Edited by
Roger Protz

Deputy Editor
Jill Adam

Assistant Editor
Kate Green

Sponsored by

Campaign for Real Ale
230 Hatfield Road, St Albans,
Hertfordshire AL1 4LW

Contents

Thanks to the following at CAMRA head office: Cressida Feiler, Publications Co-ordinator, for research and progress chasing for the Breweries section; the Campaigns teams of Mike Benner, Iain Loe, Louise Ashworth, Tony Jerome, Sofia Deus, Jonathan Mail and John Cottrell. The What's Brewing duo of Ted Bruning and Kim Adams. The Administration team: Kirk Winkler, Malcolm Harding, Jean Jones, Gary Fowler, Michael Green, Angie Nergaard, Carwyn Davies and Owen Ingram. Special thanks to Peter Feiler for crunching the first draft of the Breweries section.

Beer Index compiled by Jeff Evans.

Thanks to 65,000 CAMRA members who carried out research for the pubs; the Campaign's Regional Directors, who co-ordinated the pub entries; CAMRA's Brewery Liaison Officers for their reports on the country's breweries; Paul Moorhouse for assembling the brewery tasting notes; and CAMRA's National Executive for their support and enthusiasm.

The Good Beer Guide production team: Designed by Rob Howells of Howells Design, London W13. Typeset by Ken Millie, T&O Graphics, Bungay, Suffolk. Maps by David and Morag Perrott, PerroCarto, Machynlleth, Montgomeryshire, Wales. Colour reproduction by DDP Imaging.
Printed by WS Bookwell Ltd, Finland; British representative David Sowter.

Published by the Campaign for Real Ale Ltd, 230 Hatfield Road, St Albans, Herts, AL1 4LW. Tel 01727 867201. Fax 01727 867670. Action Line 0845 60 30 20 8

E-mail camra@camra.org.uk Web-site www.camra.org.uk ISBN 1-85249-176-0

The 30th edition of the Good Beer Guide is dedicated to the memory of Abi Maddock and Jim Fox

Jim Burrows of Brakspear (left) received the British Guild of Beer Writers' British Beer and Brewing Award in 2001 from Roger Protz. Now Burrows is quitting and selling his beers.

Beer and pubs duopoly is a threat to drinkers' choice

The discount game played by global brewers and giant pubcos fleeces beer lovers and drives competitors out of business, argues **Roger Protz**

LOVERS OF QUALITY beer were horrified to learn in July 2002 that W H Brakspear of Henley-on-Thames, one of Britain's most revered regional brewers, planned to close its plant by the end of the year. Brakspear will become yet another pub retailer, while the beers – sold to Refresh UK – will be brewed elsewhere. The Henley company was defeated by forces that are also attacking other middle-ranking brewers: it was producing more beer than at any time in its history, yet as a result of the rampant greed of the giant pub companies it could not make a sufficient return on its sales to justify staying in brewing.

As we celebrate the thirtieth edition of the Guide, many of the problems that faced beer drinkers in the early 1970s have come back to haunt us in the twenty-first century. When the Guide was first published, the brewing industry was changing from one in which a large number of regional brewers flourished to one dominated by six new

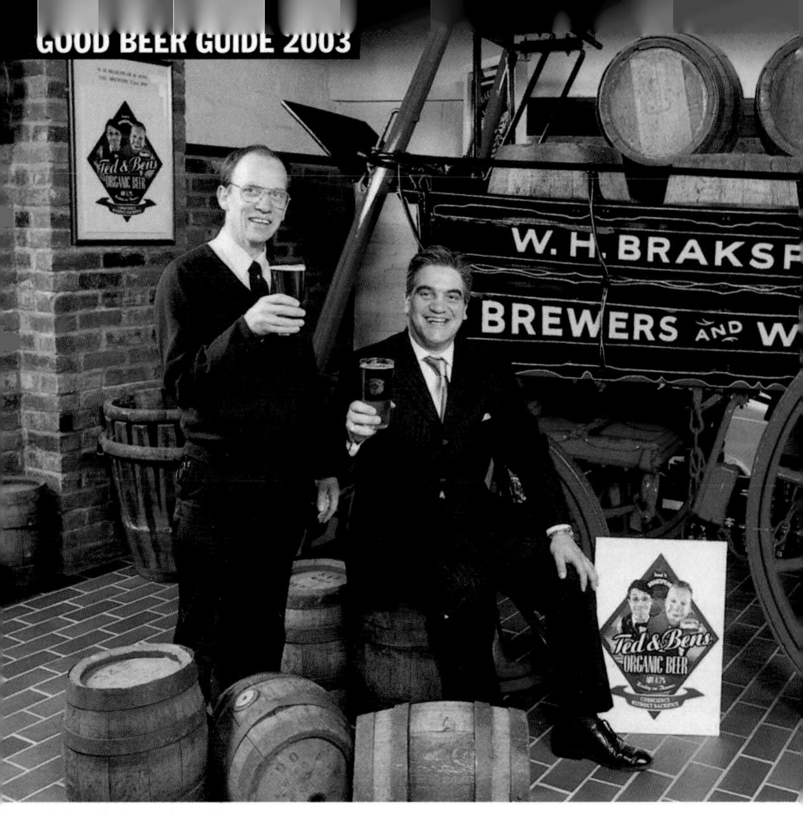

Empty glass...Ted Emmett (left) and Ben Iannacone gave their names to Brakspear's successful organic beer Ted & Ben's. But Ted's job as security officer at the Henley brewery will go, while Ben, a national salesman, will be transferred to Refresh UK

national combines. The 'Big Six', as they were known, were the result of a series of mergers and takeovers. The nationals accounted for more than 70 per cent of all the beer brewed in Britain and – crucially – they attempted to wean drinkers from cask-conditioned beer to new filtered, pasteurised and pressurised keg beers. Keg's hey-day was a brief one. The style was soundly rubbished by CAMRA in its early years, and drinkers were sceptical. The big brewers rapidly moved on to the even more profitable pastures of fake British lager. But keg had a lasting impact: many regional brewers, convinced that the days of real draught beer were numbered, either switched to keg production or accepted takeover and closure at the hands of the Big Six. The 1970s saw the culling of some of the country's finest family-owned breweries.

The impact made by CAMRA and its beer festivals, and the resurgence of support for cask beer in the 1980s and early 90s, have turned those early struggles into sepia-toned history. But the big brewers never went away. On the contrary, they became ever more powerful. A consumer movement can change perceptions and tastes, and encourage people to prefer one type of beer to another. But only government can prevent the monopolisation of an industry. And governments of both stripes in the 1990s have acquiesced in the growing power of the national producers and their siblings, the new pub companies.

The recommendations of a Monopolies and Mergers Commission report in 1989 to open up the brewing industry and pub trade to rigorous competition were cynically aborted by the big brewers. The most important MMC proposal – the right of tenants in national brewers'

pubs to buy 'guest beers' from other suppliers – went to the heart of the Big Six cartel. They sabotaged the guest beer policy, which offered both drinkers and tenants undreamt of choice and diversity, by divesting themselves of thousands of pubs. The pubs were sold as large parcels of real estate to new pub companies, many of them set up by former Big Six executives with munificent golden handshakes. As the pub companies did not brew, they were not required to offer guest beers to their customers. Not surprisingly, they preferred to take the bulk of their supplies from the national brewers that had spawned and financed them.

In recent years the number of national brewers has declined still further as they have become part of global corporations. At the same time, driven by grossly inflated property prices in Britain, many of the leading pub companies have been taken over by banks keen to sell them on at the first opportunity for maximum profit. For example, the Laurel Pub Company, formed by Morgan Grenfell/Deutsche Bank to run the former Whitbread pub estate, sold the bulk of the pubs to Enterprise Inns a year later. The Japanese banker Nomura, once Britain's biggest pub owner, has now sold most of its pub interests and is immeasurably the richer as a result.

The cosy duopoly of global brewers and giant pubcos has been a disaster for independent brewers and consumers. Beer is disgracefully expensive, and retailers can no longer fall back on the argument that price is dictated solely by high rates of excise duty. Pubco profits have an important role to play. In the South-east of England pubgoers find they are frequently charged more than £2.50 for a pint of beer. One reason for the increasing consumption of wine is that it is now cheaper for two people to share a bottle of good quality wine at home than it is to purchase two pints of beer in a pub.

Not worth the candle

The root cause of high beer prices is the discount game. The pubcos demand beer at low wholesale prices and then sell those beers for high retail prices. In between lie obscene profits. The national brewers are happy to play the discount game. Marginal profit on one cask becomes big profit when they are brewing millions of barrels a year. But for small brewers, the discounts demanded mean the game is not worth the candle. Some sell beer to the pubcos in the knowledge that the return is neglible but the sales give them a higher national profile. Others refuse to supply the pubcos, but see their business decline. The results are plain to see: more than 40 breweries have closed in the past ten years. Many were once flourishing regional or family-owned companies that saw no future in beer production and turned themselves into pub retailers, selling national brands. This was the dilemma that faced Brakspear.

It's not hard to work out the rules of the discount game. The 'list price' or wholesale price of a barrel of standard bitter produced by a regional brewer, with an ABV of around 3.8 per cent, is £250. A national pub company will demand a discount of at least £100 off the list price. If it's not a strong brand, lacking a high profile among pubgoers, the pub company will demand an even bigger discount. This puts smaller brewers at a clear disadvantage. They cannot afford to advertise their beers. Promotion is by word-of-mouth by discerning drinkers, or in CAMRA publications. The position of small brewers, the micros in particular, is made worse by the fact that their list prices are often lower than those of the bigger regionals in an attempt to win sales to the free trade. By the time a discount of around £120 a barrel has been deducted from a beer with a list price of £230, the brewer is often selling his beer at cost price. There's no living in it for him, which explains why regional brewers are closing and many micros don't last the pace.

Pound of flesh

But the pubcos haven't finished yet. There's another pound of flesh to be carved from the body of the helpless small brewer in the shape of 'listing fees'. These are charges made by the pub companies to list a brewery and its brands in the promotional material sent to pubs. One of the national pub companies charges brewers a listing fee of £1,700 every six months for each of their brands. A small brewery owner in Yorkshire, who cannot be identified as he is frightened of losing his business with a pub company, told the Guide: 'I produce four regular beers. The pubco takes all four. So that's £13,600 in listing fees – £13,600 of my annual profits – before it sells a drop of my beer. And I have to deliver the beers myself to a depot in Liverpool because the pubco won't pick up from me in Yorkshire.'

The discounts are not passed on to publicans. They pay the full wholesale price for the beer or may get tiny discounts. The pubcos pocket the difference. The result is high prices for beer at the bar, and fat profits for the pub companies. The discount scam was exposed in May 2002 by the publicans' trade paper, the Morning Advertiser (see left).

In the 1990s, the Conservative government allowed the big brewers to make a mockery of the Beer Orders, the guidelines that resulted from the MMC report of 1989. The most infamous abuse of the orders was the 'pubs-for-

Invoice gaffe puts focus on discounts

An administrative cock-up by brewer Scottish Courage has forced the issue of pubco discounts into sharp focus.

An invoice misdirected to an Enterprise Inns tenant in Yorkshire indicates the pubco was pocketing 40% of the wholesale price.

The Scottish Courage invoice should have gone direct to Enterprise but went to the licensee instead. It showed goods delivered to the pub that week totalled £1,171.03 but the tenant had been charged £2,000.42.

Enterprise chief executive Ted Tuppen said his company offered a range of agreements and dealt with each licensee individually.

"If a tenant is on full tie he knows he is going to be paying the full wholesale price to us for his beer, but that he will be charged a lower rent," explained Tuppen.

"On the other hand, we have tenants who are on £40-a-barrel discounts. It's swings and roundabouts."

Lost bottle? The fate of Brakspear's small volume but highly regarded bottle-fermented beers is in doubt. It's expected that new owner Refresh UK will concentrate on such core brands as Bitter and Special.

Sands of time...CAMRA's innovative Ask For Cask campaign adopted a modern version of Ninkasi, the Ancient Egyptian goddess of brewing

breweries swap' between Grand Metropolitan/Watneys and Courage. The Department of Trade and Industry gave its blessing to a deal that meant that GrandMet sold its breweries to Courage, and in return Courage sold its pubs to GrandMet. The result was that neither was bound by the Beer Orders and did not have to offer guest beers to tenants. GrandMet pubs, renamed Inntrepreneur, naturally took the bulk of their beer supplies from Courage.

Beer drinkers have fared no better under a Labour government. It has reneged on a promise to bring in legislation that will end the scandal of short measure in pubs, a scandal that costs drinkers millions of pounds a year in lost beer. And, lobbied by the national brewers and the pubcos, the DTI in 2002 announced that the Guest Beer provision would be scrapped.

Beer drinking in Britain will be a poorer place if the sublime pale ales produced by Brakspear disappear, and their pubs offer instead the rare delights of Boddingtons, John Smith's and Tetley. Brakspear and independent brewers of all sizes can survive only if there is government action to tackle the scandal of the big brewer-pubco duopoly and their control of choice and prices in a majority of Britain's pubs. The now-mouldering MMC report called for an outright ban on discounts that, with great prescience, it saw as strengthening the wholesale and retail muscles of the biggest brewers. That demand should now be implemented. As Prime Minister Tony Blair is fond of the well-spun, telly-friendly phrase, he may care to campaign for 'the People's Pint'. While we keenly await his intervention to save Britain's independent brewers, the Good Beer Guide advises its readers to seek out the beers of the craft producers listed in the Breweries section and to consume them, wherever possible, in hostelries free from the cold embrace of the voracious pub companies.

My Love Affair with Beer

Real ale is a civilised drink. Keg beer is – well – a dead parrot, says **Terry Jones**

LONG BEFORE I'D HEARD OF CAMRA I'd virtually given up drinking in pubs in London. All you could get was Watney's Red Barrel and Double Diamond. It was the late Sixties and I'd grown up drinking Friary Meux in Guildford and Morrells in Oxford. I didn't know anything about how beer was made or anything about the politics of the big breweries. I just knew that the liquid stuff that came out of a small tap instead of a handpump was gassy and didn't have a good taste.

It was many years later that I began hearing about 'Real Ale'. What CAMRA did for me was to put the whole thing in perspective. It taught me about beer, and I shall always be grateful for that education. In 1977 Richard Boston (who was then famous as the Guardian's Beer Correspondent), Martin Griffiths and I set up a micro-brewery in Hereford. We reckoned it was the first one of the new wave of micro-breweries. CAMRA very kindly let us run a story about it and helped us to recruit a brewer, Peter Austin, who had been head brewer at Hull Brewery.

CAMRA helped get us publicity, and other would-be brewers came and learnt from our mistakes. David Bruce, for one, who realised that we spent a lot of time filling barrels and transporting them to pubs, and that it would be better to brew and sell on the same spot. That was the birth of the Firkin chain. It's wonderful to see how the micro-breweries have flourished since our first attempt – there are around 450 of them now. Just take a look at the Directory of Independent Breweries at the end of this book.

Beer, for me, is more than something I like drinking. It's a litmus of civilisation. If the society is making good beer, then it's a healthy society. If that's sounds a bit preposterous, look at it like this. Beer – real beer – is something that you can only make if you love it. If you want to make money, then you won't make beer – not real beer – you'll end up making something that looks like beer but that isn't really beer at all. By the time you've filtered it to take out the yeast sediment, sterilised it, and put it under the pressure of CO2 you'll end up with an inert, lifeless corpse of a drink, dolled up with gas to pass itself off as living. Making real ale demands dedication and affection for the product. It's a real and alive thing. That's what makes it difficult to keep and that's what makes it worth looking for. A society that can still produce real beer has still preserved some values that are not based on greed and profit.

So let's lift a glass to CAMRA's Good Beer Guide for keeping one element of our society healthy for over thirty years. Happy Birthday, Good Beer Guide!

*Terry Jones is a writer, producer and one of the founders of Monty Python.

Triple A for effort...Terry Jones tries his hand at cask rolling at Young's brewery

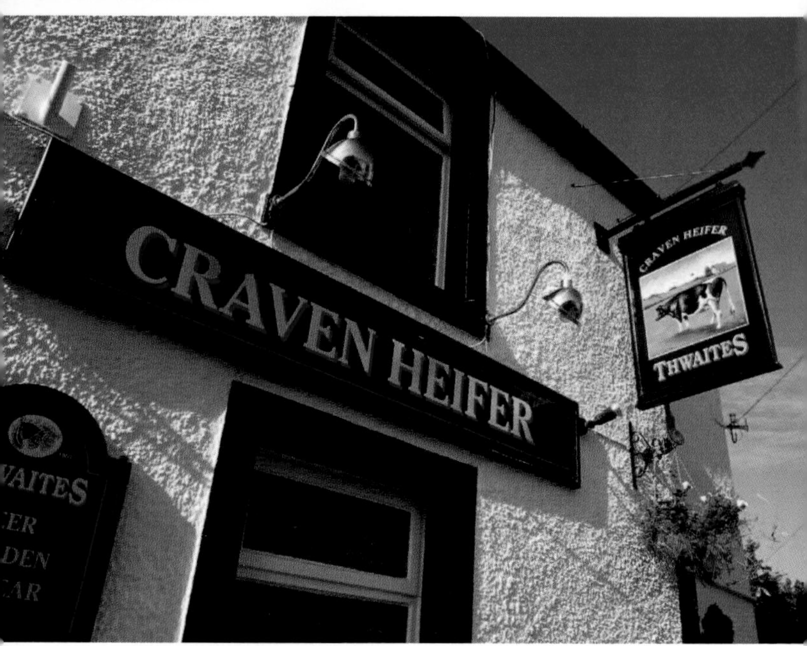

Hang on to the Hub

Jeff Evans reports that the campaign to save the village pub has won support from beer lovers, publicans, brewers...and the Prince of Wales

IN HIS HEART-WARMING and amusing memoir, The Landlord's Tale, Yorkshire writer Barrie Pepper drifts back into his more youthful days, nostalgically recalling life in the pub his parents used to run in the 1950s. Through such rose-tinted reminiscences, it's easy to describe the past as 'the good old days', without due thought for the hardships and privations of life at the time. But, in one sense, 'good old days' those were indeed. For this was a time when the pub was truly the bustling heart and soul of a community.

Take Barrie's dad's pub, cunningly disguised as the Coach and Four in the fictitious town of Oldford, to protect the privacy of those depicted in his pages. Here was a small town pub, by no means the only hostelry in the patch, but one that positively bristled with activity. It featured a bar, a tap room, a snug and a large lounge/concert room, and employed numerous members of staff, who even offered waiter service. It attracted all sectors of the local populace and acted as an oasis of refreshment, nourishment, entertainment and, not least, community spirit.

Regrettably, we have moved on half a century, and the pub, in many

Photographs: Andy Tryner

Pints and postal orders...the Craven Heifer in Stainforth, North Yorkshire, was chosen by the Prince of Wales to launch his Pub is the Hub campaign. The Thwaites' pub doubles as the village post office

instances, has lost its heart and soul. New fangled demands on leisure time like television, the revitalised cinema, the Internet, bowling alleys and affordable restaurants mean that the humble boozer can no longer rely on a steady trade. A decline in traditional rural employment and the obvious deterrent – however wise – of drink-driving legislation have aggravated the problem.

Like unpicked hops on the bine, many pubs have simply withered and died. Villages that once boasted half a dozen pubs now struggle to maintain just one, and in far too many instances that, too, has poured its last pint and taken on a new, rather sad role as a private dwelling. The chilling fact is that country pubs in England are closing at a rate of six a week.

Reversing the trend

It is a source of great encouragement therefore that an attempt has been made to breathe new life into the community local. In an initiative dubbed The Pub is the Hub, The Countryside Agency, assisted by the British Beer and Pub Association and Business in the Community, has set out to reverse the trend of pub closures. In December 2001, it published a fascinating document outlining ways in which a pub might secure its future by providing new and important services for the local population.

It enlisted the help of The Prince of Wales, whose foreword stressed the need for pubs to draw on their resourcefulness and resilience and adapt to changing circumstances. 'Practical action, not just fine words,' is what is required, according to the Prince, and that's what the booklet – subtitled 'A Good Practice Guide' – sets out to encourage by giving examples of 34 pubs around Britain that have gone that extra mile to ensure their future, and indeed the future of services in their communities.

Take the pub chosen by Prince Charles as the launch pad for the campaign. The Craven Heifer Hotel at Stainforth, North Yorkshire, is a

Thwaites house where a pint of fine Lancashire ale is not the only attraction. At one end of the pub, owners Debbie and Michael Price have established a post office and grocery store, preserving a facility that looked like dying out in the village. Senior citizens collecting their pensions can even stay on for a special pensioners' lunch once a month. To top up trade even further, the pub has four bed and breakfast rooms.

Similar services are provided by pubs like the White Hart at Blythburgh, Suffolk, and the aptly-named Pint and Post at St Giles on the Heath in Devon (although in the latter's case a pub was added to make the post office business more viable). CAMRA's National Pub of the Year for 2001, the Blisland Inn, near Bodmin in Cornwall, is yet another post office provider.

The Pub is the Hub
available free of charge from The Countryside Agency, on 0870 120 6466.

The Landlord's Tale
by Barrie Pepper, is available from CAMRA Books at £6.99 (£4.99 for CAMRA members) on 01727 867201.

But pubs, if they need to diversify, need to do so on their own terms. Selling stamps is not always the answer, at least on its own. For the Diamond Inn at Butterknowle, County Durham, the solution to slow trade lay in not just installing a post office but a separate bookmaker's shop, too. For the Miners Arms at Brassington, Derbyshire, conversion of an upstairs room into a computer training club has boosted business, while the Weir Hotel near Bacup, Lancashire, has put its faith in hosting Sunday morning church services, reaping rewards from a grateful congregation that had nowhere left to pray in the village.

Other pubs use the hook of community service to place themselves once again at the heart of village life, without necessarily tagging on ancillary businesses. The Crown Inn at Bathley, Nottinghamshire, is one such hostelry. In a village with no village hall, church, shop or other pubs, its existence is vital to the well-being of the neighbourhood. Now the parish council meets in the pub, the skittle alley is a focus for friendly rivalries, a soup kitchen is organised for the elderly in winter and the school holds its parties in the pub grounds. As a result, the whole community, from the young to the old, appreciates the role the pub has to play.

Equally worthy of recognition is the Cock Inn at Combe, Oxfordshire, where villagers can drop off prescriptions and pick up medication, thanks to a link up with a

Short head...bookmaker Trevor Dunn watches the nags and takes bets in the Diamond Inn, Butterknowle, Co Durham

Holy hour...a Baptist minister conducts a service in the Wier Hotel, Bacup, Lancs

pharmacist from a neighbouring village, and the Olde Mill at Upwell, Norfolk, which works closely with the local waterways trust and sports clubs, and lays on tea dances for the elderly.

Thankfully, publicans are not alone in meeting the challenge. Brewers like Adnams, Hall & Woodhouse and St Austell have proved ready and willing to invest in diversification. Grants may be available from local development agencies and financial assistance with start up and security costs may be forthcoming from the Post Office. Such services are well detailed in The Pub is the Hub, along with case studies of pubs that have been rescued from oblivion by the community itself. The Beauchamp Arms at Dymock, Gloucestershire, is a good example. As it happens, the village still has its own post office, shop and petrol station, but its last remaining pub's days seemed numbered. It was placed on the market in 1996 and failed to attract a buyer, until the parish council stepped in.

By securing a loan from the Public Works Loan Board, it purchased the pub and installed a manager to run it. Thus, a vital community facility has been preserved and, as a bonus, villagers have been able to extend the existing parish hall into part of the pub's car park.

Such instances of community ownership are not new. In 1983, in a similar vein, the villagers of Preston in Hertfordshire saved their local, the Red Lion, from being converted to a steak house by banding together into a company and buying the property. Now, with managers in charge, the pub is a flourishing local for its shareholders and other villagers.

With its useful guide to sources of potential funding for all these schemes, The Prince of Wales hopes The Pub is the Hub will encourage other publicans to think imaginatively about ways to diversify. For most of us beer lovers, the pub is, and always has been, the hub of the community. If this initiative makes other people realise that, too, then the future of many of our wonderful pubs may soon appear as golden as our comforting memories of the old days.

* Jeff Evans is the author of the Good Bottled Beer Guide (CAMRA Books, £8.99/£5.99 for CAMRA members). He was awarded the Gold Tankard/Beer Writer of the Year accolade by the British Guild of Beer Writers in December 2001.

Brewing in the Global Village

Michael Jackson says that innovation and enthusiasm among American craft brewers are influencing a new generation of producers in Britain, too. The result is beers rich in malt and hop character

JUST AS THE SWEEPING FASHIONABILITY of New World wines has influenced viticulture in Europe, so the American beer revolution is stimulating creativity among some British breweries. In making that observation, I am committing two heresies: 1.Talking about wine in a beer publication; 2.Daring to suggest that American brewers might having something to teach us.

The New World wine revolution started in California, and set a precedent for the subsequent uprising of small beers. I believe the wine comparison also helps consumers understand the joys of beer in all its diversity. Even people who have never had a glass of wine know that it can be red or white, sweet or dry, sparkling or still. Some beer-drinkers have only ever enjoyed Bitter. Others have only ever experienced (true enjoyment is hard to imagine in this instance) what passes in Britain for Lager. For many drinkers, the choice of beers in Britain does not extend beyond Bitter and Lager. Even the word Stout can be greeted with uncertainty until the name Guinness is mentioned.

In the United States, a handful of Ales and Porters or Stouts, dating from colonial times, hung on until the beer revolution began, but they were hard to find in the sea of light Lager. In the era when Bill Clinton was at Oxford, a proportion of his American contemporaries (post war baby-boomers) were interested not only in cannabis but also in its closest neighbour, botanically-speaking, the hop. When they returned to the U.S., they drank Bass and the unlamented Watney's, in awful, fake pubs. The beer revolution ended all that.

The American beer revolution

Another Southern Democrat, Jimmy Carter, subsequently became President and, in a last act of post-Prohibition tidying, legalised home-brewing. Around the same time, my book The World Guide to Beer was published in the U.S. This book, loosely modelled on Hugh Johnson's World Atlas of Wine, looked at the classic styles of beer; their historical and geographical origin; ingredients and production processes; and the ways in which they were typically served. Beers deemed to be classic examples were shown, many from Britain, Belgium and Germany.

Soon, many of these beers were being imported. Better yet, young Americans were making beers in these styles, at first as amateurs and later as professionals. The first of these micros was the New Albion brewery established at Sonoma, in the wine country of Northern California,

Hops across the sea...American interpretations of pale ale have been influenced by English originals but tend to be more aggressively hopped

in 1976. Charlie Papazian, a beer-loving atomic physicist, who was teaching infants' school in Boulder, Colorado, was a key figure in the revolution. He started a national organisation for home-brewers, and later for micros and brewpubs. In 1981, he visited Europe for the first time, stayed at my house, and attended the Great British Beer Festival. 'Do you think we could do this in America?' he asked. He says that I responded: 'Yes, but what would we do for beers?'. There were only four or five micros at the time, and fewer than 20 regionals, but he somehow managed to create a festival.

US beers today

The Great American Beer Festival has just celebrated its 21st birthday. Every beer offered to the public at the festival is also entered into a blindfold judging. There are typically around 1,200 beers, categorised in about 50 styles. The judging panels comprise mainly American brewers, but also a good leavening of tasters from other brewing nations. There have been several British judges: myself, fellow writer Roger Protz, publican Mark Dorber, brewing scientist Keith Thomas, and brewers such as Ken Don, of Young's; Reg Drury, of Fuller's; Sean Franklin, of Rooster's; and Nick Funnell, who once oversaw pub breweries in London and now does the same in Washington, D.C. All the beers judged are American. Nowhere in the world is there such a large judging of the beers from a single nation. The only judging with more styles is the Beer

Toddle on down...the Real Ale Festival in Chicago has become an annual showcase for American brewers who have adopted the British tradition of cask conditioning

World Cup, organised on alternate years by the same organisation. The mass-market American lagers are all represented, but in their own categories. Only a minority of micros and brewpubs produce lagers, but these support a number of categories at the judging. Over the years, these have included Bohemian-style and German-style Pils; Dortmunder Export; Vienna-style; Bock and so forth. Ale categories will cover Mild as well as Bitter; Pale; IPA; Porter; Sweet, Dry and Imperial Stouts. Very often the new American breweries' versions of classic styles are more robust than the European originals.

Some breweries have taken a classic style and turned it into something distinctively American. The much-admired Sierra Nevada Pale Ale is very well hopped, but with less emphasis on bitterness than aroma. This has led to the emergence of what might be regarded as a New American Pale Ale. On the other hand, an IPA made in the U.S. is likely to have a very pale malt character but huge hop bitterness. Oatmeal Stout is a style that was revived, originally for the American market, by Samuel Smith's, likewise Imperial Stout. Both styles are extensively made by American brewers, variously with additions of honey, chocolate, coffee, or fruit, or finished in Bourbon casks. The Alaskan Brewing Company took the notion of smoked malt and incorporated it into a Porter. Other brewers have used local woods such as mesquite in smoked beers. Local honeys, chili, sagebrush and juniper are typical local ingredients.

Influencing Britain's brewers

To taste such distinctive beers, in such numbers, subject them to critical analysis, and engage in sometimes passionate debate about their merits, over two or three days, in closed sessions, with other brewers, is an

In the past decade, it's become clear that increasing folate intake may provide protection against cardiovascular disease and cancer. Recent research shows that vitamin B6 in beer gives drinkers additional protection against cardiovascular disease.

Beer is also a source of antioxidants, which play a role in the fight against cancer. Much has been made about the presence of antioxidants in wine. What is less well known is that they are also present in beer, where they come from both malt and hops. Beer contains more than twice as many antioxidants as white wine, although only half the amount of red wine.

However, many of the antioxidants in red wines are large molecules and may be less readily absorbed by the body than the smaller molecules found in beer. Additional research shows that we absorb antioxidant material from beer more readily than from solid foods.

Beer is part of a balanced diet, providing essential vitamins and minerals. In particular it has a beneficial balance of minerals. It is also high in potassium and low in sodium – the right balance for healthy low blood pressure. It is rich in calcium and rich in magnesium, which may help to protect against gallstones and kidney stone formation.

Risk factor

Beer drinkers are protected from the organism heliobacter pylori, which is known to cause stomach ulcers and may be a risk factor for stomach cancer. Beer is also a source of soluble fibre, a liquid bread rich in vitamins derived from the cell walls of malted barley. As well as aiding a healthy bowel function, it has a further benefit of slowing down the digestion and absorption of food.

Indeed, the term beer belly is better-called 'bad diet belly'. If it is drunk moderately and is part of a sensible diet, beer will not make you fat. A glass of milk a day is more likely to do that.

But if all beer has health giving qualities is real ale even healthier? British real ales are potentially better at protecting against certain cancers because they contain more hops than most other brews, but much more research needs to be done in this field.

Beer is the only alcoholic drink to contain hops, and scientists believe any specific hop-associated health benefits are therefore unique to beer. Traditionally hops have been used for a range of therapies including sedation, to combat stress, for their sleep-inducing properties, counteracting complaints related to the menopause, anti-cancer activity, anti-inflammatory action, stimulation of the digestive tract, bacteriostasis and diuresis.

Work by German Cancer Research has isolated one of the hop components in beer that could stop some cancers developing. Cancer is caused by multiple and diverse factors, some genetic, as well as external factors such as diet. Beer contains Xanthohumol, a very promising agent with several hitherto unknown activities indicative of cancer prevention.

So next time you enjoy the conversation and relaxation that comes with a pint of good real ale remember beer is made from wholesome ingredients: malt, other cereals, hops, yeast and water – and a glass or two a day is indeed good for you.

* Tim Hampson is a beer writer and a member of the committee of the British Guild of Beer Writers.

Cask Marque Quality Guaranteed

CASK MARQUE IS A NON-PROFIT-MAKING ORGANISATION that makes awards to licensees (not the pubs) where the outlet can pass the twice-yearly Cask Marque inspections. All licensees with this award included in the Good Beer Guide are highlighted by the use of this symbol ✔ by the side of their entry.

When we inspect a licensee, what do we look for? We test temperature in the glass which should be cellar-cool ie 11-13°C (53-57°F). The beer should be crystal clear and have a taste and aroma true to type for that product.

Why is quality so important? Today the consumer demands consistent quality and unless we can deliver this to the customers' satisfaction, we will not retain customer loyalty or attract new drinkers. A recent survey showed that:

- 34% of customers would go to a DIFFERENT outlet if quality is poor;
- 49% would not order the SAME drink again if quality is poor;

53% of customers would pay MORE for quality;

- 67% of bar staff do not believe they RECEIVE sufficient training.

(Source: Interbrew UK)

A good licensee should therefore see the benefits both in satisfied customers and in increased profitability.

Quality Guarantee

When you see the Cask Marque plaque on a pub it guarantees beer quality and the opportunity to 'Try Before You Buy' – a useful marketing initiative when you are unfamiliar with the beers on sale or there is a guest beer proposition.

Consumer Role

If the cask beers are in excellent condition, compliment the licensee. Why not recommend the outlet for the Cask Marque award? Conversely, challenge the licensee if the beer is not to your liking. If you are still unhappy about the beer quality and the licensee holds the Cask Marque award, do write to Cask Marque with the details.

Wider Industry Role

As well as being a cask ale Quality Champion, Cask Marque is becoming involved in other industry initiatives to assist in training and the promotion of cask beer.

‘Cask Marque is a brilliant step forward. Now beer drinkers have champions on both sides of the bar’

Roger Protz

Cellar Card

With many pubs now owned by pub groups and supplied by a number of breweries, Cask Marque have produced a generic Cellar Card setting out best practice in keeping and preparing the beer for sale. Do request a copy from Cask Marque.

Distributors Charter

Cask beer spends twice as much time in the supply chain as it does in the licensees' cellar. Cask Marque have therefore laid down an industry standard for the handling and distribution of cask beer and encourage both pub groups and licensee to demand these quality standards from their supplier.

Training Video

As you will see from the survey, 67% of staff feel they do not receive sufficient training. Cask Marque have responded to this by producing a 20-minute video which outlines to bar staff their responsibilities both to their customers and their employers, and at the same time giving them product knowledge on how beer is brewed and the activities that take place in the cellar in preparation for them delivering the 'perfect pint'.

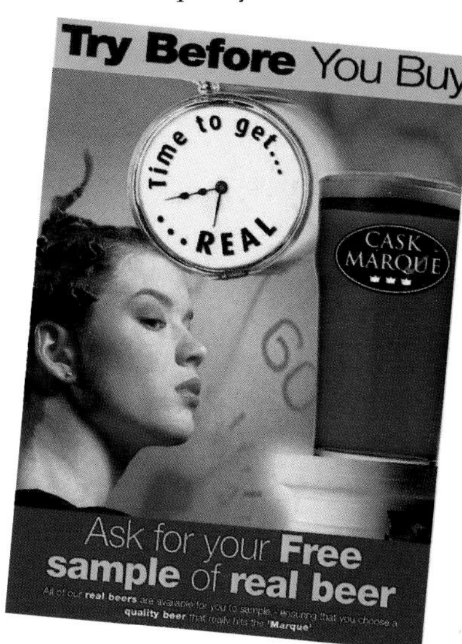

Regional Guides

As well as sponsoring the CAMRA Good Beer Guide, Cask Marque also produces 28 of its own regional guides which are free to consumers and can be downloaded from our Website on www.cask-marque.co.uk.

Real Beer Week

Real Beer Week takes place in the first week of October and gives the opportunity for licensees and brewers to heavily promote all that is good about cask beer and the opportunity to attract new drinkers. Cask Marque will be encouraging all their licensees and corporate members to become involved in this industry initiative, and we welcome CAMRA members active participation.

www.visitabrewery.co.uk

To encourage consumers to learn more about cask beer, we have created a Website which lists and gives details of brewery visits. Why not visit your own local brewery?

Do let us have your feedback – look out for the Cask Marque plaque – and visit our Website on www.cask-marque.co.uk to find the nearest Cask Marque licensee to you.

The Cask Marque Trust

Seedbed Centre, Severalls Park, Colchester, Essex CO4 4HT
Tel: 01206 752212 Fax: 01206 751198 E-mail: info@cask-marque.co.uk
www.cask-marque.co.uk

Pubs in all 30 editions

We salute the Magnificent 17

Penny plain, tuppence coloured, but united by a love of good beer

England

Bedfordshire
Cock, Broom
Rose & Crown, Ridgmont
Sow & Pigs, Toddington

Cambridgeshire
Queens Head, Newton

Cornwall
Blue Anchor, Helston
New Inn, Tywardreath

Devon
Ship, Axmouth
New Inn, Kilmington

Dorset
Square & Compass, Worth Matravers

London
Britannia, Kensington W8
Buckingham Arms, Westminster SW1
Star Tavern
Belgravia SW1

Merseyside
Roscoe Head, Liverpool

Northumberland
Star, Netherton

Oxfordshire
Crown & Tuns, Deddington

Wales

Gwent
Cherry Tree, Tintern

Scotland

Tayside
Fisherman's Tavern, Broughty Ferry
(The Fisherman's Tavern has appeared in 29 editions: there were no Scottish pubs in the first Good Beer Guide.)

The Blue Anchor, ancient home-brew pub in Cornwall

How the Good Beer Guide is compiled

It's more than just a pub guide. We start with the quality of the beer in a pub...and then everything else falls into place

IT IS NOT HYPERBOLE to claim that the Good Beer Guide is unique. For a start, it's far more than just a pub guide. Thanks to CAMRA, with its 65,000 members, its branch structure covering the whole country, and its chain of Brewery Liaison Officers – volunteers attached to every brewery – the Guide offers in the Breweries section an annual report on the state of the industry.

Beer is the belt and braces of the Guide. Cask-conditioned real ale is a living product. It requires attention, respect, even a little love in the pub cellar to bring it to fruition. Landlords who care for cask ale need more than the 'skill' required to serve keg beer or lager, a skill confined to the ability to connect a cylinder of gas to a sealed dustbin. A cask of real ale has to be tapped, vented, checked and tasted over the course of several days to ensure it has ripened and is ready to fill your glass at the bar.

For 30 years, the Good Beer Guide has been driven by the belief that if a pub landlord cares about the quality of the beer in the cellar, then everything else – the welcome, the food, the wine, and such important considerations as the state of the toilets – will fall into line. In keg-only pubs, on the other hand, you are likely to find micro-waved food, stale sandwiches, Blue Nun and Lambrusco, and toilets that answer to the name of bogs.

In the Good Beer Guide, the term 'pub' is not a synonym for 'twee'. There are rural pubs in abundance – CAMRA has been at the forefront of the campaign to save country pubs – but even in rural areas we make every effort to choose a good cross-section of hostelries, the penny plain as well as the tuppence coloured. The real strength of the Guide is that it does not ignore pubs in towns and cities. It would be foolish to do so: while Britain's national tally of pubs – around 60,000 – has remained unchanged for a decade, there has been a shift from country to town, with many new pubs opening in urban areas in recent years. Most people live in towns and drink in town pubs. The Good Beer Guide reflects that situation by offering a wide choice of urban pubs.

The pubs in the Guide are chosen democratically. CAMRA branches monitor pubs on a regular basis. Their choice for the Guide is a result of research, discussion and often a vote at branch meetings. The new format of the Guide still offers 5,000 pubs, but 4,000 have been given longer descriptions. The aim is to provide readers with as much information as possible about each pub before you embark on your travels.

Pubs in the Guide are listed county by county in England, and by regions or local authority areas in Scotland and Wales. The Key Map on the inside back cover shows the boundaries used. Greater London and Greater Manchester are listed under L and M respectively. Each county, region or area has a location map pinpointing the pubs and also independent breweries and brew-pubs.

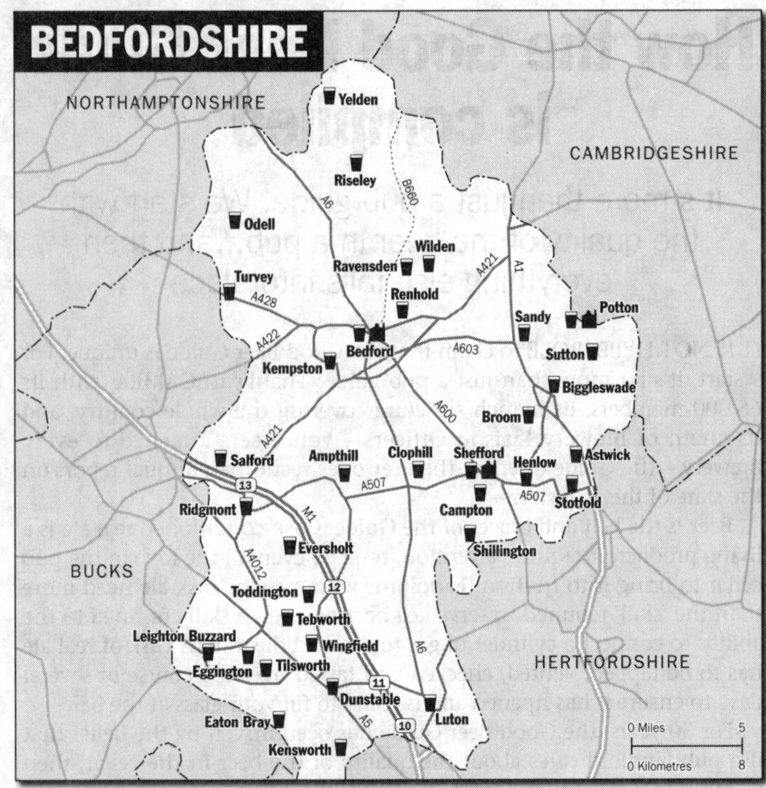

AMPTHILL

Engine & Tender
11 Dunstable Street

11 (12 Sat)-2.30, 5-11; 11-11 Fri; 12-4, 7-10.30 Sun

☎ (01525) 403319

Greene King IPA, Abbot; guest beer H

Friendly, one-bar local on the main road, with a good 'pubby' atmosphere, frequented by the local rugby club. A large patio area to the rear is used for summer drinking. Bar snacks are served 12-2 Mon-Fri. Darts and dominoes are played. The landlord possesses an unusual 'snuff engine' – if the pub is not too busy, ask to try it. Ampthill is an attractive market town popular for its antique shops.

ASTWICK

Tudor Oaks
Taylors Road (A1)

11-11; 12-3.30, 7-10.30 Sun

☎ (01462) 834133

website: www.thetudoroakslodge.co.uk

Beer range varies H

The Oaks consists of a restaurant, lodge and heavily beamed bar. A true free house, it stocks beers from regional breweries but majors on the micros. Seven handpumps serve a range from Heather Ale to Cottage brews. Real cider and perry, always on offer, are served chilled! The menu, in the comfortable dining area offers a wide choice of fresh dishes – fish and steaks are specialities. Look for the large model traction engine on the end of the bar.

BEDFORD

De Parys Hotel
45 De Parys Avenue (off A6, end of High St)

12-11; 12-10.30 Sun

☎ (01234) 352121

Wells Eagle; H **guest beers** H/G

Popular hotel bar with an adjacent restaurant and a conservatory which houses the resident parrot. The restaurant which has a no-smoking area features fish and Tex-Mex dishes. There is a pool room and function rooms. Guest beers tend to come from the Wells list but occasional beer festivals offer micro-brewers' beers served by gravity dispense. Children's certificate held; the large garden includes a children's playground. P

Wellington Arms
40-42 Wellington Street

(off A6, N of one-way system)

12-11; 12-10.30 Sun

☎ (01234) 308033 website: www.wellingtonarms.co.uk

Adnams Bitter; B&T Two Brewers Bitter, Shefford Bitter, Dragonslayer; guest beers H

Small, one-bar, back-street B&T pub operated as an ale house. It stocks an ever-changing range of guest beers from micros and regional breweries on its 13 handpumps, alongside the regular Shefford brews. It fields a number of pub games teams, including Northamptonshire skittles and also hosts regular music nights. A rare outlet for real draught cider, it also sells a variety of foreign bottled beers. North Beds and East Anglia CAMRA Pub of the Year 2001. ❀♣●✔

BIGGLESWADE

Brown Bear
29 Hitchin Street
⏲ 12-3, 5-11; 11-11 Fri & Sat; 12-3, 7-10.30 Sun
☎ (01767) 316161
Beer range varies Ⓗ
Pleasant pub, serving a changing range of beers, including foreign bottled beers. Six real ales are normally available on the handpumps. Two bars cater for a large open seating area, with no smoking permitted at the rear. The lighting is somewhat on the gloomy side, but the service is cheery and helpful. Live music is performed on Friday evenings; no meals Thu or Fri eves.
❀◐◑≠⚡

Wheatsheaf
5 Lawrence Road (from library, continue down Chestnut Ave 200 yds)
⏲ 11-4, 7-11; 11-11 Fri & Sat; 12-10.30 Sun
☎ (01767) 222220
Greene King XX Mild, IPA Ⓗ
Small, unpretentious, one-bar local tucked well away, with a loyal and mostly male clientele. No frills – just good beer, good conversation and very active crib and dominoes teams. Racing and football talk predominates with live TV when appropriate. Weekly meat raffles and frequent trips to the races are organised. No food, but occasional summer barbecues are hosted in the pleasant garden. Not many pubs like this are left; this traditional friendly working man's pub is a little gem.
❀≠♣✔

CAMPTON

White Hart
Mill Lane
⏲ 12-3 (not Mon-Thu), 6.30-11; 12-11 Sat; 12-3, 7-10.30 Sun
☎ (01462) 812657
Hook Norton Best Bitter; Marston's Pedigree; Theakston Best Bitter; guest beers Ⓗ
This traditional, family-run village free house has been in the Guide since 1976. A 300-year-old, Grade II listed pub, it features quarry-tiled floors, two inglenooks and a wealth of bygones and memorabilia. A large garden and patio with a pétanque piste and a well-equipped children's play area complete the picture. No food is served, but buffets are available for special occasions.
♨Q❀♣P

CLOPHILL

Stone Jug
10 Back Street (off A6, N of Flying Horse)
⏲ 12-4, 6-11; 12-11 Fri; 11-11 Sat; 12-10.30 Sun
☎ (01525) 860526
B&T Shefford Bitter; Courage Best Bitter; John Smith's Bitter; guest beers Ⓗ
Classic village local and a Guide regular, it is convenient for walkers of the Greensand Ridge, but check before arriving with children. Converted from three 17th-century stone cottages in the early 20th century, a single L-shaped bar serves two areas, plus a function/children's room. Excellent home-made lunches are served (12-2). A rear patio garden and picnic tables at the front prove useful in summer. Parking can be difficult at the pub, not in the village as a whole. Q❀◐♣P▯

DUNSTABLE

Victoria
69 West Street
⏲ 11-11; 12-10.30 Sun
☎ (01582) 662682
Beer range varies Ⓗ
Friendly, town-centre local, strong on pub games and TV sport. One bar, but a comfortable function room can be used when not booked. The house beer, Victoria Bitter, is brewed by Tring, while four constantly changing guest beers come from micro and regional brewers. The paved patio to the rear hosts summer barbecues, and quarterly beer festivals are held. Lunches are good value at this local CAMRA Pub of the Year, 1995-2000. ❀◐♣

EATON BRAY

Hope & Anchor
63 Bower Lane
⏲ 11-2.30 (not Wed), 5-11; 12-5, 7-10.30 Sun
☎ (01525) 220386
Courage Best Bitter; Vale Black Swan Dark Mild, Wychert; guest beers Ⓗ
Hospitable village pub that holds a supper licence until 1am. Two frequently changing guest beers are usually sourced from micro-breweries. The comfortable bar features darts, dominoes and a (subdued) juke box. The restaurant is a no-smoking area, offering good food at reasonable prices; no evening meals are served Sunday. The garden has an enclosed children's play area.
❀◐◑♣P

EGGINGTON

Horseshoes
High Street
⏲ 11-2.30 (not Mon), 6-11; 12-10.30 Sun
☎ (01525) 210282
Theakston Best Bitter; Wadworth 6X; guest beer Ⓗ
Picture-postcard pub with four rooms, consisting of a bar with scrubbed wooden tables, much used for cards and dominoes, a snug, a restaurant and an unusual upstairs room. Originally three farm cottages, it dates from around 1750. The large garden has a lawned area that is a real suntrap in summer. The food (not served Mon) is superb, and so popular that booking is recommended. ♨Q❀◐◑♣P

EVERSHOLT

Green Man
Church End
⏲ 12-11; 12-10.30 Sun
☎ (01525) 280293
Theakston Best Bitter; guest beers Ⓗ
The pub is situated opposite the church in

INDEPENDENT BREWERIES

B&T Shefford
Potton Potton
Wells Bedford

the centre of a village that is an amalgamation of 13 'ends' (small hamlets), two miles from Woburn Abbey and Safari Park. The bar has bay windows at one end and a pool table at the other. The restaurant specialises in Indian food (no meals Sun eve). The garden features an aviary, guinea pigs and a bouncy castle. Two ever-changing guest beers come from independent brewers.
⛫Q❀◑♣P

HENLOW

Engineers Arms
66 High Street
✪ 12-11; 12-10.30 Sun
☎ (01462) 812284 website: www.engineersarms.co.uk
Beer range varies 🄷
Beers from Everards and micro-breweries are stocked alongside those brewed occasionally by Kevin, the landlord, at the Bass Museum Brewery. A beer festival in October is supplemented by regular mini festivals throughout the year. Draught cider is sometimes available. This traditional village pub attracts a wide range of age groups. A pub in the true sense of the word – if you visit the Engineers a stranger, you are sure to leave as a friend.
⛫❀⊟♣●

KEMPSTON

Half Moon
108 High Street
✪ 12-3, 6 (5 Fri)-11; 12-4, 7-11 Sat; 12-3, 7-10.30 Sun
☎ (01234) 852464
Wells Eagle, Bombardier 🄷
Conventional, friendly local boozer; in the oldest part of town, it is handy for pleasant walks by the River Great Ouse. The public bar has a large games area where skittles and darts are played; quiz nights are held alternate Sundays. The cheerful landlord will stay open later at lunchtimes if customers are still drinking. A large grassed area has picnic tables and children's play equipment, including swings and a rocking horse.
❀⊟♣P

LEIGHTON BUZZARD ❄

Stag
1 Heath Road
✪ 12-2.30, 6-11; 12-3, 7-10.30 Sun
☎ (01525) 372710
Fuller's Chiswick, London Pride, ESB, seasonal beer or guest beer 🄷
This comfortably furnished, wedge-shaped pub is larger inside than it looks from without. Attracting a good cross-section of local drinkers, it features a long, wood-panelled bar with a brass footrest. Good home-cooked food is served (not on Sun eve) with a no-smoking area available to diners. A weekly quiz is held (Tue eve). The car park is unsuited to limousines, although ample parking is available nearby.
❀◑♣P✔

LUTON ❄

Bricklayers Arms
10-12 Hightown Road
✪ 12-2.30, 5-11; 12-11 Fri & Sat; 12-10.30 Sun
☎ (01582) 611017
Bateman Mild; Everards Beacon, Tiger; guest beers 🄷
Friendly, unpretentious town pub, where the two ever-changing guest beers are usually sourced from micro-breweries. A good range of Belgian bottled beers is also available. Food served 12-2 weekdays includes filled rolls, toasted sandwiches, ploughmans and burgers with chips. A quiz is held every Monday evening and Sky TV football is shown. It can be crowded on Luton Town match days. ❀⥂♣P

Mother Redcap
80 Latimer Road
✪ 11-11; 12-10.30 Sun
☎ (01582) 730913
Greene King IPA, Abbot, Old Speckled Hen 🄷
Large, one-bar pub where a games area with darts and pool is separated from the bar area by a central chimney breast. Home-cooked food (served Mon-Sat) includes a number of vegetarian options. Sky TV is shown on a large screen, for major sporting events. The small paved area in front of the pub is very popular in summer. The Mother Redcap is a Guide regular of many years' standing.
❀◑⥂♣P

INN BRIEF

BEDFORD

Devonshire Arms
32 Dudley Street
5.30 (4 Fri)-11; 11-11 Sat; 12-3, 7-10.30 Sun
(01234) 359329
Wells Eagle, Bombardier; guest beers 🄷
Pleasant, two-bar local near a park and river garden. Traditional pub games. Cask Marque accredited.

Phoenix
45 St Johns Street
11-11; 12-10.30 Sun
(01234) 352862
Wells Eagle, Bombardier; guest beers 🄷
Welcoming local, with oodles of Irish charm, at the end of the A6 one-way circus, south of river. No food Sun.

Pilgrim's Progress
42 Midland Road
11-11; 12-10.30 Sun
(01234) 363751
Courage Directors; Greene King Abbot; Hop Back Summer Lightning; Shepherd Neame Spitfire; Theakston Best Bitter; guest beers 🄷
Large town-centre Wetherspoon's, where up to five guests complement the usual house beers. No-smoking area available. Good value food. Cask Marque accredited.

BROOM

Cock ☆
23 High Street
11-3, 6-11; 12-4, 7-10.30 Sun
(01767) 314411
Greene King IPA, Abbot; guest beer 🄶
Popular village pub without a bar; the beer is served on gravity from the cellar. It has featured in every edition of this Guide.

White Horse
The Village Green, 30 Southill Road
12-3, 5.30-11; 12-3, 7-10 Sun
(01767) 313425
Greene King IPA, Old Speckled Hen 🄷
Busy village pub with a striking decor. Cask Marque accredited.

KENSWORTH

Old Red Lion
86 Common Road
11.30-3.30, 5.30-11; 11.30-11 Sat; 12-10.30 Sun
(01582) 872438
Tring Side Pocket for a Toad; Wadworth 6X; guest beer 🄷
18th-Century pub with a U-shaped bar, a conservatory-style restaurant enjoying panoramic views and a large garden with play area. Good food.

Two Brewers
43 Dumfries Street
12-11; 12-10.30 Sun
☎ (01582) 616008
Tring Side Pocket for a Toad, Jack O' Legs; guest beers H
Friendly, street-corner local run by Tring Brewery, it offers up to four guest beers (usually from micros). Split into two bar areas, the rear section has darts and displays a large collection of football photos. Regular events include a quiz every Sunday night, acoustic music sessions (Thu), live jazz (alternate Wed) and four beer festivals a year. Very popular on match days with both home and away supporters; Sky Sports is shown. Weekday lunches are served.

ODELL

Bell
Horsefair Lane
11-3, 6-11; (closed lunch), 7-10.30 Sun
☎ (01234) 720254
Greene King IPA, Ruddles County, Abbot, guest beers H
Attractive, thatched pub at the heart of the village, boasting an aviary of exotic birds and a garden running down to the River Great Ouse. With Harrold-Odell Country Park just down the lane, this is an excellent stop for breaking a walk. Although the cooking deserves its place in Good Pub Food, this is first and foremost a pub with good food rather than a restaurant with good beer. No evening meals are served Sunday. Q P

POTTON

Old Coach House
12 Market Square
12-2.30, 5.30-11; 12-11 Sat; 12-10.30 Sun
☎ (01767) 260221
Adnams Bitter; Potton Shannon IPA, Shambles; guest beer H
This Grade II listed former 17th-century coaching inn is located in Potton's picturesque market square. The family-run hotel regularly serves Potton Brewery beers and guest ales are always available. A warm, friendly welcome is offered. Meals are served in the no-smoking restaurant (not Sun eve), specialising in freshly-prepared home-cooked food. It makes an ideal base for visiting the many attractions of Bedfordshire and Cambridgeshire. Pétanque is played.
Q P

RAVENSDEN

Horse & Jockey
Church End
12-3 (4 Sat), 6-11; 12-4, 7-10.30 Sun
☎ (01234) 772319
Courage Directors; Theakston Best Bitter; guest beer (occasional) H
Two-bar village pub situated next to the church, serving a variety of food from bar snacks to full meals in a restaurant that caters for 35 diners. A good view of Bedford can be enjoyed while you dine. It hosts regular themed food evenings, for example St George's night and Indian curry nights with fancy dress. No meals are served Sunday evening or Monday. Pub games played here include darts and skittles.
Q P

RENHOLD

Three Horseshoes
42 Top End (1 mile N of A421)
11-3, 6-11.30; 11-11 Sat; 12-10.30 Sun
☎ (01234) 870218
Greene King XX Mild, IPA; guest beer H
This friendly, traditional country pub serves fresh, home-cooked food (no meals Tue eve or Sun). Specialities include home-made soup, meat pies, fresh fish (from Grimsby) and steaks. It also hosts occasional themed evenings. With plenty of walks in nearby woods the pub provides an ideal stop for ramblers. The two regular beers are complemented by regular guests. P

RIDGMONT

Rose & Crown
89 High Street
10.30-2.30 (12-3 Sat), 6-11; 12-3.30, 7-10.30 Sun
☎ (01525) 280245
Adnams Broadside; Wells Eagle, Bombardier; seasonal beer or guest beer H
Attractive pub dating back some 300 years, its two comfortably furnished bar areas house a collection of English sheepdog china and Rupert Bear memorabilia – note the Nutwood Ales sign in the car park. The tree-lined garden has approved facilities for camping and caravanning. Children are welcome in the dining area. Run by the same licensees for well over 20 years, the pub has been in every edition of this Guide.
P

RISELEY

Fox & Hounds
High Street (3 miles off A6 at Sharnbrook)
11-2.30, 6.30-11; 12-3, 7-10.30 Sun
☎ (01234) 708240
Wells Eagle, Bombardier; guest beers H
This extended old village inn enjoys a reputation for good food – charcoal-grilled steaks sold by weight are a speciality (not served Sat lunch). A dining room can be reserved for groups, but no booking is necessary for normal bar meals – meet and drink in the bar while your food is cooked. Food service can be busy at weekends. The large lawned garden has a covered patio with heating for inclement weather.
Q P

SALFORD

Red Lion Hotel
Wavendon Road (off M1 jct 13)
11-2.30, 6-11; 12-2.30, 7-10.30 Sun
☎ (01908) 583117
Wells Eagle, Bombardier; guest beer (occasional) H
Small country inn with a restaurant and busy bar warmed by a log fire in winter. The large garden has seating and a safe, well-equipped play area. Good home-cooked food, with daily specials and vegetarian choices, is served in both the bar and restaurant. En-suite accommodation includes four-poster beds. Easily accessible

from the M1, it is close to Woburn Abbey and Safari Park. ᗰQ❀⇌◑⊟♿♣P

SANDY

Sir William Peel
39 High Street
⊛ 12-11; 12-3, 7-10.30 Sun
☎ (01767) 680607
Everards Beacon; guest beers Ⓗ
One-bar traditional English pub where a warm welcome is extended to a well-behaved clientele of all ages. The three guest beers are normally supplied by small independent breweries, making for adventurous drinking. Friday nights can be hectic and occasional live music is performed. No food available, but the pub is flanked by a chip shop and Indian restaurant. ❀♿⇌♣P

SHEFFORD

Brewery Tap
14 North Bridge Street
⊛ 11.30-11; 12-10.30 Sun
☎ (01462) 628448
B&T Shefford Mild, Shefford Bitter, Dragonslayer, seasonal beers; guest beer Ⓗ
Single-bar, basic drinkers' pub where the decor features breweriana and bottled beers. Over the years it has been the Green Man, Grape Vine and Countryman, but was rescued by B&T Brewery and renamed in 1996. Popular games include table football; live music is presented most Friday evenings. Six handpumps offer B&T beers at reasonable prices and usually two guests. Food is restricted to hot pies and filled rolls. ❀♣P

SHILLINGTON

Musgrave Arms
16 Apsley End Road
⊛ 12-3, 5-11; 12-11 Sat; 12-4, 7-10.30 Sun
☎ (01462) 711286
Greene King XX Mild, Ⓗ **IPA, Abbot; guest beer** Ⓖ
Cosy country pub boasting original Tudor beams; the raised 'pub' end, with scrubbed wooden tables, is popular with dominoes players. The no-smoking dining room (where children are welcome) offers good food (steak night is Tuesday). A large garden includes children's play equipment and two pétanque pitches. This Guide regular was voted South Beds CAMRA Pub of the Year in 2001. ᗰQ❀◑♣P

STOTFOLD

Stag
35 Brook Street
⊛ 2 (12 Fri & Sat)-11; 12-10.30 Sun
☎ (01462) 730261
Adnams Bitter; Jennings Cumberland Ale; guest beers Ⓗ
Built in the early 19th century, this pub has no pretences. It is an out-and-out drinkers' pub, serving three top quality ales. The cosy bar area is augmented by pool and darts rooms. There is always a warm welcome from the bar staff enhanced by a real fire in the bar area. Look for the model railway track above the bar. Well-behaved dogs are welcome. No food is served.
ᗰ❀♣P

SUTTON

John O'Gaunt Inn
30 High Street
⊛ 12-3, 7-11; 12-3, 7-11 Sun
☎ (01767) 260377
Greene King IPA, Old Speckled Hen; guest beer Ⓗ
This traditional pub, with two beamed bars, exudes a timeless feel, and is very active in all aspects of village life. It serves a good range of home-cooked food (no meals Sun eve). There is a floodlit boules pitch and Northamptonshire skittles, open to all; it also has its own golf society. Social evenings with a buffet can be arranged. It hosts occasional informal folk sessions and morris men dance in summer in the large garden. Admire the village quilt in the lounge.
ᗰQ❀◑⊟♣P⊭

TEBWORTH

Queen's Head
The Lane
⊛ 11.30-3, 6.30-11; 12-3, 7-10.30 Sun
☎ (01525) 874101
Adnams Broadside; Ⓖ **Wells Eagle;** Ⓗ **guest beer** Ⓖ
This village local, with two small bars, was built in 1926, following the destruction of the former thatched pub by fire. The landlord oversees a public bar, with darts and a rickety pool table, and a comfortable lounge bar which hosts a weekly quiz (Thu eve), and live music on Friday evenings. It has featured in this Guide continuously for over 20 years.
ᗰ❀⊟♣P

INN BRIEF

LEIGHTON BUZZARD

Hunt Hotel
19 Church Road
12-3, 5-11; 12-3, 7-10.30 Sun
Fuller's London Pride, ESB; guest beers Ⓗ
Family-owned hotel near the rail station, with a comfortable lounge bar and restaurant (no food Sun eve). Children welcome in daytime.

Globe
26 Union Street
11-11; 12-10.30 Sun
Greene King IPA; guest beers Ⓗ
Street-corner local with an enclosed patio, offering two ever-changing guest ales and regular beer festivals. Good value food.

LUTON

Black Horse
23 Hastings Street
12-11; 12-10.30 Sun
Beer range varies Ⓗ
Much-improved, single bar serving two ever-changing guest beers, often from local micros.

TILSWORTH

Anchor
1 Dunstable Road
11-11; 12-10.30 Sun
Greene King IPA, Abbot; guest beers Ⓗ
Friendly village local offering good food at all times, a welcome to families and a large garden. Cask Marque accredited.

TODDINGTON

Bedford Arms
64 High Street
12-11; 12-10.30 Sun
Wells Eagle; seasonal beer or guest beer Ⓗ
Attractive former farmhouse with two lounge bars and a large garden. Quiz night Tue. Meals available.

✻ symbol next to a main entry place name indicates there are Inn Brief entries as well.

TODDINGTON ❊

Oddfellows Arms

2 Conger Lane

12-3 (not Mon-Thu), 5-11; 12-3.30, 7-10.30 Sun

☎ (01525) 872021

website: www.theoddfellowsarms.com

Adnams Broadside; Courage Best Bitter; Fuller's London Pride; guest beer H

Attractive, but reputedly haunted, 15th-century pub on the village green, featuring a heavily beamed and brassed L-shaped bar and a restaurant. Over 20 Belgian bottled beers, plus Hoegaarden Wit beer on draught, are all served in the correct glasses. A sheltered patio area is available for summer drinking. The extensive menu offers good value food (no meals Sun eve). Beer festivals are held in the spring and autumn at this South Beds CAMRA Pub of the Year 2002.

Sow & Pigs

19 Church Square

11-11; 12-10.30 Sun

☎ (01525) 873089 website: www.sowandpigs.co.uk

Greene King IPA, Abbot; seasonal beer or guest beer H

19th-century commercial inn with one long, narrow, dog-friendly bar, heated by three real fires, displaying assorted pigs and golfing memorabilia. No hot food, but a selection of cold platters and home-made soup are always available. The upstairs banqueting room can be booked for parties of 16-24 people, and the spread of food provided has to be seen to be believed! Accommodation offers comfortable rooms at reasonable prices. The Sow has appeared in every edition of this Guide.

Q P

TURVEY

Three Cranes

High Street (off A428)

11-2.30, 6-11; 12-3, 7-10.30 Sun

☎ (01234) 881305

Adnams Bitter; Greene King IPA, Abbot; Hook Norton Best Bitter; guest beers H

Comfortable, 17th-century coaching inn serving a good range of food in both the bar and restaurant, with a vegetarian choice always available. The split-level bar provides inviting corners for drinking and conversation. The 11-arch bridge spanning the River Great Ouse dates from the 15th century, but the picturesque olde-worlde village is mainly Victorian. Book ahead for bed and breakfast. Q P

WILDEN

Victoria

23 High Street

12-2.30, 6.30-11; 12-11 Sat; 12-3, 7-10.30 Sun

☎ (01234) 772146

Greene King IPA, Abbot; guest beer (occasional) H

This friendly, one-bar country village pub has a separate no-smoking dining room where food specials include fish and chips on Tuesday, senior citizens' meals (Wednesday lunchtime) and 'a pie and a pint' on Thursday. Themed evenings are also hosted, as well as summer barbecues in the garden. Evening meals are available Tue-Sat. P

WINGFIELD

Plough

Tebworth Road

12-3, 5.30-11 (11-11 summer Sat); 12-4, 6-10.30 (closed winter eve) Sun

☎ (01525) 873077

Adnams Bitter; Fuller's London Pride, ESB; seasonal beer or guest beer H

Attractive, thatched village inn dating from the 17th century. Beware the low beams and entrance. The conservatory to the rear doubles as a restaurant, where children are welcome, and a function/meeting room. The bar is decorated with Royal Navy memorabilia and rural scenes featuring ploughs. The food is of a high standard (no meals Sun eve). Tables are set out to the front of the pub for summer drinking, and the enclosed, prize-winning garden to the rear has children's play equipment. P

YELDEN

Chequers

High Street

12-2.30 (not Mon or Tue), 5-11; 12-11 Sat; 12-10.30 Sun

☎ (01933) 356383

Fuller's London Pride; H **Greene King Abbot;** G **Thwaites Bitter; guest beers** H

Traditional village pub, serving five real ales and two traditional ciders. It has a family-cum-skittles room and a small, no-smoking restaurant. The large garden offers a range of children's play equipment. Good value bar food is available Wed-Sun (Sunday meals finish at 5pm). An annual real ale festival is held over the spring bank holiday weekend. Yelden village is on the Three Shires Way walkers' route and boasts the impressive earthworks of a Norman castle.

P

Stout

A poet starving in a garret
Connings old Topicks like
a Parrot
Invokes his mistress and
his muse,
And stays at home for
want of shoes.
Should but his muse
descending drop
A slice of bread and
mutton chop
Or kindly when his
credit's out
Surprise him with a pint
of stout.

Jonathan Swift,
Poem to Stella,
London 1720.

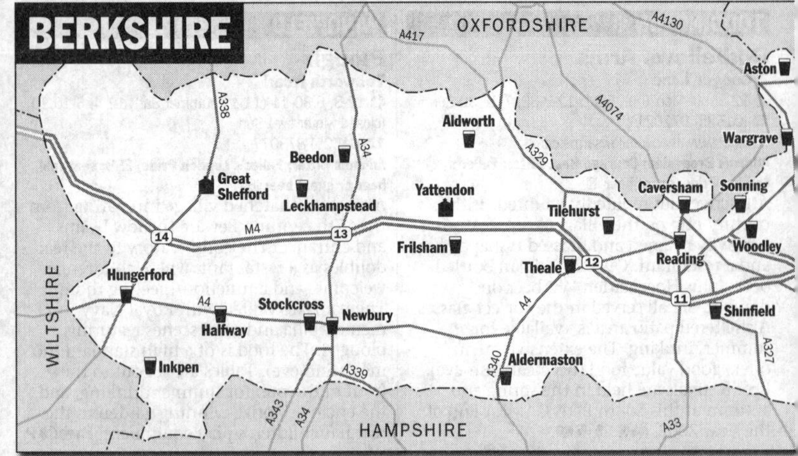

ALDWORTH

Bell ☆

Bell Lane (off B4009) OS556797

11-3, 6-11 (closed Mon); 12-3, 7-10.30 Sun

☎ (01635) 578272

Arkell's 3B, Kingsdown; West Berkshire Maggs Magnificent Mild, seasonal beers; guest beers H

Absolute gem: just what a traditional rural beer house should be. The same family has run the pub for 200 years – the current licensees since 1974. A glass-fronted serving hatch protrudes into the tiny bar, where ancient wooden furniture stands before painted brick walls. Exposed bread ovens allow more seating. There is a tap room and a lavender-scented garden leads to the cricket pitch. The nearby Ridgeway Path attracts visitors. Old Tyler is West Berkshire's Good Old Boy rebadged. Splendid filled rolls are available. CAMRA national Pub of the Year runner-up 2002.

Q P

ASCOT

Swinley

29 Brockenhurst Road, South Ascot (A330 S of racecourse)

11-11; 12-10.30 Sun

☎ (01344) 621743

Greene King IPA, Ruddles Best Bitter, Ruddles County H

Unpretentious, friendly pub with a genuine local feel, run by the same landlady for over 30 years. Built in the 1880s as a stores for the nearby railway, it was formerly known as the Railway Arms, but renamed after an ancient name for the local district. The comfortable lounge, which is bigger than at first appears, has a real fire and TV. The authentic, unspoilt public bar is unusual for the area. A member of the local cribbage league; darts and shove-ha'penny are also played. It gets very busy during Royal Ascot week.

P

BEEDON

Langley Hall Inn

Oxford Road, World's End (1 mile S of village, near M4 jct 13) OS484761

11-11; 12-7.30 Sun

☎ (01635) 248332

Brakspear Bitter; West Berkshire Good Old Boy; guest beers H

Named after a long-demolished manor house, this was a busy roadhouse until the new A34 bypassed it. After several recent changes of name and owner, it has settled down as a popular, welcoming local. The large, single horseshoe bar bears distinctly modern minimalist decor. An adjoining restaurant is popular with local business people. Breakfasts are on offer before the pub opens. Outdoor seating is on a gravel area out front. Piped music can be very loud later in the evening.

P

BINFIELD

Stag & Hounds

Forest Road (B3034, E of village)

11-11; 12-10.30 Sun

☎ (01344) 483553

Courage Best Bitter, Directors; G **guest beer** (occasional) H

Beautiful two-bar pub, parts of which are 600 years old. This whitewashed and timbered building boasts a large inglenook in the main bar and lots of nooks and crannies with seating, but beware of low beams. It once stood at the centre of Windsor Great Park, indicating the extent of the ancient forest, now greatly reduced. Parking is possible at front and rear, with outside seating in the summer. The extensive menu includes daily specials.

Q P

Victoria Arms

Terrace Road North (B3018, N of village centre)

11.30-3, 5-11; 11-11 Sat; 12-10.30 Sun

☎ (01344) 483856

Fuller's Chiswick, London Pride, ESB, seasonal beers H

Friendly pub located in a residential area just north of the village centre, enjoying a strong local trade and drawing visitors from neighbouring Bracknell. The pub is open plan with a substantial bottle collection displayed in the roof timbers, plus an old Simonds of Reading brewery sign. A basic food selection includes daily specials (no food Sun eve).

P

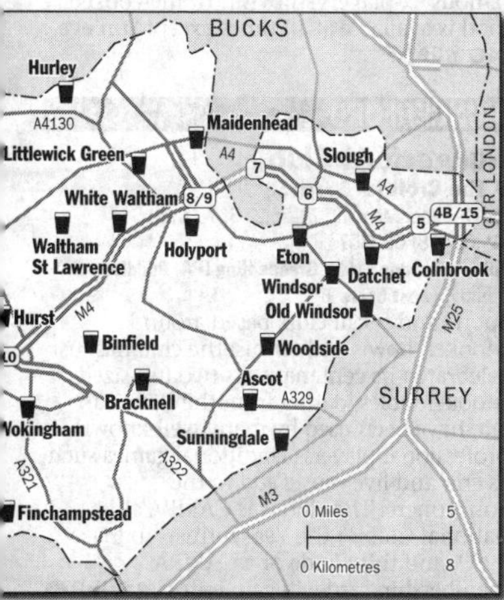

BRACKNELL

Old Manor

Grenville Place, High Street
11-11; 12-10.30 Sun ☎ (01344) 304490
Courage Directors; Theakston Best Bitter; guest beers Ⓗ
Large two-bar Wetherspoon's, converted from a former manor house. The interior retains several original features, including a priest's hole in the monk's room. The walls carry a mix of pictures of old Bracknell, along with various other curios. One bar is completely no-smoking and children are allowed in this area until 9pm if dining.
Q❀◐◑♿≠P⊬✓

CAVERSHAM ❊

Prince of Wales

76 Prospect Street (A4155)
11-3, 6-11; 11-11 Sat; 12-10.30 Sun
☎ (0118) 947 2267 website: www.nicktill.com
Brakspear Bitter, Special, seasonal beers Ⓗ
Large town pub on the northern edge of Caversham centre. Dating back to around 1890 and not over-modernised, this pub has a wood-panelled interior; the public bar houses a pool table. Live music is staged on the first Friday of each month – essentially mature pop performed by '60s-'80s cover bands. A strong sporting theme is supported by extensive TV coverage. ❀⊟♣P

COLNBROOK

Ostrich

High Street
12-3, 5.30-11; 12-3, 6.30-10.30 Sun
☎ (01753) 682682
Badger Best; Courage Directors; Wells Bombardier; guest beers Ⓗ
This famous, architecturally interesting, old pub continues to serve excellent food (including of course ostrich steaks) and ale. On the old London to Bristol coach road, many folk have stopped here for refreshment or accommodation (the latter no longer available). One landlord used to murder guests as they slept, and the grisly details are displayed in the bar. Bus No. 81 from Slough to Hounslow passes the door. Not the cheapest pub around; the cider varies. ♨❀◐◑●P

DATCHET

Royal Stag

The Green
11-11; 12-10.30 Sun
☎ (01753) 584231
Fuller's London Pride; Tetley Bitter, Burton Ale Ⓗ
A pillared porchway and heavy oak door open on to an old coaching inn that has been an ale house since the mid-17th century. One side of the building is Elizabethan. Originally called the Five Bells, the present name was adopted in 1857. The comfortable lounge is partially clad with antique wooden champagne crates. The ghostly print of a child's hand appears on the window overlooking the churchyard. The pub is owned by the Barker Bridge Trust, whose profits go towards the village upkeep. No food Sun eve.
♨◐◑⊟≠♣P

ETON

New College

55 High Street
11-11; 12-10.30 Sun
☎ (01753) 865516
Badger K&B Sussex, Best, Tanglefoot, seasonal beers Ⓗ
This Georgian-style building was taken over and extensively renovated by Badger five years ago. The open-plan, Victorian-style interior is broken up by wood and leaded glass partitions. An imaginative menu at reasonable prices is served 12-9 in summer, lunch and eve winter. Children are welcome in the dining area to the left of the bar until early evening.
❀◐◑≠(Windsor & Eton Riverside) ♣✓

FINCHAMPSTEAD

Queen's Oak

Church Lane (off B3016)
11-3, 5.30-11; 12-10.30 Sun
☎ (0118) 973 4855
website: tiggers.co.uk/home/queensoak
Brakspear Bitter, Special, seasonal beers; Coniston Bluebird Ⓗ
Fine old village pub tucked away in a hamlet opposite the church. There is a small no-smoking bar decorated with a country kitchen look, while the wood-panelled main bar leads into an informal dining area serving reasonably-priced pub meals (no food Sun eve). The current licensee has worked hard to re-establish the pub and has been rewarded with two Brakspear awards. The large garden, which houses an Aunt Sally, attracts ramblers, cyclists and families; well-behaved children are also welcome in the dining area.
♨Q❀◐◑♣P⊬

FRILSHAM

Pot Kiln ☆

1 mile S of Yattendon on road to Bucklebury
OS552781
12-2.30 (not Tue), 6.30-11; 12-3, 7-10.30 Sun
☎ (01635) 201366

INDEPENDENT BREWERIES

Butts Great Shefford
West Berkshire Yattendon

Arkells 3B; West Berkshire Brick Kiln Bitter, Gold Star, seasonal beers Ⓗ
Isolated and hard to find, this rural gem is surrounded by meadows and woodlands beloved of walkers. With bare floors and simple wooden benches and stools, it has changed little since it opened in the 1920s after a long private history of quenching local brickmakers' thirsts. Three small bars lead from a tiny tap room. A basic menu is offered, including outstanding warm filled rolls (no food Tue), but the accent is firmly on old-fashioned liquid refreshment and lively conversation. Brick Kiln Bitter is unique to the Pot Kiln.
⋔Q❀◑◑⊟♣P⊬

HALFWAY

Halfway Inn

Bath Road (A4, between Newbury and Hungerford)
⏲ 11-2.30 (3 Sat), 6-11; 12-3, 7-10.30 Sun
☎ (01488) 658215 website: www.the-halfway-inn.co.uk
Badger Best, Tanglefoot Ⓗ
This 18th-century coaching inn lies 63 miles from London and Bath – hence the name. With little local trade, it is obliged to focus on food, but the restaurant at the back is separate from the roomy oak-beamed bar. The polished wood furnishings are topped by a collection of commemorative beer bottles. Drivers should take care when using the car park – the main road traffic can be dangerously fast.
⋔❀◑◑P✔

HOLYPORT

Belgian Arms

Holyport Street (off A330)
⏲ 11-3, 5.30-11; 12-3, 7-10.30 Sun
☎ (01628) 634468
Brakspear Bitter, Special Ⓗ
Once known as the Eagle, the name of this unspoilt, wisteria-clad pub was changed after German POWs saluted it in WWI. 400 years old, it is deservedly popular all year round. The beams and open fires in winter give an 'olde-worlde' atmosphere. The garden overlooks the village green, site of Holyport Fair each June, where international cricket used to take place; famous ex-players still visit. Home-cooked food is available at all times except Sun eve.
⋔Q❀◑◑♿P

HUNGERFORD

Hungerford Club

3 The Croft (off Church St)
⏲ 12-3 (not Mon-Fri), 7-11; 12-3, 7-10.30 Sun
☎ (01488) 682357
Fuller's London Pride; Greene King IPA, Ruddles County; guest beers Ⓗ
Sports and social club, based around snooker, bowls and tennis; the club has just celebrated its centenary. Its two full-sized snooker tables, dating from the Victorian era, have been used by many well-known professional players. Traditional games such as crib and live music add to the atmosphere. The club was CAMRA's national Club of the Year runner-up in 1999, and this Guide or a CAMRA membership card will gain entry. ❀≷♣P✔

HURLEY

Dew Drop Inn

Batts Green, Honey Lane (off A423, turn up road by Grassland Research Centre) OS824815
⏲ 12-3, 6-11; 12-3, 7-10.30 Sun
☎ (01628) 824327
Brakspear Bitter, Special, seasonal beers Ⓗ
Remote, hard-to-find hostelry, located on Ashley Hill, the pub was originally cottages used by the workers from the nearby estate. Recently extended, it was a beer house until the 1960s. Reputedly haunted, the ghost only appears in the original part of the pub, especially near the gents' toilets. The pub is a venue for a vintage car club.
⋔Q❀◑◑♿♣P

HURST

Green Man

Hinton Road (off A321)
⏲ 11-3, 5.30-11; 12-3, 7-10.30 (extended hours summer) Sun
☎ (0118) 934 2599 website: www.greenman.uk.com
Brakspear Bitter, Special, seasonal beers Ⓗ
This lovely, oak-beamed, 17th-century village pub, tucked down a side road, was

INN BRIEF

ALDERMASTON

Hind's Head
Wasing Lane
11-11; 12-10.30 Sun
(0118) 971 2194
Gale's GB, HSB, seasonal beers Ⓗ
Comfortable, recently refurbished village inn, dating from 1630, with its own clockhouse, bell tower, disused brewery and jail. Cask Marque accredited.

ASTON

Flower Pot
11-3, 6-11; 12-3, 7-10.30 Sun
(01491) 574721
Brakspear Bitter, Special, Old, seasonal beers Ⓗ
Late 19th-century hotel on the Thames path with a bare-boarded public bar and a modernised extended lounge bar. No food Sun eve.

CAVERSHAM

Griffin
10-12 Church Road (A4074)
11-11; 12-10.30 Sun
(0118) 947 5018
Courage Best Bitter, Directors; Theakston XB; guest beer Ⓗ
Chef & Brewer branded conversion of a 100-year-old pub. An extensive range of restaurant quality food is served at all times. The guest beer is usually from regional or micro-breweries.

MAIDENHEAD

Ark
20 Ray Street
12-11; 12-10.30 Sun
(01628) 418707
Courage Best Bitter Ⓗ
Small corner pub in a residential area to the east of the town centre.

Hobgoblin
34 High Street
12-11; 6-10.30 Sun
(01628) 784786
Wychwood Hobgoblin; guest beers Ⓗ
Town-centre pub, handy for shoppers during the day and popular with younger drinkers in the evening.

North Star
91 Westborough Road
12-11; 12-10.30 Sun
(01628) 622711
Courage Best Bitter; Fuller's London Pride Ⓗ
Small local in a residential area. It hosts frequent events, such as quizzes and 'open the box'; table skittles played.

sympathetically extended in 1999 to form several small rooms and dining areas for smokers and non-smokers. Emphasis is on reasonably-priced and good quality food, but it remains a local beer drinkers' pub. Daily specials are shown on a blackboard. The attractive garden boasts hanging baskets and rural views. Children have a well-equipped play area and are welcome inside until 8.30pm. Wheelchair WC.
⌂Q❀◐◑♿P⊬

INKPEN

Crown & Garter

Inkpen Common (signed from A4 at Kintbury) OS378638

✪ 12-2.30 (not Mon or Tue; 3 Sat); 6.30 (6 Sat)-11; 12-3, 7-10.30 Sun

☎ (01488) 668325 website: www.crownandgarter.com

Archers Village; West Berkshire Good Old Boy, seasonal beers; guest beers Ⓗ

Set in an area of outstanding natural beauty, this recently renovated 17th-century inn offers excellent en-suite accommodation in a quadrangle of rooms surrounding a private garden. An imaginative menu is offered in the bistro-style single horseshoe bar, but drinkers will not feel out of place and there is a thriving local trade. Family-friendly; colouring books and crayons are offered to children. Combe Gibbet can be seen from the delightful garden where the landlady's green fingers are much in evidence. No eve meals Sun-Tue, except for residents. ⌂❀⇄◐◑P

Swan Inn

Craven Road, Lower Green (3 miles from Hungerford, off A338) OS359643

✪ 11-2.30, 7-11 (11-11 summer Sat); 12-3, 7-10.30 (12-10.30 summer) Sun

☎ (01488) 668326

website: www.theswaninn-organics.co.uk

Butts Bitter; Hook Norton Mild, Best Bitter; guest beers Ⓗ

This 17th-century inn was carefully extended by a local farmer to include a 10-room hotel, restaurant and organic shop. It remains at heart a friendly village local, where regulars cluster round the bar or adjourn to the flagstoned games room to play darts. Good quality organic produce features on both bar and restaurant menus, much of the pub is no-smoking, and ramps make the entire ground floor wheelchair-friendly. A large terraced patio is popular with hikers and cyclists. Guest ales are often organic; Lambourn Valley supplies the cider. Local CAMRA Pub of the Year 2000.
⌂❀◐◑♿♣●P⊬

LECKHAMPSTEAD

Stag

Shop Lane (off B4494) OS765438

✪ 11-3 (not Mon-Thu); 5.30 (6.30 Sat)-11; 12-4, 7-10.30 Sun

☎ (01488) 638436

Hook Norton Old Hooky; guest beers Ⓗ

Converted to a single L-shaped bar in the 1960s, this rural pub, catering for locals in a small downlands village, retains a two-bar feel. The old public bar has a bar billiards table, while a large sofa and a wood-burning stove provide comfort in the former saloon. A small dining room serves meals, with an emphasis on Greek recipes. The pleasant rear garden is complemented by a decked seating area at the front. ⌂❀◐◑♿♣P

LITTLEWICK GREEN

Cricketers

Coronation Road (off A4 near Maidenhead Thicket)

✪ 11-3, 5-11; 11-11 Sat; 12-10.30 Sun

☎ (01628) 822888

Brakspear Bitter; Fuller's London Pride; guest beer Ⓗ

This pleasant free house overlooks the green and cricket pitch in a pretty village, often seen on TV. A sporting theme features in the decor and a factory clock dominates the main bar. The friendly atmosphere, with a cosy open fire in winter and tables out front, make this village pub attractive all year. It is handy for the nearby business park. ⌂❀⇄◐◑♿♣P

MAIDENHEAD ❊

Vine

20 Market Street

✪ 11-11; 12-10.30 Sun

☎ (01628) 782112

NEWBURY

Lock, Stock & Barrel
104 Northbrook Street (next to canal bridge)
11-11; 12-10.30 Sun
(01635) 42730
Fuller's London Pride, ESB, seasonal beers Ⓗ
Airy, one-bar pub off the main shopping street with a popular riverside patio and roof top terrace. Meals served lunch and eve. Wheelchair WC.

READING

3B's Café Bar
Old Town Hall, Blagrave Street
(in town hall, next to information centre)
10-11; closed Sun
(0118) 939 9803
Beer range varies Ⓗ
Frequented by older people and shoppers during the day, students eves, it is invariably busy. Four handpumps serve an ever-changing beer range. Wheelchair WC.

Back of Beyond
104-108 Kings Road
11-11; 12-10.30 Sun
(0118) 959 5906
Courage Directors; Greene King Abbot; Hop Back Summer Lightning; Shepherd Neame Spitfire; Theakston Best Bitter; guest beers Ⓗ
Spacious Wetherspoon's, on the eastern fringe of the town centre on the Kennet Canal. Two guest beers change regularly.

STOCKCROSS

Rising Sun
Ermine Street
12-2 (not Mon), 5.30-11; 12-2.30, 7-11 Sat; 12-3, 7-10.30 Sun
(01488) 608131
Greene King IPA; West Berkshire Good Old Boy Ⓗ
Comfortable, down-to-earth, main road village local with a piano and occasional live bands. Car park exits on to a dangerous bend.

WOKINGHAM

Crispin
45 Denmark Street
11-11; 12-10.30 Sun
(0118) 978 0309
Cains Dr Duncans IPA; Wadworth 6X; guest beer Ⓗ
Reputedly the oldest building in the town, situated just off the market place serving food and a good choice of guest beer.

Hope & Anchor
11 Station Road
11.30-11; 12-10.30 Sun
(0118) 978 0918
Brakspear Bitter, Special Ⓗ
16th-century inn, formerly combined with a bakery. Caters for a wide clientele with sports TV, music and food lunchtime and early eve.

Brakspear Mild, Bitter, Special, seasonal beers Ⓗ
Cosy, traditional town-centre local where internal alterations in 2001 increased the customer area without changing the character of the pub. Real mild is now a fixture – unusual for the area. An extensive lunchtime menu of mostly traditional pub grub is served Sun-Fri. The decor includes a collection of spirit and liquor miniatures. Satellite TV shows live football matches; darts night is Wed and quiz night Sun. Public car parks are available nearby.
❀◖⇌♣✔

NEWBURY ❊

Hogshead

1-3 Wharf Street (between wharf and market place)
✪ 12-11; 12-10.30 Sun
☎ (01635) 569895
Greene King Abbot; Taylor Landlord; Wadworth 6X; guest beers Ⓗ/Ⓖ
Converted in 1997 from an agricultural auction mart, this large, light and airy split-level pub affords picture-window views of the canal. Solid wood rafters, furniture and bar combine with tiled and wood floors and a high ceiling to create an echoing single bar that is always busy. The half-dozen ales in the week are increased to 12 at weekends, mostly sourced from small regional or craft breweries. There is a good selection of bottled continental beers and choice of ciders. Wheelchair WC.
♨◖◗♿⇌●⚡

Monument

57 Northbrook Street (near Broadway clock tower)
✪ 11-11; 12-10.30 Sun
☎ (01635) 41964
website: www.themonumentonline.co.uk
Butts Bitter, Barbus Barbus; Greene King Old Speckled Hen; Theakston Old Peculier; guest beers Ⓗ
Lively, and often noisy 16th-century High Street boozer. The single, small bar is split into three sections, focusing on MTV or table football. A wide range of bar games includes electronic machines while the 400-CD juke box and Internet access are free. Entertainment is frequent and varies from stand-up comedy to live blues bands, often performing in the new rear covered courtyard. Part of Enterprise Inns' Tap & Spile chain, it is Butts Brewery's only regular Newbury outlet.
◖♣

OLD WINDSOR

Jolly Gardeners

92 St Lukes Road
✪ 11-11; 12-10.30 Sun
☎ (01753) 740893
Ansells Mild; Courage Directors; Greene King IPA Ⓗ
Genuine community local where the single horseshoe-shaped bar keeps a public bar/lounge feel. While the beer range is subject to change, mild is a fixture – unusual in the area. The publicans' aim to maintain a traditional pub is as successful as it is laudable. Breakfast is available 9-10.30 Tue-Sat and 10-11.30 Sun. Local CAMRA Pub of the Season winter 2001-2.
❀P

READING ❊

Butler

89-91 Chatham Street (just outside inner ring road)
✪ 11-11; 12-3, 7-10.30 Sun
☎ (0118) 939 1635
Fuller's Chiswick, London Pride, ESB, seasonal beers; guest beer Ⓗ
Originally a Victorian wine merchants' premises, it was acquired by Fuller's in the late 1970s. The Butler retains the appearance and feel of a Victorian establishment with high ceilings and bare floorboards. The pub is close to the town centre, but is well established, enjoying a good mix of customers, with a strong local base. No food Sun eve. ♨◖◗⇌P

Fisherman's Cottage

224 Kennet Side
✪ 11-11 (11-3, 6-11 winter); 12-10.30 Sun
☎ (0118) 957 1553
Fuller's London Pride, ESB, seasonal beers Ⓗ
A pleasant stroll beside the River Kennet from the town centre leads to this riverside pub, adjacent to Blakes Lock. It can also be reached from the opposite direction with a short detour from the Thames path. A conservatory-style extension has doubled the size of the original building without losing its traditional character. There is plentiful patio seating at the front overlooking the river and a terraced rear garden where barbecues are held in the summer. ❀◖◗♣P

Hobgoblin

2 Broad Street
✪ 11-11; 12-10.30 Sun
☎ (0118) 950 8119
Beer range varies Ⓗ
A Reading institution. The obvious pull being the range of five or six ever-changing, contrasting and often rare micro-brewery beers from all over the UK and sometimes further afield. Particularly worth celebrating, given its location opposite the Oracle Centre, is that the pub sticks shamelessly to catering exclusively for the discerning drinker. An eclectic mix of customers in the front bar guarantees interesting conversations; the faint-hearted might prefer the more secluded areas in the back room.
⇌●

Hop Leaf

163-165 Southampton Street (A33, one-way system, towards town centre from M4)
✪ 12-2 (not Mon or Tue), 4-11; 12-11 Sat; 12-10.30 Sun
☎ (0118) 967 2330
Hop Back GFB, Crop Circle, Entire Stout, Thunderstorm, Summer Lightning Ⓗ
The name comes from the sign of the old Simonds Brewery (later taken over by Courage), to whom the pub belonged. It is a basic, friendly ale house, of a kind becoming too rare today. One of Hop Back Brewery's few tied pubs, it has a small brewhouse, which ceased production in 2002. A real, no-frills, community pub, it fields keen darts and cribbage teams. If coming by car, try parking at the Oracle Shopping Centre and walk back up Southampton Street. **Q**♣

Retreat

8 St John Street (off A329)
⏲ 12-2, 5-11; 12-11 Fri & Sat; 12-10.30 Sun
☎ (0118) 957 1593
Brakspear Bitter; guest beers Ⓗ
True back-street local – unique in Reading and increasingly rare throughout Britain. The new landlord has slightly shifted the emphasis, but the pub itself remains unchanged. Expect three to five guest beers, quiet background jazz and interesting conversations. The regulars, a diverse bunch, select which of the two distinctive rooms suits them best. Though not nostalgic, the pub effortlessly reminds its customers of that time before the mega-pub was born.
⊟♣

SHINFIELD

Magpie & Parrot

Arborfield Road (A327 just S of village)
⏲ 12-7; 12-3 Sun
☎ (0118) 988 4130
Fuller's London Pride Ⓗ
Magnificent, refined, if idiosyncratic, village pub. Despite the fact that the single gabled room barely seats 20 and that the pub closes in the early evening, everyone visiting and sharing the ambience will be rewarded with a relaxing experience. The decor, furnishings and somewhat bizarre collections of artefacts contribute to the congenial atmosphere. Even Spencer, the pub's dog, has his own armchair. Don't miss the beer garden, an ornithologist's paradise. The 144 Reading-Wokingham bus stops outside.
⌂Q❀P

SLOUGH

Rose & Crown

312 High Street
⏲ 11-11; 12-10.30 Sun
☎ (01753) 521114
Beer range varies Ⓗ
Genuine free house at the east end of the High Street, first licensed in 1820. An ever-changing range of beers is stocked, often from unusual breweries. Small and traditional, despite Friday karaoke, the pub is popular with workers from the local sorting office and those avoiding the 'disco and doorstaff' venues prevalent in the area. Outdoor seating is on a pavement patio. Sunday lunch is available.
❀⇌

Wheatsheaf

15 Albert Street, Upton
⏲ 11-11; 12-10.30 Sun
☎ (01753) 522019
Fuller's Chiswick, London Pride, ESB, seasonal beers Ⓗ
This single bar, traditionally-styled pub was formerly a bakery, but has been licensed since 1897. The red phone box in the bar is complemented by an old pillar box in the heated, covered, garden area. A selection of agricultural tools and musical instruments adorn the walls. Two trophy-winning football teams are formed from the regulars; a weekly quiz is held Thu eve.
❀◐✔

SONNING

Bull Hotel

High Street (off B481, next to church)
⏲ 11-3, 5.30-11; 11-11 Sat; 12-10.30 Sun
☎ (0118) 969 3901
Gale's Butser, GB, HSB, seasonal beers; guest beer (occasional) Ⓗ
Always busy, upmarket pub in the village centre, it is owned by the adjacent church and leased to Gale's Brewery. Two bars boast oak beams and inglenooks, the 'locals' bar being reserved for drinkers only. Expensive, but good quality, meals are served in the main bar and rear (no-smoking) dining room; snacks are available all afternoon at weekends. The exterior is particularly attractive in summer when the hanging baskets are in bloom. Plentiful outside seating in peaceful surroundings is a bonus.
⌂Q❀⇌◐◑⊟P✔

SUNNINGDALE

Nag's Head

28 High Street
⏲ 11.30-11; 12-10.30 Sun
☎ (01344) 622725
Harveys XX Mild, BB, Old, seasonal beers Ⓗ
Well worth the short detour from the A30, this is a typical friendly local, situated at the heart of the village. One of the more far-flung outposts of Harveys of Sussex, the excellent beer cannot be faulted. It comprises two bars: a public bar where various games are played, including darts; and a lounge bar with a small side room for quieter drinking/eating (meals served weekdays). A friendly pub cat takes pride of place in front of the fire on winter days. A large garden is a summer attraction.
❀◐⊟♣P

THEALE

Fox & Hounds

Station Road, Sunnyside (between Theale and Burghfield, 1/2 mile S of canal bridge)
⏲ 11-3, 5-11; 12-3.30, 7-10.30 Sun
☎ (0118) 930 2295
Badger Tanglefoot; Draught Bass; Wadworth IPA, 6X, JCB; guest beers Ⓗ
This Wadworth house has one long bar with a separate restaurant area. There is a large collection of earthenware bottles, and paintings are occasionally displayed for sale. Friendly locals, bar billiards and attentive bar staff add to the enjoyment. Jazz nights (Tue) and other occasional live music events are staged. A small garden has tables and a play area for children. No food Sun eve.
⌂❀◐◑♣P✔

TILEHURST

Butcher's Arms

9 Lower Armour Road
⏲ 11-3 (3.30 Sat), 6-11; 12-3, 7-10.30 Sun
☎ (0118) 942 4313 website: www.butchersarms.org.uk
Archers Best Bitter; Flowers IPA Ⓗ
Pre-dating most of the surrounding suburban housing, this former Wethered's tied house retains its character and its licensee of 25 years. It has no special disabled facilities, but access is convenient.

Local documents show the history of the pub and its land from 1841 onwards. A pub for all ages and all seasons of the year. ❀⊟♣P

WALTHAM ST LAWRENCE

Bell

The Street

11.30-3, 5-11; 12-10.30 Sun

☎ (0118) 934 1788

Brakspear Bitter; guest beers Ⓗ

This 14th-century free house stands close to the village church. The regular Brakspear bitter is complemented by four changing guests, with the emphasis on breweries from Berkshire and Oxfordshire, such as West Berkshire and Wychwood. The pub consists of a series of interlinked rooms; a small no-smoking snug to the left of the entrance corridor, a room to the rear (used mainly for eating) and a main bar area which leads to a small lounge with an open fire. No meals Sun eve. ⌂Q❀◑◐⊟P⅟

WARGRAVE

Bull Hotel

Church Street

11-3, 6-11; 12-4, 7-10.30 Sun

☎ (0118) 940 3120

Brakspear Bitter, Special, seasonal beers Ⓗ

Unspoilt, 17th-century hostelry, featuring exposed beams, brasses and a log fire. A converted terrace provides an extra room for eating and drinking. Renowned for top quality, appetising food, children are welcome in this new area and the garden, but no under-sevens after 7pm, please. Can be reached by 328 bus (not Sun or eve), train or by the Reading-Wargrave cycleway. Beer is pricey but on a par with the Henley area. ⌂Q❀⊭◑◐⇌✓

WHITE WALTHAM

Beehive

Waltham Road (off B3024)

11-3.30, 5-11; 11-11 Sat; 12-11 Sun

☎ (01628) 822877

Brakspear Bitter; Flowers Original; Fuller's London Pride; guest beer Ⓗ

Near a large private airfield and historic church, the Beehive is the hub of local social activity. Its three areas comprise a public bar, lounge with real fire, and a no-smoking conservatory/restaurant. Home-cooked food is always available. The garden overlooks the village cricket pitch; at the rear, bowls or pétanque may be played. A plaque beside the large car park records that the building burned down in May 1861, but was rebuilt by late June. ⌂❀◑◐⊟♣P⅟

WINDSOR

Black Horse

Dedworth Road (opp. Tesco)

11-2.30, 5-11; 11-11 Fri & Sat; 12-10.30 Sun

☎ (01753) 861953

Draught Bass; Brakspear Bitter; Fuller's London Pride; guest beer Ⓗ

Friendly, community local in west Windsor. Guest beers are rotated throughout the seasons and mild is a regular feature. The main bar, in mock-Tudor style, is enhanced by a real coal fire. Cribbage and darts matches and fund-raising events take place regularly throughout the year. A wide-screen TV, towards the back of the pub, relays sports events. A small crazy-paved garden area to the side of the pub allows for outdoor drinking. Special menus are available at lunchtime. ⌂❀◑♣P

Mitre

Oxford Road

11-11; 12-10.30 Sun

☎ (01753) 862510 website: www.mitrewindsor.co.uk

Fuller's London Pride; guest beers Ⓗ

Street-corner pub, serving a mainly local trade in a residential area. Team activities and sports are an important aspect, including hockey, five-a-side football and clay pigeon shooting, while in the pub itself there is a pool room and a large-screen TV where most sports events, especially football, can be viewed. Quiz nights take place on Sundays, with questions often being set by the previous week's winner. Weekday meals available.
◑◐⇌(Windsor & Eton Central) ♣

Vansittart Arms

105 Vansittart Road

12-11; 12-10.30 Sun

☎ (01753) 865988 website: www.chipfreezone.co.uk

Fuller's London Pride, ESB, seasonal beers; guest beers Ⓗ

Chip-free pub that offers enticing, imaginative dishes. Old settles and recesses provide a cosy atmosphere and rugby memorabilia abounds in the bar billiards room. A special feature is a colossal montage of pub revellers. Close to the entrance, blackboards advertise forthcoming special evenings which now include live music on Sunday, when no meals are served. A summer beer festival is a regular event, taking place on the heated rear patio. Guest beers now feature regularly.
⌂❀◑◐⇌(Windsor & Eton Central) ♣✓

WOKINGHAM ❄

Broad Street Tavern

29 Broad Street

11-11; 12-3, 7-10.30 Sun

☎ (0118) 977 3706

Wadworth IPA, 6X, JCB, seasonal beers; guest beers Ⓗ

Popular, town-centre pub run by an enthusiastic landlord who is Cask Marque accredited. Mini-beer festivals are held every February and November. This Grade II listed building offers a number of drinking areas, including a large garden. It hosts monthly live music (first Thu) and has just formed its own Aunt Sally team; crib and dominoes are also played here. Wheelchair WC.
Q❀◑⇌⅟✓

Crooked Billet

Honey Hill (off Nine Mile Ride) OS826867

11-11; 12-10.30 Sun

☎ (0118) 978 0438 website: www.wootoninns.com

Brakspear Bitter, Special, seasonal beers Ⓗ

Superb country pub, situated a mile and a half south-east of the town centre. This Grade II listed building has a welcoming fire in the winter, with a snug at one end of the single bar. The pleasant garden is popular in summer for families, as well as cyclists and ramblers from nearby Finchampstead Ridges (NT); an Aunt Sally is an added attraction. ⛫Q❀◐◑♿♣P⚡

Duke's Head

56 Denmark Street

11.30-3, 5.30 (5 Fri)-11; 11.30-3, 6-11 Sat; 12-3, 7-10.30 Sun

☎ (0118) 978 0316

Brakspear Bitter, Special, seasonal beers H

This whitewashed pub is just a short walk from the market square, overlooking Denmark Street. The traditional bar opens on to the games bar and a cosy seating area. At the far end are extra seats and French doors that give access to the walled patio garden with bench table seating. There is a plush feel to the decor. The comprehensive menu includes vegetarian choices and filled baked potatoes. A no-smoking area is available at lunchtime. ❀◐⇌P⚡✔

WOODLEY

Inn on the Park

Woodford Park, Haddon Drive

11-2.30, 6-11; 11-11 Fri & Sat; 12-10.30 Sun

☎ (0118) 962 8655

website: www.inn-on-the-park.co.uk

Brakspear Bitter, Special; Fuller's London Pride; guest beers H

Comfortable and friendly one-bar pub within the sports centre, located in Woodford Park. It is convenient for the local shopping centre and a large patio is next to the park's children's play area and paddling pool, making it an ideal choice for families. ❀♿P

WOODSIDE

Duke of Edinburgh

Woodside Road (off A332)

11-3, 5-11; 11-11 Sat & summer Fri; 12-10.30 (6 winter) Sun

☎ (01344) 882736

Arkell's 2B, 3B, Kingsdown, seasonal beers H

Reputedly once the local post office this is Arkell's most easterly, and furthest pub from the brewery. It has three main bar areas and an à la carte restaurant. The 'sports' bar has a wide-screen TV, dartboard and football memorabilia. Other bars are decorated with prints of Arkell's old advertisements and dried hops. The corner garden is always busy during the summer with visitors to Windsor Great Park or Ascot racecourse. ⛫❀◐◑♣P

Future of Brakspear's Beers

W H Brakspear of Henley-on-Thames, whose beers are widely available in the Thames Valley area, will close its brewery by the end of 2002. The brands have been sold to Refresh UK, a company originally set up to market the Usher's beers from the former Trowbridge brewery, which now also owns the Wychwood Brewery in Witney. Brakspear will remain in business as a pub owner. In the short term, Refresh will have Brakspear's beers brewed mainly at Thomas Hardy in Burtonwood, with some brewed at Wychwood. Refresh plans to build a new brewery as close to Henley as possible. The problem will be finding a site that is not prohibitively expensive, and getting planning permission. Refresh is holding talks with local authorities anxious to provide employment in some areas of Oxfordshire. As Refresh's plans are to build a 'micro-brewery' it's clear that Brakspear's volumes are expected to be dramatically reduced, and low volume seasonal brands will probably disappear. Wychwood has a bottling facility and it's to be hoped that some of Brakspear's fine bottled beers, including the organic range, will survive.

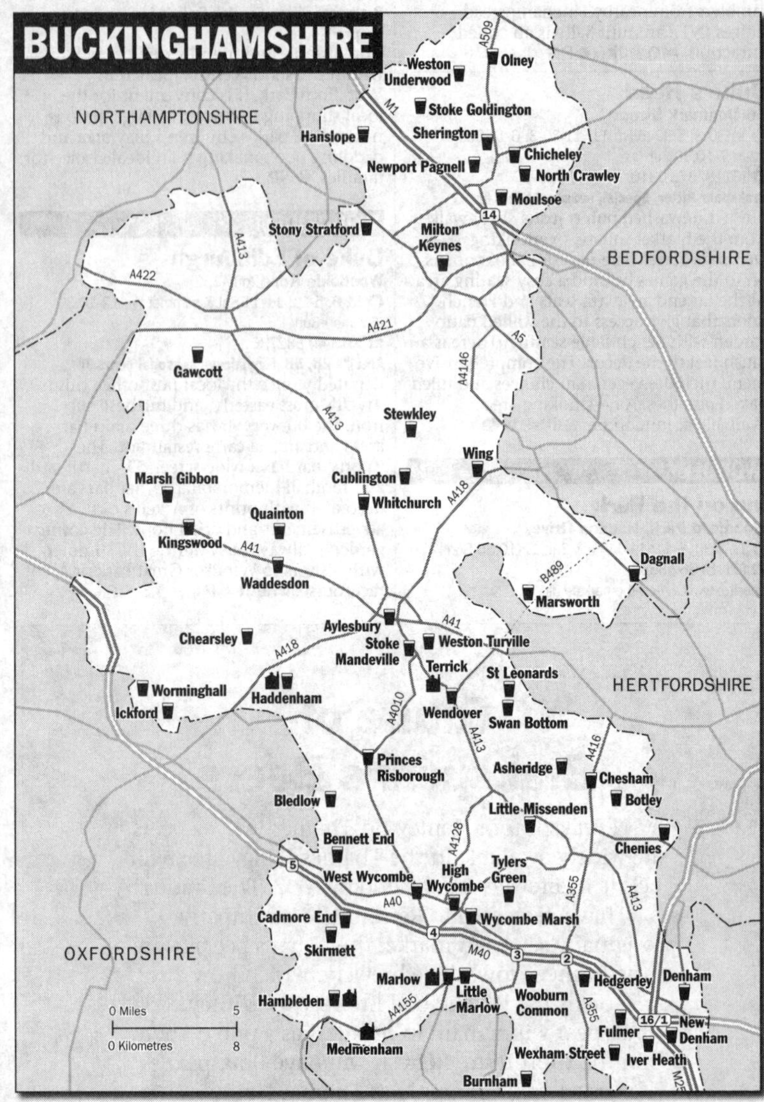

ASHERIDGE

Blue Ball

Asheridge Road (2 miles NW from Chesham, through Asheridge Rd Ind Est) OS938046
✪ 12-2.30, 5.30-11; 12-11 Fri & Sat; 12-10.30 Sun
☎ (01494) 758263
website: www.blueball.org
Fuller's London Pride; Wells Bombardier; guest beer Ⓗ

Located in a hamlet two miles from Chesham, this busy family pub is the sort every village should possess. The hard-working landlord and his family run a three-day beer festival in June with 25 ales, music, barbecue, historical re-enactments and children's day. A large field is used by groups for camping (book in advance). It hosts a quiz night (Thu) and evening entertainment (Fri and Sat). A good menu completes the amenities at this rural gem.

⌂❀◑▲♣P

AYLESBURY

Queen's Head

1 Temple Square
✪ 11.30-3, 5.30-11; 11.30-11 Fri & Sat; 12-5, 7-10.30 Sun
☎ (01296) 415484
Adnams Bitter; Courage Directors; Flowers IPA; guest beer Ⓗ

Friendly pub near the Roald Dahl Museum, it is the closest thing to a village pub in a town. Very popular, especially at lunchtime, it offers four real ales with a range of daily specials on the food menu. No juke box or fruit machines spoil the atmosphere which is enhanced by oak beams throughout the pub. The Queen's Head is the sister pub to the nearby King's Head, a 16th-century coaching inn owned by the National Trust, and run by the same landlord.

⌂Q❀⇆◑≉

BLEDLOW

Lions of Bledlow

Church End (off B4009, Chinnor-Princes Risborough road) OS776020
11-3, 6-11; 12-3, 7-10.30 Sun
☎ (01844) 343345
Marston's Pedigree; Wadworth 6X; guest beers H
Rambling, unspoilt 16th-century pub, complete with beams and inglenooks and a particularly large log fire in winter. It comprises a games room, restaurant and a large bar where a wide range of food is available from the blackboard menus. Pictures and notes of the pub's earlier days are displayed on the wall. The extensive rear garden is busy in summer with walkers and families, while tables at the front of the pub enjoy a picturesque setting at the junction of footpaths and bridleways. Q P

BURNHAM

George

20 High Street
11-11; 12-10.30 Sun
☎ (01628) 605047
Courage Best Bitter, H **Directors;** P
Vale Notley Ale H
This 16th-century, Grade II listed coaching inn has been run by the same licensee for 35 years. The bare-boarded single bar has seating to one side and a pool table. 'Alice' is the locals' name for Directors, raised by electric pump and served through a keg-style font in a mirror behind the bar. When the front door is locked in the afternoon access is via the rear courtyard/car park. P

CHEARSLEY

Bell

The Green
12.30-2.30 (not Mon; 12-3 Sat), 6-11; 12-3, 7-10.30 Sun
☎ (01844) 208077
Fuller's Chiswick, London Pride, ESB, seasonal beers H
Traditional, thatched country pub by the village green, renowned for its excellent range of food at reasonable prices – bar snacks, an à la carte menu and Sunday lunches are all available, together with vegetarian and children's options. Evening meals are served Wed-Sat. Its comfortable atmosphere is enhanced by open fires. The large, safe garden has a play area. Aylesbury Vale Council's Best Village Pub winner 1998 and 2000. Q P

CHENIES

Red Lion

Off A404, between Chorleywood and Little Chalfont
11-2, 5.30-11; 12-3, 7-10.30 Sun
☎ (01923) 282722
Wadworth 6X; guest beers H
Popular free house in a picturesque village, close to the River Chess. Enjoy superb home-cooked food from an always interesting menu. A lovely tiny snug bar can be found towards the back. Guest beers are usually sourced locally or from micro-breweries; local bottled ales are also available. House beers: Lion Pride is brewed by Rebellion and the Ben's Bitter comes from Vale Brewery. This immaculate pub is worth a visit. Q P

CHESHAM

Queen's Head

120 Church Street
12-2.30, 5-11; 12-11 Sat; 12-10.30 Sun
☎ (01494) 778690
Brakspear Bitter; Fuller's London Pride, ESB H
Corner pub in Old Chesham comprising two bars and a restaurant. The public bar displays beer and cricket memorabilia and is a fine example of its type. The saloon is divided into two areas for drinkers and diners partaking of the Thai food from the upstairs restaurant (no evening meals Sun). The River Chess runs around and under the pub. With excellent beer (mainly Fuller's) this makes a popular drinking and meeting place, and a cosy, cheerful retreat.
Q

CUBLINGTON

Unicorn

High Street
12-3 (not Mon), 5.30-11; 12-11 Sat; 12-10.30 Sun
☎ (01296) 681261
website: www.chilterncountryinns.com
Brakspear Bitter; Shepherd Neame Spitfire; guest beers H
Five ales are now always available at this unspoilt, low beamed country free house. Set in a quiet village, five miles north of Aylesbury and popular with all, the effort of finding it will be well rewarded. Food is available at all times (except Sun and Mon eves), including snacks and bar meals, with daily specials. Monthly theme nights featuring Chinese, Italian, Thai, Indian and Mexican cuisine are also proving successful.
Q P

DAGNALL

Golden Rule

Main Road South (A4146)
11.30-3, 5.30-11; 12-3, 7-10.30 Sun
☎ (01442) 843227
Fuller's London Pride, ESB, H **seasonal beers; guest beers** H/G
This rural gem of a free house may be in a small village location, but it is renowned for miles around for the landlord's warm welcome and great beers that are constantly changing. Four beer festivals a year, offering summer and winter ales, including customers' requests, keep plenty of interest in this busy pub. It is well placed to quench the thirsts of the many walkers drawn to the area. Please note: food is no longer available. Q P

DENHAM

Falcon

Village Road (off A40 and A412)

INDEPENDENT BREWERIES

Chiltern Terrick
Old Luxters Hambleden
Rebellion Marlow Bottom
Trueman's Medmenham
Vale Haddenham

⏲ 11-3, 5.30-11; 12-3, 7-10.30 Sun
☎ (01895) 832125
Brakspear Bitter; Flowers IPA; Marston's Pedigree; guest beer [H]
Delightful, traditional pub, steeped in history. Originally called Emmots Deyes from before Henry VIII's accession to the throne, it is now named after the bird on the Boyer family crest (local landowners in the 17th century). Excellent food is served – fresh fish on Fridays. Parking can be difficult, but Gerrards Cross to Uxbridge buses run on the main road, 400 yards away. ❀◑ ≢⁄

FULMER

Black Horse
Windmill Road
⏲ 11-3, 5.30-11; 11-11 Sat; 12-10.30 Sun
☎ (01753) 663183
Greene King IPA, Ruddles County, Abbot [H]
Comfortable and welcoming, with a traditional pub atmosphere, this early 17th-century building once housed the workers who built the church opposite. Although the original three bars are no longer separate, much of the cosy feel that they gave remains. Meals are served in the bar or restaurant area. ♨Q❀◑♿P⁄●

GAWCOTT

Cuckoo's Nest
Back Street
⏲ 11-2.30, 5.30-11; 11-11 Sat; 12-10.30 Sun
☎ (01280) 812092
Vale Notley Ale, Grumpling Old Ale; guest beers [H]
Every aspect of this modest-looking inn, in a pleasant but unexceptional village, combines to create a near-ideal country pub: spotlessly clean; polished wood and soft lighting; Vale Brewery's superb ales with a bonus of draught Budvar; food freshly prepared from locally-sourced ingredients; real fires and welcoming hosts. Parking can be tricky. Evening meals (Thu-Sat) must be booked. Sir George Gilbert Scott, architect, was born in Gawcott in 1811.
♨Q❀◑⊟♿⁄

HADDENHAM

King's Head
52 High Street
⏲ 12-2.30, 5-11; 12-11 Fri & Sat; 12-10.30 Sun
☎ (01844) 291391
Fuller's London Pride; Greene King IPA, [H] **Abbot;** [G] **guest beer** [H]
Traditional pub, parts of which date back to the 16th century. It is in the old part of the town and can be difficult to find, despite having two entrances, one on Townside. It enjoys a thriving trade, especially in summer when the patio drinking area can be a suntrap. Sky Sports are screened and there are occasional music evenings. The guest beer alternates on a weekly basis.
♨Q❀◑⊟♣P

Red Lion
Church End
⏲ 11.30-3, 5.30-11; 11-11 Sat; 12-10.30 Sun
☎ (01844) 291606
Adnams Bitter; Ansells Mild; Marston's Pedigree; Young's Bitter [H]
Friendly local, fielding thriving dominoes, crib, darts and quiz teams. Built in 1939, it remains unaltered, with its original oak floor and polished tables. There have only been four landlords since it opened and the present incumbent recently celebrated 30 years in the pub by signing up for a further three years. The outdoor drinking area at the front is popular in summer as it looks out on to the village green, church and duckpond.
♨Q❀⊨◐⊟♣P

INN BRIEF

BENNETT END

Three Horseshoes Inn
12-2.30, 7-11, closed Mon;
12-2.30 (closed eve) Sun
Brakspear Bitter, seasonal beers [H]
Fine old pub in splendid countryside, with cosy bars and a small restaurant area. Note the duckpond in the garden.

BOTLEY

Hen & Chickens
119 Botley Road
11-3, 6-11; 12-3.30, 7-10.30 Sun
(01494) 783303
Adnams Bitter; Courage Directors; Wells Bombardier [H]
17th-century, cosy country pub, boasting three real fires in its two rooms. No food Sun eve.

CADMORE END

Old Ship
Marlow Road
(Stokenchurch road, B482)
11-3, 5.30-11; 12-3, 7-10.30 Sun
(01494) 883496
Brakspear Mild, Bitter, Special, Old; guest beer [G]
Recently restored small, traditional country pub. Cask beers are carried up from the cellar. Bar meals served (except Sun eve, snacks only Mon lunch).

CHICHELEY

Chester Arms
Bedford Road
11-2.30 (not Mon), 5.30 (6 Sat)-11;
12-3, 8-10.30 Sun
(01234) 391214
Greene King IPA, Ruddles County [H]
Old whitewashed, roadside inn, with a pleasant, split-level drinking area. Top quality food (not served Sun eve or Mon).

HIGH WYCOMBE

Wycombe Wines
20 Crendon Street
10.30 (10 Sat)-10; 12-2, 6.30-9.30 Sun
(01494) 437228
Beer range varies [G]
Off-licence near the station, selling draught beer and (usually) a real cider, plus a range of bottled beer.

KINGSWOOD

Plough & Anchor
Bicester Road
12-3, 6-11; 12-8 Sun
(01296) 770251
Fuller's London Pride; guest beer [G]
Comfortable, food-oriented roadside pub with Cask Marque accreditation. The guest beer is from regionals and micros.

MARLOW

Hogshead
82-84 High Street
11-11; 12-10.30 Sun
(01628) 478737
Adnams Bitter; Boddingtons Bitter; Brakspear Bitter; Marston's Pedigree; Rebellion IPA; [H] **guest beers** [H]/[G]
Large, popular ale house on the site of the former Wethered Brewery. It offers nine ales and food every day.

MILTON KEYNES

Nag's Head
30 High Street, Great Lingford
12-11; 12-10.30 Sun
(01908) 607449
Draught Bass; Greene King IPA; Tetley Bitter [H]
Splendid, 16th-century thatched pub in an unspoilt village on the edge of the new city. Meals served 12-9 daily.

NEW DENHAM

Nine Stiles
52 Newtown Road
12-2.30 (3 Sat), 5-11; 12-3, 7-10.30 Sun
(01895) 272692
Greene King IPA, Ruddles County, Abbot [H]
First and last pub in Buckinghamshire, run by a true real ale enthusiast. Stays open afternoons if busy.

HAMBLEDEN

Stag & Huntsman

1 mile N of A4155 OS785866
⏲ 11-2.30 (3 Sat), 6-11; 12-3, 7-10.30 Sun
☎ (01491) 571227
website: www.stagandhuntsman.com
Brakspear Bitter; Wadworth 6X; guest beer Ⓗ
Unspoilt, characterful local gem, in a picturesque brick and flint NT village. This country pub comprises a locals' public, a cosy front bar and a lounge. An extensive menu is served throughout the three bars and the dining room (no food Sun eve). The weekly changing guest beer is usually sourced from either Cottage, Eccleshall or the local Rebellion Brewery. Thatcher's dry cider is always available on handpump.
♨❀🛏◐◑⊟♣●P

HANSLOPE

Globe

50 Hartwell Road (Longstreet Village between Hanslope and Hartwell on unclassified road)
⏲ 12-2.30 (not Tue), 6-11; 12-3, 7-10.30 Sun
☎ (01908) 510336
Banks's Bitter, Ⓗ/Ⓟ **guest beer** (occasional) Ⓗ
This classic country pub has twice won a Best-Cellar award from Banks's. A games room and lively public bar contrast with a comfortable lounge and (no-smoking) dining room. The pub is heavily involved in village life – a mixed farming and commuter community – hosting shooting dinners and other events. A pleasant garden has an aviary and play area (the pub has a children's certificate). It offers separate bar and restaurant menus (must book for the latter), but no evening meals served Tue or Sun. Q❀◐◑⊟P🁢

HEDGERLEY

White Horse

Village Lane OS969874
⏲ 11-2.30, 5.30-11; 11-11 Sat; 12-10.30 Sun
☎ (01753) 643225
Greene King IPA; Rebellion IPA; guest beers Ⓖ
15th-century, Grade II listed pub, which has been run by the Hobbs family since 1979. The small public bar features an inglenook, flagstone floor and bench seating. In the lounge you can trace the history of the village back to Roman times. With always seven ales on tap, it hosts a beer festival in the garden each spring bank holiday, plus barbecues most bank holidays. Local CAMRA Pub of the Year four times running. The campsite is only for caravans.
♨Q❀◐⊟▲♣●P

ICKFORD

Rising Sun

36 Worminghall Road
⏲ 12-3 (not Mon), 5-11; 12-11 Sat; 12-10.30 Sun
☎ (01844) 339238
Adnams Bitter; Marston's Pedigree; guest beers Ⓗ
Friendly village local, parts of which date back to the 15th century. Although food is served, it in no way dominates the pub, and accounts for only a small part of the turnover. There are always four ales available. The pub is very active in local leagues for darts, crib, pool and quizzes; Aunt Sally is played in the garden. The pub is known locally as the Woodcutter's Arms because the landlord is a forestry contractor.
♨Q❀◐◑♣P

IVER HEATH

Black Horse

Bangors Road North (A4007 jct)
⏲ 12-11; 12-10.30 Sun
☎ (01753) 653044
Badger IPA, Best, Tanglefoot, seasonal beers Ⓗ
There has been a pub on this site since the early 18th century, but the current building dates from the 1920s. During WWII this was the local Home Guard's base, but nowadays most of its trade is from lunchtime diners and the homeward-bound in the evenings. Popular with workers from the nearby Pinewood Film Studios, the pub has a conservatory dining area (no eve meals Sun-Tue). Bus No. 58 (Slough-Uxbridge) passes the door half-hourly until 7pm Mon-Sat. ❀◐◑♣P🚭✔

LITTLE MARLOW

King's Head

Church Road
(A4155 between Marlow and Bourne End)
⏲ 11-3, 5-11; 11-11 Sat; 12-10.30 Sun
☎ (01628) 484407
Brakspear Bitter; Fuller's London Pride; Rebellion IPA; Taylor Landlord; guest beer Ⓗ
This 14th-century village inn of fine character attracts a busy dining trade due to the extensive home-cooked menu. Families are welcome throughout the pub, which has a pleasant rear garden. A function room is also available at the rear of the building. A real fire is lit for the winter weather to thaw the chill while you enjoy any of their four, sometimes five, ales on offer. Wheelchair WC. ♨Q❀◐◑♿P🚭

LITTLE MISSENDEN

Crown

Off A413
⏲ 11-2.30, 6-11; 12-2.30, 7-10.30 Sun
☎ (01494) 862571
Adnams Bitter; Brakspear Special; Fuller's London Pride; guest beer Ⓗ
Classic, unspoilt hostelry in a quiet village, next to the River Misbourne. The Crown is a small pub with a discerning following providing ale and food (not Sun) to a very high standard in friendly surroundings. In the How family for nearly 100 years, it has a good atmosphere, with a stone-flagged floor at one end of the single room, and oak block flooring at the other. ♨Q❀◐♣P

MARLOW ❄

Carpenter's Arms

15 Spittal Street
⏲ 11-11; 12-10.30 Sun
☎ (01628) 473649
Morrells Oxford Blue, Varsity Ⓗ
Genuine working man's local, the only one left in the town, where lively banter, conversation and debate can still be enjoyed. Acquired by Morrells in 1992, old carpentry tools adorn the walls, while matchboxes decorate the ceiling. The landlady's deluxe sandwiches offer the best value for money in town. Sky football draws

fans, but does not intrude on the homely atmosphere. A meat raffle takes place on Sunday lunchtime. A tiny patio is used for outdoor drinking.

MARSH GIBBON

Greyhound

West Edge

12-3.30, 6-11 (closed Mon); 12-4, 7-10.30 Sun

(01869) 277365

Fuller's London Pride; Greene King IPA, Abbot H

Country pub in a quiet Domesday village. A listed building, with some 17th-century brickwork, it was rebuilt after a fire in 1740. An oak-beamed interior comprises a wood-panelled bar, two drinking areas and a restaurant; bar seating is on comfortable benches and stools and a log fire burns in the main bar area. Historical documents, bills and receipts dating back to 1813 are displayed. The Greyhound specialises in Thai food, freshly prepared to order (book weekend eves). Q P

MARSWORTH

Red Lion

90 Vicarage Road

(off B489, by canal bridge 130) OS919147

11-3, 6-11; 12-3, 7-10.30 Sun

(01296) 668366

Fuller's London Pride; Vale Notley Ale; guest beer H

This 17th-century free house lies close to the Aylesbury arm junction of the Grand Union Canal. A four-sided central bar serves the public and lounge rooms. The bright split-level lounge bears an eclectic mix of furniture, including sofas, and displays several large brewery mirrors. A large, dimly-lit public bar harbours a piano in the corner and leads to a games room housing an oche, skittle alley and bar billiards. Children are restricted to the games room. No meals Sun eve. Q P

MILTON KEYNES

Moon under Water

Unit 10, Sports Village

(N side of X-scape leisure complex)

11-11; 12-10.30 Sun

(01908) 528854

Courage Directors; Greene King Abbot; Shepherd Neame Spitfire; Theakston Best Bitter; guest beers H

Modern Wetherspoon's pub situated in the X-scape leisure complex. The single bar has two no-smoking areas, one with easy wheelchair access. Very popular with all ages, it stocks two or three guest beers. Food is served all day, every day. The X-scape complex houses the snow-dome (the UK's only ski slope with real snow), restaurants and a multi-screen cinema. Q

Wetherspoon's

201 Midsummer Boulevard, Bouverie Square

11-11; 12-10.30 Sun

(01908) 606074

Courage Directors; Greene King Abbot; Hop Back Summer Lightning; Shepherd Neame Spitfire; Theakston Best Bitter; guest beers H

Opened in 1995, this large, airy public house with its wavy roof and 'greenhouse' windows is based in the business area of central MK near the bus and rail stations. It offers good value food and cask ales at low prices, with at least three guest beers on tap most days. It can get very busy Friday and Saturday evenings. The large no-smoking area takes up about a third of the pub. It hosts two beer festivals every year.
Q

MOULSOE

Carrington Arms

Cranfield Road

11-3, 6-11; 12-3, 7-10.30 Sun

(01908) 218050

Brakspear Bitter, Special; guest beer H

The pub and village are part of the Carrington estate of Lord Carrington. This fine building was once the estate manager's house and became a public house around 1916. It now specialises in seafood and Aberdeenshire beef steaks, cooked on a special stove in the middle of the (well-ventilated) room for all to see. Located 10 minutes from junction 14 of the M1, north of Milton Keynes, it is well worth finding.
Q P

NEWPORT PAGNELL

Cannon

50 High Street

INN BRIEF

NORTH CRAWLEY

Cock Inn
16 High Street
12-3, 6-11; 12-3, 7-10.30 Sun
(01234) 391222
Wells Eagle, Bombardier; guest beers H
Sport- and food-oriented pub near Cranfield University, in the shadow of St Fermin's Church, serving bar and restaurant menus.

PRINCES RISBOROUGH

Bird in Hand
47 Station Road
12-3, 5-11; 12-4, 7-10.30 Sun
(01844) 345602
Greene King IPA, Abbot, Old Speckled Hen H
Mid-terrace, cosy, L-shaped local, attracting all ages. Accent on games, as testified by the trophy cabinet.

ST LEONARDS

White Lion
Jenkins Lane
11.30-11; 12-10.30 Sun
(01494) 758387
Bateman XB, seasonal beers; guest beers H
Traditional village pub, licensed premises since 1754. Outside play area for children; close to the Chiltern Way. No food Sun eve.

STOKE MANDEVILLE

Bull
5 Risborough Road
12-3, 5.30-11; 12-11 Fri & Sat; 12-10.30 Sun
(01296) 613632
Draught Bass; Courage Directors; Fuller's London Pride; Tetley Bitter H
Small village local with two contrasting bars, well served by public transport. Ample garden. Lunches served.

Missing?

If a pub is not listed in the Guide that you think is worthy of consideration, please let us know at GBG, CAMRA, 230 Hatfield Road, St Albans, Herts, AL1 4LW or camra@camra.org.uk. All recommendations are forwarded to CAMRA branches, which are responsible for choosing pubs.

11-11; 12-10.30 Sun
☎ (01908) 211495
Draught Bass; guest beers Ⓗ
This partially-listed building was the site of the last local brewery. The oldest parts of the structure date from the 15th century, but the Cannon has only been a pub since Victorian times. It features military memorabilia at one end, together with a stoutly individualistic juke box and, although essentially one room, it divides into three distinct areas. A live acoustic/roots jam session happens Wed. Several languages are spoken here.
Q♣P

OLNEY

Swan Inn & Bistro
12 High Street South
11-11; 12-3.30, 7-10.30 Sun
☎ (01234) 711111
Fuller's London Pride; Hook Norton Best Bitter; Morrells Oxford Blue; Shepherd Neame Best Bitter; guest beers Ⓗ
At the heart of an attractive market town, this 17th-century inn retains most of its original ceilings and beams. The wood burning in the old fireplaces gives a cosy feel. This warm welcome, along with excellent value food, makes you feel at home. The staff are always willing to help those needing disabled access. No food Sun eve. The car park is small. Two rooms provide overnight accommodation.
Q♣P

QUAINTON

White Hart
4 The Strand
12-2 (not Thu; 3 Sat), 7 (5.30 Mon)-11; 12-3, 7-10.30 Sun
☎ (01296) 655234
Adnams Bitter; Thwaites Bitter; guest beer Ⓗ
Completely rebuilt in the 1930s, this unpretentious pub is at the southern end of a pretty village. The Buckinghamshire Railway Centre is near Quainton and the North Bucks long-distance footpath runs through the pub garden. The plain public bar, with pool table, is separated from the lounge area by a chimney breast, complete with blazing fire in winter. Cheap and cheerful bar meals are served every day except Thursday. The landlord's preserved double-decker bus resides in the car park.
P

SHERINGTON

White Hart
1 Gun Lane
12-11; 12-10.30 Sun
☎ (01908) 611953
website: www.whitehartsherington.com
Fuller's London Pride; Young's Bitter; guest beers Ⓗ
This old village pub was saved by the local community in 1995, after it was sold as a private house. The inn is welcoming and cosy with a real community feel. The food is always excellent and home cooked (including tapas). No food Sun eve. Accommodation is in the old stable block. A beer and sausage fest is held on May bank holiday. Live music is staged every other Wed (phone for details). Boules is played. Local CAMRA Pub of the Year 2002.
Q♣P

SKIRMETT

Frog
Off M40 at jct 5, through Ibstone to Skirmett
OS775903
11.30-3, 6.30 (6 Fri)-11; 11-3, 6-11 Sat; 12-10.30 (12-4 Nov-Apr) Sun
☎ (01491) 638996 website: www.thefrog.tables.r.com
Brakspear Bitter; Fuller's London Pride; guest beer Ⓗ
Affording views across outstanding countryside, this 300-year-old free house is situated in the beautiful Turville Valley. The Frog is a family-owned-and-run concern exuding warmth and tranquillity. It offers a fine restaurant menu and high quality accommodation. Snacks are available in the bar area where an inviting log fire is always burning in winter. A guest beer is usually available. No evening meals served in winter. Q♣P

STEWKLEY

Swan
High Street North
12-3, 5.30-11; 12-4, 7-10.30 (12-10.30 summer) Sun
☎ (01525) 240285
Courage Best Bitter, Directors; Fuller's London Pride Ⓗ
Fine Georgian village pub, which always has a good atmosphere in its old beamed bars and dining area. Very much at the centre of village life, its clientele includes the local drama group and sports teams. Live music or a disco take place fortnightly and barbecues on summer Sundays (no food Tue lunchtime or Sun eve). Arch and Joy Grainger have run the Swan for 14 years and this is its 20th consecutive appearance in this Guide. Q♣P

STOKE GOLDINGTON

Lamb
16-20 High Street (B526)
12-3, 5-11; 12-11 Fri & Sat; 12-10.30 Sun
☎ (01908) 551233
Hook Norton Best Bitter; guest beer Ⓗ
The village is postcard-pretty, the pub informal, and friendly in a country manner. There is a smart dining room and a large bar with real fire, homely furniture, and Northamptonshire table skittles (you must try this game which is only played in this area). The cellar trapdoor is on the customers' side of the bar, which can be disconcerting when it suddenly opens at your feet! Cheerful hosts, two daft dogs, a pleasant garden, and excellent food and ale makes this a pub to linger in.
Q♣P

STONY STRATFORD

Bull Hotel & Vaults Bar
64 High Street
12-11; 12-10.30 Sun
☎ (01908) 567104 website: www.vaultsbar.co.uk
Adnams Bitter; Ansells Bitter; Draught Bass; Fuller's London Pride; Greene King Abbot; Young's Special Ⓗ
Busy, flagstone-floored bar with seven beers on handpump, serving food all day from the hotel's Mexican restaurant. Three beers

are available in the Bull Hotel bar, which closes 2.30-5.30 weekdays and 3-7 Sundays. The Vaults Bar, which was once an antique shop, displays memorabilia and bric-à-brac around the walls. ❀⇌◐◑♣P

Fox & Hounds

87 High Street

⊙ 12-11; 12-10.30 Sun

☎ (01908) 563307 website: www.stonystratford.co.uk

Adnams Bitter, Broadside; Draught Bass; Shepherd Neame Spitfire; Smiles Best; guest beer Ⓗ

Two-bar pub where meals are served in the lounge at lunchtimes (not Sun), when smoking is not permitted. A variety of bar games are played here, including Northamptonshire skittles. Live blues/folk and jazz are performed regularly; photographs of musicians grace the walls. The cider comes from Addlestone's.
❀◐⊟♿♣●P⚟

SWAN BOTTOM

Old Swan

Kingswood, The Lee

(100 yds from Chesham-Wendover road) OS902055

⊙ 12-3, 6-11; 12-11 Sat; closed Mon; 12-7 (12-10.30 summer) Sun

☎ (01494) 837239

Adnams Bitter; Brakspear Bitter; Fuller's London Pride; guest beer (summer) Ⓗ

Footpaths run close by this 16th-century Kingswood inn, referred to by locals as being in Swan Bottom. Inside, there are two distinct areas, one exclusively a restaurant specialising in seafood, the other a genuine retreat for drinkers. Flagstone flooring around the bar, a large open fire and beamed ceilings provide a welcoming atmosphere. A guest supplements the three regular ales in summer when Sunday opening times are extended and the large garden comes into its own. No food Sat eve or Sun. ⌂Q❀◐◑♣P

TYLERS GREEN

Horse & Jockey

Church Road

⊙ 12-2.30, 5.30-11; 12-3, 7-10.30 Sun

☎ (01494) 815963

Adnams Broadside; Brakspear Bitter; Greene King Abbot; Tetley Bitter; guest beer Ⓗ

Change for change's sake is not the creed here. A fiercely traditional pub near the village church, the setting is firmly apart from the big town, although the commuter belt is fast encroaching. Many of the regulars support Wycombe Wanderers. The pub mainly relies for its income on food which is available almost all the opening hours. ⌂❀◐◑♣P

WADDESDON

Lion

High Street

⊙ 12-2.30, 5.30-11; 12-2.30, 7-10.30 Sun

☎ (01296) 651227

Draught Bass; Fuller's ESB; guest beer Ⓗ

The Lion offers an excellent range of food, two regular beers and a weekend guest ale. Its deceptively large bar and dining area has big, comfortable tables. The landlord and chef, Jean Marie Descrettes, comes from Normandy and his varied menu includes over 30 main courses, (not by any means all French) and daily specials. The menus change according to season, are reasonably priced, and the portions generous. You must allow over an hour for lunch! No food Sun eve.
Q❀◐◑♣P⚟

WENDOVER

End of the World

Aylesbury Road, World's End

(1 mile N of Wendover)

⊙ 11.30-2.30, 5.30-11 (12-11 summer); closed Mon; 12-10.30 Sun

☎ (01296) 622299

website: www.endoftheworld.supanet.com

Brakspear Bitter; guest beers Ⓗ

Formerly called the Swan, this popular bar and restaurant dates back over 350 years. Four regularly changing real ales are always available, one at a reduced price. A wide range of food is offered in the three restaurant areas and the bar, although English cuisine is predominant. All the food is prepared on the premises by a team of chefs, and the fresh fish and daily specials are very popular. There is an enclosed garden where regular barbecues are held, and there is an annual music festival.
❀◐◑●P⚟

WEST WYCOMBE

George & Dragon

On A40

⊙ 11-2.30 (3 Sat), 5.30-11; 12-3, 7-10.30 Sun

☎ (01494) 464414

website: www.george-and-dragon.co.uk

Fuller's London Pride; Wells Bombardier; guest beers Ⓗ

The NT owns this rustic, oak-beamed, 18th-century inn, where the cobbled entrance is through an archway. The food is exemplary. A vintners is also run by the tenants. Two bedrooms have four-poster beds. The garden has children's play equipment. West Wycombe Park and House (NT) stand behind the village; the famous Hellfire Caves, mausoleum and church with golden ball on top can also be visited. Buses run from High Wycombe centre; No. 331 stops in the village, No. 332 on the outskirts. ⌂Q☺❀⇌◐◑P⚟

WESTON TURVILLE

Chequers

35 Church Lane (road parallel to B4544)

⊙ 12-3 (not Mon), 6-11; 12-3, 7-10.30 Sun

☎ (01296) 613298

Adnams Bitter; Fuller's London Pride; Greene King IPA; Wadworth 6X Ⓗ

The stone-flagged floor, real fire and exposed stone walls create a genteel atmosphere in the main bar of this pub which is situated in the older part of the village, near the church. A lower bar at one end leads through to the à la carte restaurant in a former barn (book eve meals); the bar lunches are good quality (no food Mon). The half-hourly bus No. 54 from Aylesbury or Wendover stops nearby (not eves or Sun).
⌂❀◐◑P

WESTON UNDERWOOD

Cowpers Oak

High Street (on Gayhurst-Olney road)
✪ 12-3, 5.30-11; 12-3, 5.30-10.30 Sun
☎ (01234) 711382
Adnams Bitter; Greene King IPA; Marston's Pedigree; guest beers Ⓗ
Fine, split-level pub, once four rooms, now only two. However, the clever use of pillars and partitions has divided it into three more intimate spaces round the central bar, plus a dining room. One section shuts off the noisier skittles and darts area. The largest room is used for bar snacks (served lunchtime and eve) and crib and dominoes-players. Various ciders are stocked in summer.
⌂Q❀◐◑⊟♣●P⊬

WEXHAM STREET

Plough

✪ 11 (12 Sat)-11; 12-10.30 Sun
☎ (01753) 662613
Courage Best Bitter; Fuller's London Pride; guest beers Ⓗ
With its listed frontage (originally three 17th-century cottages) low, beamed bar and attractive function room (originally the stables), this is a lovely little rural pub. Usually two guest ales are on offer and at lunchtimes a good selection of home-cooked meals and snacks can be enjoyed in front of one of two real fires. It is known by some as the 19th hole due to its proximity to Wexham Golf Club.
⌂Q❀◐♣P

WHITCHURCH

White Swan

10 High Street
✪ 11-11; 12-3, 7-10.30 Sun
☎ (01296) 641228
Fuller's Chiswick, London Pride, ESB, seasonal beers Ⓗ
Attractive, part-thatched 16th-century pub with an intimate atmosphere, it boasts a huge mature garden and distinctive wood panelling in the lounge bar. Good value food is available, except Sunday evenings, with daily specials (Tue-Sun) and occasional food theme nights. You can eat in either of the bars or the small, no-smoking dining room. The landlord, Vic Hinde, is Fuller's Master Cellarman No. 22, and has several appearances in this Guide to his credit.
⌂Q❀◐◑⊟♣P

WING

Cock

26 High Street
✪ 11.30-3, 6-11; 12-3, 7-10.30 Sun
☎ (01296) 688214
Courage Directors; Webster's Yorkshire Bitter; guest beers Ⓗ
A former coaching inn, the Cock appeals to diners and drinkers, as well as families. Four of its six real ales come from independent or micro-breweries, often beers that are unusual for this area. The bar has three main drinking areas, one with a dartboard. Food is served both in the bars and the spacious carvery restaurant which can get very busy at weekends. The car park is very large but has a rather narrow entrance.
S⌂Q❀◐◑♿♣P

WOOBURN COMMON

Royal Standard

Wooburn Common Road
(follow signs to Odds Farm)
✪ 12-3, 5.30 (6 Sat)-11; 12-10.30 Sun
☎ (01628) 521121
Beer range varies Ⓗ
Semi-rural roadside pub, a short detour from the A40, but well worth it. A rectangular drinking area greets customers, leading to a lower dining area behind the chimney breast. Four interesting ever-changing beers are chosen from the Interbrew portfolio, with a further guest ale of the landlord's choosing. Occasional dinner theme nights and other functions are held throughout the year. Two disabled parking spaces are provided. A pétanque piste is for hire. ⌂❀◐◑♿P

WORMINGHALL

Clifden Arms

75 Clifden Road OS640083
✪ 12-3, 5.30-11; 12-4, 6-11 (12-11 summer) Sat; 12-4, 7.30-10.30 (12-10.30 summer) Sun
☎ (01844) 339273
Adnams Broadside; Brakspear Bitter; Hook Norton Best Bitter; guest beer Ⓗ
Off the beaten track, between Oxford and Thame, this really is a hidden gem. A picturesque village local, its two bar areas feature beams and local memorabilia. The restaurant area serves a wide choice of meals and snacks, including vegetarian and children's options. Specials include curry nights (Thu) and takeaway fish and chips. The extensive secluded garden houses the local game of Aunt Sally. Bar billiards is also played at this local CAMRA Pub of the Year 2001. ⌂❀◐◑⊟♣P

WYCOMBE MARSH

General Havelock

114 Kingsmead Road (S of A40)
✪ 12-2.30, 5.30-11; 11-11 Fri & Sat; 12-10.30 Sun
☎ (01494) 520391
Fuller's Chiswick; London Pride, ESB, seasonal beer Ⓗ
Commemorating a general who died at the Siege of Lucknow, this is an imposing building on a road parallel to the A40. It has been run by the same landlord since it was acquired by Fuller's. The friendly atmosphere is generated and appreciated by the regulars. For sporting types, netball, cricket, rugby and ski-ing are all possible nearby. Evening meals are served Fri and Sat, 5.30-9. ⌂❀◐◑♣P

> That ale is a wholesome drinke contrary to many men's conceits.
>
> *Panala Alacatholica* 1623.

CAMBRIDGESHIRE

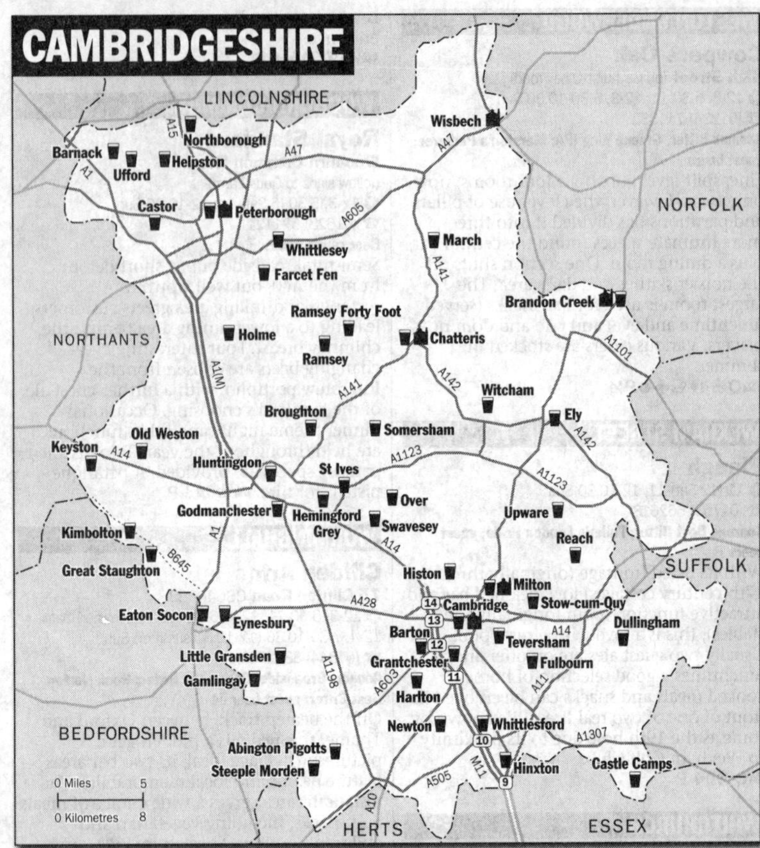

ABINGTON PIGOTTS

Pig & Abbot

High Street (off A505 towards Litlington) OS306444
⏲ 11-3, 6-11; 11-11 Sat; 12-10.30 Sun
☎ (01763) 853515
Adnams Bitter; Fuller's London Pride; guest beers Ⓗ

The only pub in this small, rural south Cambs village. Formerly known by the geriatric name of Darby & Joan, new owners attempted to bring the pub up to date with a more striking name, it failed, the pub closed, fortunately it was saved by a village buyout in 1997. Deceptively large for a village local, it features a comfortable restaurant and well-appointed lounge bar where a large inglenook holds a wood-burning stove. An imaginative menu includes blackboard specials. A good range of beers is always on tap. ⌂Q❀◐◑♣P⚟Ⓣ

BARNACK

Millstone

Millstone Lane (down lane off Main Street and 'Hills and Hollows')
⏲ 11.30-11; 12-10.30 Sun
☎ (01780) 740296
Adnams Bitter; Everards Tiger, Original; guest beer Ⓗ

The Millstone is now even more popular with drinkers as the old cellar has been converted to a traditional bar with pub games. Winner of numerous awards for beer quality and excellent food, the landlord has run the pub for 18 years. Enjoy the summer sun in the large walled patio and conservatory. An ancient quarry, known as the 'Hills and Hollows', is part of the village. Stone was extracted from here to build Peterborough Cathedral. The site is a now a pleasant nature reserve. Q❀◐◑⊟♿♣P⚟

BARTON

Hoops

1 School Lane
⏲ 12 (4 Mon)-11; 12-10.30 Sun
☎ (01223) 262230
Greene King IPA, Abbot Ⓗ

Village pubs that do not serve food are rare in this area – the fact that the Hoops can rely on its 'wet trade' is a testament to the quality of its ale – if only Greene King IPA always tasted this good! The cosy, little public bar, with its tiled floor, huge open fireplace and upholstered benches is a delight; the lounge has considerably less character. A large informal garden is another attraction. ⌂☺❀⊟♣P

BRANDON CREEK

Ship

On A10, 7 miles N of Ely
⏲ Summer: 12-3, 6.30-11; closed Mon; Winter: 12-3 Mon-Fri; 6.30-11 Fri & Sat; 12-10 Sun
☎ (01353) 676228
Beer range varies Ⓗ

The home of Captain Grumpy's Brewery, situated on the riverbank at the junction of

setting on the River Great Ouse. The real ales are served in a simple unpretentious small bar with basic furnishings and a solid fuel stove. There is a relaxing atmosphere and a firm emphasis on well-kept local ales. The large restaurant offers great scope with its modern, imaginative menu; it attracts visitors from a wide area. Booking is advisable for the restaurant at all times (no food is served in the bar). No meals offered on Sun eve or Mon. ♔Q✿◖◗P

HINXTON

Red Lion
High Street
⌚ 11-2.30, 6-11; 12-2.30, 7-10.30 Sun
☎ (01799) 530601
Adnams Bitter; Greene King IPA; Woodforde's Wherry; guest beer Ⓗ
16th-century coaching inn with a compartmented L-shaped bar and an ever-busy award-winning dining room extension. It blends sympathetically with the original brickwork which is punctuated throughout by fine old clocks, horse brasses and a menagerie of stuffed animals. The garden is home to more animated pets, including a horse. Note the unusual polished copper doorsteps. The pub fields a cricket team and cribbage is popular (Wed). Morris men visit each June as do passing participants in the annual London-Cambridge cycle ride. Note the one-way car park. ♔Q✿◖◗♿♣P⊬

HISTON

Red Lion
27 High Street
⌚ 11.30-3, 5 (4 Fri)-11; 11.30-11 Sat; 12-6, 7-10.30 Sun
☎ (01223) 564437
Bateman Mild; Everards Beacon, Tiger; Oakham Bishops Farewell; guest beers Ⓗ
Two-bar free house, comprising a quiet lounge, where food is served, and a more boisterous public bar that displays a fine collection of bottled beers in wall cabinets. There is a diverse range of breweriana throughout, including old pub signs and water jugs, plus photographs of the pub's cricket team and old village scenes. Two beer festivals are staged each year: an Easter 'aperitif' and the main event in early September with a marquee in the garden and live entertainment each evening. A selection of Belgian bottled beers is always stocked. An anti-mobile phone policy is upheld. ♔Q✿◖⊟♣P

HOLME

Admiral Wells
41 Station Road
⌚ 12-2.30, 5-11; 12-11 Sat; 12-10.30 Sun
☎ (01487) 831214
Oakham JHB; Woodforde's Wherry; guest beers Ⓗ
2001 CAMRA gold award-winner, this Victorian yellow-brick pub is situated next to the main east coast railway line. Named after one of Nelson's pall bearers at his funeral, the pub is in the 'sinking fens' area. The Holme posts are nearby which show how much the fenland has sunk over the years. Up to five beers are on offer. Three drinking areas are available as well as a separate dining room. A large, part-shaded garden lies to the side of the pub. ♔Q☋✿◖◗♿♣P⊬

HUNTINGDON

Old Bridge Hotel
1 High Street
⌚ 11-11; 12-10.30 Sun
☎ (01480) 424300
Adnams Bitter; guest beers Ⓗ
This relaxing hotel bar provides splendid surroundings for local real ale drinkers, residents and diners. The handsome, ivy-clad 18th-century building was a former private bank and stands next to the River Great Ouse in the birthplace of Oliver Cromwell. A local brewery often supplies one of the two guest beers. The imaginative, quality food and fine wine are stylishly served in the informal atmosphere of the mural-adorned 'terrace' or the intimate dining room. ♔Q✿⛟◖◗⇛P✔

Samuel Pepys
146 High Street
⌚ 11-11; 12-10.30 Sun
☎ (01480) 437877
Beer range varies Ⓗ
A welcome boost to Huntingdon's real ale scene, this former 'Irish' theme pub previously offered only keg beers, but is now firmly focused on cask beer following an extensive refurbishment. Busy at lunchtime, catering for town office workers, in the evening it becomes a lively part of the local circuit. The cask beer range usually comprises varied styles as well as a selection from Cambridgeshire brewers, such as Elgood's; Oldershaw in Lincolnshire and Nethergate in Suffolk also feature. Draught Belgian wheat and fruit beer are also stocked. Families with children are welcome until 7pm. Home-made food is served daily (eve meals Mon-Thu). ✿◖◗⇛✔

KEYSTON

Pheasant
Village loop (off A14)
⌚ 12-3, 6-11; 12-3, 7-10.30 Sun
☎ (01832) 710241
Adnams Bitter; Potton Village Bike; guest beers Ⓗ
A series of thatched cottages in an idyllic setting, the Pheasant has a number of open-plan rooms featuring oak beams and farm implements. The main bar is a lounge drinking area with a large fireplace. There are three dining sections, two are informal with simple wooden furniture, and there is the Red Room restaurant. A constantly changing range of real ales is drawn from local micro-breweries and independents. A range of Belgian beers is also stocked. The food is modern with an emphasis on Mediterranean cuisine. ♔Q☋✿◖◗P⊬

KIMBOLTON

New Sun
20 High Street
⌚ 11 (11.30 Sat)-2.30, 6 (6.30 Sat)-11; 12-10.30 Sun
☎ (01480) 860052
Greene King Old Speckled Hen; Wells Eagle, Bombardier Ⓗ
Impressive Georgian-fronted building that

opens into a comfortable lounge with exposed beams, sofas and a fireplace. The door to the left opens on to a formal dining room and the passage in front leads to the main bar with tiled floor. A second dining area leads to a patio housing potted plants. Food includes an à la carte restaurant menu with an extensive wine list, and a frequently changing blackboard of traditional pub food. All the food is home made. Evening meals are served Tue-Sat. ⌂⚭❀◐◑

LITTLE GRANSDEN

Chequers
71 Main Road
⏲ 12-2.30, 5-11; 11-11 Sat; 12-3, 7-10.30 Sun
☎ (01767) 677348
Adnams Bitter; guest beers H
Run by the same family for the last 50 years, its history has been well researched and documented by the landlord, and provides interesting reading. While retaining an excellent basic public bar, a comfortable lounge bar has been added. The landlord has devised a secret weapon to stop people hanging around in front of the bar in winter; you will find out if you linger too long. There is always an interesting guest beer at this local CAMRA Pub of the Year 2001. ⌂⚭❀⊟♣P

MARCH

Rose & Crown
41 St Peter's Road (B1099, off old A141)
⏲ 12-2.30 (not Wed; 12-3 Sat), 7-11; 12-3, 7-10.30 Sun
☎ (01354) 652879
Woodforde's Wherry; guest beers H
Traditional, family-owned free house just south of the town centre. A large comfortable bar plus a highly popular no-smoking lounge cater for a broad range of locals and visitors. The five guest pumps always include a mild and around 1,700 different beers have now been served. Two or three ciders plus a perry are always on gravity from the ultra-modern cellar. Over 100 whiskies fight for space on the back bar in this CAMRA multi-award winning pub, where bar meals are offered Thu-Sat. There is no juke box and, be warned, do not move the chairs around the bar! A small patio is available. Q❀◐⊟♿♣●P⊬

Warm Beer

It is said that the Maids of Honour of the Tudor Court, who we have seen were ale-ladies, if they cannot be called ale-knights, frequently liked their beer warm, and had it placed upon the hob of the grate 'to take the chill off'. It was therefore natural for their attendants to ask the question, 'From the hob or not from the hob?', which in process of time became 'hob or nob?'

John Bickerdyke 1889

MILTON

Waggon & Horses
39 High Street
⏲ 12-2.30 (3 Sat), 5 (6 Sat)-11; 12-3, 7-10.30 Sun
☎ (01223) 860313
Elgood's Black Dog Mild, Cambridge, Pageant Ale, seasonal beers; guest beers H
Elgood's first acquisition for 55 years, this imposing mock-Tudor one-roomed pub boasts a large collection of hats. The sizeable garden houses chickens and is safe for children. Games include bar billiards and pétanque. A popular quiz is staged on Wednesday. Baltis are the speciality Thursday evening, but all meals represent good choice and value. The real cider stocked is from local producer, Cassels. ⌂❀◐♣●P

NEWTON

Queen's Head
Fowlmere Road
⏲ 11.30-2.30, 6-11; 12-2.30, 7-10.30 Sun
☎ (01223) 870436
Adnams Bitter, Broadside, seasonal beers G
Unchanging gem: a village local that has appeared in every edition of this Guide. Just 18 landlords have presided here since 1729. The traditional public bar has wooden benches, a high-backed settle, tiled floor and the comforting tick of a large old clock. Squeezing past the piano into the games annexe, you can enjoy shove-ha'penny and devil among the tailors, among others. The cosy saloon features a roaring fire and built-in seating. Simple, satisfying food is freshly prepared to order. The outdoor drinking area extends to the green opposite. ⌂Q❀◐⊟Ⓐ♣●P⊬

OLD WESTON

Swan
Main Street (B660, off A14)
⏲ 6.30-11; 12-3, 7-11 Sat; 12-3, 7-10.30 Sun
☎ (01832) 293400
Adnams Bitter, Broadside; Greene King Abbot; guest beers H
16th-century beamed village local with a central bar area, a dining area and a games section offering hooded skittles, darts and pool. The central bar has a large inglenook. The pub started life as two private houses that have since been merged, and the building has grown over the years. At the turn of the century the pub had its own brewery. In the 1950s and '60s it was known as the Mucky Duck, due to the barmaids' risqué attire. A varied menu of home-cooked traditional pub food includes good puddings (Wed-Sat eves and Sun lunch). ⌂Q❀◐♣P

PETERBOROUGH ❄

Bluebell
St Paul's Road, Dogsthorpe
(1/2 mile off old A15, near city fire station)
⏲ 11-2.30, 6-11; 11.30-3, 6-11 Sat; 12-3, 7-10.30 Sun

☎ (01733) 554890
Elgood's Black Dog Mild, Cambridge, Pageant Ale, Greyhound Strong; guest beer Ⓗ
Said to be Peterborough's oldest pub, it has been a regular Guide entry for a number of years. It is one of Elgood's three city outlets and has the full range of ales on sale alongside a guest beer. This stone-built, two-roomed pub has a tiny snug with a cosy atmosphere and aircraft pictures displayed on the walls. The main bar is spacious and good lunchtime meals are served weekdays. A large patio and children's play area are added attractions. ❀◐⊟♿P⁄

Bogart's
17 North Street (near bus station)
⏲ 11 (12 Sat & Mon)-11; 12-10.30 Sun
☎ (01733) 703599
Oakham JHB; guest beers Ⓗ
This regular Guide entry of more than 10 years is a small, single-roomed bar. Originally called the Ostrich, the Humphrey Bogart theme is unusual as the pub is more like a street-corner local. A cosy suntrap courtyard is at the rear of the building. It features up to six beers, mainly from micro-breweries. The regulars find the close proximity of bus, rail and taxis very handy. Quiet at lunchtime, more boisterous in the evening, Bogart's is one of the few city-centre pubs not to have 'greeters' at weekends. It is a few minutes' walk from the north entrance of Queensgate Shopping Centre. Lunchtime food is served Tue-Sun. ❀◐⇌

Brewery Tap
80 Westgate (opp. bus station)
⏲ 12-11 (1.30am Fri & Sat); 12-10.30 Sun
☎ (01733) 358500
Oakham JHB, seasonal beers; guest beers Ⓗ
Largest brew-pub in Europe, set alongside the award-winning Oakham Ales Brewery. A large glass partition allows you to see the brewing process in action. The many awards bestowed on the beers produced by Oakham adorn the walls of the pub. Champion beer at the Great British Beer Festival 2001, JHB is brewed here. The authentic Thai food (served daily) is highly recommended. A late licence (Fri and Sat) means door controls and an entrance charge after 10.30pm. ◐◑♿⇌⁄

Charters
Town Bridge
⏲ 12-11 (1.30am Fri & Sat); 12-10.30 Sun
☎ (01733) 315700
Draught Bass; Everards Tiger; Fuller's London Pride; Oakham JHB; guest beers Ⓗ
This converted Dutch grain barge (circa 1907) is moored on the River Nene. Having celebrated 10 years in this Guide in 2002, the pub boasts a great variety of customers and guest ales. Oakham ales from the award-winning brewery are featured, as the pub is in joint ownership. A peaceful garden is a welcome retreat, in fact a refuge from the hustle of the shopping centres and city close by. A footpath along the river leads to Railworld and Nene Valley Railway. A new oriental restaurant 'East' is on the top deck. Restricted entry applies on football match days and on Fri and Sat eves. ❀◐◑⇌⁄

Cherry Tree
9 Oundle Road, Fletton (A605, S of city, near football ground)
⏲ 12-2.30, 6-11; 12-11 Sat; 12-10.30 Sun
☎ (01733) 703495
website: www.thecherrytreeinn.co.uk
Draught Bass; Marston's Pedigree; Tetley Bitter; guest beers Ⓗ
Local community pub set on the south side of the River Nene, near Railworld and Nene Valley Railway. A popular music venue with regular live performances from bands; the function room is ideal for any special occasions and meetings. The Cherry Tree won an award as a community pub and hosts plenty of fund-raising events for charity. The pub fields a football team and regulars enjoy the quiz nights and games played. It is very busy on match days due to the close proximity of the football ground. ⋒♘❀◐◑♿⇌P

Goodbarns Yard
64 St John Street (500 yds from market place)
⏲ 11 (12 Sat)-11; 12-10.30 Sun
☎ (01733) 551830
Adnams Broadside; Black Sheep Best Bitter; guest beers Ⓗ
Situated on the edge of the city centre, this pub has had a revival in the last two years due to an enthusiastic manager and team. It has leapt from serving no real ale to selling a regular choice of changing guest beers. The two-roomed pub has plenty of local memorabilia and features a spacious conservatory, used for family gatherings or local meetings. An annual beer festival is held at this local CAMRA Pub of the Year 2001. Lunchtime food is served weekdays. ♘❀◐⊟♿⇌P⁄✔

Palmerston Arms
82 Oundle Road, Woodston (A605)
⏲ 12-11; 12-10.30 Sun
☎ (01733) 565865
Beer range varies Ⓗ
This 400-year-old, stone-built listed building makes a welcome return to the Guide. Up to 14 ales are brought to you direct from the cellar to its two rooms which are drenched in old artefacts and breweriana. Cider and country wines are also on offer, and an extensive array of malt whiskies. Beware, this pub operates a highly restrictive entry policy, which may be activated by the licensee at any time! A tiny courtyard serves as a garden. Q❀⊟♣●

RAMSEY

Jolly Sailor
43 Great Whyte (B1040)
⏲ 11-3, 5.30 (6 Sat)-11; 12-3, 7-10.30 Sun
☎ (01487) 813388
Adnams Broadside; Bateman XB; Tetley Bitter; Wells Bombardier; guest beers Ⓗ
Three very different rooms in this Grade II listed pub are served from a central bar, where the half-dozen handpumps make it a favourite venue in this market town on the south-west edge of the Fens. The street outside is above a river culverted 150 years ago when Ramsey ceased to be an inland port. Modern boat moorings are five minutes' walk away. Much decorative brass and copper add to the traditional, cosy

atmosphere. A mature clientele, enjoying good beer and conversation, meet here away from the distractions of food and loud music. Note the very narrow door from the street into the snug. A sheltered courtyard is available for outdoor drinking. Parking is accessible via Newton Road. ⛼Q❀♣P

RAMSEY FORTY FOOT

George Inn
1 Ramsey Road (B1096, 3 miles NE of Ramsey)
12-4, 6-11; 12-4, 7-10.30 Sun
☎ (01487) 812775
John Smith's Bitter; guest beers Ⓗ
Popular, family-run free house, the two guest beer pumps and an expanding range of home-cooked meals make a trip into the Fens well worthwhile. A small split-level bar serves two similarly divided rooms and a huge open fire in the inglenook keeps everyone cosy. The family room doubles as a pool room. Boat moorings on the adjacent Forty Foot drain are popular with summer tourists. A limited daytime bus service links this small village with Ramsey and Peterborough – otherwise transport by car or boat is essential! ⛼Q❀◑♿♣P

REACH

Dyke's End
8 Fair Green
12-3, 6-11; 12-3, 7-10.30 Sun
☎ (01638) 743816
website: www.the-dykesend-pub.com
Adnams Bitter; Greene King IPA; Woodforde's Wherry; guest beers Ⓗ
Situated at the end of the Devil's Dyke (a 6th-century defensive earthwork), Reach was in danger of losing its pub, so in 1999 a group of villagers clubbed together to buy it. Since then it has thrived, providing locals and visitors alike with an excellent selection of ales, it is also renowned throughout the area for food (booking advisable for the restaurant section). Local artists exhibit their work alongside interesting items relating to this historic village.
⛼Q❀◑♿P⚟

ST IVES ❄

Floods Tavern
27 The Broadway
11.30-11; 12-10.30 Sun
☎ (01480) 467773
Elgood's Cambridge, Greyhound Strong, seasonal beer Ⓗ
Friendly lounge bar in a town pub taken over by Elgood's in 2001. In fine weather the rear riverside garden is an idyllic refuge, close to the Holt Island Nature Reserve and with splendid views across the River Great Ouse and water meadows. Interesting enlarged photographs of local flood scenes adorn the walls in the bar. Steak night (Wed) is the only evening that food is served, karaoke is held on Thursday and jam sessions on Tuesday. Satellite TV is available but is not disruptive. ⛼❀◑

Royal Oak
13 Crown Street
11-11; 12-10.30 Sun
☎ (01480) 462586
Draught Bass; Marston's Pedigree; Tetley Bitter Ⓗ

Good ale, raw onions, and no ladies

John McSorley, founder of McSorley's Ale House, New York City, 1854.

Historic market pub in the town whose most famous inhabitant was Oliver Cromwell. The characterful room layout and many original features were thankfully preserved in a refurbishment in the 1990s. Most of the building is 18th century, despite the date '1502' over the door. A constantly changing range of three guest beers keeps the customers happy and provides a focus for local real ale drinkers. Entertainment is provided by quiz nights (Thu), card nights and unobtrusive satellite TV. ❀◑♣P✔

SOMERSHAM

Windmill
St Ives Road (B1086, 1 mile from Somersham)
11.30-2.30, 5.30 (6 Sat)-11; 12-3, 7-10.30 Sun
☎ (01487) 840328
Greene King IPA, Ruddles County, Old Speckled Hen Ⓗ
Popular country pub retaining a small, original public bar and a jug and bottle hatch. The lounge has been extended into two adjacent cottages, creating an ample dining area and a sociable drinking environment. Food includes Mexican dishes and themed food events are a feature. No food is served on Sunday evening, which is quiz night. Occasional fantasy role play entertainments are staged. It is reputedly haunted by the last locally-hanged arsonist, Tom Savage. ❀◑♣P✔

STEEPLE MORDEN

Waggon & Horses
19 Church Street
12-3, 7-11; 12-11 Sat; 12-10.30 Sun
☎ (01763) 852829
Greene King XX Mild, IPA; guest beers (summer) Ⓗ
Deep in the heart of south Cambridgeshire's rambling countryside, this traditional 300-year-old village pub provides a welcoming retreat. Your thirst can be slaked with an excellent pint of the rare XX Mild. The tile-floored public bar, complete with pool table, leads to a cosy lounge boasting a large inglenook (children welcome). There is a CC-registered site at the rear of the pub (must be booked). Pétanque is played. Look out for the former WWII American Air Force base memorial close by.
⛼❀▲♣P

STOW-CUM-QUY

White Swan
11 Main Street
11-3, 6-11; 12-3, 7-10.30 Sun
☎ (01223) 811821
Adnams Bitter; Greene King IPA; Woodforde's Wherry; guest beer Ⓗ
Convivial meeting place for connoisseurs of interesting beers and outstanding food. The two bars are at different levels. The lower,

partly sculpted out of adjoining cottages, is used primarily as a restaurant and has a collection of drinking pots. The upper bar has a collection of mirrors and is a cosy place for a beer and/or meal. Milton Brewery ales often feature. Q❀◑♣P⚟

SWAVESEY

White Horse

1 Market Street

12-2.30, 6-11; 11.30-11 Sat; 12-10.30 Sun

☎ (01954) 232470

Taylor Landlord; guest beers H

Large well-run pub in the village centre. The lounge is comfortable and food-oriented, while the public bar is more characterful with a tiled floor and roaring fire in winter. At the back is a pool/family room. The spacious garden hosts barbecues and has a children's play area. There are four changing guest beers, often including one from a local brewery. The Sunday lunchtime roasts are renowned (no meals Sun eve).

⚟❀◑♣⚟

TEVERSHAM

Rose & Crown

1 High Street

11.30-2.30, 6 (5 Fri)-11; 12-11 Sat; 12-3, 7-10.30 Sun

☎ (01223) 292245

Ansells Mild; Greene King IPA; guest beer H

Friendly village pub with plenty to offer. The extended garden includes a children's play area. The bar area is Z-shaped and usually has adequate seating; well-behaved children are welcome. A pool table is at one end and local radio is sometimes played without being intrusive. The beer is always of a high standard with a regular mild and a frequently changing guest. Pub games, including darts, are available on request.

❀◑♿♣P

UFFORD

White Hart

Main Street

11-3 (not Mon), 6-11; 12-3, 7-10.30 Sun

☎ (01780) 740250

Brakspear Bitter; Wadworth 6X; guest beers H

This 17th-century former farmhouse makes a welcome return to the Guide after an absence of five years. The small, homely bar has a tiled fireplace with old bench seats and tables. At the rear is a popular restaurant with a small cocktail bar. Games nights are held on a regular basis and small groups of different associations meet here. An old piano is located in the bar for the occasional keyboard maestro. A safe garden for children is to the rear of the pub. No food is served on Sun eve or Mon.

Q❀◑♿P⚟

UPWARE

Five Miles from Anywhere Inn

Old School Lane (2 miles off A1123, between Wicken and Stretham)

11-3, 7-11 (12.30am Wed, 2am Fri); closed Mon; (11-2am summer Sat); 12-10.30 Sun

☎ (01353) 721654 website: www.fivemiles.co.uk

City of Cambridge Hobson's Choice; guest beers H

Unusual pub that successfully caters for many different types of customer, including walkers, boaters and families with children. Outside, almost four acres of grounds include a fully-equipped children's play area, extensive moorings and a heated terrace for dining. Children love the bouncy castle in summer. Live entertainment is hosted (Fri and Sat eves) and monthly jazz (on third Sun lunchtime). The lounge bar stocks a wide range of real ales, the public has a large-screen TV. The pub holds a children's certificate.

❀◑P

WHITTLESEY

Bricklayers Arms

9 Station Road (B1093, 200 yds S of market place)

11-4 (may extend Fri & Sat), 6.30-11; 12-4, 7-10.30 Sun

☎ (01733) 202593

John Smith's Bitter; guest beer H

A CAMRA gold award-winning pub and HQ for the famous Whittlesea Straw Bear Festival. This great two-roomed community local often has up to five guests on offer; and one is usually a mild. The long, plainly furnished public bar contrasts with the smaller cosy lounge. Strong language is not tolerated and the clientele spans the ages in full harmony. Situated close to council boat moorings, handy for the station and near regular buses on the Peterborough route; caravans and tents can be accommodated on the rear lawn by arrangement. Wheelchair access is via the garden door from the car park. ❀♿⚟♣P

Hero of Aliwal

75 Church Street (B1040, 1/4 mile S of A605 jct)

11-3 (not Mon), 7 (6 Sat)-11; 12-3.30, 7-10.30 Sun

☎ (01733) 203736

Adnams Bitter; H **guest beers** H/G

Family-owned fenland free house with a large public bar and lounge which is mostly given over to a 70-seat restaurant. There is a large, floodlit pétanque terrain and pool, darts and dominoes make up the pub games. On a riverside site, the pub is handy for boat moorings. Usually two guest ales are on offer, sometimes more, and occasionally on gravity dispense. Oakham and Rudgate breweries are often featured. Irish music evenings are a popular attraction, as are visits by local morris and sword dancers. Wheelchair access to public bar WCs only. The patio and children's play area is ideal on summer days. Lunchtime food is served Tue-Sun.

❀◑♿♣P

WITCHAM

White Horse

7 Silver Street

12-3 (not Mon & Tue), 6.30-11; 12-3, 7-11 Sun

☎ (01353) 778298

Adnams Bitter; guest beers H

Now the only pub in Witcham village, this tucked-away local is worth finding. Apart from a little nook as you walk in, the pub is open plan. Wonderful relaxing, comfortable environment – a warm welcome is always assured here. Delicious food available Tue-Sat eve, on Sunday a roast is the speciality.

Q◑P

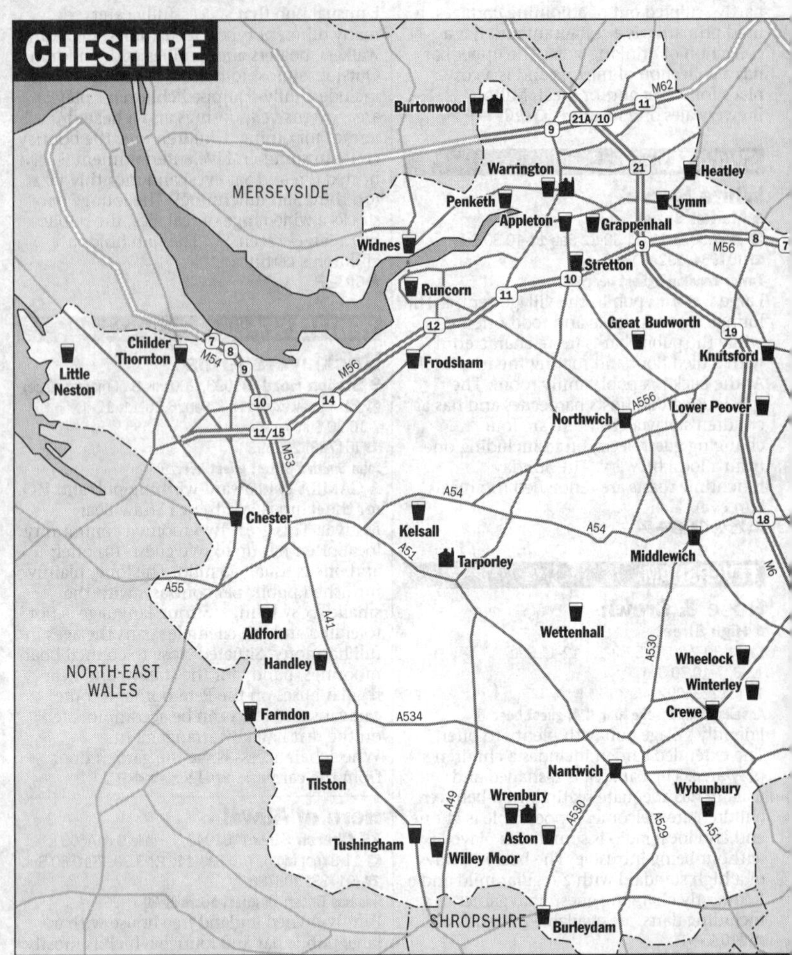

ALDFORD

Grosvenor Arms

Chester Road (B5130)
⊕ 11.30-11; 12-10.30 Sun
☎ (01244) 620228
Bateman XB; Flowers IPA; guest beers Ⓗ

Stylishly refurbished Victorian free house with a large open-plan interior and a lively atmosphere. There are also several well-furnished quieter areas and a pleasant conservatory with an attractive terracotta floor. In addition to the regularly changing well-kept ales, there is an extensive wine list and a good range of whiskies. Families are welcome and there is a large neat lawn with picnic tables. An emphasis on food, with a justified reputation, attracts many diners. The menu is imaginative and meals are delicious. ♨Q❀◑♿P

ALSAGER

Mere

58 Crewe Road (B4077)
⊕ 11-11; 12-10.30 Sun
☎ (01270) 882019
Flowers IPA; guest beers Ⓗ

Lively town-centre pub catering for all ages. An excellent range of ales includes five guest beers, rotating weekly; a monthly list and week's description board is displayed by the bar. Themed memorabilia decorate the walls, along with details of the pub's past 110 years of licensees. Tuesday is live music night and themed days are a regular occurrence. The pub has a large-screen satellite TV in the bar, plus a games room with TV and pool. Hot snacks are served all day.
❀⇌♣P

APPLETON

Birchdale Hotel

Birchdale Road (opp. London Bridge on A49)
⊕ 6 (8.30 Fri & Sat)-11; 8.30-11 Sun
☎ (01925) 263662
Taylor Landlord; guest beer Ⓗ

This unspoilt hotel is located just south of Stockton Heath village in a quiet residential area near the Delamere Way and Bridgewater Canal. Dating from the 1800s, it features a large, split-level lounge, a games room and rear gardens. Traditional home-cooked food is served Mon-Thu, 6.30-8. A friendly welcome is extended to residents, locals and visitors. It stands on the Warrington-Northwich bus route.
Q❀⇔◑♣P☐

large public bar, offering pool and table football, welcomes dogs. A cosy front lounge serves good food at fair prices. Guest beers constantly change and are clearly described on a board over the bar. The upstairs restaurant welcomes children. This pub is popular with walkers, cyclists and photographers and is a frequent winner of CAMRA awards. Draught cider is occasionally sold in summer. Q❀◖◗⊟♣P⊬

HANDFORTH

Railway

Station Road

✪ 12-3.30, 5.30-11; 12-3.30, 7-10.30 Sun

☎ (01625) 523472

Robinson's Hatter Mild, Best Bitter, seasonal beers (summer) Ⓗ

Large, multi-roomed 100-year-old pub facing the railway station. In winter it is a rare outlet for handpulled Robinson's Old Tom. The pub is frequented by a good cross-section of people and always seems to be busy and welcoming, with a pleasant array of plants and flowers. The no-smoking room at the back has no piped music (but televised football at times). Lunches, which range from snacks to full meals, including vegetarian options, are served Mon-Sat, 12-2. The bandleader, Syd Lawrence, was a previous landlord. The current incumbent has won an award for the best garden for the past four years. Q☋❀◖⊟⇌♣P⊬

HEATLEY

Railway

42 Mill Lane (B5159)

✪ 12-11; 11.30-11 Sat; 12-10.30 Sun

☎ (01925) 752742

Boddingtons Bitter; Taylor Landlord; guest beer Ⓗ

Victorian community local with five rooms served by a central bar. The welcoming snug retains some memorabilia of the long-dismantled railway which now forms the course of the adjacent Pennine Trail. It is home to many societies and clubs, including a folk club (Thu). The huge garden and play area is particularly popular with families in summer. Good value, freshly prepared lunches (no meals on Sun) include daily specials. Rolls and pies are sold at all times. Check out the imaginative Christmas lunches.
Q☋❀◖⊟♣P

HIGHER HURDSFIELD

George & Dragon

61 Rainow Road (last pub on Whaley Bridge Road, B5470, out of Macclesfield)

✪ 12-3 (not Sat), 7 (5 Fri)-11; 12-4, 7-10.30 Sun

☎ (01625) 424300

Wells Bombardier; guest beers Ⓗ

Small, friendly free house set back off the road with outside tables in summer. Built of local stone, part of the pub is reputed to be 400 years old. A true community inn, it is especially lively on match nights. The inviting bar area has a colourful display of pump clips, there is also a long room, a pool section and a snug. This local CAMRA Pub of the Season 2001 often features local brews as guests.
❀◖♣P

HIGHER SUTTON

Hanging Gate

Meg Lane

(follow Ridge Hill Road from village centre for 1½ miles)

✪ 12-3, 7 (5.30 Fri)-11; 12-11 Sat; 12-10.30 Sun

☎ (01260) 252238

Hydes Bitter, Jekyll's Gold, seasonal beers Ⓗ

An unusual building, dating from 1621, built on the hillside with small rooms on three levels; the lowest affords a wonderful panorama of the hills and the Cheshire Plain, stretching to the Welsh Mountains. Despite its exposed position, inside is cosy and welcoming with blazing fires in winter.

INN BRIEF

HANDLEY

Calveley Arms

12-3, 6-11; 12-4, 7-10.30 Sun

(01829) 770619

Boddingtons Bitter; Theakston Black Bull; guest beers Ⓗ

Popular 16th-century inn usually offering two guest beers. Well regarded for its food.

HOLMES CHAPEL

George & Dragon

Middlewich Road

11-11; 12-10.30 Sun

(01477) 537785

Robinson's Hatters Mild, Best Bitter Ⓗ

This modern building, with public bar and quiet lounge offers a patio, a children's certificate and serves bar meals.

KETTLESHULME

Bull's Head

Macclesfield Road (B5470)

3 (5 Mon; 12 Fri & Sat)-11; 12-10.30 Sun

(01663) 733225

Boddingtons Bitter; guest beer Ⓗ

Terraced stone pub in village centre, a homely country local with real fire and 1960's/70's background music.

MOBBERLEY

Roebuck

Mill Lane

11.45-3, 5-11; 11.45-11 Sat; 12-10.30 Sun

(01565) 873322

Taylor Landlord; Tetley Bitter; guest beers Ⓗ

Fashionable restaurant converted from traditional pub. Wine bar atmosphere, with excellent food. Cask Marque accredited.

NANTWICH

Oddfellows Arms

97 Welsh Row

12-3 (not Mon), 6-11; 12-11 Fri & Sat; 12-4, 7-10.30 Sun

(01270) 624758

Burtonwood Bitter, Top Hat; guest beer Ⓗ

Recently refurbished pub near the canal. Regular live music staged.

RAINOW

Rising Sun

Hawkins Lane

12-3, 5-11; 12-10.30 Sun

(01625) 424235

Marston's Bitter, Pedigree; guest beer Ⓗ

Traditional community pub on the road through Rainow. Good views of Kerridge Ridge from the garden. Appetising food.

TILSTON

Carden Arms

Church Road

12-2.30 (not Mon & Tue), 5-11; 11-11 Fri & Sat; 12-10.30 Sun

(01829) 250214

Greenalls Bitter; guest beers Ⓗ

350-year-old coaching inn with well regarded restaurant.

WHEELOCK

Cheshire Cheese

466 Crewe Road

12-11; 12-10.30 Sun

(01270) 760319

Hydes Bitter, seasonal beer Ⓗ

Split-level, canalside local, acquired by Hydes in 1999.

WINTERLEY

Foresters

473 Crewe Road

12-11; 12-10.30 Sun

(01270) 762642

Marston's Pedigree; Tetley Dark Mild, Tetley Bitter; guest beers Ⓗ

A single room, this friendly local has good home-cooked lunches and play area/garden and guest beers from Weetwood.

A family-run pub, it is popular with walkers and diners, with a well-deserved reputation for fresh home-cooked food. This local CAMRA Pub of the Year 2000 is a rare outlet for Hydes in the area.

KELSALL

Morris Dancer

Chester Road

(from A54 follow signs for Kelsall Village)

11-11; 12-10.30 Sun

(01829) 751291

Weetwood Best Bitter; guest beers

Old village pub that has been extended without losing its character. Beams, oak settles and bare wooden floors create a relaxed, traditional atmosphere. The pub attracts a good 'early doors' trade. It is the site of Chester folk festival at Whit weekend. There are plans to operate a restaurant under a separate name and to open accommodation. Live football via satellite is shown in the bar on Sat. This friendly pub is at the centre of the village, both geographically and socially. The licensee has won Wm Youngers Excellence Award. Q P

KETTLESHULME

Swan

Macclesfield Road (B5470)

12-3 (not Mon), 5.30-11; 12-11 Fri & Sat; 12-10.30 Sun

(01663) 732943

Thwaites Bitter; guest beers

15th-century, white-walled pub in a hollow alongside the B5470. The classic interior of this small country inn features original timber beams, stone fireplaces, and real log fires in winter. Three ever-changing guest beers are always available, usually from micro-breweries. Families and hikers are welcome. This picturesque Peak District National Park village is surrounded by excellent walking country. P

KNUTSFORD

Cross Keys

52 King Street

11.30-3, 5.30 (7 Sat)-11; 12-3, 7-10.30 Sun

(01565) 750404 website: www.hotel.knutsford.co.uk

Boddingtons Bitter; Taylor Landlord; guest beers

Largely rebuilt in 1909, this former 18th-century coaching inn is set on Knutsford's attractive 'Bottom Street'. A glass and timber screen separates the lounge from the vault with its pool table and TV. Bar meals can be had at lunchtimes, while the restaurant, reached by a barrel-vaulted tunnel, opens Tue-Sat evenings. The fine choice of cask ales sets the Cross Keys apart: a gleaming bank of polished brass handpumps features three constantly changing guest beers. Real cider is often available. P

LITTLE NESTON

Harp Inn

19 Quayside

11-11; 12-10.30 Sun

(0151)336 6980

Holt Bitter; Taylor Landlord; guest beers

Delightful, two-roomed pub served by a single bar. Converted from two cottages, it subsequently became a miners' pub and obtained a full licence in 1960. The superb public bar has a roaring fire and low beams. Enjoy the wonderful views across the Dee, but beware high tides. This pub may be difficult to find, but it is well worth the effort. Q P

LOWER PEOVER

Crown

Crown Lane (B5081, off the A50 S of Knutsford))

11.30-3, 5.30-11; 12-3, 7-10.30 Sun

(01565) 722074

Boddingtons Bitter; Flowers IPA; Greene King Old Speckled Hen; Taylor Landlord; guest beer

This homely 17th-century country inn tempts the passer-by with its cobbled frontage, flower tubs and hanging baskets. Three rooms cluster around a central bar; the first has benches, scrubbed tables and a well-used dartboard. Low ceilings, beams and brasses abound. The smart front room is used mainly by diners. An annual gooseberry competition is held on the last Saturday in July. Mild is usually available, and the guest beer is usually from one of Cheshire's independent brewers, typically Weetwood. P

LYMM

Barn Owl

Agden Wharf, Warrington Lane

(off A56 Lymm-Altrincham road)

11-11; 12-10.30 Sun

(01925) 752020

Marston's Bitter, Pedigree; guest beer

Open-plan pub in a former boatyard building overlooking the Bridgewater Canal. Walkers on the opposite towpath, on ringing a bell, summon the ferry from the pub. Despite the rural location, it enjoys a thriving local trade, while delicious food and a children's certificate, make it popular with diners. Canal-based tourists and local cruising clubs regularly use the pub. It hosts live music on Saturday and a quiz on Thursday. The conservatory is a pleasant spot for a peaceful drink. Q P

MACCLESFIELD

Boarhound

37 Brook Street

12-11; 12-10.30 Sun

(01625) 421200

Robinson's Hatters Mild, Best Bitter

Spacious, well-maintained pub formerly known as the Commercial. Its sizeable upstairs function room is the meeting-point for many of the town's clubs and societies. The large bar serves a lounge, pool room and games area. Apart from hosting the usual pub teams, the Boarhound is also the home of the town's premier amateur football team: Brook Celtic.

British Flag

42 Coare Street

7 (4 Sat)-11; 12-3, 7.30-10.30 Sun

(01625) 425500

Robinson's Hatters Mild, Best Bitter, Old Tom (winter), seasonal beers

This is an old-fashioned and friendly town

local, where four rooms surround a central bar. Pub games are popular, with table skittles played and one room dedicated to pool. The tap room, apart from darts and cards, is home to the landlord's local trophy cabinet of Macclesfield Town FC memorabilia. There is also a large-screen TV for sport. In the 1860s the pub was a ginger beer brewery. It has a reputation for being the local of the neighbouring King's School, being frequented by many of its staff. ⇌♣

Dolphin

76 Windmill Street

12-2.30, 5.30-11; 12-11 Sat; 12-10.30 Sun

☎ (01625) 616179

Robinson's Hatters Mild, Best Bitter, Ⓗ **Old Tom** (winter), Ⓖ **seasonal beers** Ⓗ

Friendly, traditional street-corner local, opposite open playing fields, with two distinct drinking areas served by the central bar. There is another room to the left. This is a true community local, with darts, dominoes and crib teams, and is popular with several generations of local families. Robinson's seasonal beers are always available, as well as the award-winning Old Tom strong ale in the winter months. Home-cooked food is sold at lunchtime.

Railway View

Byrons Lane (off London Rd, off A523, at lights on Langley-Wincle road)

12-3 (not Mon-Thu), 6-11; 12-3, 7-10.30 Sun

☎ (01625) 423657

Boddingtons Bitter; Cains Mild; guest beers Ⓗ

Very pleasant pub, 100 years from the main London road. The beer range includes a house beer from Coach House, and four changing guests from around the country. Home-made food is always on offer with a good selection of tasty pies. This is a pub that is well worth visiting. Monday evening features beer at a reduced price. ⇌♣

Waters Green Tavern

98 Waters Green

11.30 (11 Sat)-3, 5.30 (7 Sat)-11; 12-3; 7-10.30 Sun

☎ (01625) 422653

Taylor Landlord; guest beers Ⓗ

Close to the bus and rail stations, this pleasant town pub originally had three storeys; the half-timbered front is false. Traditional home-cooked food is served. Slightly opened out to create three areas and a pool room to the rear, the long bar to the left stocks seasonals and more unusual beers; up to five guests are sold, often including some from north of the border. This local CAMRA Pub of the Year 1999 fields thriving darts, pool and quiz teams.
Q⇌♣

MIDDLEWICH

Royal British Legion Club

100 Lewin Street

12-3, 7-11; 11-11 Sat; 12-3, 7-10.30 Sun

☎ (01606) 833286

Hydes Bitter; guest beers Ⓗ

This cavernous club returned to real ale in 2001 after 40 years of keg – an achievement due to the enterprising committee and new landlord. Sports are well supported, with three snooker tables close to the bar, and a bowling green at the rear, with outdoor seating. There is a rear lounge and spacious main room, but no children's facilities. Show this Guide or CAMRA membership card to gain entry to this regional CAMRA Club of the Year 2001. Beartown beers are often featured. ♣P

MOBBERLEY

Bull's Head

Mill Lane

11-11; 12-10.30 Sun

☎ (01565) 873134

Boddingtons Bitter; Tetley Bitter; guest beers Ⓗ

This is a traditional country local, very much a part of its community, with all manner of activities and a good reputation for its food. There is a cobbled frontage and bowling green to the rear. An unusual fireplace divides the main room. The pub hosts occasional beer festivals, traction engine rallies and music. Bucking the trend for a Punch house, it has three guest beers, and turnover is building up well. Follow signs from the B5085, the Bull's Head is found down a quiet lane. P

NANTWICH

Black Lion

Welsh Row

4 (12 Fri & Sat)-11; 1-10.30 Sun

☎ (01270) 628711

Titanic White Star; Weetwood Best Bitter, Old Dog, Oasthouse Gold Ⓗ

Small timber-framed black and white pub with the date 1664 above the door. Three small rooms downstairs are lit by candles; upstairs there are two rooms, the front one has a TV and is sometimes used for meetings. Chess is played every evening and there is live music at weekends. At the side is a small paved area for outdoor drinking. This is a friendly pub, where conversation predominates.
Q♣

NORTHWICH

Freemasons Arms

45 Castle Street

11-11; 12-10.30 Sun

☎ (01606) 79310

Webster's Yorkshire Bitter; guest beers Ⓗ

Welcoming town pub on the Northwich 'curry trail', an honest, down-to-earth local that has avoided change. There are two small front rooms, and a compact side room where dominoes are played and an active darts team is based. The pub is within walking distance of the town and bus station, or you will find off-street parking nearby. ♣

Kingfisher

15 Kingsmead Square, Regency Way (in local shopping centre of Kingsmead development)

11.30-11; 12-10.30 Sun

☎ (01606) 354720

Lees Bitter, Moonraker, seasonal beers Ⓗ

This is a brand-new, purpose-built family pub. In response to community needs, provision is made for all: an outside play area, small 'rooms' for board games, function rooms that are safe for toddlers and a large child-free upstairs section. Each

area has its own distinct atmosphere. There are two events monthly, celebrating, for example, Charlie Chaplin's birthday and Mother's Day, with live music staged and themed menus. The restaurant can cater for any dietary need. Comfy sofas are ideal for a relaxing drink.
⛰Q🍼❀☾◗♿P⚟

PENKETH

Ferry Tavern

Station Road (off Tannery Lane, off A562)
⏲ 12-3, 5.30-11; 12-11 Sat & summer; 12-10.30 Sun
☎ (01925) 791117
Boddingtons Bitter; Courage Directors; Wells Bombardier; guest beers Ⓗ
Worth seeking out, the pub is located between the river and the Sankey-St Helens Canal. It is especially popular with walkers in the summer months. Access to the pub from the car park is by crossing a railway line. Six handpumps in the bar area are complemented by over 300 whiskies. Home-made food is served Mon-Sat in either the bar area, or upstairs in the more formal surroundings of the small, no-smoking restaurant. ⛰Q❀◗P

PEOVER HEATH

Dog Inn

Well Bank Lane
(off A50 at the Whipping Stocks pub)
⏲ 11.30-3, 5 (5.30 Sat)-11; 12-10.30 Sun
☎ (01625) 861421
Hydes Bitter; Moorhouses Black Cat; Weetwood Best Bitter, Old Dog Ⓗ
This comfortable inn, set on a quiet lane and converted from a row of 18th-century cottages, features in CAMRA's Good Pub Food. The tap room offers pool and darts, a real fire warms the lounge, and the restaurant boasts local produce. Beams, dried flowers and photos of old village life add interest. A splendid array of flower tubs and hanging baskets surround the benches on the patio. Regular quiz nights feature.
⛰Q❀🛏☾◗⊟♿♣P⚟

PRESTBURY

Admiral Rodney

New Road (200 yds downhill from train station)
⏲ 11-3, 5.30-11; 11-11 Fri & Sat; 12-3, 7-10.30 Sun
☎ (01625) 829484
Robinson's Hatters Mild, Best Bitter Ⓗ
Situated at the village centre, less than five minutes' walk from the station, this Grade II listed building dates from 1730. The interior is most attractive, with small rooms, low ceilings and exposed beams. The furnishings are also appealing, with some of the tables being constructed from old barrels. Named after a famous British naval officer in the Napoleonic Wars, the pub benefits from a total lack of juke box, pool table or other annoying machines.
Q❀☾⇌P

RUNCORN

Weaver Hotel

South Parade, Weston Point
(off A557 Weston expressway)
⏲ 12-11; 12-10.30 Sun
☎ (01928) 572239
Oakwell Barnsley Bitter, Old Tom Ⓗ
An imposing, refurbished (1913) building, that takes the name of its predecessor nearer the docks. It is adjacent to the ex-ICI chemical works but popular with local village characters. On one side is an open-plan lounge, on the other a basic public bar used by darts, pool and football teams. Noteworthy features include some original internal wall tiling and a few Groves & Whitnall window panes. There is a grassed area to the side with views over the Mersey estuary. ❀☾◗⊟♣P

STRETTON

Ring O' Bells

Northwich Road, Lower Stretton
(A559, off M56 jct 10)
⏲ 12-3 (3.30 Sat), 5.30 (7 Sat)-11; 12-3, 7-10.30 Sun
☎ (01925) 730566
Greenalls Bitter; Tetley Mild; guest beer Ⓗ
Traditional pub in an area dominated by family eating houses – a real gem. What was once a row of cottages is now a small, cosy, friendly local. No fruit machines or music, so conversation tends to be lively. The bar serves the main room with an inviting real fire, the unusual tables are made from old sewing machines. Two smaller rooms are quieter and the rear snug has a collection of local views. A small outdoor drinking area is adjacent to the rear car park. ⛰Q❀P

TUSHINGHAM

Blue Bell Inn

Signed Bell 'o t'Hill from A41, 4 miles N of Whitchurch
⏲ 12-3, 6-11; 12-3, 7-10.30 Sun
☎ (01948) 662172
Hanby Drawwell; guest beers Ⓗ
This part-14th-century, timber-framed pub positively exudes atmosphere. Floodlit and imposing on the outside, access is via a cobbled frontage and two hefty oak doors. The back rooms are mainly for dining and quiet conversation, but the front bar is dominated by friendly locals and the pub dogs. It is full of ancient artefacts, many found in the pub. The bar is a very sociable place, presided over by the larger-than-life American landlord. There are tales of a duck haunting. ⛰Q❀☾◗⛺♣P

WARRINGTON

Bull's Head

33 Church Street
⏲ 12-11; 12-10.30 Sun
☎ (01925) 635680
Cains Bitter; Courage Directors; Greenalls Bitter; Tetley Mild; guest beer Ⓗ
Attractive, rambling, 17th-century building, converted from a row of cottages. This multi-roomed pub has a lounge to the front, a bar area with pool table and two smaller, quieter rooms to the rear. At the back you will find a large function room and a bowling green. This welcoming, unspoilt pub, just outside the town centre, is home to many sports clubs.
❀☾⊟⇌(Central) ♣

Wilkies

25 Church Street (A49, 500 yds from centre)
⏲ 2 (12 Fri & Sat)-11; 12-10.30 Sun

☎ (01925) 416564
Beer range varies Ⓗ
A single room bar with an Irish theme. A continually changing range of four beers is invariably sourced from smaller/micro-breweries. Two beer festivals, at Easter and early December, are held in the rear courtyard. Irish beers feature in March and milds during May (usually one dark beer is available). Sky TV on the big screen attracts many customers at weekends when live rugby league or football is shown.
≉ (Central) ♣ ⍞

WETTENHALL

Little Man
Winsford Road OS628601
✪ 12-3 (not Tue), 7-11; 12-3, 7-10.30 Sun
☎ (01270) 528203
Beer range varies Ⓗ
Friendly, rural pub, popular with local equestrian and farming communities. Excellent, good value food and ever-changing real ales are available. The pub welcomes children and dogs. It is thought to be the only pub of this name in the country – look above the front door to see the little man watching you. This charming hostelry is well worth seeking out. ♨❀◐P

WIDNES

Horse & Jockey
18 Birchfield Road (300 yds S of station)
✪ 11-11; 12-10.30 Sun
☎ (0151) 420 2966
Greenalls Bitter; Tetley Bitter; guest beer Ⓗ
A warm welcome is guaranteed at this local CAMRA Pub of the Year 2001. This cosy, one-roomed pub, close to the town centre benefits from excellent links to train and bus services. Over a century old, it backs on to a park and has a fully enclosed garden with a children's play area. It is much favoured by the local community and has no juke box. The guest beer changes weekly.
❀≉P

WILLEY MOOR

Willey Moor Lock Tavern
Tarporley Road (300 yds off A49) OS534452
✪ 12-2.30 (3 summer), 6-11; 7-10.30 Sun
☎ (01948) 663274
Theakston Cool Cask; guest beers Ⓗ
An attractive, red-brick and whitewashed, ex-lock keeper's cottage. Access from the car park is across a narrow bridge over the Llangollen Canal. There is easy access from boats (front door by the lock). There are several eating and drinking areas served by one bar. Paintings of canal life and a collection of teapots and toby jugs create interest. Two guest beers in winter are increased to four in summer, to cater for boaters and walkers on the Sandstone Trail. The large garden is popular. Take care when arriving by car due to unforgiving sleeping policemen. ♨Q☋❀◐P

WRENBURY

Dusty Miller
Cholmondley Road
✪ 11.30-3, 6.30-11; 12-3, 7-10.30 Sun
☎ (01270) 780537
Robinson's Best Bitter, Old Tom (winter), **seasonal beers** Ⓗ
Converted from a mill, it became a pub, originally a free house, in 1977. Situated in an idyllic setting, where the Llangollen Canal crosses the River Weaver, the lounge bar, decorated with hop bines, and upstairs dining room overlook the towpath and lift bridge. Mooring is available. The Dusty Miller lies on the Cheshire Cycleway, one mile from Wrenbury station. ❀◐▲P

Paradise Brewery Bar
2 Creamery Industrial Estate, Wrenbury Road (follow the brown signs marked 'micro-brewery')
✪ 11-11 Fri & Sat early spring to late autumn; 12-3 Sun
☎ (01270) 780916
Beer range varies Ⓗ
Cosy bar at the Paradise Brewery. Usually up to five Paradise beers are available, including a mild, plus a guest ale. Beer festivals are held through the year, including one between Christmas and New Year, and another at Easter. There is a function room for hire. To find out more about the brewery, go to the viewing area, or join one of the tours which are often run.
Q

WYBUNBURY

Swan
2 Main Road (B5071)
✪ 11.30-11; 12-10.30 Sun
☎ (01270) 841280
Greene King Abbot; Jennings Mild, Bitter, Cumberland Ale, Cocker Hoop, Sneck Lifter Ⓗ
Spacious village inn, bow-fronted with low beamed ceilings, acquired by Jennings in 1999. Popular with locals, walkers and cyclists, top quality food is served. A homely atmosphere is enhanced by inviting log fires. The pub has an attractive setting, next to a leaning tower, all that remains of the original parish church, a prominent local landmark.
♨Q❀⇔◐◗♿P⚟

> There is by now sufficient information available to indicate that moderate use of alcoholic beverages is pleasurable and beneficial for older adults... the lower ethanol beverages such as beer and wine may have their place in the lifestyles of some older adults.
>
> **Professor Robert Kastenbaum, 1988, United States.**

Blowing in the Wind

Why barley is the preferred grain of craft brewers

HAVE YOU EVER WONDERED WHY some beers are golden in colour, others are amber or copper hued, while still more are as black as night? The answer lies in barley malt and the way it's prepared for the brewing process.

Brewers call barley malt 'the soul of beer'. It provides flavour, colour, and natural sugar. Other grains can be used in brewing, but even wheat beers are a mix of both wheat and barley. Barley is the preferred grain in brewing because it's remarkably hardy and grows in many parts of the world, withstanding great differences in climate and temperature. It produces high levels of starch and natural enzymes that are vital to fermentation, and – unlike other grains such as wheat – it also has a husk that acts as a filter during the mashing stage of brewing.

And, most important for both the brewer and the drinker, it gives a delightful juicy, biscuity flavour to beer. That essential characteristic, the main building block of malt, is embellished by darker versions that add nutty, vinous, chocolate, coffee, liquorice and roasted notes.

Finest

Pale malt is the basis of all beer, even dark stouts. The finest form of barley is known as 'maritime', grown close to the coast in soil that is dark and rich, often reclaimed from the sea. In Britain, areas such as Norfolk and the Scottish Lowlands are ideal for growing top quality maritime varieties. When barley has been harvested, it's taken to maltings where it's dried and then steeped or washed repeatedly in large troughs of fresh water for three days. This cleans the grain, and kills wild yeasts and bacteria that would impede germination and, later, fermentation.

When steeping is finished, the soaked grain is either laid out on warm floors or, in modern maltings, loaded into rotating drums. The grain begins to germinate: its starch becomes soluble and rootlets break through the husks. Inside each ear of grain, the plant's embryo – the main root or acrospire – start to grow, triggering a change that turns proteins into enzymes.

Only partial germination is allowed by the maltster, who measures the growth of the embryo and the solubility of the starch, a stage known as modification. If germination were allowed to continue, the grain would start to consume its own sugars.

Germination is stopped by heating or curing the grain in kilns. The floors are made of slotted metal and heat comes blasting up from below. Malt stays in the kilns for 48 hours.

The main types of malt used in ale brewing in Britain are as follows (EBC is a colour rating laid down by the European Brewing Convention):

Pale malt (4-7.5 EBC). The basis of all beers. It is kilned at 100-105 degrees C/212-221 F. The barley must be of the highest quality and low in nitrogen: nitrogen is converted into protein and can cause a haze in the finished beer. The high level of enzymes in the malt convert starch into sugar during the mashing process in the brewery.

Mild Ale malt (7 EBC). A type of malt used, as the name implies, to make Mild Ale. It's darker than pale malt as a result of slightly higher kilning temperatures. It can be made from barley higher in nitrogen, as any haze will be masked by the colour of the finished beer, and will be diluted by the use of brewing sugar and cereal adjuncts. As a result of diminishing demand for Mild, many brewers use pale malt and add either darker malts or adjuncts such as caramel for colour.

Crystal malt (100-300 EBC). This is a stewed malt that gives both colour and body to classic English pale ales. After germination in specialist maltings, the 'green' (unfinished) malt is loaded into a sealed kiln where the moisture cannot escape. The temperature is raised to 45C/113F, which matches the mashing temperature in a brewery. The enzymes inside each kernel of grain convert some of the starches into sugar. Vents in the kiln are opened and the temperature is increased so that the sugar crystallises: it is a similar process to making toffee. Not all the sugar is converted and much of it is dextrin rather than maltose. As dextrin cannot be converted into alcohol by brewer's yeast, the sugar remains in the beer, giving a fullness of palate and a pleasing nutty flavour. Brown malt, rarely used these, is also a type of stewed malt.

Chocolate malt (1,000 EBC) is kilned at high temperatures until the grains look like coffee beans. The malt is used primarily to add colour and a luscious chocolate or coffee character to dark milds, porters and stouts. As a result of high kilning temperatures, dark malts have few enzymes and therefore lack the 'diastatic power' to convert starch into sugar.

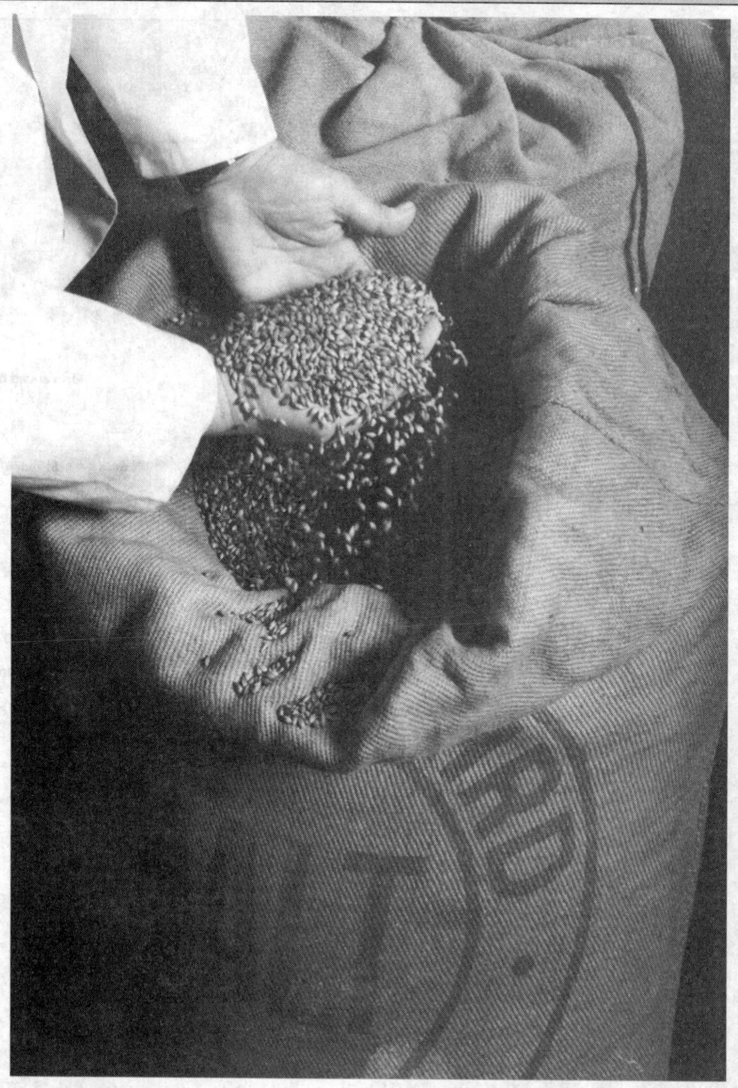

Roasted barley (1,000-1,500 EBC). The barley is not malted but is roasted until it turns black. It gives a dry and burnt aroma and flavour to stouts, in particular the style known as 'Dry Irish Stout'. It also helps create a dense collar of foam on beer, another distinguishing feature of stout.

Black malt (1,250-1,500 EBC). This type of malt gives a tart, slightly astringent character to dark beers, and an acrid bitterness. It imparts a flavour similar to that of espresso coffee, and must be used sparingly to avoid unbalancing the flavour of beer. Scottish brewers often add a minute amount of black malt to their ales for both colour and flavour.

Wheat malt (5 EBC). This is a major constituent of wheat beers brewed in Germany and the Netherlands and, increasingly, in Britain. Wheat beers are usually a 50-50 blend of wheat and barley malts. Wheat malt has a pronounced grainy and fruity character. It is often used in small amounts by traditional ale brewers as it creates a good head of foam on finished beer.

Adjuncts are cereals or sugars used in the brewing process. They can be used for cheapness, as is the case with American light lagers, where high proportions of rice or maize are used. British brewers often use tiny amounts of wheat flour, flaked [gelatinised] or torrefied [scorched] grains, with 'invert sugars' [glucose and fructose] to encourage fermentation, reduce haze and add subtle colour and flavour. Caramel, which is burnt sugar, is also used for colour and flavour, often in Milds. Most cask-conditioned beers are brewed with at least 90% pale malt, sometimes a much higher proportion.

CORNWALL

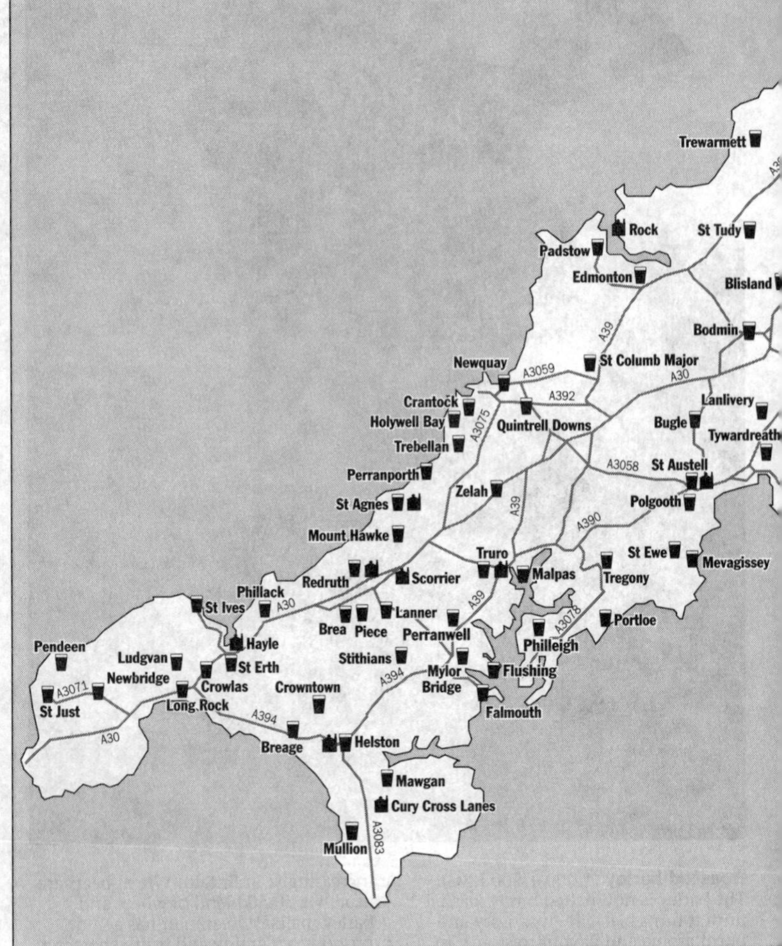

ALTARNUN

Rising Sun

1 mile N of village on Camelford road
11-3, 6-11; 11-11 Sat & summer; 12-10.30 Sun
(01566) 86332

Beer range varies H

Originally a 16th-century farmhouse, this pub retains many original features. There are normally four ever-changing real ales, increasing to five at weekends and six in summer. Camping is allowed in the pub grounds – caravans welcome. It offers an excellent value food menu. Near the Inny Valley recreational walk, dog-friendly – but watch out for Eric, the cat with attitude! Pool is played here.

BLISLAND

Blisland Inn

The Green (signed from A30, 1½ miles N of Bodmin)
11.30-11; 12-10.30 Sun
(01208) 850739

Beer range varies H/G

CAMRA's award-winning pub beside the only village green in Cornwall is at the centre of community life. It normally has six or seven ales available, with two or three from Cornish brewers and various ciders. Bar food and à la carte meals are available, all made with local produce – booking is advised for full meals. A collection of barometers, toby jugs and clay pipes decorates the two bars; the family room is presided over by a silent, but watchful, iguana.

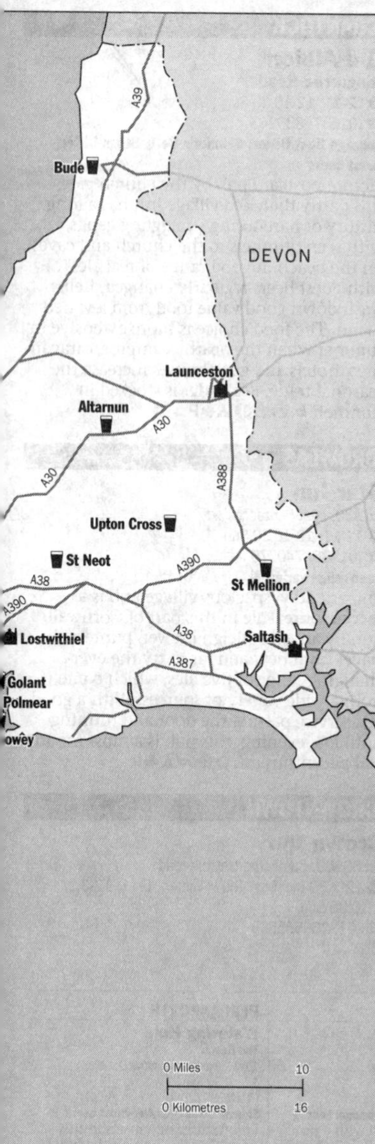

BODMIN

Hole in the Wall

16 Crockwell Street (off ring road)

12-2.30, 5-11; 12-10.30 Sun

(01208) 72397

Draught Bass; Sharp's Doom Bar; guest beers Ⓗ

Formerly the town's Debtors' Prison, this warm, welcoming pub is entered through a leafy garden with bubbling stream, presided over by a stuffed lion. The single bar, which is divided by archways, houses an eclectic collection of antiques and military memorabilia. The pub draws a good mix of locals and passing trade, and guest ales are changed regularly. Meals are served in the bar, while the Lion's Den restaurant is upstairs. Use the council car park (free after 5pm). Q

Mason's Arms

5-9 Higher Bore Street

(by town wall, on Lanivet road)

11-11; 12-10.30 Sun

(01208) 72607

Sharp's Cornish Coaster; Taylor Landlord; guest beers Ⓗ

Dating from before Napoleonic times, this pub claims to be the oldest licensed premises in town. The lively, slate-flagged public bar provides games and music, including occasional live entertainment. The lounge is quieter and preferred by locals seeking a more relaxed pint and general chat. Traditional bar meals are served at lunchtime. On the edge of the town, the Mason's largely relies on local custom, but visitors are always welcome. Q P

BREA

Brea Inn

Higher Brea (near Pool Ind. Estate)

12-2.30 (not Mon), 7 (6.30 Sat)-11; 12-3.30, 7-10.30 Sun

(01209) 713706

Flowers IPA; Sharp's Doom Bar; guest beer Ⓗ

Nicely modernised village local with a good reputation for food, most of it sourced locally. Set in the thick of Camborne's mining district, it was once a mine captain's house before becoming a tinners' ale house. The single, cosy bar is dedicated to drinking matters in the evenings, when food is confined to a tiny elevated restaurant in the next room. Booking is essential for meals (not served Sun-Tue eves). Get there by 44C bus weekday lunchtimes. Q P

BREAGE

Queen's Arms

Off A394

11.30-2.30, 6.30-11; 12-10.30 Sun

(01326) 573485

website: www.thequeensarmsinn.co.uk

Draught Bass; Sharp's Doom Bar; guest beers Ⓗ

Thriving village pub in the shadow of the church, runner-up in 2001 Cornwall CAMRA Pub of the Year. One long bar has a fire at each end, and a games area around the corner. It always stocks six real ales and Bulmers West Country cider on handpump. A wide range of food is available until 9pm in the no-smoking dining room. Beams are festooned with a plate collection. A large outside area includes a safe playground

INDEPENDENT BREWERIES

Ales of Scilly St Mary's
Bird in Hand Hayle
Blackawton Saltash
Blue Anchor Helston
Doghouse Scorrier
Driftwood St. Agnes
Keltek Lostwithiel
Organic Cury Cross Lanes
Redruth Redruth
Ring O'Bells Launceston
St Austell St Austell
Sharp's Rock
Skinner's Truro

across the lane. Children are welcome in the pub, too.
♨❀◐◑♣●P

BUDE

Bencoolen
Bencoolen Road
12-11 (11-11 summer); 12-10.30 Sun
☎ (01288) 354694
Beer range varies Ⓗ
Welcoming pub named after the ship wrecked in Budehaven in 1862. Some of the timbers were used in the pub's construction. Take time during your visit to read the account of the shipwreck detailed on one of the walls. Although handpumps are used, all beers can be served by gravity if requested. This pub, normally quiet, becomes a hive of activity during Bude Jazz Week (August bank holiday). Bar snacks and restaurant meals are served.
♨❀⇌◐◑▲P

BUGLE

Bugle Inn
57 Fore Street (A391)
11-11; 12-10.30 Sun
☎ (01726) 850307 website: www.bugleinn.co.uk
St Austell IPA, Tinners, Tribute, seasonal beers Ⓗ
Situated at the village crossroads, this inn has been newly refurbished to a comfortable standard, serving St Austell beers in the single L-shaped bar. Its five en-suite bedrooms have become very busy due to the 'Eden' effect. Breakfast for residents and visitors is served from 8am until mid-morning, and meals (with an all-day breakfast) are served continuously from midday until 10.30pm. Bugle stands in the Cornish china clay district.
♨❀⇌◐◑⇄P✔

CRANTOCK

Old Albion
Langurroc Road
12-11; 12-10.30 Sun
☎ (01637) 830243
Courage Best Bitter; Skinner's Betty Stogs Bitter; guest beers Ⓗ
Picture-postcard pub by the church gate, this partly thatched village inn has a long history of harbouring smuggling gangs, with secret tunnels to the church and caves on the beach. A good range of real ales, with guest beers regularly changed, helps wash down good value food from a varied menu. The food choice is more extensive in summer when the nearby camping/caravan sites, hotels and guesthouses increase the seasonal trade. Real cider is stocked in summer. ♨⛀❀◐◑▲●P

CROWLAS

Star Inn
On A30, near Penzance
11-11; 12-10.30 Sun
☎ (01736) 740375
Beer range varies Ⓗ
This friendly, spacious village pub is a mecca for real ale in this part of Cornwall. Run by an ex-Cotleigh brewer, punters travel from near and far to try the ever-changing range of five ales, which come from a wide variety of sources. With a good bus service passing the door and running until late evening, this pub is a must for any real ale enthusiast. Q❀⇌▲♣P

CROWNTOWN

Crown Inn
On B3303, Camborne-Helston road
12-2.30 (not Mon-Thu in winter), 6-11; 12-3, 7-10.30 Sun
☎ (01326) 565538

INN BRIEF

GOLANT

Fisherman's Arms
Fore Street
12-3, 6-11 (11-11 summer); 12-10.30 Sun
(01726) 832453
Courage Best Bitter; Sharp's Doom Bar; Usher's Best Bitter or Founders Ale; guest beer Ⓗ
Riverside pub with a single bar, pub games, home-cooking, accommodation and a summer beer festival. Beware tides!

HELSTON

Rodney Inn
31 Meneage Street
11-11; 12-10.30 Sun
(01326) 572417
St Austell IPA, Tribute, HSD, seasonal beer Ⓗ
Bustling, modern, town pub, popular with younger drinkers evenings, but all are welcome. Have a pint and a haircut on Sunday! Cask Marque accredited.

LONG ROCK

Mount View Hotel
11-11; 12-4, 7-10.30 Sun
(01736) 710416
Courage Best Bitter, Directors Ⓗ
Friendly, one-bar village inn, with a no-smoking dining area (no food Sun). Families are welcome. Good bus services.

LUDGVAN

Old Inn
Lower Quarter
12-3, 5.30-11; 12-11 Sat; 12-3, 5.30-10.30 Sun
(01736) 740419
St Austell IPA, Tribute, seasonal beer Ⓖ
Pleasant, two-bar pub with a no-smoking area in the main bar. A limited, but tasty menu includes good value Sunday lunches.

MULLION

Mounts Bay Hotel
Churchtown
11-2.30, 6-11 (11-11 summer); 12-3, 7-10.30 (12-10.30 summer) Sun
(01326) 240221
Skinner's Betty Stogs Bitter, Cornish Knocker Ⓗ
Rambling, friendly free house in the village centre, with two bars and a no-smoking dining area. Good bus service.

NEWQUAY

Lanherne Pub & Restaurant
32 Ulalia Road
11-3, 6-11 (11-11 summer); 12-3, 7-10.30 (12-10.30 summer) Sun
(01637) 872308
Beer range varies Ⓗ
Spacious pub near the zoo and Waterworld leisure park. Two bars: one for drinkers, one for diners.

PERRANPORTH

Watering Hole
The Beach
11-11 (closed weekdays Oct-Mar); 12-10.30 Sun
(01872) 572888
Skinner's Spriggan Ale; guest beers Ⓗ
Enjoy stunning sunsets in this unrivalled location on the beach. Quality ale and food; regular live music (Fri and Sat).

PERRANWELL

Royal Oak
Perranwell Station
11-3, 6-11 (may vary summer); 12-10.30 Sun
(01872) 863175
Draught Bass; Flowers IPA; guest beer Ⓗ
Small, friendly, cottage pub dating from the 18th century, now a free house specialising in excellent food.

PHILLEIGH

Roseland Inn
11-3, 6-11; 12-3, 6-10.30 Sun
(01872) 580254
Draught Bass; Marston's Pedigree; Sharp's Doom Bar; Ringwood Best Bitter Ⓗ
Classic, 16th-century country inn offering award-winning home-cooked food. On a cycle trail; families and dogs are welcome.

Skinner's Betty Stogs Bitter; guest beers Ⓖ

Once a hunting lodge for the nearby Trevarno estate, this large, friendly, granite roadside inn dispenses real ale direct from the cellar, in spite of the correctly-badged handpumps on the bar, which helps maintain consistent quality on warm summer days. This is a community pub where conversation dominates, although there may be occasional live entertainment or a quiz. The guest ales change frequently, with the emphasis always on Cornish breweries. Note the limited winter opening times.

Q❀⇌◐♣P

EDMONTON

Quarryman

Just off A39

⌚ 12-11; 12-10.30 Sun

☎ (01208) 816444

Beer range varies Ⓗ

Once a school and shop, and part of a 19th-century purpose-built housing complex for local quarrymen, this popular family-friendly inn exudes character and bonhomie. The cosy, single bar has several drinking areas, the decor reflecting sport and field activities. The beer list includes examples from the Sharp's and Skinner's ranges plus a varying guest or two, and complements the high quality meals. Adjoining holiday cottages form a quadrangular setting around the garden. It is handy for the Camel Trail and county showground.

⛰Q❀◐⛺P✔

FALMOUTH

Mason's Arms

31 Killigrew Street

⌚ 11-11; 12-10.30 Sun

☎ (01326) 311061

St Austell Tribute, HSD Ⓗ

Town-centre pub, just off the bus terminus. The emphasis is on its 'traditional' nature – a locals' local: no discos, no karaoke, as stated by a board on the pavement, although there is a juke box. The tiny bar serves good ale to a small but comfortable single room, which nevertheless has space to form one or two separate drinking areas. No food is served, but you may bring in your own – choose from a list of takeaways by the door.

⛰♣

Seven Stars ☆

The Moor

⌚ 11-3, 6-11; 12-3, 7-10.30 Sun

☎ (01326) 312111

Draught Bass; guest beer Ⓖ

Wood dominates the bar of this unspoilt old Grade II* listed town-centre pub, also on the CAMRA National Inventory of historic pub interiors. The lively, narrow tap room, where conversation is the entertainment, has a steadfast following of locals and displays an impressive collection of keyrings; there is a quieter 'snug' at the back. The 'bottle and jug' hatch still exists for outside drinkers. The bus terminus is outside – services run until late evening to Truro and Camborne.

Q❀⊟⇌(Town)

FLUSHING

Royal Standard

St Peters Hill (off A393 at Penryn)

⌚ 11-2.30 (3 Fri & Sat), 6.30-11 (varies winter); 12-3, 7-10.30 (varies winter) Sun

☎ (01326) 374250

Draught Bass; Sharp's Cornish Coaster, Doom Bar Ⓗ

Friendly local, run by the present landlord for over 30 years. Home-made pasties and apple pies are specialities on the menu. Fine views of Falmouth and the Penryn River can be enjoyed from the front patio. Drivers beware of swans in the road nearby. The pub is accessible from Falmouth by foot ferry across the river. ⛰❀◐♣

FOWEY

Galleon

12 Fore Street

⌚ 11-11; 12-10.30 Sun

☎ (01726) 833014

Draught Bass; Flowers IPA; Skinner's Cornish Knocker; guest beer Ⓗ

This 400-year old pub has recently been comprehensively refurbished and provides congenial drinking areas, including a patio beside the town quay, overlooking the river. This view can also be enjoyed from the lounge windows. The traditional feel of the public bar is provided by imaginative use of timber beams and solid wood furniture. There is access for the disabled and children are welcome (nappy-changing facilities provided); guest accommodation includes two family rooms. Live music is usually performed Sunday lunchtime. Cider is sold in summer. ⛰Q⊏❀⇌◐⊟♿⛺●

HELSTON ❊

Blue Anchor

50 Coinagehall Street

⌚ 11-11; 12-10.30 Sun

☎ (01326) 562821

Blue Anchor Middle, Bragget (summer)**, Special, seasonal beers** Ⓗ

Flagship brew-pub, dating from the 15th century, this is a totally unspoilt, rambling old granite building with several rooms in which to drink the 'Spingo' beers and enjoy the atmosphere and conversation. The main bar at the front has a well-worn flagstone floor, low, beamed ceiling and old wooden tables and settles; the smaller rear bar is dominated by the inglenook and fire in winter. This pub has featured in every edition of this Guide. It enjoys good bus connections with other west Cornwall towns until late evening. Skittles played.

⛰Q⊏❀⇌◐⊟♣

HOLYWELL BAY

St Piran's Inn

⌚ 11 (7 winter)-11; 12-10.30 (varies winter) Sun

☎ (01637) 830205

St Austell Tribute; guest beers Ⓗ

Situated almost on the golden sands of a picturesque bay, this free house offers up to four guest ales, many from local micros. The landlord tends to rename some beers and produces his own pump clips. There may be a refundable parking fee in summer to ensure only pub customers use the car park, as it is close to the beach. The many camping and other holiday facilities in the area boost summer trade, when good value meals and evening barbecues may be enjoyed. ⩕Q🛡❀◐◑♿ΔP

LANLIVERY

Crown Inn

Turn off A390, 1 mile W of Lostwithiel OS080590
✪ 11-3, 6-11; 12-3, 6-10.30 Sun
☎ (01208) 872707
Sharp's Doom Bar, Eden Ale 🄷
This popular pub is opposite the church and on the Saints Way footpath. The stone-flagged public bar is large in contrast to the tiny snug. Sharp's Brewery supplies the house ale, Glory. A lounge leads to the à la carte restaurant, which has a conservatory extension; snacks are served in the bars. Vegetarians and vegans are catered for. There are two bed and breakfast cottage rooms in the large garden.
⩕Q🛡❀⛾◐◑ΔP

LANNER

Lanner Inn

The Square (A393, Redruth-Falmouth road)
✪ 12-3, 4.30-11; 12-11 Fri & Sat; 12-3, 7-10.30 Sun
☎ (01209) 215611
Sharp's Cornish Coaster, Doom Bar; guest beer 🄷
Real village community local where the emphasis is on sport, with the pub fielding teams for the usual bar games. The two small bars can get crowded at times, but the atmosphere is always friendly and convivial. The guest ale is regularly varied, often as recommended by the locals. Four bed and breakfast rooms make this an ale drinker's ideal holiday call. Frequent buses connect the pub to local towns, including weekday evenings. ⩕Q❀⛾♣P

LONG ROCK ❊

Mexico Inn

Gladstone Terrace (off A30 near Marazion)
✪ 11-2.30, 5-11; 12-3, 7 (5 summer)-10.30 Sun
☎ (01736) 710625
Sharp's Doom Bar, Eden Ale; Skinner's Figgy's Brew; guest beer (summer) 🄷
Local free house with a single L-shaped beamed bar and bare granite walls, characteristic of the mine of which this building was once a part. The summer guest beer is varied. The pub is especially popular in season, being only 50 yards from the beach. Good bus services pass the door until late evening on weekdays; car parking is very limited. Good quality food is available in the bar, or the no-smoking restaurant (evenings). ⩕Q❀◐◑♿ΔP

LOSTWITHIEL

Royal Oak

Duke Street (behind Royal Talbot)
✪ 11-11; 12-10.30 Sun
☎ (01208) 872552
website: www.angelfire.com/ky/royaloak/main.html
Draught Bass; Fuller's London Pride; Marston's Pedigree; Sharp's Own; guest beers 🄷
This popular pub is a 13th-century inn, just off the A390. The stone-flagged public bar is a noisy and convivial place for socialising. A plush lounge bar runs into a restaurant area, then into a family room. The six en-suite rooms are busy with Eden Project visitors. The inn serves excellent food and selects many beers in their guest range from independent and local breweries.
⩕Q🛡❀⛾◐◑ΔΔ⥱P

LUDGVAN ❊

White Hart

Churchtown (signed from A30 at Crowlas)
✪ 11-2.30, 6-11; 12-3, 7-10.30 Sun
☎ (01736) 740574
Draught Bass; Flowers IPA; Marston's Pedigree 🄶
14th-century inn with an authentic atmosphere, maintained by an interesting mix of old chairs and tables. Wooden partitions create quiet corners in the two rooms. Large, wood-burning stoves keep the place snug throughout. It serves generous portions of food, much of it local (not winter Mon eve). A place for quiet conversation, it is popular with locals and tourists alike. The beer is served direct from barrels at the back of the bar. A small car park is shared with the church.
⩕Q❀◐◑♣P⊁

MALPAS

Heron Inn

From A390 in Truro, take road signed Malpas, next to Radio Cornwall OS843426
✪ 11 (11.30 winter)-2.30, 6-11; 11-2.30, 6-10.30 Sun
☎ (01872) 272773
St Austell IPA, Tribute, seasonal beer (summer) 🄷
This picturesque village pub, just outside Truro, can be reached by road or river. Set above the road, it benefits from wonderful views over Truro River and surrounding woodland – look for herons. The terrace is a popular choice for a drink, while inside natural slate and oak combine with a blue colour scheme, enhanced by artefacts from local artists and craftsmen. A good menu is supplemented by a specials board, all home-cooked. Children are welcome. ❀◐◑P⊘

MAWGAN

Old Court House

Off Helston-St Keverne road (B3293)
✪ 12-3, 6-11 (11-11 summer); 12-3, 7-10.30 (12-10.30 summer) Sun
☎ (01326) 221240
Beer range varies 🄷
Very friendly country pub tucked away down a leafy lane. Keen licensees justifiably call it a 'proper village pub', with food limited to simple but wholesome fare including an all-day breakfast. Up to four real ales may be on offer, with local Cornish brews much favoured, although the odd 'foreign' beer from across the Tamar may find its way on to the bar. Originally called the Ship Inn, its current name commemorates incorporation of the local courtroom into the pub. Opening times may be varied in winter. The 'Lizard Rambler' bus (T3) passes nearby. ❀◐◑ΔP

MEVAGISSEY

Fountain Inn

3 Cliff Street
✪ 11.30-11; 12-10.30 Sun
☎ (01726) 842320

St Austell Tinners, HSD Ⓗ
The inn's slate floors and low, beamed ceiling declare its 15th-century origins. The two bars have a cosy feel and abound in interesting features. Just off the end of Fore Street, close to the harbour, the pub is within easy motoring distance of the Lost Gardens of Heligan and the Eden Project. The friendly landlord, once a fisherman, keeps the ales in tip-top condition. There are five guest rooms; evening meals are served in summer. Regular buses run to St Austell.

MOUNT HAWKE

Old School Pub
W of B3277
12-3 (not Mon-Fri), 7-11 (midnight Fri & Sat); 12-3, 7-10.30 Sun
☎ (01209) 891158
Tetley Bitter; guest beer Ⓗ
Near the coast, this popular watering-hole is frequented by locals and tourists. Originally the village school, now a family-run free house. Externally unaltered, the spacious interior contains a comfortable bar with no-smoking area, dining room, function room and skittle alley. The atmosphere is friendly and relaxing. The ever-changing beers are complemented by excellent value meals. The hub of the community, activities include regular music nights. Easily accessed by public transport.

MYLOR BRIDGE

Lemon Arms
Off A393 at Penryn
11-3, 6-11; 12-3, 7-10.30 Sun
☎ (01326) 373666
St Austell Tinners, Tribute, HSD Ⓗ
Friendly, one-bar village-centre pub frequented by local sports teams. Good home-cooked food is available, and families with children are made welcome. The real ales are always from the St Austell Brewery, but the range may vary from time to time. There is a patio for summer drinking. Hourly buses from Falmouth serve the pub on weekdays.

NEWBRIDGE

Fountain Inn
On A3071
12-2 (not winter Mon), 6-11; 12-11 Fri & Sat; 12-10.30 Sun
☎ (01736) 364075
St Austell IPA, Tinners, Tribute, HSD, seasonal beer Ⓗ/Ⓖ
The Fountain is a busy, friendly village local, known for its real ale and good food. It was awarded Cornwall CAMRA Pub of the Year in 2002. A wine glass by each handpump contains a sample of the beer, so you can see what is on offer. A Grade II listed building, it has solid walls, a flagstone floor and partly-carpeted lounge area with a vast granite fireplace. Among other community activities, the pub hosts Cornish language lessons. A frequent bus service from Penzance stops outside the door.

NEWQUAY ❊

Skinner's Ale House
58 East Street
12-11; 12-10.30 Sun
☎ (01637) 876391 website: www.skinnersbrewery.com
Skinner's Betty Stogs Bitter, Cornish Knocker, Blonde, seasonal beers; Ⓗ **guest beers** (occasional) Ⓖ
Although set amidst the theme bars of this boisterous Cornish resort, the 'theme' here is real ale. Characterised by varnished wood and bare wooden floorboards, free monkey nuts provide the 'sawdust' on the floor, but good value, more substantial meals can be enjoyed. The Goofy Ale is a house beer and all the latest Skinner's beers are available in this tied house. Live music is popular most weekend evenings, while the pub supports football and darts teams in winter. Two beer festivals are generally held each year in spring and autumn.

PADSTOW

London Inn
Lanadwell Street
11-11; 12-10.30 Sun
☎ (01841) 532554
St Austell IPA, Tinners, HSD Ⓗ
Unspoilt pub, close to the harbour in the heart of this classic tourist village and

INN BRIEF

POLMEAR

Ship Inn
Polmear Hill
11.30-3, 6-11 (11-11 summer); 12-10.30 Sun
(01726) 812540
Draught Bass; Marston's Pedigree; Sharp's Doom Bar; guest beer Ⓗ
At the entrance to Par beach, this large inn has an attractive single bar and a restaurant. In summer, bands perform in the garden.

QUINTRELL DOWNS

Two Clomes
East Road
12-3, 7-11 (12-11 summer); 12-3, 7-10.30 (12-10.30 summer) Sun
(01637) 871163
Sharp's Doom Bar; guest beers Ⓗ
Named after its fireside ovens, the emphasis here is on food, while the guest beers change regularly.

ST ERTH

Star Inn
1 Church Street
11-11; 12-10.30 Sun
(01736) 752068
Beer range varies Ⓗ
Up to four real ales may appear at busy times in this traditional 17th-century village pub. Families welcome.

ST JUST

King's Arms
5 Market Square
11-11; 12-10.30 Sun
(01736) 788545
St Austell Tinners, Tribute, seasonal beer Ⓗ
Fine old granite pub in a typical mining town, catering for locals and visitors. Good bus service from Penzance. Cask Marque accredited.

TREGONY

King's Arms
55 Fore Street
11-2.30 (3 Sat), 6-11; 12-3, 7-10.30 Sun
(01872) 530202
Flower's Original; Sharp's Doom Bar; Skinner's Betty Stogs Bitter; guest beer Ⓗ
16th-century coaching inn with home-cooked food and children's play area at rear. At least two ales always available.

❊ symbol next to a main entry place name indicates there are Inn Brief entries as well.

fishing port, made famous by TV chef Rick Stein. Converted from a terrace of fishermen's cottages, it has a single main bar, plus a room used mainly for meals. The atmosphere is friendly and welcoming, often enhanced by spontaneous folk music. It provides an excellent base to enjoy the famous 'Obby Oss' celebrations on 1st May. The freshly-prepared meals are good value.
♛⇄◐◑♿⛺♣✔

PENDEEN

North Inn
On B3306, St Ives-Lands End road
⏲ 12-11; 12-10.30 Sun
☎ (01736) 788417
website: www.cornwall-online.co.uk/north-inn
St Austell IPA, Tinners, HSD, seasonal beer Ⓗ
The wall photographs and memorabilia reflect this friendly pub's position in the Penwith tin mining district. The mine artefacts are from nearby Geevor, the last mine to close in the area and now a museum. Popular with locals, the inn also attracts summer visitors situated as it is in an area of outstanding natural beauty and handy for the coastal path – try also the local buses on the coast road. The beer range may vary to accommodate a seasonal brew.
♛Q❀⇄◐◑⛺♣P✔

PHILLACK

Bucket of Blood
14 Churchtown Road
⏲ 11 (12 winter Mon)-2.30 (3 Sat), 6-11; 12-4, 7-10.30 Sun
☎ (01736) 752378
St Austell IPA, HSD, seasonal beer Ⓗ
Very low beams (getting lower by the year, according to the landlord!) are the dominant feature of this old inn near the holiday beaches of Hayle Towans. Welcoming to locals and holidaymakers alike, its name stems from a gory legend involving the pub well – see the story by the door. The beers may vary within the St Austell range, depending on the season and demand. There is usually no food during the winter, nor lunchtimes Sun or Mon in summer.
♛Q❀◐◑⛺♣P✔

PIECE

Countryman Inn
Off Redruth-Helston road, near Four Lanes
⏲ 11-11; 12-10.30 Sun
☎ (01209) 215960
Courage Best Bitter; Greene King Old Speckled Hen; Skinner's Cornish Knocker; Theakston Old Peculier; guest beers Ⓗ
'Traditional pub, traditional values' is the landlord's slogan at this one-time miners' grocery store set among the old engine houses of Camborne's copper mining district. Deservedly popular, it manages to keep up to nine real ales in good condition, several of them from local brewers; the house beer is from Sharp's. There are two separate bars, the larger hosting some form of entertainment most nights as well as Sunday lunchtime. Good value pub food is available all day, every day.
♛❀◐◑⊟⛺P

POLGOOTH

Polgooth Inn
Ricketts Lane
⏲ 12-3, 6-11; 12-3, 6-10.30 Sun
☎ (01726) 74089
St Austell Tinners, HSD, seasonal beer Ⓗ
The building originally belonged to the local tin mine and some of its timbers were recycled from mine use. This popular inn has been modified into an attractive version of a traditional village pub. Families are welcome: there is a children's playground, a family room and an outside garden area for drinking. Food is served daily in the no-smoking dining room and the public bar.
♛♨❀◐◑⛺P✔

PORTLOE

Ship Inn
OS933394
⏲ 12-3, 6.30-11 (11-11 summer); 12-10.30 Sun
☎ (01872) 501356
St Austell Tinners, Tribute, HSD or seasonal beer Ⓗ
This small, friendly local is situated in a working fishing village on the Roseland Peninsula. Sympathetic refurbishment has kept a traditional feel to the pub, which is close to the coastal footpath and NT-protected coastline. The home-cooked menu includes locally-caught fish and is served in the no-smoking dining room. The pub has two en-suite bedrooms and also rents out a nearby two-bedroomed self-catering cottage. Children and pets are welcome. The car park is small.
♛Q♨❀⇄◐◑♿P✔

REDRUTH

Rose Cottage
Chapel Street
⏲ 12-11; 12-10.30 Sun
☎ (01209) 212129
Draught Bass; guest beers Ⓗ
Welcome watering-hole in something of a real ale desert, this busy pub at the bottom of the town is much larger inside than the exterior suggests, being three old cottages knocked into one. There are two bars and several distinct drinking areas, as well as a pool room. The two guest beers are constantly varied. Younger drinkers take over on Friday and Saturday evenings, but the pub generally enjoys a broad spread of customers. Good food uses local provisions. Limited parking.
◐◑⊟⇌♣P✔

Tricky Dickie's
Tolgus Mount (off old Redruth bypass, A3047)
OS686427
⏲ 11-3, 6-11; 11-11 Fri & Sat; 12-10.30 Sun
☎ (01209) 219292 website: www.trickydickies.com
Sharp's Own; guest beers Ⓗ
Spacious conversion of an isolated, former tin mine smithy, with several corners for privacy. A wide choice of good wines, a comprehensive menu of good value food, and exemplary service are hallmarks here. Families are welcome. The accommodation block includes a fitness centre and conference facilities. Live jazz bands perform Tuesday evenings; other entertainment is staged on Thursday. A partially-

covered outside barbecue is available for hire. Well worth finding.

ST AGNES

Driftwood Spars Hotel

Trevaunance Cove

11-11 (midnight Fri & Sat); 12-10.30 Sun

(01872) 552428 website: www.driftwoodspars.com

Draught Bass; Driftwood Cuckoo Ale; St Austell HSD; Sharp's Own; Tetley Bitter; guest beers H

By the coast, this fine family-run free house with micro-brewery is an oasis for cliffwalkers. It's a former mine warehouse and sail loft built from granite, slate and enormous ships' spars. Beamed ceilings, leaded light windows, granite fireplaces plus a 'wreckers' tunnel form a cosy, atmospheric three-bar interior. The nautical decor includes a fine collection of ships' clocks. An extensive menu offers excellent meals. Besides live music and theatre, charity events range from alternative dog shows to plastic duck races.

ST AUSTELL

Stag Inn

5 Victoria Place (near church)

11-11; 12-10.30 Sun

(01726) 67148

Draught Bass; Greene King Old Speckled Hen; guest beer H

Built in the 1700s, this inn was the second to be established in the then village of St Austell. It is now a small, friendly, town-centre house currently owned by Pubmaster, who provide an excellent selection of ales. Conversion to a single bar has not spoiled this traditional drinkers' pub where conversation remains the main entertainment. A comfortable pub despite bare floorboards, it provides meals daily except Sun. Live entertainment is usually staged Friday evening.

Western Inn

West Hill

12-3, 5-11; 12-11 Fri & Sat; 12-10.30 Sun

(01726) 72797

St Austell Tinners, Tribute, HSD or seasonal beer H

St Austell tied pub, much modified; it consists of an L-shaped area with a raised games section. Refurbishment has proved successful, providing pleasant, attractive spaces for eating and drinking with separate areas for different functions. Interesting use has been made of old chapel pews and woodwork in the bar. A pleasant venue for socialising outside the town centre, there is a patio for outside drinking.

ST COLUMB MAJOR

Ring O' Bells

3 Bank Street

12-2 (not Mon), 5-11; 12-3, 7-10.30 Sun

(01637) 880259

Sharp's Doom Bar, Eden Ale; H **guest beers** G

This atmospheric 15th-century free house was opened to celebrate the parish church tower, hence the name. A former brew-pub, it is the oldest in town, the narrow frontage belying the extensive, beamed, slate-floored three-bar interior. Each bar has its own character and custom: youngsters frequent the front bar, older drinkers the middle and back. Decor is rustic throughout, with assorted wood furniture including settles. Wood-burning stoves add comfort. A cosy restaurant, the former brewery, offers a cosmopolitan menu.

ST EWE

Crown Inn

OS978461

12-3, 5-11 (11-11 summer); 12-3, 6-10.30 (12-10.30 summer) Sun

(01726) 843322

St Austell Tinners, Tribute, HSD, seasonal beer (summer) H

Situated in an unspoilt village near the Lost Gardens of Heligan, this cosy old local features a working spit over the open fire, and its own well. The bar has a slate-flagged floor and is for drinking only; meals are served in a dining room extension (all day in summer). Food is a speciality here, with the deservedly popular meals being prepared on the premises. A double room is available for overnight guests.

ST IVES

Western Hotel

Gabriel Steet

11-11; 12-10.30 Sun (01736) 795277

St Austell Tribute, HSD, seasonal beer H

The main real ale outlet at this comfortable town-centre hotel is actually the Kettle & Wink, a separate bar slightly below pavement level, which nevertheless functions as a popular local pub. Quiet at lunchtimes when the clientele are mostly local shoppers or holidaymakers, it is busier in the evenings especially when there is live entertainment at the hotel featuring folk or jazz, among other music styles. A second saloon bar opens during busy summer periods.

ST JUST ❄

Star Inn

1 Fore Street

11-11; 12-10.30 Sun

(01736) 788767

St Austell XXXX Mild, H **Tinners,** G **Dartmoor,** H **HSD,** G **seasonal beer** H

Reputed lodging of John Wesley, this 18th-century inn is St Just's oldest. Slate floors, an open fire and wooden seats add character to the beamed bar, whose surroundings bear witness to a long association with tin mining. The adjacent 'snuggery' forms a cosy family room. Food is limited to substantial lunchtime snacks. A lively folk scene produces singalongs most evenings; traditional games also thrive. It is essentially a drinkers' pub, where locals spin a yarn or two, and laughter is the byword.

ST MELLION

Coryton Arms

12-2.30, 5.30-11; 12-11 Fri & Sat; 12-10.30 Sun

(01579) 50322

Beer range varies Ⓗ

Two ever-changing guest ales, one of which is normally Skinner's, are sold at this dog-friendly pub where everyone is made to feel as if they are part of the family. It is easily accessible from either Plymouth or Launceston and is not far from St Mellion golf club. Fine views can be enjoyed from the rear of the pub, over the Tamar Valley. A good food selection represents excellent value. The 76 bus stops outside the door.

ST NEOT

London Inn

12-3, 6.30-11; 11-11 Sat & summer; 12-10.30 Sun

☎ (01579) 320263

Courage Best Bitter; Sharp's Doom Bar, Own; Ⓖ **John Smith's Bitter; guest beer** (summer) Ⓗ

Popular 16th-century coaching inn with flagstoned floor and exposed beams, on the old route to London, next to a church famed for its stained glass window. Gravity-dispensed beers are kept on an impressive stillage behind the bar; the guest ale appears in summer. There is a comprehensive food menu. The pub supports darts, euchre, and skittle teams who play in the traditional skittle alley. A daytime bus service connects with Liskeard. It has a small car park and some tables and benches outside.

Q P

ST TUDY

Cornish Arms

Off A391

12-3, 6.30-11; 12-4, 7-10.30 Sun

☎ (01208) 850656

Draught Bass; St Austell XXXX Mild; guest beer (summer) Ⓗ

16th-century beamed village pub, boasting a classic slate floor in the bar. It has a games area and several other rooms, including a restaurant where the varied menu is based on local produce. The guest beer tends to be restricted to the occasional pint in summer; the cider varies, but is usually local. The pub is family-friendly, with a room equipped to keep children occupied. The determined can get here by No. 126 bus from Bodmin at lunchtime on weekdays.

Q P

STITHIANS

Seven Stars

Church Road

12-2.30, 7 (6 Fri)-11; 11-11 Sat; 12-3, 7-10.30 Sun

☎ (01209) 860003

Sharp's Doom Bar; Skinner's Betty Stogs Bitter; guest beers Ⓗ

Village community local, over 100 years old; an extension to what was once a farmhouse. Friendly and lively, it serves up to four real ales which are constantly varied, although mainly Cornish. Not strictly a 'quiet' pub, conversation nevertheless dominates the single bar area, which has a stone-flagged floor and beamed ceiling. Euchre is the main pub game. Buses pass nearby until late evening. Meals are served lunchtimes (not Tue) and Wed-Sat eves.

TREBELLAN

Smugglers' Den Inn

Off A3075 towards Cubert, then signed

12-2.30 (not winter Mon-Wed), 6-11 (11-11 summer); 12-10.30 Sun

☎ (01637) 830209

website: www.smugglers-den-inn.co.uk

Beer range varies Ⓗ/Ⓖ

Tucked down a steep, narrow lane, this 400-year-old thatched inn boasts an Elizabethan courtyard, as well as a garden. The popular no-smoking restaurant serves daily specials. The large fireplace is a focal point in winter. The friendly owners offer a varying range of ales, with mainstays from St Austell, Skinner's and Sharp's; Callestick farm cider is available in summer. An ale and pie festival is a regular spring event. A good bus service stops 10 minutes' walk from the pub. P

TREWARMETT

Trewarmett Inn

Opp. garden centre

12-2.30 (not Mon), 7-11; 12-2.30, 7-10.30 Sun

☎ (01840) 770460

Sharp's Doom Bar, Eden Ale, Special Ⓗ

Welcoming village pub, parts of which date back 300 years, and which once operated as a kiddleywink for workers at the nearby quarry. A traditional Cornish local, it features low beams, slate floors and stone walls in its two drinking rooms and dining area where the food is home-made. The garden offers distant sea views. Folk music is much in evidence, with instruments on the walls and live sessions twice a week. Daytime buses serve Wadebridge and Bude.

Q P

TRURO

Bunter's Bar

58 Little Castle Street

11-11; 12-10.30 Sun

☎ (01872) 241220

Sharp's Doom Bar; Skinner's Betty Stogs Bitter; guest beer Ⓗ

This lively bar serves an immaculate pint from a selection of local beers, the 'guest' usually being from the St Austell range. Competitively priced, the pub occupies a one-time shopping arcade, as can be seen by its capacious interior and distinct drinking areas. The emphasis is on sport – one of the spaces houses three pool tables. Popular with older drinkers at lunchtime, Bunter's becomes more of a youngsters' pub at night. You may bring your own food.

City Inn

Pydar Street (B3284, Perranporth road)

11-11; 12-10.30 Sun

☎ (01872) 272623

Draught Bass; Courage Best Bitter; Sharp's Doom Bar; Skinner's Betty Stogs Bitter; guest beers Ⓗ

This popular pub is situated just away from the shopping centre, and prides itself on being a traditional 'local'. The regular ales are supplemented by constantly-changing guest beers and Haye Farm cider is available by gravity dispense. Good value, fresh food is complemented by reasonably-priced wines. The comfortable lounge has cosy drinking corners and lots of memorabilia,

almost next door, is also owned by Dent Brewery; it is rare for both to be closed at the same time. ⛰Q❀⇌◑▲♣P⊭

DUFTON

Stag Inn

⏲ 12-3 (not winter Mon), 6-11; 12-11 Sat & summer; 12-10.30 Sun

☎ (017683) 51608

Black Sheep Best Bitter; Flowers IPA; guest beers Ⓗ

Fronting a large village green, the Stag offers a warm welcome to those exploring this area, between the north lakes and the Pennines. A superb kitchen range dominates the front bar, which has a dining area to the left. The side bar includes another (no-smoking) dining area. It has a safe garden, plus a front patio. An adjoining cottage forms part of the accommodation. ⛰Q❀⇌◑▲♣P

EAGLESFIELD

Black Cock

⏲ 8 (7 Sat & summer)-11; 7-11 Sun

☎ (01900) 822989

Jennings Bitter Ⓗ

This unspoilt village local is a delight to those who make the effort to seek it out. A hidden gem, dating back to probably the 17th century, it has not been altered for around 30 years, when the two front rooms were opened out. Low beams and wood panelling are decorated with gleaming brassware. The landlady is one of the longest serving in West Cumbria, earning local CAMRA's Pub of the Season award, summer 2001. ⛰Q

ELTERWATER

Britannia Inn

⏲ 11-11; 12-10.30 Sun

☎ (0153 94) 37210 website: www.britinn.co.uk

Coniston Bluebird; Dent Aviator; Jennings Bitter; guest beers Ⓗ

A truly 'quiet' pub; it has no juke box, machines or TV. Set in one of the most popular Lakeland locations, it is often necessary to press the village green into service when the bar, hall, slate-floored back room and patio are all full. Booking is advisable for evening meals in the no-smoking dining room. Nautical memorabilia is displayed in a glass case, opposite a splendid sideboard in the entrance hall. ⛰Q❀⇌◑▲

ENNERDALE BRIDGE

Shepherd's Arms Hotel

⏲ 11-11; 12-10.30 Sun

☎ (01946) 861249 website: www.shepherdsarmshotel.co.uk

Courage Directors; Jennings Bitter; Theakston Black Bull; guest beers Ⓗ

Local CAMRA Pub of the Season in 2002, this small hotel has an informal atmosphere. Located on Wainwright's Coast-to-Coast footpath, it offers a welcome break for walkers in quiet, comfortable surroundings. Good home-cooked food is served in the bar, while specialities are available in the restaurant. In five years under the current owner this hotel has become a retreat for beer lovers. Buses between Cleator and Cockermouth run through the village. ⛰❀⇌◑▲P

FOXFIELD

Prince of Wales

On A595, opp. station

⏲ 5 (12 Fri & Sat)-11; closed Mon & Tue; 12-10.30 Sun

☎ (01229) 716238

Beer range varies Ⓗ

Friendly pub, it is ideally situated for buses and the station (no trains Sun). Darts, board games and bar billiards are available. The ever-changing beers always include a mild and usually a beer from their own Tigertops or Foxfield breweries. Speciality beers include draught foreign wheat beer, plus a good selection of bottled continental beers; the cider varies. Speciality beer weekends and themed mini-beer festivals are a regular feature, but the hospitality is permanent. ⛰Q⇌≋♣●P▯

GARRIGILL

George & Dragon Inn

Off B6277, 4 Miles S of Alston

⏲ 12-3, 7-11; 12-3, 7-10.30 Sun

☎ (01434) 381293 website: www.cumbria1st.com

Castle Eden Ale; Flowers IPA; Marston's Pedigree Ⓗ

High in the North Cumbrian Pennines, at the centre of the village, this characterful hostelry was built in the 17th century as a coaching inn. Originally serving the local lead and zinc miners, visitors following the Pennine Way and Coast-to-Coast cycle and walking routes are more in evidence now. Over the bar, the hinged cover has eight glass panels with very nice original drawings depicting Ritson's The Rights of the Dragon, along with hand-written descriptions. No food Tue eve. ⛰❀⇌◑♣

GRASMERE

Traveller's Rest

1/2 mile N of village on A591

⏲ 11-11; 12-10.30 Sun

☎ (015394) 35604 website: www.lakelandinns.com

Jennings Bitter, Cumberland Ale, Sneck Lifter; guest beer Ⓗ

This cosy pub is conveniently situated for serious mountain walking on Helvellyn and Fairfield. The Coast-to-Coast path also passes nearby. A roaring winter fire warms the cosy bar area which has a family/games/lounge room up a few steps. Two dining rooms (one no-smoking) serve good value meals (all day in summer). The same family own the King's Head at Thirlspot (on A591, six miles north towards Keswick). ⛰Q☋❀⇌◑P✔

GREAT BROUGHTON

Punchbowl

19 Main Street (off A66)

⏲ 11 (7 Mon)-11; 12-10.30 Sun

☎ (01900) 824708

Jennings Bitter; guest beer (occasional) Ⓗ

Tiny, low-ceilinged village pub where visitors are sure of a warm welcome. The building dates back to the 17th century and was a coaching inn, as testified by the presence of a blacksmith's shop for reshoeing horses. There is a roaring fire in winter and the pub fields quiz and darts teams. It is a free house which stocks occasional guest beers in summer.

GREAT CORBY

Corby Bridge Inn

Off A69, E of Carlisle
12-11; 12-10.30 Sun
(01228) 560221
Thwaites Mild, Bitter; guest beer H

Grade II listed building, of architectural and historical significance, it is situated alongside the Carlisle-Newcastle railway line, a short, but stunning, walk across the viaduct from Wetheral Station. The pub offers a friendly welcome in its three open-plan rooms, and holds special gourmet food nights (no food Mon). Solway CAMRA Pub of the Year 2002.
Q (Wetheral) P

GREAT LANGDALE

Old Dungeon Ghyll

11-11; 12-10.30 Sun
(015394) 37272 website: www.odg.co.uk
Black Sheep Special; Jennings Cumberland Ale; Theakston Cool Cask, Old Peculier; Yates Bitter; guest beers H

Surrounded by dramatic mountain scenery, the basic bar, adjacent to the hotel, is ideally located for weary adventurers to dry off in. A hard floor, wooden benches, kitchen range and good honest pub grub characterise the bar, where the absence of piped sound, pool or machines encourages story-telling and impromptu music-making. The hotel and dining room is open to non-residents (book for meals).
Q P

GREAT STRICKLAND

Strickland Arms

12-3 (not Wed), 6-11; 12-10.30 Sun
(01931) 712238
Black Sheep Best Bitter; Greene King Old Speckled Hen; Jennings Bitter; Tetley Bitter, Burton Ale; guest beer H

Fine example of a village pub as it should be: two bars, a games area, quiet classical music, home-made, good value meals and a large garden. Add a good range of beers, comfortable accommodation and here is the ideal base for exploring the northern Lake District and the Pennines. The front bar boasts a superb corner clock, the rear lounge an extensive collection of china dolls.
P

HAWKSHEAD

King's Arms Hotel

11-11; 12-10.30 Sun
(015394) 36372
Black Sheep Best Bitter; Coniston Bluebird; Tetley Bitter; guest beer H

This pretty Lakeland pub sits in a small square at the heart of Hawkshead in the beautiful Vale of Esthwaite. A seated area outside is a lovely place to enjoy your pint and observe the many visitors to this idyllic area. The dining room serves home-cooked food. It has no pool or juke box but stages occasional live music. Well worth a visit; there is a campsite in this National Park village. Q

Sun Inn

Main Street
11-11; 12-10.30 Sun
(015394) 36236
Black Sheep Best Bitter; Barngates Cracker Ale; guest beers H

Sound village pub, well used by locals and tourists, it has a good rotation of guest beers. An open fire, pool and darts feature on the upper level of this split-level house. It has a quarry-tiled floor and table tops. This welcoming pub can become hectic in summer with tourists but, like all the pubs in this village, it is well worth a visit.

HAYTON

Stone Inn

1/2 mile S of A69
11-3, 5.30-11; 11-11 Sat; 12-4, 7-10.30 Sun
(01228) 670498
Jennings Cumberland Ale; Thwaites Mild, Bitter H

Popular, traditional and superbly welcoming local, a community pub where you can learn many things including Spanish, computing and how to grow leeks! Strong naval connections are in evidence throughout the pub, including Pussers naval rum sold (like all spirits) in quarter gills. A fine pair of 1904 Christ Church Boat Club oars adorns one wall, a Heriot Brewery mirror another. Toasties are usually available; summer barbecues are held in the garden. Q P

HESKET NEWMARKET

Old Crown

1 mile SE of Caldbeck
12-3 (not Mon), 5.30-11; 12-11 Sat; 12-3, 7-10.30 Sun
(016974) 78288
Hesket Newmarket Great Cockup Porter, Blencathra Bitter, Skiddaw Special Bitter, Doris's 90th Birthday Ale, Catbells Pale Ale, Old Carrock Strong Ale H

Regional CAMRA's award of Pub of the Year 2001 indicates how highly this pub is regarded by real ale fans. Situated on the edge of the Caldbeck Fells, it is the start and finish point for many walkers. It serves as the tap for the village brewery, situated in a converted barn to the rear of the pub. Saxon cider is sold. Curries are a speciality on the evening menu. The rooms may be small and cosy but the welcome is always large.
Q

HIGH NEWTON

Crown

Off A590
12-2.30, 6-11 (12-11 summer); 12-10.30 Sun
(015395) 31793
website: www.thecrowninn.lakeland.com
Theakston Cool Cask; Yates Bitter; guest beer H

17th-century coaching inn in beautiful surroundings, three miles from Lake Windermere. It boasts flagged floors, a huge fireplace and an oak beamed ceiling. The only survivor of three pubs in the village, not much has changed here since the last coach came in. A split-level bar serves both the distinctive upper and lower rooms; there is also a pool room reputedly haunted, the ghost, for reasons only known to himself, only ever presents himself to women. ⚜❀⇆◑◗♣P

INGS

Watermill Inn

Just off A591, near church
⌚ 12-11; 12-10.30 Sun
☎ (01539) 821309 website: www.watermillinn.co.uk
Black Sheep Best Bitter; Coniston Bluebird; Jennings Cumberland Ale; Lees Moonraker; Theakston Old Peculier; guest beers Ⓗ
Originally a timber mill, then a guesthouse, since 1990 it has been a family-run pub. Among the many awards which adorn almost every wall, is runner-up national CAMRA Pub of the Year 1990. It offers a staggering selection of up to 16 cask beers, but no piped music, machines, pool or TV. The 'top' bar is popular with families and diners (meals all day). The 'bottom' bar attracts a regular coterie of real ale enthusiasts. The impressive cellar can be viewed via a cartwheel-shaped window. ⚜Q❀⇆◑◗♿♣P

KENDAL ❊

Burgundy's Wine Bar

19 Lowther Street
⌚ 11.30-3.30 (not Mon-Wed), 6.30-11 (not Mon); 7-10.30 Sun
☎ (01539) 733803
website: www.burgundyswinebar.com
Beer range varies Ⓗ
Town-centre, multi-level, bistro-style bar serving an ever-changing range of real ales as well as an above-average choice of draught and bottled continental beers; the cider varies. It hosts the annual Cumbria Beer Challenge in early spring and celebrates St George's Day in some style. Evening meals can be provided by prior arrangement. Several destinations are served from the nearby bus station. Q◑◗⇌

Castle Inn

13 Castle Street
⌚ 11-11; 12-10.30 Sun
☎ (01539) 729983
Dent Aviator; Jennings Bitter; Tetley Bitter; guest beer Ⓗ
Busy, two-bar pub with a lounge (housing an impressive fish tank) to the left and a bar with TV to the right (note the etched Duttons Brewery window). An adjacent games room is up a step. Excellent value lunches are popular with staff from nearby offices; evenings attract darts, pool and quiz teams, when it becomes a true community local. Families are welcome until 6pm. A couple of benches are set on the pavement in summer. ◑⇌♣

KESWICK ❊

Dog & Gun

2 Lake Road (off market sqare)
⌚ 11-11; 12-10.30 Sun
☎ (017687) 73463
Theakston Best Bitter, Old Peculier; Yates Bitter; guest beers (summer) Ⓗ
Popular with both locals and visitors, this pub provides two bar areas, one stone-flagged with an open seating area, the other has high-backed settles for more secluded drinking. A regular quiz (Thu eve) raises funds for local charities – often the mountain rescue team. A good range of food is offered – the goulash has remained a firm favourite for many years. Guest beers are stocked from Easter. ⚜◑◗▲

KIRKBY LONSDALE

Snooty Fox Tavern

Main Street
⌚ 11-11; 12-10.30 Sun
☎ (015242) 71308
website: www.mortal-man-inns.co.uk
Taylor Landlord; Theakston Best Bitter; guest beers Ⓗ
Imposing Jacobean hotel in the centre of this pleaant market town. The two bars are encircled by several interconnecting roms set out for dining. The front bar has a collection of tunics hanging on the walls and horse bits fixed to the beams, while the rear bar is stone-floored and has a juke box. It is noted for its high quality meals and superior accommodation. A spring beer festival is held under canvas in the rear courtyard. ⚜Q❀⇆◑◗▲P

LITTLE CORBY

Haywain

500 yds off A69, 5 miles E of Carlisle
⌚ 12-3 (not Mon-Fri), 6 (7 Mon-Thu)-11; 12-10.30 Sun
☎ (01228) 560598
Robinson's Hartleys Cumbria Way, Best Bitter Ⓗ
This was the only pub in the area not under State Management control from WW1 to the early 1970s. Close to the River Eden, this recently altered village pub, now has a larger bar area, but has lost none of its character. It boasts a stone-flagged floor and bar stools made from old tractor seats. Hunting pictures adorn the walls in the lounge area. Local CAMRA Pub of the Season 2002. ◑◗♿♣P

LOWESWATER

Kirkstile Inn

Opp. church OS141209
⌚ 11-11; 12-10.30 Sun
☎ (01900) 85219 website: www.kirkstile.com
Coniston Bluebird; Jennings Bitter, Cumberland Ale Ⓗ
Classic Lakeland inn, replete with original beams and stone walls. Close to Crummock Water, it benefits from a fantastic setting, dominated by Melbreak Fell. It has a games room and delightful garden. Good food is served to accompany the beer from Cumbrian breweries. A fourth beer (Yates XB) is on sale in summer. ⚜Q❀⇆◑◗♿P

LOW ROW

Railway Inn

3 miles E of Brampton, N of A69
⌚ 12-3, 5.30-11; 12-3, 6.30-10.30 Sun
☎ (016977) 46222
Thwaites Bitter; guest beer Ⓗ
Built as a byre, and converted into an inn around 1850, it is tucked away in its own grounds, just off the main road through the village. It takes its name from the Carlisle-Newcastle railway line; even the footrest at the bar is an old section of rail. On a clear

day the views across the Pennines are superb. Lanercost Priory and Hadrian's Wall are nearby. Q❀◑ ⅄P

MELMERBY

Shepherd's Inn

11.30-3, 6-11; 12-3, 7-10.30 Sun
☎ (0870) 745 3383 website: www.shepherdsinn.net
Dent T'Owd Tup; Jennings Cumberland Ale; guest beers H

Circa 1789, this fine pub is at the village centre. An attached barn has been converted into a bar area, creating two split-level rooms, one with a raised pool table area. A relaxed atmosphere is enhanced by fine oak beams in the barn and a stone-flagged floor. Excellent food includes an award-winning cheeseboard. Saxon cider is sold. A collection of pub mirrors adorns the high wall in the barn. ⌂Q❀◑ ⅄♣●P□✔

NEAR SAWREY

Tower Bank Arms

On B5285 OS370956
12-3, 6-11; 12-3, 6-10.30 Sun
☎ (015394) 36334
Theakston Best Bitter, Old Peculier; Wells Bombardier; guest beer H

Large country pub which featured in Beatrix Potter's Jemima Puddleduck. The bar area, with extremely comfortable seats, is a gallery for signed photographs of the many celebrities who have stayed here over the years. The guest beers tend to be local brews, but some are from micro-breweries. A varied selection of bottled continental beers is also stocked. The atmosphere is that of a typical Lakeland pub. ⌂Q❀⇌◑P

NETHER WASDALE

Screes

11-11; 12-10.30 Sun
☎ (019467) 26262
website: www.thescreesinnwasdale.com
Black Sheep Best Bitter; Worthington Bitter; Yates Bitter H

The Screes is one of two first-class sources of real ale in this tiny hamlet, hidden deep in the Lake District. Close by are Scafell Pike, Great Gable and the brooding Wast Water. Loyal clientele support jazz and folk nights and the Wasdale real ale festivals, that the two pubs plan together. The Screes is homely and friendly, the bar being on two levels with oddly-placed beams supporting an ancient structure. Walkers and families are welcome. ⌂Q☕❀⇌◑ ⅄P

PARSONBY

Horse & Jockey

On B5301
11-11; 10.30-10.30 Sun
☎ (016973) 20482
website: www.horseandjockeypub.co.uk
Jennings Mild, Bitter H

Good, old-fashioned village roadside pub near Aspatria. An open stone fireplace, oak beams and flagged floor feature in this friendly hostelry. Generous portions of home-cooked food are served daily (12-9). Interest is added by pub mirrors, the aquarium and the amazing ever-growing collection of pigs in various forms. Customers' children are invited to draw pictures to add to the existing 'gallery'. ⌂❀◑ ⅄♣P

PENRITH ❋

Agricultural Hotel

Castlegate (by station)
11-11; 12-10.30 Sun
☎ (01768) 862622
Jennings Mild, Bitter, Cumberland Ale, Cocker Hoop, Sneck Lifter H

Comfortable pub, close to the station, and a short uphill walk from the town centre. The Aggie (as it is known locally) has a friendly atmosphere and provides a good range of home-cooked meals. The pub is just a stone's throw from the ruins of Penrith Castle, which remain as testimony to the turbulent history of the border counties, and are worth a visit. ⌂❀⇌◑♿⇌P✔

POOLEY BRIDGE

Sun Inn

12-11; 12-10.30 Sun
☎ (017684) 86205
Jennings Bitter, Cumberland Ale, Sneck Lifter, seasonal beers H

Traditional pub, set in the centre of this popular north Lakes village. The no-

INN BRIEF

KESWICK

Bank Tavern
47 Main Street
11-11; 12-10.30 Sun
(017687) 72663
Jennings Bitter, Cumberland Ale, Sneck Lifter; guest beers H
One of the oldest pubs in Keswick, it serves an extensive lunch and evening menu. Outdoor drinking area. Cask Marque accredited.

MILNTHORPE

Cross Keys Hotel
1 Park Road
12-11; 12-10.30 Sun
(015395) 62115
Robinson's Hartleys XB, Best Bitter, seasonal beers H
Spacious, town-centre pub with a ground-floor bar and dining room – upstairs function room and outside tables and chairs.

PENRITH

Gloucester Arms
Great Dockray (town centre)
11.30-11; 12-10.30 Sun
Beer range varies H
Grade I listed 16th-century inn, with many original features, including three large fireplaces. King Richard I is known to have stayed here.

PORT CARLISLE

Hope & Anchor
11-3 (not Wed), 5.30-11; 11-11 Sat; 12-10.30 Sun
(01693) 51460
Beer range varies H
Nestling on the shore of the Solway Firth where beautiful sunsets abound, this is a very popular local.

SCALES

White Horse Inn
12-3, 6-11; 12-3, 6.30-10.30 Sun
(017687) 79241
Black Sheep Best Bitter; Jennings Bitter H
Coaching inn at foot of Blencathra on Coast-to-Coast cycle trail, which welcomes walkers. Extensive menu.

TROUTBECK

Mortal Man
12-11; 12-10.30 Sun
(015394) 33193
Jennings Bitter; Theakston Best Bitter; guest beer H
Comfortable hotel affording fine views: two bars, a no-smoking lounge and dining room. Hosts events on celebratory days.

smoking, panelled 'top' bar attracts diners and has a log fire in winter. The 'bottom' bar has large-screen TV and a pool table (winter). Dogs are welcome in both bars. Snacks are served all day in summer; there is a dining room for main meals and a large, safe garden. The steamer pier for summer cruises on Ullswater is a short walk away.

ROWRAH

Stork

Rowrah Road

12-2.30, 5.30-11; 12-11 Sat; 12-10.30 Sun

(01946) 861213

Jennings Bitter; guest beer (occasional) H

Traditional Cumberland local, close to the western fells of the Lake District, an area of remote beauty which is less populous and thus quieter in the tourist season. The Stork has a strong community focus, but visitors also enjoy the tasty, home-cooked food and cosy atmosphere. Attractions nearby include go-karting, the Coast-to-Coast walk and cycle path, and Cumberland sports such as wrestling, hound trailing and fell-running.

ST BEES

Queen's Hotel

Main Street

12-3, 5.30-11; 12-3, 7-10.30 Sun

(01946) 822287

website: www.queenshotel-stbees.com

Jennings Bitter; Yates Bitter; guest beer (summer) H

17th-century pub and hotel in the middle of the village. An extensive food menu of mainly traditional fare includes Cumberland sausage and Waberthwaite ham. The guest beer is likely to be from the Jennings range. The village, home to a medieval priory and a 400-year-old public school, is close to the western fells and stands at the start of the Coast-to-Coast walk (St Bees to Robin Hood's Bay). Parking is limited.

SILLOTH

Golf Hotel

Criffel Street (opp. main green)

11-11; 12-10.30 Sun

(016973) 31438

Derwent Carlisle State Bitter; guest beers (summer) H

Opened in 1865, the Golf Hotel overlooks the green and the Solway Firth. There is a comfortable, spacious lounge with a small bar in the corner. The various rooms display pictures of old Silloth; all are mobile phone-free zones. The hotel is used by various groups as a meeting place. Guest beers, in summer, come from the local Derwent Brewery.

STAVELEY

Eagle & Child

Kendal Road

11-11; 12-10.30 Sun

(015394) 821320

Beer range varies H

Victorian inn that has been sympathetically refurbished to provide larger drinking and dining areas within the U-shaped ground floor. Guest beers are usually from local micros. A secluded rear garden is complemented by one across the road by the bank of the River Kent. Good walking country is nearby; a regular bus service between Kendal and Keswick has a stop in both directions outside the front door.

TALKIN

Blacksmith's Arms

3 miles S of Brampton, off B6413

12-3, 6-11; 12-3, 7-10.30 Sun

(016977) 3452

Black Sheep Best Bitter; Jennings Cumberland Ale; Tetley Bitter H

Excellent, multi-roomed, free house at the heart of a quiet, pretty village on the edge of the Pennines. Built in the 17th century as a village smithy, it gradually expanded to serve refreshments to waiting customers. When, as part of the Temperance Movement, Lady Caroline Howard closed all pubs on her estate, the Blacksmith's became very popular with local miners and quarrymen. It remains deservedly popular today, selling superb meals.

TIRRIL

Queen's Head

12-3, 6-11; 12-11 Fri & Sat; 12-10.30 Sun

(01768) 863219 website: www.queensheadinn.co.uk

Tirril John Bewsher's Best Bitter, Charles Gough's Old Faithful; Thomas Slee's Academy Ale; guest beer H

Multi-level inn with two bars and a large (no-smoking) dining room. An imaginative menu is served throughout and is complemented by several house beers brewed by the owner at the new, larger Tirril Brewery at nearby Brougham Hall. New brews are tested at the Queen's before going into full production. The magnificent fireplace in the partly slate-floored front bar has won many awards. The rear bar has a juke box and pool table.

ULDALE

Snooty Fox

12-2, 6.30-11; 12-2, 6.30-10.30 Sun

(016973) 71479

Black Sheep Best Bitter; Theakston Best Bitter H

The building became a pub in the late 1600s, and was originally known as the George & Dragon; it was sold to the Workington Brewery in 1940. Following a period of closure in the 1980s it was reopened as the Snooty Fox. The house beer Uld Ale is brewed at Hesket Newmarket Brewery. The oak beams date from the 1700s; old framed maps make interesting conversation pieces.

ULVERSTON

Farmer's Arms

Market Place

11-11; 12-10.30 Sun

(01229) 584469

website: www.farmersulv.freeserve.co.uk

Theakston Best Bitter; guest beers H

Popular, town-centre pub overlooking the market (Thu and Sat). An extensive dining area at the rear serves good quality meals.

The original, imposing fireplace enhances the bar area at the front of the pub. Coffee and soft drinks are available before 10.30am, as is the all-day breakfast. Daily newspapers are provided. It gets very busy at weekends, especially evenings. A good range of quality wines is always available. Children are welcome until 9pm (if not too crowded).

UNDERBARROW

Punchbowl Inn

12-3.30 (not Tue), 6-11; 12-4, 7-10.30 Sun
(015395) 68234
Black Sheep Best Bitter; Jennings Cumberland Ale; guest beer H

The spacious bar area has a small counter and boasts many interesting features, including heavy ceiling beams, a spice cupboard beside the fireplace and a set of brass hanging balances. There is a side room with tables and chairs, plus a room that can be hired for functions or meetings. The good value meals are especially popular on Friday (fresh fish). P

WASDALE HEAD

Wasdale Head Inn

11-11; 12-10.30 Sun
(019467) 26229 website: www.wasdale.com
Derwent Carlisle State Bitter; Great Gable Great Gable, Wasd'ale; Yates Bitter; guest beers H

There are two ways to reach this superb pub: a nine-mile drive down a mainly single-track road, winding around mountain and lakeside, or climb across a mountain to it! A good choice of mainly Cumbrian brews, includes their own; good home cooking is based on local produce. A variety of accommodation is available, from tents and a camping barn – to a four-poster suite. Ask about Will Ritson and the biggest liar in the world; be amazed at the stark beauty of Wast Water and Scafell Pike.
Q P

WESTNEWTON

Swan Inn

Off B5301
12-3 (not winter), 6-11; 12-3, 6-10.30 Sun
(016973) 20627
Jennings Bitter; Yates Bitter H

Friendly, traditional village pub that has been recently renovated. Westnewton is a charming village, lying between the northern fells and the coast. It is also home to Yates Brewery; their bitter is badged Swan Bitter for this local outlet. Food is served daily in the bar or restaurant, which has a no-smoking section. Q

WETHERAL

Wheatsheaf

On B6263, off A69
12-2.30, 5-11; 12-11 Fri, Sat & summer); 12-11 Sun
(01228) 560686
Greenalls Bitter; Marston's Pedigree H

One-roomed, comfortable village local in the attractive village of Wetheral, six miles east of Carlisle. Situated on the bank of the River Eden, the village is excellent for walking and fishing. The pub serves good quality bar food. Its regular quiz nights are very popular with the locals. P

WINSTER

Brown Horse

11-11 (may vary winter); 12-10.30 Sun
(015394) 43443 website: www.thebrownhorse.com
Black Sheep Best Bitter; Jennings Bitter, Cumberland Ale; guest beer H

An equally warm welcome awaits drinkers at one end and diners at the other, at this rural pub set in the unspoilt Winster Valley. No juke box, pool or machines invade here, just quiet background music and above-average quality meals. The Winster Room, up a broad flight of stairs, is no-smoking, has its own bar and can be hired for functions. P

WINTON

Bay Horse

1-4 (not Tue), 7-11; 12-3, 7-10.30 Sun
(017683) 71451
Black Sheep Best Bitter; Theakston Cool Cask; guest beers H

Homely local, on the edge of the village green, it has a stone-flagged public bar, a dining area and a raised games room at the rear. A children's certificate applies. Well worth the minor detour from the A685, it is handy as a base from which to explore the Pennines to the east and the Howgills to the west.
Q P

WORKINGTON

George IV (Minnie's)

Stanley Street
11-3, 7-11; 12-3, 7-10.30 Sun
(01900) 602266
Jennings Bitter H

End-of-terrace, quiet, cosy and friendly local on one of the oldest streets in the town; not to be missed. It is convenient for the rugby league, football and speedway stadia, and the attractive harbour development. The pub is affectionately known as Minnie's, after the long-serving landlady.

The Beauty of Hops

Appreciating the aromas, flavour and bitterness imparted by the small green plants

Hops have just as many flavour profiles and 'beauty spots' as grapes, but brewers in the 1970s and '80s used to blend hops together to achieve a consistent grist rather than asking just one hop to show its individual beauty and character.
This is not to claim that single hop beers are better. They are just different. But times have changed and there are now more than 30 single hop varietal beers in Britain including award winners such as Fuller's 1845 (Goldings); Hop Back's Summer Lightning (Goldings); Hogs Back's TEA (Goldings); Brakspear's Coniston Bluebird (Challenger); Adnams Broadside (First Gold); and Caledonian's Golden Promise (Target).
So what clues can you use to try to recognise each hop, in the knowledge that barley, yeast and water will do their best to influence the result?

Fuggles At 3-5.6% alpha acid (bitterness ratio), it has the lowest bitterness of all English hops, which go as high as 17% alpha. The Fuggle is perhaps the most famous of English hops. It has what I hope (as an Englishman) is the 'typical English flavour': smoky, grassy, sensual, earthy and moreish. Developed in 1875 in Kent, it was hit hard in the 20th century by the disease VerticilliumWilt. It is frequently blended with English Goldings as the Fuggle gives balance, depth and subtlety of flavour.

Goldings The Golding has a low bitterness level at 4.4-6.7% alpha acid and is a delicate creature giving lemon/orange flavours designed to refresh. It is the quintessential summer-time hop, a traditional English hop variety, whose gently floral flavours have been described by beer writers as having a 'perfumed lemon aroma, citrus sweet, with flavours of lemon sherbet, fresh orange, lychees and perfumed violets'.

Bramling Cross This is a Golding crossed with a wild Manitoban male. It shows an alpha acid of 6-7.8%, higher than its Golding parent, and has a distinctive 'American aroma'. This refers not to popcorn or cola but to the citric/catty flavours shown by many American hops. This demonstrates itself as blackcurrant and lemon flavours, a Sauvignon Blanc/Cabernet Sauvignon equivalent, which is great for autumnal beers that need edge, or fruit beers or Porters showing a vinous character.

The Fuggle Hop

Challenger This hop variety, at 6.5-8.5% alpha acid, was always regarded as 'dual purpose', able to give both flavour and bitterness at the same time. It has a wonderful lime edge to it which drinkers find refreshing, and this helped gain the title 'Ultimate Fem'ale' beer in 2001 for Coniston Bluebird in the Beauty of Hops competition. It would perform well with curry (think lime chutney) or strong cheese.

First Gold This 5.6-8.7% alpha hop is another Goldings relation and its flavours are like a double dose of that hop ie rich orange and dried apricot, like the fashionable white Viognier grape. It is the first of the new English hedgerow hop varieties (grows to 8 feet instead of the traditional 20 feet) which means it needs less chemical treatments to keep it healthy and can be picked by machine. It is already being used in single varietal beers and gives a wonderful deep Christmas Pudding flavour. It would also add a wonderful deep apricot quality to wheat beers.

Target At 9.9-12.6% alpha acid, this hop was previously thought to have little flavour benefits. But brewers such as Caledonian (Golden Promise) have shown that it can be a clever aroma hop as well. Adjectives such as 'spicy, orange, tangerine, tinned peaches, sage, peppery spice and citrus sweet' have all been used to describe it. More English hedgerow and traditional height hops are in the pipeline, brimming with flavour and more disease resistant than current varieties. With hops such as these to play with, who needs grapes?

Rupert Ponsonby

The National Hop Association of England organises the annual Beauty of Hops competition. The winners in 2002 were: Ultimate Wedding Beer – Smiles Bristol IPA (Challenger/First Gold/Fuggles); Ultimate Spiced/Fruit Beer – S A Brain Ultimo (Challenger/Fuggles/Goldings); Ultimate BBQ Beer – Harveys Bonfire Boy (Bramling Cross/Fuggles/Goldings/Progress; and Greene King Strong Suffolk (Challenger/Northdown/Target).

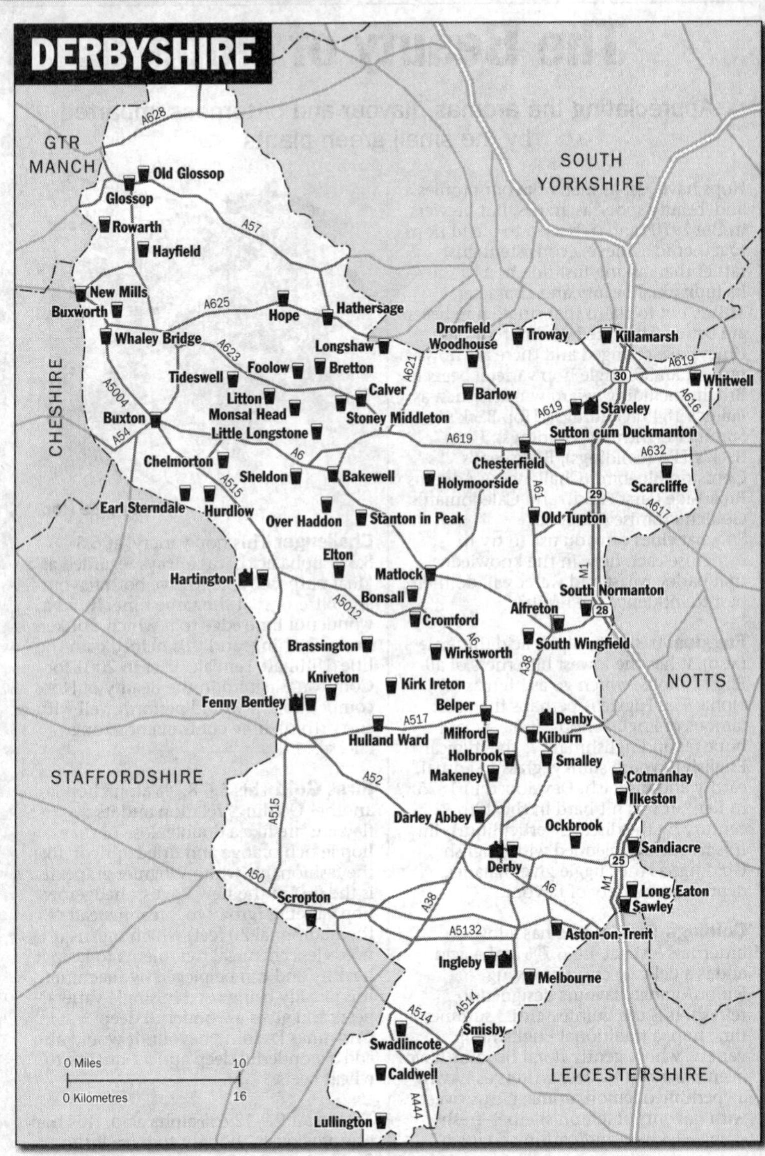

ALFRETON

Victoria Inn

80 Nottingham Road (B600)

🕓 1-11; 12-11 Sat; 12-10.30 Sun

☎ (01773) 520156

Taylor Landlord; guest beer Ⓗ

Extensively refurbished, busy two-roomed local served by a central bar where a friendly welcome is assured. The lounge features an illuminated aquarium while pump clips of previously featured beers are displayed on beams in the public bar which has a pool table and Sky TV. Guest beers change regularly and showcase local micro-breweries; a summer beer festival is held. The outdoor terrace is illuminated, and houses long alley skittles. A limited snack menu is available. Parking is difficult; Alfreton town centre is nearby.

❀⊡≉♣

ASTON-ON-TRENT

Malt Shovel

16 The Green (off Derby Rd)

🕓 11.30-11; 12-10.30 Sun

☎ (01332) 792256

Draught Bass; Fuller's London Pride; Marston's Pedigree; Wells Bombardier; guest beers Ⓗ

The brewer's Tudor exterior marks this as a latecomer among the hand-made bricks of surrounding buildings. It has two rooms, plus a restaurant extending the original lounge. The bar retains unspoilt inter-war oak-panelled decor, while the quieter lounge is decked out with copper, brass and horse tack. A reference library provides reading matter. Guest beers vary between regionals and micros. The licence is now in the hands of the younger generation of the same family. Regular buses run from Derby.

♨Q❀◐⊡♿▲♣P

Railway Porter; Marston's Pedigree; Taylor Landlord; Ⓗ **guest beers** Ⓗ/Ⓖ
Built by Midland Railway as the centrepiece of the railway village that is now a conservation area; then as now it had its own brewhouse, but no bars, the beer being served by pot-boys. It was later acquired by Hardys & Hansons who ran it until 1974, when it closed and fell into disrepair. Restored and reopened 14 years later, it is now one of the best-known free houses in the country and a committed champion of small brewers. Q

Crompton Tavern

45 Crompton Street
11-11; 12-10.30 Sun
☎ (01332) 733629
Banks's Bitter; Marston's Pedigree; Taylor Landlord; guest beers Ⓗ
Tucked away in a cul-de-sac off Green Lane and picked out at night by a fringe of fairylights, this was originally a guesthouse for visiting actors at the nearby Grand Theatre, where the first performance of Bram Stoker's Dracula was staged in 1924. Two front doors open on to different ends of the same bar, with lower level wings on either side. The pub doubles as a free gallery for local artists.

Falstaff

74 Silver Hill Road, Normanton
12-11; 12-10.30 Sun
☎ (01332) 342902
Greene King Abbot; Marston's Pedigree; guest beers Ⓗ
Known locally as the Folly, the Falstaff was built as a latter-day coaching inn for Pountain, Girardot & Forman (see the terracotta monogram outside). Formerly owned by Allied, it is now free and the best real ale pub in Normanton. The curved bar is flanked on one side by a small lounge, and on the other by a games room. Not posh, but a real local.
Q

Flowerpot

23-25 King Street
11-11; 12-10.30 Sun
☎ (01332) 204955
Draught Bass; Ⓖ **Marston's Pedigree; Whim Arbor Light;** Ⓗ **guest beers** Ⓗ/Ⓖ
Just up from the cathedral, this is one of the pubs that spearheaded Derby's free trade growth in the 1990s to become a showcase for small breweries. Much expanded from the original premises, it reaches far back from the small, roadside frontage and divides into several interlinking rooms; the furthest is a lively venue for gigs. See the glass cellar wall, revealing rows of stillaged firkins.
Q

Furnace Inn

9 Duke Street
11-11; 12-3, 6.30-10.30 Sun
☎ (01332) 331563
Hardys & Hansons Best Mild, Best Bitter, Classic, seasonal beers Ⓗ
Just off St Mary's Bridge, with its 15th-century bridge chapel, the Furnace stands on the west bank of the Derwent at the edge of Darley Park. The name preserves its close connection with Handyside's Britannia foundry of which it was once part. Scenes of bygone Derby decorate the walls and bar-top, but it is the atmosphere, rather than the building itself, that gives this local boozer its appeal. It hosts karaoke weekend evenings.
P

Olde Dolphin Inne ☆

5a Queen Street
10.30-11; 12-10.30 Sun
☎ (01332) 267711
Adnams Bitter; Draught Bass; Black Sheep Special; Cains Mild; Caledonian Deuchars IPA; Greene King Abbot; guest beers Ⓗ
Below the great gothic tower of the cathedral, the timber-framed Dolphin is Derby's oldest pub, although much restored latterly. The beamed interior divides into bar, upper and lower lounges and a snug, each of distinct character; but the raised patio attracts most drinkers in warm weather. It opens for breakfast at 9am. It is best to book the upstairs steak bar; good value bar food. CAMRA's City Pub of the Year 2002, it holds an annual beer festival (July).
QP

SMISBY

Smisby Arms
Main Street
12-3, 6 (5.30 Fri; 7 Sat)-11; 12-3, 7-10.30 Sun
(01530) 412677
Marston's Pedigree; guest beer Ⓗ
Popular, three-roomed village free house of character, with a good reputation for food (not served Sun eve).

STONEY MIDDLETON

Moon Inn
Town End
12-2.30 (not Mon-Wed), 6-11; 12-11 Sat; 12-3, 7-10.30 Sun
(01433) 630203
Stones Bitter; guest beers Ⓗ
Cosy, low-ceilinged pub in a quarrying village.

TROWAY

Black-a-Moor
Snowdon Lane
12-3, 6-11; 12-10.30 Sun
(01246) 413180
Beer range varies Ⓗ
Comfortable roadside pub with an emphasis on food, yet always two or three ales, often from micros. Summer beer festival. Cask Marque accredited.

WIRKSWORTH

Royal Oak
North End
8-11; 12-3, 8-11 Sun
(01629) 823000
Draught Bass; Taylor Landlord; Whim Hartington IPA; guest beers Ⓗ
Small, mid-terraced, beamed, coaching inn circa 1757, in an interesting side street, near the market place.

Old Silk Mill
19 Full Street (near cathedral)
10.30-11; 12-10.30 Sun
☎ (01332) 369748
Draught Bass; Black Sheep Special; Boddingtons Bitter; Fuller's London Pride; guest beers Ⓗ
The Old Silk Mill selling Nottingham Rock ales was demolished in 1924, its namesake being built four years later. Distinguished by an elegant stone front and mural depicting the historic silk trades lock-out of 1833, the pub attracts custom as much for its food as for its beer (opens 9am for breakfast). The Silk Mill Museum (well worth visiting) is close by, while on the green opposite stands an equestrian statue of Bonnie Prince Charlie where his incursion into England ended.
❀◑◐♿

Rowditch Inn
246 Uttoxeter New Road (1 mile from centre)
12-2 (not Mon-Wed), 7-11; 12-2, 7-10.30 Sun
☎ (01332) 343123
Hardys & Hansons Best Bitter, Classic, seasonal beers; Marston's Pedigree; guest beers Ⓗ
On the borough's ancient boundary, once marked by a defensive dyke or rough ditch (whence Rowditch), stands this plain-fronted but warmly welcoming roadside pub. The busily cluttered bar-back is a veritable gallery of guest beers, past and present. At the start of the last century this was one of a thousand houses owned by nearby Strettons, by far the biggest brewer in the county, bought by Allsopp's in 1927. Regular beer festivals are held.
❀♣⚟

Smithfield
Meadow Road (downriver from market place)
11-11; 12-10.30 (12-3, 7-10.30 winter) Sun
☎ (01332) 370429
Draught Bass; Oakham JHB, Bishops Farewell; Whim Arbor Light, Hartington IPA; guest beers Ⓗ
Bow-fronted riverside pub, built to serve the old cattle market, which has since moved to a new site leaving the 'Smithy' in a bit of a backwater. Just downriver from the market place, your first sight on entering is the front bar's regimental row of black handpulls. To the left is a games room that admits children until 9pm. To the right is a cosy back room, looking out over a riverside patio, with a stone fireplace flanked by wooden settles.
❀◑♣P

Station Inn
12 Midland Road
11.30-2.30, 5 (7 Sat)-11; 11.30-11 Fri; 12-3, 7-10.30 Sun
☎ (01332) 608014
Draught Bass; Ⓖ **Marston's Pedigree** Ⓗ
This modest, but elaborately-fronted pub was built to serve Midland Railway's classical station nearby, needlessly swept away in 1983 to be replaced by the present functional, but uninspiring edifice. The traditional bar features a panelled counter, cast-iron footrail and quarry-tiled floor; the large rear lounge acts as dining area and function room. Many cellar awards on display attest to the skills of the well-established licensee.
◑♿≠♣

DRONFIELD WOODHOUSE

Jolly Farmer
Pentland Road (off B6056)
12-11; 12-10.30 Sun
☎ (01246) 418018
Black Sheep Best Bitter; Taylor Landlord; Tetley Bitter; guest beers Ⓗ
Built by the lamented former Nottingham brewers Shipstone's, this pub opened in 1976 as the Gorsey Brigg. It later became a Greenalls ale house, renovated in farmhouse style, open-plan with many alcoves. Subsequent changes of ownership have not dented the manager's enthusiasm for stocking a range of guest beers. A glass-fronted cellar is visible behind the bar, and no lager or keg fonts are to be seen. The pub, serving a large private housing estate, is well supported by local residents. No evening meals Sun. ❀◑◐♿♣

EARL STERNDALE

Quiet Woman
Off B5053
12-4, 7-11; 12-3, 7-10.30 Sun
☎ (01298) 83211
Adnams Bitter; Marston's Bitter, Pedigree; guest beers Ⓗ
Unspoilt local in the heart of the Peak District National Park, opposite the village church and green. Walkers are welcome in the cosy, beamed room with a real fire and a small bar. One of the beams displays a collection of Marston's pump clips from long-lost beers. Traditional games are played, with dominoes tables in the main bar, plus a games room. Local cheeses, fresh eggs and traditional pork pies can be purchased from the bar. Live folk music is staged (Sun). Q❀◑♣P

ELTON

Duke of York ☆
Main Street
8.30-11; 12-3, 8.30-10.30 Sun
☎ (01629) 650367
Adnams Bitter; Mansfield Cask Ale Ⓗ
Extremely well-kept traditional village pub in the heart of the Peak District. The same owner has kept this unspoilt public house for the last 35 years. The three rooms all boast real fires and it is worth a visit simply to admire the original decor which makes it worthy of its inclusion in CAMRA's National Inventory. QP

FENNY BENTLEY ❊

Bentley Brook Inn
(A515)
11-11; 12-10.30 Sun
☎ (01335) 350278
website: www.bentleybrookinn.co.uk
Leatherbritches Ashbourne Ale, Hairy Helmet, Bespoke; Marston's Pedigree; guest beers Ⓗ
Just inside the National Park, the pub is home to Leatherbritches Brewery and an award-winning restaurant. Its well-established spring bank holiday beer and music festival offers up to 100 beers. This small, friendly, family-run hotel affords excellent views and ever-improving facilities. It is within easy reach of Derbyshire's major tourist attractions. A

pleasant outdoor terrace overlooks an extensive garden area where camping facilities and a skittle alley are available. ♨♉❀⇌◑◗♿▲♣●P⊬

GLOSSOP

Crown Inn

142 Victoria Street
⏲ 5 (12 Fri & Sat)-11; 12-10.30 Sun
☎ (01457) 862824
Samuel Smith OBB Ⓗ
Friendly local, in the Whitfield area of town, where a central curved bar serves two small snugs, a bar area and a large games room. Built at the end of a terrace in 1846, it has been a Sam Smith's house since 1977 – the only one in the entire High Peak. The Crown is testament to the fact that pubs do not need to have their interiors ruined to be a popular and pleasant place in which to drink; a fine example of the type of local that is sadly disappearing. ♨Q❀♿≹♣⊬

Friendship

3 Arundel Street
⏲ 4 (3 Fri; 12 Sat)-11; 12-3, 7-10.30 Sun
☎ (01457) 855277
Robinson's Hatters Mild, Best Bitter, seasonal beers Ⓗ
Street-corner local run by a committed licensee whose sympathetic refurbishments have kept the pub's character. A semi-circular bar and a wood-panelled interior are features of the open-plan lounge. A corner is dedicated to local cricket enthusiasts who frequent the pub, along with those from Glossop FC. The back tap room is served by a hatch. Up to 30 malt whiskies are sold. Children are welcome until 8pm. Note the impressive lamp over the front door, circa 1900. The garden is now fully open. ♨♉❀≹♣

Old Gloveworks

Riverside Mill, George Street
⏲ 12-11 (may close early eve Mon-Wed); 12-10.30 Sun
☎ (01457) 858432
John Smith's Bitter; Theakston Cool Cask; guest beers Ⓗ
Converted mill, previously a wine bar, affording elevated views over Glossop Brook. Entertainment includes local bands (Thu), discos (Fri and Sat) and cabaret (from 3.30pm Sun). Four ever-changing guest beers are stocked. A discretionary age limit (over 25) is imposed by the landlord. A licence extension until midnight applies Friday and Saturday (no admittance after 10.45pm). Outside, enjoy the riverside patio and roof terrace. Weekday lunches are served. ❀◑≹P

Star Inn Ale House

2 Howard Street
⏲ 11-11; 12-10.30 Sun
☎ (01457) 853072
Boddingtons Bitter; Pictish Brewers Gold; Taylor Landlord; guest beers Ⓗ
Highly regarded ale house, selling around 12 guest beers each week. Bare floorboards and the back tap room, served by a hatch, create an authentic atmosphere. Background music does not intrude on conversation. Built in 1837, it became a Boddingtons house in 1889 and remained so until acquired by Greenalls in 1993. Local tastes ensure that only rarely is a dark beer on sale, but Pictish and Phoenix beers appear frequently. Handy for buses, it stands across from the rail station. ≹♣P

HATHERSAGE

Little John Hotel

Station Road
⏲ 11-11; 12-10.30 Sun
☎ (01433) 650225
Beer range varies Ⓗ
Spacious stone building, encompassing bar areas, hotel rooms and holiday cottages. The five seating areas have benefited from recent investment, notably the lounge, family areas and the large function room. The four ever-changing real ales from independent breweries are popular with locals and walking and caving groups alike. Generous portions of home-cooked food are prepared using fresh produce; meals are served all day Saturday and Sunday. Baby changing facilities are available. ♉⇌◑◗⊞♿▲≹♣●P⊬

Scotsman's Pack

School Lane
⏲ 11.30-3, 6-11; 11.30-11 Sat; 12-10.30 Sun
☎ (01433) 650253
Burtonwood Bitter, Top Hat; guest beers Ⓗ
Built around 100 years ago, the comfortable interior, with Edwardian features, is decorated with horse brasses and plates. There are three seating areas: a particularly pleasant one by the fire; an alcove by the bar and a larger area with more of a restaurant feel. A flagship pub for Burtonwood, it is noted for the quality of its food and accommodation. Look for the nearby grave of Little John, and walk in the surrounding Peak District National Park. ❀⇌◑◗≹♣P⊬

HAYFIELD

Royal Hotel

Market Street
⏲ 11-3, 6-11; 11-11 Fri & Sat; 12-10.30 Sun
☎ (01663) 742721
Marston's Pedigree; Tetley Bitter; guest beers Ⓗ
Imposing stone pub, entirely in keeping with its surrounding environment. In an attractive Peak District village, this former vicarage stands near the church and cricket ground. The River Sett, in front of the pub, flows down from Kinder Scout. The traditional interior boasts original oak panels and pews which, aided by real fires, give a pleasant, relaxing atmosphere. There is also a restaurant. ♨Q♉❀⇌◑◗♿▲P⊬

HOLBROOK

Dead Poets Inn

Chapel Street
⏲ 12-2.30, 5-11; 12-11 Fri & Sat; 12-10.30 Sun
☎ (01332) 780301
Greene King Abbot; Ⓖ **Sarah Hughes Dark Ruby Mild;** Ⓗ **Marston's Pedigree;** Ⓖ **Shardlow Goldenhop; guest beers** Ⓗ
Dramatic transformation from an ailing Allied house to a thriving free house, it now attracts custom from outside the village. Built in 1800, the high-backed pews, stone-flagged floors and an inglenook combine to create atmosphere. The licensee, a former

coffin maker, believed that many of our famous poets gained inspiration for their work from atmospheric taverns such as this; poetry readings are held monthly (first Tue). Bottled Belgian beers augment the draught ales. Regular beer festivals are held.
♕❀☾♣P

Wheel Inn
14 Chapel Street
⊙ 12-2.30 (not Mon), 5-11; 11.30-11 Sat; 12-3, 7-10.30 Sun
☎ (01332) 880006
Archers Golden; Ⓖ **Courage Directors; Marston's Pedigree; Theakston Black Bull;** Ⓗ **Whim Hartington Bitter;** Ⓖ **guest beers** Ⓗ
Warm 18th-century pub entirely different in character to its close neighbour, the Dead Poets. The restaurant area offers a good range of reasonably-priced, home-cooked food (not served Sun eve or Mon). The patio and award-winning garden are a joy to behold in summer. Two beer festivals a year are held and up to 40 single malt whiskies are stocked. This exceptional village for real ale enthusiasts is served by the No. 71 bus from Derby. ♕❀☾◗

HOLYMOORSIDE

Lamb Inn
16 Loads Road
⊙ 12-3 (not Mon-Fri), 7-11; 12-4, 6-10.30 Sun
☎ (01246) 566167
Home Bitter; guest beers Ⓗ
Cosy, two-roomed pub in a village close to the Peak District National Park, warmed by a real fire in one room. The holder of numerous local CAMRA awards, it keeps up to six guest ales. A pleasant outdoor drinking area is ideal for summer evenings. Note that the pub is closed lunchtime except weekends and bank holidays.
♕Q❀♣P

HOPE

Cheshire Cheese
Edale Road
⊙ 12-3, 6-11; 12-11 Sat; 12-4, 6-10.30 Sun
☎ (01433) 620381
website: www.hopenet.co.uk/cheshirecheese
Barnsley Bitter; Black Sheep Best Bitter; Taylor Landlord; Wentworth WPA; guest beer Ⓗ
16th-century free house situated in the famed walking country of the Peak District National Park. The car park is small, and the road outside narrow, so walking the last few yards is recommended. The pub has three seating areas furnished with a variety of cushioned chairs and benches. The lower area serves as a restaurant at mealtimes. Children are welcome (except in the immediate vicinity of the bar). A quiz is held alternate Wednesday evenings.
♕Q❀⛟☾◗▲P

HULLAND WARD

Black Horse Inn
On A517
⊙ 12-2.30, 6-11; 12-3, 7-10.30 Sun
☎ (01335) 370206
Draught Bass; Marston's Pedigree; guest beers Ⓗ
This traditional 300-year-old country inn stands in an elevated village, in some of the most picturesque country outside the Peak, close to Carsington Water. Its split-level, multi-roomed drinking area, with low, beamed ceilings and quarry-tiled floors, is served by a central bar offering two rotating guest ales. An extensive bar menu is complemented by a popular Sunday carvery in the restaurant. Some rooms boast four-poster beds. ❀⛟☾◗♣P⚟✔

ILKESTON

Dewdrop Inn
Station Street (off A609)
⊙ 11.30-3 (not Sat), 7-11; 12-4.30, 7-10.30 Sun
☎ (0115) 932 9684 website: www.eggpie.com
Draught Bass; Taylor Best Bitter; Whim Hartington IPA; guest beers Ⓗ
Three-roomed local: a bar, family room and lounge with a log fire burning most of the time. It stocks over 50 malt whiskies, an occasional real cider and a house beer from Broadstone. The doorstep sandwiches are legendary. It was CAMRA East Midlands Pub of the Year in 1997 and is a frequent local award-winner. Long alley skittles is played on the patio. It hosts beer festivals throughout the year and regular wine and cheese evenings. ♕Q♘❀⊟♣●

KILBURN

Traveller's Rest
114 Chapel Street (1 mile off B6179)
⊙ 12-4 (not Mon-Thu), 5.30-11; 12-4, 7-10.30 Sun
☎ (01332) 880108
Greene King Abbot; Tetley Bitter, Burton Ale; guest beer Ⓗ
Traditional, friendly two-roomed village local, in a former mining area, dating back to the 1850s. Known locally as Mamma's after a former landlady, it enjoys a good standing in several pub games leagues. Look for the photograph of old Kilburn Station which stood nearby. A small rear garden houses an open skittle alley. The local tourist attraction of Denby Pottery, with its visitor centre and shop, is just a mile away. Good bus services run from Derby (91 and 125). ♕❀⊟♣P

KIRK IRETON

Barley Mow ☆
Main Street (off B5023)
⊙ 12-2, 7-11; 12-2, 7-10.30 Sun
☎ (01335) 370306
Hook Norton Old Hooky; Marston's Pedigree; guest beers Ⓖ
Exceptionally characterful country pub respectfully converted from a dour Jacobean farmhouse that would have made a perfect setting for a gothic novel. With several interconnecting rooms of differing size and character, the heart of the place is the bar, featuring a low, beamed ceiling, quarry-tiled floor, wooden bench seating, stone fireplace, slate-topped tables and bar-back stillage. A free-standing outhouse now serves as the village post office. There are not many left like this; a real gem.
♕Q❀⛟⊟▲♣●

LITTLE LONGSTONE

Packhorse Inn
Main Street
⊙ 11.30-3, 5 (6 Sat)-11; 12-10.30 Sun

☎ (01629) 640471
Marston's Bitter; guest beer Ⓗ
Genuine village local, a pub since 1787, retaining many original features. Located where the Monsal Trail emerges from fields on to the minor road leading to Monsal Head, it is popular with walkers, but also enjoys a local trade. Its three small rooms are well decorated; the garden is up a flight of steps at the back. Live folk music is performed (Wed eve) – singers and players are welcome. ♨Q❀◑◐▲♣

LITTON

Red Lion

Main Street
⏲ 12-3, 6-11; 12-11 Sat; 12-10.30 Sun
☎ (01298) 871458
Jennings Cumberland Ale; Oakwell Barnsley Bitter; Shepherd Neame Spitfire; guest beer Ⓗ
This gem acts as the hub of village life as a true local should. It faces south across a village green, complete with stocks. Three small rooms surround a huge open fireplace and a bit more space is created by the unusual sliding front door. Bar skittles is played; quizzes and other special events take place on Monday evening. No food is served Sunday evening. ♨Q❀◑◐▲♣P⊁

LONG EATON

Hole in the Wall

6 Regent Street
⏲ 10.30-3.30, 5.30-11; 10.30-11 Fri & Sat; 12-4.30, 7-10.30 Sun
☎ (0115) 973 4920
website: www.hiw.pub@ntlworld.com
Courage Directors; Nottingham Extra Pale Ale; Wells Bombardier; guest beers Ⓗ
Called the Regent Inn until the 1950s, this 100-year-old back-street local is a CAMRA award-winning boozer. With two rooms, plus small serving hatch, it is a keen supporter of micro-brewery products; the beers from the Nottingham Brewery are particular favourites. Strong on pub games, it supports local rugby football and hockey teams. The enclosed rear patio hosts long alley skittles and barbecues in the summer. Bar snacks are available. A pay and display car park is opposite, and the Erewash Canal is nearby.
❀⊟♣

LONGSHAW

Grouse Inn

On A625 OS258779
⏲ 12-3, 6-11; 12-11 Sat; 12-10.30 Sun
☎ (01433) 630423
Banks's Bitter; Barnsley Bitter; Marston's Pedigree; guest beer Ⓗ
Isolated moorland pub, thought to have been converted from a farmhouse to slake the thirsts of men building the nearby Totley tunnel. A long-standing free house, in the same family since 1965, its front lounge is decorated with photographs of local gritstone edges. The more basic tap room doubles as a function room, and a conservatory completes the accommodation. It stocks a fine range of malt whiskies. Evening meals are served Wed-Sun.
♨Q☕❀◑◐⊟♣P⊡

LULLINGTON

Colvile Arms

Main Street
⏲ 12-2 (not Mon-Fri), 7-11; 12-3, 7-10.30 Sun
☎ (01827) 373212
Draught Bass; Marston's Pedigree; guest beer Ⓗ
Popular, 18th-century free house in a hamlet at the southern tip of the county. The central snug features high-backed settles, reminiscent of an earlier era, and there are two comfortable lounges, one converted from two cottages. Three quiz teams and the local cricket team meet here, leading to lively conversation. The garden area includes a bowling green. Local CAMRA Country Pub of the Year 2001.
♨❀♣P

MAKENEY

Holly Bush Inn

Holly Bush Lane OS352447
⏲ 12-3, 5-11; 12-11 Fri & Sat; 12-10.30 Sun
☎ (01332) 841729
Brains Dark; Ⓗ **Greene King Ruddles County; Marston's Pedigree;** Ⓖ **guest beers** Ⓗ
Grade II listed, and once a farmhouse with a brewery on the Strutt Estate, this late 17th-century, former Offilers house positively oozes character. It stood on the Derby turnpike before the Strutts opened the valley route in 1818; Dick Turpin is known to have drunk here. The enclosed wooden snug is sandwiched between two bars. Little changes here, least of all the licensees (only two families have run the pub since 1939). Up to five guest beers are offered; regular beer festivals are held. ♨Q☕❀⊟P

MATLOCK ❄

Thorn Tree Inn

48 Jackson Road (off Wellington St)
⏲ 12-2.30 (not Mon or Tue), 7-11; 12-10.30 Sun
☎ (01629) 582923
Draught Bass; Whim Hartington Bitter; guest beers Ⓗ
This cosy gem, hidden away, high above the Peak District spa town, affords panoramic views over the picturesque Derwent Valley. Circa 19th century, it consists of two small rooms and a patio area with a heater and canopy. Popular outdoor beer festivals are held over bank holiday weekends. At the start of the Limestone Way, this local also attracts walkers, and is within easy reach of many tourist attractions. The night-time views have made this the centre of the 'Matlock Triangle', famous for UFO sightings.
Q❀◑◐▲⇌♣

MILFORD

King William

The Bridge, Derby Road (A6)
⏲ 12-3, 5.30-11; 12-11 Sat; 12-10.30 Sun
☎ (01332) 840842
Marston's Pedigree; Taylor Landlord; Wells Bombardier; guest beers Ⓖ
Single-roomed, stone-built roadhouse at the foot of a sandstone cliff and contemporary with the elegant stone bridge which straddles the adjacent River Derwent. A warm welcome is assured from the landlady who has restored the interior to its former glory, retaining softwood beams and the

original tiled floor. The Derwent Valley, whose mills and factories were seminal in the Industrial Revolution, is now a World Heritage site. Regular buses run from Derby.
⛼◑♿

MONSAL HEAD

Monsal Head Hotel
On B6465
⏲ 11-11; 12-10.30 Sun
☎ (01629) 640250 website: www.monsalhead.com
Courage Directors; Taylor Landlord; Theakston Best Bitter, Old Peculier; Whim Hartington Bitter; guest beers Ⓗ
The hotel owes its existence to the now-closed Derby-Manchester railway line which plunged into a tunnel underneath here, before emerging on to a viaduct (now open to walkers) over the River Wye. Monsal Head remains a popular beauty spot. Real ale is kept in the stable bar to the rear, decorated appropriately. Guest beers, from Kelham Island and Abbeydale are regularly available. ⛼Q❀🛏◑▶▲♣P

NEW MILLS ❊

Beehive
67 Albion Road
⏲ 5-11; 4-10.30 Sun
☎ (01663) 742087
Boddingtons Bitter; guest beers Ⓗ
A first-class renovation of this once ordinary local (formerly a tollhouse) has produced an excellent place to drink. It is comfortable and friendly, with a beer range which is a positive asset to the area. Note the old photos of New Mills and the surrounding area. After a few pints downstairs you can go upstairs and eat in the very good Indian restaurant. ❀▶⇌(Newtown/Central)

Pack Horse
Mellor Road (1 mile from centre)
⏲ 12-3, 5-11; 12-11 Sat; 12-10.30 Sun
☎ (01663) 742365
Tetley Bitter; guest beers Ⓗ
Stone pub, in keeping with the farmhouses dotted around in the surrounding countryside, it nestles in a fold of the back road from New Mills to Mellor and Marple Bridge. There are good views up the valley to Hayfield and Kinder Scout and south over Ollersett Moor. A comfortable, well-appointed single room serves good quality food until late. Catering for all tastes, this is a friendly, relaxing place to drink and dine.
⛼Q❀🛏◑▶P

OCKBROOK ❊

Royal Oak
55 Green Lane (off A52, follow Ilkeston signs)
⏲ 11.30-2.30 (3 Sat), 6.30-11; 12-3, 7-10.30 Sun
☎ (01332) 662378
Draught Bass; guest beers Ⓗ
Set back from the road across a cobbled courtyard, this fine pub was CAMRA East Midlands Pub of the Year 2000. In the same family since coronation year and little changed, its every aspect speaks of good old-fashioned values. No dizzy lights or thumping music intrude. Each room has its own character and clientele. It hosts a beer festival every October. Three ever-changing guest beers showcase local micro-breweries. Excellent home-cooked food is served. Separate gardens cater for adults and families.
Q❀◑♿♣P⚟

OLD TUPTON

Royal Oak Inn
Derby Road (A61, 3 miles S of Chesterfield)
⏲ 12-11; 12-10.30 Sun
☎ (01246) 862180
Daleside Bitter; John Smith's Bitter, Magnet; Wells Bombardier; Whim Hartington IPA; guest beers Ⓗ
Traditional, mellow red brick structure, with small-paned windows dating from 1861. Recently refurbished, its open-plan interior has four distinct areas: games room (with full-sized Jenga), tap room, snug and a best room. Outside is a well-equipped children's play area, tables, seats and a skittle alley. The centre of the local community, it is very welcoming to walkers; regular bank holiday walks by the locals raise money for charity.
⛼❀◑▶♿▲♣P🗑✔

OVER HADDON

Lathkil Hotel
From Bakewell, take B5055 for 1 mile, then follow signs OS206665
⏲ 11.30-3, 7-11; 11.30-11 Sat; 12-10.30 Sun
☎ (01629) 812501 website: www.lathkil.co.uk
Wells Bombardier; Whim Hartington Bitter; guest beer Ⓗ
Free house in an idyllic setting, benefiting from spectacular views across the picturesque Lathkil Dale Nature Reserve. The bar features fine oak panelling and a welcoming fire, much appreciated by walkers. The Lathkil usually stocks two guest beers. The dining room offers quality food, and an extensive specials board applies to the bar menu, too. Superior accommodation is also available. The children's room opens lunchtimes.
⛼Q🚼❀🛏◑▶P🗑

ROWARTH

Little Mill
Rowarth Village (signed off Siloh Rd)
⏲ 11-11; 12-10.30 Sun
☎ (01663) 743178
Banks's Bitter; Camerons Strongarm; Marston's Pedigree; guest beer Ⓗ
Spacious pub of character with a history that tells a tale. Originally a candle wick mill, it features a fully working waterwheel. A large open area bordering a stream is at the front of the pub, which lies in a pleasant, secluded spot. The pub also has a garden and adventure playground. A huge log fire dominates the lounge and home-cooked food is served all day.
⛼Q🚼❀🛏◑▶♿▲P🗑

SAWLEY

Harrington Arms
392 Tamworth Road (B6540)
⏲ 11-11; 12-10.30 Sun
☎ (0115) 973 2614
website: www.harringtonarms.co.uk
Hardys & Hansons Best Bitter, Classic, seasonal beers Ⓗ
This former coaching inn stands close to

the River Trent and the Trent and Mersey Canal. It has traditional decor of panelled walls, low, beamed ceilings and a large open-plan area. An open fire and wood-burning stove add to its charm. The extended patio and garden area, with large outdoor heaters, hosts the annual beer festival (Aug). Freshly-cooked food, with international dishes, is served in the restaurant area, but the bar menu is just as good.
⛰❀◑♿≋(Long Eaton) P⚟✔

SHELDON

Cock & Pullet
Main Street (off A6)
⌚ 11-11; 12-10.30 Sun
☎ (01629) 814292
Draught Bass; Taylor Landlord Ⓗ
Set in Peak District walking country near the former Magpie lead mine (now frequented by potholers), this is only a recent pub. Converted from a derelict barn in 1995, it brought ale back to Sheldon after a gap of 24 years. The pub is L-shaped with three rooms (snug, bar and games) and houses 24 clocks! Home-made meat pies are a speciality, but there are usually at least two vegetarian dishes, plus specials on offer.
⛰❀🛏◑⊟▲♣P

SMALLEY

Bell Inn
35 Main Road (A608)
⌚ 11.30-3, 5-11; 11-11 Sat; 12-10.30 Sun
☎ (01332) 880635
Adnams Broadside; Fuller's London Pride; Mallard Duckling; Whim Hartington Bitter, Hartington IPA; guest beer Ⓗ
This mid 19th-century inn comprises three rooms, a large, attractive child-friendly garden and accommodation – three flats in a converted stable adjoining the pub. Brewing and other memorabilia adorn the walls. Top quality beer and food have helped earn the Bell the local CAMRA Pub of the Year award 2002. Situated on the main Derby-Heanor road, near Shipley Country Park, it can be reached via the H1 bus service (every 20 minutes from Derby bus station).
⛰Q❀🛏◑⊟♿P✔

SOUTH NORMANTON

Boundary
Lea Vale, Broadmeadows
⌚ 12-3, 5-11; 12-11 Fri & Sat; 12-10.30 Sun
☎ (01773) 819066 website: www.the boundary.co.uk
Draught Bass; Bateman XXXB; Fuller's London Pride; Greene King Old Speckled Hen; Titanic seasonal beers; guest beers Ⓗ
Popular, multi-roomed estate pub, with an adjoining 14-bedroom lodge and conference facilities. Up to seven real ales include local micro-breweries' products and national favourites. A guest beer club allows regulars to choose their own beer at a reduced price. An extensive menu includes daily specials and a Sunday carvery. A big screen shows Sky TV in the sports lounge. Live entertainment (Fri and Sat eves), indoor and outdoor play areas, and regular quizzes are all on offer here.
🐴❀🛏◑⊟♿♣P⚟

Clock Inn
107 Market Street
⌚ 11-11; 12-10.30 Sun
☎ (01773) 811396 website: www.theclockinn.co.uk
Camerons Strongarm; Mansfield Dark Mild; Marston's Bitter; Shepherd Neame Spitfire; guest beers Ⓗ
Cask Marque-accredited, family-run free house. The Clock Inn All Stars Jazz Band play on the first Monday of every month; a blues and rock theme night is held every Sunday. Tasty home-cooked food (12-2.30 and 5.30-8.30) includes good value specials and Sunday lunches. A driver-friendly soft drinks pricing policy is offered. A no-smoking lounge bar and tap room complete this local.
Q❀◑⊟♣P⚟✔

SOUTH WINGFIELD

Old Yew Tree
51 Manor Road
⌚ 5-11; 12-3, 6.30-11 Sat; 12-4, 7-10.30 Sun
☎ (01773) 833763
Cottage seasonal beers; Leadmill seasonal beers; Marston's Pedigree; guest beers Ⓗ
A regular Guide entry, this very busy family-run free house is situated near the magnificent remains of the 15th-century Wingfield Manor, destroyed by Cromwell during the Civil War. Guest beers regularly feature local micros. Good home-cooked food includes excellent Sunday lunches (no food Sun eve). The award-winning landlord was runner-up Ind Coope Master Cellarman and the pub won the Amber Valley Clean Air award. Limited parking.
⛰❀◑♿▲P⚟

STANTON IN PEAK

Flying Childers Inn
Main Road (off B5056, Bakewell-Ashbourne road)
⌚ 12-2 (3 Sat; not Mon), 7-11; 12-3, 7-10.30 Sun
☎ (01629) 636333

Ralph Harwood

Harwood my townsman
He invented first,
Porter to rival wine and
Quench the thirst.
Porter which spreads itself
Half the world o'er,
Whose reputation rises
More and more.
As long as porter shall
Preserve its fame
Let all with gratitude our
Parish name.

18th century doggerel by a man named Gutteridge

In honour of Ralph Harwood of the Bell Brewhouse in Shoreditch, East London, the first brewer of porter or 'entire butt' beer.

Beer range varies Ⓗ
Created out of four cottages in the 18th century, this free house stocks changing guest beers from a range of brewers including Bateman, Whim and Eccleshall. The cosy, timeless bar features a real fire, wooden settles and beams, while the lounge has leather seating; both rooms are heavily adorned with brass. Cobs and sandwiches are sold at lunchtime. Handy for walkers exploring the magical Stanton Moor, the pub commemorates the fourth Duke of Devonshire's favourite racehorse.
♨Q❀▲♣P

STAVELEY

Speedwell Inn
Lowgates (A619)
6-11; 6-10.30 Sun
☎ (01246) 472252
Townes Speedwell Bitter, Best Lockoford Bitter, IPA, Pynot Porter; guest beer Ⓗ
Those who enjoy good beer in simple surroundings will love this pub. Situated in a former coal mining village on the main A619, this former John Smith's house closed in 1995 and became the home of Townes Brewery in 1998. The comfortable local was voted Chesterfield CAMRA Pub of the Year 2000, just a few months after reopening to the public. A different special beer, of over 4.5% ABV, is brewed each month. Saxon cider is sold. Q♣●⚟

SUTTON CUM DUCKMANTON

Arkwright Arms
Chesterfield Road (A632)
11-11; 12-10.30 Sun
☎ (01246) 232053 website: www.arkers.co.uk
Marston's Pedigree; guest beers Ⓗ
Friendly, mock-Tudor free house on the road from Chesterfield to historic Bolsover Castle. A U-shaped central bar serves both the public bar and the wrap-around lounge. Three real fires enhance the relaxed drinking atmosphere. Local micro-breweries are well represented in the ever-changing range of five guest ales. Good value, home-cooked food is served lunchtime and Friday evening. A grassed play area and patio tables are available. Worth searching out all year round. ♨❀◑♣P

SWADLINCOTE

Sir Nigel Gresley
Market Street (near bus station)
11-11; 12-10.30 Sun
☎ (01283) 227560
Greene King Abbot; Hop Back Summer Lightning; Shepherd Neame Spitfire; Theakston Best Bitter; guest beers Ⓗ
New Wetherspoon's pub in the town centre, next to the market, created from the semi-derelict Granville Arms. It is named after the famous railway engine designer, scion of a local family, who is buried at nearby Netherseal. The large, open-plan main drinking area, with low ceilings and a green and burnt orange decor, inevitably features pictures and photographs on a railway theme. The airy conservatory doubles as a family room. Nearby public car parks are free. Q◑♿⚟●

TIDESWELL

Star
High Street
5 (12 Sat)-11; 12-10.30 Sun
☎ (01298) 872397
Barnsley Bitter; Tetley Bitter; guest beer Ⓗ
Under new ownership, this pub is now open all day at weekends. It has also undergone refurbishment, but retains the atmosphere of a village local, with several small rooms surrounding a central bar. The guest beers are wide ranging and change rapidly. The menu often includes locally-produced beef, and trout caught in a nearby reservoir (Sunday meals are served 12-7). Bar billiards is played here.
◑♿▲♣⚟

TROWAY ❄

Gate Inn
Main Road (from B6056, Snowdon Lane, turn at Black-a-Moor)
12-3, 7-11; 12-3, 7-10.30 Sun
☎ (01246) 413280
Burtonwood Bitter, Top Hat; guest beer Ⓗ
Relax and soak up the charm of this small, friendly pub in good walking country on the south side of the Moss Valley. Burtonwood's monthly guest beer policy adds welcome variety to the beer range. There is usually a dog or two sprawled in front of the fire in the bar, keeping a watchful eye open for the resident cats. The annual marrow contest (Oct) provides much entertainment, especially in the 'Best Dressed' class. ♨Q❀♣P

WHALEY BRIDGE

Shepherd's Arms
7 Old Road
12-11; 12-10.30 Sun
☎ (01663) 732840
Banks's Original; Marston's Bitter, Pedigree, seasonal beers Ⓗ
Attractive, whitewashed stone pub, formerly a farmhouse. This is an ageless local of the type that is sadly becoming rare. It has an interesting layout with a comfortable lounge. However, the pub's pride and joy is its traditional tap room with open fire, stone flags and scrubbed tables, making it one of the best examples for miles around. The garden has recently been extended. Worth a visit. ♨Q❀◑≈♣P

WHITWELL

Mallet & Chisel
Hillside (off Bakestone Moor)
12-3, 5.30-11; 12-11 Sat; 12-10.30 Sun
☎ (01909) 720343
Mansfield Dark Mild; guest beers Ⓗ
Traditional, small village local, tucked away in the back streets, originally called the Hammer & Tool. The cosy lounge area has real fires and a beamed ceiling. Local artist, Shirley Mottershead, has depicted the pub and also Whitwell Woods in two paintings that adorn the bar front. The public bar leads off the lounge and has a pool table, darts and TV. Three guest beers change regularly. The No. 77 bus, Chesterfield-Worksop passes nearby. Evening meals are served 5.30-7.30. ♨Q❀◑≈♣P

STYLE MONITOR

Mild Ale

MILD ALE NOW CONSTITUTES such a small proportion of beer production in Britain that it's hard to imagine it was once the country's dominant beer style. Until the 1950s, it was the biggest-selling type of beer, and as late as 1959 it constituted a formidable 42 per cent of all the beer drunk in Britain. Its decline has been rapid since then, victim of the country's weakening industrial base and a general tendency to drink pale-coloured alcoholic beverages.

Pandered

It has suffered, too, from a belief that 'mild' equals 'weak'. Many brewers have pandered to this by reducing the strengths of their milds to the range of 3.2% to 3.5%. There is nothing wrong -- indeed, it is sensible – to drink beers low in alcohol, but, in an age dominated by the word 'premium', mild has suffered from an out-dated image. While it is no longer badged as a mild, Sarah Hughes Dark Ruby, brewed to an early 20th-century recipe and with an ABV of 6%, gives us a good indication of what mild ales used to taste like.

At the turn of the 20th century, when mild easily outsold porter, stout and pale ale, the average strength of beer in Britain was 5.5% ABV. The style was called mild not because it was low in alcohol but because it was less heavily hopped than other types of beer. In fact, mild ale had appeared and thrived in the late 18th and early 19th centuries as beer drinkers' tastes changed.

Guilty

Porter, the leading style of the 18th century, had earned a bad reputation as brewers were found guilty of using adulterants – some of them poisonous – to give the beer its colour and flavour. Mild found favour with drinkers who wanted a slightly sweeter and less bitter beer. Improvements in malt production enabled brewers to make a beer using better quality brown malts that were considerably cheaper than the new pale malts. Using fewer hops – which were taxed at the time – and by producing the beer quickly (whereas porters and stouts were stored for months), brewers were able to offer mild as both a tasty and cheaper alternative to existing beers. At a time when great industrial cities were appearing, with a mass working class living and working in poor conditions, mild appealed as both a cheap drink and – with a degree of unfermented sugars – one that restored energy after long hours in factories.

After its years of decline, mild has undergone a small renaissance in recent years. Many craft brewers produce milds, while large regionals such as Banks's and Brains are leading producers of the style. The Highgate Brewery in Walsall is considered by many to brew a classic mild. It is 3.4%, is brewed from a blend of pale, crystal and black malts, with maltose sugar and caramel added for flavour and fermentability. Fuggles and Goldings hops create 22 units of bitterness.

Mild doesn't have to be weak – neither does it have to be dark. In its hey-day, mild ale would come in both light and darker versions. Robinsons of Stockport still produces a succulent light mild, while McMullen's AK, even though the term mild has been dropped, is another fine example of a light mild.

DEVON

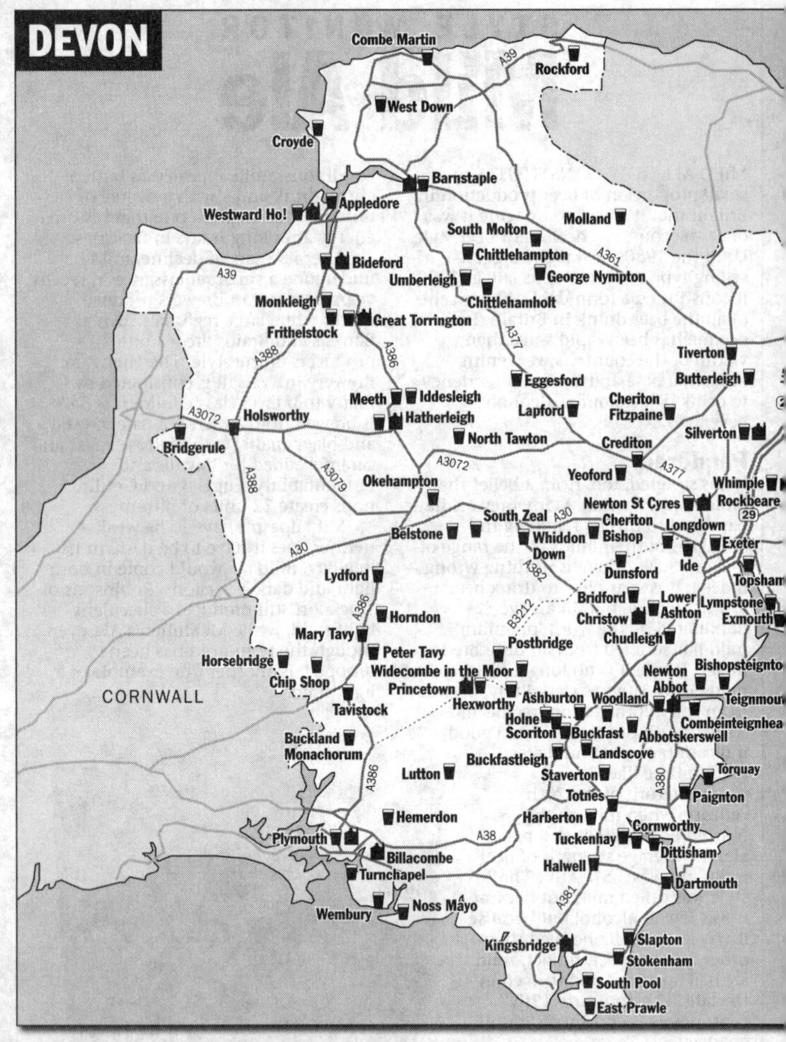

ABBOTSKERSWELL

Court Farm Inn

Wilton Way

⏲ 11-11; 12-10.30 Sun

☎ (01626) 361866

Draught Bass; Ⓖ **Flowers IPA; Fuller's London Pride; Wadworth 6X** Ⓗ

Classic, 17th-century manorial Devon longhouse, converted to a pub in 1972. Owned by a brewery group, it retains many original features such as flagstones, large fireplaces, oak beams and panelling. Its food range and daily specials are very popular, making it especially busy at lunchtimes. There is a public bar and a pleasant lawned seating area, looking across the large car park to the old church. ⌂❀◐⊟♣P

Two Mile Oak

Totnes Road

⏲ 11-11; 12-10.30 Sun

☎ (01803) 812411

Draught Bass; Flowers IPA; Greene King Abbot Ⓖ

15th-century coaching house on the main Newton Abbot-Totnes road. Superb dark wood panelling is the keynote of the public bar which is full of character. All real ales are served on gravity, but they are slightly expensive. The lounge bar includes an oak beamed dining area and stone walled alcoves. An excellent range of food is served. Large car park. ⌂Q❀◐⊟▲♣P

APPLEDORE

Beaver Inn

Irsha Street (take A386 N from Bideford)

⏲ 11-3.30, 6-11; 11-11 Sat; 12-10.30 Sun

☎ (01237) 474822

Draught Bass; guest beers Ⓗ

The Beaver has a fairly modern interior with a raised eating area overlooking the estuary. The pub name comes from an association with the fur trade in the early part of the century. There is a games room area for pool and darts. After sampling the real ales why not try one of the large collection of whiskies from around the world? One of the two guest beers is usually from a local brewery, the cider is Ostlers. ❀◐▲♣

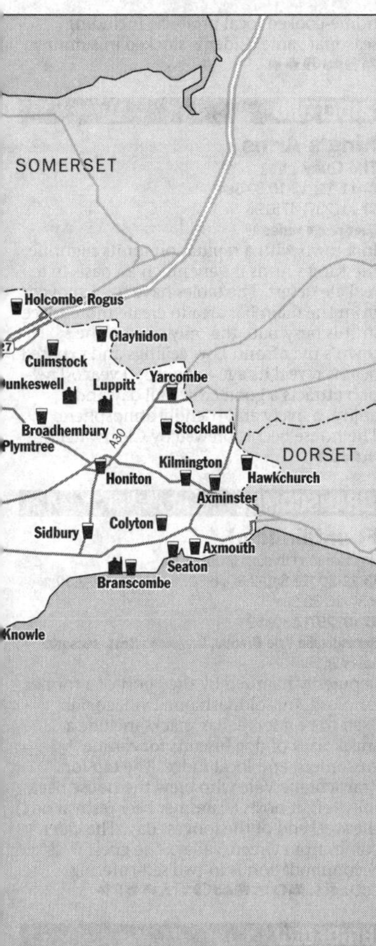

Coach & Horses

5 Market Street (take A386 N from Bideford)

12-11; 12-10.30 Sun

(01237) 474470

Fuller's London Pride; Greene King Abbot; Marston's Pedigree; Wells Bombardier; guest beer H

Friendly establishment with a selection of five local guest ales to choose from, a real fire in the bar and a games area that can be serviced from its own section of the bar. The pub dates from the 17th century and, so the story goes, was a favourite haunt of smugglers. During the week there are monthly food theme nights and quiz nights. Its traditional association with music is continued, hosting Irish folk, jazz and jam sessions.

ASHBURTON

Exeter Inn

26 West Street

11-2.30, 5-11; 12-3, 7-10.30 Sun

(01364) 652013

Badger Best; Greene King IPA H

The oldest public house in Ashburton, built in 1131 to house men building the church. The inn was frequently used by Sir Francis Drake on his many journeys from Plymouth to London. Extended in the 17th century, it features a rustic, dark wood-panelled, L-shaped bar and canopy, with two drinking areas where settles provide the main seating. A small serving hatch at the rear serves the lounge bar. Drinks are dispensed from a disused fireplace, the sides of which are formed by two old millstones.

Q

AXMINSTER

Red Lion

Lyme Street

12 (11 Thu)-2.30, 7 (5 Thu)-11; 11-11 Sat; 12-2.30, 7-10.30 Sun

(01297) 32016

Branscombe Vale Draymans Best, BVB; Otter Bitter; guest beers H

Town pub where TV is usually on in the background, often with sport – Saturdays with a big match are busy. There is a quiet dining area off the main bar, and the food is good value; an interesting specials board usually offers organic options. Children are welcome. The big car park opposite can get full on Thursday, market day. The landlord always stocks four real ales, plus a cider in summer. P

AXMOUTH

Ship Inn

Church Street

11-2.30, 6-11; 12-10.30 Sun

(01297) 21838 website: www.axmouth.com

Draught Bass; Otter Bitter, Ale H

This creeper-clad village pub was rebuilt in 1880 after a fire destroyed the original 10th-century building. Admire the collections of Guinness memorabilia and costumed dolls from around the world. The decked garden area provides a home for convalescing owls and the skittle alley doubles as a children's room. Live music is usually performed on Sunday afternoon. The Ship has been in every edition of this Guide, and run by the same family throughout that time.

Q P

INDEPENDENT BREWERIES

Barum Barnstaple
Beer Engine Newton St Cyres
Blackdown Dunkeswell
Blewitts Kingsbridge
Branscombe Vale Branscombe
Clearwater Great Torrington
Country Life Westward Ho!
Exe Valley Silverton
Jollyboat Bideford
O'Hanlon's Whimple
Otter Luppitt
Points West Plymouth
Princetown Princetown
Scattor Rock Christow
Summerskills Billacombe
Sutton Plymouth
Tally Ho! Hatherleigh
Teignworthy Newton Abbot

BARNSTAPLE

Check Inn
Castle Street
11-11; 12-10.30 Sun
(01271) 375964
Beer range varies H/G
North Devon CAMRA's Pub of the Year 1998 and 2001. The Check Inn has put real ale on the local map. The range changes constantly so it is worth popping in every day to see what is available. It is a treat to be served by people who are so interested in what you are drinking, and care about the product they are serving. Home to countless darts, pool, quiz and football teams, it has also welcomed top darts players for charity tournaments.

Reform Inn
Reform Street, Pilton
12-11; 12-10.30 Sun
(01271) 323164
Beer range varies H
The Reform has established itself at the heart of the Pilton area community, and the skittle alley out the back is the place to be for the annual beer festival, during the Green Man celebrations in July. As you walk in the pub pool is played to background music on the left, while the quieter bar with a fire is on the right. The beer comes from the award-winning Barum Brewery which is just out the back. There are bottles or plastic containers to take away.

BELSTONE

Tors
OS619935
11-2.30, 6-11 (11-11 summer); 12-3, 7-10.30 (12-10.30 summer) Sun
(01837) 840689
Sharp's Doom Bar; guest beers H
Large granite building, next to the church in an unspoilt North Dartmoor village. The long, single bar acts as a friendly local while catering for the many walkers who enjoy the open moorland or river valleys leading to the moor. The Tarka Trail passes through the village and pony trekking is also available nearby. Although the beer range varies regularly, the accent is on West Country products. The menu is based on home-cooked local produce, including seasonal game. Cider is stocked in summer.

BIDEFORD

King's Arms
The Quay
11-11; 12-10.30 Sun
(01237) 475196
Beer range varies H
In a town with a reputation for its nightlife, the King's Arms is very much an oasis in a real ale desert. The tables have been moved from the main bar area to create more space in this busy pub, the only one on the town's river front. Low ceilings and exposed beams reveal its age – some 350 years. The pub attracts a good crowd all day and enjoys a lively and friendly atmosphere. The house beer is brewed by Clearwater.

BRANSCOMBE

Fountainhead
On main road through linear village
11.30 (11 Sat)-2.30, 6.30 (6 Sat)-11; 12-2.30, 6.30-10.30 Sun
(01297) 680359
Branscombe Vale Branoc, Draymans Best, seasonal beers H
Reputedly haunted by the ghost of a former landlord, this old-fashioned village pub used to be a forge. Bar snacks include a snack pack of dog biscuits for canine customers, and local fudge. The tap for Branscombe Vale who brew the house beer, Jolly Jeff, it hosts a summer beer festival on the weekend of the longest day. The cider comes from Green Valley. The guest accommodation is in two self-catering cottages.

BRIDFORD

Bridford Inn
Off B3193, turn left in centre of village OS815864
12-2.30, 6-11; 12-3, 7-10.30 Sun
(01647) 252436
Draught Bass; Scattor Rock Teign Valley Tipple; guest beer H
Large village pub, this 17th-century Devon longhouse boasts beamed ceilings and a

INN BRIEF

BARNSTAPLE

Marshals
95 Boutport Street
11-11; 12-10.30 Sun
(01271) 376633
Draught Bass; H **guest beers** H/G
Situated in the town centre near Queen's Theatre, a local with ever-changing guest beers. Popular for lunchtime meals.

BISHOPSTEIGNTON

Bishop John de Grandisson
Clanage Street
11-2.30, 5-11; 11-11 Sat; 12-10.30 Sun
(01626) 775285
Draught Bass; Greene King Old Speckled Hen; guest beers H
Delightful old village pub: an L-shaped bar leads to a cosy, split-level lounge/diner.

CHITTLEHAMHOLT

Exeter Inn
11.30-2.30, 7-11 (11.30-11 summer); 12-3, 7-10.30 Sun
(01769) 540281
Greene King Abbot; St Austell Dartmoor Best H
Fine village pub with a reputation for serving good food. Six guest rooms available.

DITTISHAM

Red Lion
The Level
12-2.30 (3 Fri & Sat), 6-11; closed Mon; 12-3, 7-10.30 Sun
(01803) 722235
Butcombe Bitter; Palmer IPA; guest beer H
1750s coaching house, now a single bar with open fires, a children's room and patio garden. Good food.

EXETER

Royal Oak
81 Fore Street, Heavitree
11-3 (3.30 Sat), 6 (7 Sat)-11; 11-11 Fri; 12-3, 7-10.30 Sun
(01392) 254121
Brakspear Special; Otter Ale; Wadworth 6X H
This multi-roomed 14th-century ex-manor house boasts the only fully thatched roof in Exeter. Good value lunches.

Welcome Inn
Haven Banks
12-2.30, 6.30-11; 12-3, 7-10.30 Sun
(01392) 254760
Beer range varies H
Two-roomed gaslit classic, by the canal with flagged floors and an untouched, 1960s interior.

single, very wide, bar that originated from the Boots pharmacy in Exeter. Converted to a pub in 1968, it has an open-plan seating area for drinkers and diners, an area where children are allowed, plus a snug and a meeting room. The large fireplace houses a wood-burning stove and an old bread oven. An excellent selection of food caters for all tastes. Dogs are welcome. Various ciders are stocked in summer.
⌂Q⊛❀◑♣P

BRIDGERULE

Bridge Inn

Take A39 Bideford-Bude, then B3254
⊛ 12-2 (not Mon-Fri), 6.30-11; 12-3, 7-10.30 Sun
☎ (01288) 381316
Flowers Original; Sharp's Doom Bar Ⓗ
The Bridge Inn is a delightful village pub where a real fire, set in a central fireplace in the main bar greets the winter visitor. Good value snacks are served in one bar; the menu caters for children, with small portions on request. As with all traditional village pubs the Bridge is a focal point for the community, but it also enjoys a good summer trade from visitors who want to get away from the coast. There is an aviary at the rear.
⌂❀◑♣P

BROADHEMBURY

Drewe Arms

⊛ 11-3, 6-11; 12-3, 7-10.30 (closed winter eve) Sun
☎ (01404) 841267
Otter Bitter, Bright, Ale, Head Ⓖ
Picturesque, relatively unspoilt, thatched, Grade II listed inn, set in a village of cob and thatched cottages, owned by an offshoot of the Drewe family, who own Castle Drogo in the Teign Valley. Predominantly a food pub, the award-winning restaurant specialises in fish dishes (booking essential). The old-fashioned public bar is very small and displays cinema memorabilia, while the main bar features wickerwork. The beers are served direct from the casks housed in a wooden chilled cabinet.
⌂Q❀◑⊟♣♣P

BUCKFAST

Abbey Inn

Off A38 on route to Buckfast Abbey
⊛ 11-2.30, 6-11; 12-10.30 Sun
☎ (01364) 642343
St Austell IPA, Dartmoor Best, HSD Ⓗ
Large inn, situated inside the Dartmoor National Park, close to the famous Buckfast Abbey. The spacious oak-panelled bar is traditionally furnished, creating a warm, welcoming interior. The large dining room offers an excellent range of food. In an idyllic setting, the outside terrace overlooks the unspoilt River Dart, and there are many visitor attractions close by.
⌂Q❀⇌◑♿ÅP⊘

BUCKFASTLEIGH

White Hart

2 Plymouth Road
⊛ 12-3 (not Mon), 6-11; 12-11 Fri & Sat; 12-3, 7-10.30 Sun
☎ (01364) 642337 website: www.stayanight.com
Greene King Abbot; Teignworthy Beachcomber; guest beer Ⓗ
Pleasant pub with a single, open-plan bar and separate dining area, plus a restaurant that is not open all year. Outside, a large courtyard provides additional seating and a barbecue in summer. A good range of fresh, home-cooked food is served at reasonable prices. The house beer is brewed in Teignworthy. The guest ales are varied, sourced from all over the country with one always on tap; Sam's Dry Cider is supplied by Winkleigh. ⌂⊛❀⇌◑♣♣⍻

BUCKLAND MONACHORUM

Drake Manor Inn

The Village
⊛ 11.30-2.30 (3 Sat), 6.30-11; 12-3, 7-10.30 Sun
☎ (01822) 853892
Courage Best Bitter; Greene King Abbot; Sharp's Doom Bar Ⓗ
16th-century, two-bar village pub. The public bar has a small cellar bar at the rear that admits children. There is a relaxed lounge/snug bar and a restaurant that enjoys a good reputation, using local produce as much as possible for its 'specials'. A peaceful garden stands next to a

GEORGE NYMPTON

Castle Inn
12-2.30, 5-11; 12-2.30, 7-10.30 Sun
(01769) 572633
Barum XTC, Jester Ⓗ
Comfortable, friendly village local with a growing reputation for food. The second Barum Brewery is across the car park.

HATHERLEIGH

George Hotel
11-11; 12.30-10.30 Sun
(01837) 810454
Draught Bass; guest beer (summer) Ⓖ
Coaching inn with a restaurant. The front bar has a 'Mad Monk' theme, with a house beer from St Austell.

HEXWORTHY

Forest Inn
12-3, 6-11 (may extend summer); 11-11 Sat; 12-10.30 Sun
(01364) 631211
Teignworthy Reel Ale; guest beer Ⓗ
Isolated, attractive inn on Dartmoor, a haven for walkers, riders and anglers. Meals, snacks and accommodation available.

HOLNE

Church House Inn
12-2.30 (3 Sat), 7 (6 Sat)-11; 12-3, 7-10.30 Sun
(01364) 631208
Butcombe Bitter; guest beers Ⓗ
Grade II listed, 14th-century, two-bar inn in the National Park. Excellent local fresh food. Families welcome.

HONITON

Three Tuns
133 High Street
11-11; 12-4, 7-10.30 Sun
(01404) 42902
Draught Bass Ⓗ
360-year-old coaching inn in this famous lace-making town. Two cosy bars with comfy seating; pub lunches.

HORNDON

Elephant's Nest Inn
11.30-2.30, 6.30-11; 12-2.30, 7-10.30 Sun
(01822) 810273
Boddingtons Bitter; Palmer IPA; St Austell HSD; guest beers Ⓗ
Picturesque, 16th-century pub affording superb moorland views. The bar features elephantine items; two family rooms.

stream. Log burners warm both bars in winter; in summer, the floral displays are impressive. The pub can be reached by Citybus No. 55 from Yelverton (daytime service).

BUTTERLEIGH

Butterleigh Inn

12-2.30, 6 (5 Fri)-11; 12-3, 7-10.30 Sun
(01884) 855407
website: www.thebutterleighinn.co.uk
Cotleigh Tawny, Barn Owl, Old Buzzard; guest beers (occasional) H

This is what a country pub should be. In a charming spot, this splendid 400-year-old Devon cob building is full of character in each of its rooms, including a snug, main bar and an adjoining lounge/dining area. The open fire in an ancient fireplace, helps make this a warm, welcoming place. In summer, enjoy the views of the surrounding rolling hills from the attractive secluded garden. Old Buzzard is often replaced by guest ales from local breweries.

CHERITON BISHOP

Old Thatch Inn

Just off A30 from Exeter
11.30-3, 6-11; 12-3, 7-10.30 Sun
(01647) 24204
Branscombe Vale Branoc; Otter Ale; guest beer H

Large 16th-century thatched free house, on the north-eastern edge of Dartmoor with beams and an open stone fireplace. The pub is on several levels, comprising a small bar area, a larger area with tables and a no-smoking room. The three ales come from independent breweries with at least two from the south-west. The à la carte menu offers a varied selection of food; en-suite accommodation is also available. The pub holds an annual beer festival in May.

CHERITON FITZPAINE

Ring of Bells

11-2.30 (not winter Mon-Fri), 6.30-11; 11-3.30, 7-11 (11-10.30 summer) Sun
(01363) 866374
Beer range varies H

This charming, 14th-century inn is situated in beautiful countryside. It boasts a thatched roof, real fires and exposed beams. The central bar serves both the pub and the dining area. It is the hub of the Crediton Folk Festival held annually in the village in spring. Boules and skittles are played. Excellent bar/restaurant menus are prepared by a progressive chef – look out for theme nights. Three beers are available in the winter, up to six in summer.

CHIP SHOP

Chip Shop Inn

Off A384, 3 miles W of Tavistock OS437751
12-2.30, 5-11; 12-10.30 Sun
(01822) 832322
Draught Bass; Sharp's Doom Bar; guest beers H

This remote, popular pub offers a friendly welcome to visitors and locals alike. Chip Shop was once a busy mining village where the miners exchanged their wages of company-issued chips for goods. The L-shaped bar boasts a fine collection of mirrors. The skittle alley is often in demand and supports two teams. The garden has a children's playhouse. The pub is dog-friendly.

CHITTLEHAMPTON

Bell Inn

The Square (take B3227 from South Molton to Umberleigh)
11-3, 7-10.30; 11-11 Sat; 12-3, 7-10.30 Sun
(01769) 540368
Beer range varies H/G

The only remaining pub in a village which at the turn of the century had at least six public houses and a brewery. You are assured of a warm welcome and a fine selection of up to six ales, either on beer engine or gravity. There is much local activity here, particularly in the cricket season. A newly-built conservatory restaurant overlooks the garden and an excellent home-cooked menu makes this a pub well worth visiting. Cider is stocked in summer.

INN BRIEF

MARY TAVY

Mary Tavy Inn
Lane Head
11.45-3, 6-11; 12-3, 7-10.30 Sun
(01822) 810326
Princetown Jail Ale; guest beer H
Cosy, friendly pub on edge of Dartmoor, reputedly haunted by the son of a blacksmith. Good views from garden.

MEETH

Bull & Dragon
11-3, 6-11; 12-3, 7-10.30 Sun
(01837) 810325
Adnams Broadside; Ring o' Bells Bodmin Boar; guest beer H
14th-century thatched inn with a small bar, restaurant and games room. Accommodation available; good food.

MOLLAND

London Inn
12-2.30, 6-11; 12-2.30, 7-10.30 Sun
(01769) 550269
Cotleigh Tawny; Exmoor Gold G
Delightful old village pub and restaurant, popular with visitors to Exmoor. Can be very busy in the shooting season.

MONKLEIGH

Bell Inn
12-11; 12-10.30 Sun
(01805) 622338
Barum XTC, Original H
Focal point of the village, this partially thatched pub is based on a 15th-century building. Good garden.

PLYMOUTH

Brasserie
Ocean Quay Marina, Richmond Walk, Devonport
11-3, 7-11; 12-3, 7-10.30 (not winter eve) Sun
(01752) 500008
Summerskills Best Bitter H
Restaurant that sells real ales, situated in a large marina with outdoor seating. Locally caught fish is a speciality.

London Inn
Church Road, Plympton St Maurice
11-11; 12-10.30 Sun
(01752) 337025
Courage Best Bitter; Greene King Ruddles County; guest beer H
Two-bar, 17th-century former coaching inn set in conservation area of much interest. Regular food nights feature ethnic cuisines.

CHUDLEIGH

Bishop Lacy

Fore Street (signed off A38)
⏲ 11-11; 12-10.30 Sun
☎ (01626) 854585
website: thebishoplacyinn@btinternet.com
Banks's Bitter; Courage Directors; Ⓗ **Princetown Jail Ale; Skinner's Cornish Knocker; guest beers** Ⓖ

Grade II listed, 14th-century church house, now a bustling local. It has built up a reputation for serving a good selection of real ales, mostly on gravity. The pub has two bars, both with open fires. Home-cooked food is served in a no-smoking restaurant area. Beer festivals are a regular event at this local CAMRA Pub of the Year 2000 (and regional winner in 1998). Children (and dogs) are welcome.
♨Q❀◐◑⊟♣P

CLAYHIDON

Half Moon Inn

⏲ 12-2.30, 7-11 (closed Mon); 12-3 (closed eve) Sun
☎ (01823) 680291
Cotleigh Tawny, Old Buzzard; guest beers Ⓗ

This traditional country inn is set in the Blackdown Hills, close to the Somerset border, affording outstanding views over the Culm Valley. It is very popular with both locals and visitors to the area. The Half Moon is believed to have originated as a cottage, built by stone masons for their own use while building the church in the 18th century, and was first known as the Church House. ♨Q♉❀◐◑♿⛺♣P⚡

COLYTON

Gerrard Arms

Rosemary Lane
⏲ 11-3, 6-11; 12-3, 7-10.30 Sun
☎ (01297) 552588
Draught Bass; Ⓗ **Branscombe Vale Branoc;** Ⓖ **guest beers** Ⓗ

Busy, one-bar pub next to the church in a delightful little town, with lots of lovely old cottages in tangled narrow streets and alleyways. Popular with locals, it has a well-used skittle alley at the rear, and a garden for families. The home-made food is good value; a traditional roast is served on Sunday. It is possible to take the tramway from Seaton in summer, with an easy walk from Colyton station. It hosts occasional mini beer festivals. ❀◐◑⛺⊖

COMBEINTEIGNHEAD

Wild Goose

Between Newton Abbot and Shaldon, S of Teign estuary
⏲ 11.30-3, 6.30-11; 12-3, 6.30-10.30 Sun
☎ (01626) 872241
Beer range varies Ⓗ

17th-century free house at the heart of the village. The long single bar has large open fireplaces and seating areas at each end. There are normally six constantly changing ales, nearly always from small independent breweries, many of them local. On the other side of the pub is a recently revamped dining area, benefitting from rural views across the River Teign. All food is home cooked, with fresh fish and vegetarian options always available.
♨Q❀◐◑♿⛺♣P

COMBE MARTIN

Castle Inn

High Street (near town hall)
⏲ 12-11; 12-10.30 Sun
☎ (01271) 883706 website: www.thecastleinn.com
Draught Bass; Worthington Bitter; guest beers Ⓗ

Beer drinkers' paradise, with two ever-changing guest ales (tending to be 5% ABV or above) sourced from micro-breweries all over the UK. A display of previous guest beer clips keeps a good record. The bar floor is reclaimed floorboards and railway sleepers, while the bar itself has a large elm top. The pub has a sound-proofed no-smoking restaurant, serving exclusively local produce (no meals Tue lunch). In the back of the pub darts, pool and skittles can all be played. ♨♉❀⛟◐◑⛺♣P

CORNWORTHY

Hunter's Lodge Inn

⏲ 11.30-2.30, 6.30-11; 12-3, 7-10.30 Sun
☎ (01803) 732204 website: www.hunterslodgeinn.com
Teignworthy Reel Ale; guest beers Ⓗ

In the middle of a Devon village, mentioned in the Domesday Book, the Hunter's Lodge is all a village pub should be, complete with resident ghost. Built in 1740, it opened in 1804 as the New Inn, became the Globe in 1880, and finally the Hunter's Lodge. Characterised by low, beamed ceilings and log fires, quiz and jazz nights compete for space with local meetings, but there is plenty of room for parking. ♨Q❀◐◑♿♣●P⚡

CREDITON

Crediton Inn

28a Mill Street (opp. Somerfield on Tiverton road)
⏲ 11-11; 12-2, 7-10.30 Sun
☎ (01363) 772882 website: www.crediton-inn.co.uk
Draught Bass; Sharp's Doom Bar; guest beers Ⓗ

Friendly free house, just off the town centre, known locally as the Kirton Inn. Four ales are always available and the two guests are often from south-western independents. A modest menu of good value cooked meals is served. The pub has its own angling club and skittle alley, and hosts occasional quiz/theme nights. This is a real gem, but do not be tempted by the chilli sherry!
◐◑⇌♣P

CROYDE

Thatched Barn Inn

14 Hobbs Hill
⏲ 11-11; 12-10.30 Sun
☎ (01271) 890349 website: www.thethatch.com
Barum Longboat; Draught Bass; St Austell HSD; guest beer Ⓗ

Outstandingly popular pub drawing a broad spectrum of customers, including, in season, surfers recovering from catching waves at the famous Croyde Beach nearby. This late medieval barn, was converted into a pub in 1978, retaining much of the original structure. It is a fair size, but sympathetic divisions of space and soft lighting afford an intimate atmosphere normally enjoyed by much smaller venues. Happily, its renowned food does not usurp drinkers' space.
❀⛟◐◑⛺♣●P

...ley Inn

...11 (12-11 summer Sat); 12-3, 7-10.30 Sun
...34) 840354
...ange varies G

...is 300-year-old inn stands by the River Culm where it emerges from the Blackdown Hills. The car park was formerly the railway sidings of the Tiverton Light Railway – the pub was previously called the Railway Inn. The menu is based on local produce, often free range and organic. Up to six real ales change regularly. The cobbled yard houses a converted barn used for B&B or holiday lets. The pub may stay open all day in fine weather.

DARTMOUTH

Cherub Inn

13 Higher Street
11-2.30, 5.30-11 (11-11 summer); 12-10.30 Sun
☎ (01803) 832571 website: www.the-cherub.co.uk
Beer range varies H

Reputed to be the oldest house in Dartmouth this Grade II listed building started life as a wool merchant's house, becoming a pub in 1972. A small, cosy, oak beamed bar is welcoming and friendly to visitors and locals alike. A steep spiral staircase leads to the restaurant which has earned a good reputation for local fish. Three beers (two in winter) mainly from south-western breweries complement the house beer from Summerskills.

Windjammer Inn

23 Victoria Road (opp. old market hall)
11-3, 5.15-11; 12-3, 6-10.30 Sun
☎ (01803) 832228
Draught Bass; Princetown Dartmoor IPA; guest beers H

A typical town pub exterior conceals a large single bar, furnished in light coloured woods. The pub bears a nautical and yachting theme, providing yachting information on a blackboard. It has a growing reputation for good quality, reasonably-priced food. The two regular beers are supplemented by an ever-changing range of guests from all over the country.

DUNSFORD

Royal Oak

7 miles W of Exeter, on Moretonhampstead road
12-2.30, 6.30 (7 Mon)-11; 12.30-2.30, 7-10.30 Sun
☎ (01647) 252256 website: www.troid.co.uk
Dartmoor Best Bitter; Greene King Abbot; Princetown Jail Ale; Sharp's Own; guest beers H

Popular Victorian local on the edge of Dartmoor National Park. The single bar incorporates three areas, plus a lower room with a pool table. Dining areas at either end of the bar serve a range of reasonably-priced home-cooked food from a regular menu and chalkboards (Tue is fish and chip night). Spring and autumn beer festivals feature 12 different beers, while Friday is mystery beer night, at £1.50 a pint. Regular visitors come to stay from all over the UK.

EAST PRAWLE

Pig's Nose Inn

12-2.30, 7 (6.30 Sat)-11; 12-3, 7-10.30 Sun
☎ (01548) 511209 website: www.pigsnoseinn.co.uk
Fuller's London Pride; Sutton Comfort; guest beers (summer) G

Three-roomed old smugglers' inn, set on the village green. Children and dogs are welcome, adults are asked to behave themselves. A haven for birdwatchers and coastal walkers alike, home-made meals are produced, using local ingredients. Occasional live music at weekends makes this a popular venue.

EGGESFORD

Eggesford Country Hotel

On A377, near station
11-11; 12-10.30 Sun
☎ (01769) 580345 website: www.eggesfordhotel.co.uk
Badger Best; Cotleigh Tawny; Scattor Rock Teign Valley Tipple; guest beers H

Set in the beautiful Taw Valley, in 10 acres of gardens and river walks, this is a family-run hotel where the Fox and Hounds bar serves guest ales. These tend to be from local brewers. During the season it is popular with fishermen, so salmon and trout appear regularly on the extensive home-cooked menu. A beer festival is held annually on the first weekend in August.

INN BRIEF

ROCKBEARE

Jack in the Green
11-3, 5.30-11; 12-10.30 Sun
(01404) 822240
Cotleigh Tawny; Otter Ale; Theakston Best Bitter; guest beers (summer) H
Mainly a restaurant, serving excellent, varied food and good beer. Home of Exeter Balloons (hot air).

SEATON

King's Arms
55 Fore Street
11-3, 6-11; 11-11 Sat; 12-10.30 Sun
(01297) 23431
Branscombe Vale Branoc, BVB; Flower's Original H
Neat little pub on the edge of town, popular with locals for beer and food.

STAVERTON

Sea Trout Inn
11-3, 6-11 (11-11 Fri & Sat in summer); 12-3, 7-10.30 (12-10.30 summer) Sun
(01803) 762274
Palmer Dorset Gold, IPA, 200 H
15th-century pub: two bars and a good restaurant, near the River Dart and preserved steam railway. Accommodation available.

STOKENHAM

Tradesman's Arms
6.30-11 (not Mon); 12-3 Sun
(01548) 580313
Adnams Bitter; guest beer H
Two-roomed beamed village pub, very popular with locals for food, but limited opening hours. Sells Heron Valley cider.

TAVISTOCK

Trout & Tipple
Parkwood Road
12-2.30 (11-3 summer), 6-11; 12-3, 7 (6 summer)-10.30 Sun
(01822) 618886
Princetown Jail Ale; guest beer H
Near a trout fishery; a traditional bar, games room and large conservatory/dining room. Children's certificate until 9pm.

TEIGNMOUTH

Blue Anchor
Teign Street
11-11; 12-10.30 Sun
(01626) 772741
Beer range varies H
Small local near the docks. A single bar with pool table, dartboard and juke box, serving up to seven ales.

Let the train take the strain – the station is just 150 yards away.
♨⛵❀⇄◐♿⇌♣P

EXETER ❄

Brook Green
31 Well Street
⊙ 12-2.30, 5-11; 11-3, 6-11 Sat; 12-3, 7-10.30 Sun
☎ (01392) 495699
Butcombe Bitter; guest beers Ⓗ
Friendly, community local, always offering six beers at reasonable prices. Close to St James Park football ground, it is student-friendly and furthers its community spirit by fielding two league darts teams and hosting regular meetings of the 'Victorians' cricket club. It has a very small car park and parking in the vicinity is difficult. However, it is only 100 yards from St James station on the Exmouth line from the central station.
Q⇌(St James)♣

Double Locks Hotel
Canal Banks (follow lane from Marsh Barton trading estate) OS933901
⊙ 11-11; 12-10.30 Sun
☎ (01392) 256947
Adnams Broadside; Branscombe Vale Branoc; Everards Original; Ⓖ **Young's Bitter, Special;** Ⓗ **guest beers** Ⓖ
On the banks of Exeter's historic canal, with extensive outdoor areas, this famous pub is popular with walkers and cyclists. Dogs are welcome. It hosts live music (Thu, Fri and Sat). A wide range of food is served all day. New owners, Young's have wisely not attempted to alter any aspect, although improved toilets and kitchens are planned. A stronger influence of Young's beers is evident but there is still plenty of choice, with up to 12 cask ales available. ♨❀◐●P

Great Western Hotel
St David's Station Approach
⊙ 11-11; 12-10.30 Sun
☎ (01392) 274039
website: www.greatwesternhotel.co.uk
Adnams Broadside; Draught Bass; Branscombe Vale Branoc, Exe Valley Dob's Best Bitter; Fuller's London Pride; Taylor Landlord Ⓗ
It takes a very special landlord to turn an old railway hotel into a mecca for real ale. A choice of 10 ales all week increases by possibly another four at weekends. The emphasis is on West Country brews, but others are sourced from all over the UK. No wonder this is the local CAMRA Pub of the Year 2002 (again). The August festival offers up to 150 ales. An excellent menu with generous portions and reasonable prices is a bonus. ❀⇄◐⇌(St Davids) P

Hour Glass
21 Melbourne Street
⊙ 12-2.30, 5.30-11; 12-2.30, 6.30-10.30 Sun
☎ (01392) 258722
Draught Bass; Greene King Abbot; Otter Bitter; guest beer Ⓗ
Delightful back-street pub in a 19th-century artisans' terrace. It has quietly been here for over a century, and the name certainly goes back at least to the 1930s. Over the past couple of years new landlords have made a serious effort to promote ales, alongside its thriving food trade which includes seafood as a speciality and imaginative vegetarian dishes. Unspoilt old timbers and panelling create a warm atmosphere in one of Exeter's hidden gems. Q◐

Well House
Cathedral Yard
⊙ 11-11; 12-5 Sun
☎ (01392) 223611
Skinner's Ice Blonde; guest beers Ⓗ
Oasis in the city centre, this single-roomed pub overlooks the cathedral. Why not visit the Roman well in the cellar, but note you are not alone – a skeleton is there to keep you company. This bar is vibrant, with a cross-section of customers, and can get very busy. Real ales are to the fore, with regular imaginative beer festivals organised. Rich's cider is stocked. ◐⇌(Central) ●

EXMOUTH

Bicton
5 Bicton Street (opp. Trinity Church)
⊙ 11-11; 12-10.30 Sun
☎ (01395) 272589 website: bictoninn@lineone.net
Draught Bass; Branscombe Vale Branoc; guest beer Ⓗ
This is a good example of a small pub serving the local community, that has survived in a town dominated by pubs for tourists and the younger age group. This lively, friendly corner pub offers a warm welcome. The main room is supplemented by a pool room. Other pub games are very popular, including darts, cards and dominoes. All beers are reasonably priced. A good value set meal is served weekday lunchtimes – no other food is available.
◐⇌♣

Powder Monkey
2-2A The Parade
⊙ 11-11; 12-10.30 Sun
☎ (01395) 280090
Courage Directors; Hop Back Summer Lightning; Shepherd Neame Spitfire; Theakston Best Bitter; guest beers Ⓗ
Wetherspoon's town-centre pub is named after local Nancy Perriam, who was a powder monkey (naval slang, normally for young boys, who filled shells and cartridges). Inside, read the history of some of Exmouth's more famous inhabitants including Lord Rolle and Lady Nelson. Popular with all ages during the day and early evening, it is frequented by the under 30s at night. The patio is very popular in summer. Of the five guest ales, one or two are always from major local brewers.
♨Q⛵⇄◐♿⇌⅟✔

FRITHLESTOCK

Clinton Arms
Off A386 from Torrington, or A388 Holsworthy-Bideford road
⊙ 12-3, 6-11; 12-3, 7 (6 winter)-10.30 Sun
☎ (01805) 623279
Clearwater Cavalier; guest beer Ⓗ
17th-century inn by the village green named after Lord Clinton, it comprises one small bar with an adjoining lounge and a pool room. There is also a large walled garden and a function room. The ruins opposite are a medieval priory and can be visited (by permission). Close to the Tarka Trail; fishing permits are available at the bar for the mile and a

half stretch of river that provides a catch for the pub menu.
♨⚇❀⛺◑◗▲♣P

GREAT TORRINGTON

Black Horse Inn

High Street
⊛ 11-3, 6-11; 11-11 Sat; 12-4, 7-10.30 Sun
☎ (01805) 622121
Courage Best Bitter, Directors; John Smith's Bitter; guest beer Ⓗ
This 16th-century coaching inn was used by Hopton and Fairfax during the Civil War Battle of Torrington. It has seen some modest alterations since then, but retains its atmosphere. The oak-panelled lounge wall on the right is probably the oldest part of the inn. The ceiling of the bar is decorated with guest ale pump clips. The portrait by the fire was painted by a local artist after New Year's eve 2000. The 70-seater restaurant has just been refurbished.
♨⛺◑◗♣

HALWELL

Old Inn

On A381, Totnes-Kingsbridge road
⊛ 11-3, 6-11; 12-3, 6-10.30 Sun
☎ (01803) 712329
website: www.the-old-inn.freeserve.co.uk
RCH PG Steam, East Street Cream Ⓗ
Friendly, family-run roadside pub, with a warm village atmosphere, situated next to the beautiful Norman church. The present inn was built in 1874 after the original Old Inn had been destroyed by fire in the 17th century. The single bar has seating, and dining tables in the bar area; there is also a no-smoking dining room. Excellent food at reasonable prices features oriental dishes as a speciality. En-suite accommodation and cider in summer complete the picture.
♨Q⚇❀⛺◑◗♣●P⊬

HARBERTON

Church House Inn

Off main Totnes-Kingsbridge road
⊛ 12-3, 6-11; 12-3, 7-10.30 Sun
☎ (01803) 863707
Draught Bass; guest beers Ⓗ
Friendly, 12th-century pub, originally built to house the masons working on the church. It then became a chantry house for monks. In 1327 the Abbot handed the property to the poor and in 1950 it passed out of the church's hands. A Tudor window frame and latticed window containing panes of 13th century hand-made glass can still be seen. Heavy beams and a flagstoned floor characterise the bar and dining area. An extensive range of excellent food is available. ♨Q⚇⛺◑◗●P⊬

HAWKCHURCH

Old Inn

⊛ 11.30 (12 winter)-3.30, 6.30-11; 12-3.30, 7-10.30 Sun
☎ (01297) 678309
Cotleigh Tawny, Barn Owl, Snowy Ale; Flowers Original; guest beers Ⓗ
This village pub, opposite the church, is the only one for miles. Although food-oriented, people who just want a quiet pint are welcome. There's a good car park behind the pub, but to reach it you need to go through the village hall car park a little way down the road. What was the skittle alley at the back now houses a model railway layout. Open most weekends – to find out if it's open 'phone (01297) 678398. Q❀◑◗P

HEMERDON

Miner's Arms

Between Cornwood and Plympton
⊛ 11-2.30, 5.30-11; 12-3, 7-10.30 Sun
☎ (01752) 343252
Draught Bass; Ⓗ/Ⓖ **Sutton XSB; guest beers** Ⓗ
Completely unspoilt and friendly village pub that has been run by the same family since 1870. The main bar, replete with beams and flagstoned floor, bears many mementos from the days when the area and pub were connected with the now-disused Hemerdon mine. Leading off the bar is a smaller drinking area that has a window overlooking the well-kept garden. The pub stands on a hill, commanding a good view over Plymouth, especially at night when the city is lit up. ♨Q❀♿♣P

HOLCOMBE ROGUS

Prince of Wales

Centre of village
⊛ 12-3 (not winter Mon-Thu), 6.30-11; 12-3, 7-10.30 Sun
☎ (01823) 672070
Cotleigh Tawny; Otter Bitter; guest beers Ⓗ
Pleasant, 17th-century country pub, not far from the Grand Western Canal, which is popular with cyclists and walkers. It has unusual cash register handpumps which have been lovingly restored. The guest beers change regularly and cider is sold in summer. A large restaurant area offers home-cooked food (including vegetarian options) or you can relax in the lounge by the log-burning stove. A skittle alley, pool and darts areas and an attractive walled garden complete the picture. ♨Q❀◑◗♣●P

HOLSWORTHY

King's Arms ☆

The Square
⊛ 11-11; 12-3, 7-10.30 Sun
☎ (01409) 253517
Draught Bass; Sharp's Doom Bar Ⓗ
Whichever way you enter this pub you are certain of a warm welcome and fine ale. This 17th-century inn comprises three bars, with entrances on two streets, resulting in two postal codes! The snug and public bars are separated by a snob screen – an original feature. The displays of pub and beer memorabilia are noteworthy, particularly the pictures. ♨Q

HORSEBRIDGE

Royal Inn

Between B3362 and A388
⊛ 12-3, 7-11; 12-3, 7-10.30 Sun
☎ (01822) 870214 website: www.royalinn.co.uk
Draught Bass; Sharp's Doom Bar; guest beers Ⓗ
The inn stands on the banks of the River Tamar by an historic bridge linking Devon with Cornwall. Monks built the bridge and the pub – originally as a nunnery. It stands

in an acre of ground with summer terraces. The main bar is half-panelled; the lounge features hops and horse brasses, a third room is no-smoking. Up to six guest ales are stocked in summer. Bar billiards is played here. ⋒Q❀◑♣P

IDDESLEIGH

Duke of York

Next to church
11-11; 12-10.30 Sun
☎ (01837) 810253

Adnams Broadside; Cotleigh Tawny; guest beers Ⓖ

A bit off the beaten track, but once found never forgotten. This 15th-century village inn does not have juke boxes, fruit machines or karaoke nights, but with old beams, inglenooks and a friendly homely atmosphere, it is the perfect place to relax and enjoy good food and ale. Much of the produce for the kitchen comes from the landlord's farm and an extensive menu is available all day everyday. The cider (Sam's) is produced by Winkleigh.
⋒Q❀◑♣

IDE

Poacher's Inn

11.30-2.30 (not Mon), 5.30-11; 12-4, 7-10.30 Sun
☎ (01392) 273847

Draught Bass; Branscombe Vale Branoc; Otter Ale; guest beers Ⓗ

This traditional village pub, with its welcoming, friendly atmosphere, is found in a small village on the outskirts of Exeter, near the A30. It is well known for its interesting menu of varied fare, including fish and seafood specials, all at reasonable prices. It hosts occasional live music (Wed eve, usually mid-month). The guest beers are sourced from West Country breweries.
⋒Q❀◑♿P⚟

KILMINGTON

New Inn

The Hill (100 yds S of A35)
11-2.30, 6-11; 12-3, 7-10.30 Sun
☎ (01297) 33376

Palmers BB, Dorset Gold (summer), **IPA** Ⓗ

In a wonderful location overlooking the Axe Valley, the safe garden houses many aviaries and boasts impressive summer flower displays. The photogenic thatched building dates from the 14th century, but it only became a pub around 1800, hence the name. It has been in every edition of this Guide. Well supported by locals, with a good skittle alley, it serves snacks lunchtime, a full evening menu, daily specials and Sunday roasts. No children in the bar, but they are welcome in a small no-smoking dining area or family room.
⋒Q❀◑♣P

KNOWLE

Dog & Donkey

24 Knowle Village
11-2.30 (3 Fri & Sat), 6-11; 12-3, 7-10.30 Sun
☎ (01395) 442021

Draught Bass; guest beers Ⓖ

Lively, friendly, village pub, retaining many original features. Note the old photos of the village on the walls. A haven for walkers and cyclists, it is free from electronic music, but hosts regular music evenings, singalongs and live bands. The guest ales change weekly. Local produce features on an interesting, great value menu. Skittles, pool and euchre teams play regularly. The pub has achieved an award of excellence from the local Environmental Health Department.
⋒Q❀◑♿♣P⚟

LANDSCOVE

Live & Let Live Inn

On main road through village
11-2.30, 6.30-11; 12-3, 7-10.30 Sun
☎ (01803) 762663

Draught Bass; Teignworthy Reel Ale; guest beer Ⓗ

Small, beamed village pub: a wood-panelled L-shaped bar, with a small drinking area close to the bar, and two dining alcoves with beamed doorways. Large stone fireplaces make attractive focal points. A small walled garden at the front is complemented by an orchard garden next to the car park, opposite the pub. A good selection of home cooked food is served at reasonable prices. Originally built as a house, it became a pub around 1840.
⋒Q❀◑P

LAPFORD

Old Malt Scoop Inn

Signed from A377
12-3, 6-11; 11-11 Sat; 12-4, 7-10.30 Sun
☎ (01363) 83330

Adnams Broadside; Ⓖ **Marston's Pedigree; Sharp's Doom Bar; guest beer** Ⓗ

Popular village local, about a mile from the A377 and Lapford station. Dating from the 16th century, it was formerly a coaching inn and now comprises many rooms. A smallish public bar area is dominated by a large inglenook and adjacent bread oven in what used to be the kitchen. It also has a large dining area (no eve meals Tue), a games room and a skittle alley. The cider, Cheddar Valley, is from Thatcher's.
⋒Q❀◑♣P

LONGDOWN

Lamb Inn

On B3212, 2 miles from Exeter towards Mortenhampstead
11-11; 12-10.30 Sun
☎ (01392) 811711

Courage Best Bitter; Greene King Old Speckled Hen; Teignworthy Beachcomber; guest beer Ⓗ

Substantial stone building in a small village amid rolling hillside, opened out inside into a single area, one part is separated as a popular, no-smoking restaurant. The main area, served from a central bar with timber panelling and solid oak bartop, is carpeted and furnished with comfortable settees, Chesterfields, and plenty of bar stools. Dogs are welcome in the bar. No food is served on Monday. ⋒Q❀◑♣P

LOWER ASHTON

Manor Inn

Off B3193, Teign Valley road
12-2, 6.30-11; closed Mon; 12-2.30, 7-10.30 Sun
☎ (01647) 252304

Princetown Jail Ale; RCH Pitchfork; Teignworthy Reel Ale; guest beer [H]

A Devon gem: pitched in the heart of the Teign Valley on the edge of the National Park, it affords outstanding views over Dartmoor. Two bars provide a good balance of dining and drinking areas. Four real ales are always available, plus a Christmas special for the festive period. An excellent menu of home-cooked food is supplemented by extensive chalkboard specials (fish, steaks, etc) and West Country cheeses, all at reasonable prices. Families can enjoy the sunny garden.

⛫Q❀◑⊟▲♣P

LUTTON

Mountain Inn

Old Chapel Road (off Plympton-Cornwood road)
OS596594
⏲ 11-2.30 (3 Sat), 7 (6 summer)-11; 12-3, 7-10.30 Sun
☎ (01752) 837247
Sutton XSB; guest beers [H]

Traditional village pub on the edge of Dartmoor. Popular with locals and visitors alike, it is frequented by horse riders. The house beer, Dark Side is brewed by Summerskills; cider is stocked in summer. The interior is distinctive with cob walls and a large fireplace. The pub name is a corruption of a local landowner's name, Montain. Boules is played in summer and the location is convenient for visiting Sparkwell Wildlife Park.

⛫Q♉❀◐♣P

LYDFORD

Mucky Duck Inn

Lydford Gorge (next to White Lady Falls)
⏲ 11-11; 12-10.30 Sun
☎ (01822) 820208
Sharp's Doom Bar; guest beer [H]

The duck theme was revived when the present licensees acquired this 170-year-old property in 1993. It has been completely refurbished and now features an attractive bar with a display of ducks of all varieties (and a lone leprechaun). 1960s music and a relaxed atmosphere are the norm. The pub has bar billiards, a skittle alley and a garden, unfenced to the car park. Guest accommodation is in four self-catering holiday flats. Meals are served all day.

⛫Q♉❀⇔◑♣P

LYMPSTONE

Redwing

Church Road
⏲ 11.30-3, 6-11; 11.30-11 Sat; 12-10.30 Sun
☎ (01395) 222156
Greene King Abbot; Palmer IPA; Ushers Best Bitter; guest beers [H]

This pub was under a (widely publicised) threat of closure, due to the ending of its lease. Eventually a new owner bought the freehold and granted the resident tenant a new lease, so happily there has been no change and this friendly, lively, local continues to thrive. Four beers and Thatcher's cider are complemented by excellent food (not served Sun eve). Live music (Tue and Fri), quizzes and local sports teams combine to make this a seriously good village pub.

Q❀◑⊟≠♣♣P

NEWTON ABBOT

Dartmouth Inn

63 East Street (opp. hospital)
⏲ 12-3, 4.30-11; 11-11 Sat; 12-10.30 Sun
☎ (01626) 353451
Princetown Dartmoor IPA; [H] **guest beers** [H]/[G]

This 17th-century free house has been locally described as the village pub in the town. This warm and friendly three-roomed pub boasts open fires and a good selection of South-Western micro-breweries' ales. Well-prepared traditional pub food of excellent value is served weekday lunchtimes at this frequent South Devon CAMRA Pub of the Year winner. Fruit wines and Sam's Dry Cider make this pub complete. Children are welcome at lunchtime.

⛫♉❀◐≠♣♣

INN BRIEF

TIVERTON

White Ball
Bridge Street
11-11; 12-10.30 Sun
(01884) 251525
Courage Directors; Exmoor Stag; Hop Back Summer Lightning; Shepherd Neame Spitfire; Theakston Best Bitter; guest beers [H]
Friendly pub, near the town centre, where many regulars enjoy Wetherspoon's inexpensive ale and food. Cask Marque accredited.

TOTNES

Kingsbridge Inn
9 Leechwell Street
12-3 (not winter Mon), 6-11; 12-3, 7-10.30 Sun
(01803) 863324
Draught Bass; Theakston Old Peculier; guest beers [H]
Busy and at times crowded: a subtly-lit bar with alcoves. Live music and entertainment staged. Good food.

UMBERLEIGH

Rising Sun
11-3, 6-11; 12-3, 6-10.30 Sun
(01769) 560447
Beer range varies [H]
Dating back to the 13th century, with beautiful views over the River Taw. Award-winning menu; accommodation.

YARCOMBE

Yarcombe Angel
11.30-3.30, 6.30-11; 12-3, 7.30-10.30 Sun
(01404) 861676
Draught Bass; Black Sheep Best Bitter; Fuller's London Pride; Otter Bitter; Taylor Landlord; guest beers [H]
14th-century building, part of the estate given to Francis Drake by Elizabeth I. Roomy bar and a room with pool table.

Check it out

Pubs in the Good Beer Guide may change ownership and the facilities listed could alter. If a visit to a pub involves a long journey, it's advisable to check before leaving that full meals, family facilities, accommodation or camping sites are still available.

NEWTON ST CYRES

Beer Engine

1 mile off A377 near station
⌚ 11-11; 12-10.30 Sun
☎ (01392) 851282
Beer Engine Rail Ale; Piston Bitter; Sleeper Heavy, seasonal beers Ⓗ

Built as a railway hotel, around 1850, on the present Barnstaple branch line, the pub is now home to Devon's oldest brewery (opened in 1983). The brewery is visible behind glass downstairs (tours by arrangement). The single room has bar and eating areas (children encouraged). The bar is decorated with hops and artwork, including the original Beer Engine pub sign. Varied home-cooked food, using local ingredients, is designed to suit all tastes including vegetarian. ♛Q❀◐◑♿≠♣P⊬▯

NORTH TAWTON

Railway Inn

Whiddon Down Road (off A3124, 1 mile S of North Tawton) OS666001
⌚ 12-2 (not Mon, Wed or Thu), 6-11; 12-3, 7-10.30 Sun
☎ (01837) 82789
Teignworthy Reel Ale; guest beers Ⓗ

Set in a rural location, the Railway is a friendly, single-bar local that is part of a working farm. The pub stands next to the former North Tawton station (closed 1971), which it predates, and the bar decor includes railway memorabilia and old photos of the station. The beer range, although changing regularly, is generally West Country based, as is the cider stocked in summer. The pub has a dining room and a games room. ♛▭◐◑♣●P

NOSS MAYO

Ship Inn

⌚ 11-11; 12-10.30 Sun
☎ (01752) 872387 website: www.nossmayo.com
Exmoor Gold, Shepherd Neame Spitfire; Summerskills Tamar; guest beers Ⓗ

The pub has been refurbished recently in such a stylish way that all the original character has been kept. Situated alongside the River Yealm, it has its own moorings (contact the pub to ascertain tides and availability). Comfortable seating can be found on both floors and outside. Daily papers and magazines are provided for those who do not wish to watch the river. The pub is an ardent supporter of craft ales and local food products. It is handy for walkers on the South Devon coastal path. ♛Q❀◐◑♣●P▯

OKEHAMPTON

Plymouth Inn

26 West Street
⌚ 12-3, 7-11; 12-11 Sat; 12-10.30 Sun
☎ (01837) 53633
Beer range varies Ⓖ

16th-century former coaching inn, near the bridge over the West Ockment river, this friendly pub brings the welcome and atmosphere of a village pub to an old market town. Walking and cycling groups are informally organised in summer, and two beer festivals are held (normally May and Nov). The constantly changing beer range places the accent on West Country breweries. Occasional live music is performed in the bar, usually acoustic, and sometimes impromptu. Home-cooked food includes pizzas (takeaways available). ♛≈❀◐◑▲♣⊬

PAIGNTON

Devonport Arms

42 Elmbank Road (behind the zoo)
⌚ 11-11; 12-10.30 Sun
☎ (01803) 558322
Courage Best Bitter; John Smith's Bitter; guest beers Ⓗ

Built on a corner site in the 1930s, this traditional pub has remained basically unaltered. Multi-roomed, it has a large bar with a wide-screen TV, a small family room and a lounge bar. Skittles is played in the barn behind the pub. Well-prepared, basic, but good value meals are served lunchtime (Mon-Sat) and evenings (Thu-Sat). ♛Q≈❀◐◑P

Isaac Merritt

54-58 Torquay Road
⌚ 11-11; 12-10.30 Sun
☎ (01803) 556066
Courage Directors; Greene King Abbot; Shepherd Neame Spitfire; Theakston Best Bitter; guest beers Ⓗ

Busy town-centre ale house, popular with all ages. Its comfortable, friendly atmosphere is enhanced by cosy seated alcoves and it is accessible to wheelchair-users, with a designated ground-floor WC. This superb Wetherspoon's has a deserved reputation for its excellent quality and ever-changing guest beers from all over the country; the house beer, Isaac's Tipple, is brewed by Blackawton. Superb value meals are available all day. Fully air conditioned, it was local CAMRA Pub of the Year 2001. Q◐◑♿≠●⊬⊘

PETER TAVY

Peter Tavy Inn

⌚ 12-2.30 (3 Sat), 6.30 (6 Fri & Sat)-11; 12-3, 6-10.30 Sun
☎ (01822) 810348
Draught Bass; Badger Best; Princetown Jail Ale; Summerskills Tamar; guest beers Ⓗ

Pleasant, 15th-century inn, situated in a quiet village. There is a small, but welcoming, bar with two large rooms (one no-smoking) and a patio area at the front. Seek out the hidden garden. Children (and dogs) are welcome. Located on the No. 27 cycle route, a caravan and campsite is one mile away at Harford Bridge. The pub is popular for food but drinkers are equally welcome. ♛≈❀◐◑▲P⊬

PLYMOUTH ❄

Britannia Inn

1 Wolseley Road, Milehouse
⌚ 11-11; 12-10.30 Sun
☎ (01752) 607596
Courage Directors; Greene King Abbot; Shepherd Neame Spitfire; Theakston Best Bitter, Old Peculier; guest beers Ⓗ

Typical Wetherspoon's conversion from a run-down Edwardian pub into a real local that is usually busy. Three miles from the

city centre, it can truly be called a community pub, attracting mostly regular locals. It stands by a busy road junction, near the Mayflower sports centre in Plymouth's largest public park. The pub sponsors a player from nearby Plymouth Argyle and admits football supporters on match days, when the atmosphere always remains good-humoured. A cider is occasionally stocked.
⛰Q❀◐◑♿⇌(North Rd) ●⚡✔

Butcher's Arms
160 Cremyll Street, Stonehouse
⏲ 1-11; 12-3, 7-10.30 Sun
☎ (01752) 660510
Courage Best Bitter; guest beer Ⓗ
This cosy, single bar local with its friendly atmosphere stands next to the Navy's Grade I listed King William Victualling Yard (now empty, its further use is undetermined). Also close by is the pedestrian ferry across the River Tamar to Cornwall, and a public park called Devil's Point. At the narrowest point on the Tamar, this is a spectacular place to watch ships in Devonport Dockyard; the pub's enclosed garden is safe for children. A cider (varies) may be available in summer. Q❀◐♣●

Clifton
35 Clifton Street, Greenbank
⏲ 5 (12 Fri & Sat)-11; 12-10.30 Sun
☎ (01752) 266563
Draught Bass; Worthington Bitter; guest beers Ⓗ
Summerskills produce the popular house beer, Clifton Classic, for this spacious back-street, one-bar pub, near the city centre. There is always a warm welcome from the landlord and landlady. The large clock is correct only twice a day. Numerous pub teams are fielded. Television screens at each end of the bar provide excellent viewing for sports fans but disturb conversation.
♿⇌(North Rd) ♣

Dolphin
The Barbican (opp. Dartington Glass)
⏲ 10-11; 12-10.30 Sun
☎ (01752) 660876
Draught Bass Ⓖ
A must: the only unspoilt pub in Plymouth's historic centre. Opposite the old fish market, it is convenient for the National Aquarium and Mayflower Steps. Paintings of the landlord by celebrated artists decorate the walls. The pub windows depict the original Octagon Brewery, which was sold in turn to Plymouth Breweries, then Courage, passed to Bass and is now Punch Taverns. The Tolpuddle Martyrs stayed here on their return to England. The ladies' WC is not very user-friendly.
⛰Q

Fortescue
37 Mutley Plain
⏲ 11-11; 12-10.30 Sun
☎ (01752) 660673
Badger Tanglefoot; Draught Bass; guest beers Ⓗ
This local is situated in a student area, but frequented by a cross-section of the community. Live sport is not shown in the main bar so as not to spoilt the conversational atmosphere, but the cellar bar houses a large screen for sporting events, and is a venue for musical evenings and private functions. The patio garden at the rear is popular in the summer. A changing range of two or three guest beers, includes some exotic and unusual brews.
❀◐⇌(North Rd) ✔

Hogshead
12-14 Royal Parade
⏲ 11-11; 12-10.30 Sun
☎ (01752) 260442
Boddingtons Bitter; Hook Norton Old Hooky; Marston's Pedigree; guest beers Ⓗ
Not your usual real ale venue, this newly designed Hogshead is a bright, airy, food-focussed, female-friendly, café-bar during the day (meals are served 11-6). The modern decor features bare wood and stainless steel, with brightly-coloured sofas and pine tables and chairs. The pub's chameleon nature has it darken down in the evenings, becoming youth and music-oriented, as a feeder to Plymouth's clubland. ◐◑♿

Lounge
7 Stopford Place, Stoke
⏲ 11-2.30, 7-11; 12-2.30, 7-10.30 Sun
☎ (01752) 561330
Draught Bass; guest beer Ⓗ
A gem of an old-fashioned pub in a back-street leading to Devonport Park. This is Devonport's only recommended real ale outlet. A comfortable, homely atmosphere prevails in the single, large carpeted bar. Although hidden away, it is well worth seeking out. The changing guest beer is now dispensed by handpump, after years of gravity dispense. There is an emphasis on good value food at lunchtime, which is very popular with the local retired population.
⛰Q◐⇌(Devonport)

Prince Maurice
3 Church Hill, Eggbuckland
⏲ 11-3, 7-11; 11-11 Sat; 12-4, 7-10.30 Sun
☎ (01752) 771515
Adnams Broadside; Badger Tanglefoot; Draught Bass; Courage Best Bitter; Summerskills Best Bitter; guest beers Ⓗ
Cosy, friendly, two-bar pub close to the church, dating from the 16th century, in an area which still has a village atmosphere, despite being now surrounded by residential development. It was named after the nephew of Charles I who stayed nearby while leading the Royalist offensive against the local Parliamentarian stronghold. Plymouth CAMRA Pub of the Year 2000 and 2001.
⛰❀⊟♣P

Providence
20 Providence Street, Greenbank (off A386, turn into Clifton Place, first right)
⏲ 5 (4 Fri; 11 Sat)-11; 1-10.30 Sun
☎ (01752) 228178
Greene King Abbot; Summerskills Best Bitter; guest beer Ⓗ
Classic example of a cosy back-street boozer. On the corner of a row of terraced houses, the atmosphere is redolent of someone's front lounge. Hosting a mixed bag of friendly regulars and providing a wide selection of background music, this pub, not too far from the city centre, is well worth a visit. The beer range includes a house ale.
⛰⇌

Royal Albert Bridge Inn

930 Wolseley Road, Saltash Passage

11-11, 12-10.30 Sun

(01752) 361108

Draught Bass; Courage Best Bitter; guest beers H

Small, friendly pub enjoyed by locals and visitors alike. In the shadow of Brunel's famous railway bridge, it affords views across the Tamar River to Cornwall, and features many maritime artefacts and local memorabilia. It serves good, freshly-cooked food, including very popular Sunday roasts, and a tempting range of desserts. An Italian motorcycle club meets here monthly (third Mon). See the impressive memorial to US troops, who left from here on D-Day, on the river bank.

Q (St Budeaux/Ferry Rd)

Thistle Park Brewhouse

32 Commercial Road, Coxside (between Aquarium and Warner leisure complex)

11-2am; 12-12.30am Sun

(01752) 204890

Sutton Plymouth Pride, XSB, Sutton Comfort, seasonal beers; guest beers H

This friendly, basic pub, can be reached by foot, via a swing bridge from the historic Barbican. It has bare floorboards and an air of a village pub within the city. The link with Sutton Brewery is now firmly established by the recent renaming to Thistle Park Brewhouse. Those with strong jaws should try the biltong, a delicacy from the landlord's native South Africa; lunches are served until 5pm. Pavement tables are set out in fine weather. Live music is staged regularly. Note the late licence.

PLYMTREE

Blacksmith's Arms

$3^1/_2$ miles E of M5 jct 28

12-2.30 (not Mon), 6 (5 Fri)-11; 12-3, 7-10.30 Sun

(01884) 277474

Banks's Original, O'Hanlon's Fire Fly, Otter Ale; guest beers H

18th-century, popular village pub, with a reputation for good quality food, the ingredients for which are sourced locally wherever possible; a children's menu is available. It hosts occasional live music and quiz nights; skittles (five teams) and boules are also played. From easy chairs around the log burner, admire the oak beamed interior, decorated with blacksmith's tools, diving memorabilia and deer antlers. In summer this friendly local plays host to cricket teams and offers barbecues. Q P

POSTBRIDGE

Warren House Inn

On B3212, Postbridge-Mortonhampstead road

11-3, 6-11; 11-11 Fri, Sat & summer; 12-10.30 Sun

(01822) 880208

Badger Tanglefoot; Moor Old Freddy Walker; Sharp's Doom Bar, Special H

The third highest pub in England stands in wild Dartmoor, a winter shelter and summer oasis for walkers, campers, tourists, locals and riders. A dining area has been added to the existing rooms, which are rustic and homely. A light lunch menu is complemented by a full evening one, offering many home-cooked dishes. The fire has been burning here since 1845. Breathtaking views can be enjoyed from the tables outside. Countryman cider is stocked.

Q P

PRINCETOWN

Plume of Feathers

The Square

11-11; 12-10.30 Sun

(01822) 890240

website: www.plumeoffeathers-dartmoor.co.uk

Draught Bass; Princetown Dartmoor IPA, Jail Ale H

Princetown's oldest building (1785) features copper-topped bars, a slate floor and granite walls. Always busy, locals and visitors spread themselves through the different rooms, including a family room, with its own bar, and out on to the paved courtyard and garden, weather permitting. The pub has its own campsite, plus dormitory accommodation in two bunkhouses. Facilities for disabled customers are very good. The cider is from Countryman. Food ranges from snacks to full meals, with a specials board. Q P

Prince of Wales

Tavistock Road

11-11; 12-10.30 Sun

(01822) 890219

Draught Bass; Princetown Dartmoor IPA, Jail Ale H

Welcoming, single bar with a children's certificate opposite the famous prison. Pub games include pool and darts. The restaurant doubles as a no-smoking area for drinkers; food is served all day until 9.30pm. Occasional live music includes informal folk evenings on the last Thursday of the month. The pub acts as the tap for Princetown Brewery sited at the rear. The Yelverton-Princetown cycle route ends, conveniently, behind the pub.

P

Railway Inn

Two Bridges Road

11-11; 12-10.30 Sun

(01822) 890232

Sutton Dartmoor Pride; Wadworth 6X; Teignworthy Old Moggie H

This cosy pub is well worth a visit, offering a homely alternative to its famous neighbour (the prison!) Comprising several rooms and a skittle alley, the wood-panelled walls are hung with memorabilia from the steam railway that once served Princetown. The pub supports darts and skittles teams. The Luscombe organic cider is certainly worth trying, even though kept in a keg. Food from the excellent menu is served all day. Q P

ROCKFORD

Rockford Inn

Brendon OS756478

12-3, 6 (6.30 winter)-11 (not Tue eve); 12-10.30 (closed winter) Sun

(01598) 741214 website: www.therockfordinn.com

Clearwater Cavalier, 1646; Cotleigh Tawny; guest beer H/G

This pub is tricky to find, but the scenery you will enjoy en-route makes it worthwhile. Set by the East Lynn River, along the Brendon Valley, the Rockford is an oasis for ramblers. This cosy, four-

roomed pub offers both excellent beer and traditional pub grub. Guest accommodation includes two rooms for families. Beers are served on gravity dispense in winter.
⛫Q🚼❀🛏◑▲●P⚟

SCORITON

Tradesman's Arms

On Holne road OS704684
⏲ 11-2.30 (3 summer), 6.30 (6 summer)-11; closed winter Mon; 12-2.30, 6-10.30 (closed winter eve) Sun
☎ (01364) 631206
website: www.thetradesmansarms.com
Draught Bass; Princetown Dartmoor IPA, Jail Ale Ⓗ
This 17th-century village pub was originally an ale house, built for the tin miners. The single bar incorporates an open-plan bar area and a dining alcove; there is also a family room. This friendly pub hosts a quiz night (Thu), folk music (Fri) and jazz on Sunday lunchtime. Look out for the Scoriton 'mystery beer' each month on a fourth handpump. It serves a good choice of quality food, as well as wines and 34 malt whiskies. ⛫Q🚼❀🛏◑P

SIDBURY

Red Lion Inn

Fore Street
⏲ 12-2.30, 5-11; 12-11 Sat; 12-10.30 Sun
☎ (01395) 597313 website: www.theredlion.info
O'Hanlon's Fire Fly; Ringwood Best Bitter; guest beers Ⓗ
Popular with walkers, this 400-year-old coaching inn is full of character. Its cosy beamed bars are strewn with hops and bric-a-brac. Go through the archway into the suntrap patio garden for an al fresco meal on warmer days; the excellent menu offers home-made fare based on local ingredients. Along with an interesting selection of guest ales, the licensee will source a favourite brew. It hosts an annual beer festival, regular folk evenings, weekly darts and skittles, and is home to Sidbury CC.
Q🚼❀🛏◑⊟♿♣⚟

SILVERTON

Lamb Inn

Fore Street
⏲ 11-2.30, 6-11; 11-11 Sat; 12-10.30 Sun
☎ (01392) 860272 website: www.lamb-inn.com
Draught Bass; Ⓗ **Exe Valley Dob's Best Bitter; Greene King Abbot; Shepherd Neame Spitfire** Ⓖ
Family-run village pub of stone floors, stripped timbers and old pine tables and chairs. Most ales are served from a temperature-controlled stillage behind the bar. A multi-purpose function room houses a skittle alley and bar. Good value home-cooked food includes a specials board that always features a vegetarian option; monthly steak nights are held, with low prices. Village organisations, such as bell-ringers and short mat bowlers congregate here. ⛫◑♿♣⚟

SLAPTON

Queen's Arms

Signed off A379
⏲ 12-3, 6-11; 12-3, 7-10.30 Sun
☎ (01548) 580800
website: www.slapton.org/queensarms
Badger IPA; Princetown Dartmoor IPA; guest beers Ⓗ
One of the famous free houses of south Devon: a single bar with a traditional atmosphere and large open fire.It stocks up to two guest ales depending on the time of year. A full traditional menu is served, with the chef's home-made pies a speciality (takeaways available). See the many old photos of the area, including those of wartime evacuation. Peaceful, secluded walled gardens and patio add to its appeal. Children (and dogs) are welcome.
⛫Q❀◑▲●P

SOUTH MOLTON

George Hotel

Broad Street
⏲ 12-2 (not Mon or Tue), 6-11; 12-2, 7-10.30 Sun
☎ (01769) 572514
Draught Bass; Jollyboat Mainbrace Bitter; guest beer Ⓗ
Sympathetically refurbished, 16th-century coaching inn in the town's main square. It hosts live music (folk and jazz), plus films in the large function room. It is also used by several local organisations, and serves as a centre for the local business community. No meals are served Sunday lunchtime.
⛫Q🚼🛏◑⊟P⚟

King's Arms

4 King Street
⏲ 10.30-11; 12-10.30 (may close 4-7) Sun
☎ (01769) 572679
Draught Bass; Cotleigh Tawny; guest beer Ⓗ
No-nonsense local, attracting a wide range of customers, depending on the time of day. No food is advertised, but basic snacks are available on request. It can be noisy, but the pool table, TV and games machines are all at one end of the long bar; a quiet area, with ample seating, overlooks the town square. Here you will find a warm welcome and plenty of conversation – everyone seems to know each other. The guest beer is supplied by Cotleigh. ♣●

SOUTH POOL

Millbrook Inn

Off A379 at Chillington, E of Kingsbridge OS776402
⏲ 12-2.30, 6-11; 12-3, 7-10.30 Sun
☎ (01548) 531581 website: www.millbrookinn.co.uk
Draught Bass; Ⓖ **Fuller's London Pride; Wadworth 6X** (summer)**; guest beer** Ⓗ
The Millbrook is situated at the head of the Salcombe estuary. The main section of the pub dates back to the early 17th century, with the top bar (children welcome) added later. The pub is busy in summer, with most of its trade coming from boaters and walkers. It famed for its crab sandwiches and Aylesbury ducks. No Sunday evening meals are served Jan-March. Note, no debit or credit cards are accepted.
⛫Q❀🛏◑⊟▲♣

SOUTH ZEAL

King's Arms

⏲ 12-2.30, 5.30 (5 Fri)-11; 11-11 Sat; 12-10.30 Sun
☎ (01837) 840300
Adnams Bitter; Draught Bass; Greene King Abbot; Otter Ale Ⓗ
Thatched 14th century ale house (or probably more accurately a former cider

house), which is still a popular meeting place, situated towards the top of the hill at the western end of the village. The landlord is active in the local folk music scene, so live music is not an uncommon occurrence in one of the two bars, usually acoustic – sometimes jazz – sometimes impromptu. ⛬❀◑♿⛺♣P

STOCKLAND

King's Arms Inn

⌚ 12-3, 6.30-11; 12-3, 6.30-10.30 Sun
☎ (01404) 881361 website: www.kingsarms.net
Courage Directors; Exmoor Ale, Gold; Otter Ale Ⓗ
Popular large pub, once a coaching inn, in the centre of a village on the eastern edge of the Blackdown Hills. The spacious public bar leads through to a smaller lounge, with a piano, and to a well-used skittle alley. This pub enjoys a good reputation for food, with bar meals served lunchtime, and an à la carte evening menu in the no-smoking restaurant. Regular folk evenings are held. Inch's and Jack Rat cider are served in summer. ⛬Q❀🛏◑⊟♿♣●P⊓

TEIGNMOUTH ❄

Golden Lion

85 Bitton Park Road (A379)
⌚ 12-4, 6-11; 12-4, 7-10.30 Sun
☎ (01626) 776442
Beer range varies Ⓗ
Friendly, welcoming, typical two-bar pub, overlooking the docks. There is a cosy L-shaped lounge bar with beamed ceilings and a larger public bar with an L-shaped bar and a pool table. Three ever-changing real ales are served on handpump at very reasonable prices. There is limited parking at the front of the pub. ⊟≠♣P

TOPSHAM

Bridge Inn ☆

Bridge Hill (from Exeter follow road through Topsham to Exmouth)
⌚ 12-2, 6-10.30 (11 Fri & Sat); 12-2, 7-10.30 Sun
☎ (01392) 873862 website: www.cheffers.co.uk
Adnams Broadside; Blackawton Westcountry Gold; Branscombe Vale Branoc; Exe Valley Exeter Old Bitter; Otter Ale; guest beers Ⓖ
This CAMRA National Inventory listed, 16th-century gem is unspoilt by modern additions such as juke box, fruit machines or optics. All beer is gravity served from the cellar, predominantly, but not exclusively, from local breweries. In March 1998 Queen Elizabeth II made this her only 'official' pub visit. There is home-made soup in winter and usually ploughmans lunches, too. In the same family for 105 years, a waterfront area is perfect for enjoying balmy summer evenings. ⛬Q❀⊟≠P

Lighter Inn

The Quay, Fore Street
⌚ 11-11; 12-10.30 Sun
☎ (01392) 875439
Badger Best, Tanglefoot, seasonal beers Ⓗ
This attractive, substantial pub, formerly a customs house, benefits from a stunning location on the harbourside and looks across the Exe estuary to the wildlife sanctuary. Comfortably furnished with various small areas for drinkers, diners and families, this is Hall & Woodhouse's most westerly pub. The menu is varied, specialising in fresh fish. Always popular with locals, from Easter onwards it gets busy with tourists. Live music features, often performed outside in good weather. ⛬♨❀◑≠⚡✔

TORQUAY

Crown & Sceptre

2 Petitor Road, St Marychurch
⌚ 11-3 (4 Sat), 5.30 (6.30 Sat)-11; 12-3, 7-10.30 Sun
☎ (01803) 328290
Draught Bass; Courage Best Bitter, Directors; Fuller's London Pride; Greene King Old Speckled Hen; Young's Special; guest beers Ⓗ
This 200-year-old coaching house has stalls for seating in the public bar; the lounge bar boasts some exposed stone walls, while chamber pots and flags hang from the ceilings. Furniture is made out of reclaimed floorboards. It has been in this Guide for 26 years and still attracts old and new customers alike, to its friendly atmosphere. Jazz is staged (Tue and Sun eves), and folk on the second Thursday of the month. No food is served Sunday. The beer can be expensive.
⛬Q❀◑⊟♣P

TOTNES ❄

Steam Packet Inn

St Peter's Quay
⌚ 11-11; 12-10.30 Sun
☎ (01803) 863880
website: www.thesteampacketinn-totnes.co.uk
Draught Bass; Courage Best Bitter; guest beers Ⓗ
Three 18th-century cottages were converted a long time ago into an atmospheric riverside pub. Only a few minutes' walk from the town centre, this free house is comfortable and warm, with vibrant colours, exposed bricks, panelling and leather sofas. A striking conservatory restaurant, overlooking the River Dart, has a supper licence. Private moorings are available for four boats. Live jazz is performed Sunday lunchtime. Guest ales come from all over the UK; cider is sold in summer.
⛬❀🛏◑♣●P

TUCKENHAY

Maltster's Arms

Bow Creek (signed from A381, Totnes-Kingsbridge road)
⌚ 11-11; 12-10.30 Sun
☎ (01803) 732350 website: www.tuckenhay.com
Princeton Dartmoor IPA; guest beers Ⓗ
Marvellous, waterside pub overlooking the peaceful, wooded Bow Creek. Waterside tables and boat moorings are available. The pub has a narrow main bar, linking two other cosy rooms – the snug and another with red-painted seats and kitchen chairs on a wooden floor. The restaurant area serves excellent quality food; barbecues and live music are staged outside in summer beside the creek. A 10% discount on accommodation is given to card-carrying CAMRA members, but the beer is expensive. Heron Valley cider is stocked in summer.
⛬Q♨❀🛏◑♣●P

TURNCHAPEL

Boringdon Arms

13 Boringdon Terrace (A379, Plymstock)
⌚ 11-11; 12-10.30 Sun
☎ (01752) 402053 website: www.bori.co.uk
Butcombe Bitter, RCH Pitchfork; Summerskills Best Bitter, Sutton XSB; guest beers Ⓗ
Regular CAMRA award-winner in a village on Plymouth's outskirts. It holds bi-monthly beer festivals and is home of the Cattewater Gig Club. Formerly a quarrymaster's house, but a pub for over 200 years, the garden is part of the old quarry. Residents may request their favourite beer as a guest. The pub is served by local buses or by water taxi from Plymouth's Barbican, and stands on the south-west coastal footpath. Try the legendary pies. ♨Q❀⇌◑⊟♣

New Inn

1 Boringdon Road (A379, follow signs to Mountbatten and Turnchapel)
⌚ 12-3 (not Mon-Thu), 6-11; 12-11 Sat; 12-10.30 Sun
☎ (01752) 402765
Draught Bass; Princetown Jail Ale; Sharp's Doom Bar; Taylor Landlord; guest beers Ⓗ
This village pub was originally three buildings, a bakery, a butcher's and a tavern. On the outskirts of Plymouth, the New Inn stands at the waterside, looking out across the Cattewater to Plymouth Hoe. Enjoying an excellent reputation for both beer and food, the pub is accessible from Plymouth city centre by bus, or water taxi from the Barbican. Some of the inn's five quiet, en-suite guest rooms benefit from sea views. ♨Q⇌◑♣P

WEMBURY

Odd Wheel

Knighton Road
⌚ 12-3, 6.30-11; 12-11 Sat; 12-4, 7-10.30 Sun
☎ (01752) 862287
Courage Best Bitter; Princetown Jail Ale; Shepherd Neame Spitfire; Skinner's Coast Liner; Sutton XSB Ⓖ
Friendly pub, in the South Hams, on a regular bus route from Plymouth. It comprises a large lounge with dining tables and comfortable seating, plus a lively public bar. The bar runs its own golfing society and is the meeting place for a sailing club, darts and football teams. The garden affords views of the rolling countryside. Close to Wembury Bay and the Mewstone, it makes a good start or finishing point for a coastal walk. Light lunchtime meals are supplemented by a fuller, home-cooked evening menu. ♨Q❀◑⊟♿P

WEST DOWN

Crown Inn

1 mile from A3123
⌚ 12-2 (3 summer), 7 (6 summer)-11; 12-10.30 Sun
☎ (01271) 862790
Barum Original; guest beer Ⓗ
Very much the village inn – set in the square of this rural village. Dating from the 17th century and delightfully refurbished, there is a level run to the family room, then one step down to the main bar and the open-plan dining area that seats 20 candlelit diners. On a summer's evening take pleasure in the wonderful country garden. Thatchers cider is stocked in summer. No lunches are served on winter Monday. ♨Q♉❀⇌◑⊟♿⅄●P⊭

WESTWARD HO!

Nelson Inn

5 Nelson Road (follow A39 from Barnstaple to Bideford)
⌚ 11-11; 12-10.30 Sun
☎ (01237) 474745
Fuller's London Pride; guest beers Ⓗ
Cheery, welcoming pub that belies its architecture. Located in a tourist area, it caters well for visitors, but still manages to impart the atmosphere expected of a local. It supports local breweries in its range of guest beers. The restaurant area serves a good variety of meals and snacks. ❀⇌◑⅄P

Pig on the Hill

Pusehill (off A39, Bideford-Abbotsham road) OS427282
⌚ 12-3, 6 (6.30 winter)-11; 12-3, 7-10.30 Sun
☎ (01237) 425889 website: www.pigonthehill.co.uk
Country Life Old Appledore, Wallop, Golden Pig; guest beer (occasional) Ⓗ
This converted farm is also home to the Country Life Brewery, which can be viewed through a large window at the far end of the lounge. The interior is decorated with all things porcine, and if the weather is kind, you can relax in the extensive garden watching the large pig and goats. The atmosphere in the intimate bar is friendly and relaxed; the lounge (or patio in summer) hosts occasional live jazz. Pétanque is played. Q♉❀⇌◑⅄♣P

WHIDDON DOWN

Post Inn

Exeter Road (old main road, near A30 services)
⌚ 11-11; closed Tue; 12-10.30 Sun
☎ (01647) 231242
Beer range varies Ⓗ
Built in the 16th century as the post office on the old coaching road to the West, the Post is a pleasantly refurbished country pub, handy for the A30 and keen to cater for modern travellers (meals are served 11-11). The central bar serves three rooms, with the two side rooms, although generally laid out for diners, available for no-smoking drinkers. The ales follow a West Country theme, and the cider is local. Occasional beer festivals are held. ♨Q❀◑⅄●P⊭

WHIMPLE

New Fountain Inn

Church Road (leave A30 at Daisymount, follow signs)
⌚ 12-3, 6.30-11; 12-3, 7-10.30 Sun
☎ (01404) 822350
Branscombe Vale Branoc; Teignworthy Reel Ale; guest beers (occasional) Ⓖ
Friendly, welcoming village pub, serving an excellent menu at superb value prices. Well-behaved children are welcome. Special events here include wassailing in January (the village was the original home of Whiteways Cider), occasional charity quiz nights and live music. The cider is now provided by Thatcher's. The village museum is next door.
♨Q❀◑⊟≹♣●P

WIDECOMBE IN THE MOOR

Rugglestone Inn ☆

1/4 mile S of village centre (signed) OS721766

11-2.30 (3 Sat), 7 (6 summer)-11; 12-3, 7 (6 summer)-10.30 Sun

☎ (01364) 621327 website: www.rugglestone.f9.co.uk

Butcombe Bitter; St Austell Dartmoor Best G

Unspoilt, cosy pub in a splendid Dartmoor setting. The small bar area has seating and a stone floor. Beer is also served through a small hatch in the passageway. The lounge area is warmed by an open fire. The pub is named after a local 'logan' stone. Children under 14 are not allowed inside, but across the stream is a large grassed seating area with a shelter for use in bad weather. Home-cooked food is served. The pub's car park is just down the lane.

WOODLAND

Rising Sun

Village signed from the Plymouth-bound A38, pub on left (1 1/2 miles) OS790697

11.45-3 (not Mon), 6-11 (not winter Mon); 12-3, 7-10.30 Sun

☎ (01364) 652544

website: www.risingsunwoodland.co.uk

Princetown Jail Ale; guest beers H

Lovely, spacious free house, set in beautiful countryside between Torbay and Dartmoor. The long single bar serves a large open-plan bar and dining area where small screens offer some privacy. An additional area off the main bar serves as the family room. The extensive grounds have seating and a children's play area. An excellent range of home-made food includes renowned pies.

YEOFORD

Mare & Foal

12-2.30 (4 summer), 6-11; 12-2.30, 7-10.30 Sun

☎ (01363) 84348

Sharp's Doom Bar, H **Special;** G **guest beer** H

This pub was built in this small, mid-Devon village in the 1830s to serve the expanding railway. The character, however, is that of a pub, rather than a railway hotel, with a real fire, interconnecting rooms and a skittle alley for drinkers, plus a dining room. The house speciality is steaks. Traditional beer is to the fore, but do not be disappointed if the gravity beer is off – the locals cannot get enough of it. Boules and croquet are played.

Fizz warning

Some national breweries produce both cask-conditioned and 'nitro-keg' versions of their beers. Boddingtons Bitter, John Smith's Bitter, Tetley's Bitter and Worthington fall into this category. Nitro-keg beers, often promoted as 'smooth' or 'cream-flow' products, are filtered and pasteurised in the brewery, and served in pubs by a mix of applied carbon dioxide and nitrogen gases. They are bland, served extremely cold, and any hop character is lost by the use of applied gas. To add insult to injury, the keg founts that serve such beers are often topped by small dummy handpumps.

As a result of lobbying by CAMRA, some producers of cask and nitro versions of the same beer now include the word 'cask' on pump clips for the genuine article. For example, both John Smith's Bitter and Tetley's Bitter now carry the word 'cask' on pump clips for the real thing. For the sake of brevity, and as the Good Beer Guide lists only cask-conditioned beers, we refer simply to John Smith's Bitter and Tetley Bitter.

The Coors Brewing brand, Worthington, is labelled Worthington Bitter in cask form, and – bizarrely – Worthington Best Bitter in the nitro-keg version. Always choose the living rather than the dead.

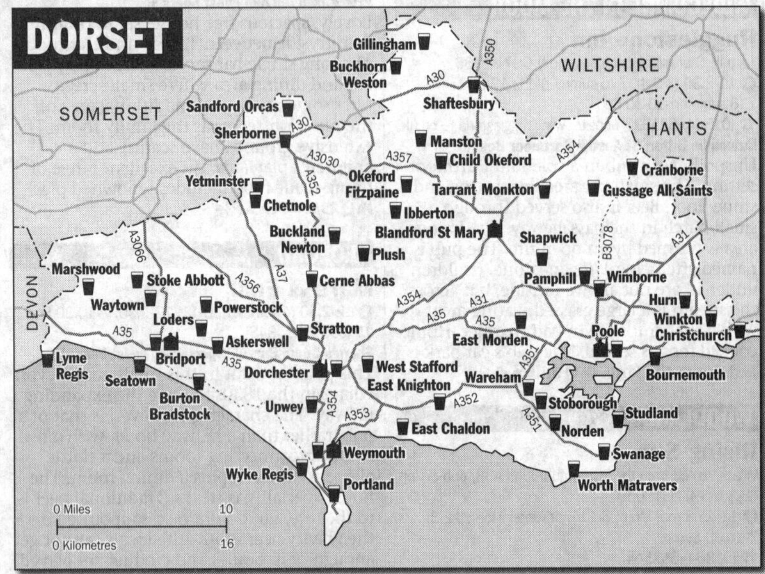

ASKERSWELL

Spyway

N of A35, pub is 1/2 mile N of village OS529933

11.30-2.30, 6-11; closed Mon; 12-3, 7-10.30 Sun

☎ (01308) 485250

Adnams Bitter; Branscombe Vale Drayman's Best; Greene King Abbot; guest beer (summer) H

Situated above the village on an old road called 'Spyway', this smugglers' inn dates from 1600. The south-facing garden provides stunning views of the surrounding walking country. Inside is a comfortable lounge, dining room and cosy, beamed bar with open fire, settles and horse brasses. The gluten-free menu uses local farm produce and features interestingly flavoured home-made ice cream; eve meals served Tue-Sat. Vegetarians are amply catered for but please 'phone beforehand. Q P

BOURNEMOUTH

Goat & Tricycle

27-29 West Hill Road

12-3, 6-11; 12-3, 7-10.30 Sun

☎ (01202) 314220

Draught Bass; Red Shoot Tom's Tipple; Wadworth IPA, 6X, JCB; guest beers H

On two levels, with a central bar, this was formerly two neighbouring pubs that have been cleverly knocked together. The lower section has a run of eight real ale handpumps, featuring the full Wadworth range and up to three changing guest ales. A lovely courtyard, filled with tubs and baskets of flowers, gives an extra dimension to the pub. Good food is served to locals and those holidaymakers who find this superb ale house. Q

Porterhouse

113 Poole Road, Westbourne

11-11; 12-10.30 Sun

☎ (01202) 768586

Ringwood Best Bitter, Fortyniner, Old Thumper, seasonal beers; guest beer H

Quaint, busy but welcoming pub in the heart of Westbourne. The light, open bar features a wood floor, panelling, seating around the walls and settles. The complete range of Ringwood beers is supplemented by seasonal brews and guests; a traditional cider is also stocked. This Ringwood house has won local CAMRA's Pub of the Year award five times in seven years. Lunches are served Mon-Sat.

Q (Branksome)

Shoulder of Mutton

1010 Ringwood Road, Bear Cross

12-2.30, 6-11; 12-3.30, 7-10.30 Sun

☎ (01202) 573344

Flowers Original; guest beers H

Bournemouth's third oldest pub stands alongside the original Ringwood road, which is now overshadowed by the dual carriageway. The pub has been extended at both ends of the building, but has retained its heart, where the flagstoned floor was laid over 200 years ago. In the public bar there is a century-old shove-ha'penny slate to play on (ask behind the bar). This small back-street boozer is well worth a visit.

P

Sir Percy Florence Shelley

673-675 Christchurch Road, Boscombe

11-11; 12-10.30 Sun

☎ (01202) 300197

Courage Directors; Ringwood Old Thumper; Theakston Best Bitter; guest beers H

Popular, atmospheric suburban Wetherspoon's where the decor reflects the building's early life as a theatre. Pictures also show the Boscombe area in the 19th and 20th centuries, along with a brief history of the Shelley family. The wide area of polished floorboards in front of the bar is complemented by a raised no-smoking section and seating booths at the rear, leading to a quiet courtyard. It hosts beer festivals in spring and autumn.

(Pokesdown)

BRIDPORT ❊

Hope & Anchor

13 St Michaels Lane

⌚ 11-11; 12-10.30 Sun

☎ (01308) 422160

Beer range varies Ⓗ

Unspoilt, back-street local presided over by a welcoming landlady. Live, mainly blues, music is staged Sunday lunchtime and most Friday and Saturday evenings. The ever-changing selection of three real ales, usually from West Country brewers, is supplemented by occasional beer festivals in summer. Three ciders are also served from Taunton, Burrow Hill and Cheddar Valley. The pub has no car park but both the bus station and municipal car park are next door. 🔥❀♣🍎

Woodman

61 South Street

⌚ 11-3, 7-11 (11-11 summer); 11-3, 7-10.30 Sun

☎ (01308) 456455

Draught Bass; guest beers Ⓗ

This beamed local on the southern approach to town stocks two guest beers, mainly from south-west independents. The comfortable bar offers ample seating, supplemented in summer by tables on the wide pavement outside. Good quality lunches including Sunday roasts and evening meals (seasonal) are served in the skittle alley area. Popular with tourists on market days (Wed and Sun), it is well worth the walk from the town centre. ❀◐◑♿♣

BUCKHORN WESTON

Stapleton Arms

Church Hill (signed from A30)

⌚ 11-3, 6-11; 12-3, 6-10.30 Sun

☎ (01963) 370396

website: www.thestapletonarms.co.uk

Butcombe Bitter; Ringwood Best Bitter; guest beers Ⓗ

New owners have turned a drowsy village inn into a vibrant pub for real ale and cider drinkers and for foodies too, with custom drawn from neighbouring towns as well as locals. Restaurant tables are set apart from the bar. Outside, there is a popular garden, with a children's play area being developed in the next field. The excellent atmosphere here makes it a welcome addition to the Guide. 🔥Q❀🛏◐◑♣🍎P

BUCKLAND NEWTON

Gaggle of Geese

E of village, 600 yds from B3143

⌚ 12-2.30, 6.30-11; 12-3, 7-10.30 Sun

☎ (01300) 345249

Badger Best; Ringwood Best Bitter, Fortyniner; guest beer Ⓗ

This village pub, at the top of the quaintly named Piddle Valley, features several drinking areas and a dining area where an extensive menu, including home-made curries, can be enjoyed. Although in a quiet village, customers may keep in touch with the outside world via the internet access provided. Very popular with ramblers and cyclists, there are goose auctions in May and September. The adjacent caravan site is also run from the pub. Guest beers come from Butcombe or Oakhill. 🔥❀◐◑⛺♣P

BURTON BRADSTOCK

Three Horseshoes

⌚ 11-11; 12-10.30 Sun

☎ (01308) 897259

Palmer Dorset Gold, Copper Ale, IPA, Tally Ho! Ⓗ

Thatched building in the middle of a pretty village, close to the western end of Chesil Beach. Run by an ale-loving landlord, this is one of the few Palmer's houses to carry the excellent Tally Ho! It has two drinking areas outside: a secluded garden and a series of south-facing benches to the side. Low beams and a blazing fire in winter make this one of the most attractive pubs in the area, however beer prices are above average. 🔥❀◐◑⛺P

CERNE ABBAS

Royal Oak

⌚ 11-3, 6-11; 12-3, 7-10.30 Sun

☎ (01300) 341797

Butcombe Bitter; Greene King Old Speckled Hen; Wadworth 6X; guest beers Ⓗ

This delightful thatched pub, whose stone walls are draped with ivy, was built in 1540. Three flag-floored adjoining rooms are furnished with a miscellany of chairs, armchairs and settles. The village is well known for its risqué chalk outline of a giant fertility figure on the adjacent hillside. The food is excellent and imaginative but does not overwhelm the pub atmosphere. There is a small patio to the rear. 🔥Q❀◐◑⛺♣

CHETNOLE

Chetnole Inn

1 mile E of A37

⌚ 11-2.30, 6-11; 12-2.30, 7-10.30 Sun

☎ (01935) 872337

Branscombe Vale Branoc; Palmer IPA; guest beers Ⓗ

This classic village pub, positioned opposite the church, is a 20-minute stroll along country lanes from Chetnole Halt on the Weymouth to Bristol line and makes an excellent day out. The public bar, warmed by a blazing fire, has a skittle alley behind. Excellent food is served in the lounge, restaurant or garden on sunny days. Guest beers come from West Country brewers, with the Easter weekend seeing the annual beer festival. 🔥Q❀◐◑⊟⇌♣P

CHILD OKEFORD

Saxon Inn

Gold Hill OS829135

⌚ 11-2.30 (3 Sat), 7-11; 12-3, 7-10.30 Sun

☎ (01258) 860310

Butcombe Bitter; guest beers Ⓗ

This friendly pub stands at the north end of a village, nestling against the foot of Hambledon Iron Age hill fort which offers spectacular views across the River Stour and Vale of Blackmoor. Converted from three

INDEPENDENT BREWERIES

Badger Blandford St. Mary
Goldfinch Dorchester
Thomas Hardy Dorchester
Palmer Bridport
Poole Poole
Quay Weymouth

cottages in 1949, but looking much older, with low, beamed ceilings and settles, two rooms are served from one small bar. Excellent food is cooked to order (no eve meals Tue or Sun). To the rear of its whitewashed walls is a large secluded garden. A rural classic. ♨Q❀◑♿⛺♣P

CHRISTCHURCH

Olde George Inn

2A Castle Street

11-11; 12-10.30 Sun

☎ (01202) 479383

Flowers Original; Hampshire Strong's Best Bitter; Ringwood Fortyniner; guest beers Ⓗ

Former Tudor coaching inn, dating back 600 years, comprising two low-ceilinged rooms – one is dedicated to diners. A covered courtyard that admits children, and is heated in winter, leads to barn bar that stages jazz bands (Thu eve) and Irish folk/rock bands (Fri eve) – admission free. The pub gets very busy on music nights. Two ciders are normally on tap. Try the excellent summer menu. ❀◑●

CRANBORNE

Sheaf of Arrows

4 The Square

11-11; 12-10.30 Sun

☎ (01725) 517456

Draught Bass; Ringwood Best Bitter; guest beer Ⓗ

Set in the middle of Cranborne, the pub comprises a large, friendly, locals' public bar with pool, darts and TV, a smaller, snug/lounge bar and a function room-cum-skittle alley. Children are not allowed in the public bar, but may dine (accompanied) elsewhere, and use the pleasant, walled patio garden under supervision. Very popular at weekends with walkers and cyclists, the good menu offers takeaways. Food theme evenings and an annual beer festival (early summer) are added attractions. ♨Q❀◑⛺♣

DORCHESTER

Blue Raddle

Church Street

11.30-3, 7-11; 12-3, 7-10.30 Sun

☎ (01305) 267762

Greene King Abbot; Sharp's Cornish Coaster; guest beers Ⓗ

Friendly, town-centre free house, serving beers from West Country micro-breweries. Two of the most realistic flame-effect gas fires imaginable are often mistaken for the real thing. The public lounge-style bar displays lewd and suggestive paintings on the walls. The menu often includes game dishes, but vegetarians are also well catered for. Check out the unusual pub sign: the Cerne Giant is on one side in the background, but omitted on the other. Q◑♿⇌

Tom Brown's

47 High East Street

11-11; 11-3, 5.30-11 Tue & Wed; 12-4, 7-10.30 Sun

☎ (01305) 264020

Goldfinch Tom Brown, Midnight Sun, Flashman's Clout (occasional), **Midnight Blinder** Ⓗ

The tap of the Goldfinch Brewery takes the form of an old public bar – bare floorboards accompanied by plain wooden tables and chairs. Conversation rules in this friendly pub, only occasionally disturbed by the ancient, outstandingly good value, juke box. The brewery is situated to the rear of the building in what used to be a night club, and is partially visible from the corridor. Three Goldfinch beers are always available, Flashman's Clout only makes infrequent appearances nowadays. ◑⇌♣

EAST CHALDON

Sailors Return

1 mile S of A352 OS791834

11-2.30, 6-11 (11-11 Easter-autumn); 12-2.30, 7-10.30 Sun

☎ (01305) 853847

Hampshire Strong's Best Bitter; Ringwood Best Bitter; guest beers Ⓗ

This thatched inn is situated on the fringe of a small hamlet. It provides a welcome refreshment stop for ramblers on the nearby Dorset Coastal Path and can get extremely busy on summer weekends. Excellent food in generous portions dominates the numerous flag-floored rooms, while the main bar retains the air of a local pub. Up to seven beers are served in high season, five

INN BRIEF

BRIDPORT

Bull
East Street
10-11; 12-10.30 Sun
(01308) 422878
Draught Bass; Otter Bitter, Ale Ⓗ
Small bar in an historic hotel, hosting live music most Saturdays. A pleasant courtyard provides welcome space in summer.

Greyhound
2 East Street
11-11; 11-11 Sun
(01308) 422944
Courage Directors; Elgood's Greyhound Strong; Theakston Best Bitter; guest beers Ⓗ
Popular Wetherspoon's, offering unusual guest ales; very busy in the evening. Cask Marque accredited.

EAST KNIGHTON

Countryman
Blacknoll Lane
11-3, 6-11; 12-3, 7-10.30 Sun
(01305) 852666
Courage Best Bitter, Directors; Greene King Old Speckled Hen; Ringwood Best Bitter, Old Thumper; Wadworth 6X Ⓗ
Country pub, just off the main road with a good restaurant, children's room and large bar area.

NORDEN

Halfway Inn
11-11; 12-10.30 Sun
(01929) 480402
Badger Best, Tanglefoot, seasonal beers; Gribble Fursty Ferret Ⓗ
Allegedly used by Oliver Cromwell; two lounge areas, a spacious main bar and a superb range of quality food. Cask Marque accredited.

POOLE

Central Hotel
81 Commercial Road, Lower Parkstone
12-3, 5-11; 12-11 Sat; 12-10.30 Sun
(01202) 743970
Badger Best, Tanglefoot, seasonal beers Ⓗ
Superb 19th-century main bar, a modern side bar and a music room upstairs; a local institution.

POWERSTOCK

Three Horseshoes
11-3, 6-11; 12-3, 7-10.30 Sun
(01308) 485328
Palmer Copper Ale, IPA, 200 Ⓗ
Attractive pub, commanding views over the village and splendid countryside. An extensive menu specialises in fish dishes.

normally. A tented beer festival is held in late spring. Weston's traditional cider is sold.
Q❀◑♣●P

EAST MORDEN

Cock & Bottle

On B3075, off A35 near Wareham
✪ 11-3, 6-11; 12-3, 7-10.30 Sun
☎ (01929) 459238
Badger K&B Sussex, Best, Tanglefoot Ⓗ
Lovely, traditional village pub, unspoilt by development. An open fire is the main feature in the warm public bar which is well used by locals. It attracts a lot of custom for its meals served in the cosy dining area. Bar snacks are also available – all at reasonable prices. The garden is well situated for the summer, as the village is off the main road. Wheelchair access is excellent with a designated WC.
♨Q◑⊟♿♣P

GILLINGHAM

Buffalo

Lydfords Lane, Wyke (150 yds from B3081, Wincanton road)
✪ 12-2.30, 5.30-11; 12-3, 7-11 Sat; 12-3, 7-10.30 Sun
☎ (01747) 823759
Badger K&B Sussex, Best Ⓗ
Just outside Gillingham stands the former Matthews Brewery, a landmark for Lydfords Lane, leading to the Buffalo. This once rural pub, now surrounded by housing, still maintains a friendly, country atmosphere. Two compact, linked bars – one intriguingly named Drum & Monkey – feature stone floors, exposed beams and, in one bar, an impressive display of hanging jugs. Meals, mainly lunchtime, are home-cooked, simple but satisfying (no food Sun eve). Monthly quizzes and occasional piano singsongs provide entertainment.
♨Q❀◑♣P

Phoenix

High Street
✪ 10-2.30, 7-11; 10-3, 7-11 Sat; 12-3, 7-10.30 Sun
☎ (01747) 823277
Badger K&B Sussex, Best, seasonal beers Ⓗ
Gillingham's historic 18th-century coaching inn has reclaimed some of the space lost over recent years. The former cake shop next door is now the pub's restaurant. This leaves the bar dedicated to drinkers, who will find a friendly, conversational welcome. All customers benefit from the air filtration system – so efficient that you are never aware of the nearby tandoori. There is always a seasonal beer from Badger on tap. Outside, the patio overlooks the quiet town square. ♨❀◑⇌♣✔

GUSSAGE ALL SAINTS

Drovers Inn

Between A354 and B3078 OS003106
✪ 11.45-3, 6-11; 12-3, 7-10.30 Sun
☎ (01258) 840084
Ringwood Best Bitter, Fortyniner, Old Thumper, seasonal beers Ⓗ
This part-thatched, 17th-century brick village inn (formerly the Earl Haig) boasts flagstoned floors, exposed beams, and an old bread oven. Two bar areas are divided (and warmed) by a large inglenook. The large front garden, with picnic benches, affords good views over the downs. Excellent home-cooked food can be ordered from two blackboards, but no table bookings are taken (no food Mon eve). Well behaved children (and dogs) are welcome. Ringwood's fourth tied house is popular with walkers and locals. ♨Q❀◑♣P

HURN

Avon Causeway Hotel

Off B3073, behind road bridge
✪ 11-11; 12-10.30 Sun
☎ (01202) 482714 website: www.avoncauseway.co.uk
Red Shoot Forest Gold; Ringwood Best Bitter, Old Thumper; Wadworth IPA, 6X, JCB Ⓗ
This pub was the Hurn railway station until 1935. The old platform is complete and houses a carriage, used as a restaurant and a venue for Murder Mystery evenings. The public bar, which welcomes walkers with dogs, has a wood floor and bears a railway theme with many old artefacts. The lounge bar leads through to the family area and garden, where a children's play area has swings and a slide, as well as an aviary. The hotel has 10 rooms – one is a bridal suite.
♉❀⇔◑♿⛺●P⚟✔

IBBERTON

Crown Inn

Church Lane (4 miles off A357) OS788077
✪ 11-2.30 (not Mon), 7-11; 11-11 summer; 12-3, 7-10.30 (12-10.30 summer) Sun
☎ (01258) 817448
Ringwood Best Bitter; guest beer Ⓗ
Idyllic country pub nestling below Bulbarrow Hill. Its 15th/16th-century origins can be discerned in the massive door, flagstoned floor and inglenook. A small brook runs alongside the attractive garden. This Guide regular usually stocks a guest beer from the Cottage Brewery and cider from Burrow Hill. Although off the beaten track, it is well worth making the effort to find this charming pub.
♨Q♉❀◑♿♣●P

LODERS

Loders Arms

OS492943
✪ 11-3, 6-11; 12-3, 7-10.30 Sun
☎ (01308) 422431
Palmer BB, IPA, 200 Ⓗ
Situated in a remote village, deep in rambling countryside, the pub is best approached from the A3066 Bridport-Beaminster road. With stone-flagged floors and a long bar area, the bar itself is adorned with hops. The restaurant has a well-deserved reputation for its excellent food. For those not eating, the bar contains such distractions as a piano, chess and Connect Four. Families are welcome in all areas; camping is possible in the grounds.
♨Q⇔◑♿⛺♣●P

LYME REGIS

Nag's Head

Silver Street
✪ 11-3, 6-11; 10-11 Fri & Sat; 12-10.30 Sun

☎ (01297) 442312
Beer range varies Ⓗ
This fine brick and flint coaching inn, situated above the town, is well worth the effort to find. It affords superb views across Lyme Bay towards Portland Bill from the good-sized garden. A deceptively large local, the pub has two linked bars, a lower level pool room and a renowned first-floor restaurant, famous for its speciality of Tipsy Cod. The house beer, Sark Lark, is brewed by Quay of Weymouth; Channel Island beers are also occasionally stocked.
♨Q❀⛐◐◑♣P

Volunteer

31 Broad Street
⏲ 11-11; 12-10.30 Sun
☎ (01297) 442214
Draught Bass; Otter Ale; guest beer Ⓗ
The pub name refers to the Volunteer Regiment founded in 1794 to combat the threat of a French invasion, but the pub is a lot older than this. The double-fronted, pebbledashed building contains two rooms: a low, beamed bar and a dining/family room where a comprehensive menu is served. The house beer, Donegal, brewed by Branscombe Vale, indicates the origin of the cheerful landlord, a popular publican in Lyme for over 30 years. ♨Q◐◑♣

MANSTON

Plough

Shaftesbury Road (B3091, $2^{1}/_{2}$ miles NE of Sturminster Newton)
⏲ 10.30-2.30, 6-11; 12-3, 7-10.30 Sun
☎ (01258) 472484
Sharp's Cornish Coaster; Ⓗ **guest beers** Ⓗ/Ⓖ
Rescued from disaster five years ago, the Plough has been transformed into an exceptional, highly popular free house, winning seasonal and annual awards from local CAMRA. Drinkers and diners happily share the single bar, enjoying interesting guest beers from both pump and cask. Summer attractions include the well-used pétanque pitch, and the beer festival (usually in July) held in a marquee in a corner of the large garden.
♨❀◐◑♣P

MARSHWOOD

Bottle

On B3165, close to Devon border
⏲ 12-3, 6.30-11 (closed winter Mon); 12-3, 7-10.30 Sun
☎ (01297) 678254
Otter Bitter; Quay Organic Gold; guest beers Ⓗ
This thatched country inn enthusiastically embraces the provision of natural products, with organic beer, food, wine and even organic cola available. The wholesome menu includes vegetarian and vegan choices, as well as locally reared GM-free beef and pork. A single bar serves two small rooms, one no-smoking, with a family room and skittle alley at the rear leading to a large garden overlooking Marshwood Vale. The pub plays host to a nettle eating competition in June, organic of course!
Q❀◐◑▲♣P⚟

OKEFORD FITZPAINE

Royal Oak

Lower Street (2 miles off A357)
⏲ 12-3, 5.30-11; 12-11 Sat; 12-3, 7-10.30 Sun
☎ (01258) 861561
Ringwood Best Bitter Ⓗ
This two-bar, friendly village local has a large garden, games room and a skittle alley. It also serves good, home-cooked food (no meals Sun eve). The cosy public bar, with its flagstoned floor and a huge central wooden pillar, is dominated by an inglenook, whose open fire is more than welcome on a cold winter's evening. The lounge bar-cum-

INN BRIEF

SHAFTESBURY

Olde Two Brewers
24 St James' Street
11-3, 6-11; 12-3, 7-10.30 Sun
(01742) 852210
Courage Best Bitter, Directors; Theakston XB; guest beers Ⓗ
Popular local at the foot of Shaftesbury's Gold Hill, serving excellent meals.

SHERBORNE

Skippers
1 Terrace View, Horsecastles
11-2.30, 5.30 (6 Sat)-11; 12-2, 7-10.30 Sun
(01935) 812753
Wadworth IPA, 6X, JCB, seasonal beers Ⓗ
This Wadworth house is deservedly popular for its food. Ornaments include pigs and walking sticks.

SHAPWICK

Anchor
West Street
11-3, 6-11; 12-3, 7-10.30 Sun
(01258) 857269
Greene King Abbot; Ringwood Best Bitter; guest beer Ⓗ
Recently reopened village free house, with a boules court and good food, close to Badbury Rings Iron Age hill fort.

STOBOROUGH

King's Arms
3 Corfe Road
11-11; 12-10.30 Sun
(01929) 552705
Greene King Abbot; Ringwood Best Bitter; Taylor Landlord; guest beer Ⓗ
17th-century pub affording excellent views. A traditional menu can be served outdoors in this good walking area.

SWANAGE

Red Lion
63 High Street
11-11; 12-10.30 Sun
(01202) 423533
Greene King Old Speckled Hen; Ⓖ **Ringwood Best Bitter; Taylor Landlord;** Ⓗ **guest beers** (summer) Ⓖ
Popular, friendly, Purbeck stone pub with a patio and garden. Addlestones cider is stocked.

WAREHAM

Duke of Wellington
7 East Street
11-11; 12-10.30 Sun
(01929) 553015
Fuller's London Pride; Wadworth 6X; guest beers Ⓗ
Cosy, welcoming town pub with a large patio. An excellent range of food is served (all day in summer).

WYKE REGIS

Wyke Smugglers
76 Portland Road
11-2.30, 6-11; 12-3, 7-10.30 Sun
(01305) 760010
Greene King Old Speckled Hen; guest beers Ⓗ
Community pub with guest beers from Pubmaster's list. Darts and skittles teams predominate. Children are not encouraged inside.

Poor beer

If you consider beer quality in a pub is not up to standard please let us know immediately. Write to GBG, CAMRA, 230 Hatfield Road, St Albans, Herts, AL1 4LW or camra@camra.org.uk. If the pub has a Cask Marque symbol, write to Cask Marque at the address in its editorial feature at the front of the Guide.

restaurant is bright and airy; well-behaved children are welcome for meals.
⛼☺❀◐♣●P

PAMPHILL

Vine ☆
Vine Hill (off B3082)
✪ 11-2.30, 7-11; 12-3, 7-10.30 Sun
☎ (01202) 882259
Beer range varies Ⓗ/Ⓖ
Pretty pub, built as a bake house over 200 years ago, it is close to Kingston Lacy House and Badbury Rings (both NT). Run by the same family for three generations, it has two small bars and a games room upstairs. A large garden, with ample seating, is very popular with walkers and cyclists. Sandwiches and ploughmans are served at lunchtime. A true free house, this former local CAMRA Rural Pub of the Year serves real ales from many small breweries.
Q❀⊟♣●P⊓

PLUSH

Brace of Pheasants
1½ miles off B3143 OS715024
✪ 12-2.30, 7-11; 12-3, 7-10.30 Sun
☎ (01300) 348357
Fuller's London Pride; guest beer Ⓖ
Originally a row of 16th-century cottages, this heavily beamed thatched inn serves real ale from a stillage behind the bar, with not a keg font in sight. Cider is available in summer. Solid comfortable seating, an open fire and inglenook complete the picture. The restaurant enjoys an excellent reputation, using local produce whenever possible (booking is advised). Note the unusual pub sign: two stuffed pheasants inside an illuminated glass case.
⛼Q☺❀⊨◐♣●P⚟⊓

POOLE ❊

Bermuda Triangle
10 Parr Street, Lower Parkstone
✪ 12-2.30, 5.30 (5 Fri)-11; 12-11 Sat; 12-10.30 Sun
☎ (01202) 748087
Beer range varies Ⓗ
Refurbished and reopened as a free house in 1990, this gem soon established itself as a mecca for real ale fans and remains popular. The small bar stocks four constantly changing guest beers. Note the rowing boat and lifebuoy outside; the Triangle mystery is explored throughout the split-level interior, with maps, newspaper cuttings and even a section of aircraft wing suspended from the ceiling.
❀◐⇌(Parkstone)

Blue Boar
29 Market Close (opp. Guildhall)
✪ 11-3, 5 (6 Sat)-11; 12-3, 7-10.30 Sun
☎ (01202) 682247
Cottage Southern Bitter; Courage Best Bitter, Directors; guest beers Ⓗ
Former merchant's house, dating back to 1750, this popular free house is located in Old Poole, near the High Street. The lounge bar is comfortable and stylish, while the atmospheric cellar bar stages live music Wednesday (folk club), Friday and Sunday. Both bars are bedecked with nautical artefacts. The outdoor drinking area is used by morris dancers on May Day. A magnificent function/conference room is available on the second floor. Local CAMRA Pub of the Year 2002. ❀◐⇌

Branksome Railway Hotel
429 Poole Road
✪ 11-11; 11-10.30 Sun
☎ (01202) 769555
Fuller's London Pride; Hampshire Strong's Best Bitter; guest beer Ⓗ
Built in 1894, this Victorian hotel is situated halfway between Bournemouth and Poole town centres, on the main road opposite Branksome Station. Its two bars are connected by an arch: the saloon houses a pool table and dartboard; the lounge bar has plenty of seating and is dominated by a large fireplace. The hotel has six luxury en-suite bedrooms at reasonable prices (discount for CAMRA members). Former local CAMRA Pub of the Season.
⊨◐⇌(Branksome)♣P

Brewhouse
68 High Street
✪ 11-11; 11-5, 6-11 Sat; 12-10.30 Sun
☎ (01202) 685288
Poole Bitter, Bosun, seasonal beers Ⓗ
Good, basic local, home of Poole Brewery. The single bar serves a split-level room, divided by the Poole Brewery logo. At the front, a seating area overlooks the pedestrian precinct; to the rear, two pool tables are in constant use. This busy town-centre pub sells its own beers at a very reasonable price and, although it has TV and juke box, it is a place where cheerful conversation reigns; an oasis in an area rapidly sprouting modern 'plastic' pubs.
⇌♣

Bricklayer's Arms
41 Parr Street, Lower Parkstone
✪ 12-2.30, 5-11; 12-3, 6-11 Sat; 12-3, 7-10.30 Sun
☎ (01202) 740304
Greene King Abbot; Hop Back Summer Lightning; Ringwood Best Bitter, Fortyniner Ⓗ
Upmarket, single-roomed free house, with an L-shaped layout: to the right is a real fire and comfortable armchairs, to the left a sofa, leading to more seating at the rear. Indoor greenery provides a breath of fresh air, while outside, a small seating area is complemented by a secluded rear garden.
⛼❀◐⇌(Parkstone)

Hogshead
382 Ashley Road, Parkstone
✪ 11-11; 12.30-10.30 Sun
☎ (01202) 740596
Boddingtons Bitter; Flowers Original; Greene King IPA, Abbot, Old Speckled Hen; Taylor Landlord; Ⓗ **guest beers** Ⓗ/Ⓖ
Single bar, converted from a former Co-operative store. The interior features much wood, stone floors, with seating on two levels and a large open fire at one end. Very popular with shoppers during the day, it becomes lively at weekends, when the policy is to turn the music up loud. Sky Sports TV is provided for live football matches. Five handpumps are supplemented by two casks on stillage behind the bar. Food is served daily until 7pm.
⛼◐♿P

Oakdale
Kingsmill Road, Oakdale
11-11; 12-10.30 Sun
(01202) 672055
Beer range varies H
The Oakdale has a public bar and a lounge bar, with separate entrances from the car park, but inside there is an internal door between them. The bar runs the length of both rooms. The public bar is basic, with a hard floor, pool table and a dartboard; the lounge bar is more plush with carpets, Tudor-style decor and an open fire. It is a popular choice for Sunday lunch.

Royal Oak & Gas Tavern
25 Skinner Street
11-11; 12-10.30 Sun
(01202) 672022
Greene King Abbot; Hampshire Strong's Best Bitter H
Traditional, back-street pub, dating back to 1798, where many original features remain. Old pictures of Poole hang on wood-panelled walls and help create a warm welcoming atmosphere. Close to Poole Quay, it boasts a pleasant enclosed garden that you would not expect to find in the back streets of Poole. The function room has space for up to 100 people.

PORTLAND

George Inn
133 Reforne, Easton
11-11; 12-10.30 Sun
(01305) 820011
Ringwood Best Bitter, Fortyniner H
This 17th-century pub stands across the road from the cricket ground, a location that is appreciated by locals on summer evenings. The original bar has beams from long-gone sailing ships, and is a place for conversation. By contrast, the larger Quarr Bar, a recent addition, hosts live bands (Sat eve). The menu is unpretentious but wholesome, with generous portions.

SANDFORD ORCAS

Mitre Inn
OS626205
11.30-2.30, 7-11; 12-3, 7-10.30 Sun
(01963) 220271
Adnams Bitter; Greene King Abbot; guest beers H
Entering the Mitre (mind your head) is to experience a pub that really knows its role in life. The welcome is warm, the home-cooked food excellent, the seating comfortable (armchairs in the bar) and the beer in top condition. Flagged floors extend from the bar area to the dining room; well-behaved children are welcome. Outside is an elevated garden. No food is served Monday. Guest beers are selected from the Punch Tavern list.

SEATOWN

Anchor
S off A35 in Chideock
12-3, 6-11 (12-11 summer); 12-3, 7-10.30 Sun
(01297) 489215
Palmer BB (summer), G **Dorset Gold, IPA, 200** H
Accessed by a single track road from Chideock, or by foot along the Dorset Coastal Path, this comfortable inn is situated nearly on the beach. Run by a friendly landlord, it is popular with tourists and local walkers alike. Public parking is available opposite. Live jazz groups feature occasionally at weekends. Opening times may vary, depending on sea conditions and the season – 'phone beforehand if travelling far. There is a caravan site nearby.

SHAFTESBURY

Ship Inn
24 Bleke Street
11-3, 5-11; 11-11 Thu-Sat; 12-10.30 Sun
(01747) 853219
Badger Best, Tanglefoot, seasonal beers H
Until 1930, this 16th-century inn was a doctor's surgery. Now it is a picturesque pub of several bars and a small cosy snug, with an open fire. Exposed beams are everywhere and the sloping floors are appropriately reminiscent of an old ship. This is a popular local, serving Badger's seasonal beers as guests, and excellent, well-priced meals. Entertainment includes occasional music nights; pétanque is played outside in summer.

SHERBORNE

Britannia
Westbury
11-2.30, 6-11; 12-3, 7-10.30 Sun
(01935) 813300
Beer range varies H
Welcoming, 300-year-old inn, believed to be the oldest in town. Collections of model cars, brewing equipment and other artefacts adorn the walls. There are normally five real ales on tap, one usually from Ringwood, with the others from the south-west or Wales; the cider varies. Classical music or jazz provides the background in the lounge, with rock (not deafening) in the public bar. Home-made bread is used in the sandwiches and ploughmans.

Digby Tap
Cooks Lane
11-2.30, 5.30-11; 12-2.30, 7-10.30 Sun
(01935) 813148
Ringwood Best Bitter; guest beers H
Lively, long-established, free house close to the abbey, station and town centre. It is divided into four drinking areas, with flagged floors and cosy corners. Enjoying a strong regular trade, it is a favourite haunt of rugby and hockey players. Unpretentious food is served Mon-Sat and occasional live music is performed. Three or four ever-changing beers mostly come from independent brewers, usually one from each. Mobile phone use is banned.

STOKE ABBOTT

New Inn
11-2.30, 6-11; 12-3, 7-10.30 Sun
(01308) 868333

Palmer IPA, Dorset Gold, 200 [H]
Comfortable, 17th-century inn, situated in the middle of a picturesque village. Good quality freshly-cooked food is offered, which can mean a very busy bar in the tourist season. The bar's unusual thatched canopy reflects the thatch covering the roof. A very impressive fireplace warms the pub in winter. It makes an ideal resting point for walkers on the many paths and bridleways that cross this area.
⛼Q❀⇔◑♿♣P

STRATTON

Saxon Inn
Dorchester Road
(off A37, 2 miles N of Dorchester)
⏲ 11-3; 6-11; 12-3, 7-10.30 Sun
☎ (01305) 260020
Fuller's London Pride; Greene King Abbot; Palmer IPA [H]
This brand-new (2001) thatched country pub was constructed as part of the village extension and features flagged floors, a real fire and good food. Located next to the village church, it is frequented by villagers and tourists alike. The experienced landlord has ensured that this is no transient, trendy pub but one that is destined to mature and acquire great character with time. The house beer is from Palmer – Dorset Gold in summer, Copper Ale in winter.
⛼❀◑♿P

STUDLAND

Bankes Arms
Watery Lane
⏲ 11-11; 12-10.30 Sun
☎ (01929) 450225
Beer range varies [H]
NT-owned, this lovely building of Purbeck stone overlooks the sea near the start of the magnificent coastal clifftop walking route. This split-level, one-bar pub with a no-smoking restaurant, serves eight ever-changing real ales, often from local breweries such as Poole, Quay and Hampshire. An annual summer beer festival offers 50-plus ales and a hog roast. It is very popular, especially with walkers, and on weekend lunchtimes, particularly in winter when the roaring log fire is very welcome.
⛼❀⇔◑⛺🍎

TARRANT MONKTON

Langton Arms
Off B3082 from Wimborne
OS944088
⏲ 11.30-11; 12-10.30 Sun
☎ (01258) 830225
website: www.thelangtonarms.co.uk
Beer range varies [H]
This multi-award winning, 17th-century gem is in a picturesque hamlet of the Tarrant Valley. The rustic public bar houses a pool table and dartboard; the beamed lounge bar bears an array of handpumps, selling over 30 guest beers every month. The restaurant-cum-function room serves excellent food, while the accommodation is of superior quality. A beer festival is held annually, and the pub is a venue for clubs and events; it also has a skittle alley.
⛼Q♨❀⇔◑⊟♿♣P⚟

UPWEY

Royal Standard
700 Dorchester Road
⏲ 11-3, 6-11; 12-10.30 Sun
☎ (01305) 812558
Archers Village; guest beers [H]
Two-bar pub selling two guest beers. The lounge reflects the landlord's interest in railways, with pictures and models. Outside at the rear is an aviary containing a magnificent eagle owl, which could be said to be the licensee's pride and joy, were it not for his equal passion for vintage motorcycles. More modern pursuits are not forgotten – there is internet access – but beware the fine should your mobile ring in the public bar.
⛼Q❀⊟≉♣P

WAYTOWN

Hare & Hounds
⏲ 11.30-3, 6.30-11; 12-3, 7-10.30 Sun
☎ (01308) 488203
Palmer Dorset Gold, IPA [G]
Tucked away in a small hamlet, best reached from the Netherbury end, this unspoilt country pub has a single counter serving two drinking areas. The garden offers superb views and it makes an excellent stopping-place for the many walks that you can take in one of the prettiest parts of west Dorset. No food is served Sunday evening or Monday in winter. Taunton cider is stocked.
⛼Q❀◑♿⛺🍎P

WEST STAFFORD

Wise Man
⏲ 11-3, 6-11; 12-4.30 (closed eve) Sun
☎ (01305) 263694
Ringwood Best Bitter; guest beers [H]

This 400-year-old thatched, ivy-clad pub in a quiet village, has retained its public bar, but the lounge is now almost exclusively used as a restaurant, serving a wide selection of food. Now owned by a local businessman, the pub is rapidly returning to being a thriving local. Appropriate menus, linked with suitable guest beers, are served on special occasions, such as Burns Night and St Patrick's Day.
⌂Q❀◑◐⊟♣P

WEYMOUTH

Boot

High West Street
⚙ 11-11; 12-10.30 Sun
☎ (01305) 770327
Ringwood Best Bitter, Fortyniner, Old Thumper, seasonal beers; guest beer Ⓗ
Weymouth's oldest pub, it can be difficult to find (hidden behind the fire station) but it is well worth the effort. The single wood-floored bar area gives way at each end to rooms with comfortable seating and warming fires. The full Ringwood beer range is supplemented by the landlord's choice of guests and Cheddar Valley cider. The pub's popularity leads to a spillage of customers on to the pavement (seating provided) in clement weather. A true pub, where conversation rules.
⌂Q❀⇌♣●

Weatherbury

7 Carlton Road North
⚙ 11-11; 12-10.30 Sun
☎ (01305) 786040
Draught Bass; Fuller's London Pride; guest beers Ⓗ
Large corner pub, situated in a residential area, 400 yards from the beach. The guest beers usually come from small, established breweries. There is a small patio area, while the interior is open plan, with a pool table dominating one end. A further small side room can be used for meetings or families. The menu is varied without being over elaborate. Happy hours are a feature in the late afternoon.
❀⇔◑◐♿⇌♣P

WIMBORNE

Cricketers

Park Lane
⚙ 11-11; 12-10.30 Sun
☎ (01202) 882846
Marston's Pedigree; Ringwood Best Bitter, Fortyniner; guest beer Ⓗ
Popular, busy (especially at weekends) town-centre pub. The cricketing theme is appropriate as the garden overlooks the town's cricket pitch. The large single bar has a pool table one end and a comfortable area with armchairs at the other. RATS, the Real Ale Tasting Society, meets every Monday and Thursday; members can buy beer at a discount. Beer festivals are held summer and winter.
⌂❀◑♣●

Crown & Anchor

6 Wimborne Road, Walford Bridge
⚙ 11-2.30, 6-11; 12-3, 7-10.30 Sun
☎ (01202) 841405
Badger K&B Sussex, Best Ⓗ
A pub since 1823, rebuilt in 1917 and refurbished in 2000, this friendly local is one of the finest outlets for Badger beers in east Dorset, hence its tenth consecutive listing in this Guide. It also offers splendid lunches. A small garden on the River Allen overlooks Walford Craft Mill. It is a 10-minute walk from the centre of this ancient town, via the footpath that follows the river. This charming gem eschews juke box and fruit machines, but hosts a folk night (Thu).
⌂Q❀◑▲P⊘

WINKTON

Lamb Inn

Burley Road (off B3347)
⚙ 11-3, 5-11 (11-11 summer Sat); 12-10.30 Sun
☎ (01425) 672427
Fuller's London Pride; Ringwood Best Bitter, Fortyniner; guest beer (summer) Ⓗ
A pub since at least the 1780s, it is surrounded by fields – one of them a former wartime airfield. Retaining two bars, the public has a piano, dartboard and history of the airfield. The comfortable lounge offers an interesting menu, much of which is displayed on a large blackboard (children welcome if eating) – come on Tuesday for curry, followed by a quiz. Wednesday is jazz night. The restaurant has its own Sunday lunch menu. The garden has tables and a children's play area.
⌂❀◑◐⊟♣P

WORTH MATRAVERS

Square & Compass ☆

Off B3069 OS974777
⚙ 12-3, 6-11; 12-11 Sat; 12-3, 7-10.30 (not winter eve) Sun
☎ (01929) 439229
Badger Tanglefoot; Ringwood Best Bitter; guest beers Ⓖ
Step back in time into this treasure trove of a remote, yet thriving inn. Run by the Newman family since 1907 and listed in every edition of this Guide, some highlights are the rare drinking corridor, flagstone floors and its own museum which boasts the largest possible fossil collection from the Purbeck coastline – a World Heritage Site. It stages a beer festival (Oct); cider festival (Nov) and frequent live music. Very popular with walkers; do not miss this superlative ancient Purbeck stone inn.
⌂Q❀▲♣●

YETMINSTER

White Hart

High Street
⚙ 12-2.30, 7-11; 12-3, 7-10.30 Sun
☎ (01935) 872338
Greene King IPA; guest beers Ⓗ
This 400-year-old thatched inn is located in the village centre, a pleasant stroll from the railway halt. The convivial public bar is basically furnished and caters for pub games. An imaginative menu, including vegetarian options, is served in the more comfortable lounge. The pub provides accommodation in an adjoining converted barn. The skittle alley at the rear has its own bar; the garden has a play area for children.
Q⇔◑◐⊟♿⇌♣P

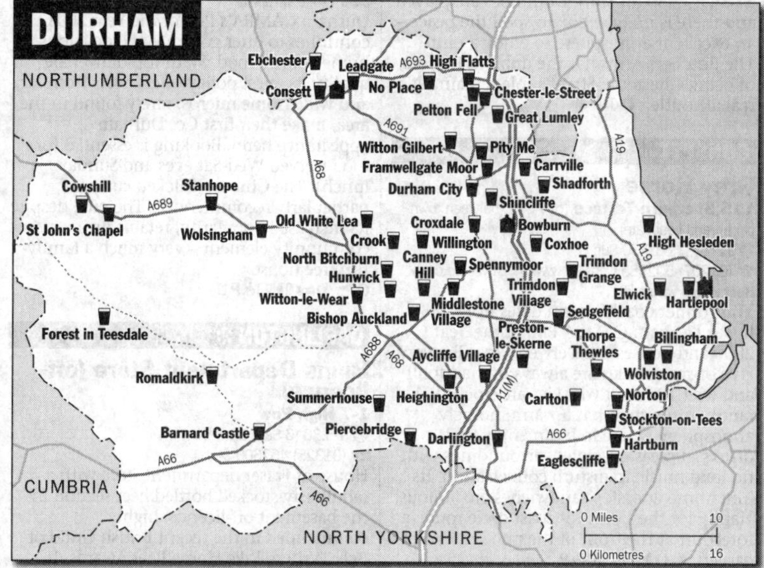

Co Durham incorporates part of the former county of Cleveland

BARNARD CASTLE

Coach & Horses

22 Galgate

11-11; 12-10.30 Sun

☎ (01833) 638369

Jennings Bitter, Cumberland Ale H

18th-century inn situated in the centre of this historic market town, gateway to the reaches of Upper Teesdale with the 12th-century castle also close by. Friendly atmosphere; popular with locals, visitors and walkers. One of the few Jennings outlets in this area despite the close proximity of Cumbria.

BISHOP AUCKLAND

Newton Cap

1 Newton Cap Bank

12-4 (not Tue), 7-11; 12-3, 7-11 Sun

☎ (01388) 605445

John Smith's Bitter; guest beer H

Friendly, traditional working men's pub with a warm welcome for all. A quiet haven in a town dominated by keg theme pubs. The landlady takes a great pride in the quality of the ales. If the bar is not too busy try your hand at a game of ringo – not easy after a couple of pints. Guest beers are sold at very reasonable prices, when available, contrary to trends elsewhere! Camerons Strongarm is once again stocked occasionally. The pub is conveniently located only 200 yards from the bus station.

Q

CANNEY HILL

Sportsman

Canney Hill

12-2.30 (4 Sat; not Mon), 5 (7 Mon & Sat)-11; 12-4, 7-10.30 Sun

☎ (01388) 603847

Camerons Strongarm; guest beer (occasional) H

Situated on the A689 on the outskirts of Bishop Auckland, the Sportsman is a popular pub renowned for an excellent pint of Strongarm and good meals; it is advisable to book for Sunday lunch. The extension has created a larger dining section and has also provided an area suitable for meetings. The pub now has a bar, snug and eating area. It is well served by public transport and the bus stop is by the front entrance.

Q P

CARLTON

Smith's Arms

12-2 (not Mon & Tue), 5-11; 11-11 Fri & Sat; 12-10.30 Sun

☎ (01740) 630471

Camerons Strongarm; guest beer H

Fine end-of-terrace, red-brick pub in the centre of the village. The bustling public bar has a large-screen TV and is usually full on big match nights. The quieter lounge has a dining area at one end and comfortable settees on which it is all too easy to nod off after a few pints. The chef uses fresh local ingredients and the meals represent excellent value for money. At busy times reserving a table is a smart move. No food is served on Sun eve.

P

CHESTER-LE-STREET

Butchers Arms

Middle Chare (off Front Street)

11-3 (4 Sat), 6.30-11; 12-3, 7-11 Sun

☎ (0191) 388 3605

Camerons Strongarm; Marston's Pedigree; guest beer H

This friendly, one-roomed town pub caters for the more mature customer. Emphasis is placed on the traditional lunches served

INDEPENDENT BREWERIES

Castle Eden & Camerons Hartlepool
Derwent Rose Consett
Durham Bowburn

11-3 (12-2.30 on Sun). Dominoes are played and there is no juke box to spoil the peace – an excellent atmosphere to enjoy a pint. The Butchers Arms has the dubious honour of being Chester-le-Street's sole remaining real ale outlet. Q ◐ ⇌ ♣

CONSETT

Grey Horse

115 Sherburn Terrace (off A692, between town centre and Leadgate)

12-11; 12-10.30 Sun

☎ (01207) 502585 website: www.thegreyhorse.co.uk

Beer range varies H

This former coaching inn dates from 1848. It was Durham CAMRA Pub of the Year 2000 and houses the Derwent Rose Brewery. Five or six real ales are always on handpull and over 100 malt whiskies are stocked. A family-run pub, it has a warm, homely atmosphere where folk can enjoy their drinks in pleasant, quiet surroundings with no loud music to disturb conversation. Its lunchtime doorstep sandwiches are famous. Handy for the Coast-to-Coast cycle route, a forecourt at the front of the pub serves as a garden. Q ❀ ◐ ♣ P

COXHOE

Cricketers

Victoria Terrace (off A177)

7-11; 12-3, 7-10.30 Sun

☎ (0191) 377 0510

Camerons Strongarm; Marston's Pedigree; guest beer H

Although now owned by Pubmaster, the Cricketers still retains the 'look' of a Vaux pub. It is open plan with one large, U-shaped bar/lounge. It is very much a well-used village local and the Coxhoe football and cricket teams (hence the pub's current name) use it as their base. The beer garden has good facilities for children. ❀ ♣

CROOK

Uplands Hotel

Acacia Gardens (off B6298)

11-3, 7-11; 12-2.30, 7-10.30 Sun

Beer range varies H

Imposing early 20th-century house built for a local colliery manager. The once massive colliery and chemical works are long gone but a heritage trail remains. The building was sympathetically refurbished in 1999 and includes a lounge/conservatory, restaurant and traditional bar; accommodation includes a bridal suite. Four cask ales are usually on offer from a broad range which normally includes a Black Sheep beer. 2002 saw the start of seasonal beer festivals and also the award of the local CAMRA Pub of the Season. Take bus no. 1b from Darlington, Crook and Tow Law to the Uplands Hotel, the stop is adjacent.
❀ P

CROXDALE

Daleside Arms

Front Street (B6288, 3 miles S of Durham, off A167 roundabout)

12-2.30 (3 Sat; not Mon-Thu), 7-11; 12-3, 7-10.30 Sun

☎ (01388) 814165

Beer range varies H

Durham CAMRA's Pub of the Year 2001 continues to offer good ale and delicious home-cooked food. With top-drawer ale quality its guest policy offers beers from far and wide (some micros, rarely found in the area, make their first Co. Durham appearance here). Booking is essential for food (served Wed-Sat eves and Sunday lunch). The Chinese chicken curry is particularly recommended. The pub, despite its increased popularity, retains its community element – very much a family-run free house.
Q ❀ ◐ ♿ P

DARLINGTON

Binns Department Store (off-licence)

1-7 High Row

9-5.30 (6 Sat); 11-5 Sun

☎ (01325) 462606

House of Fraser department store with a fabulously-stocked bottled beer section in the basement off-licence, highly commended in the recent British Guild of Beer Writers Take Home Beer Awards. It stocks over 400 quality beers to take away, including dozens of British and Belgian bottle-conditioned ales; the own-label Binns' beer comes from Springhead. Frequent tasting sessions are held (Sat), often hosted by brewers. A good selection of special glasses available, they are kept out of sight due to space limitations. ⇌

Britannia

Archer Street

11.30-3, 5.30-11; 11-11 Fri & Sat; 12-3, 7-10.30 Sun

☎ (01325) 463787

Camerons Strongarm; John Smith's Bitter; guest beers H

Relaxed, friendly old local just across the ring road from the town centre but well-removed from the frenetic circuit. A bastion of cask beer for 140 years, it is a frequent entry in this Guide. The Britannia retains much of the appearance and layout of the private house it originally was, with a modestly-enlarged bar and domestic-proportioned parlour (used for meetings) either side of a central corridor. Listed for historical associations, it was the birthplace of teetotal, 19th-century publisher, J.M. Dent. Up to three guest beers are on offer, usually from larger independents.
Q ⇌ ♣ P

Number Twenty-2

22 Coniscliffe Road

11-11; closed Sun

☎ (01325) 354590

Burton Bridge Burton Festival Ale; Hambleton Bitter; Village White Boar, Bull, Old Raby; guest beers H

Popular, stylish bar with a passion for cask ale, on the edge of the town centre. It has won numerous CAMRA awards since it was converted from a shop and restaurant in 1995, including local Pub of the Year 2002. Huge, curved windows and a high ceiling give an airy character even when packed, but visit off-peak to savour at its best. In all, 13 handpumps serve nine beers, mainly from small independent brewers; this is the home pub of Village Brewer beers, commissioned from Hambleton. Nightmare is sold here as Yorkshire Stout. Q◐⇌🍷✔

Old Yard Tapas Bar

98 Bondgate

⏲ 11-11; 12-10.30 Sun

☎ (01325) 467385 website: www.tapasbar.fsnet.co.uk

John Smith's Magnet; Theakston Cool Cask, Old Peculier; guest beers Ⓗ

Interesting mixture of small town-centre bar and Mediterranean-style taverna, with a range of five real ales sold alongside the sangria, ouzo, tapas and mezes. Regular theme nights are organised with live bouzouki, plate-smashing and flamenco – but participation is not compulsory! It is perfectly acceptable to simply pop in for a pint. The guest beers generally come from larger independent breweries. Licensed for pavement drinking in summer, when tables are set out. Public car parks are within 50 yards. ❀◐◑⇌

Quaker Coffee House

2 Mechanics Yard (yard next to Binns store in High Row)

⏲ 11-11; 12-10.30 Sun

☎ (01325) 468364

website: www.welcome.to/the.quaker

Beer range varies Ⓗ

Unusual bar in one of Darlington's oldest buildings, tucked away in one of the hidden town-centre yards. It features an unusual bar with an upstairs restaurant, which acts as a function room in the evenings (lunches are served Mon-Sat). A popular venue for visiting football fans, it also stages live music twice a week. It was awarded local CAMRA Pub of the Year for two years running. Quaker Ghost is the house beer, brewed by Darwin in honour of Ethel, the resident ghost. ◐♿⇌♣🍷

Tanners Hall

63-64 Skinnergate

⏲ 11-11; 12-10.30 Sun

☎ (01325) 369938

Courage Directors; Shepherd Neame Spitfire; Theakston Best Bitter; guest beers Ⓗ

Typical town-centre Wetherspoon's pub, it is spacious with a no-smoking area, and plenty of old pictures of Darlington are displayed. A single, long bar serves drink and food. A wide range of drinks at highly competitive prices draws the crowds, particularly at weekends, when the pub tends to be very busy. Good value meals are served all day. A patio area is available for outdoor drinking.
♨Q❀◐◑♿⇌⊬✔

DURHAM CITY ❄

Cathedrals

Court Lane, Old Elvet

⏲ 11-11; 12-10.30 Sun

☎ (0191) 370 9632

Beer range varies Ⓗ

This new brew-pub is one of only three breweries in County Durham: brewing was suspended as the Guide went to press, but the management hopes to start again soon. Situated in a former police station, the brewing plant is located behind the main bar.
◐◑♿⇌P

Colpitts

Hawthorne Terrace (near bus and rail stations)

⏲ 12-11; 12-10.30 Sun

☎ (0191) 386 9913

Samuel Smith OBB Ⓗ

Durham has three timeless pubs in its centre – Victoria, Shakespeare and Colpitts. An intimate, atmospheric, old-style boozer with a busy bar, small lounge and compact pool room. The welcome is friendly and the no-frills approach is a refreshing change from the run-of-the-mill, artificial pubs the marketing men think we want. Another feat amazing for Durham is the price of a pint – the cheapest – and what is more important, the beer is excellent.

Court Inn

Court Lane

⏲ 11-11; 12-10.30 Sun

☎ (0191) 384 7350

Draught Bass; guest beers Ⓗ

Standing next to the Crown Court and prison, this popular pub affords an imposing view looking westwards to the cathedral. The comfortable, well-appointed bar has a congenial atmosphere. A larger, no-smoking area with tables is used by drinkers and diners. A wide range of quality bar snacks and meals is sold throughout the day. It is popular with locals, students and tourists. Guest ales are often from local breweries. ❀◐◑♿⊬

Dun Cow

37 Old Elvet

⏲ 11-11; 12-4, 7-10.30 Sun

☎ (0191) 386 9219 website: theduncow.com

Boddingtons Bitter; Castle Eden Ale; guest beer Ⓗ

This historic pub, full of character, is situated opposite the Crown Court and prison. The intimate snug (entered by a passageway) has remained unchanged in living memory. Continue further down the passageway to reach the more spacious lounge. Popular with locals and students, its congenial atmosphere attracts all ages. The pub boasts the highest sales of Castle Eden Ale in the country. The guest beers come from local breweries. Good value snacks are sold at lunchtime with a more extensive range available on Friday. Folk music is staged on Thursday evening.
Q◐◻♿♣⊬

Elm Tree

12 Crossgate

⏲ 12-3, 6-11; 11-11 Sat; 12-10.30 Sun

☎ (0191) 386 4621

Adnams Bitter; Draught Bass; Camerons Strongarm; Tetley Bitter Ⓗ

Old ex-Vaux coaching inn just off the city centre with a bar and a smaller lounge. Former Durham CAMRA Pub of the Year when Vaux was in charge, the decor and furniture have deteriorated since the destruction of the brewery. Popular with all ages and busy at weekends; students flock to the seats at the rear of the pub on summer nights. Entertainment includes a regular quiz and live music. Remains of the original elm tree are found in the bar. There is a large car park, and two bed and breakfast rooms are available.
Q❀🛏◻⇌♣P

Half Moon

New Elvet (opp. Royal County Hotel)
11-11; 12-10.30 Sun
☎ (0191) 386 4528
Draught Bass; Worthington Bitter; guest beers Ⓗ
The Half Moon occupies a splendid position by the River Wear, which itself allows wonderful, meandering walks and superb views of Durham's magnificent cathedral. This classic pub has a listed interior; its back bar is particularly noteworthy. Customers include a good mix of students, tourists and locals, and it is handy for the town centre and market place. One of the guest beers usually comes from Durham Brewery. Sandwiches are available at lunchtime. Disabled access is via a side passage. ✿♿

Hogshead

58 Saddler Street (between market place and cathedral)
11-11; 12-10.30 Sun
☎ (0191) 386 9550
Black Sheep Best Bitter; Caledonian Deuchars IPA; Castle Eden Ale; Hook Norton Old Hooky; Tetley Bitter; guest beers Ⓗ
When Whitbread sold its pubs, including the Hogshead chain, ale drinkers waited to see how choice would be affected. There are limits, as expected of most pub chains, but here a few surprises still appear. The good ale quality attracts young and old but be warned, the place is often busy on weekend evenings. The pub is extremely popular with students and it would be nice to think they drink the cask! An adventurous manager puts on as varied a beer range as possible in this typical Hogshead.

King's Lodge

Waddington Street, Flass Vale
11-11; 12-10.30 Sun
☎ (0191) 370 9977
website: www.kingslodge-leisure.co.uk
Darwin Durham Light Ale; Fuller's London Pride; Wadworth 6X Ⓗ
This modern-style, smart hotel/pub has undergone continuous refurbishment over the past four years, owing to fire damage. The comfortable, contemporary bar area has an array of Durham photos. The plush 80-seater restaurant has prices to match. A pianist plays (Wed and Thu) and alternates on Sunday evening with a singer who also performs on Friday and Saturday. Bar snacks are available from the bistro. The beer prices in the bar tend to be high. Conference facilities are available. Q✿P

Queen's Head Hotel

2 Sherburn Road, Gilesgate
11-3, 5-11; 12-3, 7-10.30 Sun
☎ (0191) 386 5649
Greene King Old Speckled Hen; Marston's Pedigree; Tetley Burton Ale; guest beer Ⓗ
A good mix of locals and hotel residents drink here, and it is a meeting place for darts, dominoes, pool and leek clubs. The distinctive bar attracts plenty of regulars, while the lounge is more traditional. A good range of reasonably-priced meals are offered. The accommodation has been recently refurbished. Bus routes 22, 63, 64, 154 and 220 serve the Queen's Head.
✿♿P

Shakespeare Tavern ☆

63 Saddler Street (between market place and cathedral)
11-11; 12-10.30 Sun
McEwan 80/-; Theakston Best Bitter; guest beers Ⓗ
This pub, long-absent from this Guide, has become a positive haven for real ale drinkers. A change of management brought superb beer quality and the return of guest ales. Another gem, like the Victoria, this pub is on CAMRA's national inventory. With its back room and amazing snug comes a tiny main front bar, even with 12

INN BRIEF

AYCLIFFE VILLAGE

County
13 The Green
12-3, 5.30-11; 12-3 Sun
(01325) 312273
John Smith's Magnet; Wells Bombardier; guest beers Ⓗ
Overlooking the broad village green, this pub is considered a fully-fledged restaurant, despite the choice of good beer.

BILLINGHAM

Station Hotel
Station Road
12-11; 12-10.30 Sun
(01642) 366911
Draught Bass Ⓗ
Spacious hotel on the site of several earlier pubs. There is a lively atmosphere in the one large room, hosting a weekly quiz.

BISHOP AUCKLAND

Pollards Inn
104 Etherley Lane
12-3, 6-11; 12-3, 7-10.30 Sun
(01388) 603539
Camerons Bitter, Strongarm; guest beer Ⓗ
On the western edge of town near the hospital. Meals are served 12-2 and 6-9 (no food Sun eve).

Tut 'n' Shive
68 Newgate Street
11-11; 12-10.30 Sun
(01388) 603252
Beer range varies Ⓗ
Busy pub, near the bus station, popular with younger drinkers at weekends; live music Thu eve.

CARRVILLE

Grange Inn
High Street
11-11; 12-10.30 Sun
(0191) 384 6750
Castle Eden Nimmo's 4X; guest beer Ⓗ
Basic, but comfortable, pub. Two Castle Eden ales usually sold; the food is worth a try.

COWSHILL

Cowshill Hotel
12-2.30, 7-11 (afternoon opening flexible); 12-2.30, 7-11 Sun
(01388) 537236
Tetley Bitter Ⓗ
Imposing, three-storey, stone-built hotel near Kilhope Lead-mining Centre, run by the same family for 35 years. Bus Weardale No. 101.

DARLINGTON

Darlington Cricket Club
South Terrace
7.30 (7 Fri; 4 Sat)-11; 12-3, 7-10.30 Sun
(01325) 250044
Theakston Cool Cask; guest beers Ⓗ
Traditional-style pavilion set in a shared venue for league football and cricket. Show this Guide or CAMRA membership to gain entry.

DURHAM CITY

Garden House
North Road
11-11; 12-10.30 Sun
(0191) 384 3460
Black Sheep Best Bitter; guest beers Ⓗ
City pub in the style of a country inn. Above-average bar snacks and meals. Guest ales are on rotation.

FRAMWELLGATE MOOR

Salutation
Dryburn View
11-11; 12-10.30 Sun
Draught Bass; Greene King Old Speckled Hen; Tetley Bitter; Wells Bombardier Ⓗ
Busy, food-oriented pub with a lively clientele. With four cask ales, a guest beer would be appreciated.

people drinking here it can feel packed. The intimate, friendly atmosphere where strangers are treated like regulars makes this pub unmissable when visiting Durham.
Q⊞≥

Victoria ☆

86 Hallgarth Street
⊙ 11-3, 6-11; 12-2, 6-10.30 Sun
☎ (0191) 386 5269
Darwin Durham Light Ale; McEwan 80/-; Marston's Pedigree; Theakston Best Bitter Ⓗ
What a cracker! This consistent entry sits like a time warp with a compact, friendly bar and unspoilt snug with its own serving hatch and bell pushes. Both young and old mingle in the genial environment, the real fire is especially welcome in winter. This pub offers an impressive range of malt whisky, in addition to the cask ale. The house beer comes from Durham Brewery. If you choose not to venture far, accommodation is available. The landlord, continues to keep this impressive pub just as it should be. A gem.
ᗑQ⊟⊞≥

Woodman Inn

23 Gilesgate (10 minutes walk uphill from the market place)
⊙ 12-11; 12-10.30 Sun
☎ (0191) 386 7500
Beer range varies Ⓗ
Locals and students gather at this popular pub with its constantly changing, well-kept real ales from micro-breweries. The October beer festival is supported and manned by Durham CAMRA and offers a minimum of 25 real ales. The public bar area has reduced sound levels of music (juke box), and serves a good stottie. ◑♿

EAGLESCLIFFE

Blue Bell

663 Yarm Road
⊙ 11-11; 12-10.30 Sun
☎ (01642) 780358
Courage Directors; Theakston Old Peculier; guest beers Ⓗ
This pub was rebuilt from an old roadhouse on the north bank of the River Tees, adjacent to Yarm Bridge. This was replaced by an iron bridge in the 1800s, which collapsed on the opening evening! The stone bridge was widened instead. The pub enjoys extensive views over the river from its gardens and decking. A popular eating place, but the Blue Bell also has an unswerving commitment to real ale, with regular guest beers from small brewers. It is part of the JT Barras chain.
❀◑♿♣P

EBCHESTER

Derwent Walk

Ebchester Hill (B6309, Leadgate road)
⊙ 12-3, 6-11; 12-11 Fri & Sat; 12-10.30 Sun
☎ (01207) 560347
Jennings Bitter, Cumberland Ale, Cocker Hoop, Sneck Lifter; guest beer Ⓗ
This pub continues to be popular with locals, walkers and diners alike. Situated in picturesque surroundings, it offers fine cask ale and a varied food menu. A comfortable hostelry with wooden flooring and memorabilia, it possesses an extra dimension that more modern restaurant-style pubs lack. A warm welcome is assured, it is a pity about the prominence given to the Cumberland smooth pump as you enter the pub, hopefully it will not hit cask sales.
Q❀◑⊞♿P⍞✔

ELWICK

Spotted Cow

The Green
⊙ 11.30-11; 12-10.30 Sun
☎ (01429) 266373
Camerons Strongarm Ⓗ
One of two whitewashed pubs overlooking the village green, the Spotted Cow is a long, low building with two separate rooms. The large public bar is furnished with plain wooden furniture and a large-screen TV, while the lounge is more comfortable and peaceful. The pub has been part of the Camerons estate for longer than most people round here can remember. Good food is served daily.
◑⊞♣P⍞

FOREST IN TEESDALE

High Force Hotel

On B6277, S of village
⊙ 11-3, 7-11 (11-11 summer); 7 (12 summer)-10.30 Sun
☎ (01833) 622222
High Force Teesdale Bitter, Forest XB, Cauldron Snout Ⓗ
Small, unpretentious, 19th-century residential hotel, popular with walkers and visitors to England's highest and most spectacular waterfall, High Force, secreted in woods just opposite. The stepped, two-roomed public bar is simply furnished and has a preponderance of panelling, exposed stone and well-used open fires – snow comes early 1,060 feet up in the Pennines. A former stable behind the hotel became home to High Force Brewery in 1995 but due to the many pressures on the licensees' time the frequency of brewing has been reduced with Darwin having taken over production of the draught brands in the last year.
ᗑ❀⊟◑♣P⍞

FRAMWELLGATE MOOR ❄

Tap & Spile

27 Front Street (off A167 bypass, 1½ miles from Durham centre)
⊙ 11.30-3 , 6 (5 Fri)-11; 12-3, 7-10.30 Sun
☎ (0191) 386 5451
Black Sheep Best Bitter; Jennings Cumberland Ale; guest beers Ⓗ
Despite Enterprise Inns' policy of restricting the choice of guest ales, this pub continues to offer a good choice of beer and Weston's Old Rosie cider. Devotees still frequent this popular watering-hole remembering the choice of ales available in the Tap's infancy. This four-roomed pub is finished in typical bare boarded ale house-style and has a bar billiard table in the family room. Light bar snacks and hot drinks are available. Credit goes to the licensee who does his best to offer the best ale choice possible despite limits.
Q♉⊞♿♣●⚟

GREAT LUMLEY

Old England

Front Street (on main street through village)
Public: 11-11; 12-10.30 Sun; Lounge: 12-2, 6.15-11; 12-3, 7-10.30 Sun
(0191) 388 5257
Beer range varies H

Large, friendly, family-run pub. It offers a wide range of guest beers, usually three on tap, including ales from small local breweries in Northumberland and Durham. The spacious, split-level lounge is comfortable and divided into distinct areas by wood and coloured glass panels. The atmosphere here is peaceful and it attracts a regular clientele, including diners (a no-smoking eating section is also available). The popular public bar is more boisterous with a pool table, dartboard, satellite and large-screen TV and a juke box. Other entertainment includes a quiz, held twice a week, (Tue and Thu eves). Q

HARTBURN

Masham Hotel

87 Hartburn Village
11-11; 12-3, 7-10.30 Sun
(01642) 580414
Draught Bass; Black Sheep Special H

Excellent, unspoilt local in a tree-lined village on the outskirts of Stockton. Its origins as a private house are clear for all to see. A central bar serves a large room, a snug via a hatch and two other rooms via the corridor. To the rear are extensive gardens where barbecues feature in summer. Regular live music events are held, often with an Irish theme with the licensee jamming along. Note that no meals are served Saturday evening or Sunday. Q P

HARTLEPOOL

Causeway

Vicarage Gardens, Stranton (off A689, behind Stranton Church)
11-11; 12-10.30 Sun
(01429) 273954
Camerons Bitter, Strongarm; Marston's Pedigree; guest beers H

Hidden behind its Victorian red-brick frontage lies this three-roomed gem. A large public bar serves the needs of the serious drinker. Two quieter side rooms (one of them is no-smoking) have drinks dispensed from a hatch in the corridor. Universally regarded as the brewery tap, the pub is popular with Camerons' workers, as well as those of Pubmaster's nearby offices. The licensee is a keen musician, so the pub hosts regular live music evenings. Q

Nursery Inn

Hopps Street
12 (11.30 Sat)-11; 12-10.30 Sun
(01429) 268994
Camerons Strongarm H

Set in the appropriately named Hopps Street, the pub occupies the site of the Mary Willett Excursionists Day Nursery Garden (hence the name). This fine white-painted pub has won recent awards for Camerons Best-Kept Cellar and Hartlepool civic society. The music room plays host to the Hartlepool folk club and other live music events. The pub has its own pigeon club and Sunday football team. The walls of the pub are adorned with old photographs of local interest. P

HEIGHINGTON

George & Dragon

East Green (5 miles N of Darlington)
12-3, 5.30-11 (11-11 summer Sat); 12-3, 7-10.30 Sun
(01325) 313152
Black Sheep Best Bitter; John Smith's Magnet; Wells Bombardier; guest beers H

Friendly village pub, with locals happily mixing with people from further afield. It is an old coaching station, complete with stables yet refurbished in a more modern style. The spacious, bright, cheery lounge has a separate bar area. Bar meals are served in the lounge, with a separate restaurant area in a conservatory-style extension. The outstanding home-cooked food has an excellent reputation locally (no meals served on Sun eve). Live music is performed on alternate Saturdays. P

HUNWICK

Quarryburn

1 Helmington Square (B6286)
12-2.30 (not Wed), 5.30 (7 Wed)-11; 12-11 Sat; 12-10.30 Sun
(01388) 607236
Ansells Best Bitter; Tetley Mild H

INN BRIEF

HARTLEPOOL

Jackson Arms
Tower Street
12-11; 12-10.30 Sun
(01429) 862413
Draught Bass; guest beers H
Traditional pub in an old part of the town, named after a founding father, Ralph Ward Jackson. Lunches available.

HIGH FLATTS

Plough Inn
11-11; 11-10.30 Sun
(0191) 388 2068
Black Sheep Special; Wadworth 6X H
Spacious one-roomed bar in the countryside. Friendly atmosphere, the landlords are enthusiastic about real ale.

HIGH HESLEDEN

Ship Inn
12-3, 6.30-11; closed Mon; 12-3, 7-10.30 Sun
(01429) 836453
Beer range varies H
Newly reopened village pub with three constantly changing cask ales and excellent food.

LEADGATE

Jolly Drovers
12-11; 12-10.30 Sun
(01207) 503994
Adnams Bitter; Bateman XB H
In an area short on real ale, this pub has not gone for a predictable choice. The food is recommended.

SHADFORTH

Plough
South Side
7 (12 Sat usually)-11; 12-10.30 Sun
(0191) 372 0375
Beer range varies H
Friendly, two-roomed village pub, traditional bar with real fire and larger lounge. Suffers from stay-at-home TV brigade. No food.

SPENNYMOOR

Frog & Ferret
Coulson Street, Low Spennymoor
4 (11 Thu-Sat)-11; 12-10.30 Sun
(01388) 818312
Camerons Strongarm; Courage Directors; Theakston Cool Cask, XB; guest beers H
Small, quiet local worth a visit for the range of beers in this area. Local CAMRA Pub of the Year.

The dining room of this hostelry, now standing for two centuries, is adorned with theatrical memorabilia and complements the fine foods on offer. The beer range has changed and the pub is one of the few outlets for cask mild in the area – well worth a detour. The ghost can still be heard treading the boards upstairs, and it managed to smash the landlord's pride and joy Friary Meux mirror to coincide with the launch of the 2002 edition of this Guide. Buses on the 108 Willington-Bishop Auckland route pass the front door – ask for the Wheatsheaf. ♔Q◑▲♣

MIDDLESTONE VILLAGE

Ship Inn

Low Road

✪ 5 (12 Fri & Sat)-11; 12-10.30 Sun

☎ (01388) 810904

Beer range varies Ⓗ

The pub that Vaux tried to close, reopened following a local CAMRA campaign and it has gone from strength to strength. It now has six handpumps, and the beer includes examples from small, independent breweries with always one from Daleside and Durham. Local CAMRA Pub of the Year 2001 and 2002, it was national runner-up 2001. A regular quiz night is held (Thu) and beer festivals are hosted in May and November. Bar games include toad in the hole and skittles, and there is a darts league on Monday. A regular bus service stops outside the front door. Popular for food, especially Sunday lunch, meals are served lunchtime Fri-Sun and Thu-Sat evenings. A roof-top patio is an unusual spot to enjoy a drink. ♔❀◑♣P⌸

NO PLACE

Beamish Mary Inn

Front Street (600 yds off A693)

✪ 12-11; 12-10.30 Sun

☎ (0191) 370 0237

Black Sheep Best Bitter, Special; Jennings Cumberland Ale; Theakston Old Peculier; guest beers Ⓗ

The Beamish Mary Inn remains one of Durham's finest real ale outlets. While the pub has been tidied up in recent years, its design and furnishings must be experienced to be appreciated. It enjoys good local support and is well worth a visit, especially in February for the annual beer festival. The pub offers a good combination of above-average food and live music (many evenings a week), and a wide range of guest ales; Big Lamp Lamplight is the house bitter. ♔Q❀⛟◑⊟✔

NORTH BITCHBURN

Red Lion

North Bitchburn Terrace (A689, 3 miles NW of Bishop Auckland)

✪ 12-3, 7-11; 12-3, 7-10.30 Sun

☎ (01388) 763501

Black Sheep Special; Greene King Abbot; Marston's Pedigree; John Smith's Bitter; guest beer Ⓗ

Old roadside free house, in the same hands for over 15 years, this friendly inn has long held a wide-reaching reputation for ale and food. Enter the compact pool room off the comfortable, bright bar; down two steps to a surprisingly spacious restaurant. The rear patio offers spectacular views over the Wear Valley. Look for the caricature of the landlord in the pub sign. Guest beers are from all over Britain, and change regularly. Bus No. 1B, Darlington-Tow Law, stops 50 yards away. ♔Q❀◑♣●P

NORTON

Unicorn

147 High Street (next to duck pond)

✪ 12-3.30, 5.30-11; 11-11 Fri & Sat; 12-4, 7-10.30 Sun

☎ (01642) 643364

John Smith's Magnet Ⓗ

Superb old village gem with interesting layout which the landlady and customers would go to war to defend! This nearly happened a few years ago when a well-meaning brewery wanted to box in a steel girder bearing the name Dorman Long Steel. Pride in local craftmanship prevailed. The pub has a small public bar and several side rooms served by a hatch in the corridor. In a world of pubs serving a host of beers, the Unicorn keeps only one, supremely well: ask for cask. Q☋❀◐⊟♿♣

OLD WHITE LEA

Dun Cow Inn

Turn W at Royal George, Billy Row, then 1 mile

✪ 7-11 Wed, Fri & Sat; 7-10.30 Sun

☎ (01388) 762714

Darwin Evolution Ⓗ

Genuine traditional, rural pub that has hardly changed since it was taken over by the present incumbent's forefathers in the early 19th century. New visitors will be surprised by the welcome offered, although it is best to ring and check times before travelling. It may open at other times for group visits when extra ales from the Darwin range may be available with sufficient prior notice. Fine collections of drinking and brewing memorabilia adorn the bars, some of which date back to the days of the first licensee in 1830. Take bus No. 1B to Billy Row, then walk for approximately one mile. ♔Q❀⊟P⚟

PELTON FELL

Moorings

Hett Hills

✪ 11.45-11; 11.45-10.30 Sun

☎ (0191) 370 1597

Black Sheep Special; Theakston Cool Cask; guest beer Ⓗ

This country pub oozes character and has been reborn, based on high quality food and real ale. Built on a hill, it has a downstairs bar and a large restaurant upstairs, specialising in seafood. The landlord is attentive and hospitable, and has the Master Cellarman certificate, as is evident in the beer quality. Food is served from 12-9.30 daily. ❀◑⊟P⚟

PIERCEBRIDGE

Carlbury Arms

Just off A67

✪ 11-11; 12-10.30 Sun

☎ (01325) 374286

website: www.britnett.com/carlburyarms
Jennings Cumberland Ale; John Smith's Magnet; guest beer Ⓗ
Traditional inn formerly known as the Wheatsheaf, set in this picturesque village which dates back to the Roman times, when it was a fort and settlement known as 'Magis'. The pub has two rooms along with a restaurant, both the beer range and food on offer have something to suit everyone. There is a quiz every alternate Monday. The garden is a picnic area with rustic water features. ⛰Q❀◐▶♣P

PITY ME

Lambton Hounds

62 Front Street (off A167 roundabout, 2 miles N of Durham)
11-11; 12-10.30 Sun
☎ (0191) 386 4742
Black Sheep Best Bitter; Everards Tiger; guest beer Ⓗ
This 250-year-old coaching inn, now operated by Enterprise Inns, is a former Vaux house. Good food, fine ale and a warm welcome are assured in a cosy environment. It is popular with locals, and visitors from near and far. The public bar has a pool table and is separated from the lounge by the original bar from the Titanic's sister ship, the Olympic. The pub also offers a snug and a separate dining room that has been recently refurbished.
Q❀◐▶♿♣P

PRESTON-LE-SKERNE

Blacksmith's Arms

Ricknall Lane (off A167 at Gretna Green)
☎ (01325) 314873
website: www.blacksmithsarms.co.uk
12-3, 6.30-11 (12-11 summer); 6.30 (12 summer)-10.30 Sun
Beer range varies Ⓗ
Long, narrow, family-run free house standing by itself and offering an unusual combination of pub, nursery and more. A long corridor separates the bar and lounge, while the beamed lounge follows a 'farmhouse' style, complete with a Welsh dresser. Up to three guest ales are available, the special cask ale night on Sunday offers excellent value for money. Tasty home-cooked meals are served (no food on Sun eve). The plants and vegetables are for sale, while hens, peacocks and guinea fowl roam free in the garden, and there is even a helicopter landing pad. ❀◐▶P

ROMALDKIRK

Kirk Inn

The Green
12-2.30 (not Mon-Wed), 6-11; 12-3, 7-10.30 Sun
☎ (01833) 650260
Boddingtons Bitter; Fuller's London Pride; Greene King Abbot; guest beers Ⓗ
Family-run pub built in 1745 overlooking the large, attractive village green. The cosy single room doubles as the village post office before lunchtime, but it is almost impossible to detect this at other times. Fine home-cooked food appears from the labyrinthine kitchen area; Sunday lunches are popular – best to book. Evening meals are served daily (except Tue and Sun). Background classical music creates a restful atmosphere. The pub is very popular with walkers. Guest beers come from local, independent brewers.
⛰❀◐▶♿▲♣P

ST JOHN'S CHAPEL

Blue Bell Inn

12 Hood Street
5 (11 Sat)-11; 12.30-3, 6.30-10.30 Sun
☎ (01388) 537256
Tetley Bitter Ⓗ
One of the region's rare outlets for cask cider (Addlestone's). This traditional village pub is located in excellent walking and cycling country. In an area known as 'England's Last Wilderness', the weather is unpredictable in winter and spring. The bar contains many ornaments and curios and photos of the local football team. Bus No. 101 from Stanhope passes, but please check return times before travelling. ▲♣●

SEDGEFIELD

Ceddesfield Hall

Sedgefield Community Association, Rectory Row (behind the church)
7.30-10.30; 8-11 Sat; 8-11 Sun
☎ (01740) 620341
Beer range varies Ⓗ
Run by volunteers of the Sedgefield Community Association, the building (dating from 1791), was the rectory and is set in seven acres of grounds. It is now used

INN BRIEF

STOCKTON-ON-TEES

Sun Inn
Knowles Street
11-11; 12-10.30 Sun
(01642) 623921
Draught Bass Ⓗ
Classic local, widely renowned for its ale. Lager sales are minimal. Stockton folk club meets Mon in back room.

SUMMERHOUSE

Raby Hunt
6.30-11; 12-3, 7-10.30 Sun
(01325) 374604
Mansfield Riding Bitter; Marston's Bitter; guest beer (occasional) Ⓗ
Welcoming, stone-built free house in a whitewashed hamlet, consisting of a lounge and two-part locals bar. Snacks available.

WITTON GILBERT

Glendenning Arms
Front Street
4 (3 Fri; 11 Sat)-11; 12-10.30 Sun
(0191) 371 0316
Draught Bass; Tetley Bitter; Worthington Bitter; guest beer Ⓗ
Unspoilt and comfortable sums up this friendly village pub with open fires, original 1970s handpulls, and seat dividers in the bar.

WOLSINGHAM

Mill Race
West End
11-11; 12-10.30 Sun
(01388) 526551
McEwan 80/-; guest beers Ⓗ
Fine example of 1920s pub style, this very friendly local is on the outskirts of the village. Bus No. 101.

Check it out

Pubs in the Good Beer Guide may change ownership and the facilities listed could alter. If a visit to a pub involves a long journey, it's advisable to check before leaving that full meals, family facilities, accommodation or camping sites are still available.

for a wide range of activities – everything from Bonsai to squash. There is a compact bar, a large lounge and a function room. The atmosphere is very friendly, with excellent cheap beer sold (40-50 different ales per year). A beer festival is held the first weekend in July, usually with at least 10 beers. Awarded CAMRA Club of the Year 1999, it claims a resident ghost, 'the pickled parson'. Q❀⊞♿P▯

Dun Cow Inn

23 Front Street

⏲ 11-3, 6.30-11; 11.30-3, 7-10.30 Sun

☎ (01740) 620894

Theakston Best Bitter; guest beers Ⓗ

This is a small country hotel which has excellent and imaginative food available in the large restaurant, also a very fine selection of wines. The bar/lounge is the main room where meals are also served. There is an intimate, traditional back bar and an old-fashioned snug. In summer the exterior is noted for its splendid floral displays. See if you can spot the 'glass' chimney. Q⇌◖◗⊞P

Nag's Head

8 West End

⏲ 12 (5 Mon)-11; 12-10.30 Sun

☎ (01740) 620234

Theakston Cool Cask; guest beers Ⓗ

The Nag's Head is conveniently situated in the village close to Sedgefield racecourse. It is a free house, run as an old-fashioned local to attract all age groups; families with well-behaved children are most welcome. There is a compact, comfortable bar and a smaller, quaint lounge, plus a separate restaurant (no food Sun eve). The two guest beers are usually mid-strength (4-5%). There are traditional pub games available, such as shove-ha'penny. The landlord and landlady both originally come from the village.
❀◖◗⊞♣P⊬

SHINCLIFFE

Seven Stars

High Street North (A177, 1¾ miles S of Durham)

⏲ 12-11; 12-10.30 Sun

☎ (0191) 384 8454 website: www.sevenstarsinn.co.uk

Black Sheep Best Bitter; Courage Directors; Marston's Pedigree; Theakston Best Bitter Ⓗ

This olde-worlde coaching inn sits on the edge of a picturesque village, beside the busy A177. A characterful pub with an unspoilt charm, it boasts a varied but pricey food menu. It is a pity that the guest beers appear to have dried up. The Seven Stars is within easy reach of Durham, local attractions, and there are plenty of good local walks, ideal for creating a thirst.
Q❀⇌◖◗⊞

SPENNYMOOR ❊

Ash Tree

Carr Lane (10 mins from town centre on Greenways Estate)

⏲ 6 (12 Sat)-11; 12-10.30 Sun

☎ (01388) 814490

Camerons Strongarm; Tetley Bitter; guest beers Ⓗ

The hub of the local estate, this pub has constantly sold real ale since opening in 1980. It is a Pubmaster house, following the demise of Vaux; the former owners had just completed an excellent refurbishment. It is a single-room layout but is broken up into a separate bar and lounge area by a central partition. Outdoor drinking is very popular in summer and everyone is made to feel welcome. The guest is from Pubmaster's approved range. ❀♣P▯

STANHOPE

Queen's Head

Front Street

⏲ 12-11 (may vary winter); 12-10.30 Sun

☎ (01388) 528160

Beer range varies Ⓗ

19th-century, stone pub on three floors, popular with locals and visitors. It is a handy base for walkers and cyclists with exceptional hillwalking routes virtually on the doorstep. The Coast-to-Coast cycle route passes the pub. The beer range may be restricted in winter but up to three cask ales are stocked during summer. The No. 101 bus from Crook and Bishop Auckland stops at the pub, while the X21 service from Newcastle (on Wed and Sat) stops in the market place. ⇌◖◗⛺♣

STOCKTON-ON-TEES ❊

Fitzgeralds

9-10 High Street

⏲ 11.30-3 (3.30 Fri; 4 Sat), 6.30-11; 7-10.30 Sun

☎ (01642) 678220

Greene King Old Speckled Hen, Abbot; guest beers Ⓗ

This grandiose stone edifice with granite pillars was built originally as a gentlemen's club with an upstairs billiards room. Converted to a pub many years ago, it later changed its 1960s image to something altogether better, all carved mahogany, cut glass and little snob screens. All this architectural detail was removed for future use from long-demolished pubs by previous owners, Sir John Fitzgerald. Always a good range of interesting guest beers is stocked from breweries not often featured in the area. ◖⇌♣

Senators

Bishopton Road West (off Stockton ring road at Whitehouse Farm shopping centre)

⏲ 11-3, 6-11; 11-11 Fri & Sat; 12-10.30 Sun

☎ (01642) 672060

Courage Directors; Marston's Pedigree Ⓗ

White-painted pub forming one corner of a Safeway supermarket. Opened by Vaux as the Thirsty Senator in the late 1960s, the pub retains its Vaux windows and trappings, but sadly not the beer. Inside, is a single split-level room with a bar at one end and an alcove used for lunchtime diners. Despite its austere exterior, the pub is warm and welcoming inside. Regular quiz nights are held, and the pub offers players the chance to visit golf courses. ❀◖♣P

THORPE THEWLES

Hamilton Russell Arms

Bank Terrace

⏲ 12-11; 12-10.30 Sun

☎ (01740) 630757

Courage Directors; John Smith's Magnet; Wells Bombardier; guest beer Ⓗ

Historic pub overlooking the village green. Originally part of the estate of the

Marchioness of Londonderry, it was named after the 1929 marriage between Gustavson Hamilton and Emma Russell. Recently extended and refurbished, the pub retains its snug and games room, together with a large no-smoking area. There is an extensive south-facing garden, while open fires feature in winter. Cheery staff, and a much-praised, extensive menu with fish and vegetarian options, make this a pub for all tastes. ⛫Q❀◖◗⊟♿P⁄

TRIMDON GRANGE

Dovecote Inn

Salters Lane (B1278)

⏲ 7 (12 Fri & Sat)-11; 12-10.30 Sun

☎ (01429) 880967

Beer range varies 🄷

Built originally for the local pit and coke oven workers, now a traditional welcoming one-roomed village local with an open fire. The owner is a real ale enthusiast, although the brewing of his Trimdon cask ales has been suspended for the time being. The usual pub games are played. Food is available on Sunday lunchtimes. ⛫◖◗

TRIMDON VILLAGE

Bird in Hand

Salters Lane (B1278)

⏲ 11-11; 12-3, 7-11 Mon; 12-10.30 Sun

☎ (01429) 880391

Black Sheep Best Bitter; guest beers 🄷

Large, friendly locals' pub, dating from the 1950s on the very edge of the village, overlooking open country. It has a central serving area, with a bar at one side and a large lounge/restaurant at the other. The landlord is very committed to promoting real ale and stages six themed beer weekends a year. Old-fashioned pub games nights are also held; games played include shove-ha'penny and devil among the skittles. A special event on August bank holiday is the 'Battle of the Bands' (rock and blues), and there is regular live entertainment. Trimdon folk club meets on the first Friday of the month. ❀◖◗⊟♣P

WILLINGTON

Black Horse Inn

42 Low Willington

⏲ 7 (12 Sat)-11; 12-10.30 Sun

☎ (01388) 746340

Beer range varies 🄷

Busy local on the edge of town and one of the few to sell cask ale. Two beers are always available from both regional and local breweries. A quiz night is held on Sunday. Situated near Roman roads and encampments, the pub is reputedly haunted by a Roman soldier who rearranges table decorations. Easily accessible by public transport, it is on the X46 bus route from Durham to Crook and the 108 bus from Bishop Auckland stops at the door. Local CAMRA Pub of the Year 2000. Q❀⊟♣P

WITTON GILBERT ❄

Travellers Rest

Front Street (off A691, Consett Road, 2 miles from Durham city centre)

⏲ 11.30-3, 6-11; 11-11 Sat; 12-10.30 Sun

☎ (0191) 371 0458

Theakston Best Bitter; guest beers 🄷

Traditional country-style inn that has been recently refurbished to improve the conservatory and main bar area. The no-smoking room is now called the Sports room, with memorabilia such as old editions of this Guide. A separate restaurant makes four rooms in all, but the diverse range of food is served in all rooms, and caters for most tastes. This contemporary, comfortable pub is popular with families. Boules is played in summer.

⛫Q❀◖◗♣P⁄

White Tun

Sacriston Lane (A691)

⏲ 12-3, 6-11; 12-11 Sat; 12-10.30 Sun

☎ (0191) 371 0734

Castle Eden Bitter; guest beers 🄷

This estate-style pub has a spacious bar and a smaller, comfortable lounge. It is a regular outlet for Castle Eden and Camerons beers. A friendly atmosphere prevails and the bar has a large-screen TV for football. Food from a traditional set menu is usually served during all opening hours (except on Sun eve). The White Tun is very popular with locals.

Q◖◗♣P

WITTON-LE-WEAR

Dun Cow

19 High Street

⏲ 6 (12 Fri & Sat)-11; 12-10.30 Sun

☎ (01388) 488294

Bateman XXXB; John Smith's Bitter; guest beer 🄷

This traditional village pub (c1799) has a pleasant setting on the village green. It is popular with locals and users of the Wear Valley Way long-distance footpath and is centrally situated for tourist attractions such as Witton Castle, Low Barns Nature Reserve and Hamste~rley Forest. The pub has a thriving leek club with a show held in September. It is well situated for public transport with bus stop at the door. This quiet pub has no juke box, pool table or piped music, although it is reputed to have a ghost with a preference for shoes, and running up and down the passage at night, so watch out!

⛫Q❀Ѧ♣P

WOLSINGHAM ❄

Black Bull Inn

27 Market Place (opp. town hall)

⏲ 12-11; 12-10.30 Sun

☎ (01388) 527332

Ansells Best Bitter; guest beer 🄷

Imposing, stone-built former coaching house in the market place of an ancient village. There are some good walks locally, and many fine examples of architectural styles are to be found nearby. The pub has an enviable reputation for food, being run by a chef of national repute; it is often worth booking in advance, especially at holiday times. The bar can become busy on darts nights but the lounge is usually a quiet haven. The Weardale bus No. 101 from Bishop Auckland and Crook stops in the market place.

⛫Q❀⛿◖◗⊟♣

WOLVISTON

Ship

50 High Street

12-3, 6-11; 12-3, 7-10.30 Sun

☎ (01740) 644420

Black Sheep Best Bitter; guest beer Ⓗ

Dating from the early 1900s, this former coaching inn, whose stables still stand to the rear, occupies an even older site, in use since the 1800s. The pub has a homely atmosphere, with a no-smoking area and efficient ventilation system. All the food is freshly prepared and cooked on the premises – no portion control or microwave 'pings' happen in this kitchen. Guest beers come mainly from independent breweries. Voted local CAMRA Pub of the Season 2000, it is still as good today. ❀◑♣P⊬

Wellington

High Street

12-11; 12-4.30, 7-10.30 Sun

☎ (01740) 646901

Draught Bass Ⓗ

Old whitewashed village pub on the crossroads of what was once the main road north. The interesting façade sits happily beneath the pantiled roof and blends into its setting. There is a large function room available, used for regular live music events, and a long lounge area leading into a public bar. Lunches are served daily, and evening meals, 5-9, Sun-Mon. ❀◑♣P

What's Brewing CAMRA

NEWSPAPER OF THE CAMPAIGN FOR REAL ALE

August 2002

Queen starts Jubilee mash

Former MD's buy-out bid thwarted at last-minute

CAINS GOES NATIONAL AFTER SALE

by TIM HAMPSON & JOHN REYNOLDS

LIVERPOOL-brewed real ale is set to keep on flowing on Merseyside and beyond following the sale of Cains to a drinks distribution company for £3.4 million.

The new owner of the Stanhope Street site and its 10 pubs is Midlands-based wholesaler Gardner-Shaw, which has depots nationwide. It has bought the company as a going concern and pledged to make turn Cains – which was loss-making thanks to its involvement in low-cost supermarket lagers – into a success story.

The sale ends months of speculation over the future of brewing in Liv...

Sudarghara Dusanj said. "Cains has been important to Liverpool's economy for many years. We recognise the importance of preserving the heritage of the company and firmly believe we can take this piece of history and transform it into a modern day success story.

"We will continue to produce beers under the award-winning Cains brand and maintain production on the current site.

"We believe ...

the region are treating the purchase with caution. The Supporters of Cains Action Group, formed by members of Merseyside, Wirral and Southport CAMRA in February, has vowed to continue its campaign to ensure Cains beers continue to be sold in over 300 pubs in the area.

And CAMRA National Chairman Dave Goodwin, who has been personally involved in the campaign to support Cains, said: "The sale of the brewery and pubs as a single entity is ...d news, but we have ... meet the new man... to discuss the fu... quality real ale ... and the

Inside this Month

Indies push real ale p3

Ridley's buys up Tolly p4

Short pint law attacked p5

Help for rural pubs p6

Festival preview p7-9

Your Letters p10-11

Classifed ads p12

PLUS CAMRA festivals p13

Brakspear to go

BRAKSPEAR of Henley is to close its brewery with over ... job losses. As What's

Hold the front page...

Members of CAMRA receive a free monthly newspaper, What's Brewing. It is packed with up-to date information about beer, brewing and pubs, and will keep you informed about all the latest developments in the beer world. What's Brewing also lists CAMRA beer festivals throughout the country, along with CAMRA branch and regional activities.

What's Brewing has the best and most authoritative writers. It is edited by Ted Bruning, and regular columnists include Jeff Evans, Good Beer Guide editor Roger Protz, and Arthur Taylor. John Reynolds surveys the City scene while laughter is provided by veteran cartoonist Bill Tidy with his Kegbuster strip.

What's Brewing is worth the price of CAMRA membership alone. To receive your monthly copy, sign up for membership by using the form at the back of the Guide.

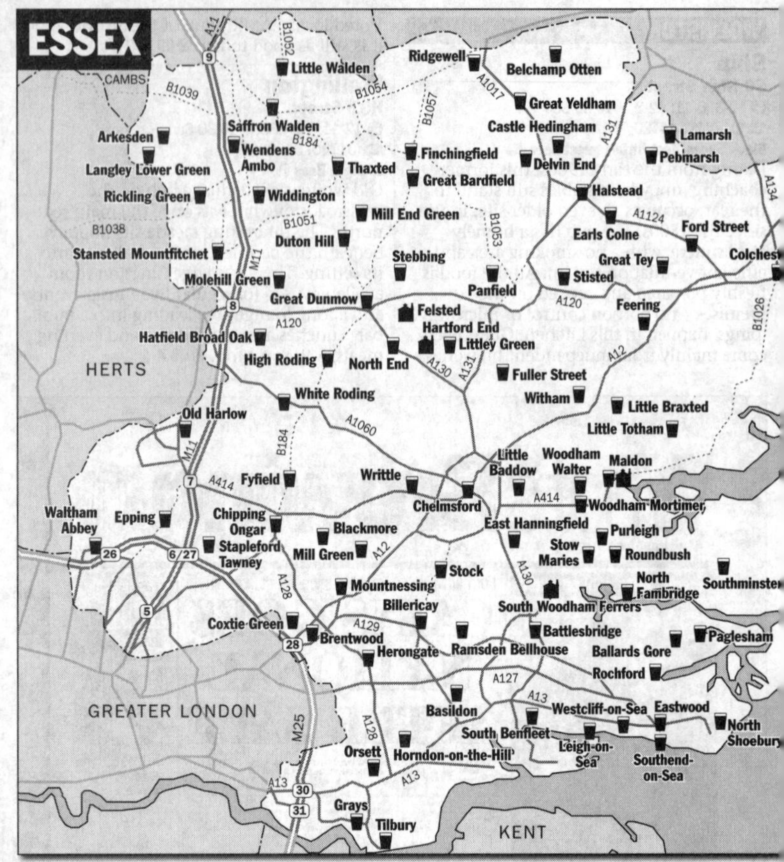

ARKESDEN

Axe & Compasses

(opp. Post Office, 2 miles N of B1038) OS483344
☼ 12-2.30, 6-11; 12-2.30, 7-11 Sun
☎ (01799) 550272
Greene King IPA, Ruddles Best Bitter, Old Speckled Hen; guest beer Ⓗ
Partly-thatched, 17th-century village inn with a public bar and restaurant that has won awards for good food. A community pub with a very friendly atmosphere, it is the centre for much of village life and locals actually talk to strangers here. It is frequented by walkers exploring this beautiful locality on an extensive local network of footpaths.
⌂Q❀◐⊟♣P

BALLARDS GORE

Shepherd & Dog

Gore Road $2^1/_2$ miles from Rochford, between Stambridge & Paglesham OS906928
☼ 12-3, 6-11; 12-10.30 Sun
☎ (01702) 258279
Beer range varies Ⓗ
With a range of three regularly changing cask ales from small and independent breweries, plus real cider in summer, this quiet traditional, country pub is an ideal place for a relaxing drink. In the child-free bar (or in the restaurant) you can also enjoy a meal. The pleasant garden hosts summer barbecues and family garden parties. With its lovely rural surroundings, it is popular with walkers and cyclists. Q❀◐♿♣P

BATTLESBRIDGE

Barge Inn

Hawk Hill (off A130, follow signs to antiques centre) OS781947
☼ 11-11; 12-10.30 Sun
☎ (01268) 732622
Adnams Bitter; Draught Bass; Tetley Burton Ale; guest beers Ⓗ
400-year-old weatherboarded pub, opposite an antiques and craft centre. Barges used to moor at what is now the rear of the building. It can be busy with visitors to the many antiques outlets in this historic village. Serving up to seven varied guest ales a week, Tuesday is games and curry night. Bring your own games, if you like! Old photographs and wooden seats lend a rustic atmosphere. The menu is unpretentious, but varied.
♘❀◐≠♣P

BELCHAMP OTTEN

Red Lion

Fowes Lane OS799415
☼ 12-3 (not Mon-Fri), 7-11; 12-3, 7-10.30 Sun
☎ (01787) 277537
Greene King IPA; guest beer (occasional) Ⓗ
Village local with a friendly

handpump; the guest beers are changed regularly to include local beers as well as some rarities. There is also a good range of malt whiskies. The restaurant serves a large selection of dishes, including a good choice of vegetarian meals. ❀◐◑P

FULLER STREET

Square & Compasses

Leave A131 for Great Leighs, turn right at St Anne's Castle OS748161

11.30-3, 6.30 (7 winter)-11; 12-3, 7-10.30 Sun

☎ (01245) 361477

Nethergate Suffolk County; Ridleys IPA G

A country pub for country people, specialising in quality food, including seasonal game and local produce (booking advised at weekends). The menu makes mention of 'proper bread' for all sandwiches. The pub has a tap room, a large dining area and an upstairs room with its own bar can be booked for groups. Take time to examine the copious quantities of agricultural tools, taxidermy and old photographs, all of local origin.

Q❀◐◑ ♿▲♣P

FYFIELD

Queen's Head

Queen's Street (off B184)

11-3.30, 6-11; 11-11 Sat; 12-4, 7-10.30 Sun

☎ (01277) 899231

Adnams Bitter, Broadside; guest beers H

Busy country pub in the middle of the village. It retains a cosy feeling with a long bar, some partitions, a beamed ceiling and wood flooring around the bar. Popular for food, it can get very busy at lunchtimes; evening meals are served Tue-Sat. The garden overlooks the Roding River. The guest beers – normally four – are usually from small micros, sometimes one guest is replaced by a real cider. ❀◐◑P

GRAYS

Grays Athletic Football Club

Bridge Road (2 minutes' walk from centre)

5 (12 Fri & Sat)-11; 12-10.30 Sun

☎ (01375) 377753

Greene King IPA; guest beers H

The social club of the Grays Athletic Football Club admits card-carrying CAMRA members, or bearers of this Guide. The bar overlooks an indoor five-a-side football pitch, and a full-sized outdoor pitch – when the curtains are drawn back. TV sports are shown on a large screen. There are usually two guest beers, often of a higher strength – 5%-8% ABV is not uncommon – and sometimes a mild. Limited parking. ◐♣

Theobald Arms

King's Walk (near B189)

10.30-3, 5-11; 10.30-11 Fri & Sat; 12-4, 7-10.30 Sun

☎ (01375) 372253

Courage Best Bitter; guest beers H

Family-run, two-bar pub in a recently-rejuvenated riverside area – opposite is the revamped town wharf fronting on to the Thames. The three guest beers change often. The pub fields several darts teams and the public bar features an unusual revolving round pool table. There are outdoor drinking areas for both the public and saloon bars. A beer festival is held in June, in one of the former stables, converted into a bar. Excellent value food is served weekdays. ❀◐ ♿⇌♣P

GREAT BARDFIELD

Bell

Dunmow Road (B1057)

11-11; 12-10.30 Sun

☎ (01371) 811097

Adnams Bitter; Greene King IPA, Abbot; guest beer H

Cosy, friendly, two-bar local in the village centre, popular with locals. The 500-year-old structure leaves the lively public bar at a higher level than the saloon bar, which houses a large brick open fireplace and an inlaid games table. The pub is said to be haunted by two ghosts. ◐◑ ♣P

GREAT CLACTON

Plough

1 North Road (near B1032)

11-11; 12-10.30 Sun

☎ (01255) 429998

Adnams Broadside; Flowers Original; Greene King IPA; Tetley Bitter; guest beers H

The building that is now this two-bar pub, dates back to the 16th century and much of the original structure has survived. It became a pub in the 19th century as a result of a family dispute, leaving two adjacent pubs, which, by a quirk of fate, are now run by a brother and sister. The pub supports darts and football teams, while a cricket team uses it as a base in summer. A warm welcome is assured. ❀♣

GREAT DUNMOW ❄

Boar's Head

37 High Street (B184)

11-11; 12-10.30 Sun

☎ (01371) 873630

Adnams Bitter; Greene King Abbot; Young's Bitter H

Town-centre pub by the main public car park. Around 400 years old, low ceilings, beams, pictures of old Dunmow and a tropical fish tank are notable features of the pub. This timber-framed, lathe and plaster building 'bends' when delivery lorries 'bump' it while negotiating the tight bend. Quiet at lunchtimes, it gets lively evenings and weekends, but is mainly frequented by locals. This little pub with a big atmosphere is run by a former thatcher.

❀P

GREAT TEY

Chequers

The Street (1½ miles N of A120)

11.30-3, 6.30-11; 12-4, 7-10.30 Sun

☎ (01206) 210814

Greene King XX Mild, IPA, Abbot; guest beer H

Locals and visitors alike receive a warm welcome at this large, 16th-century pub at the centre of the village. A varied menu is served in the spacious restaurant. It is one of the few pubs to regularly serve Greene King mild. The pub hosts men's and women's darts matches during the winter months.

❀◐◑ ♣P✔

GREAT YELDHAM

Waggon & Horses

High Street (A1017)
⌚ 11-11; 12-10.30 Sun
☎ (01787) 237936
website: www.waggonandhorses.net
Greene King IPA, Abbot, guest beers 🄷

16th-century inn at the village centre, where ales come from various Anglian brewers, including the ever-changing guests. This popular village local serves traditional pub food, all day at weekends. Games vary from pool to shove-ha'penny. Reasonably-priced B&B is provided in a recently-built annexe, handy for visiting nearby Hedingham Castle and the steam railway museum. It attracts all ages and a friendly welcome from the landlord is assured.
⚘🛏◑◐♿♣P

White Hart

Poole Street (A1017)
⌚ 11-3, 6-11; 12-3, 7-10.30 Sun
☎ (01787) 237250
website: www.whitehartyeldham.co.uk
Beer range varies 🄷

Imposing, timber-framed inn, at the edge of the village, built in 1505. Original beams, a Norfolk pammet floor in the bar and octagonal chimneys are all features of this Grade I* listed building, with extensive riverside gardens. Guest ales from local brewers such as Adnams and Mighty Oak change weekly and Belgian bottled beers are stocked. High quality, freshly-prepared food is served in the bar and restaurant.
♛Q⚘◑◐♿P

HALSTEAD

Dog Inn

37 Hedingham Road (A1124)
⌚ 11 (5 Mon)-11; 12-10.30 Sun
☎ (01787) 477774
Adnams Bitter, Broadside; Mauldons Moletrap; guest beers 🄷

This two-bar pub at the top of the historic town has gone from strength to strength. To the rear, there is a beautiful outlook over the valley of the River Colne. The building has all the ingredients for a traditional old pub – exposed beams, brickwork, brasses, and always an interesting range of beers. It fields two quiz teams and has good accommodation, with some rooms en-suite.
♛⚘🛏◑◐♣P

HARWICH

Hanover Inn

65 Church Street (near B1352)
⌚ 10.30-2.30, 6.30-11; 12-4, 7-10.30 Sun
☎ (01255) 502927
website: www.hanover-inn-harwich.co.uk
Greene King IPA; guest beers 🄷

Harwich today has nothing like the density of pubs for which it was once renowned, but this free house still offers a cosy nautical charm and a good pint. Very much at the heart of its community, this vibrant local also offers accommodation, making it an ideal base for exploring the Tendring peninsula. ♛🛏⇌ (Town) ♣

HATFIELD BROAD OAK

Cock

High Street (B183)
⌚ 12-3, 6-11; 12-3, 7-10.30 Sun
☎ (01279) 718273
Adnams Bitter; guest beers 🄷

Typical, olde-worlde village pub, totally unspoilt by time or over-zealous owners, with a wood floor, bar and old furniture. A lick of paint would be preferable to the green and nicotine colours on display at present, but this does not detract from the

INN BRIEF

LEIGH-ON-SEA

Elms
1060 London Road
10-11; 12-10.30 Sun
(01702) 474687
Courage Best Bitter, Directors; Shepherd Neame Spitfire; Theakston Best Bitter; guest beer (occasional) 🄷
Spacious Wetherspoon's served by many bus routes out of Southend via A13. Cask Marque accredited.

PANFIELD

Bell
37 Kynaston Road
11-11; 12-10.30 Sun
(01376) 324641
Ridleys IPA, Old Bob 🄷
Cosy 16th-century village local near B1053 with camping by arrangement. Darts and pool; good food.

RIDGEWELL

White Horse
Mill Road
11-3 (not Tue), 6-11; closed Mon; 12-3, 7-10.30 Sun
(01440) 785532
Adnams Bitter; Ridleys IPA; guest beers 🄷
Wide-ranging menu in bar and restaurant. Low ceiling and beams in a popular village local.

ROCHFORD

Milestone
Union Lane
10-11; 12-10.30 Sun
(01702) 544229
Greene King IPA, Abbot; guest beer (occasional) 🄶
Opposite the station, TVs dominate this sport-oriented bar. Acclaimed Thai restaurant upstairs (book).

SAFFRON WALDEN

Axe
60 Ashdon Road
12-2.30, 6-11; 12-10.30 Sun
(01799) 522235
Greene King IPA, Abbot 🄷
Popular local, with a wealth of Victoriana and military memorabilia. Award-winning garden with boules pitch – Cask Marque accredited.

King's Arms
Market Hill
11-3, 5-11; 11-11 Sat; 12-10.30 Sun
(01799) 522768
Greene King IPA; Marston's Pedigree 🄷
Town-centre pub near market square, comfortable and friendly. Note the display of caricatures.

Temeraire
55 High Street
11-11; 12-10.30 Sun
(01799) 516975
Courage Directors; Greene King IPA; Shepherd Neame Spitfire; Theakston Best Bitter; guest beers 🄷
The younger generation gather in the evening but at lunchtime frequented by all ages. Large garden. Cask Marque accredited.

STANSTED MOUNTFITCHET

Queen's Head
3 Lower Street
11-3, 5.30 (7 Sat)-11; 12-3, 7-10.30 Sun
(01279) 812458
Draught Bass; Flowers IPA; Tolly Cobbold Original; guest beer 🄷
Comfortable village-centre pub, bearing an eclectic collection of brass and old agricultural implements. Refuge for commuters. No food Sun.

STEBBING

White Hart
High Street
11-3, 5-11; 11-11 Sat; 12-10.30 Sun
(01371) 856383
Greene King IPA; guest beers 🄷
15th-century beamed pub with good value food. Live music Sun afternoon and sometimes Sat. Caters for local clubs.

excellent pub which draws a varied clientele, from hikers at lunchtime to local villagers of all ages later in the day. Games played here include shut the box. No evening meals are served Sunday.
₼Q❀☽◗♿♣P⊬

HERONGATE

Green Man

11 Cricketers Lane (near A128)
11-11; 12-10.30 Sun
☎ (01277) 810292
Adnams Bitter, Broadside; Draught Bass; Tetley Bitter; H guest beers G
This pub is located in a small lane just off the A128. There is a comfortable main bar area, plus several rooms at the back, sometimes used for meetings. As well as handpumps, casks are also stocked behind the bar (cooling jackets are used). This local CAMRA Pub of the Year 1999 has a children's play area in the garden and holds regular quizzes. Well worth a visit.
₼Q❀☽◗⊬

HIGH RODING

Black Lion

3 The High Street (B184, 3 miles S of Dunmow)
12-3, 6-11; 12-11 Sat; 12-10.30 Sun
☎ (01371) 872847
Ridleys IPA, H Witchfinder, G/H Rumpus, H Old Bob; guest beer G
This beautiful, timber-framed building dates back to the mid-1400s and is one of the oldest pubs in Essex. There is a restaurant, seating up to 24 people where the food is good value, with fresh fish available daily.
₼❀☽◗P

HORNDON-ON-THE-HILL

Swan

121 High Road (near B1007)
11.30-2.30 (not Mon; 12-4.30 Sat), 6-11; 12-4.30, 7-10.30 Sun
☎ (01375) 640617
Adnams Broadside; guest beers H
This welcoming 400-year-old coaching inn looks surprisingly fresh and lively. The two bars are connected at the front and back of the pub. Hops hang from exposed beams, some sporting memorabilia is displayed around the walls, and the bar top is covered with pre-decimal coins. Excellent live folk music is performed on Sunday evening.
Q☽◗⊟P

LAMARSH

Lamarsh Lion

1½ miles NW of Bures OS892355
12 (11 Sat)-3.30, 6-11; 12-3, 7-10.30 Sun
☎ (01787) 227918 website: www.lamarshlion.com
Beer range varies H
Originally a 14th-century coaching inn, this free house offers a genuinely warm welcome. The large bar area is divided by numerous beams. The bar dispenses three beers that change on a regular basis. The restaurant is deservedly popular, so booking is advisable (no meals Mon or Sun eve). The garden overlooks the delightful Stour Valley and, to make this pub the perfect all-rounder, en-suite accommodation is available in a converted stable block.
₼❀⇔☽◗⋏♣P

LANGLEY LOWER GREEN

Bull

Turn N off B1083 at Clavering OS436345
12-2.30, 6-11; 12-3, 7-10.30 Sun
☎ (01279) 777307
Greene King IPA, Old Speckled Hen H
Classic Victorian village local, boasting original cast-iron lattice windows and fireplaces, in a small, isolated hamlet. It has a devoted band of regulars and is used by local groups, including football and cricket teams. This friendly pub, in beautiful rolling countryside, is worth a visit. A pitch penny game (penny in the hole) is concealed beneath a bench in the saloon bar. Meals can be arranged with advance notice.
❀⊟♣P

LEIGH-ON-SEA ❊

Broker

213-217 Leigh Road (500 yds from A13)
11-3, 6-11; 11-11 Fri & Sat; 12-10.30 Sun
☎ (01702) 471932
website: www.brokerfreehouse.co.uk
Shepherd Neame Spitfire; guest beers H
Single, large, open-plan bar with a no-smoking children's area (until 7.30pm). Situated in a main road, near a shopping centre, it has a small restaurant to one side; a comprehensive menu includes bar snacks and vegetarian options. Two guest beers is the norm here. Music or quizzes are staged on Sunday evening; the television is for sports. The pub runs a bonus ball lottery to support various charities. This free house has a small patio for outdoor drinking.
❀☽◗♿⇌(Chalkwell)⊬

LITTLE BADDOW

Rodney

North Hill OS778080
11.30-2.30 (3 Sat), 6-11; 12-10.30 Sun
☎ (01245) 222385
Greene King IPA, Old Speckled Hen; guest beer H
A pub since the early 1800s, when it would have sold beer from the Chelmsford Brewery, the Rodney was built as a farmhouse around 1650 and has also served as a grocer's and a bakery. This comfortable two-roomed beamed pub has a public bar with a pool table, a small snug and a compact drinking/dining area displaying many brasses, posters and seafaring prints. The food is all home made and includes good value daily specials. Q❀☽◗⊟⋏♣P

LITTLE BENTLEY

Bricklayer's Arms

Rectory Road (off A120 and A133)
12-3, 6.30-11; 12-4, 7-10.30 Sun
☎ (01206) 250405
Greene King IPA, Ruddles Best Bitter H
This family-run village pub promotes real ale, real food and real people. Home-made lunches and evening meals are available every day, plus a traditional roast on Sunday. Its location makes it an ideal stop to or from Harwich international port and the Tendring holiday resorts. Pots, plates,

porcelain and pictures abound in the bar. The regulars mostly come from the farming community – their wit is dry whatever the weather. Q❀◐◑P

LITTLE BRAXTED

Green Man

Green Man Lane, Kelvedon Road ($1^1/_2$ miles SE of village) OS849130
⌚ 11-3, 6-11; 12-3, 7-10.30 Sun
☎ (01621) 891659
Ridleys IPA, Prospect, Old Bob [H]

This delightful pub offers a choice of cosy, beamed saloon bar, basic public and a secluded garden – take your pick. It enjoys a very attractive setting, especially in the spring. The food is good, with an extensive menu renowned for the generous sandwiches and French bread snacks (try the haggis). Note the collection of model vehicles in the public bar and wooden hop shovels in the saloon bar. ⛼Q❀◐◑⊟♣P

LITTLE OAKLEY

Olde Cherry Tree

Clacton Road
⌚ 11-2.30, 5-11; 12-3, 7-10.30 Sun
☎ (01255) 880333 website: www.cherrytreepub.com
Adnams Bitter, Broadside; Fuller's London Pride; guest beers [H]

Steeped in history, this attractive village local once fronted a large cherry orchard. With its views of the North Sea, award-winning open fire and restaurant, the pub is a cosy oasis for those who enjoy excellent ales and superb home-cooked food. Five handpumps take centre stage on the bar and include two constantly changing guests. The pub has won a host of awards and stages its own beer festival and hog roast in June. ⛼❀◐◑♣P⊽

LITTLE TOTHAM

Swan

School Road (2 miles SE of B1022)
⌚ 11-11; 12-10.30 Sun
☎ (01621) 892689
website: www.theswanpublichouse.co.uk
Beer range varies [G]

Delightful Grade II listed cottage pub set behind a pleasant garden. A good selection of beers includes a house ale from Mighty Oak. Essex CAMRA Pub of the Year 2000 and 2000, the cosy saloon, with its low ceiling and beams is complemented by a traditional public bar with a 1950s bar billiards table. The new dining room offers good value meals. The hub of the village, it supports many local activities; a beer festival is held in June.
⛼Q❀◐◑⊟♿⛺♣●P⊬⊽

LITTLE WALDEN

Crown

On B1052, 2 miles NE of Saffron Walden
⌚ 11.30-2.30, 6-11; 12-10.30 Sun
☎ (01799) 522475
Adnams Broadside; City of Cambridge Boathouse Bitter; Greene King Abbot; Fuller's London Pride [G]

Charming 18th-century, beamed country pub featuring a large inglenook and offering an extensive menu. Racked cask stillage is used for dispensing an excellent selection of real ales. There is a large car park at the rear, plus patio. This quiet country hamlet pub attracts many locals and business folk from Saffron Walden. It is used for local club meetings and offers a welcoming atmosphere. ⛼Q♉❀◐◑♣P

LITTLEY GREEN

Compasses

Turn off B1417 at Ridleys Brewery OS699172
⌚ 12-3, 6 (7 Sat)-11; 12-3, 7-10.30 Sun
☎ (01245) 362308
Bateman Mild; Ridleys IPA, Prospect, Rumpus, Old Bob, seasonal beers [G]

Isolated country pub, restored in traditional Victorian style. The pub is considered to be the Ridleys' brewery tap, and the full range of their beers is generally available; all beer is served by gravity from the cellar. Large filled rolls called 'huffers' are available at lunchtime. No games machines or pool table, and no music invade the peace here, except for the frequent folk evenings.
⛼Q♉❀♣P⊬

MALDON

Queen's Head

The Hythe
⌚ 10.30-11; 12-10.30 Sun
☎ (01621) 854112
Greene King IPA, Abbot; Mighty Oak Burntwood [H]

Situated on the Hythe, overlooking the Blackwater estuary, this three-bar Grays pub has a nautical atmosphere and affords views of the sailing barge moorings, especially from its own riverside patio. Each of the bars has its own distinct atmosphere, one benefiting from river views. There is always someone to chat to and the pub get busy in summer, but is more of a local in winter. Crib and dominoes are played. Limited parking. The no-smoking area is the family room. ⛼Q♉❀◐◑⊟♿♣P⊬

MILL END GREEN

Green Man

1 mile E of B184 OS619260
⌚ 12-3, 7-11; 12-5, 7-10.30 Sun
☎ (01371) 870286
Adnams Bitter; Greene King IPA; Ridleys IPA [H]

15th-century pub on a quiet country road in open countryside. Oak studwork and very low beams feature in a cosy bar with padded settles. The adjacent dining area has seating for 30-plus. The central open fireplace is controlled by an adjustable hood. The landlord is also the chef, offering a varied menu of home-prepared fresh food. The excellent large garden has a mesh-covered pond and a tennis court available for hire, as well as the more usual patio and barbecue area.
⛼Q❀⛟◐◑P

MILL GREEN

Viper

Mill Green Road OS641018
⌚ 12-3, 6-11; 12-3, 7-10.30 Sun
☎ (01277) 352010
Ridleys IPA; [H] **guest beers** [H]/[G]

In the same family for three generations, this wonderful unspoilt country pub has a wood-panelled public bar and snug, plus a comfortable lounge. Three or four guest beers often include one from Mighty Oak, and a dark beer is generally offered. Good food includes real ale sausages, and excellent home-made chilli pickled eggs are usually available, but the landlord's chilli vodka experiments are even more dangerous! Local CAMRA Pub of the Year 1997-99. ⛼Q❀◐⊟♣●P

MOLEHILL GREEN

Three Horseshoes

Off Takeley-Elsenham road, 1 mile from Stansted Airport OS564247
11-11; 12-10.30 Sun
☎ (01279) 870313
Draught Bass; Greene King IPA, Abbot Ⓗ

Very attractive, thatched country pub with low beams and an inglenook. Originally a drovers' inn, now 500 years old, it still offers a warm welcome to walkers and to airline personnel and other workers at Stansted Airport; note the aircraft mementos in the bar. The old barn is a venue for impromptu music sessions on summer weekends. Camping is possible in the paddock by prior arrangement. There is extensive outdoor seating. ⛼❀◐◑P

MOUNTNESSING

Prince of Wales

199 Roman Road (B1002)
12-3, 5-11; 12-3, 7-10.30 Sun
☎ (01277) 353445
Ridleys IPA, Prospect, Old BOB Ⓗ

This Ridleys tied house is situated on the old A12, a mile from the new trunk road, opposite a large cricket field and a windmill. The timbered interior has two distinct drinking areas, one of which has a no-smoking section with individual partitioned tables. The local cycling club congregates here after races, on Wednesday evenings, in summer. Evening meals are served Tue-Sat. ⛼◐◑⊟P⊬

NORTH END

Butcher's Arms

Dunmow Road (A130, between Chelmsford and Dunmow)
12-3,7-11; 11-11 Sat; 12-10.30 Sun
☎ (01245) 237481
Ridleys IPA, Prospect, Rumpus, Old Bob Ⓗ

Attractive, welcoming, 16th-century roadside pub with many original features – note the beams and fireplace. The full range of Ridleys beers is permanently available. Very good, home-cooked food includes locally-renowned fish and chips, served in the bar or no-smoking restaurant (booking advised at busy times; no eve meals winter Mon). An award-winning garden makes this a pleasant place for families in summer. ⛼Q❀◐◑♣P

NORTH FAMBRIDGE

Ferry Boat Inn

Ferry Road (off B1012) OS853968
11.30-3, 7-11; 12-4, 7-10.30 Sun
☎ (01621) 740208
Shepherd Neame Best Bitter, Spitfire, Bishops Finger Ⓗ

Large, weatherboarded 500-year-old building by the River Crouch. It has been extended by an additional dining area, which doubles as a family room. Popular with locals, walkers and sailors – also smugglers in the past – the main bar area boasts flagstoned floors, oak timbers and naval memorabilia. Good home-cooked food is served in a homely atmosphere. Close to riverside walks and a nature reserve, in a peaceful spot, a separate block contains six double suites. ⛼ᗢ❀⛟◐◑♣P

NORTH SHOEBURY

Angel Inn

Parsons Corner (A13, 400 yds N of Asda)
11-3, 5.30-11; 12-3, 7-10.30 Sun
☎ (01702) 589600
Greene King IPA, Abbot; guest beers Ⓗ

The licensee has taken this collection of blacksmith's, wheelwright's and post office cottages from 'at risk' to a full sympathetic restoration. This timber-framed building, circa 1650, features Essex weatherboarding, a thatched roof, oak beams and flagstones. Loud music and gaming machines are banned; conversation rules the bar and no-smoking restaurant areas. It offers four guest beers per week, plus an annual charity beer festival (usually Whitsun). The pub is on several bus routes. Q❀◐◑♿P⊬

OLD HARLOW

Crown

40 Market Street
12-3, 5 (7 Sat)-11; 12-3, 7-10.30 Sun
☎ (01279) 868969
Greene King IPA, Old Speckled Hen Ⓗ **guest beers** Ⓖ

Historic country pub, in the middle of the old town, that has served the local community for over 350 years. A recent extensive refurbishment has exposed a wealth of old beams and ships' timbers, which have been preserved along with wall paintings that can be enjoyed for the first time in centuries. Usually two guest beers from regional breweries are served. It hosts regular live music (often jazz), although at Christmas a brass band may lead a night of carol-singing.
⛼ᗢ❀⛟◐◑♿⥱(Harlow Mill) ♣⊬

ORSETT

Foxhound

18 High Road
11-3.30, 6-11; 11-11 Sat; 12-3.30, 7-10.30 Sun
☎ (01375) 891295
Courage Best Bitter; Crouch Vale Essex Boys Bitter; Greene King IPA; guest beers Ⓗ

A pub that has retained its traditions and individuality. The saloon bar bears many hunting artefacts, including a striking carpet featuring foxhound heads. The public bar is basic, but full of character. The Fox's Den dining room provides excellent meals at lunchtime and Wed-Sat evenings (other times are bookable). It hosts a lively monthly quiz and, several times a year, even livelier auctions that raise funds for guide dogs. ⛼Q❀◐⊟♿♣P

PAGLESHAM

Punchbowl

Church End (off A127, to Rochford, signed Canewdon

and Paglesham)
11.30-3, 6.30-11; 12-3, 6.30-10.30 Sun
(01702) 258376
Adnams Bitter; Ridleys Old Bob; guest beers H
16th-century pub in white Essex weatherboard, situated in the sole village street. Originally a sailmaker's, it has a single, beamed bar decorated with brassware and old pictures. The regular bitter is complemented by three changing guests. The small restaurant offers a varied menu, including vegetarian choices, a specials board and pensioners' menu. A children's play area is at the rear and tables set out at the front of this south-facing free house.
Q P

PEBMARSH

King's Head
The Street (1½ miles E of A131)
12-3, 6-11; closed Mon; 12-3, 7-10.30 Sun
(01787) 269306
Greene King IPA; guest beers H
This family-run pub nestles in a picturesque valley where lies the isolated village of Pebmarsh. The pub is very much the hub of the community. A vast brick-built chimney and fireplace dominate the main bar. The beers come mainly from micro-breweries – the tally of guest ales is fast approaching 1,000. The food is excellent and represents good value. It hosts Independence Day celebrations in July and an annual beer festival (Oct).
Q P

PURLEIGH

Bell
The Street (off B1010)
11-3, 6-11; 12-3, 7-10.30 Sun
(01621) 828348
Adnams Bitter; Ridleys IPA; guest beer H
Attractive old pub, extensively refurbished in the 16th century. It is situated in a conservation area, near the church and original village buildings, on top of a hill. The garden affords fine views over the Blackwater estuary. Popular with walkers using St Peter's Way and other footpaths, well-behaved dogs are welcome. Good food is available at this friendly, traditional hostelry.
Q P

RAMSDEN BELLHOUSE

Fox & Hounds
Church Road
11.30-11, 12-10.30 Sun
(01268) 710286
Greene King IPA, Ruddles County, Old Speckled Hen; guest beers H
Popular village pub, where a family-friendly beer festival is held on the last weekend in July. On the bar there is a changing range of interesting guest beers, alongside the three regulars. There are also three menus: a Sunday carvery, and an à la carte menu are served in the no-smoking restaurant; snacks and light meals are served in the bar. Children are welcome – a pets' corner and play area in the extensive garden will keep them amused.
P

RICKLING GREEN

Cricketer's Arms
½ mile W of B1383 OS511298
12-11; 12-10.30 Sun
(01799) 543210
website: www.cricketers.demon.co.uk
Flowers IPA; Fuller's ESB; Wadworth 6X G
Cricket is a dominant theme in this inn, which adjoins the green (still regularly used by two clubs), where in 1882, the highest score – 920 runs – ever scored in a single innings on a single day was achieved. A famous one day pro-am cricket tournament is held annually. The pub, dating from the 17th century, has been extended to provide accommodation for tourists and Stansted Airport passengers, which is conveniently near (but not so close as to disturb).
P

ROCHFORD

Golden Lion
35 North Street
12-11; 12-10.30 Sun
(01702) 545487
Fuller's London Pride; Greene King Abbot; guest beers H
Small, unspoilt 300-year-old, weatherboarded pub, walkable from the station, with some free parking outside. Conversation rules inside and you could imagine yourself in the 18th century when the juke box is off. Weapons, pump clips and four local CAMRA Pub of the Year plaques adorn the bar. Four guests include a mild or porter. Loud music on Friday draws crowds, otherwise peace and tranquillity reign, apart from occasional live music.

ROUNDBUSH (PURLEIGH)

Roundbush
Fambridge Road (B1010, between Fambridge and Maldon) OS858019
11-3, 6-11; 12-10.30 Sun
(01621) 828354
Greene King IPA, Abbot; guest beer G
This 300-year-old Grays pub boasts two bars and a function room, plus its own adjoining café (open 8.30am-2pm). A friendly, rural pub, popular with locals and visitors, it is simply furnished and well decorated. Access to the serving area is a via a hatch from the public bar. Parking is available for lorries, which are welcome. Children are admitted to the public bar. Q P

ROWHEDGE

Walnut Tree
Fingringhoe Road (1 mile E of B1025) OS021216
12-3 (not Mon-Fri), 8 (7.30 Fri; 7 Sat; not Mon or Wed)-11; 12-3, 7.30-10.30 Sun
(01206) 728149
Beer range varies H
No beers from national breweries and no keg or lager dispensing equipment are to be seen in this pub, just five handpumps offering a range of ales from micro-breweries. Three miles from Colchester's Town Station, this village pub is lively and friendly, offering a vinyl juke box, pool,

pinball machine and good value food. Nutty, the one-horned goat, lives in the garden along with chickens – try the omelettes. Dogs and their well-behaved owners are welcome. Beware limited opening hours. ♨❀◐◑♣●P

SAFFRON WALDEN ❊

Old English Gentleman

11 Gold Street (near B184/B1052)

11-11; 12-10.30 Sun

☎ (01799) 523595 website: www.gourmet-guide.com

Adnams Bitter; Greene King IPA; guest beers Ⓗ

18th-century, town-centre pub with log fires and a welcoming atmosphere, serving a selection of regularly changing guest beers. A dining area has been added and an extensive menu is prepared by a trained chef, with special dishes changing daily. Saffron Walden's market days are Tuesday and Saturday. The pub has a pleasant patio at the rear. ♨❀◐♣

SOUTH BENFLEET

Hoy & Helmet

24-32 High Street (200 yds from station)

11-11.30; 12-10.30 Sun

☎ (01268) 792307

Courage Best Bitter, Directors; Greene King IPA; guest beer Ⓗ

Historic, wood-framed building, dating in part from the 15th century – the Hoy is a boat and the Helmet its hard stand. Built on the site of the Battle of Benfleet, the pub displays a history of this important event of 894 AD. A magnificent open fire dominates one bar; it can get noisy. Meals are served all day until 9.30pm.
♨❀◐◑⇌(Benfleet) ♣

SOUTHEND ON SEA

Cork & Cheese Ale House

10 Talza Way, Victoria Plaza (lower ground floor of shopping centre)

11-11; closed Sun

☎ (01702) 616914

Beer range varies Ⓗ

This free house is an oasis nestling in the basement of the concrete monstrosity that is the Victoria Plaza shopping centre. Voted local CAMRA Pub of the Year on five occasions, it specialises in new ales and an ever-changing range of beer from craft and independent breweries. Over 2,000 different guest ales have been stocked since 1992. The bar area displays an impressive collection of pump clips and brewery memorabilia. Weekday lunches served. Local CAMRA Pub of the Year 2002.
❀◐⇌(Central/Victoria) ♣●

SOUTHMINSTER

Station Arms

39 Station Road (near B1020/B1021 jct)

12-2.30, 6-11; 12-11 Sat; 12-4, 7-10.30 Sun

☎ (01621) 772225

Crouch Vale Brewers Gold; guest beers Ⓗ

This delightful, weatherboarded pub is a former winner of CAMRA East Anglian Pub of the Year, and is a must for beer lovers. A good variety of beers often showcases micros. Traditionally furnished on a railway theme, a warm welcome and friendly atmosphere are assured here. Beer festivals are held on late May and August bank holidays. Live blues and folk evenings take place each month. Meals are served Thu-Sat evenings in the restaurant.
♨Q❀◑⇌♣●

STANSTED MOUNTFITCHET ❊

Rose & Crown

31 Bentfield Green (1/2 mile W of B1383)
OS507255

11-3.30, 6-11; 12-3.30, 7-10.30 Sun

☎ (01279) 812107

Adnams Bitter; Fuller's London Pride Ⓗ

Typical Victorian pub near a duckpond on the edge of a small hamlet that has expanded to become part of Stansted Mountfichet village. This free house has been modernised to provide one large bar, but maintains the friendly, caring atmosphere of a village local. Note the outstanding floral display at the front. The landlady, who seems to know every customer's name, makes everyone welcome and the pub is well used by locals. Food is simple, but reliably excellent and very good value (no eve meals Sun).
❀◐◑♣P

STAPLEFORD TAWNEY

Moletrap

Tawney Common (from Epping, down Stonards Hill, left at Fiddlers Hamlet, first left to Ongar and Toot Hill, second right Tawney Common, pub 1/2 mile on right)
OS501014

12 (11.30 summer)-3; 6.30 (6 summer)-11; 12-4, 6-10.30 Sun

☎ (01992) 522394

Beer range varies Ⓗ

In a 'Bermuda Triangle' between Ongar, Epping and Stapleford Abbotts, the Moletrap is difficult to find, but well worth the effort for the welcome provided. It owes its unusual name to Joseph Treader who, in the early 1900s, designed a very successful mole trap. He invested his wealth in the pub and named it after his invention. A popular venue, especially at weekends, for walkers and cyclists, it stands on the Three Forests Way. The food here is home made (no meals Sun eve). Local CAMRA Pub ofhe Year 2002.
♨Q❀◐◑P

STOCK

Hoop

21 High Street (B1007)

11-11; 12-10.30 Sun

☎ (01277) 841137

Adnams Bitter; guest beers Ⓗ/Ⓖ

Small pub in an upmarket village, a long-standing supporter of real ale. Ever-changing guest beers (usually at least four) are mostly on gravity dispense; the cider varies. The cosy, beamed bar has a dartboard and local sports teams are supported. All the food (available all day) is prepared on the premises. Behind the pub you will find some friendly dogs, outside toilets and a large garden with covered seating area – home to the legendary May beer festival. Regular buses from Billericay and Chelmsford.
Q❀◐◑♣●

STOW MARIES

Prince of Wales
Woodham Road
11-11; 12-10.30 Sun
☎ (01621) 828971
Beer range varies H/G
Popular, friendly pub in an attractive 17th-century building where the beer choice includes Belgian brews. The excellent food represents good value; themed menu evenings add variety and the home-made pizzas are cooked in the pub's own traditional bread ovens. Live music and beer festivals are hosted throughout the year, otherwise it is a fairly quiet place.
Q P

TENDRING

Cherry Tree Inn
Crow Lane (B1035)
11-3, 6-11; 12-7 Sun
☎ (01255) 830340
Adnams Bitter; Greene King IPA, Abbot; guest beers H
This warm, friendly pub is situated at a crossroads – the floodlit church steeple lights the way at night. The small restaurant area is dominated by a brick fireplace, and exposed beams, brickwork and brasses throughout typify a rural inn. Three centuries ago it was three cottages, today the pub is host to bellringers, cricketers and the Tendring Gentleman's Golf Society. The village link bus daytime service passes the door regularly. P

THAXTED

Star
Mill End (B184)
11-11; 12-10.30 Sun
☎ (01371) 830368
Adnams Bitter, Broadside; guest beers H
Popular with locals and visitors, the Star is now open plan, but exposed beams and a vast open fireplace have been retained. Thaxted is an architectural gem, not to be missed, with its steep High Street, Guildhall, windmill, almshouses and towering above all, the parish church of cathedral proportions. Home of a month-long festival, Thaxted also hosts the annual national weekend morris men gathering, when teams dance in the street.
P

TILBURY

Anchor
Civic Square (near A126)
11-11; 12-10.30 Sun
☎ (01375) 850560
Courage Directors; Hop Back Summer Lightning; Shepherd Neame Spitfire; Theakston Best Bitter; guest beers H
Sympathetic Wetherspoon's conversion of an old Charrington's house that has brought excellent value and interesting guest beers to a formerly keg town. Locals favour the front of the pub, the no-smoking rear area is used mainly by diners, although the children's licence means that this area can be noisy. Scenes from Tilbury Docks, together with profiles of local characters feature in the decor. Low prices for beer and food (even by Wetherspoon's standards) mean that it can get very busy.
P

WALTHAM ABBEY

White Lion
11 Sun Street (near B194)
11-11; 12-10.30 Sun
☎ (01922) 718673
McMullen AK H
Small, one-bar pub, wood-panelled throughout. It is a rare McMullen's outlet, where the tenant does not use a cask breather. Darts dominate here, with local leagues playing on Monday, Tuesday and Wednesday, and a knockout on Sunday evening. Live music is staged on Saturday night. No food is available at any time, just a friendly local in a pedestrianised shopping area.

WEELEY

White Hart
Clacton Road, Weeley Heath (B1441)
11-2.30, 4.30-11; 11-11 Fri & Sat; 12-10.30 Sun
☎ (01255) 830384
Beer range varies H/G
This no-frills pub has an L-shaped drinking area that caters for pool and darts players. The publican opted for a no-food regime which many would regard as hardly a recipe for success. However, by concentration on an ever-changing range of real ales from micro-breweries near and far, and introducing gravity dispense, he has been able to establish an excellent reputation among real ale fans. A regular bus service passes the door; the station is about a mile away.
P

WENDENS AMBO

Bell
Royston Road (B1039)
11.30-2.30, 6-11; 12-10.30 Sun
☎ (01799) 540382
Adnams Bitter; Ansells Mild; guest beers H
Beamed, country pub, at the centre of a picturesque village, with a large rear garden, which boasts a crazy golf course and hosts a

INN BRIEF

STISTED

Dolphin
Coggeshall Road
11-3, 6-11; 12-3, 7-10.30 Sun
(01376) 321143
Ridleys IPA G
Quiet, unspoilt, beamed country pub with much community involvement. No food Tue or Sun eves. Other Ridleys beers stocked.

WHITE RODING

Black Horse
Chelmsford Road
11-11; 12-10.30 Sun
(01279) 876322
Ridleys IPA, G **Rumpus,** H/G **Old Bob** G
Busy local. Some of the handpumps are for show, with the beer actually dispensed by gravity from the cellar.

WITHAM

Woolpack
7 Church Street
11.30-11; 12-10.30 Sun
(01376) 511195
Beer range varies G
Two-bar, back-street local – the oldest pub in the town.

beer festival in May. The Bell has been local CAMRA Pub of the Year in previous years. There is easy access from Audley End Station (Cambridge-Liverpool Street line) and buses from Saffron Walden will bring you to this welcoming pub which serves excellent home-made food.
⛫Q❀◐▶ ⇌ (Audley End) ♣P

WESTCLIFF-ON-SEA

Cricketer's Inn

228 London Road (A13/Milton Rd jct)
⏲ 11-11; 12-10.30 Sun
☎ (01702) 343168
Greene King IPA, Abbot; guest beers Ⓗ
Spacious Grays pub, offering Greene King

Calculating Beer Rip Off

Beer drinkers can work out by how much they are being short changed by using a new rip-off calculator launched by the Campaign for Real Ale. The credit card sized device clearly states the cost in pence of pints which fall short of 100 per cent liquid.The consumer group is urging drinkers to stand up for their rights in pubs that serve short pints in response to the government's proposals to make it legal to serve only 95 per cent liquid.

Mike Benner, CAMRA's Head of Campaigns and Communications said, 'Despite policies dating back thirty years to bring in a full pint law, the Labour government has published proposals which will make it legal for pubs to sell short measures. There have been thousands of consumer complaints about short measure, but big business is being put before consumer rights.'

The Rip-Off Calculator shows that a customer paying £2.20 for a pint could be paying 50 pence too much if the liquid in the glass is only 2.5 centimetres below the brim of the glass. That could be costing someone drinking two pints a day a staggering £365 a year!

Mike Benner added, 'You don't have to be a rocket scientist to work out that the big pub chains are making millions out of short measure and the government is now playing into their hands by legalising the practice. It's time for consumers to fight back by letting the government know they care about this issue and voting with their feet by taking their custom elsewhere when served a short pint.'

CAMRA's research shows that:

- 89.4 per cent of pints are less than 100 per cent liquid
- More than one in four pints (27.7 per cent) are less than the industry's guidelines of 95 per cent liquid
- Pubs that already serve 100 per cent liquid pints are cheaper on average than pubs which do not guarantee full pints.

Rip Off calculators are available from CAMRA on 01727 867201 or from 230 Hatfield Road, St Albans, Herts, AL1 4LW

beers and two weekly guests from Grays' list. The cider is Thatchers. Of the two bars, one is used as a family room until 9pm. The menu ranges from bar snacks to Sunday roasts and special prices are available on food and drink at certain times. Music lovers can visit the adjacent Club Riga, which stages live bands several times a week.

≠(Westcliff) ♣P

Hamlet Court

54 Hamlet Court Road (near A13)

11-11; 12-10.30 Sun

☎ (01702) 391752

Courage Directors; Fuller's London Pride; Greene King Abbot; John Smith's Bitter; guest beers Ⓗ

Former bank put to better use as a pub, offering a good selection of real ales, with two from independent brewers, and hosting regular beer festivals. This one-bar pub offers table service. Old pictures of the local area are displayed. An extensive menu includes daily specials; it opens at 10am for breakfast. In summer the french doors open on to a patio with heaters for cool evenings. Quizzes and party evenings are held regularly.

≠

WIDDINGTON

Fleur de Lys

High Street (1½ miles E of B1383, follow signs for Mole Hall Wildlife Park) OS538316

12-3, 6-11; 12-3, 7-10.30 Sun

☎ (01799) 540659

Adnams Bitter, Broadside; Greene King IPA; guest beers (summer) Ⓗ

Friendly village local that attracts walkers from the extensive footpath network. The 400-year-old building is said to be haunted. Close to Priors Barn (English Heritage) and Mole Hall Wildlife Park (worth a visit), this pub was saved by the local CAMRA branch some years ago, and is used by groups such as morris dancers and bridge club (Monday evening, when no meals are served). The games room has pool and machines.

♣P

WIVENHOE

Horse & Groom

55 The Cross (B1028)

10.30-3, 5.30 (6 Sat)-11; 12-3.30, 7-10.30 Sun

☎ (01206) 824928

Adnams Bitter, seasonal beers; guest beers Ⓗ

This is a pub that caters for all. The public bar is home to five darts teams, including a highly successful ladies' team. The lunches are very popular. The landlady and her bar staff are always welcoming and friendly. The landlord acquired a sort of fame when he became the Adnams fisherman on the local CAMRA calendar – much to the amusement of his regulars. This pub is accessible by bus from Colchester.

♣P

WOODHAM MORTIMER

Hurdlemaker's Arms

Post Office Road (between A414 and B1010) OS813045

11.30-3, 6.30-11; 12-4, 7-10.30 Sun

☎ (01245) 225169

Greene King IPA, Abbot; guest beers Ⓗ

Classic country pub – and the only Hurdlemaker's in the country. The two linked bars are both simply furnished: the public, with its tiled floor, has a dartboard, while the flagstoned lounge displays blackboards showing a varied menu (no food Sun eve). The turnover of guest beers averages four per month. The large country garden is ideal for summer days and occasional barbecues are held. A small barn has been refurbished as a characterful club room – the TVR club meet here monthly.

Q♣P

WOODHAM WALTER

Bell

The Street

(off A414, near Danbury)

12-3, 7-11; 12-3, 7-10.30 (not winter eve) Sun

☎ (01245) 223437

Adnams Broadside; Greene King IPA; guest beer Ⓗ

Picturesque, 16th-century coaching house, timber-framed with exposed beams. Central to the village, this traditional pub is popular with ramblers and is close to the Chelmer Navigation and areas of common land. This friendly, relaxing pub offers good home-produced food, with daily specials, grills, fish and vegetarian dishes, plus eight varieties of ploughmans! A separate room is available for parties; evening meals are served Tue-Sat.

Q♣P

WRITTLE

Inn on the Green

57 The Green (near A1060)

11-3, 6-11; 11-11 Wed-Sat; 12-10.30 Sun

☎ (01245) 420266

Brakspear Bitter; Mighty Oak IPA, English Oak; Nethergate IPA; Ⓗ **guest beers** Ⓗ/Ⓖ

The long, single bar is open plan, with two distinct drinking areas and a dining area on a raised platform. Two or three guest beers usually come from independent breweries. Good home-cooked food includes many daily specials; there is a function room-cum-restaurant upstairs. A beer festival is held every Easter in a marquee in the large garden, featuring over 30 beers. Popular with ramblers, the inn features in a book of Essex walks.

♣P

Wheatsheaf

70 The Green (near A1060)

11-2.30 (3 Fri), 5.30-11; 11-11 Sat; 12-10.30 Sun

☎ (01245) 420695

Greene King IPA, Abbot; Mighty Oak Oscar Wilde, Burntwood; guest beer Ⓗ

Small, locals' pub on the village green, selling beer since 1851. A door connects the tiny public bar, with wooden benches, to the more comfortable lounge. The only traditional, old-fashioned pub in the village, it attracts local bellringers, morris dancers and folk musicians – other people are welcome! The old Gray and Sons sign in the public bar was rescued from the brewery, which closed in 1974.

Q♣P

shops and offices, it enjoys a lively lunchtime trade and good food is served weekdays. The mostly business clientele at lunchtime is replaced by locals in the evening. Q ◐ ⇌ (Temple Meads)

Merchants Arms

5 Merchants Road, Hotwells

11-3, 5-11; 11-11 Fri & Sat; 12-10.30 Sun

☎ (0117) 904 0037

Bath SPA, Gem, Barnstormer; guest beer Ⓗ

Lovingly restored, award-winning Bath Ales pub, with a friendly, cosy atmosphere. It is easily noticed, with its brightly-painted orange exterior. The bar is wood-panelled and usually serves three Bath Ales beers, along with a regularly changing guest beer. At the back is a small no-smoking area. Bar snacks are served and satellite TV is available. Several bottle-conditioned and continental beers are also stocked; four-pint jugs are available at a small discount. Limited parking.

Old Fox

60 Fox Road, Eastville

7.30-11 (closed August and Christmas/New Year); 7.30-10.30 Sun

☎ (0117) 952 2674

RCH Pitchfork, Old Slug Porter; Taylor Landlord; guest beers Ⓗ

This 300-year-old, back-street free house, next to the M32 motorway, features a panelled interior and lots of local memorabilia, especially relating to colliers. WG Grace is said to have drunk here. Strong emphasis laid on traditional games, including shove-ha'penny and shut the box as well as chess and backgammon. Six beers are usually available, plus a good range of bottled beers and over 20 malt whiskies; not the cheapest though. Check opening times before making the journey.
Q ⇌ (Stapleton Rd) ♣

Post Office Tavern

17 Westbury Hill, Westbury-on-Trym

11-11; 12-3, 7-10.30 Sun

☎ (0117) 940 1233

Draught Bass; Ⓖ **Bath SPA; Butcombe Bitter; Courage Best Bitter; Otter Bitter; Smiles Best; guest beer** Ⓗ

Smart, popular pub, where a dress code applies. Formerly the old village post office, it displays plenty of memorabilia, including a red telephone box in the bar. This free house keeps six real ales, plus a guest beer. It has a bar for non-smokers. Evening food is restricted to pizzas, served Mon-Sat. It is a rare outlet for Otter beer in Bristol. ◐ ▶

Prince of Wales

84 Stoke Lane, Westbury-on-Trym

11-3, 5.30 (5 Fri)-11; 11-11 Sat; 12-4, 7-10.30 Sun

☎ (0117) 962 3715

Draught Bass; Bath SPA; Brakspear Bitter; Butcombe Bitter; Courage Best Bitter; guest beers Ⓗ

One of the few landlord-owned free houses left in Bristol, this very popular pub, with an attractive garden, is five minutes' walk from the centre of Westbury village. Various comfortable seating areas are decorated with unusual sporting prints and memorabilia. The imaginative menu features daily specials at competitive prices. The pub sponsors badminton, football, rugby and cricket teams; it gets busy when rugby is shown on the large foldaway TV screen. A nitro-keg free zone, a no-smoking area is available at lunchtime. Q ✿ ◐

Reckless Engineer

Temple Gate (opp. Temple Meads Station)

12 (7.30 Sat)-11; 12-10.30 Sun

☎ (0117) 929 0425

Otter Ale; Tetley Bitter; guest beers Ⓗ

Combining real ale with real live music, it hosts live bands every Saturday and most Friday evenings – free entry to card-carrying CAMRA members and uniformed postal and rail staff. Styles vary from rock and punk to soul music. The bareboarded, low-ceilinged pub can get smoky. The long-standing landlord has resisted takeover attempts by the hotel that was built above and beside it. Otter Ale is easily the biggest seller here. Weekday lunches served.
◐ ⇌ (Temple Meads)

Sugar Loaf

51 St Mark's Road, Easton (near Stapleton Rd Station)

11-11; 12-10.30 Sun

☎ (0117) 939 4498

Greene King Abbot; Marston's Pedigree; Tetley Bitter Ⓗ

This popular community pub is situated in the heart of Easton, near possibly the best spice shops in Bristol. The pub has two bar

---

CAM

Berkeley Arms
High Street
11-2.30, 5-11; 11-11 Fri & Sat; 12-10.30 Sun
(01453) 542424
Wickwar BOB; guest beers Ⓗ
Friendly local, circa 1890. The imposing Stroud Brewery frontage bears the Berkeley family crest. Beer festival in May.

CHELTENHAM

National Hunt
Benhall Avenue
11-11; 12-10.30 Sun
(01242) 527461
Fuller's London Pride; Wadworth 6X; guest beers Ⓗ
Refurbished pub on Cheltenham's western edge. Up to seven real ales include one from Goff's. Good value meals.

CHIPPING SODBURY

Squire Inn
67 Broad Street
11-3, 6-11 (Mon-Thu); 11-11 (Fri & Sat); 12-10.30 Sun
(01454) 312121
Draught Bass; Marston's Pedigree; Wadworth 6X; Wickwar BOB Ⓗ
Large ex-coaching inn with open fireplace, flagged floors and restaurant (good food), skittle alley and garden.

CINDERFORD

Forge Hammer
115 Victoria Street
12 (7 Mon)-11; 12-10.30 Sun
(01594) 826662
Freeminer Bitter; guest beer Ⓗ
Probably the oldest pub still open in Cinderford, located on the outskirts. Well-behaved children welcome. Meals are good value.

CLEEVE HILL

High Roost
On B4632, at top of Cleeve Hill
11.30-2.30 (3 Sat), 7-11; 12-4 (closed eve) Sun
(01242) 672010
Hook Norton Best Bitter; guest beer Ⓗ
Spectacular views from Cotswold's highest point, a popular venue for walkers. Good value food; traditional English puddings.

DOWNEND

Downend Tavern
125 Downend Road
11-11; 12-10.30 Sun
(0117) 987 3413
Draught Bass; Butcombe Bitter; Courage Best; Worthington Bitter Ⓗ
Street-corner pub staging live music Thu, Fri and Sat eves, and a quiz Sun. Lunchtime food (not Sun).

areas, one of which features a CD juke box that satisfies most musical tastes. The other bar area is quieter. The pub also boasts a pool room with three tables. There is a pleasant garden to the rear. A house beer, Easton Bitter, is brewed by Moles. It stages live music (free admission) on Thursday. ❀◐ ⇌ (Stapleton Rd) ●

Victoria

20 Chock Lane, Westbury-on-Trym

✪ 12-2.30, 5.30-11; 12-3, 5.30-10.30 Sun

☎ (0117) 950 0441

Draught Bass; Wadworth IPA, 6X, JCB; guest beer Ⓗ

This pub is hidden down the quiet Chock Lane. The sloping garden, with patio heaters, is perfect for summer evenings. A comfortable local, built in the early 18th century, it has previously been a courthouse and a cider house. Good food is served lunchtime and evening until 8pm (home-cooked pizzas available until 10pm). The walls are hung with prints and photographs of old Westbury. Q❀◐♣✔

White Horse

24 High Street, Westbury-on-Trym

✪ 11-11; 12-10.30 Sun

☎ (0117) 950 7622

Draught Bass; Butcombe Bitter, Gold Ⓖ

Multi-roomed pub serving the villagers of Westbury for over two centuries. Known as the 'Hole in the Wall', the beer is served through the window of the original building into the Georgian extension; the beers are kept cool in a 14th-century vault. The main bar has a flagstoned floor, with seating ranging from modern tables and chairs to ancient carved settles and a chaise longue. It can be lively on weekend evenings. Children are welcome in rooms without a bar until 7pm, when evening meals finish. Q❀◐⊟♣●

BROAD CAMPDEN

Baker's Arms

(signed from B4081)

✪ 11.30-2.30, 4.45-11; 11.30-11 Sat & summer; 12-10.30 Sun

☎ (01386) 840515

Donnington BB or SBA; Hook Norton Best Bitter; Stanway Stanney Bitter; Wells Bombardier; guest beer Ⓗ

Fine old country pub (circa 1724), free of machines and music. A 1905 photograph shows it as a bakery and grain store. It is characterised by Cotswold stone walls, exposed beams, an inglenook and an attractive oak bar counter. A framed hand-woven rug, depicting the inn, took one thousand hours to make in 1969. Bar meals are home cooked and there is a children's play area in the garden, which has a terrace with flower tubs. It hosts monthly folk music (third Tue). ♨Q❀◐♣●P

CHARLTON KINGS

Merryfellow

2 School Road

✪ 11-11; 12-10.30 Sun

☎ (01242) 525883 website: www.merryfellowinn.co.uk

Black Sheep Best Bitter; Gale's HSB; Greene King IPA; Wadworth 6X; guest beer Ⓗ

Comfortable, modernised local in a busy village centre, this pub retains its original Stroud Brewery window. An excellent, extensive outdoor area, housing an aviary, is suitable for supervised children. Reasonably-priced meals are served until 9pm. Entertainment is provided by a skittle alley, pool table and large-screen TV for sports. Note the Jack Russell print, signed by both the England and Australia cricket teams. Stagecoach service B runs from Cheltenham throughout the day. ❀◐P

CHELTENHAM ❄

Adam & Eve

8 Townsend Street (near Tesco)

✪ 10.30-3, 5-11; 10.30-11 Sat; 12-3, 7-10.30 Sun

☎ (01242) 690030

Arkell's 2B, 3B, seasonal beer Ⓗ

Unpretentious, friendly, terraced local, 15 minutes' walk from the centre. The public bar and small, comfortable lounge provide a strong community focus. The skittle alley fields many teams, and the pub takes part in the local quiz league. Almost unnoticed are the flowers on each table. The friendly landlady has run Cheltenham CAMRA's Pub of the Year 2002 for the past 24 years. Off the main Tewkesbury road, it is readily accessible by public transport (Stagecoach C and 41), but parking is limited. Q⊟

Hewlett Arms

Harp Hill

✪ 11-2.30 (3 Thu & Fri; 5 Sat), 6-11; 12-5, 7-10.30 Sun

☎ (01242) 228600

Black Sheep Best Bitter; Stanway Stanney Bitter; Tetley Bitter Ⓗ

Attracting a wide range of people from all walks of life, this comfortable, relaxed pub can be very busy, so booking for meals is recommended. Located on the outskirts of town, it is handy for the football ground and racecourse. A small car park is located beside the large garden and patio. A fine collection of mugs and jugs hang on the beams, and naval memorabilia peppers the walls. It is a few minutes' walk from Stagecoach service A bus stop. ❀◐P⊬

Kemble Brewery Inn

27 Fairview Street (off ring road)

✪ 11.30-2.30 (3 Fri), 5.30-11; 11.30-11 Sat; 12-4, 7-10.30 Sun

☎ (01242) 243446

Archers Village, Best Bitter, Golden; guest beer Ⓗ

Cheltenham CAMRA Pub of the Year 2001 is a small, but deservedly popular back-street local. Hard to find, but well worth the effort, it is Cheltenham's major outlet for Archers and offers good value, home-made food (not served Sun eve). The first owner came from Kemble and made cider from apples picked in the rear orchard, now an attractive walled garden. Popular with race-goers and home football supporters, the single room can get smoky on event days. Q❀◐

Mitre's Bar

23 Sandford Street

✪ 12-11; 12-10.30 Sun

☎ (01242) 516655

Goff's Jouster; guest beer Ⓗ

Despite its wine bar appearance, this modernised free house remains very much a popular back-street pub. Up to three beers,

MORETON-IN-MARSH

Inn on the Marsh

Stow Road (A429)

12-2.30, 7-11; 11-3, 6-11 Fri, Sat & summer; 12-3, 7-10.30 Sun

(01608) 650709

Banks's Original; Marston's Bitter, Pedigree; guest beer H

This former bakery has a bar which is reminiscent of an Amsterdam 'brown café', with comfortable armchairs, old photographs, duck prints and hanging hops. The no-smoking area, with baskets hanging from the rafters, is a reminder of Moreton's basket-weaving past. The menu for the dining area conservatory bears the Dutch East Indies influence of the Dutch landlady/chef (no food Mon eve). The garden has a duckpond, a former coach wash. Q P

NAILSWORTH

George Inn

Newmarket (1/2 mile up hill from bus station)

11-3, 6-11; 12-3, 7-10.30 Sun

(01453) 833228

Draught Bass; Moles Tap Bitter; Taylor Landlord; Uley Old Spot H

Traditional village local, with a friendly atmosphere, looking southwards over the valley above Nailsworth. Three chimneys confirm that the inn was originally three cottages, becoming a pub in 1820, and renamed in 1910 to honour the incoming George V. The George features in CAMRA's Good Pub Food and the award-winning chef uses only fresh ingredients; even the rolls are home made. The imaginative menu is keenly priced and served in the small restaurant (booking essential) or the bar. Q P

OAKRIDGE LYNCH

Butcher's Arms

OS915038

11-3, 6-11; 12-4, 7-10.30 Sun

(01285) 760371

Archers Best Bitter; Greene King Abbot; Tetley Bitter; Wickwar BOB; guest beer (occasional) H

Popular, two-bar stone local, whose restaurant opens Wednesday-Saturday and Sunday lunchtime. Food is also available in the bars at all times (except Sun eve and Mon). There is a skittle alley, and the pub runs a team in the local league. It also fields its own cricket team which plays friendly matches against neighbouring pubs. Noted for its consistently good beer and excellent food, the pub boasts a fine garden. Q P

OLDBURY-ON-SEVERN

Anchor

Church Road

11.30-2.30, 6.30-11; 11-11 Sat; 12-10.30 Sun

(01454) 413331

Draught Bass; Butcombe Bitter; Theakston Best Bitter, Old Peculier H

Country inn, a two-bar classic, circa 17th century. The accent here is on food with a varied menu. The main bar is L-shaped, with a beamed ceiling and roaring fire; the public bar is smaller, displaying local photographs, including some of Severn salmon fishermen. At the rear is a dining room (children admitted). The large garden, next to a river, is safely fenced, at the end is a pétanque pitch. Opposite the pub a footpath goes to the River Severn. Q P

OLD DOWN

Fox

Inner Down, Tockington

11-3 (2.30 Sat), 6-11; 12-10.30 Sun

(01454) 412507

Draught Bass; Flowers IPA; Moles Best Bitter H

Pleasant, cosy, 18th-century country pub. The L-shaped bar, with low wooden beams and a roaring log fire, displays old prints of the pub and historic Bristol. A wide choice of food, presented on a blackboard menu, is of high quality. There is a small children's room. Outside is a lit verandah area covered by a grapevine, and a small garden with children's play area. Moles Black Rat cider is on tap. Note the handmade pub sign. P

OLD SODBURY

Dog Inn

Badminton Road (between Chipping Sodbury and A46)

11-11; 12-3, 7-10.30 Sun

(01454) 312006

Fuller's London Pride; Marston's Pedigree; Wadworth 6X; Wickwar BOB H

Historic, 16th-century roadside pub with a traditional decor of stone beams and wood in its large lounge, smaller rooms and skittle alley. Situated close to the Cotswold Way footpath, it is hugely popular for its excellent food; the menu includes over 20 vegetarian options. Children are welcome; the large garden has benches and a play area. Rooms are available for overnight stays in the pub and neighbouring properties. Q P

PRESTBURY

Royal Oak

The Burgage

11.30-2.30, 5.30-11 (11.30-11 summer Sat); 12-3.30, 7-10.30 (12-10.30 summer) Sun

(01242) 522344

Archers Village; Taylor Landlord; guest beer H

Small, popular local in reputedly Britain's most haunted village. The public bar features exposed beams and low ceilings, while the lounge serves as a restaurant until 9pm. All food is home made and features cheeses from a local producer; meat is mainly sourced directly from Smithfield. A large garden at the rear leads to a skittle alley/function room. Q

PUCKLECHURCH

Rose & Crown

68 Parkfield Road

11.30-3, 6-11; 12-4, 7-10.30 Sun

(0117) 937 2351

Draught Bass; Wadworth IPA, 6X, JCB, seasonal beers H

Located close to the Bristol-Bath cycle path, this large, popular village pub enjoys a good reputation for meals (booking advised), which are served in the dining area and the lounge (eve meals Tue-Sat). The bar tends to be quieter. Children are welcome in the restaurant where good value pensioners' specials are served (not Sun eve). This smart pub is decorated in a traditional manner, with much wood. P

Star

37 Castle Road

11-11; 12-10.30 Sun

(0117) 937 2391

Draught Bass; G Wadworth 6X H

Located on the 689 Bristol bus route, this excellent community local is friendly and family-oriented. Bass is the biggest seller, served in jugs brought up from the cellar. Three real ciders are also stocked. The conservatory serves as a no-smoking restaurant for the justly popular food, based on local ingredients (no food Sun eve). This is a sporting pub where golf, fishing, crib and darts have a good following. The June beer festival coincides with the Pucklechurch 'Revels'.

P

SHEEPSCOMBE

Butcher's Arms

Signed from A46 and B4070 OS892104

11.30-3, 6.30 (6 Fri & Sat)-11; 12-3.30, 7-10.30 Sun

(01452) 812113 website: www.cotswoldinns.co.uk

Hook Norton Best Bitter; guest beers H

Cosy, 17th-century village pub and restaurant, part of Blenheim Inns, a privately-owned company which successfully breathes life into tired pubs. Quoits is played here. Its sign of a butcher sipping a pint of ale with a pig tied to his leg is probably the most photographed in the country. It is thought that butchering went on here when Henry VIII hunted deer in Sheepscombe Valley. Take in the staggering views from the tables on the steep grass behind the pub. Q P

SHIREHAMPTON

Lamplighters

Station Road

11-3, 6-11; 12-10.30 Sun

(0117) 982 3549

website: www.the-lamplighters.co.uk

Draught Bass; Bath Gem; Butcombe Bitter; Smiles Best H

Opposite the village of Pill on the bank of the River Avon, this 18th-century pub is in an area not noted for real ale. A spacious single bar is complemented by a function room and a children's room. Bar billiards is played. The large garden has a children's play area, and stands next to council playing fields. It is convenient for the station. An annual beer festival is held in September. No food is served Sun eve.

P

SLAD

Woolpack

On B4070

11-3, 6-11; 11-11 Sat; 12-10.30 Sun

(01452) 813429

Uley Bitter, Old Spot, Pig's Ear; guest beers H

Popular 16th-century inn clinging to the side of the Slad Valley, benefiting from superb views. Well used by walkers, it achieved fame through the late Laurie Lee, author of Cider with Rosie, who was a regular. Thoughtfully restored, with the addition of wooden settles in the end bar, well-behaved children are welcome in the end room. Three bars serve the award-winning Uley beers; ciders and perries are sold in the summer. Evening meals are served Tue-Sat.

Q P

STAPLE HILL

Humper's Off-Licence

26 Soundwell Road (Kingswood-Downend road)

12-2, 5-10.30 (12-10.30 summer Sat); 12-2, 5-10.30 (12-10.30 summer) Sun

(0117) 956 5525

Draught Bass; Butcombe Bitter; Smiles Best; Wickwar BOB; H guest beers G

Enterprising off-licence which has featured in the last 11 editions of this Guide. Four regular beers on handpump, plus up to three guests on gravity are further supplemented by four real ciders. All of these are sold at prices a third cheaper than most pubs. Bring your own container or

INN BRIEF

QUEDGELEY

Little Thatch Hotel

141 Bristol Road

12-2.30 (not Sat), 6.30-11; 12-3, 7-10.30 Sun

(01452) 720687

Otter Bitter; guest beers H

Wonderfully preserved building of 1351 with excellent modern hotel added. Craft brewery guest beers; quality food.

SAPPERTON

Daneway Inn

11-2.30 (3 Sat; 5 summer Sat), 6-11; 12-3 (5 summer), 7-10.30 Sun

(01285) 760297

Wadworth IPA, 6X, seasonal beers H

Excellent old characterful pub, near Sapperton Canal Tunnel. Food lunchtimes and eves. Family room; large garden.

STROUD

Golden Fleece

Nelson Street

12-3, 5-11; 11.30-11 Sat; 12-10.30 Sun

(01453) 764850

Draught Bass; Black Sheep Best Bitter; Greene King Abbot; guest beer H

Coal fires and a south-facing walled garden add to this homely pub. Light lunches in week. Gentle jazz played; live music Thu.

WOODCHESTER

Ram Inn

Station Road, South Woodchester

11-11; 12-10.30 Sun

(01453) 873329

Archers Best Bitter; John Smith's Bitter; Uley Old Spot; Wickwar BOB; guest beers H

400-year-old pub that runs an Irish beer festival for the National Hunt Festival in March. Good value food. Used by walkers.

Service

If you are unhappy with any aspect of service in a pub in the Guide, you should first complain to the manager or tenant of the pub, and then, if not satisfied, to the owner of the pub. Send a copy of your complaint, with any corrrespondence to GBG, CAMRA, 230 Hatfield Road, St Albans, Herts, AL1 4LW

buy one here. An ever-increasing range of bottled beers includes many bottle-conditioned ones. Hours may vary.

STOW-ON-THE-WOLD

Queen's Head

The Square

11-2.30 (3 Sat), 6-11; 12-2.30, 7-10.30 Sun

(01451) 830563

Donnington BB, SBA H

This 14th-century stone building has been licensed since at least the 1630s when a coin was held by the licensee in Cirencester. It stands at the heart of the town square, virtually unchanged as a near perfect example of a small Cotswold town pub, popular with locals and tourists alike. The two bars are full of character and packed with fascinating pictures, clocks and other artefacts. No food Sunday. Q

STROUD

Lord John

Russell Street

11-11; 12-10.30 Sun

(01453) 767610

Greene King Abbot; Hop Back Summer Lightning; Shepherd Neame Spitfire; Theakston Best Bitter; guest beers H

Wetherspoon's sympathetic conversion of the old postal sorting office has produced an L-shaped bar with a south-facing walled garden. A comfortable bar, with no music and a no-smoking area, produces a relaxing atmosphere in which to enjoy the range of ales. There is an input from the regulars as to the choice of guest ales from the Wetherspoon's list, giving a greater variety of guests than in other JJW outlet in Gloucestershire. Q

SWINEFORD

Swan

Bath Road (A431, 1 mile SE of Bitton)

11-3, 5-11; 12-3, 7-10.30 Sun

(0117) 932 3101 website: www.downourlocal.com/theswan-swineford

Draught Bass; G **Butcombe Bitter;** H **Courage Best Bitter** G

Comfortable free house in a tiny hamlet between Bristol and Bath, near the River Avon. The pub is famed for its Bass on gravity, and is popular with locals and walkers. The main room has a log fire and a curving wood and leather bar; there is another room for drinking, and a small restaurant. Home-prepared food is served daily (booking advisable for Sunday lunch). Children are welcome. A house beer, Morrells Firkin IPA (ABV 3.6%) is normally available. P

TEWKESBURY

Berkeley Arms

8 Church Street

11.30-3, 5-11; 11.30-11 Fri & Sat; 12-2.30, 7-10.30 Sun

(01684) 293034

Badger Tanglefoot; Wadworth IPA, 6X, JCB; guest beer H

Popular, two-bar pub, just off Tewkesbury Cross. Music evenings, every Saturday, attract a wide range of talented musicians. A good choice of meals is served in both the bars which usually keep a good selection of real ales. The pub also sells cider. It is reputed to have a resident ghost. Almost next door is Tewkesbury Abbey, which is another excellent reason to visit the town. Q

Nottingham Arms

129 High Street

11-11; 12-10.30 Sun

(01684) 292012

Adnams Broadside; Greene King IPA, Abbot; Tetley Bitter H

16th-century town-centre pub, opposite the Town Hall. A heavily timbered front bar, with roaring fire, leads to a cosy rear dining area, the traditional cellar is accessible from a side passage. Widely popular for its consistently good beers and food, it hosts live music on Thursday during the summer. The pub gets busy at lunchtime with visitors to this historic town.

White Bear

Bredon Road

11-11; 12-10.30 Sun

(01684) 296614

Wye Valley Bitter; guest beers H

Lively, friendly pub: one L-shaped bar with a pool table one end and a dartboard at the other. Family-run, it serves the best value pint in town from an ever-changing beer list, plus real cider. Close to Tewkesbury Marina, it is popular with boaters. It fields crib, darts and pool teams, while its skittle alley doubles as the home of Tewkesbury winter ale festival in February. Note the possibility of flooding in winter. P

TORMARTON

Portcullis Inn

High Street (near M4 jct 18)

12-3, 6-11; 12-3, 7-10.30 Sun

(01454) 218263

Draught Bass; Butcombe Bitter; Otter Bitter; Wadworth 6X; guest beers H

This pub is the focal point of the ancient village of Tormarton. Its modest Virginia creeper-covered stone frontage belies its spacious, unassuming main bar. It has an oak-panelled no-smoking restaurant which provides freshly-cooked generous meals at modest prices, weekday evenings and lunchtime at weekends. The friendly landlord/owner takes pride in his fine selection of beers sourced mainly from local breweries. Seven en-suite guest rooms are available. Q P

ULEY

Old Crown

The Green

11.30-2.30 (3 Sat), 7-11; 12-3, 7-10.30 Sun

(01453) 860502

website: www.oldcrown@tiscali.co.uk

Uley Bitter, Pig's Ear; guest beers H

Attractive, whitewashed 17th-century free house in the picturesque Uley Valley, it has a pleasant walled garden. The main bar has a low, timbered ceiling. Close to Uley Brewery and the Cotswold Way, it is popular with walkers. Live music can be enjoyed on Tuesday and Friday. The pub was local CAMRA Pub of the Year 2001. The

landlady serves over 150 guest ales each year, mainly from micro-breweries. The home-cooked food is good value.
♛Q☕❀⇌◑♣P

WATERLEY BOTTOM

New Inn

Signed from North Nibley OS758964
⌚ 12-2.30 (not Mon), 6 (7 Mon)-11; 12-11 Sat; 12-10.30 Sun
☎ (01453) 543659
Bath SPA, Gem; Cotleigh Tawny; Greene King Abbot; guest beer Ⓗ
Lovely free house situated in a small hamlet, surrounded by steep hills. During the 19th century it was a cider house, frequented by mill workers on their daily journeys; cider is still served straight from the cask. A beer festival is held the last weekend of June; on the following Tuesday a traditional ball-throwing event takes place. The pub has two bars and an attractive garden with a boules piste. No food is served on Monday. ♛Q❀◑⊟♣●P

WHITECROFT

Miners Arms

The Bay
⌚ 12-11; 12-10.30 Sun
☎ (01594) 562483
Freeminer Speculation; guest beers Ⓗ
Spacious, newly and sympathetically refurbished pub containing two bars and a large skittle alley. The pub offers a number of games including quoits, and a boules pitch is located in the front garden. A smaller garden is at the rear. Drawing a lively and varied clientele, it is always friendly. The Dean Forest steam railway runs next to the pub (passenger stops are scheduled, but not yet available). Belgian beers are stocked. ❀♣P

WHITMINSTER

Old Forge Inn

On A38, close to M5 jct 13
⌚ 12-3 (not Mon), 5-11; 12-11 Sat; 12-4, 7-10.30 Sun
☎ (01452) 741306
Black Sheep Best Bitter; Exmoor Ale; Wickwar Cotswold Way; guest beer Ⓗ
This mainly timber-framed building, bearing a strange mix of window styles, dates back at least to the 16th century. It was once the Swan or Swan with Two Necks (see sign above the door) before becoming a forge. Today the compact bar has a very homely feel with its beamed ceiling, attractive open fireplace and fashionable curtains. Home-cooked food is offered from a menu and specials board (no meals Sun eve or Mon). Thatcher's cider is stocked.
Q❀◑♣●P⚟

WITHINGTON

King's Head

King's Head Lane (Yanworth road) OS036153
⌚ 11-11; 12-10.30 Sun
☎ (01242) 890216
Hook Norton Best Bitter; guest beer (summer) Ⓖ
Unspoilt village local that can be hard to find but is worth the effort. In the same family for 90 years, it is a true free house, providing a strong community focus by hosting traditional games such as Aunt Sally. Although no food is served, other than pies and crisps, the landlady can rustle up bread and cheese on request. A Wickwar beer is usually available. Chedworth Villa is close by. Q❀♣●P

WOOLASTON COMMON

Rising Sun

1 mile off A48 at Woolaston OS590009
⌚ 12-2.30 (not Wed), 6.30-11; 12-3, 7-10.30 Sun
☎ (01594) 529282
Freeminer Bitter; Fuller's London Pride; Hook Norton Best Bitter Ⓗ
Lovely country pub affording excellent views; off the beaten track but well worth finding. The good value, home-produced meals are recommended. The landlord and locals together make this a welcome refuge. The 350-year-old pub has undergone many sympathetic improvements over the years, including a large bar and a small snug. On the route of the circular pub walks of the Forest of Dean, it is popular with walkers and cyclists. ♛Q❀◑Å♣P

Good Old Ale

When schoolboy friends meet once again, who
  have not met for years,
Say, over what will they sit down, and talk of
  their careers.
Your 'wishy washy' wines won't do, and fiery
  spirits fail,
For nothing blends the heart of friends like good
  old English ale.

J Caxton, circa 1880

STYLE MONITOR

Bitter

BITTER AND PALE ALE are often thought to be synonymous. Their origins lie in the India Pale Ales first fashioned in the early 19th century, but a century later they had become different if related styles. While some leading brewers such as Bass and Worthington continued to make strong bottled pale ales that matured in glass and threw a sediment, most brewers adopted filtration and pasteurisation to produce sterile and carbonated beers. The term 'bitter' had been used occasionally to describe the heavily-hopped draught Burton beers, but the term became a style in the early 20th century as the result of seismic changes in the way pubs were owned in England.

Rampage

From the middle of the 19th century until the turn of the 20th, brewers went on the property rampage, buying large numbers of pubs as they built tied estates that took only the products of the owning breweries. The breweries had also become public companies and they needed to offer shareholders some return on the large financial outlay that had gone to create tied estates. Beers such as porter, stout and IPA, known as 'vatted ales', took months to reach maturity. The brewers developed a new type of draught ale known as 'running beers' – the cask-conditioned real ales of today – that were ready to drink within days of reaching pubs. They gained maturity after a short secondary fermentation in cask in the pub cellar. In order to give the draught version of pale ale a fullness and roundness of palate, brewers blended with their pale malts a new type of stewed malt known as crystal (see also article on malt). Crystal malt arrives in the brewery with its starches already transformed into sugar: it doesn't require mashing. It adds nothing to fermentation but gives a pleasingly rich and nutty flavour to beer as well as colour.

Recognised

Drinkers dubbed these beers 'bitter' and the name stuck. While today there are some truly pale bitters, brewed only from pale malt and brewing sugar in the manner of the early IPAs, English bitter is recognised throughout the world as a beer style with a rich, appealing copper or amber colour.

In the 1950s, sales of bitter overtook those of mild ale. In spite of the rise of lager in the past 20 years, bitter is still seen as the quintessentially English style of beer. It's not just its colour that singles it out from other styles. It has a low level of carbonation, the result of natural conditioning in the cask: in most other countries where ale is brewed, it is filtered in the brewery and served by applied gas pressure. The low carbonation level of bitter makes it an easy as well as a pleasurable beer to drink, avoiding the unpleasant fullness of pressurised beers.

Bitter suggests a generous hop rate as well. Bitterness is measured by IBUs (International Units of Bitterness). While an English mild may have around 22 IBUs, bitters register in the 30s and even higher: the classic Holts Bitter from Manchester, for example, has 40 IBUs. This is identical to the IBUs of the classic Czech golden lager Pilsner Urquell: Holts tastes more bitter as a result of the nature of English hops. Unlike lager hops, English hops are fertilised and give a pungent, earthy, spicy and resiny character to bitter that is missing from other beer styles.

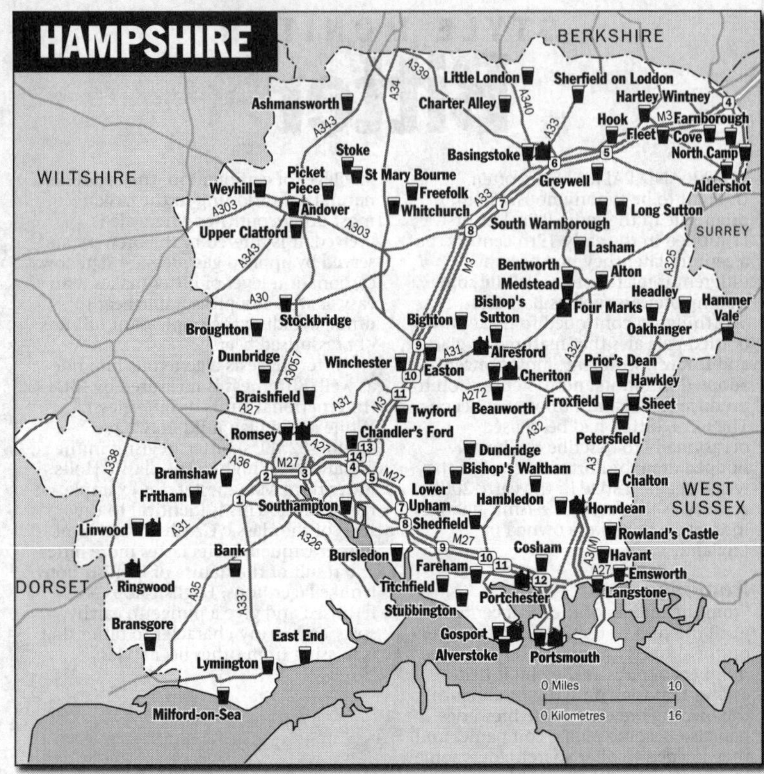

ALDERSHOT

Garden Gate

4 Church Lane East (off B3007)

11.30-3, 5.30-11; 11-11 Sat; 12-4, 6.30-10.30 Sun

☎ (01252) 321051

Greene King IPA, Abbot Ⓗ

The Garden Gate in its previous incarnation, the Peel of Bells, was established during the mid-19th century for the entertainment of Prince Albert's own soldiers from Saxony. Sadly, no evidence for this can be found in the present establishment. Entry is through the left-hand front door and opens into a comfortable single, horseshoe-shaped lounge. A small back room is occasionally used for meetings. It is close to Aldershot railway station (via footbridge, turn right and up into St George's Road). Evening meals served until 7pm. ❀🛏◐◑⇌P

Red Lion

Ash Road

12-2, 5-11; 12-11 Thu-Sat; 12-4, 7-10.30 Sun

☎ (01252) 686700

Courage Best Bitter; guest beers Ⓗ

Walking from the train station through Manor Park, or on the main road to Ash, the Red Lion is difficult to miss. The three open connected drinking areas are served from one long bar which boasts five guest ales, flying the flag for the smaller and local breweries. Some seats are from old coopers' barrels. Three log fires and collections of old plates, jugs and teapots help maintain the generally quiet, traditional village pub atmosphere. An annual beer festival is held the weekend after August bank holiday. Quiz night is Sunday. Lunches are served Tue-Fri. Oversized, lined glasses are available on request. ♨❀◐⇌P🍷

Royal Staff

37a Mount Pleasant Road (off A323 at jct with Waterloo Rd)

12-3, 5-11; 12-11 Sat; 12-10.30 Sun

☎ (01252) 408012

Fuller's Chiswick, London Pride, seasonal beers; guest beers Ⓗ

Located at the top of a steep hill (Waterloo Road) this beautifully refurbished establishment is well worth the climb. The pub is situated among some of the last late-Victorian villas remaining in the 'east end' of Aldershot and the decoration and furnishings reflect this setting. Old-fashioned hospitality is the trademark of the amiable landlord. The pub is very handy for paying supporters of Aldershot Town Football Club; non-payers watch from the top of the hill, outside the pub! Lunches are served Mon-Fri. ❀◐⇌♣✔

ALTON

Eight Bells

Church Street (off High St)

11-11; 12-10.30 Sun

☎ (01420) 82417

Brakspear Bitter; Hogs Back TEA; guest beers Ⓗ

Excellent free house, just outside the town centre, on the old Alton-Oldham turnpike. The building dates from 1640 and is steeped in history. Opposite stands the ancient St Lawrence church around which the Civil War Battle of Alton was fought. The pub

alley' (later becoming 'charter alley'). There is a delightful rural ambience, with wooden beams, a skittle alley, and fires in winter. In summer cider is stocked. From 1989 to 2002 there were 450 guest beers. Menu offerings include vegetarian meals, children's portions, a variety of steaks and their speciality – home-made pies (of course, made with real ale). No meals served on Sun or Mon eve.

CHERITON

Flower Pots Inn

3/4 mile N of A272

12-2.30, 6-11; 12-3, 7-10.30 Sun

(01962) 771318

Cheriton Pots Ale, Village Elder, Best Bitter, Diggers Gold G

Home of the Cheriton brewhouse, fine two-bar, red-brick pub built in the early 1800s. A log fire and a 30ft well in the public bar add to the charm and character of this country gem, which is situated on the edge of a pretty village, close to the source of the River Itchen. It is popular with walkers. Good quality food is served, curry night is Wednesday (no food Sun eve). A large beer festival is hosted on August bank holiday. Weston's cider is stocked. Accommodation is available in converted stables and camping is possible in the field behind the pub.

DUNBRIDGE

Mill Alms

Barley Hill (B3084, by station)

12-3, 6-11; 12-3, 7-10.30 Sun

(01794) 340401 website: www.themillarms.co.uk

Beer range varies H

Large, relaxed, comfortable inn, appealing to a wide range of customers: well-heeled fishermen sampling the River Test, families and walkers enjoying fine countryside and travellers from the Southampton-Salisbury line station opposite. The central bar serves a dining area, large conservatory, cosy lounge with a good winter fire and a public bar. House beers are Mottisfont Meddler (Hampshire Brewery) and Olde Test Tickler (Itchen Valley Brewery). There is a pleasant garden, large double skittle alley and luxurious bedrooms.

DUNDRIDGE

Hampshire Bowman

Dundridge Lane, Bishop's Waltham (1 1/2 miles E of B3035) OS578184

12-2.30 (3 Sat), 6-11; 12-3, 7-10.30 Sun

(01489) 892940

website: www.hantsbowman.f9.co.uk

Archers Village; Cheriton Village Elder; Ringwood Fortyniner; guest beers G

Headquarters of the Portuguese Sardine Racing Club, the Bowman is off the beaten track but well worth finding. This former Gale's pub, built in 1865, is almost unchanged, with brick floors, old furniture and a wood-burning stove. Real ales are served on gravity from a stillage behind the bar. It is popular with walkers, and visitors and their dogs are made very welcome. An archery club meets in the field next door. There is a regular quiz (Mon). Good pub grub is served (no food on Mon, or Sun eve).

EAST END (LYMINGTON)

East End Arms

Lymington Road (3 miles E of IOW ferry) OS362968

12-3, 6-11 (not Mon eve); 12-9 Sun

(01590) 626223

Ringwood Best Bitter, Fortyniner; guest beers H

Unpretentious, unspoilt rural pub in a quiet backwater. The traditional public bar is preferred by the friendly locals, while the lighter, more modern and homely dining/lounge bar serves good quality food (not on Sun eve or Mon). It stands near the Solent Way long-distance footpath. It holds a children's certificate until 8pm. Cider (Thatcher's) is stocked in summer. It is worth making a detour to visit this pub, which caters for everyone.

EASTON

Cricketers Inn

1/2 mile S of B3047 on Easton's main street

12-3, 6-11; 12-11 Sat; 12-10.30 Sun

(01962) 779353 website: www.thecricketersinn.com

Otter Ale; Ringwood Best Bitter; Taylor Landlord; guest beers H

At first glance this pub seems typical of inns given over to the food trade; it has a separate no-smoking dining room as well as serving meals in the main bar. In fact there is much more to it – it is a true village pub, supporting the local cricket team and offering entertainment, including Jenga and quiz nights. It also offers accommodation (three rooms) and conference facilities. The meals are excellent and menus interesting (no food on Sun eve). A guest beer is usually available and periodically complemented by small 'festivals' from the cellar. A roadside patio serves as a garden.

EMSWORTH

Coal Exchange

21 South Street

10.30-3, 5.30-11; 10.30-11 Sat; 12-10.30 Sun

(01243) 375866

website: www.thecoalexchange.co.uk

Gale's Butser, GB, HSB; seasonal beers; guest beers H

Built in the 1600s, this was originally a pork butchery and ale house. As the name suggests, it was also used as a place for merchants delivering coal by sea to exchange their wares for local produce. The nearby harbour is a popular yachting venue and the pub is decorated with local and nautical items and photographs. The curry night (Tue) and international night (Thu) are well worth a visit. The 700 bus from Portsmouth to Brighton stops close by.

Lord Raglan

35 Queen Street

11-3, 6-11; 12-10.30 Sun

(01243) 372587 website: www.thelordraglan.com

Gale's Butser, GB, HSB, seasonal beers; guest beers H

Lively, welcoming flint-built pub on the edge of town near the Sussex border. The large garden at the rear of the pub offers views of the top of Emsworth harbour. It is a rare outlet for traditional cider and has live music of varying styles every Sunday evening. The No. 700 bus from Portsmouth to Brighton stops in the town centre, five minutes' walk from the pub.

FAREHAM

White Horse

44 North Wallington (jct 11 M27, 1/2 mile from A32 Delme roundabout)

11-3 (4 Fri & Sat), 5.30-11; 12-4, 7-10.30 Sun

(01329) 235197 website: www.whitehorse-pub.com

Draught Bass; Oakleaf Bitter, Squirrel's Delight, Hole Hearted; Tetley Bitter H

Small, cosy inn tucked down a narrow lane. It stands alongside the former Saunders Brewery now converted for residential use. The two small bars offer bar meals at candlelit tables or you can opt for the separate restaurant (no meals are served Sun or Mon eve). Superb choice for outdoor drinking: a French-style patio at the rear or sit at the front, close to the Wallington River which is across the lane. Parking is available in the village hall car park.

Q

FARNBOROUGH

Prince of Wales

184 Rectory Road

11.30-2.30, 5.30-11; 12-3.30, 7-10.30 Sun

(01252) 545578

Badger Tanglefoot; Fuller's London Pride; Hogs Back TEA; Ringwood Fortyniner; Young's Bitter; guest beers H

Five regular beers on the front bar are complemented by up to five guests in the snug bar on the left, in this well-established real ale institution. Local, regional and micro-breweries are well represented in a selection, which includes a lower-priced session beer. There are several distinct drinking areas spread around a central bar, each with its own character. Situated in old Farnborough village, close to Farnborough North station, it is 15 minutes' from Farnborough Main. Lunches are served Mon-Sat. (North) P

FLEET

Prince Arthur

238 Fleet Road

11-11; 12-10.30 Sun

(01252) 622660

Courage Best Bitter, Directors; Greene King Abbot; Hogs Back TEA; Hop Back Summer Lightning; Ringwood Fortyniner H

Typical Wetherspoon's house, but smaller than many, with a long bar which leads to a raised no-smoking, family area and patio. Seven regular beers are complemented by up to three guests. The pub is named after the Duke of Connaught who lived in the area while serving as a commanding officer in nearby Aldershot. The railway station is 30 minutes' walk away and is connected by a regular bus service until early evening (less frequent on Sat). Q

FREEFOLK

Watership Down

Freefolk Priors (off B3400)

11.30-3, 6-11; 12-3, 7-10.30 Sun

(01256) 892254

Brakspear Bitter; guest beers H

Welcoming free house set back from the main road, named after the famous book by Richard Adams (he lives nearby). The story of the rabbits is set in the fine downland countryside to the north of the pub. The five handpumps serve a changing range of small brewers' beers, always including a real mild – rare in this area. There are two 'traditional' rooms with displays of old pictures and pump clips. An impressive collection of penny arcade machines features strongly. One area is adorned by CAMRA awards and table football is available. A small conservatory has been added without detracting from the fine atmosphere. Buses stop close by and the pub is popular with walkers and cyclists.

P

FRITHAM

Royal Oak

1 mile S of B3078 OS232141

11.30-2.30 (11-3 summer), 6-11; 11-11 Sat; 12-10.30 Sun

(023) 8081 2606

Cheriton Pots Ale, Village Elder; Ringwood Best Bitter, Fortyniner; guest beer H

Small, thatched pub at the end of a New Forest track, awarded local CAMRA Pub of the Year many times. Comprising one main bar and several interconnected rooms with hatchway service, it is impeccably traditional – black beams, bare floors, wainscotting… Lunchtime food is typically ploughmans, soup or quiche. 'Supper Club' meals are served on Monday and Tuesday evenings, check in advance. Vast garden; in summer a marquee hosts barbecues, hog roasts and a beer festival (Sept). The centre for all Forest life, it is perfect for walkers, cyclists or equestrians (facilities for riders). Dogs are welcome – almost mandatory!

Q

FROXFIELD

Trooper

Alton Road (3 miles from Petersfield) OS727273

website: www.trooperinn.com

12-3, 6-11; 12-3, 7-10.30 Sun

(01730) 827293

Ringwood Best Bitter; guest beers H

Remote but friendly free house which serves four beers from independent breweries. Set high up in Hampshire's rolling countryside, it has a mixed clientele, but is popular with the country set. The atmosphere is enhanced by the candlelit bar and tables. Worth seeking out for the food alone, the extensive menu varies on a monthly basis. The restaurant is open from 9am for breakfasts, then all day for coffee. Walls are adorned with paintings from local artists, some for sale. Q P

GOSPORT

Clarence Tavern

1 Clarence Road

11-11; 12-10.30 Sun

(023) 9252 9726

Oakleaf Bitter, Hole Hearted, Blake's Gosport Bitter H

This tavern is a distinctive former brew-pub famed for its food – medieval banquets are sometimes held. The building was extended when it was turned from a club to a pub in 1999, the roof of the extension came from a chapel on the Isle of Wight. Although brewing has moved a short distance, the old brew-kit can still be seen through glass windows. The pub is not on a bus route but is only 10 minutes' walk from the Gosport ferry. Evening meals and lunches are served Mon-Sat, 12-2, 7-10. ⛼Q❀◐◑♿P⚟

Five Alls
75 Forton Road
⌚ 10-11; 12-10.30 Sun
☎ (023) 9252 9773
Draught Bass; Courage Directors 🄷
This two-roomed local is named after the 'five alls' of the king, soldier, priest, judge and toff. The lounge bar has recently been refurbished which has seen the bar being shortened slightly to provide more room. The pub holds regular quizzes and darts matches when it can get busy. Make sure you pay a visit to the highly distinctive toilet, they don't make them like this anymore. The pub can be reached on bus routes 81 and 83 between Gosport and Fareham. Meals are served Mon-Sat, 10-7. ❀◐◑🚂♣

Queen's Hotel
143 Queen's Road
⌚ 11.30-2.30, 7-11; 11.30-11 Sat; 12-3, 7-10.30 Sun
☎ (023) 9258 2645
Badger Tanglefoot; Black Sheep Special; Young's Bitter; guest beers 🄷
Popular back-street local, under the same management for 18 years, with 17 entries in this Guide and many local CAMRA awards. Any bus to or from the Gosport ferry via Stoke road stops at Waitrose (five minutes' walk away). The bar is divided into three drinking areas, but the focal point is an old open fire with an elegant, carved wood surround. A new outdoor drinking area will be in use from summer 2002. Two guest beers are normally available and a sixth handpump dispenses real cider in summer and a regular dark beer in winter. ⛼❀♣🍎

GREYWELL

Fox & Goose
The Street
⌚ 11-11; 12-10.30 Sun
☎ (01256) 702062
Courage Best Bitter; Gale's HSB; guest beers 🄷
16th-century pub set in a very picturesque part of the county. The Basingstoke Canal is located a short distance from the Fox & Goose, providing very pleasant walks. At the rear of the pub is a huge garden where various events are held. Children are welcome inside the inn if dining. Customers with well-behaved dogs are also allowed in the pub and gardens. ⛼Q❀◐◑⛺♣P▯

HAMBLEDON

Bat & Ball
Hyden Farm Lane, Clanfield (2½ miles from village on Clanfield road)) OS677167
⌚ 11.30-3, 6-11; 11.30-11 summer Sat; 12-4, 7-10.30 Sun
☎ (023) 9263 2692
Gale's Butser, GB, HSB, seasonal beers; guest beers 🄷
This remote pub straddles the boundary between Hambledon and Clanfield, quite significant when they had different licensing hours. The boundary is marked on the floor and used to divide the bar too. However, the pub is far better known as the cradle of cricket and has seen many famous matches on Broadhalfpenny Down between the local team and England. The bar is full of cricketing memorabilia and has to be a 'must visit' for every fan of the great game. Bar skittles, shut the box and many other pub games are played. ⛼❀◐◑♿♣P

HAMMER VALE

Prince of Wales
Hammer Lane (1 mile S of A3, ½ mile from B3121) OS868326
⌚ 12-3, 6-11; 12-11 Sat; 12-10.30 Sun
☎ (01428) 652600
Gale's Butser, HSB, seasonal beer; guest beer 🄶
Built in 1927, the pub nestles at the bottom of a scenic wooded valley. The bar runs the length of the pub serving a public bar with a wood-burning stove, a small saloon and a no-smoking restaurant area with a real fire. Superb food from an imaginative menu includes new and traditional dishes. Thursday is curry night in winter and Sunday is barbecue time in summer. Lunches are served daily and evening meals Tue-Sat. Outside is a large children's play area and patio seating. Ramblers are welcome. Local CAMRA Pub of the Year 2002. ⛼Q❀◐◑🚂♿⛺♣P

HARTLEY WINTNEY

Waggon & Horses
High Street (A30)
⌚ 11-11; 12-10.30 Sun
☎ (01252) 842119
website: www.angelfire.com/id/waggon
Courage Best Bitter; Gale's HSB; guest beers 🄷
Welcoming village-centre pub. There are some interesting photographs just inside the entrance. The lively public bar contrasts well with the quieter lounge. The Waggon & Horses has won many local CAMRA awards. The landlady serves good food at lunchtimes. There is also a very pleasant courtyard garden at the rear. It makes a peaceful refuge after visiting the many antique shops which crowd the High Street. ⛼Q❀◐🚂♣

HAVANT ❊

Old House at Home
2 South Street
⌚ 11-11; 12-10.30 Sun
☎ (023) 9248 3464
Gale's Butser, GB, HSB, seasonal beers; guest beers 🄷
The date carved into the outside wall indicates 14th century, but this is about 200 years too early. Beams recovered from the Spanish Armada were used in its construction and it was one of only two buildings to survive the 1760 fire. It was originally five cottages and then a bakery

(note the remains of the oven in the lounge). In the public bar is a post to which the last dancing bear in England was reputedly tethered. Regular live music is staged (Sat eve). Evening meals are served Mon-Thu (6-8). ⋒❀◐▶⊟⇌♣⊁●

HAWKLEY

Hawkley Inn

Pococks Lane (up steep hill and first turning on left)
OS747291
✪ 12-2.30 (3 Sat), 6-11; 12-3, 7-10.30 Sun
☎ (01730) 827205
Beer range varies Ⓗ

Surprisingly busy considering its rural location, this pub has six regularly rotating beers (all from small breweries), plus the landlord's own cider, Swamp Donkey. A single bar serves two small but distinct areas, one is no-smoking. Two real fires warm the winter traveller and one has a moose's head above it, complete with hat and cigarette! Live music is played most Saturday evenings in winter, plus a beer festival the first weekend in June. Lunches are served daily, evening meals Mon-Sat. ⋒Q❀◐▶●⊁

HEADLEY ❄

Hollybush

High Street (B3002 W of Bordon)
✪ 11-3, 5-11; 11-11 Sat; 12-4, 7-10.30 Sun
☎ (01428) 712211
Courage Best Bitter; Greene King IPA; Young's Special; guest beers Ⓗ

Comfortable and welcoming Victorian pub with period decor. A central bar serves fine real ale to thirsty customers at the front of the main room and provides a degree of privacy for diners seated in the recently re-worked rooms at the rear (no food Sun eve). A particularly pleasing feature is the bar billiards table found just behind the front door. A bus service runs from Farnham and Haslemere – even on Sundays. Difficult to spot if motoring; pub is on a tight bend. Q❀⇄◐▶♿♣P⊁

HORNDEAN

Brewers Arms

1 Five Heads Road
✪ 12-2 (not Mon; 4 Sat); 5 (6 Sat)-11; 12-3, 7-10.30 Sun
☎ (023) 9259 1325
Draught Bass; Courage Directors; Fuller's London Pride; Ringwood Best Bitter; guest beers Ⓗ

Pre-war, half-brick tiled pub set back off the main Portsmouth road. Referred to by those who use it as 'a proper pub', it is a genuine local where people come to drink and talk. See plans in the lounge of the original 1929 layout prior to internal alterations carried out by the previous owners, Gale's, in the early 1970s. Four regular beers are stocked, plus two guest ales which go on each Friday night, generally from small breweries. Q❀⊟♣P

LANGSTONE

Ship Inn

Langstone Road
✪ 11-11; 12-10.30 Sun
☎ (023) 9247 1719
Gale's Butser, GB, HSB, seasonal beers; guest beers Ⓗ

Situated on the shore of Langstone harbour (a popular yachting venue), this pub has much to offer for both the nautically-minded and the landlubber. There are many interesting local walks along the shore and into Havant via the trackbed of the much-missed Hayling Island branch line. See if you can find the berth of the old Isle of Wight train ferry. The Roman Wade Way (circa 900 BC) crossed the harbour to Hayling Island here. All buses to Hayling stop by the pub. ⋒❀◐▶♿P

LASHAM

Royal Oak

Off A339
✪ 11-3, 6-11; 12-3, 7-10.30 Sun
☎ (01256) 381213
Ringwood Best Bitter; guest beers Ⓗ

An attractive pub in the centre of a picturesque village. The welcoming garden sits alongside the church and provides a peaceful summer setting. The garden leads to a small lounge bar popular with diners. Meals are served Tue-Sun, with sandwiches only on Mon. There is a separate entrance to a comfortable public bar which has a pool table tucked away from the bar counter. The pub is renowned for its continually changing range of micro-brewery beers. The road outside runs through nearby Lasham Airfield, a popular gliding centre. ⋒❀◐▶⊟♣P

LINWOOD

Red Shoot

Toms Lane 3 miles E of Ellingham Cross on A338
OS187094
✪ 11-3, 6-11 (11-11 Sat & summer); 12-10.30 Sun
☎ (01425) 475792
Red Shoot Forest Gold, Tom's Tipple; Wadworth IPA, 6X, JCB, seasonal beers Ⓗ

This rambling inn has only been a pub since 1963; previous lives have included a private club and a garage. Many rooms have been incorporated into a single L-shaped, multi-level bar. Comfortably furnished with an eclectic mixture of furniture, some antique, a long bar meanders through this area. Events include a music quiz (Thu) and live music (Sun), beer festivals are hosted April and October. The pub's 2½ barrel brewery is visible from the bar. Good food is available, some home made, with special OAP lunches. A large camp and caravan site adjoins the pub. ⋒Q♨❀◐▶♿▲P

LITTLE LONDON

Plough Inn

Silchester Road (1 mile off A340, S of Tadley)
✪ 12-2.30, 6-11; 12-3, 7-10.30 Sun
☎ (01256) 850628
Ringwood Best Bitter, Fortyniner, Ⓗ **guest beers** Ⓖ

In 1857 Daniel Holloway became the owner of the Plough (and local brickworks), it has remained a traditional village pub ever since. You will find no loud music or other distractions; just an informal, relaxing atmosphere in this sympathetically restored cottage. In winter there are log fires and porter is served. Baguettes are available every lunch and evening (except Sun eve) and jacket potatoes are prepared every third Monday of the month which is quiz night. There is folk music on the last Monday of every month. Ideally located for ramblers visiting nearby Roman ruins at Silchester or Pamber Woods behind the pub, a pleasant garden stands at rear. ⛫Q☺❀♿♣P

LONG SUTTON

Four Horseshoes

The Street

⌚ 12-2.30, 6.30-11; 12-3, 7-10.30 Sun

☎ (01256) 862488 website: www.fourhorseshoes.com

Fuller's London Pride; Gale's Butser, HSB; guest beers Ⓗ

Possibly one of the most picturesque pubs in Hampshire with its handsome verandah and floral decoration. The interior is immaculate from the parquet flooring to the brass decoration around the walls. A decent-sized car park contains a boules terrain. Children can let off steam in a play area. The licensees are now running their second Guide entry for Hampshire. Great care and attention is given to the excellent beers and superb food, the warm welcome ensures repeat visits. ⛫Q☺❀🛏◐◑⛺♣P

LOWER UPHAM

Woodman

Winchester Road (B1277/B3037 jct) OS524194

⌚ 12-2.30 (5.30 Sat), 7-11; 12-5.30, 7-10.30 Sun

☎ (01489) 860270

Greene King IPA; guest beers Ⓗ

The contrasting lounge bar and public bar of this part 17th-century pub are equally welcoming. Children may bounce, climb and swing in the garden, and the summer floral displays blaze with colour. Two beers from Greene King's guest range are usually available, alongside more than 200 malt whiskies. There is a Tuesday night quiz, and live blues on the first Wednesday of the month. The Winchester to Bishop's Waltham, Fareham and Southsea bus service passes hourly in both directions. ⛫❀⊟♣P▯

LYMINGTON (PENNINGTON)

Musketeer

26 North Street (off A337 at White Hart)

⌚ 11.30-3, 5.30-11; 12-3, 7-10.30 Sun

☎ (01590) 676527

Brakspear Bitter; Ringwood Best Bitter, Fortyniner; guest beers Ⓗ

Traditional, comfortable, one-bar local in the village centre. At lunchtime it offers excellent home-cooked food at affordable prices (not served Sun). An entry in this Guide for 24 years and run by the same family throughout that time, it is now well into the second generation. Pub sign aficionados are unlikely to have seen one like this before! Four real ales are always on offer and log fires guarantee a warm welcome in winter. This pub is worth seeking out; enjoy a pint on the pleasant patio. ⛫Q☺❀◐♣P

MEDSTEAD

Castle of Comfort

Castle Street (2 miles N of Four Marks on A31) OS655373

⌚ 11-2.30 (3 Sat), 6-11; 12-3, 7-10.30 Sun

☎ (01420) 562112

Draught Bass; Courage Best Bitter; Gale's Butser; Usher's Best Bitter Ⓗ

17th-century village local tucked behind the church. There is a separate public bar and a small, comfortable lounge which is more like a family living room but with a large fireplace containing a wood-burning stove. A fish tank now occupies what was the serving hatch until the bar was 'updated' in the early 1960s. It is well known for its floral displays, with the verandah running the length of the pub well decorated with hanging baskets. ⛫Q❀◐⊟♣P

MILFORD-ON-SEA

Red Lion

32 High Street (B3058 to village centre)

⌚ 11.30-2.30, 6-11; 12-2.30, 7-10.30 Sun

☎ (01590) 642236 website: www.redlionmilford.co.uk

Flowers Original; Fuller's London Pride; Ringwood Best Bitter Ⓗ

This two-bar village pub was built in 1790 and retains its original sash windows. The interior has been attractively refurbished and one end of the bar houses a pool table. One bar is no-smoking and the other larger bar has a log fire and a piano, which is occasionally the focus of a singsong. The pub has a friendly atmosphere with a good mixture of customers of all ages. Good quality food is served. Music is occasionally played. ⛫Q❀🛏◐◑♿♣●P⊁▯

NORTH CAMP

Old Ford

Lynchford Road

⌚ 11-11; 12-10.30 Sun

☎ (01252) 544840

Brakspear Bitter; Courage Best Bitter; Fuller's London Pride; Greene King Abbot; guest beer Ⓗ

Imposing pub next to, and in the same architectural style as, North Camp railway station. It has a strong local following and attracts rail travellers and walkers along the Blackwater Valley path. Enter through double doors straight in to the single bar, which has a games room to the left, seating area and real fire to the right and a dining/meeting room at the rear. The large, safe garden with children's play equipment and a pets' corner is popular for traditional Sunday lunch. Evening meals are served Mon-Sat. A skittle alley is available by arrangement. ⛫☺❀◐◑⇌♣P

OAKHANGER

Red Lion

The Street (2½ miles E of A325/B3002 jct at Bordon)

⌚ 11-3, 6-11; 12-3, (closed eve) Sun

☎ (01420) 472232

Courage Best Bitter, Directors; guest beer Ⓗ

Find a charitable nominated driver, put on your walking boots or even move to the village, but do visit this gem. At this excellent village local the traditional public bar is dominated by luxuriant hop vines, a real fire and the now legendary 32lb stuffed pike. The dining saloon is more refined but not without atmosphere. A superb garden with well-established fruit trees and shrubs, leads to

a safe children's play area. It is likely to be crowded for all the right reasons.
⛫Q❀◑⊟♿♣P

PICKET PIECE (ANDOVER)

Wyke Down Country Pub & Restaurant

Follow signs for Wyke Down from A303
⏲ 11-2.30, 6-11 (may vary); 12-3, 6-10.30 Sun
☎ (01264) 352048 website: www.wykedown.co.uk
Exmoor Ale; guest beers Ⓗ
The pub forms part of a working farm and caravan/camping site, that was formerly a petrol station. In the 1980s the petrol gave way to beer and the conversion was completed in 1997 with the introduction of cask ales. A stylish, modern restaurant was added in the same year. Rooms are available for private functions, and families are welcome in the large conservatory. In addition to the camping facilities, the pub also features a golf driving range and an outdoor swimming pool. ⛫♨❀◑⛺♣P

PORTSMOUTH ❊

Artillery Arms

Hester Road, Milton, Southsea
⏲ 11-3, 6-11; 11-11 Fri & Sat; 12-10.30 Sun
☎ (023) 9273 3610 website: www.artilleryarms.co.uk
Cheriton Pots Ale; Gale's GB, HSB; Tetley Burton Ale; guest beers Ⓗ
Popular local, hidden away behind Milton Road. There is a noisy public bar and a more relaxed lounge which extends into the once separate function room. Unusually for a Portsmouth local, it has its own parking area. A local dominoes league play on Wednesday evening. The pub has good links with Cheriton Brewery and its Village Elder is served with greater regularity than at other Pompey pubs. When it is not available, the guest beer comes from other local breweries. Lunches are served 12-3; evening meals must be booked. Take No. 18 bus from Commercial Road, and footpath to Milton Campus. ♨❀◑♣P

Connaught Arms

119 Guildford Road, Fratton
⏲ 11.30-2.30, 6-11; 11.30-11 Fri & Sat; 12-4, 7-10.30 Sun
☎ (023) 9264 6455
website: www.connaughtarms.co.uk
Cheriton Pots Ale; Hop Back Summer Lightning; guest beers Ⓗ
Imposing, Victorian 'Brewer's Tudor' pub. An enjoyable experience for the first-time customer, the quality of the beer and food guarantee a repeat visit. This spacious pub has a single L-shaped bar, with a raised seating area, and a walled patio garden. In addition to the lunch menu, enjoy the delicious home-made pasties with fillings from the standard to the eclectic. The pub has a children's certificate. It can be very busy when Pompey are playing at home, with both home and away supporters making a beeline for pre-match drinks. Local CAMRA Pub of the Year 2002.
❀◑⇌ (Fratton) 🍎✔

Fifth Hampshire Volunteer Arms

74 Albert Road, Southsea
⏲ 12-11; 12-10.30 Sun
☎ (023) 9282 7161
Gale's GB, Winter Brew, HSB Ⓗ
Popular pub situated in an area of Southsea with several good pubs and a variety of restaurants. There are two distinct bars: the public features darts, TV, a rock juke box, a rare collection of hard hats and an overcooked pizza. The lounge has a collection of military and naval memorabilia, and an array of certificates presented by the local CAMRA branch, founded here in February 1974. Guest beers are supplied through Gale's. Their Festival Mild is occasionally stocked. Take No. 17 bus from Portsmouth & Southsea railway station, and ask for the King's Theatre stop.
Q⊟♣

Florence Arms

18-20 Florence Road, Southsea
⏲ 11-11; 12-10.30 sun
☎ (023) 9287 5700
Adnams Broadside; Young's Bitter, Special; guest beer Ⓗ
Surprisingly spacious pub with a tiled façade built in the 1920s to supply the need for a local midway between Palmerston Road and South Parade Pier. The largest of the three bars normally serves as a restaurant but it

INN BRIEF

PORTSMOUTH

John Jaques
72-82 Fratton Road
10-11; 12-10.30 Sun
(023) 9277 9742
Courage Directors; Greene King Abbot; Hop Back Summer Lightning; Shepherd Neame Spitfire; Theakston Best Bitter; guest beers Ⓗ
Wetherspoon's pub located five minutes' walk from Fratton Station. Popular on football Saturdays. Cask Marque accredited.

Ship & Castle
90 Rudmore Road
11-11; 12-10.30 Sun
(023) 9269 1147
Gale's Butser, GB, HSB, seasonal beers; guest beers Ⓗ
Hidden behind motorway and commercial docks, this pub used to be almost surrounded by water. Handy place to wait for the ferry.

Sir John Baker
80 London Road, North End
10-11; 12-10.30 Sun
(023) 9262 7960
Courage Directors; Greene King Abbot; Hop Back Summer Lightning; Shepherd Neame Spitfire; Theakston Best Bitter; guest beers Ⓗ
Wetherspoon's pub in the North End shopping area; usual range of cheap, good food and beer. Cask Marque accredited.

PRIOR'S DEAN

White Horse (Pub with No Name)
11-2.30 (3 Sat); 6-11; 12-3, 7-10.30 Sun
(01420) 588387
Gale's GB, HSB; Ringwood Fortyniner, Old Thumper, guest beers Ⓗ
Famous old pub hidden in a field (second track from main road), with no pub sign. House beer is Gale's Butser.

SHERFIELD ON LODDON

Four Horseshoes
Old Reading Road
11-3, 5.30-11; 11-11 Fri & Sat; 12-10.30 Sun
(01256) 882296
Fuller's London Pride; Young's Bitter; guest beer Ⓗ
Exposed beams and attractive pews create a characterful interior. Fresh fish is a speciality. Skittle alley available.

STOCKBRIDGE

Three Cups
High Street
12-2, 5-11; 12-2, 7-10.30 Sun
(01264) 810527
Fuller's London Pride; Ringwood Best Bitter, Porter Ⓗ
15th-century coaching inn with beams, wooden pillars and old-fashioned lights. Good range of food (not served Sun eve).

1960s. Buses 34 and 72 provide a half-hourly service to or from the Gosport ferry (hourly eve and Sun) and buses run to Southampton (72, not eve) and Fareham (34). The present owners have been here for over 20 years. Three guest beers are normally available, with local breweries often represented, and occasional dark beers in winter. There is a restaurant and TV/function room. Families are welcome in some areas of the pub before 8pm (no food Mon eve). ❀◐◗P⚟

TITCHFIELD

Wheatsheaf

East Street (off A27)

12-3, 6-11; 12-11 Fri; 12-3, 7-10.30 Sun

☎ (01329) 842965

Fuller's London Pride; Woodforde's Wherry; guest beers Ⓗ

Originally a Coopers of Southampton premises, now an unspoilt village local. Recently extended at the rear, it boasts a new kitchen and a larger room with seating for dining and drinking. Special menus for occasions (such as Mother's Day) are available; eve meals are served Wed-Sat. The outside toilets are accessed via a covered walkway. The pub car park only has spaces for six cars but there is a large car park close by at the community centre. Taped music is played in the main bar area and very occasionally live music is staged. A wide selection of guest beers is offered, normally two at a time. Families are allowed in the small snug, and there is a patio.

⛼Q❀◐◗▲♣P

TWYFORD

Phoenix

High Street (B3335, 1 mile S of M3 jct 11)

11.30-2.30 (3 Fri & Sat), 6-11; 12-3, 7-10.30 Sun

☎ (01962) 713322 website: www.thephoenixinn.co.uk

Greene King IPA, Abbot; guest beer Ⓗ

This is the hub of village life. Once a long, many-roomed, roadside inn it is now a single, comfortably furnished room, entered from the car park. The eating area is no-smoking; one step down is the long bar space with stools for informal drinkers. The guest beer is from Greene King's (smallish) list. A good range of home-cooked food is available and includes Sunday roasts. Accommodation can be arranged in nearby cottages – ask for introductions. Functions can be booked in the skittle alley.

⛼Q❀◐◗♣P⚟

UPPER CLATFORD

Crook & Shears

Off A343, S of Andover

12-3, 6-11; 12-3, 7-10.30 Sun

☎ (01264) 361543

Flowers Original; Fuller's London Pride; Ringwood Fortyniner; Taylor Landlord Ⓗ

Attractive, 17th-century village pub comprising two main rooms and a small dining section leading from the bar area. Old-style wooden floors around the bar and wood panelling create an olde-worlde atmosphere enhanced by black and white photographs and agricultural implements. A skittle alley behind the pub can be hired for functions. The local beer is from Ringwood and the range changes on a fairly regular basis. A variety of competitively-priced main meals are available daily.

⛼Q❀◐◗♣

WEYHILL

Weyhill Fair

On A342, 3 miles W of Andover

11.15-3, 6 (5 Fri)-11; 12-3, 7-10.30 Sun

☎ (01264) 773631 website: www.weyhillfair.co.uk

Fuller's Chiswick, London Pride, seasonal beers; guest beers Ⓗ

Popular roadside free house on a regular bus route with a bus stop just outside. Once a private house, it was extended to provide food and accommodation for cattle and sheep drovers who attended the now-defunct Weyhill Fair, from which the pub takes its name. A mural upstairs depicts scenes from the event. There are regularly changing guest beers from all parts of the country with over 200 different ales sold each year. Families with children are welcome in the no-smoking eating area at the side. A regular beer festival is held in July. There is a good-sized field behind for camping. Local CAMRA Pub of the Year 2001. Q❀◐◗▲♣P⚟

WHITCHURCH

Prince Regent

104 London Road

11-11; 12-10.30 Sun

☎ (01256) 892179

Archers Best Bitter; Hop Back Summer Lightning; Otter Ale; guest beers Ⓗ

Unspoilt, traditional town pub with a warm welcome. The single-bar pub overlooks one of England's smallest towns and is well worth the walk up from the square. The friendly landlord is always ready for a lively

Nourishment, not Punishment

It is gratifying, in these days of hop and malt susbstitutes and other abominations, to know that the princes of the trade still adhere to malt and hops. For those who sell adulterated beer, no punishment can be too great.

W T Marchant 1888

chat and takes great personal pride in the beer quality. The pub has strong pool and quiz teams. Buses stop outside, serving the nearby towns of Basingstoke, Andover and Winchester. Limited parking. ❀◐⇌♣⚈P

Red House Inn

21 London Street

⏲ 11.30-3, 6-11; 12-3, 7-10.30 Sun

☎ (01256) 895558

Cheriton Pots Ale; Itchen Valley Pure Gold; guest beers Ⓗ

This 16th-century coaching inn, once a 'big-brewers' outlet, has been transformed in recent years. With two very separate bars of diverse character, the pub can cater for everyone. The traditional log-fired public bar, with its flagstone floor, contrasts with the pleasant lounge. Beers are always from local brewers and the pub is renowned for high quality food at reasonable prices. The atmosphere is unpretentious and welcoming. The large garden has an area set aside for young children. If visiting Whitchurch with its silk mill, trout and fine walks (not to mention seven other pubs!), the Red House should not be missed.

Q❀◐◗⊟⇌P

WINCHESTER

Bell Inn

83 St Cross Road (extreme S edge of city, on B3335)

⏲ 11-3, 5-11; 11-11 Fri & Sat; 12-4, 7-10.30 Sun

☎ (01962) 865284

Greene King IPA, Ruddles Best Bitter, Ruddles County Ⓗ

Two widely contrasting bars give a choice of drinking style in this comfortable, traditional pub. A quiet, carpeted, conversational lounge complements a busy, cosmopolitan, flagstoned public bar. A large, safe garden with children's play equipment is reached via the public bar patio doors. The Bell adjoins the Hospital of St Cross, England's oldest (1132) almshouse. The pub is a tranquil one mile stroll from the city through water meadows that inspired Keats's To Autumn. Food is good 'pub grub' and includes Sunday roasts (no eve meals on Wed or Sun). Q❀◐◗⊟♣P

Black Boy

1 Wharf Hill (off B3330, Chesil St, near M3 jct 10)

⏲ 11-3, 5-11; 12-3, 7-10.30 Sun

☎ (01962) 861754

Beer range varies Ⓗ

Genuine free house that serves beers from Hampshire breweries. It is centuries old – with oak beams and varied floor levels. The main L-shaped bar is divided by a central fireplace. To the left an old barn has been converted into a separate, evening wine bar (lunchtime bar space). Very idiosyncratic decor – a giant Newton's cradle hangs from a ceiling, itself covered in pocket watches and keys, and old engineering pieces lie about. Imaginative food is served (eve meals Tue-Thu). A wealth of table games can be played.

❀◐◗♣

Green Man

53 Southgate Street (S of High St, on B3335)

⏲ 11.30-11; 12-10.30 Sun

☎ (01962) 865429

Greene King IPA, Abbot; Ruddles Best Bitter; guest beers Ⓗ

Substantial, Victorian, flint and brick corner pub, just south of the city centre directly opposite Winchester's cinema. Although it is a Greene King pub, no external signs reflect this. The many original rooms have been somewhat opened up to leave a variety of booths around a central island bar. Plenty of dark wood, old floorboards and an attractive, but non-functional, pot-bellied stove grace the pub. Diversions include regular live music, a piano singsong (Sun) and folk/jazz (Tue), quizzes (Mon), table games and a skittle alley. Good quality food is served during all sessions (except Sun eve). There is a very small patio area.

❀◐◗♣✔

Hyde Tavern

57 Hyde Street (400 yds N of City Rd on B3047)

⏲ 12-2.30 (3 Sat), 5 (6 Sat)-11; 12-10.30 Sun

☎ (01962) 862592

Greene King IPA; guest beer Ⓗ

Small, 15th-century, timber-framed building, dominated by twin dormer windows. Located in a street where ale has been sold for over 700 years, this unspoilt, two-roomed pub is below street level – beware low beams and ceilings, undulating floors and walls. It remains a place for drinking and conversation (expect to be drawn in) with old-fashioned values. Hyde Abbey's ruins and King Alfred's grave lie close by, but the Tavern's ghost is female – her footsteps are heard in the bar after hours!

❀⊟⇌♣

St James Tavern

3 Romsey Road (B3040, near county hospital)

⏲ 11.30-2.30, 5.30-11; 11.30-11 Sat; 12-10.30 Sun

☎ (01962) 861288

Butcombe Bitter; Wadworth IPA, 6X, JCB, seasonal beers Ⓗ

Located above street level on an acute terrace corner, this pub has wood floors, tan walls with light wood panelling and lofty ceilings. A raised no-smoking extension contains a coal-effect gas fire, while at the far end of the single, L-shaped bar is Winchester's last pub bar billiards table and a TV for sports events. Popular with students and hospital staff, there is a wide selection of good value food available every session.

❀◐◗⇌♣⚟✔

Wykeham Arms

75 Kingsgate Street

⏲ 11-11; 12-10.30 Sun

☎ (01962) 853834

Draught Bass; Gale's Butser, GB, HSB Ⓗ

Rambling, many-roomed, Georgian pub, yards from the gates of Winchester College and the Cathedral Close. The bric-à-brac and antiquities could easily furnish every pub in the city – 2,000 (allegedly) tankards adorn the walls, canes cover a ceiling, Nelsoniana abounds, old school desks make compact tables. The menu rates a Michelin award, evening booking is advisable (no meals on Sun eve). Trollope called it a 'third-rate hostelry'. Now the rooms are certainly first rate, and priced accordingly. Dogs welcome. Busy, but always civilised.

Q❀⛌◐◗P✔

dates back to the 16th century. In Victorian times the premises doubled as a wheelwright's shop – hence the name. The pub is still the focus for many community events including a monthly folk jam session (first Tue). Wholesome, good value food is prepared from local ingredients (no lunches served Mon or Wed). ♔❀⛟◑◐♣

ROSS-ON-WYE

Riverside

20 Wye Street

✪ 11-11; 12-10.30 Sun

☎ (01989) 564688

Goff's Jouster; Teme Valley That; Wye Valley Butty Bach Ⓗ

Occupying a position right on the banks of the River Wye, it was recently converted from a café/restaurant to a pub. The single L-shaped bar has views of the river and a pool table in an alcove; there is a separate dining room. The licensee enthusiastically supports breweries in Herefordshire and adjoining counties and may vary the range from time to time. On-street parking is available nearby. Traditional home-cooked bar food is served. ♔❀⛟◑◐♣

ST OWENS CROSS

New Inn

At A4137/B4521 jct

✪ 12-2.30 (3 Sat), 6-11; 12-3, 7-10 Sun

☎ (01989) 730274

Draught Bass; Tetley Bitter; Wadworth 6X; guest beers Ⓗ

Excellent black and white 16th-century pub, it boasts a split-level main bar with several cosy nooks and crannies. All the beers are served through a six-gang pewter beer engine rescued from a long-closed pub in Ross-on-Wye. Traditional English home-cooked snacks and meals are served in the main bar and in the dining room. The garden, with views of the Black Mountains, features hanging baskets in summer.
♔❀⛟◑◐♣P

SELLACK

Loughpool

1 mile NW of A49 at Peterstow OS558268

✪ 11.30-2.30, 6.30-11; 12-2.30, 6.30-10.30 Sun

☎ (01989) 730236

John Smith's Bitter; Wye Valley Bitter, Butty Bach Ⓗ

A superb 16th-century black and white pub where the long, low bar has two small alcoves and an open fire at one end. There is also a no-smoking restaurant. Recently bought by a London restauranteur, the food is original and of a very high standard using local produce where possible. Drinkers are welcome and bottled local ciders and perries such as Weston's and Dunkerton's are available. A large grassed area affords views of the delightful surrounding countryside.
♔Q♉❀◑◐P

WELLINGTON

Wellington Inn

1/2 mile W of A49

✪ 12-2.30, 6-11; 12-2.30, 7-10.30 Sun

☎ (01432) 830267 website: www.thewellington.uk.com

Draught Bass; Hancock's HB; Hobsons Best Bitter; guest beers Ⓗ

This traditional village pub has a main bar, with a feel midway between a public and lounge, plus a rustic-style restaurant. It offers one of the best choices of ale in the county plus a local real cider in summer; the guest beers are mainly from local breweries. Food is a real speciality with a separate lunchtime menu and daily specials. The bar has interesting local photographs and family board games are provided. ♔❀◑◐♿♣P

WITHINGTON

Cross Keys

On A465 in Withington Marsh

✪ 5-11; 12-11 Sat; 12-4.30, 7-10.30 Sun

☎ (01432) 820616

Greene King Abbot or Old Speckled Hen; Wye Valley Butty Bach; guest beer Ⓗ

Local that has been run by the same landlord for over 30 years; since acquiring the pub from Whitbread he has transformed the interior by stripping back to bare stonework. A single bar serves two drinking areas, each with a real fire. A monthly folk jam session is held (last Thu). The pub is on the Hereford – Bromyard bus route (419/420); camping can be arranged nearby. No food is served except on Saturday, when filled rolls are available.
♔❀⛺♣P

WOOLHOPE

Butchers Arms

E end of village

✪ 11.30-3; 6.30-11; 12-3, 7-10.30 Sun

☎ (01432) 860281

Hook Norton Best Bitter, Old Hooky; Wye Valley Bitter Ⓗ

This impressive black and white pub was formed in Victorian times by combining a butcher's shop and a beer house. Original beams are much in evidence, including a very solid one at head height in the lounge (beware!). The style of the furnishing is rustic. A good mix of customers use the pub for drinking and, predominantly, for eating, with home-prepared food being served in both bars as well as the dining room. A stream runs alongside the pub and garden.
♔Q❀⛟◑◐⊞P⚟

Crown

In village

✪ 12-2.30, 7 (6.30 Fri, Sat & summer)-11; 12-3, 7-10.30 Sun

☎ (01432) 860468

Smiles Best; Wye Valley Bitter; guest beer Ⓗ

A village pub next to the church, it is deservedly popular for its food, but drinkers are also welcome and now have a new area in a conservatory at the front door. Meals are served in the restaurant, and, more informally, in the large bar. The food is all home prepared and the extensive, appetising menu includes a large choice of vegetarian dishes. Food gift vouchers are on sale; booking for weekend meals is advised.
❀◑◐P

> In heaven there is no beer,
> that's why we drink it here.
> *Polish National Anthem.*

STYLE MONITOR

Old Ale and Barley Wine

THEY ARE OFTEN LINKED in beer tastings, but Old Ale and Barley Wine are two separate styles. The modern linkage is the result of both styles being predominantly winter ones. Unlike barley wine, old ale does not necessarily have to be a beer of fearsome strength. Centuries ago, it acquired its maturity, flavour, ripe condition and smooth flavour as the result of ageing in great oak tuns. Today ageing is more likely to be in bottle or brewery conditioning tank. Historically, it was a beer brewed for blending with fresh pale and brown ales. Old or 'stale' was one of the key constituents of the early porter beers: see section on porter and stout.

Improve

The vatting of beer has long since disappeared, and the finest versions of old ale are now those that mature and improve on their yeasty sediment in bottle. Others are produced for the winter and Christmas period, cask-conditioned ales that gain in palate and flavour as the weeks go by. Among fine examples of the style are the prize-winning Old Tom brewed by Robinson's of Stockport. The 8.5% beer has been brewed since 1838 and is almost as old as the brewery. It's the result of a mash of Halcyon and Pipkin pale and crystal malts, flaked maize and torrefied wheat, with caramel for colour. It's boiled with Golding and Northdown hops and dry hopped in the cask with a further addition of Goldings. One of the best-known and certainly most widely available old ales in Theakston's Old Peculier (5.6%), while a classic of the style is the bottle-conditioned Prize Old Ale produced by George Gale of Horndean. It's matured in the brewery for a minimum of six months and is given a further addition of yeast when bottled. The 9% beer will improve in bottle for several years.

Counter

Barley wine came into use in the 18th century as brewers attempted to counter the impact of imported French wine. The new technologies of the industrial revolution made it possible to make strong but pale beers. The increasing use of lightly cured pale malt and the scientific culturing of pure strains of yeast gave brewers far greater control over the production of strong beers. These beers were variously described as October beers (brewed in the spring and stored until the autumn), malt liquors and malt wines. Eventually they were brought together under the generic title of barley wine.

The leading British barley wine for many years was Bass No 1, available only in small nip bottles. No 1 indicated that, at 10.5%, it was the strongest of all Bass's beers. It has been restored by the Museum Brewing Company in Burton-on-Trent, which specialises in recreating old Bass beers. The profile of barley wine was given a boost in 1995 when Norman's Conquest (7%) beat all-comers to pick up the Champion Beer of Britain award for the Cottage Brewery in Somerset. Other fine examples of the style are Fuller's Golden Pride (9.2%) – casks of the beer are rolled around the brewery yard to keep the yeast working – and J W Lees' 11.5% Harvest Ale, an annual bottled vintage. Visitors to the US are advised to seek out the 12% Big Foot barley wine brewed by the Sierra Nevada Brewery in California.

groups are welcome, with a loyal following from games and quiz teams. Since the last Guide, four witches have appeared over the bar. Did they arrive in Hitchin from an oddly numbered platform?
❀◐⇌♣P⊘

ICKLEFORD

Plume of Feathers

Upper Green (400 yds from A600, down Turnpike Lane)
11.30-3, 6-11; 12-4, 7-10.30 Sun
☎ (01462) 432729
Adnams Bitter; Brains Bitter; Flowers IPA; Fuller's London Pride; Shepherd Neame Master Brew Bitter; Wadworth 6X Ⓗ

Welcoming pub that has been run by two sisters for the past seven years. It is quite lively, but not too noisy. The food, which is prepared to order, is excellent value. It has a large car park to the rear, and during the summer months the small garden is a pleasant place to sit and while away the hours. There is a public bar with a separate lounge, which has changed significantly over the years. The bar has been shortened and the room at the rear is now a restaurant.
Q❀◐◑P

KIMPTON

White Horse

22 High Street
12-2.30 (3 Sat), 6-11; 12-4, 7-10.30 Sun
☎ (01438) 832307
website: www.whitehorsekimpton.co.uk
Draught Bass; Courage Directors; McMullen AK; guest beer Ⓗ

The White Horse has won several community pub awards having supported local charities and village activities. It is very popular with walkers and cyclists. The Grade II listed building was converted from three 16th-century cottages and has its own priest's hole behind the bar. The extensive menu includes many home-made dishes (no meals on Mon). Specialities include fish, vegetarian dishes and Sunday lunches. In the warmer months, there is an al fresco dining area to the rear of the pub.
♨❀◐◑♣P

KINGS LANGLEY

Saracen's Head

47 High Street (A4251, just off M25 jct 20)
11-2.30, 5-11; 11-3, 6-11 Sat; 12-3, 7-10.30 Sun
☎ (01923) 400144
Fuller's London Pride, ESB; guest beer Ⓗ

Stepping down from the High Street, this 17th-century pub reveals a large single room. A bench-lined area at the rear resembles a public bar, while the rest has a lounge atmosphere. Saracens' heads jugs hanging from the beams, antique telephones and shelves of old ale bottles provide some interesting viewing. A log fire in winter completes the traditional feel. In summer, award-winning flowering baskets can be admired from several street-side tables. No food is served on Sunday.
♨❀◐P

LETCHMORE HEATH

Three Horseshoes

The Green
11-3, 5.30-11; 11-11 Fri & Sat; 12-10.30 Sun
☎ (01923) 856084
Draught Bass; Courage Directors; Tetley Bitter; guest beers Ⓗ

A beer house since the 18th century, the building was recorded in 1586 with a smithy adjoining. The earliest part is a timber-framed hall circa 16th century, with a 17th-century frontage. Substantial reconstruction took place in 1803. The pub has featured in films since the 1920s, in addition to numerous TV appearances. There are two separate bars, a flagstoned public and genuine oak-beamed lounge. An imaginative home-cooked menu is available. Q◐◑⊞P

NORTHAW

Two Brewers

1 Northaw Road
11-11; 12-10.30 Sun
☎ (01707) 652420
Adnams Broadside; Draught Bass; Greene King IPA Ⓗ

One-bar village pub sits next to a picturesque 19th-century church. Formerly owned by Allied-Domecq, this Punch Taverns house is divided into several drinking sections which helps to maintain

---

HARPENDEN

Gibraltar Castle
70 Lower Luton Road
11-3, 5-11; 12-3, 6-10.30 Sun
(01582) 460005
Fuller's Chiswick, London Pride, ESB, seasonal beers Ⓗ
Traditional-style Fuller's pub located opposite Batford Common. Specialises in home-cooked food. Cask Marque accredited.

NEWGATE STREET

Coach & Horses
61 Newgate Street Village
11-11; 12-10.30 Sun
(01707) 873236
Adnams Bitter; Fuller's London Pride; Greene King IPA Ⓗ
Old ivy-covered pub next to the village church. Popular with horse riding, classic car and motorcycle clubs. Expensive.

ST ALBANS

Farriers Arms
35 Lower Dagnall Street
12-2.30 (3 Sat; not Mon), 5.30-11;12-3, 7-10.30 Sun
(01727) 851025
Courage Directors; McMullen AK, Country; guest beer Ⓗ
Traditional back-street boozer, birthplace of CAMRA's oldest branch.

TYTTENHANGER GREEN

Plough
11.30-2.30 (3 Sat), 6-11;12-3.30, 7-10.30 Sun
(01727) 857777
Fuller's London Pride, ESB; guest beers Ⓗ
Popular free house with good value lunches and six guests. Impressive collection of bottled beers on display. Busy garden.

WATFORD

Pub on the Corner
94-96 Queen's Road
12-11; 12-10.30 Sun
(01923) 247697
Beer range varies Ⓗ
Near town centre, selling unusual guest beers. Pinball machine, pool, table football and a loud juke box feature.

WILLIAN

Three Horseshoes
Baldock Lane
11-11; 12-10.30 Sun
(01462) 685713
Greene King IPA, Morland Original, Ruddles County, Abbot, Old Speckled Hen Ⓗ
Originally two cottages, now a cosy single bar. Popular with locals, it offers a marquee and function room for events.

an intimate atmosphere. The exterior is particularly attractive in summer when the window boxes are a blaze of colour. Plenty of outdoor drinking space, as there is a patio to the front and a garden to the rear.
♔❀◖◗♣P

NUTHAMPSTEAD

Woodman Inn

Signed off A10 OS413346
✪ 11-3.30, 5.30-11; 11-11 Sat; 12-4, 7-10.30 Sun
☎ (01763) 848328
website: www.thewoodman-inn.co.uk
Adnams Bitter; Fuller's London Pride; guest beers Ⓗ
This 17th-century free house features an L-shaped bar and wonderful open fires. The restaurant offers à la carte meals as well as house specials and snacks (no food Sun eve). Accommodation is available, making this an excellent base for visiting local attractions, such as Duxford Imperial War Museum. During WWII the USAF 398th bomber group was based locally. The B-17 flying fortresses flew many missions over Europe and the pub displays original photographs and memorabilia. A memorial is located outside. The pub has been awarded the local CAMRA Pub of the Season.
♔Q❀🛏◖◗P⊡

OLD KNEBWORTH

Lytton Arms

Park Lane OS229202
✪ 11-3, 5-11; 11-11 Fri & Sat; 12-10.30 Sun
☎ (01438) 812312 website: www.the-lytton-arms.co.uk
Draught Bass; Fuller's London Pride; Woodforde's Wherry; guest beers Ⓗ
Popular, large 19th-century Lutyens inn adjoining the Knebworth estate. Note the railway memorabilia and breweriana throughout the pub, along with fascinating photos of Knebworth House, pop concerts in the grounds, and the Lytton family. The pub has featured for over a decade in this Guide and at least 3,000 different cask ales have been served. An excellent range of Belgian bottled beers and malt whiskies are always available. Beer festivals are hosted in the spring and autumn. It has won numerous CAMRA awards.
♔Q❀◖◗♿♣🍎P⚟

OXHEY

Victoria

39 Chalk Hill
✪ 11-3, 5.30-11; 11-11 Thu-Sat; 12-10.30 Sun
☎ (01923) 227993
Beer range varies Ⓗ
Comfortable two-bar local, of unusual shape, at the junction of Chalk Hill and Aldenham Road. The public bar entrance is from the main road, while access to the lounge is via the side patio. Regular quiz nights are held and the crib club and local skiing club meets here. A Cannon Brewery mirror adorns the lounge, evidence of former owners, Taylor Walker. A Benskins pub at the time of survey, following the discontinuation of this old Watford brew, the beer range will vary.
❀◖⊟⇌(Bushey) ♣P

POTTERS CROUCH

Hollybush

Bedmond Lane (off A4147) OS116053
✪ 11.30 (12 Sat)-2.30, 6 (7 Sat)-11; 12-2.30, 7-10.30 Sun
☎ (01727) 851792
Fuller's Chiswick, London Pride, ESB; seasonal beers (occasional) Ⓗ
Attractive early 18th-century oak-beamed pub in rural surroundings. Well-furnished throughout with large oak tables and period chairs, the landlord is a top Fuller's Master Cellarman and a winner of many brewery awards. The huge array of award certificates displayed in the bar confirms that this is one of the best quality Fuller's outlets in the area. Good lunchtime snacks are served (not Sun). The pleasant large garden is ideal in summer. ♔Q❀P✔

PRESTON

Red Lion

The Green
✪ 12-3, 5.30-11; Sat hours vary; 12-3, 7-10.30 Sun
☎ (01462) 459585
Greene King IPA; guest beers Ⓗ
Attractive Georgian-style free house on the village green. It became Britain's first community-owned pub in the 1980s. The landlord and landlady came here after 20 years' service at another well-known pub with many appearances in the Guide. The guest beers are constantly changed and feature ales from many local breweries. The pub also specialises in freshly-prepared home-cooked food. It boasts numerous cricket teams and is involved in fund-raising events. Awarded local CAMRA Pub of the Year 2001, it was Hertfordshire CAMRA Pub of the Year 2000. ♔❀◖◗♣P

RADLETT

Red Lion

78 Watling Street (A5183)
✪ 11-11; 12-10.30 Sun
☎ (01923) 855341
Young's Bitter, Triple A, Special, seasonal beers Ⓗ
This Victorian hotel was originally a Temperance establishment. It was purchased by Young's in 2000. The bar area has been extended and the restaurant reduced to 60 seats. There are 14 guest rooms and a function room, plus a patio overlooking the street. Meals are served lunchtime (12-3) and evening (6-10).
❀🛏◖◗♿⇌P

REDBOURN

Hollybush

Church End
✪ 11-2.30, 5.30-11; 11-3, 7-11 Sat; 12-3, 7-10.30 Sun
☎ (01582) 782423
Adnams Bitter; Tetley Bitter; guest beers Ⓗ
Redbourn's true free house, tucked away off Chequer Lane and opposite almshouses in picturesque Church End. This pub has been in existence since 1696, as suggested by its charming appearance. The three ever-changing guest ales primarily come from regional brewers Nethergate, Mauldons (East Anglia), Archers, Cottage (West Country), and locally from Tring and Vale

breweries. There is a separate hall for private functions with a folk music night held weekly (Thu). ⛼Q❀◑⊟♣P

RUSHDEN

Moon & Stars

Mill End (off A507 between Baldock & Buntingford) OS302317
⏲ 12-2.30 (not Mon & Tue), 6-11; 12-3, 6.30-11 Sat; 12-3, 7-11 Sun
☎ (01763) 288330
website: www.moonstars.fsnet.co.uk
Greene King IPA, Old Speckled Hen Ⓗ

Lovely two-bar pub overlooking the rolling countryside. Originally built as two separate dwellings in the 1600s, it has been a pub since 1802. The public bar has an open fire which in the past was reputedly fuelled by the customers' own firewood when they came to sup locally-brewed ales. The lounge doubles as a restaurant and seats up to 24. The only inn for a few miles, it is popular with walkers and cyclists. It is community-based and fields a darts and football team. Pétanque is played. Up to 10 vegetarian choices are available (no meals Tue lunchtime or Mon). ⛼❀◑◑♣P⊡

ST ALBANS ❊

Farmer's Boy

134 London Road
⏲ 11-11; 12-10.30 Sun
☎ (01727) 766702
Verulam Best Bitter, Special, IPA, Farmers Joy, seasonal beers Ⓗ

Cosy, cottage-style pub, now the home of the Verulam Brewery, which moved here from Harpenden in 1996. It was voted local CAMRA Pub of the Year 1998. All the beers are brewed on site, including monthly seasonal beers. An assortment of German and Belgian bottled beers are also available. All the food is home made and served 11.30-9.30 every day, with roasts on Sunday and barbecues on the patio in summer. Satellite TV is provided. Look out for the unusual ashtrays on the bar.
⛼❀◑◑⇌(City) ♣

Lower Red Lion

34-36 Fishpool Street
⏲ 12-2.30, 5.30-11; 12-3, 6-11 Sat; 12-3, 7-10.30 Sun
☎ (01727) 855669 website: www.thelowerredlion.co.uk
Fuller's London Pride; Oakham JHB; guest beers Ⓗ

17th-century, two-bar pub near the cathedral and Roman Verulamium. This genuine free house stocks four changing guest beers from micro-breweries as well as the 2001 Champion Beer of Britain, Oakham JHB. Beer festivals are held during May Day and August bank holiday weekends and feature up to 50 unusual beers. It offers good B&B, with TV and tea/coffee-making facilities and two en-suite rooms. Quiz nights are hosted on Wednesday and occasional food nights on Tuesday. ⛼Q❀⇆◑P

Mermaid

98 Hatfield Road
⏲ 11.30-11; 12-10.30 Sun
☎ (01727) 837758
Adnams Bitter; Everards Beacon, Tiger; guest beers Ⓗ

Dating back to the 1830s, this pub was a beer house until 1950. The wood-floored, L-shaped bar usually boasts beers from smaller breweries such as Nethergate and B&T. Customers include students, office workers and locals. Live music, staged at weekends, attracts a lively crowd. A cashpoint machine is on hand. Baguettes and microwaved pies are served at lunchtime. ❀⇌(City) ♣P

White Hart Tap

4 Keyfield Terrace
⏲ 12-11; 12-10.30 Sun
☎ (01727) 860974 website: www.whitehartap.co.uk
Adnams Broadside; Fuller's London Pride; Greene King IPA; guest beer Ⓗ

Much-improved one-bar, back-street local that has recently been refurbished. Meals are offered every lunchtime including Sunday roasts and barbecues are held in the spacious garden in summer. Once a month themed food nights are hosted. Entertainment includes live music, with local bands performing on Saturday night and a quiz (Mon eve). The pub is twinned with the 'Bar No Limit' in Belgrade and a visit there was featured on Carlton Television. ⛼❀◑♣

White Lion

91 Sopwell Lane (off Holywell Hill)
⏲ 12-3, 6 (5 Sat)-11 (12-11 summer Sat); 12-4, 7-10.30 (12-10.30 summer Sun)
☎ (01727) 850540 website: www.white-lionpub.co.uk
Adnams Bitter; guest beers Ⓗ

Welcoming, 16th-century traditional family-run pub situated in St Albans conservation area. It offers an ever-changing selection of guest beers. The eclectic, tasty home-made food, for vegetarians and carnivores alike, uses a good proportion of organic produce and includes an imaginative sandwich selection. The delightful beer garden has a children's play area and summer barbecues. Live music, particularly blues, is performed on Saturday evening, also occasional acoustic (unplugged) live music and traditional jazz staged. A quiz is hosted every Tuesday at 9pm. ❀◑◑⊟⇌(Abbey) ♣

SANDRIDGE

Green Man

High Street
⏲ 11-3, 5.30-11; 11-11 Fri & Sat; 11-10.30 Sun
☎ (01727) 854845
Adnams Broadside; Ⓖ **Draught Bass;** Ⓗ **Bateman XXXB;** Ⓖ **Greene King IPA,** Ⓗ **Abbot** Ⓖ

An ex-Benskins pub currently owned by Pubmaster. This is a family-run pub, the landlord has been in residence for 15 years now – the longest-serving of all the village's pubs. Over half the cellar space is given to ales served straight from the cask, usually three. For cycling enthusiasts, the local 40+ cycle club meets every Thursday. Two real fires warm the pub. Evening meals are served on Friday and Saturday.
⛼Q☋❀◑◑♣P

SAWBRIDGEWORTH

Gate

81 London Road
⏲ 11.30-3, 11.30-11.30 Fri & Sat; 12-10.30 Sun
☎ (01279) 722313

Greene King Abbot; Taylor Landlord; Wells Bombardier; guest beers Ⓗ/Ⓖ

Small, but busy, pub catering for all ages. It hosts regular ale festivals and has its own brewery (Sawbridgeworth) at the rear. The pub aims to offer nine ales at all times, and has recently started keeping real cider continually available. The traditional front bar has an extensive pump clip collection from the 2,000 plus ales that have been sold. The rear bar focuses on sport; crib, dominoes and darts are played. There is a small patio and the car park takes a maximum of 10 cars.

❀◑♿⇌♣🍎P

SOUTH MIMMS

Black Horse

65 Blackhorse Lane (off B556 near A1/M25 jct)

11-3, 5.30-11; 11-11 Fri & Sat; 12-10.30 Sun

☎ (01707) 642174

Greene King IPA, Abbot, seasonal beers Ⓗ

It may not seem possible that the narrow winding Blackhorse Lane was once the main road linking the north-west of England to London. This is, of course, why there is a pub on the site. This busy two-bar local also caters for passing trade. The lively public bar has a thriving darts team. The cosy lounge has a horsy theme, an open fire, interesting furniture and bric-à-brac. The secluded garden overlooks farm buildings. The Black Horse has a reputation for good food.

❀◑▣♣P

STANSTEAD ABBOTTS

Lord Louis

36 High Street

11-11; 12-10.30 Sun

☎ (01920) 870121

Fuller's Chiswick, London Pride, ESB Ⓗ

This pub was taken over by Fuller's just prior to Christmas 2000. There used to be a number of separate rooms, the only evidence of this is the way that the floor changes, different woods, tile and stone. A quiet house during the day, it gets more lively in the evening when a younger clientele take over. It looks much more like an old town pub rather than a village house.

◑● ⇌ (St Margarets) P⊬

STAPLEFORD

Papillon (at the Woodhall Arms)

17 High Road

11-3, 5-midnight; 12-3, 6.30-11 Sun

☎ (01992) 535123

Adnams Bitter; guest beers Ⓗ

Large food-oriented pub with two separate eating areas. Bar meals are sold in addition to the full restaurant menu. Monthly food and drink themed evenings are popular. Usually three very reasonably-priced guest beers are on tap from micro-breweries. The car park has reserved space for disabled and recent alterations have made wheelchair access easier but there is a step to each separate dining area. The White Hart stood very close to the present site from 1750. It was replaced by the Woodhall Arms a century later.

❀◑● ♿P

TRING

King's Arms

King Street (Aylesbury end of town, B4635)

12 -2.30 (3 Fri), 7-11; 11.30-2.30; 7-11 Sat; 12-4, 7-10.30 Sun

☎ (01442) 823318

Wadworth 6X; guest beers Ⓗ

A grand, pillar-supported open porch dominates the King's Arms front door, with sombre pink walls and brewery/beer plaques. The character suits its back-street location, it was built in the 1820s for the then Brown's Brewery. The pine-clad interior displays brewery memorabilia and promotional posters for the local theatre. There is a no-smoking area at lunchtime and a heated patio. Top quality ales, wholesome home cooking, take-home facilities and independent brewery beers make this pub more than worth the effort to locate it.

♨Q❀◑●♣🍎⊬

Robin Hood

1 Brook Street (on roundabout at B4635/B486 jct)

11-2.30, 5.30-11; 11-3, 6.30-11 Sat; 12-3, 7-10.30 Sun

☎ (01442) 824912

Fuller's Chiswick, London Pride, ESB, seasonal beers Ⓗ

Once a small cottage dating back to the mid 1300s, this well-presented town pub radiates a country pub feel. It features a low beamed ceiling, freely adorned with horse brasses, wainscot cladded or bare brickwork, with white textured plaster above on the walls, which are covered with awards and prints including 2001/2002 Fuller's Master Cellarman of the Year. The pub specialises in fresh cooked fish dishes (no meals are served Sun eve). Bronze standard disabled facilities are provided. A courtyard is pleasant for summer drinking.

♨Q❀◑●♿♣⊬✔

WALTHAM CROSS

Vault

160 High Street (opp. McDonalds in shopping centre)

11-11 (midnight Fri & Sat); 12-10.30 Sun

☎ (01992) 631600

Beer range varies Ⓗ

Popular, friendly, family-run free house in converted bank premises: a split-level bar, with a new garden at the rear where barbecues are held in summer. Well-behaved children are welcome until 7pm. A lively atmosphere is dominated by football and sports weekends (on the big-screen TV). Pensioners' special price lunches are served on Thursday. The varied menu of home-cooked meals includes options for children and vegetarians, with Sunday lunches proving very popular. A full programme of entertainment includes: live bands (Thu eve and occasionally on Sun), disco on Friday (no admittance after 10pm, with a late licence to midnight), quiz on Tuesday and karaoke on last Saturday in month. On the other Saturdays, comedians are booked or there is a disco.

❀◑⇌ (Waltham Cross/Theobalds Grove)

WARE

Crooked Billet

140 Musley Hill

12-2.30 (not Mon, Wed or Thu), 5.30-11; 12-11 Sat; 12-10.30 Sun

(01920) 462516

Greene King XX Mild, IPA, Old Speckled Hen, seasonal beers H

Popular locals' pub, well worth finding from the town centre (20 minutes' walk from the railway station). Two distinct bars are connected by a walk-through, one has a pool table and is animated, the other is cosier and generally quieter. Carlisle United supporters are given the red-carpet treatment. Bar snacks are served and Sky Sports shown. The pub opens all day on bank holidays.

WARESIDE

Chequers

On B1004, in centre of village OS395156

12-2.30, 6-11; 12-11 Sat; 12-10.30 Sun

(01920) 467010

Adnams Bitter, Broadside; guest beers H

Once a traditional 17th-century coaching inn, this characterful, cosy pub has an interesting interior with low beamed ceilings. It offers three distinct drinking areas, and a separate restaurant converted from the old stables. All the food is freshly cooked; local game is a speciality and there is a good range of vegetarian dishes. Small independent breweries predominate among the guest beers. Live jazz is staged on Sunday evenings, and pétanque and darts are played. There is a patio at the front of the pub facing the road. Q P

WESTON

Cricketers

Damask Green Road

12-2.30, 5.30-11; 12-11 Sat; 12-3, 7-10.30 Sun

(01462) 790273 website: www.rhubarb-inns-co-uk

Fuller's London Pride; McMullen AK; guest beers H

Originally called the Thatched House, now as the Cricketers it won the award for local CAMRA Most Improved Local Pub 2002. It displays a sporting theme and offers a no-smoking section in the dining area. The land to the rear of the pub is used for various functions in summer.

Q P

WHITWELL

Maiden's Head

67 High Street (signed from B656)

11.30-3, 5 -11; 11.30-4, 6-11 Sat; 12-3, 7-10.30 Sun

(01438) 871392

McMullen AK, Country; guest beer H

One of the McMullen's flagship pubs, this splendid two-bar local has a homely feel. It is a perennial Guide entry and previous East Anglia CAMRA Pub of the Year. The landlord, who has run this hostelry for 20 years, came third in the McMullen's Cellarman of the Year this year, and a couple of years ago he won the Arnold Memorial award for Best Community Pub. He has been heavily involved in charity work – another interest is his grand Dinky toy collection. The McMullen AK has improved yet again, thanks to a new brewer at McMullen. The pub sells delicious home-cooked food.

P

WIDFORD

Green Man

High Street (B1004) OS420159

12-3, 5.30-11; 12-11 Sat; 12-10.30 Sun

(01279) 842846

Adnams Bitter; McMullen AK; guest beers H

Former McMullen's tied house but now a genuine free house after a period of closure. Very busy with locals, attracting a good mixture of younger and older customers, it makes a welcome stop for walkers and cyclists as it is approached uphill from all directions. The guest beers are from independent small breweries. Live bands are staged on Saturday evening. This is a village local that is bucking the trend of rural pub closures. No food is served Monday.

Q P

WILDHILL

Woodman

45 Wildhill Road (between A1000 and B158) OS265068

11.30-2.30, 5.30-11; 12-2.30, 7-10.30 Sun

(01707) 642618

Greene King IPA, Abbot; McMullen AK; guest beers H

An absolute gem, a small, friendly village pub which specialises in beers from micro-breweries. Popular with office workers at lunchtime it is also very busy on Sunday lunchtimes although no food is served that day. Bus service 201 stops outside the pub on Tue. The Woodman features a large display of woodsaws, mainly from the estate of the late Dame Barbara Cartland. The pub sponsors a Saracens rugby player and is a popular watering-hole for supporters. Joint local CAMRA Pub of the Year 2000.

Q P

WOOLMER GREEN

Chequers Inn

16 London Road

11-3, 5-11; 12-11 Sat; 12-10.30 Sun

(01438) 813216

Adnams Broadside; guest beers H

Large pub built in 1927 next to what was then the Great North Road. Inside, a large open-plan bar is divided by a real log fireplace. A separate restaurant area provides peace to enjoy the extensive home-made menu (no food served on Sun eve). Since being acquired by the current tenants (both chefs) in late 2000, this pub has won the local CAMRA Most Improved Pub 2001 award. Two small beer festivals are hosted annually. P

For we could not now take time for further search (to land our ship) our victuals being much spent especially our beer.
Log of the Mayflower.

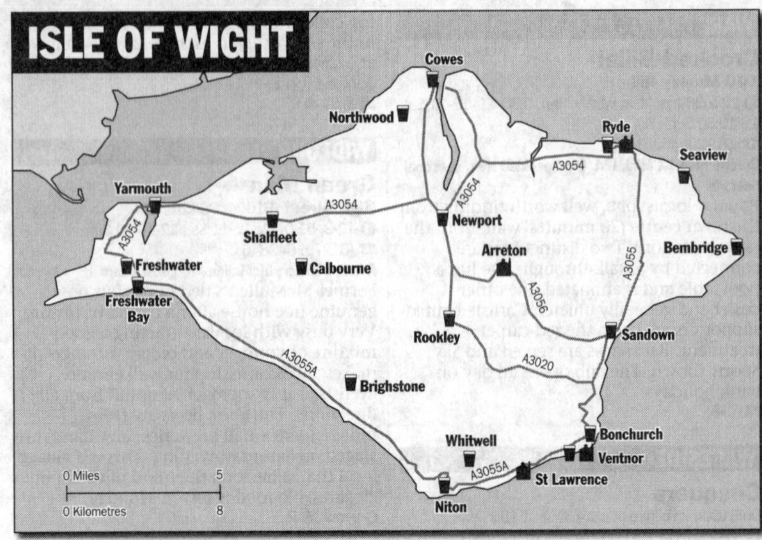

BEMBRIDGE

Crab & Lobster

32 Forelands Field Road (hard to find, take Lane End Rd and turn right past arcade of shops – follow brown direction signs)
⌚ 11-3, 6-11; 11-11 Sat; 12-10.30 Sun
☎ (01983) 872244
website: www.crab-and-lobster.co.uk
Flowers Original; Goddards Special Bitter; Greene King IPA Ⓗ
A tortuous meander through the village of Bembridge is well rewarded, when the sea is reached and the only building left is the coastguard lookout station. You will have arrived at the Crab & Lobster, renowned over the years for its seafood, and in spite of numerous refurbishments it retains much of its charm. With wild views over the English Channel and the notorious Bembridge Ledge, it is no wonder that just around the headland is the island's second lifeboat station. Bed and breakfast (with a family room and four double bedrooms) is available.
❀⇌◑P⊬

BONCHURCH

Bonchurch Inn

The Chute (off Sandown Road)
⌚ 11-3, 6.30-11; 12-3, 7-10.30 Sun
☎ (01983) 852611 website: www.bonchurch-inn.co.uk
Courage Best Bitter, Directors Ⓖ
Superbly preserved stone pub, tucked away in a Dickensian courtyard, it was once the stables of the adjacent manor house. Little has changed since it first gained a licence in the 1840s, and the pub remains one of the most unspoilt on the island. The floors are taken from a ship's deck and the chairs from a liner. Rings and bar billiards are played yet, curiously, the landlord of this very English pub is an Italian. As well as featuring in an episode of The Detectives, there are mementoes and keepsakes from many of the stars who have popped in when visiting the island. Try the Italian restaurant across the courtyard.
Q❀⇌◑♿♣P⊬

BRIGHSTONE

Countryman

Limerstone Road
⌚ 11-3, 7-11; 11-11 summer; 12-3, 7-10.30 Sun
☎ (01983) 740616
Badger K&B Sussex, IPA, Best, Tanglefoot Ⓗ
Spacious, friendly, country roadhouse with a large lounge bar and an enthusiastic landlord. This fine family pub enjoys a reputation for excellent food and beer, it is a regular finalist in the local CAMRA Pub of the Year competition. The huge function room is popular for wedding receptions and evening gatherings. A pleasant outside area has a fine view across the fields to the sea. Nearby, the village of Brighstone gained ecclesiastical fame when three successive incumbents had the privilege of progressing to become bishops. ♨Q❀◑▲♣P⊬

CALBOURNE

Blacksmith's Arms

Park Cross, Calbourne Road (B3041, Carisbrooke road)
⌚ 11-3, 6-11 (11-11 summer); 12-10.30 Sun
☎ (01983) 529263
website: www.blacksmiths-arms.co.uk
Beer range varies Ⓗ
Frequent winner of the Island Pub of the Year and 1998 runner-up for the CAMRA national title. This excellent pub offers an ever-changing range of both real ales and imported German speciality beers. The pub itself is of some considerable character and among the most venerable on the island, enjoying magnificent views to the Solent. The charismatic Bavarian landlord takes great pride in both his beer and his authentic German cuisine. He stages regular themed events, including beer festivals; an Oktoberfest is held featuring all the beers available at its larger Munich progenitor.
♨Q❀◑▲♣P⊬

COWES

Anchor Inn

1 High Street

11-11; 12-10.30 Sun
(01983) 292823 website: www.anchorcowes.co.uk
Badger Tanglefoot; Flowers Original; Fuller's London Pride; Goddards Fuggle-Dee-Dum; Wadworth 6X; guest beers
High Street pub, well placed next to the marina to tempt visiting yachtsmen to their first pint ashore. It was originally called the Trumpeters and dates from 1704. Hugely popular during the summer months, the recent conversion has integrated the stables and created a pleasant beer garden with instant cover to cope with the summer showers. A fine selection of beer is always in prime condition complemented by a good choice of fresh food served all day. Live entertainment is provided at weekends in winter and most evenings in summer. The recent addition of bed and board has been well received at this bustling pub.

Kingston Arms
176 Newport Road
11-2.30, 6-11; 11-11 Fri & Sat; 12-4, 7-10.30 Sun
(01983) 293393
Gale's HSB; guest beers
On the main road out of Cowes towards Newport, you cannot miss the Kingston Arms. A friendly, family and locals' pub near the yachting centre, it offers good value bed and breakfast accommodation. The lively public bar offers darts, pool, pétanque and any other variety of game that takes your fancy. The beer is always in good order with an interesting variety of guest ales. P

Union Inn
Watch House Lane (near the High Street)
10.30-3, 6-11 (10.30-11 summer); 12-10.30 Sun
(01983) 293163
Gale's GB, HSB; guest beer (summer)
Well-decorated town pub, just off the Parade and yards from the sea. One three-sided bar serves the lounge, a snug, a dining area and the airy conservatory that was originally the yard. The limited beer range is always in tiptop condition with a guest ale from the Gale's portfolio during the summer months. A roaring fire in the winter enhances the cosy atmosphere. The long-established landlord has acquired a following for the good value accommodation. The seafaring image is complemented by maritime pictures.
Q

FRESHWATER

Prince of Wales
Princes Road
11-11; 12-10.30 Sun
(01983) 753535
Boddingtons Bitter; Brakspear Special; Ringwood Fortyniner; Tetley Mild
Once part of the Whitbread estate and now in the free trade, this fine, unspoilt town pub is run by possibly the longest-serving landlord on the Isle of Wight. There is a strong games section that adds to the lively atmosphere. Situated just off the main Freshwater shopping centre, there is a large garden to relax in during hot summer days and a pleasant snug bar to sample the well-kept ales in winter. Should you have one too many during the evening, there is no need to phone for a taxi – the landlord has one! P

FRESHWATER BAY

Fat Cat Bar
Sandpipers, Coastguard Lane (through main bay car park, clearly visible)
11-3, 6-11; 12-3, 6-10.30 Sun
(01983) 758500 website: www.fatcattrading.co.uk
Beer range varies
Real gem of a bar tucked away within the Sandpipers Hotel situated between Freshwater Bay and the Afton Nature Reserve. An ever-changing range of well-kept ales is served in convivial surroundings, well frequented by local drinkers. If you elect to stay (and book ahead), you may well be able to choose your favourite tipple for that home-from-home feeling. Comfortable chairs add to the relaxing atmosphere, and the friendly welcome is a joy. The adjoining hotel offers a full range of accommodation and a comprehensive menu. Q P

NEWPORT

Prince of Wales
36 South Street (opp. bus station)
11-11; 12-4, 7-10.30 Sun
(01983) 525026
Goddards Special Bitter; Usher's Best Bitter; guest beers
Formerly the tap to the adjacent but now demolished Green Dragon, this excellent mock-Tudor single-bar, street-corner local has built a fine reputation for its ale and tasty food. Although in the centre of town, opposite the bus station and Safeways' supermarket, this is very much a locals' pub and it has resisted the temptation to be 'tarted up'. It still retains the feel of a public bar. Q

NITON

Buddle Inn
St Catherine's Road (follow signs to St Catherines lighthouse, undercliff road closed both to and from St Lawrence))
11-11; 12-10.30 Sun
(01983) 730243
Adnams Bitter; Flowers Original; Greene King Abbot; guest beers
16th-century inn built as a farmhouse and reputedly a smugglers' inn during the 18th century. Extensively refurbished in recent years, it still retains its ancient flagstones and beams, inglenook and many interesting photographs. The adjoining smugglers' barn was a cattle shed until 1934 when it was transformed into a dance hall. Very popular with the seasonal trade, it has ample space outside to take advantage of the south-facing vista. Enjoying an excellent reputation for good quality food, it stocks at least six ales, each chosen to suit the taste of the landlord. P

INDEPENDENT BREWERIES

Goddards Ryde
Scarecrow Arreton
Ventnor Ventnor
Yates St Lawrence

NORTHWOOD

Travellers Joy

85 Pallance Road (A3020, Yarmouth road out of Cowes)

11-2.30, 5-11; 11-11 Fri & Sat; 12-3, 7-10.30 Sun

(01983) 298024 website: www.tjoy.com

Goddards Special Bitter; guest beers

The choice of cask ales here is one of the best on the Isle of Wight. This well-renovated and extended old country inn, was the island's first beer exhibition house. Island beer drinkers owe much to the Travellers Joy and it is deservedly favoured by local CAMRA members who have voted it local Pub of the Year on no less than five occasions. Always at least eight beers are on offer from national, local and micro-breweries. The garden has a children's play area and a small pets' corner. A good range of home-cooked food is available during the lunchtime and evening sessions.

ROOKLEY

Chequers Inn

Niton Road (off A3020)

11-11; 12-10.30 Sun

(01983) 840314

website: www.chequers-inn.demon.co.uk

Courage Best Bitter, Directors; Gale's HSB; Greene King Old Speckled Hen; John Smith's Bitter

This country pub at the heart of the island has beautiful views of the surrounding countryside. It was formerly a Whitbread house, and considering its present popularity after an extensive rebuild, it is astonishing that Whitbread closed the pub and sold it. Dating back to the mid-1800s, it was once a customs and excise house. These days it is heavily food- and family-oriented, but surprisingly still retains a flagstone-floored public bar and a fine pint of beer. There are some very good children's facilities including a large outdoor play area and baby-changing room. Disabled facilities include a Braille menu. Recent achievements have seen it voted Family Pub of the Year.

RYDE

Solent Inn

7 Monkton Street (by parade of shops)

11-11; 12-10.30 Sun

(01983) 563546

Greene King IPA; guest beers

Excellent, street-corner local, with a warm, welcoming atmosphere. The pub has improved considerably under its present enthusiastic landlord, and the range of real ales has increased to four (due to demand by the regulars) and varies frequently. Parts of the pub are very ancient, and the public bar slopes downhill alarmingly! Music night (Fri) sees the landlord and many local musicians jamming together on a variety of instruments, including flutes and, astonishingly, a concert harp.

SEAVIEW

Seaview Hotel

High Street

11-2.30, 6-11; 12-3, 7-10.30 Sun

(01983) 612711 website: www.seaviewhotel.co.uk

Goddards Special Bitter; Greene King Old Speckled Hen; guest beer

It may not seem right to rave about an hotel when it is the beer that we are tasting, but here the two are intertwined. From the moment you walk in, your imagination will be captured by the history of the sea that is all around you. The public bar is quite small, but during the summer months when the pub really buzzes, there is still plenty of room to move around. Three guest beers are the norm, a fourth is added in summer. The hotel, well, that is another story – you will have to find out for yourself.

SHALFLEET

New Inn

Main Road

12-3, 6-11 (12-11 summer); 12-3, 6-10.30 Sun

(01983) 531314 website: www.thenew-inn.co.uk

Badger Best; Draught Bass; Ventnor Golden; guest beers

Unmissable as you travel through Shalfleet on the Newport to Yarmouth road, the New

INN BRIEF

NEWPORT

Bargeman's Rest

Little London Quay (visible from road bridge over river, follow signs from dual carriageway)

10.30-11; 12-10.30 Sun

(01983) 525828

Badger IPA, Best, Tanglefoot; guest beers

Superb riverside establishment with reasonably-priced food. Live music staged most evenings but quiet areas also available.

Simeon Arms

21 Simeon Street

11-3, 6-11; 11-11 Fri & Sat; 12-10.30 Sun

(01983) 614954

Courage Directors; Goddards Special Bitter; guest beers

Back-street pub with a massive local trade. Astonishing number of pub teams supported. Eve meals Fri & Sat.

RYDE

Fowlers

41-43 Union Street

10.30-11; 12-10.30 Sun

(01983) 812112

Badger IPA, Best, Tanglefoot; guest beers

Fine Wetherspoon's serving food all day and ever-changing beers. Well located. Cask Marque accredited.

SANDOWN

Castle

12-14 Fitzroy Street

11-3, 7-11; 11-11 Sat; 12-3, 7-10.30 Sun

(01983) 403169

Ventnor Golden; guest beers

Excellent town free house with a mass of darts, crib and pétanque teams. Always has five real ales.

Poor beer

If you consider beer quality in a pub is not up to standard please let us know immediately. Write to GBG, CAMRA, 230 Hatfield Road, St Albans, Herts, AL1 4LW or camra@camra.org.uk. If the pub has a Cask Marque symbol, write to Cask Marque at the address in its editorial feature at the front of the Guide.

One Hundred Years Old

I met the other day an old man, who asked me to drink. 'I am not thirsty,' said I, 'and I will not drink with you.' 'Yes, you will,' said the old man, 'for I am this day one hundred years old; and you will never again have an opportunity of drinking the health of man on his hundredth birthday.' So I broke my word and drank. 'How have you passed your time?' said I. 'As well as I could,' said the old man, 'always enjoying a good thing when it came honestly within my reach; not forgetting to praise God for putting it there'. 'I suppose you were fond of a glass of good ale when you were young'. 'Yes,' said the old man, 'I was, and so, thank God, I am still'. And he drank off a glass of ale.

George Barrow, 1857.

Inn has stood at the entrance to Mill Road for 300 years. It remains an ancient and largely unspoilt country local with a flagstone floor and immense character. The good beer and food, especially the fish and seafood for which the pub is noted, continue to entice locals from inland and seafarers up the lane from Shalfleet creek. The roaring log fire is a delight in winter and in summer, the rustic chairs and tables outside, together with the extensive garden provide ample space for families.
♨☺❀◐◑▲♣P⚟

VENTNOR

Crab & Lobster Tap

Grove Road (just off the High St by central car park and heritage centre)
✪ 10.30-11; 12-10.30 Sun
☎ (01983) 852311
Ventnor Sunfire; guest beers Ⓗ
Located close to the Ventnor Brewery, this interesting town pub has one of those warming atmospheres that immediately spells comfort. You may strike lucky and be in the pub when one of the rings league matches is played. Ventnor is one of the only places in Great Britain where there continues to be a league. A wonderful collection of memorabilia has been gathered that will intrigue the first-time visitor. The pub has a fine reputation for food, it is served lunchtime daily and on Saturday evening (table d'hôte) when it is advisable to book. ◐♣

Volunteer

30 Victoria Street
✪ 11-11; 12-10.30 Sun
☎ (01983) 852537
website: www.thevolunteer.demon.co.uk
Badger Best, Tanglefoot; Ringwood Best Bitter; Ventnor Golden; guest beers Ⓗ
Built in 1866, the Volunteer is probably the smallest pub on the Isle of Wight. It operated as a beer house between 1869 and 1871 and still retains many original features of the traditional drinkers' pub. It is well-known for the quality of its beer and cellarmanship, which have been recognised by the many awards gained in the local Pub of the Year competition. No chips, no children, no fruit machines, no video games, just a pure adult drinking house and one of the few places where you can still play rings. An absolute gem. ♨Q♣

WHITWELL

White Horse

High Street
✪ 11-3, 6-11 (11-11 summer); 12-3, 6-10.30 Sun
☎ (01983) 730375
Badger Best, Tanglefoot; Greene King Abbot; Ventnor Golden; guest beers Ⓗ
Built in 1454 and reputedly the oldest established inn on the Isle of Wight, this thatched, stone-built pub has a comprehensive menu and large garden. A recently completed extension has provided much needed additional space and the original part of the building has a Tardis-like interior offering a secluded, cosy environment. The present owners have not allowed the fine kitchen and wonderful selection of fresh food to detract from the quality of the beer. ♨☺❀◐♿♣●P⚟

YARMOUTH

Wheatsheaf Inn

Bridge Road (Wheatsheaf Lane opp. George Hotel)
✪ 11-11; 12-10.30 Sun
☎ (01983) 760456
Brakspear Special; Ⓗ **Goddards Fuggle-Dee-Dum;** Ⓖ **Greene King Old Speckled Hen; Wadworth 6X** Ⓗ
Pleasant old coaching house, that now has additional rooms. It is spacious and comfortable with a large conservatory to the rear, ideal for families and on pleasant summer evenings. The large public bar has its fair share of visiting yachtsmen tracing the few yards from the harbour. The beer is always well kept and complements the imaginative, reasonably-priced freshly cooked food. This charming inn is well worth a visit. Yarmouth Square parking is close by.
Q☺❀◐◑⇌ (Yarmouth Wightlink Ferry) ♣

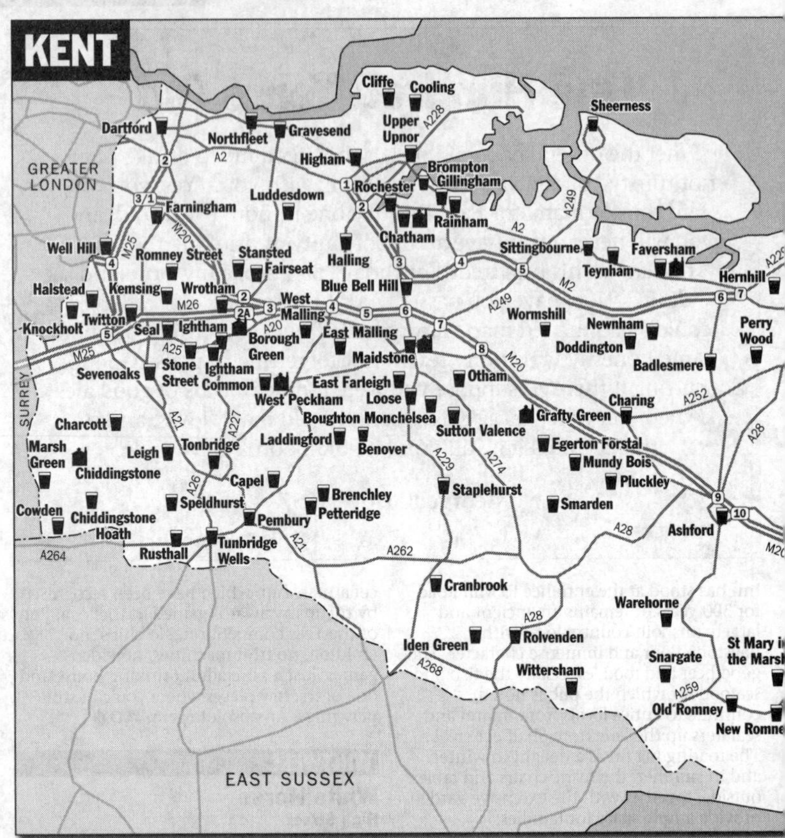

ASHFORD

County Hotel

10 High Street

11-11; 12-10.30 Sun

(01233) 646891

Courage Directors; Hop Back Summer Lightning; Shepherd Neame Spitfire; Theakston Best Bitter; guest beers Ⓗ

Large Wetherspoon's, in the centre of town, laid out on two levels with three distinct areas, one of which is for non-smokers. The walls are decorated with prints, photos and displays on local history. Popular at lunchtime during the week, the pub is very busy during the evening at weekends. The car park is small for such a popular pub.

BADLESMERE

Red Lion

Ashford Road

12-3, 6-11; 12-11 Fri & Sat; 12-10.30 Sun

(01233) 740320

Fuller's London Pride; Greene King Abbot; Shepherd Neame Master Brew Bitter; guest beers Ⓗ

A free house, dating from 1546, which was once a morgue – the naturally cool cellar is now ideal for casks of ale. The guest beers are often from micro-breweries. The meals are prepared using local produce, some from the landlady's father's farm (no food Sun eve). Beer festivals are held over Easter and August bank holiday weekends. Live bands perform on Friday evenings; happy hour is 7.30-8.30 Thursday. Johnson's farmhouse cider from Sheppey is usually available, as is a mild. P

BENOVER

Woolpack Inn

Benover Road

12-3, 6-11; 12-3, 7-10.30 Sun

(01892) 730356

Shepherd Neame Master Brew Bitter Ⓗ

This popular Shepherd Neame 15th-century beamed country inn has two interlinked bars. It serves a variety of excellent food in a friendly atmosphere. The walls are adorned with hops and antique farming implements; look out for the skeleton in the cupboard and the old beer bottles. A regular entry in previous editions of this Guide. The beers, other than Master Brew, are served under blanket pressure. The No. 23 bus stops here. P

BISHOPSBOURNE

Mermaid

The Street

12-3, 6.10-11; 12-3, 7-10.30 Sun

(01227) 830581

Shepherd Neame Master Brew Bitter, Spitfire, seasonal beers Ⓗ

Well worth the short detour from the A2, this attractive community local is in its 22nd year in this Guide. One of the three bars has a basket grate, secondhand books and darts. The pub is just off the North

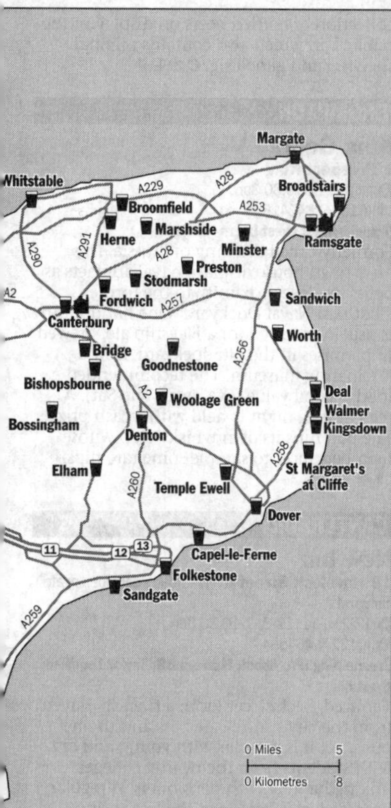

Downs Way; dogs are welcome with well-behaved owners. You can take a pleasant walk from here to the Plough & Harrow at Bridge (qv), passing the former home of author Joseph Conrad. ♨Q❀◑⊟♣

BLUE BELL HILL

Lower Bell

201 Old Chatham Road (off A229, part way up the hill)
✪ 11-11; 12-10.30 Sun
☎ (01634) 861127
Greene King IPA, Abbot; guest beer Ⓗ

Large pub, extended in recent years to provide a no-smoking restaurant/function area on two levels. Another restaurant adjoins the main bar which houses an eclectic display of artefacts and memorabilia. Close to Kit's Coty ancient monument and the North Downs Way, it is handy for walkers. The pub name stems from when stagecoaches used a single track road to the top of the hill and used bells as a signalling system. Bus No. 101 runs close by. Q❀◑♿P

BOSSINGHAM

Hop Pocket

The Street
✪ 12-3, 7-11; 12-3, 7-10.30 Sun
☎ (01227) 709866
Beer range varies Ⓗ

19th-century village pub that takes pride in using local produce. This is a good place to try Hopdaemon beers, and local apple juice. The attractive bar is hung with hops, while the modern conservatory is popular with diners. The large garden has a children's play area tucked discreetly away. It hosts occasional live music – usually for locals' birthday celebrations. Annual events include a wheelbarrow race, firework displays, and a late summer beer festival. ♨❀◑⛺♣P

BOUGHTON MONCHELSEA

Cock Inn

Heath Road (off A229, S of Maidstone) OS776508
✪ 11-11; 12-10.30 Sun
☎ (01622) 743166
Young's Bitter, Special, seasonal beer Ⓗ

This old coaching inn, with its open fireplace and wealth of oak beams, was built in 1604, to provide lodgings for travellers from London to Canterbury. Rumours suggest that King George III took refreshment here in 1778, prior to a troop inspection. The inn also featured briefly in the 1948 film Kind Hearts and Coronets. Owned by Young's since 1999, a full range of snacks and meals is served in the bar and restaurant (all day Sun). ♨❀◑♣P

BRENCHLEY

Bull of Brenchley

High Street
✪ 11.30-3, 5-11; 11-4, 6-11 Sat; 12-4, 7-10.30 Sun
☎ (01892) 722701
Greene King IPA; Harveys BB; Shepherd Neame Spitfire; guest beer Ⓗ

Sited near the ancient church at the village centre is this tall Victorian building which replaced its predecessor, destroyed by fire. The bar is in three sections and has a neo-Victorian style of decor. Children are admitted if dining. A new patio has been created in front of the pub, but this has reduced the parking area. There are seven letting rooms, some in a rear annexe. ♨❀🛏◑P

BRIDGE

Plough & Harrow

86 High Street
✪ 11-3, 5-11; 11-11 Sat; 12-3, 7-10.30 Sun
☎ (01227) 830455
Shepherd Neame Master Brew Bitter Ⓗ

This 300-year-old former maltings has no garden or food or music, but takes pride in being a traditional village pub. It is home to over 30, widely varying, clubs and teams; bar billiards and shut the box are played. The vicar works behind the bar once a month. There is a strong emphasis on conversation, and visitors are made

INDEPENDENT BREWERIES

Flagship Chatham
Goacher's Maidstone
Hopdaemon Canterbury
Larkins Chiddingstone
Old Kent Borough Green
Ramsgate Ramsgate
Shepherd Neame Faversham
Swale Grafty Green
Swan West Peckham

welcome. An easy detour from the A2, it is served by frequent buses. Walk from here to the Mermaid at Bishopsbourne (qv).
⛫Q♣P

BROADSTAIRS

Brown Jug
204 Ramsgate Road
12-3, 6-11; 12-10.30 Sun
☎ (01843) 862788
Greene King IPA, Abbot H
Olde-worlde pub, with a knapped flint façade, parts of which date back to the reign of Charles II. Previously tied to Cobbs of Margate, it served as an officers' billet during the Napoleonic Wars. Devoid of music or fruit machines, the interior is cosy and homely, enjoying a friendly atmosphere. Two things not to miss are the water clock which plays Little Brown Jug on the hour, and the superb outside loos!
⛫Q❀⊟⇌(Dumpton Pk) ♣P

Lord Nelson
11 Nelson Place
11-11; 12-10.30 Sun
☎ (01843) 861210
Greene King IPA, Abbot; Harveys BB H
Welcoming local, a short walk from the harbour. Its name commemorates the anchoring of HMS Victory, with Nelson's body on board, off Broadstairs in December 1805. The bars contain many pieces of naval memorabilia, including a piece of original oak from Victory and a magnificent bronze of the Admiral himself. Formerly tied to Tomson and Wootton of Ramsgate, the pub retains its associations with the local fishing community, along with its distinctive Victorian charm. ❀♣P

Neptune's Hall ☆
1-3 Harbour Street
11-11; 12-10.30 Sun
☎ (01843) 861400
Shepherd Neame Master Brew Bitter, Spitfire, seasonal beers H
Traditional boatmen's pub, circa 1815, it was Grade II listed after fierce campaigning by its regulars. Known as the folk music pub of Broadstairs, the Neptune holds regular gigs and jam sessions. Note the superb collection of bottled beers on display in the public bar, which also contains original shelving and panelling. Q❀⊟♣

BROMPTON

King George V
1 Prospect Row
11-11; 12-10.30 Sun
☎ (01634) 842418
Draught Bass; guest beers H
Formerly called the King of Prussia, this busy town house displays naval artefacts as befits its close proximity to the former Chatham Naval Dockyard. One handpump is usually reserved for a Flagship ale, brewed in premises in the old dockyard, now a fascinating museum. The recommended food is good value (eve meals Tue-Sat). A regular quiz night is held with a cash prize. The pub runs its own whisky club whose members meet to sample some rare nips.
◑♣

CANTERBURY ❊

New Inn
19 Havelock Street (off ring road near Queningate car park)
12-2, 5-11; 12-3, 7-10.30 Sun
☎ (01227) 464584
Greene King IPA, Abbot; Harveys BB; Taylor Landlord; guest beers H
Terraced, back-street local; a friendly haven from the city-centre café bars and theme pubs, yet it is popular with young and old, with students from the nearby colleges mixing happily with pensioners. A regular beer festival is held over the late spring bank holiday weekend, when some 30 real ales are available in the two small bars and conservatory area at the back. ❀◑⇌(East)

Phoenix
67 Old Dover Road
11-11; 12-4, 7-10.30 Sun
☎ (01227) 464220
website: www.thephoenix-canterbury.co.uk
Greene King Abbot; Wells Bombardier; Young's Bitter; guest beers H
Originally the Bridge House Tavern and dating back to the 18th century, the pub burnt down in 1962 and was appropriately

INN BRIEF

BROOMFIELD

Huntsman & Horn
Margate Road
11.30-11; 12-10.30 Sun
(01227) 365995
Ansells Best Bitter; Greene King IPA H
Traditional decor and lots of wood in a listed building: two bars, a restaurant, a no-smoking area and a children's certificate. No food Sun eve.

CANTERBURY

Hobgoblin
40 St Peter's Street
12-11; 12-10.30 Sun
(01227) 455563
Flowers Original; Fuller's London Pride; Wychwood seasonal beer H
Formerly the Black Griffin, this 16th-century pub near the Westgate has windows from Rigden's Brewery. Student discounts 2-8.

King's Head
204 Wincheap
12-2.30, 6.30-11; 7-10.30 Sun
(01227) 462885
Fuller's London Pride; Shepherd Neame Master Brew Bitter; guest beers H
15th-century oak-beamed inn on the A28 to Ashford. It offers en-suite accommodation and extensive menus. Bat and trap played.

Thomas Ingoldsby
5-9 Burgate
10-11; 12-10.30 Sun
(01227) 463339
Courage Directors; Shepherd Neame Spitfire; Theakston Best Bitter; guest beers H
Hugely successful Wetherspoon's, near the cathedral and bus station, originally a furniture shop. Weston's Old Rosie cider is sold.

CHATHAM

Tap 'n' Tin
24 Railway Street
12-11; 2-10.30 Sun
(01634) 847926
Beer range varies H
Former brew-pub, particularly popular with younger drinkers. Free rolls at lunchtimes. It has an on-site launderette.

CLIFFE

Victoria
174 Church Street
12-11; 12-10.30 Sun
(01634) 220356
Shepherd Neame Master Brew Bitter, Spitfire or seasonal beer H
Friendly, cosy little local. The wood-panelled bar has pew seats. The garden has giant chess, snakes and ladders and draughts.

renamed the Phoenix. Up to three guest beers change regularly as testified by the ever-growing collection of pump clips behind the bar. Because of its close proximity to the County ground, it displays a collection of cricketing memorabilia. Regular fun quiz nights are held. Senior citizens qualify for discounts on meal prices; food is served 11-9.30. ❀⇆◑ ⇌(East) ♣P

Unicorn Inn

61 St Dunstans Street (by level crossing)

✪ 11-11; 12-10.30 Sun

☎ (01227) 463187

Shepherd Neame Master Brew Bitter; Fuller's London Pride; guest beers 🄷

This comfortable pub on the original pilgrims' route dates back to 1604 and stands close to the ancient Westgate. The Unicorn has an attractive suntrap garden. An unobtrusive satellite TV in the back bar shows sporting events; bar billiards is played here and a quiz is held weekly (Sun). The menu is extensive but unpretentious, featuring a daily special (no food Sun eve). One of the two guest beers is usually from a local brewery. ♔❀◑ ⇌(West) ♣

CAPEL

Dovecote

Alders Road (1/2 mile W of A228, between Colts Hill and Tudeley) OS643441

✪ 12-3 (or later), 6-11; 12-3 (or 4), 7-10.30 Sun

☎ (01892) 835966

Adnams Broadside; Badger K&B Sussex; Harveys BB; Larkins Chiddingstone; guest beer 🄶

In an idyllic rural location near hopfields in the middle of a row of cottages, enjoy the warm, welcoming atmosphere in a bare brick walled interior. Four ales are served direct from the cask by a knowledgeable landlord with Cask Marque accreditation. The good value food is particularly popular on Thursday (curry night) when booking is recommended. Chiddingstone real cider is stocked. The attractive garden houses a dovecote and a children's climbing frame. ♔❀◑ ▲♣P⊘

CAPEL-LE-FERNE

Royal Oak

New Dover Road (B2011, E of village) OS263387

✪ 11.30-3 (4 Sat), 6-11; 12-4, 8-10.30 Sun

☎ (01303) 244787

Shepherd Neame Master Brew Bitter; guest beers 🄷

Originally a farmhouse and long barn, the pub lies close to the cliff edge, where the view encompasses Cap Gris Nez in France, St Mary's Bay and Dungeness bird sanctuary. The main bar acts as a talking shop and occasional cribbage school; the barn is for other games. Food is cooked to order (not Wed eve). Guest ales come from regional and micro-breweries. The coastal route is a cycle path, but beware – the track to the beach can be dangerous. ♔◑ ▲♣P

CHARCOTT

Greyhound

1/2 mile N of B2027 and Chiddingstone causeway OS522472

✪ 12-3 (not Tue), 6-11; 12-3, 7-10.30 Sun

☎ (01892) 870275

Adnams Bitter; Badger K&B Sussex; Flowers Original; Greene King Old Speckled Hen 🄷

Neat, small brick and tile pub in a little hamlet, its long, narrow bar area has seating in bay windows. A small extension to the rear forms the dining area where quality food is served (no meals Tue). The well maintained interior is decorated with assorted pictures. Parking may be difficult at busier times; Penshurst Station is a short walk along a footpath. The flat land to the south was once an airfield. Boules is played in the garden. ♔❀◑ ⇌(Penshurst) ♣

CHARING

Bowl Inn

Egg Hill Road (at jct of five Lanes) OS950514

✪ 5 (12 Fri & Sat)-11; 12-10.30 Sun

☎ (01233) 712256 website: www.bowlinn.co.uk

Fuller's London Pride; guest beers 🄷

Located on top of the North Kent Downs, this remote 16th-century pub is well worth finding. It has been a regular CAMRA award-winner since 1994, including Kent Pub of the Year. You can camp in the large garden by arrangement. An annual beer festival in July offers 20-plus real ales. A magnificent open fire in winter and an unusual revolving pool table are notable features. Three guest beers are kept. Snacks are available until 10.45pm. ♔❀⇆▲♣P⊁

CHATHAM ❄

Ropemaker's Arms

70 New Road

✪ 12-3 (not Sat), 7-11; 7-10.30 Sun

☎ (01634) 402121

Goacher's Light; Greene King IPA, Abbot; guest beer 🄷

On the A2 close to Chatham Station and the town centre, the pub's name derives from the ropery in Chatham Dockyard, which until very recently supplied ropes to the Navy. A mural by a local artist features a dockyard shed. The sign outside celebrates the long-standing association with Goacher's. Games include bar billiards and pool; monthly quiz nights are held (first Wed). No food is available on Sunday. ◑⇌♣

CHIDDINGSTONE HOATH

Rock Inn

Hoath Corner (1 1/2 miles S of Chiddingstone via Wellers Town) OS497431

✪ 11.30-3, 6-11; closed Mon; 12-3, 7-10.30 Sun

☎ (01892) 870296

Larkins Traditional, Best, Porter 🄷

Only pub owned by the local Chiddingstone brewery, Larkins, it is a fine example of an old Kentish inn with two bars, a brick floor, irregular beams and doors. Note the large wood-burning stove. An odd fact is that due to the low headroom of the cellar door, one landlord was only given the tenancy because of his height. In summer the garden and front of pub provide seating. Games include ring the bull. No meals Sun eve. ♔Q❀◑ ⊟♣P

COOLING

Horseshoe & Castle

The Street

✪ 11-3, 7-11; 12-4, 7-10.30 Sun

☎ (01634) 221691
website: www.horsehoeandcastle.co.uk
Adnams Bitter; Draught Bass; guest beers Ⓗ
Situated in the middle of a peaceful village, this pub is close to the RSPB nature and bird reserve. The pub specialises in seafood on an interesting menu (no food Mon eve). The nearby ruined castle was once owned by Sir John Oldcastle, on whom Shakespeare's Falstaff was modelled, while the local graveyard boasts the tombstones that were used in Charles Dickens' Great Expectations, where Magwitch surprised young Pip. Addlestone's cider is sold.
♔Q❀⛌◑◐♣●P

COWDEN

Fountain
High Street ($^2/_3$ mile W of B2026)
⏲ 11.30-3 (not Mon), 6-11 (10.30 Mon); 12-10.30 Sun
☎ (01342) 850528
Harveys XX Mild, Pale Ale, BB, seasonal beers Ⓗ
Approached by many steps, the Fountain, with its Kentish pegtile roof and name etched into the door panes, is the village's sole survivor. Hops adorn the beams of this two-bar Harveys' tied house. In the lounge bar, along with the dartboard and collection of football picture cards, stands a piano waiting to accompany any live entertainment. A weekly quiz is held (Wed). Meals are served Tue-Sun.
Q❀◑◐⊟♣P✔

CRANBROOK

George Hotel
Stone Street
⏲ 10.30-11; 12-10.30 Sun
☎ (01580) 713348 website: www.georgehoteluk.co.uk
Harveys BB; guest beers Ⓗ
Historic hotel, in a tranquil Weald town, dating back to 1300, although much of the interior is 15th century. In 1573 Queen Elizabeth I was entertained in what is now the function room. The high-ceilinged main lounge bar is uncluttered, with comfy sofas and armchairs blending with simple tables and chairs. The 34-place restaurant, with its impressive fireplace, adjoins this bar. A small informal wine bar provides a contrast to the peaceful lounge. Your hotel bedroom may boast a four-poster and a jacuzzi.
♔Q❀⛌◑◐P✔

DARTFORD ❊

Malt Shovel
3 Darenth Road (A226, East Hill, 50 yds)
⏲ 10.30-2.30, 5-11; 10.30-11 Fri & Sat; 12-3, 7-10.30 Sun
☎ (01322) 224381
Young's Bitter, Triple A, Special, seasonal beers Ⓗ
Traditional pub with a country atmosphere in town. It dates from the late 17th century and retains an olde-worlde charm in its low ceilings and time-worn woodwork, particularly in the public bar. Bric-à-brac hangs from the ceiling and a celebrated Dartford Breweries mirror adorns the conservatory which doubles as the family room. Good value food includes a regular specials board and various theme nights. The saloon bar is accessible to wheelchairs.
♔Q⛩❀◑◐⇌P

Paper Moon
55 High Street
⏲ 11-11; 12-10.30 Sun
☎ (01322) 281127
Courage Best Bitter, Directors; Shepherd Neame Spitfire; guest beers Ⓗ
Town-centre, corner pub converted from a bank, it is decorated in typical Wetherspoon's style featuring interesting cameo descriptions of Dartford's history. The pub name reflects the town's early local connections with paper-making. Good value food is served all day. Regular beer promotions and festivals attract a regular following. Q◑◐♿⇌⚡✔

DEAL ❊

Admiral Penn
79 Beach Street
⏲ 6-11; closed Sun
☎ (01304) 374279 website: www.admiralpenn.com
Draught Bass; Fuller's London Pride; Wells Bombardier Ⓗ
Smart bar in a prime seafront location, offering panoramic views of passing shipping. The nautical theme, combined with a Dutch flavour, works well. A range of continental spirits and liqueurs is stocked,

INN BRIEF

DARTFORD

Old Court House
43 Spital Street
11-11; 12-10.30 Sun
(01322) 226645
Young's Bitter, Triple A, Special, seasonal beers Ⓗ
Imposing, high-ceilinged former court house, converted to a pub in 1997. A popular meeting place; live music is performed Thu eve.

DEAL

Star & Garter
101-103 Beach Street
11-3.30, 6-11; 12-10.30 Sun
(01304) 375131
Shepherd Neame Master Brew Bitter Ⓗ
Seafront hotel with an old-fashioned, relaxed atmosphere. The front bar looks out towards the Goodwin Sands; cosy rear bar.

DOVER

White Horse
St James Street
12-3, 5-11; 12-11 Thu-Sat; 12-10.30 Sun
(01304) 202911
Fuller's London Pride; Greene King Abbot; guest beers Ⓗ
Recently refurbished pub with an extensive food trade. Medieval in origin, it lies below Dover Castle, next to the sports centre.

EAST FARLEIGH

Victory
Farleigh Bridge
11-11; 12-10.30 Sun
(01622) 726591
Goacher's Dark; Shepherd Neame Master Brew Bitter; Tetley Bitter Ⓗ
Cosy pub, right by the station, with a warm, friendly atmosphere. Games available include bar billiards.

FAVERSHAM

Elephant
31 The Mall
12-11; 12-10.30 Sun
(01795) 590157
Beer range varies Ⓗ
Renowned community pub near the station. A Flagship house, it also sells guest beers. Bar snacks until 10pm; Sunday lunches.

Three Tuns
16 Tanners Street
11-3, 7-11; 12-3, 7-10.30 Sun
(01795) 532663
Shepherd Neame Master Brew Bitter Ⓗ
Horatio Nelson used this pub to pay off his Faversham crew. Now a friendly local with an active social club. Food served 12-2 Tue-Sat. Pétanque played.

including such specialities as Dutch Kopstoot and Jagermeister cold from the fridge. In spite, or maybe because, of limited opening hours, the pub is invariably well patronised and lively. ⛫⇌

Saracen's Head

1 Alfred Square (N end of High St)
11-11; 12-10.30 Sun
☎ (01304) 381650
Shepherd Neame Master Brew Bitter, Best Bitter, Spitfire Ⓗ
Shepherd Neame tied house, serving the north end of town, it overlooks the distinctive Alfred Square, Deal's only square. This cheerful street-corner local is home to several darts and pool teams. The games area on the left, and the area of seating by the bar blend well together, making for a good atmosphere which attracts a wide range of customers. ❀◐♣

Ship

141 Middle Street (parallel to seafront)
11-11; 12-10.30 Sun
☎ (01304) 372222
Adnams Broadside; Draught Bass; Hook Norton Best Bitter; Shepherd Neame Master Brew Bitter; guest beer Ⓗ
Cosy, traditional pub with two drinking areas (one a secluded back room). This historic tavern in the heart of Deal's conservation area, is surely light years away from the haunt of blackguards and ruffians who must have frequented these mean streets in days gone by. The pub's walls display, naturally, a nautical theme. Freshly-made rolls and coffee are available at the bar. ⛫❀⇌

DENTON

Jackdaw

The Street (A260)
11-11; 12-10.30 Sun
☎ (01303) 844663
Beer range varies Ⓗ
Old established, but extended, family pub-restaurant which retains a distinctive frontage. Sited in a deep valley, it remains the focus for a tiny hamlet, with all facilities concentrated here – Royal Mail, phone box, bus stop and bottle bank. Featured in the 1960s Battle of Britain film, it was for many years a Whitbread Wayside Inn, with a welcome selection of real ales. These days the beers come from far and wide – a typical selection might include Nethergate, St Austell, Woodforde's and Hardys & Hansons. ❀◐▶P

DODDINGTON

Chequers Inn

The Street
11-3, 7 (6 Fri)-11; 11-11 Sat; 12-3, 7-10.30 Sun
Shepherd Neame Master Brew Bitter, seasonal beers Ⓗ
Ancient and attractive unspoilt pub, featuring a large open fire and hops hanging around the bar. It has two bars: pool is played in the public; the split-level saloon is quieter. Popular with walkers and cyclists, and used by various clubs, including the Norton owners' club, it hosts folk music now and again. Food is available, but tables are not laid, allowing drinkers to sit where they prefer. ⛫❀◐▶♣P

DOVER

Blakes

52 Castle Street (100 yds from market sq)
11-3 (summer only), 6-11; 6-10.30 (summer only) Sun
☎ (01304) 202194
Fuller's London Pride; guest beers Ⓗ
Situated just off the market square, Blakes is a cellar bar with a restaurant at ground level. The atmosphere is peaceful and welcoming and there is always a good hum of conversation. Renowned for its food (the seafood, usually including Dover sole, is to be recommended), meals are served in summer. Malt whiskies are a speciality, with up to 52 available. Five en-suite rooms can be booked. Q◐▶⇌(Priory)

Flotilla & Firkin

1 Bench Street (off A20, York St roundabout)
11-11; 12-10.30 Sun
☎ (01304) 204488
Draught Bass; Marston's Pedigree; Tetley Bitter Ⓗ
Ideally located near the seafront and the town centre, the Flotilla & Firkin is popular with locals and tourists alike; children are welcome until 6pm. Formerly the Dover Tavern, it was refurbished five years ago, displaying prints and pictures on a nautical theme. The food is well prepared and reasonably priced. The juke box plays constantly, but is kept low – except for Thursday's karaoke when Dan, the manager, becomes Tom Jones! ❀◐⇌(Priory)

Golden Lion

11 Priory Street (A256/B2011 jct)
10-11; 12-10.30 Sun
☎ (01304) 202919
Beer range varies Ⓗ
Just off the High Street, this is a one-bar street-corner local, enjoying a significant regular following, as well as making visitors feel very welcome. The Golden Lion Winkle Club, whose photos adorn the wall, is at the heart of the community, having given a lot of money to local charities, particularly schools, in the last five years. Reasonably-priced filled rolls are available from the bar. The beer range usually includes a varying brew from Brains of Cardiff.
⇌(Priory)

Mogul

5 Chapel Place (near A256/A20 jct, York St roundabout))
11-11; 12-10.30 Sun
☎ (01304) 205072
Beer range varies Ⓖ
Family-run genuine free house that has won several awards in recent years. Three beers are usually available, often including a mild; over 500 different ales have been served in the last two and a half years. The garden affords views of the castle and harbour. A log fire burns between the two bars. Pictures of old Dover and Imperial India feature alongside brewery posters and chalk representations of regular customers. Easier to find on foot than by car, it is well worth seeking out. Thatcher's cider is served. Games include quoits, bar skittles and toad in the hole.
⛫Q❀⇌(Priory)♣⚈⚟

EAST FARLEIGH ❄

Bull
Lower Road
❂ 11-11; 12-10.30 Sun
☎ (01622) 726282
website: www.the-farleigh-bull.co.uk
Adnams Bitter; Flowers Original; Fuller's London Pride; Goacher's Gold Star Ale; Shepherd Neame Master Brew Bitter 🄷
Busy, L-shaped, Victorian pub standing above the Medway Valley. The large, well-used, function room has its own bar; the garden has a children's play area with small animals. A good selection of food includes daily specials, vegetarian and children's options. A portable village convenience store is currently located in the car park. Local CAMRA Pub of the Year 2000, it was runner-up in 2001. It hosts live music on Sunday evening. ⩋❀◐◑⇌P⊁

EAST MALLING

Rising Sun
125 Mill Street
❂ 12-11; 12-10.30 Sun
☎ (01732) 843284
Goacher's Light; Shepherd Neame Master Brew Bitter; guest beers 🄷
Popular village pub, serving reasonably-priced beers. The U-shaped bar commands the centre of the pub, with comfortable seating around the perimeter, and bare bricks and timber much in evidence. Basic bar food is served Mon-Fri. Children are strictly not allowed in this genuine drinkers' pub which has been in the landlord's ownership for 12 years. It is a regular haunt for local darts and football teams. ❀◐⇌♣

EGERTON FORSTAL

Queen's Arms
Forstal Road OS893464
❂ 12-3 (not Mon or Tue), 5-11 (not Mon); 12-11 Sat; 12-10.30 Sun
☎ (01233) 756386 website: www.quarms.co.uk
Fuller's London Pride; Goacher's Mild; Harveys BB; Shepherd Neame Master Brew Bitter; guest beers 🄷
Hard to find, this rural village local is everything a country pub should be and is well worth making the effort to seek out. Up to four changing guest beers are stocked, including products from Kent brewers and further afield; a second mild is often available. Real Kentish cider is occasionally available in summer. No food is served on Sunday evening.
⩋❀◐◑▲♣P

ELHAM

Rose & Crown
High Street
❂ 11-3, 6-11; 12-3, 7-10.30 Sun
☎ (01303) 840226 website: www.roseandcrown.co.uk
Hopdaemon Golden Braid; Greene King Ruddles Best Bitter; guest beer 🄷
Cosy village pub, popular with walkers and diners. Real beams and comfortable sofas give a very welcoming ambience. A preference for keeping locally-brewed guest beers, such as Rother Valley, adds to the attraction of this pub off the beaten track. Log fires make it a cosy winter evening haunt. Six en-suite rooms in the courtyard have been converted from old stables.
⩋Q♉❀⇆◐◑♣P

FAIRSEAT

Vigo
Gravesend Road (A227, 1 mile N of A20)
❂ 12-3.30 (not Mon-Fri), 6-11; 12-3.30, 7-10.30 Sun
☎ (01732) 822547
Flagship Hardy's Kiss; Harveys XX Mild, BB; Young's Bitter, Special; guest beers 🄷
Unspoilt, ancient drovers' inn located on a main road at the top of a steep hill on the North Downs. Named in honour of a local resident who fought in the famous Crimean Battle, the pub has subsequently given its name to a village built in the 1960s nearby. Run by the same family since 1930, this no-frills pub has a quiet atmosphere except when daddlums (Kentish skittles) is being played!
⩋Q♣P⊁⊽

FARNINGHAM

Chequers
87 High Street (250 yds from A20, off M25 jct 3)
❂ 11 (12 Sat)-11; 12-10.30 Sun
☎ (01322) 865222

INN BRIEF

GRAVESEND

Windmill Tavern
Shrubbery Road
11-11; 12-10.30 Sun
(01474) 352242
Fuller's London Pride; Greene King IPA; Webster's Yorkshire Bitter; guest beers 🄷
Real country pub in the town, with three comfortable bars and an award-winning garden. Lunchtime meals. Traditional pub games.

IGHTHAM

Chequers
The Street
11-3, 6-11; 12-3, 7-10.30 Sun
(01732) 882396
Greene King IPA, Abbot, seasonal beer; guest beer 🄷
Pleasant, traditional one-bar village local with an open fireplace. Good value meals are served lunchtime and evening (not Sun eve).

KINGSDOWN (DEAL)

King's Head
Upper Street
12-2.30 (not Mon), 5-11; 11-3, 6-11 Sat; 12-5, 7-10.30 Sun
(01304) 373915
Draught Bass; Greene King IPA; guest beer 🄷
Traditional village local, with several bars and rooms, in the main village street, leading down to the sea.

KNOCKHOLT

Crown
Main Road OS468588
11-2.30 (3 Sat), 6-11; 12-3, 7-10.30 Sun
(01959) 532142
Adnams Bitter, Broadside 🄷
West of the village, Kent's highest pub, of 19th-century origin, is just north of the North Downs Way. Food served lunchtime, plus Sat eve.

LEIGH

Bat & Ball
High Street
12-3, 6-11; 12-3, 6-10.30 Sun
(01732) 833230
Hook Norton Old Hooky; Shepherd Neame Master Brew Bitter; guest beers 🄷
250-year-old, two-bar village inn close to the green and station. No food Sun or Mon eve.

LOOSE

Walnut Tree
657 Loose Road
11-3 (4 Fri), 6-11; 12-3, 7-10.30 Sun
(01622) 743493
Shepherd Neame Master Brew Bitter, Spitfire, Bishops Finger 🄷
Cosy village pub, offering meals and bar snacks (no food Sun).

Fuller's London Pride, ESB; Oakham JHB; Taylor Landlord; guest beers Ⓗ
Excellent, one-bar corner local in a charming riverside village, complete with family butcher, grocer, bank and curry house. Near the Darenth Valley footpath, and easily accessible by major roads, the pub attracts a wide range of clientele. Up to eight beers include a rotating range of guests. Note the unusual tiled roof over the bar. Nearby cottages display outstanding flower arrangements in spring and summer. It is a worthy regular Guide entry. No food Sun. ❀◑♣

FAVERSHAM ❊

Anchor

52 Abbey Street
✪ 12-11; 12-3, 6-11 Mon; 12-10.30 Sun
☎ (01795) 536471 website: www.upanchor.co.uk
Shepherd Neame Master Brew Bitter, Best Bitter, Spitfire, seasonal beers Ⓗ
One of Shepherd Neame's first three pubs, it dates from the 17th century. Set across the end of historic Abbey Street, it is yards from Standard Quay, where many preserved sailing vessels are berthed. The pub's main ceiling beams are old ships' timbers. It enjoys a well-deserved reputation for its food which is freshly prepared on the premises using local ingredients; fish and game are specialities (no food Sun eve or Mon). Live music (jazz and blues) is performed Sunday evening. The large garden is a bonus.
⛼Q❀◑◗⊟

Bear Inn

3 Market Place
✪ 10.30-3, 5.30-11; 10.30-11 Sat; 12-3.30, 7-10.30 Sun
☎ (01795) 532668
Shepherd Neame Master Brew Bitter, Spitfire, seasonal beers Ⓗ
This classic pub retains its early 19th-century layout: three bars off a long side corridor. It stands opposite the ancient Guildhall, where tables for outside drinking are set out in summer. Notable features in the back bar are a carved wooden bear and a clock on which the figures are replaced by the letters of the pub's name. The excellent, home-cooked food often features old English recipes. This typical market town pub recalls times past.
Q❀◑⊟⇌

Chimney Boy

59 Preston Street
✪ 11-4, 5.30 (6 Sat)-11; 12-4, 7-10.30 Sun
☎ (01795) 532007
Shepherd Neame Master Brew Bitter, Spitfire, seasonal beers Ⓗ
Convenient for the station, it was originally built as a convent and later became the Limes Hotel. During the 1970s, steps were found in an old chimney and it was decided to rename the pub. Around the same time, alterations were made to the interior, adding a large upstairs function room, which is used by various clubs, including the very popular Faversham Folk Club. The pub is noted for its restaurant (no food Sun eve), there is also a room with a pool table. Patio available at rear.
❀◑◗⇌♣P

Crown & Anchor

41 The Mall (400 yds S of station, towards A2)
✪ 10.30-3 (4 Sat), 5.30 (6 Sat)-11; 12-3.30, 7-10.30 Sun
☎ (01795) 532812
Shepherd Neame Master Brew Bitter Ⓗ
A high quality pint awaits you at this friendly local. The beer served here is the yardstick by which to judge others. Dating from the mid-19th century, it was soon absorbed into the Shepherd Neame estate. A single-roomed pub, with an L-shaped bar, it has an area for pool and darts. Weekday lunches are served – the goulash is recommended as the landlord is Hungarian. It has appeared in this Guide for the last 10 years. ◑⇌♣

Shipwright's Arms

Hollowshore, off Ham Road (from Priory Rd, Davington, turn right into Ham Rd, left at bottom, first right) OS017636
✪ 11-3, 6-11 (closed winter Mon); 11-11 Sat & summer; 12-10.30 Sun
☎ (01795) 590088
Goacher's Mild, Flagship Shipwrecked; Gold Star Ale; Hopdaemon Skrimshander IPA; guest beer (summer) Ⓖ
Remote and historic, 300-year-old pub, set in the marshes at the confluence of Faversham and Oare creeks; it has a very special atmosphere. Beers come only from Kentish breweries, all drawn direct from the cask. In summer there is real Kentish cider, too. Beer festivals are often held at bank holidays. Winner of the CAMRA South East super-regional Pub of the Year 2001, children and dogs are welcome. No food Sun eve, Mon or Tue (all day). Real fires, real food, real character! ⛼Q❀◑◗⛺♣●P⊬

Sun Inn

10 West Street
✪ 11-11; 12-10.30 Sun
☎ (01795) 535098
Shepherd Neame Master Brew Bitter, Spitfire, seasonal beers Ⓗ
Located on historic West Street, the Sun is one of the oldest pubs in town. Formed from two separate pubs, the main fireplace was hidden for years until the 1920s when it was put back to its rightful use. Particularly notable is the well-preserved wooden panelling. This pub is the very heart of the market town, just a hundred yards or so from the Guildhall. Patio available at rear. ⛼❀◑⇌♣

FOLKESTONE

Clifton Hotel

The Leas
✪ 11-3, 6-midnight; 11.30-3.30, 6.30-midnight Sun
☎ (01303) 851231
website: www.reservations@thecliftonhotel.com
Draught Bass Ⓗ
Hotel bar just off the Leas promenade, it is the epitome of high-ceilinged Victorian elegance. The central bar has stools and comfortable armchair seating around the perimeter. The best pint of Bass in town is served here, and the food is not bad either – try the fish and chips. Folkestone's broad promenade is ideal for a leisurely stroll and if the weather is clear you can see the coast of France. Q❀⛟◑◗⇌(Central)

Lifeboat Inn

42 North Street

11-11; 12-10.30 Sun

☎ (01303) 243958

Draught Bass; Fuller's London Pride; guest beers H

The short climb up North Street is well worth the effort, for nestling at the top is the Lifeboat Inn where you will always get a warm welcome. Just as welcoming to the visitor, however, is the sight of, on average, five real ales on tap; the two house regulars are the ever-popular London Pride and Bass, plus usually three guests. Evening meals are served Tue-Sat (no food Mon). Q

FORDWICH

Fordwich Arms

King Street (400 yds from A28 at Sturry)

11-11; 12-3, 7-10.30 Sun

☎ (01227) 710444

Flowers Original; Shepherd Neame Master Brew Bitter; Wadworth 6X; guest beer H

Classic pub with a single large bar. The garden and patio are by the side of the River Stour. Fordwich is England's smallest town; the tiny, ancient town hall stands opposite the pub. The restaurant is often very busy, although tables are also available in the bar. No food is served Sunday evening when musicians play (folk on the first and third Sundays every month). The Stour Valley Walk passes outside and Westbere Lakes are nearby. Theobold's cider is served straight from the cask. Q ♿ ⇌ (Sturry) P

GILLINGHAM

Barge

63 Layfield Road

12-3 (not Tue), 7-11; 12-11 Sat; 12-10.30 Sun

☎ (01634) 850485

website: www.myofficesecretary.com/thebarge

Wadworth 6X; guest beers H

The Flagship house beer, Joshua's Ale, is named after the landlord's son, and three guest beers are normally on tap. A new feature is the decking just outside the back door where you can sit and take in some spectacular views across the River Medway. The pub was named as Folk Venue of the Year by a local magazine; a free folk night is held every Monday. The interior walls depict life below decks, painted by local artist, Jamie Montgomery. The pub is candlelit in the evenings.

⇌ ♣

Frog & Toad

38 Burnt Oak Terrace

11-11; 12-10.30 Sun

☎ (01634) 852231 website: www.thefrogandtoad.com

Fuller's London Pride; guest beers H

This thriving town house was Medway CAMRA Pub of the Year in 2001, it now boasts four handpumps, a real cider and at least 30 Belgian bottled beers (each served in its own branded glass). A regular on one handpump will be a beer from Flagship. Two real ale festivals are held in the garden, in May and August. No juke box or fruit machines, but the pub fields many sporting teams such as football, darts, and bar billiards. Summer barbecues and live entertainment are added attractions.

⇌ ♣

Upper Gillingham Conservative Club

541 Canterbury Street (top end, near A2)

11-2.30 (3 Sat), 7 (6.30 Sat)-11; 12-2.30, 7-10.30 Sun

☎ (01634) 851403

Shepherd Neame Master Brew Bitter; guest beers H

A club that makes everyone welcome, earning it Medway CAMRA's Club of the Year award for the last three years, and national runner-up in 2001. The two guest ales will normally only be up to 4.5% ABV, but are excellent value. Show a current CAMRA membership card or a copy of this Guide to be signed in. A single U-shaped bar is supplemented by a snooker room with two full-sized tables, and a TV room. ♣ P

Will Adams

73 Saxton Street (off lower end of Canterbury St)

12-3 (not Mon-Fri), 7-11; 12-4, 8-10.30 Sun

☎ (01634) 575902

Hop Back Summer Lightning; guest beers H

This pub sells bottled beers from around the world and offers 25 malt whiskies, as well as up to four guest ales. Saturday lunchtime hours are extended when the local professional football team are playing at home. Formerly known as the Saxton Arms, its name honours the famous navigator/adventurer, whose exploits are depicted on a mural inside. The pub fields quiz, darts and pool teams. Weston's Old Rosie or Moles Black Rat cider is stocked. Meals served at lunchtime on Sat.

⇌ ♣

GOODNESTONE

Fitzwalter Arms

The Street OS255546

12-3.30, 7-11; 12-3.30, 7-10.30 Sun

☎ (01304) 840303

Shepherd Neame Master Brew Bitter H

Rural local in a picturesque village, named after the lord of the manor. Built as the bailiff's lodge to the Fitzwalter estate, it has been licensed since 1703 and retains an unspoilt Jacobean exterior. The interior has also largely survived intact, with three distinct bars giving a cosy, intimate character. The garden is accessible via the saloon bar where meals are served (booking advisable for Sunday lunch). Nearby Goodnestone Estate Gardens, once frequented by Jane Austen, are open to the public.

♣

GRAVESEND

British Tar

15 Milton Road (opp. clock tower)

11.30-3, 7-11; 12-3, 7-10.30 Sun

☎ (01474) 533891

Everards Tiger; Gale's HSB; Young's Special H

Old timber-framed building with a Dutch style pointed roof, which pre-dates the adjoining Georgian colonnade. An old-fashioned waterman's pub with a nautical theme, little has changed here since the 1960s. The licensee is the longest-serving landlord in Gravesend, and this friendly no-frills, town-centre local is usually a quiet haven away from the modern themed bars.

⇌ ♣

Crown & Thistle

44 The Terrace (just off inner ring road, near river)
✪ 11-11; 12-10.30 Sun
☎ (01474) 533918
Daleside Shrimpers; guest beers [H]
Built as a private house in Georgian times, it became an ale house in 1849. Renovated and reopened in 2001, after a short closure, this is the ideal small town pub. Strongly favouring micro-breweries, four beers come from all parts of the UK. Double Vision cider and fruit wines are also sold. Chinese and Indian meals can be ordered at the bar (eves). Note the collection of former Russell's Brewery pictures. No fruit machines, TV or children, just a relaxed drinking environment.
⇌●⁄

Jolly Drayman

1 Love Lane, Wellington Street (off A226, by BP garage)
✪ 11.30-11; 12-4, 7-11 Sat; 12-4, 7-10.30 Sun
☎ (01474) 352355
Everards Tiger; guest beers [H]
Delightful, low-ceilinged pub with a friendly, cosy atmosphere, situated in the former offices of the old Wellington Brewery, part of which still stands across the road. The coke oven, which powered the plant, was located on the site of the present car park, so the pub is known locally as the coke oven. Barbecues are held on weekend evenings in summer.
❀◐⇌♣●

HALLING

Homeward Bound

72 High Street
✪ 12-3, 5 (7 Sat)-11; 12-3, 7-10.30 Sun
☎ (01634) 240743
Shepherd Neame Master Brew Bitter [H]
Formerly a Mason's Brewery outlet, this friendly Shepherd Neame pub is part of a Victorian terrace. Various old photographs of the village adorn the walls. Every Tuesday the car park is full of assorted motorcycles of all ages as the Medway Triumph Club hold their meetings here. A traditional Kent dartboard (no trebles) is used by the darts team on Thursday evening.
♔Q❀⇌♣P

HALSTEAD

Rose & Crown

1-3 Otford Lane OS489611
✪ 12-11; 12-10.30 Sun
☎ (01959) 533120
Courage Best Bitter; Harveys seasonal beers; Larkins Traditional; guest beers [H]
Popular, two-bar pub, in a flint-faced listed building of the early 1860s, where food (served weekdays) does not predominate. Originally named the Crown, it displays a wealth of pictures showing the pub in earlier times. The garden, where bat and trap is played, is safe for children, who are also welcome in the games room. The three guest beers come from small breweries and are changed regularly. Ask the landlady about Humphrey, the benign ghost.
♔Q♉❀◐⊟♿♣P

HERNE

Smugglers Inn

1 School Lane (off A291)
✪ 11-11; 12-10.30 Sun
☎ (01227) 741395
Shepherd Neame Master Brew Bitter, Spitfire, seasonal beer [H]
The attic here was used by smugglers as a look-out post, while a tunnel linked the cellars to the church. The public bar has a nautical theme – the bar is fitted with the prow of a whaler. The saloon bar features hops, brass and wooden beams decorated with twigs. A regular bus service runs from Canterbury and Herne Bay. Just across the road is the recommended Herne Florist and Real Ale off-licence. Games include shove-ha'penny and bat and trap. No food Sun.
♔Q❀⇌◐⊟♣

HERNHILL

Three Horseshoes

46 Staple Street (1 mile N of Boughton Street)
OS080601
✪ 12-3, 5-11; 12-11 Fri & Sat; 12-3, 7-10.30 Sun
☎ (01227) 750842
Shepherd Neame Master Brew Bitter, Spitfire, seasonal beers [G]
Traditional country pub in a hamlet set among the fruit orchards near Mount Ephraim Gardens and Farming World. The pub dates from 1690 and its beers are served direct from the cask. This friendly, village pub offers a warm welcome to all except mobile phone users. Home-cooked food is served Tue-Sat. Quiz nights, and other schemes, raise money for local good causes; the Wheely Bin Grand Prix on August bank holiday is unmissable. ♔Q❀◐▲♣P

HIGHAM

Stonehorse Inn

Dillywood Lane (150 yds off B2000)
✪ 11-3, 6-11; 11-11 Fri & Sat; 12-3, 7-10.30 Sun
☎ (01634) 722046
Courage Best Bitter; guest beers [H]
A regular outlet for Flagship beers, this classic country pub is surrounded by fields, but is very close to the edge of the Medway Towns. The unspoilt wood-panelled public bar boasts a log range and a bar billiards table. Quiz nights are held Sunday evenings in the quiet saloon. Food is served lunchtimes Mon-Fri and Wed-Sat evenings. It has a large garden to the rear.
♔Q❀◐⊟♣P

IDEN GREEN (BENENDEN)

Woodcock Inn

Woodcock Lane (off Benenden-Sandhurst road)
OS807313
✪ 11-11; 12-10.30 Sun
☎ (01580) 240009
Greene King IPA, Ruddles County; Harveys BB; Rother Valley Level Best [H]
Deservedly popular rural pub where the low-ceilinged bar, complete with old timber beams and bare brickwork, is dominated by an inglenook, surrounded by comfortable sofas. The garden, appreciated by ramblers and families alike, allows food and drinks to be ordered through the back window of the bar. A full menu is available every day. All

food is home-prepared and, with up to 10 special dishes on offer each week, caters for most tastes, including vegetarians and children. ⌂Q❀◐◑♣P

IGHTHAM COMMON

Old House ☆

Redwell Lane (1/2 mile SW of Ightham village, between A25 and A227) OS590559

✪ 12-3 (not Mon-Fri), 7-11 (9 Tue); 12-3, 7-10.30 Sun

☎ (01732) 882383

Cotleigh Tawny; Daleside Shrimpers; G Flowers IPA; H Oakham JHB; guest beers G

A row of red brick and tile cottages, with a small forecourt, is difficult to discern as a pub since the sign disappeared long ago. The main bar focuses on a large open fireplace with exposed beams (part 16th-century) and the atmosphere buzzes with the convivial conversation of true locals. The parlour is altogether quieter. At least four beers are on stillage in a room behind the bar. It is a remarkable survivor from a bygone era. ⌂Q⊟ΔP

KEMSING

Rising Sun

Cotmans Ash Lane OS563599

✪ 11-3, 6-11; 12-3, 7-10.30 Sun

☎ (01959) 522683

Beer range varies H

Isolated hilltop hostelry in pleasant countryside near the North Downs Way and several local footpaths. First-time visitors are advised to 'phone for directions. The main bar area is a converted hunting lodge, with a large collection of agricultural implements and a large open fireplace, where an ageing resident African Grey parrot presides. Five handpumps dispense an ever-changing range of small independent and micro-breweries' beers from all over Britain; a cider is sometimes stocked in summer. Excellent quality, home-cooked food comes in generous portions. Not to be missed.

⌂Q❀◐◑Δ♣●⊓

KNOCKHOLT ❋

Three Horseshoes

The Pound

✪ 11.30-3, 6-11; 11-11 Fri & Sat; 12-10.30 Sun

☎ (01959) 532102 website: www.t3hsk.co.uk

Courage Best Bitter; Fuller's London Pride; Greene King IPA; Harveys BB H

Imposing white-painted building at the village centre. The roomy saloon bar is decorated with pictures of cars and trains. The panelled snug bar displays pictures of military occasions – the landlord is a former band sergeant major of the Irish Guards. There are two handpumps in each bar. The North Downs Way passes about 600 yards to the south of the pub. No meals served Sun eve. Wheelchair access is at the rear.

❀◐◑⊟♿♣P

LADDINGFORD

Chequers Inn

OS689481

✪ 11.30-3, 5-11; 11-11 Sat; 12-10.30 Sun

☎ (01622) 871266

Adnams Bitter; Badger K&B Sussex; Fuller's London Pride; guest beer H

In summer the frontage of this 15th-century weatherboarded former farmhouse is festooned with floral displays. The walls inside show awards earned by the licensee and staff. Look out also for the landlord's 'Thought of the Week'. Regular fund-raising events are held in aid of local charities. Excellent snacks and full meals are served at all sessions. There is a spacious patio and large garden with a children's play area and animal corner. A beer festival is held in April (book early for guest accommodation).

⌂❀⇔◐◑P✔

LUDDESDOWN

Cock Inn

Henley Street OS664672

✪ 12-11; 12-10.30 Sun

☎ (01474) 814208

Adnams Bitter; Goacher's Mild; Shepherd Neame Master Brew Bitter; guest beers H

Genuine free house, offering at least six real ales, three regular ciders and an occasional perry. A choice of dartboards includes quad, Kentish and London fives. Popular free quiz (Tue eve) is devised and hosted by the genial landlord. Accessible by footpath from Sole Street Station, it stands near the Weald Way and many local footpaths. The saloon bar features WWII memorabilia and the public bar bears a classic car theme. A spacious conservatory leads to the garden where pétanque is played. No food served Sat eve or Sun. ⌂Q❀◐◑⊟Δ♣●P✔

MAIDSTONE

Druid's Arms

24 Earl Street

✪ 11-11; 12-10.30 Sun

☎ (01622) 758516

Boddingtons Bitter; guest beers H

Now reverted to its former name, this busy establishment, close to the main shopping street, nevertheless maintains the Hogshead reputation for beer range and quality. Popular with shoppers and office workers by day, it is frequented by students and real ale connoisseurs at all times. The spartan interior is incidental to enjoyment of a wide and constantly changing range of up to seven guest beers, with always one on gravity. Biddenden cider is also stocked. Meas are served 12-8 (7 Fri and Sat). The garden has a covered heated area.

⌂❀◐◑⇌(East) ●

Rifle Volunteers

28 Wyatt Street (off Week St/Union St)

✪ 11-3 (may vary; 5 Sat), 6 (7 Sat)-11; 12-5, 7-10.30 Sun

☎ (01622) 758891

Goacher's Mild, Light, Crown Imperial Stout H

Great little pub – if you want to go somewhere for a quiet drink and good conversation then this is the place. This Goacher's house is a regular outlet for the mild. Delicious home-made food, using fresh ingredients, is served daily (evening meals by arrangement). It is easy to get to as both bus and train stations are nearby. Toy soldiers are employed as beer tokens and customers are welcome to bring along their own to use.

Q❀◐⇌(East) ♣

Swan
2 County Road (opp. prison)
11-11; 12-10.30 Sun
(01622) 751264
Shepherd Neame Master Brew Bitter, Bishops Finger, seasonal beers H
Regular Guide entry, and frequent Cellarmanship award-winner, the Swan is close to the County Council offices and opposite the main entrance to HMP Maidstone. The latter is reputed to be the 'stunt double' for many such film and TV establishments. The pub's street-corner site extends down a small terrace, giving an unusual split-level bar arrangement. Wholesome curries and spicy casseroles make popular lunchtime fare for office workers and shoppers. Pétanque is played in the garden. ❀◑ ≥(East) ♣

MARGATE

Orb
243 Ramsgate Road (A254)
11-11; 12-10.30 Sun
(01843) 220663
Shepherd Neame Master Brew Bitter, Best Bitter or Bishops Finger H
Excellent pub, on the edge of town, handy for the area's main hospital. It started out as a small farm cottage and stable on the Chapel Hill Estate, but its superb position on the Margate-Ramsgate road made it a good stop-off point for horse-drawn traffic. Until 1969 it was known as the Crown & Sceptre. Today, with its extensions to incorporate a dining area and games room, it is a lively local. No food is served Sat.
❀◑♣P

MARSH GREEN

Wheatsheaf
Marsh Green Road (B2028, Edenbridge-Lingfield road)
11-11; 12-10.30 Sun
(01732) 864091
Harveys BB; guest beers H
Friendly, tile-hung country pub, the focal point for the village community. At least six or seven real ales, including a mild, are always available and change regularly. An annual beer festival is held in July to coincide with the village fête, offering over 30 ales on gravity to complement the hog roast. The pub has several rooms, including a conservatory where an extensive range of good home-cooked food is served in generous portions. There is a large garden. Biddenden cider is stocked.
Q❀◑♣P

MARSHSIDE

Gate Inn
Take Chislet turning off A28 at Upstreet
11-2.30, 6-11; 12-4, 7-10.30 Sun
(01227) 860498
Shepherd Neame Master Brew Bitter, Spitfire, Bishops Finger, seasonal beers (occasional) G
Now in its 27th year in this Guide, the Gate received the accolade of being voted one of the Daily Telegraph's top ten Traditional Country Pubs in 2002. Its assets include tiled floors, hops and an attractive garden with a stream, apple trees and ducks. An excellent, reasonably-priced menu uses local produce (no meals Mon or Tue eves in winter). It is very much a community centre. The Christmas programme of mummers' plays is noteworthy.
Q❀◑♣P

MINSTER (THANET)

New Inn
2 Tothill Street
11.30-3, 5-11; 11.30-11 Fri & Sat; 12-10.30 Sun
(01843) 821294
Greene King IPA, Abbot; guest beer H
Delightful village local, oozing warmth and atmosphere; note the stained glass Cobbs windows. Built in 1837, it was a replacement for the hostelry in William Buddell's pleasure gardens complex. Today the pub's garden is all that remains of the once-ample pleasure gardens, now housing an aviary, rabbit run and a children's climbing frame. An extension has provided a better dining area and a venue for live music. No food is served Sun eve or Mon.
❀◑ ≥♣P

MUNDY BOIS

Rose & Crown
Mundy Bois Road

INN BRIEF

MARGATE

Spread Eagle
25 Victoria Road
11-3, 5.30-11; 11-11 Fri & Sat; 12-10.30 Sun
(01843) 293396
Fuller's London Pride; Greene King IPA; guest beers H
Former Guide regular, now winning back local drinkers following several ownership changes. Cask Marque accredited.

NORTHFLEET

Rose
1 Rose Street
11-11; 12-3, 7-10.30 Sun
(01474) 365791
Shepherd Neame Master Brew Bitter H
Small Victorian local with a friendly community spirit, in a modern housing estate near Gravesend football ground.

PEMBURY

Black Horse
12 High Street
11-11; 12-3, 7-10.30 Sun
(01892) 822141
Greene King Old Speckled Hen; Marston's Pedigree; Wells Bombardier H
Village pub with a large open fire. Popular with locals and business diners; the superb restaurant is next door. A house beer is sold.

PLUCKLEY

Dering Arms
Station Road
11.30-3, 6-11; 12-3, 7-10.30 Sun
(01233) 840371
Goacher's Dering Ale H
Built as a hunting lodge for the Dering Estate, with stone-flagged bars, it serves a house ale and excellent food.

ROCHESTER

Golden Lion
147-149 High Street
10-11; 12-10.30 Sun
(01634) 880521
Courage Directors; Shepherd Neame Spitfire; Theakston Best Bitter; guest beers H
Busy Wetherspoon's pub close to Rochester Castle and Cathedral. Cask Marque accredited.

RUSTHALL

White Hart
16 Lower Green Road
12-3, 6-11; 11-11 Sat; 12-3, 7-10.30 Sun
(01892) 523076
Adnams Bitter; Harveys BB; Tetley Bitter H
Small, pleasant local facing the green: two bars featuring a piano and old clocks; darts in the 'Surgery'.

⏲ 11-3, 6-11; 12-3, 7-10.30 Sun
☎ (01233) 840393
Shepherd Neame Master Brew Bitter; Hook Norton Best Bitter; guest beer Ⓗ
An ale house since 1780, it stands in a remote hamlet, in the parish of Pluckley. It has the dubious boast of being reputedly the most haunted pub in England. A two-bar pub, it offers a good range of home-cooked food, prepared by a chef who has won prizes for his steak and kidney puddings. An extensive garden includes a children's play area. Real cider is stocked in summer. ♨Q❀◐⊞♿▲♣●P

NEW ROMNEY

Prince of Wales

Fairfield Road
⏲ 12-3, 6 (5 Thu)-11; 12-11 Fri & Sat; 12-10.30 Sun
☎ (01797) 362012
Courage Best Bitter; Shepherd Neame Master Brew Bitter; Tetley Burton Ale Ⓗ
Two-bar, back-street local with low ceilings, hosting occasional quiz nights and social events. The TV shows major sports events. A short walk away you can take a trip on the delightful little narrow gauge RH&D light railway. The pub is a rare regular outlet for Burton Ale in this part of East Kent.
♨❀⊞♣

NEWNHAM

Tapster

Parsonage Farm, Seed Road
⏲ 11.30-2.30, 6-11; 11.30-11 Sat; 12-10.30 Sun
☎ (01795) 890711
Beer range varies Ⓗ
Standing in a large garden, in an attractive building away from the road, the Tapster is warmed by a large open fire. It features a wooden floor and hops around the bar. The pub is known for its imaginative menu and many tables are set aside for diners, although there is always room for drinkers. Beers are sourced from many regional and micro-breweries; six are normally available in summer, reducing to four in the winter. Now has its own cider (when available).
♨❀⛟◐●P

OLD ROMNEY

Rose & Crown

Swamp Road (off A259)
⏲ 11.30-11; 12-10.30 Sun
☎ (01797) 367500
website: www.roseandcrown-oldromney.co.uk
Greene King XX Mild, IPA, Abbot; Fuller's London Pride; guest beer Ⓗ
Pretty country inn, built in 1689, it became a pub in 1806. Under the wide skies, and surrounded by the sometimes bleak landscape of Romney Marsh, it is nonetheless easily accessible, just off the A259. The large garden offering many facilities for families, is complemented by a new conservatory. The reasonably-priced food is recommended. Biddenden cider is usually in stock; the guest ale can include a mild, a rarity in the area. Well worth seeking out; pétanque is played here.
♨Q❀⛟◐♿▲♣●P⊬

OTHAM

White Horse

White Horse Lane (between A20 and A274)
⏲ 12-3, 5.30-11; 11-11 Sat; 12-4, 7-10.30 Sun
☎ (01622) 861304
Courage Best Bitter; Goacher's Dark; guest beers Ⓗ
This village pub keeps up to six beers, mainly from Kent micros; a Flagship beer is always available. Built in 1848, it replaced a pub of the same name dating from 1603; this building still stands. Fruit pickers from around the world fill the pub in the summer months; the licensees are polyglots. Leeds Castle and Stoneacre (NT) are nearby. Morris men congregate here at the start and end of the season. Chess and dominoes are played. ❀♿▲♣P

PERRY WOOD

Rose & Crown

1 mile S of Selling OS042552
⏲ 11-3, 6.30-11; 12-3, 7-10.30 Sun
☎ (01227) 752214
Adnams Bitter; Goacher's Mild; Harveys BB; guest beer Ⓗ
Once a woodcutter's cottage, this comfortable pub, noted for its excellent food, lies in the 150-acre Perry Wood. Its guest beer comes from various independent breweries around the country. Previous joint winner of local CAMRA Pub of the Year, it boasts a magnificent award-winning garden with a bat and trap pitch and a children's play area. Its location makes it popular with walkers. No food Sun or Mon eves. ♨Q❀◐♣P

PETTERIDGE

Hopbine

Petteridge Lane (1 mile SW of Brenchley) OS668413
⏲ 12 (11 Sat)-2.30, 6-11; 12-3, 7-10.30 Sun
☎ (01892) 722561
Badger K&B Sussex, Best, K&B Old Ale Ⓗ
Attractive pub, situated on a hilly corner. The single L-shaped bar is warmed by an open fire. Once a King & Barnes house, it is now owned by the distant Badger Brewery. A range of good home-cooked food and snacks is offered, including blackboard specials of the day (no meals Wed). Children may dine if well behaved, and the garden is safe for their use. Weston's Old Rosie cider is sold here. ♨Q❀◐●

PRESTON

Half Moon & Seven Stars

The Street
⏲ 11 (6 Mon)-11; 11-10.30 Sun
☎ (01227) 722296
Shepherd Neame Master Brew Bitter; guest beers Ⓗ
On approach from Wingham, the first view of this pub is the outdoor mural of a customs officer coastwatching under a moon and star-lit sky. Inside, it is divided into three: games, bar and eating areas. Keeping as many features as possible from the original 15th-century building, it gives a cosy impression. An imaginative range of food from bar snacks to full meals, includes vegetarian options. Occasional live music is performed.
♨❀◐♣P

RAINHAM

Mackland Arms

213 Station Road

⏲ 10-11; 12-10.30 Sun

☎ (01634) 232178

Shepherd Neame Master Brew Bitter, Best Bitter, Spitfire, seasonal beers Ⓗ

Small, terraced pub near the station with an L-shaped bar. It is very popular with the local community, particularly when football matches are broadcast on Sky TV. The long-standing licensees are very welcoming and serve the full Shep's range, including the hard-to-find Best. It is one of the nicer unchanged pubs in Rainham. ⇌♣

RAMSGATE

Artillery Arms

36 West Cliff Road

⏲ 12-11; 12-10.30 Sun

☎ (01843) 853282

Beer range varies Ⓗ

Superb, unpretentious, little pub where the emphasis is on real ale, with an ever-changing roster of five beers. Allegedly built in 1812, it was used as an officers' billet and then a brothel before becoming a beer house. It was refurbished and the interior rebuilt in 1992, after a short closure. Judged local CAMRA Pub of the Year 2002, it stocks Biddenden Bushels cider. ▲♣●

Australian Arms

45 Ashburnham Road

⏲ 11-11; 12-10.30 Sun

☎ (01843) 591489

Beer range varies Ⓗ

The last beer house in Thanet, not being fully licensed until the 1960s, the origins of the pub's name remain a mystery. It is known that convict ships docked at Ramsgate en-route to the Antipodes, but the connection is somewhat tenuous. The flint building has been altered and extended over the years, giving this busy free house a cosy, yet airy, feel. Lunches are served weekdays. ♨❀◐▲⇌♣

Churchill Tavern

18-20 The Paragon (opp. Motor Museum)

⏲ 11.30-11; 12-10.30 Sun

☎ (01843) 587862

Courage Directors; Fuller's London Pride; Ringwood Old Thumper; guest beers Ⓖ

This large pub, affording views across the English Channel, evolved out of the bars and lounges of the Paragon Hotel. When it lost its hotel function in the 1980s it was rebuilt, using old beams and church pews, and was renamed. It is popular with locals, visitors and students from nearby language schools. Although there are handpumps, all the real ale is served direct from the cask. Regular events and live music are staged. ♨◐◑▲♣

Montefiore Arms

1 Trinity Place (100 yds from A255/B2054 jct)

⏲ 12-2.30, 7-11; closed Wed; 12-3, 7-10.30 Sun

☎ (01843) 593265

Tolly Cobbold Original; guest beer Ⓗ

This busy, friendly, back-street local, serving the Hereson Road district of town, started life as two cottages. Its name is unique, honouring the legendary Jewish centenarian and philanthropist, Sir Moses Montefiore, who is principally remembered locally as a benefactor to the town's poor. He lived in Ramsgate for much of his life and is buried in a mausoleum near the pub. Regular theme nights are held throughout the year.

Q♨⇌(Dumpton Pk) ♣

St Lawrence Tavern

High Street, St Lawrence

⏲ 11-11; 12-10.30 Sun

☎ (01843) 592337

Beer range varies Ⓗ

Lively pub and restaurant, formerly the White Horse, it is now part of the successful Thorley Tavern's chain. The original Cobb's Brewery pub was built in the 18th century on a site 300 yards away. Demolished in 1851 for road widening, it reappeared a little later on the present car park site and finally settled on its current site in 1969. A reference in 1817 reports the death of an insane landlord who 'precipitated himself down a 160-foot well'. ❀◐◑▲⇌♣P

Southwood Tavern

119 Southwood Road

⏲ 12-11; 12-10.30 Sun

☎ (01843) 595272

Shepherd Neame Spitfire; guest beers Ⓗ

Former Tomson & Wotton house, situated in a residential area, not far from Ramsgate FC's Southwood ground. Although the building dates from the early 19th century, there is no evidence of it being a pub until 1880. The then-landlord, a Mr J Andrews Junior, doubled as a dairyman, reflecting the district's rural past.

♨▲⇌♣P

ROCHESTER ❊

Britannia Café Bar

376 High Street

⏲ 11 (12 Sat)-11; 12-10.30 Sun

☎ (01634) 815204

Courage Best Bitter; Wells Bombardier; guest beers Ⓗ

Previously known as the Ordnance Arms, this pub changed its name during the early 1970s. An open-plan bar leads out to a patio area which is a suntrap in summer. Live music is performed every Monday evening, and occasionally on Friday or Saturday. A monthly quiz and occasional theme nights, accompanied by appropriate food, are also held. ❀◑⇌

Cooper's Arms

10 St Margarets Street (near castle and cathedral)

⏲ 11-3, 5.30-11; 11-11 Fri & Sat; 12-10.30 Sun

☎ (01634) 404298

Courage Best Bitter, Directors; guest beers Ⓗ

This ancient and attractive inn, reputedly Kent's oldest, has an overhanging upper storey and weatherboarded sides. Inside, two cosy, comfortable bars contain some fascinating items of historic interest. The food (not served Sun) is good value and includes excellent home-cooked daily specials. The prize-winning garden hosts summer barbecues (Fri eve). Besides the cathedral and castle, many other interesting buildings and the River Medway are nearby. Parking can be difficult.

♨Q❀◑⇌(Rochester/Strood) P

Man of Kent

6-8 John Street (near police station)
12-11; 12-10.30 Sun
☎ (01634) 818771
Goacher's Light, Gold Star Ale; guest beers Ⓗ
Small, back-street ale house with a single L-shaped bar. Its rare, original tiled exterior is badged Style and Winch, a Maidstone brewery taken over and closed by Courage. Specialising in beers from Kent micro-breweries, there are normally five handpulls in operation, plus a pin on the bar. Two draught ciders and occasionally a draught perry, again sourced in Kent, are normally on tap. The rear patio/garden area is used occasionally for summer barbecues.
⛫✿⇌●

ROLVENDEN

Star

30 High Street
11-11; 12-10.30 Sun
☎ (01580) 241369
Greene King XX Mild, IPA, Ruddles County, Abbot; guest beer (occasional) Ⓗ
Ancient village pub of considerable charm, it extends a warm welcome to families with children. The single bar is set out on three levels; beware the entrance to the cellar, which is a trap door immediately inside the front entrance. It serves excellent food on a varied menu, complemented by daily specials. Regular entertainment nights are staged and it is very close to the Kent & East Sussex Steam Railway. Well worth a visit, it is a rare outlet for mild. ⛫✿◑♣

ROMNEY STREET

Fox & Hounds

Up hill from Eynsford war memorial (2 miles) OS550614
12-3 (not Mon), 6-11; 12-11 Sat; 12-10.30 Sun
☎ (01959) 525428
Beer range varies Ⓗ
Remote hilltop country pub near Romney Street mobile home park. A welcoming watering-hole for both serious hikers and gentle ramblers, it supports a regular local trade. A pool table and dartboard are complemented by the more old-fashioned games of shove-ha'penny and shut the box. Good food is served lunchtimes and Thu-Sat eves. Four rotating beers include at least one from a micro-brewery. The large, attractive garden is the venue for a beer festival in a marquee in June. A wheelchair ramp and camping facilities are available on request. ⛫✿◑♿▲♣P

ST MARGARET'S AT CLIFFE

Smugglers

High Street (1 mile SE of A258)
12-3, 5-11; 12-11 Sat; 12-4, 7-10.30 Sun
☎ (01304) 853404
Fuller's London Pride; Greene King IPA; guest beers Ⓗ
St Margaret's at Cliffe supports four pubs within 200 yards of each other. The smallest, the Smugglers, is a terraced property, where a single long bar features an unusual semi-circular servery. Low-ceilinged, with much dark wood and subdued lighting, it combines a popular local and good restaurant (Mexican dishes are a speciality). Bus services to Dover and Deal operate until early evening. The guest ale only appears at weekends in winter. A late drinking extension is available to diners. ✿◑

SANDGATE

Clarendon Inn

Brewers Hill (take stepped passageway up hill by phone box next to Sandgate Hotel)
12-3, 6-11; 12-5 Sun
☎ (01303) 248684
Shepherd Neame Master Brew Bitter, Spitfire, Bishops Finger, seasonal beers Ⓗ
This hop-bedecked local pub, with a classic mahogany gantry, is run by a friendly landlord. Live music features on alternate Thursday evenings. Enjoy the coal fire and a warming sloe gin in winter. A piano and pub games (set into tables) provide entertainment for the windswept visitor. Lined glasses are an added bonus. Biddenden Bushels cider is stocked. Beware the mother-in-law's tongue when going to the ladies'! Local CAMRA Pub of the Year 2002. ⛫Q✿◑⊟♣●⚟⊔

SANDWICH ❄

Admiral Owen

8 High Street (near tollgate)
11-11; 12-10.30 Sun
☎ (01304) 620689
Greene King IPA, Abbot, Suffolk Strong Ⓗ
Low-beamed, timbered corner house, typical of this medieval Cinque Port. Church pews and wooden tables add to its character. It provides a restful haven from the traffic which still runs along the narrow streets, despite the town being bypassed; the tollgate opposite now rendered redundant. Once a Truman's house, it is now tied to a brewery which has made major inroads into this area's free trade. ⛫◑⇌

SEAL

Five Bells

25 Church Street (100 yds N of High St, A25)
11.30-11; 12-10.30 Sun
☎ (01732) 761503
Greene King XX Mild, IPA; Harveys BB; guest beers Ⓗ
Located in the back-streets of the village, formed from two 18th-century cottages, the single low-ceilinged bar is decorated with local photographs, horse brasses and cartoons of local characters. The beer range frequently features a guest beer from one of the smaller breweries and a mild is usually available. Weekday lunches are served. Roadside tables are put out for summer drinking at this local CAMRA Pub of the Year 2001. ✿◑♣

SEVENOAKS

Anchor

32 London Road
11-3 (10.30-4 Fri), 6-11; 10.30-4.30, 7-11 Sat; 12-3, 7-10.30 Sun
☎ (01732) 454898
Greene King IPA, guest beers Ⓗ
The Anchor Inn was rebuilt in the 1920s, its most striking feature being the curved entrance doors – the inner and outer doors form an almost completely circular lobby. This is a smart, but friendly pub; the

⏲ 12-2.30; 5 (6 Mon & Sat)-11; 12-4, 7-10.30 Sun
☎ (01732) 843265 website: www.thelobsterpot.co.uk
Adnams Bitter; guest beers Ⓗ
Split-level, two-bar corner pub where wood-panelled walls and subdued lighting create a cosy atmosphere. A small restaurant alongside the bar serves an appetising range of home-cooked food (additional seating in upstairs function room when busy). No food is served Sun eve. Real ales from Kent micros are always on sale, alongside an ever-changing range of countrywide beers on six handpumps. A traditional skittle alley can be set up in the function room by prior arrangement. ☎❀◑◐ ≠♣

WEST PECKHAM

Swan on the Green

The Green (1 mile from B2016) OS644524
⏲ 11-3 (4 Sat), 6-11 (9 Mon); 12-4, 7-9 Sun
☎ (01622) 812271
website: www.swan-on-the-green.co.uk
Swan Whooper Pale, Ginger Swan, Organic Swan, Trumpeter Best, Parliament Ale, Porter Ⓗ
Licensed since 1685 but built earlier, the beams, wood floor and brickwork are now exposed providing an excellent bistro-style restaurant at one end, and a drinking area at the other. Log fires provide winter warmth. Close by the church, it faces the green where cricket is played. Six handpumps serve the Swan beers brewed at the rear. Lager and wheat beer are on tap from tanks. The short menu (not served Mon eve) offers excellent, freshly-cooked meals based on local ingredients. Bus 123 runs weekdays from West Malling Station. ♨Q❀◑◐P

WHITSTABLE

New Inn

30 Woodlawn Street (side turn, nearly opp. harbour entrance)
⏲ 11-11; 12-4, 7-10.30 Sun
☎ (01227) 264746
Shepherd Neame Master Brew Bitter Ⓗ
Built in 1844 as the Bricklayer's Arms beer house, this back-street, corner pub was renamed by 1894. The original tiny bar areas are still defined by the etched window panes, and are remembered by loyal local customers. This is a true community pub, enjoyed by young and old alike, fielding darts and quiz teams. This is a corner of old Whitstable, a good place to sit at the bar and banish worries or share success. ☎≠♣

Prince Albert

Sea Street
⏲ 11.30-11; 12-10.30 Sun
☎ (01227) 273400
Fuller's London Pride; Greene King IPA; guest beers Ⓗ
Just a few yards from the beach, yet within the town centre, the Albert is a small, friendly one-bar pub. Note the original Tomson and Wootton windows and a line showing the level reached in a 1953 flood. Guest beers often showcase Kent micro-breweries. An excellent range of good value, home-cooked food, includes fisherman's pie and steak and oyster pie. ❀◑◐≠♣

Ship Centurion

111 High Street
⏲ 11-11; 12-10.30 Sun
☎ (01227) 264740
Adnams Bitter; Elgood's Black Dog Mild; guest beers Ⓗ
The only pub in town to offer mild, this busy town-centre inn is festooned with hanging baskets in summer. Fascinating old photographs of Whitstable hang in the public bar. Entertainment includes Sky TV and live music (Thu eve and Sun afternoon). Guest beers change frequently. Home-cooked bar snacks often feature authentic German produce; the only food served on Saturday is German schnitzels. A free seafood selection is put out on the bar on Sunday.
☎◑◐≠✔

WITTERSHAM

Swan Inn

1 Swan Street
⏲ 11-11; 12-10.30 Sun
☎ (01797) 270913
website: www.swan-wittersham.co.uk
Goacher's Mild, Light; Greene King Old Speckled Hen; Ⓗ **guest beers** Ⓖ
Comfortable local at the village centre, originally a drovers' pub, mentioned first in 1684. It was local CAMRA's 2001 Pub of the Year. Up to four guest beers, often featuring Kent micros, are served in the back bar. Two local ciders from Biddenden and Double Vision are also stocked. It hosts summer and winter beer festivals; other events include live music and annual conker championships. Wittersham is on the No. 12 bus route. No food is served Mon eve or Tue.
♨❀◑◐🍎P

WORTH

Blue Pigeons

The Street
⏲ 11-11; 12-10.30 Sun
☎ (01304) 613245
Beer range varies Ⓗ
Welcoming village pub drawing a strong local trade. Redesigned several times over the last few years, it presently has a traditional layout of three distinct areas: a comfortable saloon bar with dartboard, a more basic bar with a pool table, and a restaurant where children are welcome and have their own menu. It serves everything from bar snacks to full meals, including breakfast, with vegetarian options available.
❀◑◐⊟♣P

WROTHAM

Rose & Crown

High Street
⏲ 12-3, 5.30 (6 Sat)-11; 12-4, 7-10.30 Sun
☎ (01732) 882409
Shepherd Neame Master Brew Bitter, Spitfire, Bishops Finger, seasonal beer Ⓗ
Traditional old village-centre pub. The comfortably altered and modernised interior includes a pleasant dining area (eve meals Tue-Sat) serving an excellent range of food. Home to the well-established local morris dancers, it hosts many social and sporting activities, including indoor bowls and a quiz (Thu eve). It has been a local CAMRA favourite since the early 1970s.
♨❀◑◐♣P

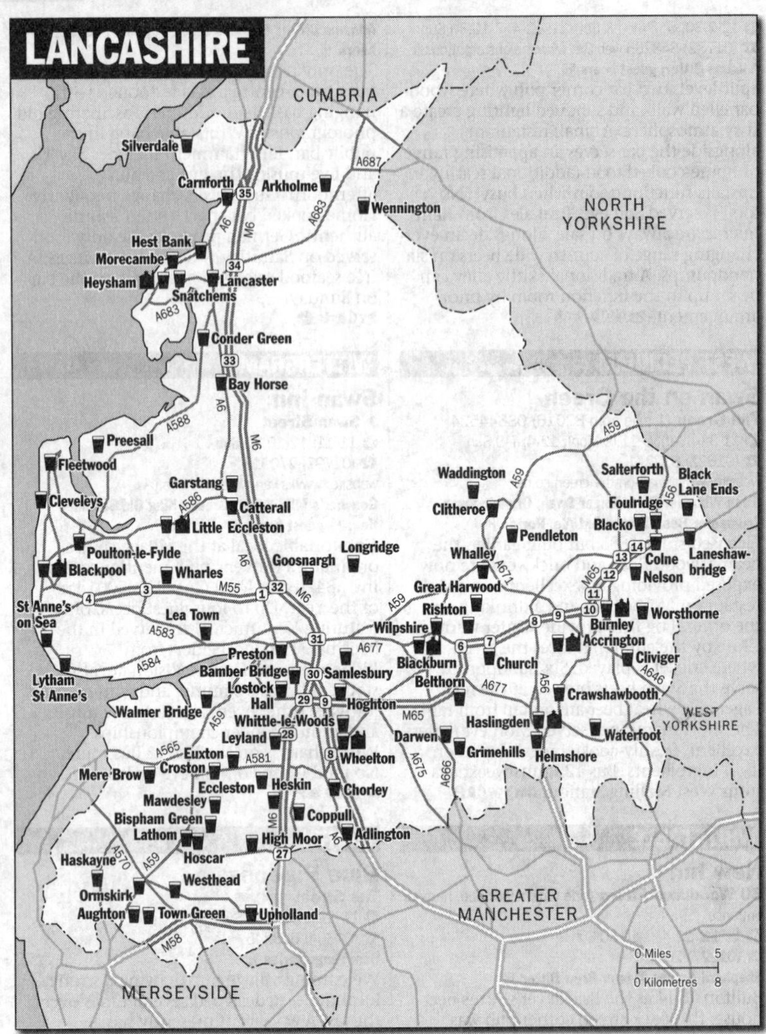

ACCRINGTON ❄

Broadway

Whalley Road

11-11 (9 Tue); 12-9 Mon; 11-10.30 Sun
☎ (01254) 395440

John Smith's Bitter; Tetley Bitter; guest beers H

One-roomed, town-centre pub that tends to be noisy at weekends when DJs appear. There are three handpumps; Tetley, John Smith's and a constantly changing guest beer which is always in good condition. A reasonably-priced extensive menu is on offer at lunchtime. The pub also sports a large-screen TV showing Sky. ✔

Grey Horse

263 Whalley Road (A680, 3/4 mile from town centre)

12-2, 4.30-11; 12-11 Fri & Sat; 12-10.30 Sun
☎ (01254) 232133

Thwaites Mild, Bitter H

Community pub set in a residential area, a typical example of a Thwaites local. It caters for those who enjoy a good conversation with their pint. It is one of only a few pubs that sell cask mild, now something of a rarity. Although the pub has been opened out, it retains distinct areas with a separate room for the pool table. Memorabilia of the landlord's favourite sports – horse racing and cricket – can be seen. Other items of interest include a gold disc of the classic Sergeant Pepper's Lonely Hearts Club Band and a large-scale model of the Grey Horse. The garden is to the front of the pub and is not fenced in. ✿♣

Red Lion Hotel

6 Moorgate, Green Haworth (off Blackburn road, 1 1/2 miles up Willows Lane)

12-3, 7-11; 12-11 Fri & Sat; 12-10.30 Sun
☎ (01254) 233194

Picks Moorgate Mild, Bedlam Bitter, Porter, Lions Pride H

Long-established pub, this is the tap of Picks Brewery. The brew-plant relocated to a more spacious industrial unit – much less cramped than the pub cellar! During the day the pub can be reached by bus, but healthy thirsts can be stimulated by a two-mile hike from Accrington! Bar food is on offer at lunchtime. At the weekend a fifth Picks beer (Lions Main or Pale Ale) is on tap. All beer is sold in oversized lined glasses. ❀◑P⊡

Sydney Street Working Men's Club
Sydney Street
⏲ 4.30 (7 Wed)-11; 11.30-11 Fri & Sat; 12-10.30 Sun
☎ (01254) 233868
John Smith's Bitter, Magnet; guest beers Ⓗ
Open-plan, typical working men's club offering a full-sized snooker table, other games and TV. The lounge is separated by a screen. There are three handpumps serving excellent ales, one of which is a changing guest beer. The club is on the site of the long-gone Sidney Street Brewery (note different spelling) and uses part of the old building. ♣

ADLINGTON

White Bear
Market Street (A6)
⏲ 11-11; 12-10.30 Sun
☎ (01257) 482357
Holt Bitter; Theakston Best Bitter; guest beers Ⓗ
Large stone-built pub on the main road, the attractive exterior is enhanced by canopies, window boxes and union flags proudly displayed. The large front bar has separate dining/drinking sections with a rear public bar and games area; a large-screen TV features sport. The rear garden and benches to the front of the pub are ideal for summer drinking. Good value home-cooked meals are offered with special promotions. Sunday lunches prove very popular. Regular bus services pass the pub. ♨❀⇄◑◐⊡≠♣

ARKHOLME

Bay Horse
On B6254
⏲ 11-3 (not winter Mon), 6-11; 12-3, 6-10.30 Sun
☎ (015242) 21425
Boddingtons Bitter; guest beer Ⓗ
Old village inn which retains a homely, rustic feel. This three-roomed pub has a bowling green and an outdoor drinking area with seats to the front. The guest beer is often from Everards. Most of the pub's customers now arrive in cars for meals. If you would prefer to take a bus, routes 443, 445 and 286 pass nearby (rather infrequent services). Q❀◑◐P⊬⊡

AUGHTON

Derby Arms
Prescot Road (B5197)
⏲ 11.30-11; 12-10.30 Sun
☎ (01695) 422237
Beer range varies Ⓗ
Traditional country pub that is full of nooks and crannies, complete with a no-smoking room. The roaring real fires, warm welcome for all and the organised clutter of interesting artefacts around the walls, combine to create a relaxing environment. Regulars request their favourite ales and every effort is made to satisfy demand; local breweries are supported. Quiz night is Tuesday and other special events are held. Three constantly changing guest beers are available. ♨❀◑◐≠(Town Green) ♣P⊬

AUGHTON (ORMSKIRK)

Dog & Gun
233 Long Lane (off A59)
⏲ 5-11; 12-3, 6-11 Sat; 12-2, 7-10.30 Sun
☎ (01695) 423303
Burtonwood Bitter, Top Hat Ⓗ
Traditional, friendly inn with plenty of character. It has a simple three-roomed layout, darts can be played in the public bar, while the lounge and snug have real coal fires. A bowling green and club house are situated at the rear, next to the car park. Recent winner of the local CAMRA summer Pub of the Year award, the Dog & Gun is a classic, unspoilt gem run by the same landlady for over 30 years.
♨Q❀⊡♿≠(Aughton Park) ♣P

BAMBER BRIDGE

Olde Original Withy Trees
157 Station Road (B6258)
⏲ 11-11; 12-10.30 Sun
☎ (01772) 330396
Burtonwood Bitter; guest beer Ⓗ
Built in the 17th century as a farmhouse, a pub that has seen many internal changes in recent years. Now effectively one large room, several separate drinking areas help to create a warm, cosy atmosphere. A well-established Guide entry, with a landlady who has recently celebrated 10 years in charge, it is now the only Withy Trees pub in the village, since its 'rival' has had a name change. There is a convenient bus stop directly outside, with regular services to Preston, Chorley and Leyland. ❀≠♣P

BELTHORN

Dog Inn
Belthorn Road (off B6232, M62 jct 5)
⏲ 12-2, 5.30-11; 12-11 Sat; 12-10.30 Sun
☎ (01254) 690794
Boddingtons Bitter; Black Sheep Best Bitter; guest beers Ⓗ
The Dog is the only pub in the village itself, the nearest competition is on the main road which bypasses Belthorn. A single-roomed, small but friendly local with an excellent, adventurous menu in the restaurant; bar food is also available. This cosy pub has stone-flagged floors, a beamed ceiling and a large open fire. There are extensive views from the restaurant at the rear towards Darwen Tower across the valley. ♨❀◑◐P

BISPHAM GREEN

Eagle & Child
Malt Kiln Lane (off B5246)
⏲ 12-3, 5.30-11; 12-10.30 Sun

INDEPENDENT BREWERIES

Blackpool Blackpool
Bryson's Heysham
Hart Little Eccleston
Moonstone Burnley
Moorhouses Burnley
Old Wheelton Wheelton
Picks Accrington
Porter Haslingden
Three B's Blackburn
Thwaites Blackburn

☎ (01257) 462297
Moorhouses Black Cat; Thwaites Bitter; guest beers Ⓗ
Outstanding, 16th-century village local with antique furniture and stone-flagged floors. Renowned for its food, a popular feature is the monthly Curry Club, usually the first Monday of the month (booking is advisable). An annual beer festival is held (from Fri to Mon) over the May bank holiday in a marquee to the rear of the pub. Saxon Cross cider is stocked. Tables around the bowling green afford wonderful views of the surrounding countryside. The front of the pub overlooks the village green.
⛰Q🐴❀◑◗♣P⊬

BLACKBURN

Fox & Grapes Hotel

3 Limefield, Preston New Road (A677)
⏲ 12-3.30, 5.30-11; 12-11 Fri & Sat; 12-4, 7-10.30 Sun
☎ (01254) 53902
Thwaites Mild, Bitter Ⓗ
Welcoming, well-furnished lounge with comfortable seating and ample bar space. The spacious snooker room has plenty of chairs and tables, making it an ideal venue for meetings. More mild is sold than bitter, and one of Thwaites' seasonal beers may occasionally be on offer. Music is played and there is a TV, but their presence is barely noticeable. Evening meals are served Mon-Sat. ⇆◗♣P

Navigation Inn

Canal Street, Mill Hill (next to bridge 96a on Leeds-Liverpool Canal)
⏲ 10.30-11; 12-10.30 Sun
☎ (01254) 53230
Thwaites Mild, Bitter Ⓗ
Unpretentious local run by one of the town's longest-serving landladies; a warm welcome is assured. A sympathetic refurbishment has enhanced the pub's character. In an ideal position for mooring a canal barge, and within walking distance of Blackburn Rovers' Ewood Park stadium, the pub's true location is Livesey, as stated on an old bottle dated 1893, belonging to the landlady. Take bus routes 18, 21 or 22 from the town centre to the pub. 🚌⇌(Mill Hill) ♣

St Mark's Conservative Club

Preston Old Road, Witton (A674)
⏲ 11.30-2.30 (not Mon-Fri), 6.30-11; 12-3, 7-10.30 Sun
☎ (01254) 52962
Thwaites Mild, Bitter; guest beer Ⓗ
Comfortable 1920s club near Witton Park with separate TV lounge and two snooker tables. A concert room extension is used for entertainment at the weekend and is hired for private functions at other times. Charity fund-raising nights take place and a brass ensemble practises here. The guest beer is usually a session bitter from a well-respected independent brewery. A warm welcome and friendly service are assured. Show a CAMRA membership card or this Guide to be signed in. Buses from the town centre are 123, 124 and 152.
Q❀⇌(Cherry Tree/Mill Hill) ♣P▯

BLACK LANE ENDS

Hare & Hounds

Take A6068 from Colne centre and follow golf club signs, 1 mile further OS929432
⏲ 12-midnight; 12-10.30 Sun
☎ (01282) 863070
Black Sheep Best Bitter; Taylor Golden Best, Landlord; Tetley Bitter; guest beer Ⓗ
Pleasant hilltop pub on the Yorkshire border. A regular Guide entry while it was a Taylor's tied house, it is now a completely refurbished free house. Popular with diners, especially for its fish menu, the barbecue area to the rear is an added attraction. The guest beer is from the Riverhead Brewery, generally Butterley Bitter or Black Moss Stout. Walkers' WC and boot wash facilities are available in the car park. If you have

INN BRIEF

ACCRINGTON

Victoria
161 Manchester Road
3 (1 Fri & Sat)-11; 1-10.30 Sun
(01254) 237727
Thwaites Mild, Bitter Ⓗ
Large, open-plan roadside pub, a single spacious U-shaped room with a pool table.

BAY HORSE

Bay Horse
Bay Horse Lane
12-2, 6.30-11; closed Mon; 12-5, 8-10.30 Sun
(01524) 791204
Everards Beacon; Tetley Bitter; guest beer Ⓗ
Rural inn with a cosy bar that aspires to gastro-pub status. On a country lane next to a closed station.

BURNLEY

General Scarlett
243 Accrington Road
1-11; 12-10.30 Sun
(01282) 831054
Moorhouses Black Cat, Premier, Pendle Witches Brew Ⓗ
This is the brewery tap, across the road from Moorhouses Brewery.

CHORLEY

Albion
29 Bolton Street
11-11; 12-10.30 Sun
(01257) 416957
Tetley Mild, Bitter Ⓗ
Unspoilt local gem with a traditional tap room and cosy lounge. Near Chorley's Big Lamp landmark.

Market Tavern
21 Cleveland Street
11-11; 12-10.30 Sun
(01257) 262815
Jennings Mild, Cumberland Ale, Sneck Lifter Ⓗ
Popular, busy local near the town's covered market. A large single bar and a raised seating area.

COLNE

Admiral Lord Rodney
Mill Green, Waterside
12-3 (summer only), 5-11; 12-11 Sat; 12-10.30 Sun
(01282) 866565
Goose Eye Brontë Bitter, Old Bear Bitter; guest beers Ⓗ
Traditional local, refurbished with some original features retained. Inexpensive, good value food is offered.

CONDER GREEN

Stork
On A588
11-11; 12-10.30 Sun
(01524) 751234
Boddingtons Bitter; guest beers Ⓗ
Long, wood-panelled building with several small rooms, main bar and restaurant. The house beer is from Interbrew.

DARWEN

Bowling Green Hotel
386 Bolton Road
12-4, 7-11 (not Tue eve); 12-11 Fri & Sat; 12-10.30 Sun
(01254) 702148
Wells Bombardier; guest beer Ⓗ
Large roadside inn with stables (dating to 1814) and beer garden at rear. Extra storey was added 1892.

Crown
24 Redearth Road
12-11; 12-10.30 Sun
(01254) 703192
Greene King Old Speckled Hen; Tetley Mild, Bitter; guest beer (summer) Ⓗ
Music-oriented pub with regular live acts and karaoke. Open-plan layout but has quiet corners.

problems finding the pub, telephone for directions. ⛫Q❀◐◗P

BLACKO

Rising Sun

330 Gisburn Road (A682)

⏲ 4.30 (7 Mon; 2 Fri; 12 Sat)-11; 12-10.30 Sun

☎ (01282) 612173

Black Sheep Best Bitter; John Smith's Bitter; Taylor Golden Best Ⓗ

Set in a row of houses, this busy, friendly pub is a community local. Small separate drinking areas create a good pub atmosphere. The locality has strong local associations with the Pendle witches. Blacko Tower is a prominent landmark just up the road. Ideally placed for delightful walks into the Pendle Hill countryside, there are views from the pub's small frontage. Q◗⊞♣P

BLACKPOOL

Bispham Hotel

Red Bank Road

⏲ 11-11; 12-10.30 Sun

☎ (01253) 351752

Samuel Smith OBB Ⓗ

This two-bar pub is very popular with locals and holidaymakers. The interior comprises a large open-plan room in original 1930s period decor. A small raised area is used for the quiz night (Thu) and other entertainment. Upstairs is a large function room and the pub retains a rare separate vault. It is home to one of the lowest priced pints on the Fylde coast. Bus route 384 stops outside, 7 and 11 nearby, it is also handy for the tram. Unobtrusive background music is played. A full menu is available 12-7 (no lunchtime meals Sun). ◐◗⊞⊖ (Bispham Tram Station)

Blue Room

139 Church Street (near Winter Gardens)

⏲ 11-11; 12-10.30 Sun

☎ (01253) 626582

Boddingtons Bitter; Fuller's London Pride; Greene King Abbot; Taylor Landlord; guest beers Ⓗ

This busy, sometimes noisy, town-centre pub is a 10-minute walk from the railway station and the promenade. It has recently reverted to its original name, having previously been called the Stanley Beer Engine. Newly painted and double-glazed, this popular pub offers food from 11-5. Two pool tables, one-armed bandits, pinball and quiz machines are added attractions. ◐⇌ (North) ♣

New Road Inn

242 Talbot Road (opp. Mecca bingo)

⏲ 12-11; 12-10.30 Sun

☎ (01253) 752666

Jennings Cumberland Ale, Sneck Lifter Ⓗ

This small three-roomed town-centre pub is the first Jennings house in Blackpool. Recently redecorated throughout, the front room is dominated by the sweeping curved bar and features posters of 1930s passenger liners. Loud music and frequent DJ nights may not be to all tastes, but the cask ale is among the cheapest in town. ⊟⇌ (North) ♣

Number 4 & Freemasons

Layton Road (B5266 at Newton Drive jct)

⏲ 12-11; 12-10.30 Sun

☎ (01253) 302877

Thwaites Bitter Ⓗ

A short stroll from Stanley Park and a mile from the seafront, this smart pub has a large split-level lounge and separate bar with pool and darts. Music and younger drinkers predominate in the evenings. Look for the landlord's specials on the GM-free menu, evening meals are served until 7pm. The small forecourt area has picnic benches. The car park is shared with the adjoining fitness centre. If you opt for the bus, take route 2 from the town centre. ❀◐◗⊞♣P

Raikes Hall Hotel

16 Liverpool Road (off A583)

⏲ 12-11; 12-10.30 Sun

☎ (01253) 757971

Draught Bass; guest beers Ⓗ

Built in 1760 and occupied in the 1860s by a religious order, from 1871 to 1901 this Grade II building was at the heart of Raikes Hall Gardens, which offered lakes, theatres, horse racing and a football ground. One large L-shaped room has lounge and bar areas. Picnic benches overlooking the pub's own bowling green provide a pleasant outdoor alternative. The first floor has a smart reception room for hire and a framed 1888 map of the gardens. Meals are served 12-8 daily (Sun 12-7). ❀◐◗P

Saddle Inn

286 Whitegate Drive (A583)

⏲ 12-11; 12-10.30 Sun

☎ (01253) 607921

Draught Bass; Hancock's HB; Worthington Bitter; guest beers Ⓗ

Blackpool's oldest pub (established 1770) has a main bar and two side rooms; the first is a cosy wood-panelled room with pictures of sporting heroes, the second is used as a no-smoking dining area at lunchtimes. It displays pictures of the brewing art and has a real fire. The reasonably-priced comprehensive menu includes daily specials. A large patio with tables is pleasant for summer drinking. The pub is well-served by buses; route No. 2 is a frequent service (South Pier to North Station and Poulton). ⛫Q❀◐◗P⚡

Shovels

260 Commonedge Road (B5261, 1/2 mile from A5230 jct)

⏲ 11.30-11; 12-10.30 Sun

☎ (01253) 762702

Beer range varies Ⓗ

Large, award-winning pub, it was local CAMRA Pub of the Year 2001. The five ever-changing guest beers are usually from small micro-breweries and brew-pubs. It hosts a week-long beer festival in October. It is home to many sports teams, including darts, dominoes and cricket. The landlord writes a regular column for the local CAMRA newsletter. There is an extensive steak and ale range menu with many specials (food served until 9.30pm). ⛫◐◗♿♣P⚡

Wheatsheaf

194-196 Talbot Road (100 yds from train/bus stations)

⏲ 10.30-11; 12-10.30 Sun

☎ (01253) 625062

Theakston Mild, Best Bitter, Old Peculier; guest beers Ⓗ
Delightfully down-to-earth, characterful boozer with collections of flags, pictures, mannequins and giant fish. Real fires are lit in spring and autumn too, adding to the homely atmosphere. If the lounge, with its chandelier, is too smart, there is an uncarpeted area with a pool table, where chess is played, and wartime posters are displayed. A small patio area is sometimes used for barbecues. A full menu is available 10.30-8. Piano night is held on Tuesday.
⇌ (North) ♣

BURNLEY

Coal Clough Hotel

41 Coal Clough Lane (200 yds E of M65 jct 10)
11-11; 12-10.30 Sun
☎ (01282) 423226 website: www.coalcloughpub.co.uk
Museum Victoria Ale, Massey's Bitter; Worthington Bitter; guest beers Ⓗ
This end-of-terrace community local is always busy and friendly. There is a separate games room and events include a folk club gathering (Tue), quiz night (Wed) and entertainment held on Thursday. The Massey's Bitter is specially brewed by Bass Museum to an old local brewery recipe. Guest ales are always available. Regular beer festivals are hosted (check the website) based on Bass Museum beers. The pub is a past winner of Bass and CAMRA awards.
⇌ (Barracks) ♣P

Garden Bar

131-133 St James Street
11-11; 12-10.30 Sun
☎ (01282) 414895
Lees Bitter Ⓗ
Friendly, popular pub located just outside the town centre. The only Lees outlet in East Lancs welcomes an interesting and varied clientele at different times and days of the week. Lunchtime trade is primarily shoppers and office workers wanting a decent bar snack and good beer, while weekday evenings and Sundays attract the local gay scene. Weekend nights are noisy and full of young (and young at heart) customers dancing the night away. This pub is a must, whatever you enjoy.
⇌ (Central)

Sparrow Hawk Hotel

Church Street (A682)
11-3, 7-11; 11-1am Fri & Sat; 12-10.30 Sun
☎ (01282) 421551
Moorhouses Premier, Pendle Witches Brew; Wells Bombardier; guest beers Ⓗ
Large hotel with superb accommodation and restaurant facilities. There is a large, popular bar, a separate games room, a café bar and upstairs restaurant. Usually six ever-changing guest beers are available from micro-breweries, plus a good selection of foreign bottled beers. Weekend entertainment and late-night opening attracts people of all ages and creates a lively atmosphere. Jazz is played Sunday lunchtime and a quiz held on Thursday evening. A large beer and blues festival is hosted at Easter. ⇌ (Central) ♣P

CARNFORTH

Canal Turn

Lancaster Road
11-11; 12-10.30 Sun
☎ (01524) 734750
Black Sheep Best Bitter, Greene King IPA, Old Speckled Hen; Worthington Bitter; guest beer Ⓗ
These premises were originally cottages built for workers at the nearby gas and iron works, and were once known as 'Pig and Piano Row'. More recently, the home of the canal bank ranger ('towpath policeman'), the pub is wedged between the A6 and the Lancaster Canal, the frontage and entrances

INN BRIEF

ECCLESTON

Original Farmers Arms
Towngate
11-11; 12-10.30 Sun
(01257) 451594
Boddingtons Bitter; Taylor Landlord; Tetley Bitter; guest beers Ⓗ
Large, split-level, whitewashed village pub that is very popular and noted for excellent food. En-suite accommodation available.

EUXTON

Travellers Rest
Dawbers Lane
12-3, 6-11; 11-3, 6-11 Sat; 12-10.30 Sun
(01257) 451184
Marston's Pedigree; guest beers Ⓗ
Roadside pub renowned for good food. Comfortable lounge, yet has retained a traditional snug. Some distance from the main village.

GREAT HARWOOD

Lomax Arms
74 Blackburn Road
2 (12 Fri & Sat)-11; 12-10.30 Sun
(01254) 882397
Wells Bombardier; guest beer Ⓗ
Friendly local, community pub with open-plan layout. Separate room for pool and darts. Well suited for televised soccer.

HASKAYNE

King's Arms
Delf Lane
12-11; 12-10.30 Sun
(01704) 840245
Tetley Mild, Bitter; guest beers Ⓗ
Four-roomed traditional country pub offering extremely good value, generous meals. Local CAMRA award-winner.

HIGH MOOR (WRIGHTINGTON)

Rigbye Arms
2 Whittle Lane
12-3, 5.30-11; 12-11 Sat; 12-10.30 Sun
(01257) 462354
Greene King Old Speckled Hen; Marston's Pedigree; Tetley Dark Mild, Burton Ale Ⓗ
16th-century pub, a Lancashire Life award-winner for its food. Log-burning stove in public bar is popular with ramblers.

HOSCAR

Railway Tavern
Hoscar Moss Road
12-3 (not Mon), 5-11; 12-11 Wed-Sat; 12-10.30 Sun
(01704) 892369
Tetley Dark Mild, Bitter; guest beers Ⓗ
Superb, unspoilt rural local, popular with cyclists. It offers a classic tap room, welcoming atmosphere and pleasant garden. Children welcome.

LANCASTER

Bobbin
36 Cable Street
11-11; 12-10.30 Sun
(01524) 32606
Everards Beacon; guest beers Ⓗ
Single, large bar renovated with a 'Lancashire cotton industry' theme. Weston's Old Rosie cider is stocked. Next to bus station.

LANESHAWBRIDGE

Hargreaves Arms
Keighley Road
12-11; closed Mon & Tue; 12-10.30 Sun
(01282) 863470
Moorhouses Black Cat; John Smith's Bitter; Taylor Golden Best Ⓗ
Locally known as the 'Monkroyd'. Well known for quality food and sponsorship of guide dogs.

NELSON

Station Free House
13 Hibson Road
11-11; 12-10.30 Sun
(01282) 877910
Beer range varies Ⓗ
Large, busy Wetherspoon's with emphasis on micro-brewery beers. It retains some Edwardian charm. Cask Marque accredited.

value home-cooked food is very popular, as are the crown green bowling and boules. Croston is twinned with Azay-le-Rideau and international matches take place during twin visits. Two beer festivals are held each year in April and October. Monthly entertainment nights are held and occasional charity sportsman's dinners. No food is served Monday evening. Buses to Preston, Chorley and Southport serve the village. ⛰❀◐◑⊟♿⛺≠♣P

DARWEN ❊

Black Horse

72 Redearth Road (200 yds from Sainsbury's)
✪ 11-11; 12-10.30 Sun
☎ (01254) 873040 website: www.rarebeerfest.ic24.net
Bank Top Flat Cap; Holt Bitter; guest beers 🄷
This friendly, welcoming community local serves from five handpumps; there are two changing guests from micros or unusual brews alongside the regulars. Ciders from Red House Farm in Somerset are available. There is a small car park at the front and a large enclosed patio beer garden to the rear. This fine, traditional pub holds a rare beer festival the first weekend in June with over 40 new and unusual beers. ❀◐≠♣●P

Britannia

104 Bolton Road (A666)
✪ 1 (2 Tue & Wed)-11; 11-11 Sat; 12-10.30 Sun
☎ (01254) 701326
Thwaites Mild, Bitter 🄷
Unchanged pub that is partly tiled floor to ceiling and features the original front window 'H. Shaw & Co's Noted Ales'. It overlooks the 200-foot India Mills chimney, a preserved mill engine and paper print machines. Inside there is a model and 1987 painting of the pub and a photo of the long-gone Spring Vale pub with brewery behind. Separate rooms are provided for darts and dominoes, and pool. There is a large outdoor flagged and grassed area, with children's playground at the rear. ❀♣

Pub

210 Duckworth Street (100 yds N of town centre, on A666)
✪ 11-11; 12-10.30 Sun
☎ (01254) 708404
Moorhouses Black Cat; Thwaites Bitter; guest beers 🄷
Succinctly-named free house just north of the town centre. This open-plan, busy pub has an original tiled main entrance with red lions in view. A corner swing two-door entry is also in use. The lively central bar has a large-screen TV and raised seating area with juke box, two pinball machines, quiz game, pool and table football. Five handpumps serve two regular beers and three ever-changing guests. Enjoy the beer garden on summer days. ❀≠♣P

FLEETWOOD

North Euston Hotel

The Esplanade
✪ 11-11; 12-10.30 Sun
☎ (01253) 876525
Moorhouses Black Cat; Webster's Yorkshire Bitter; guest beers 🄷
Historic building with spectacular semi-circular frontage. It was the work of Decimus Burton, the Victorian architect who designed the new town of Fleetwood in the 1840s. A focal point of old Fleetwood, its location is full of interest with superb views across the Wyre Estuary and Morecambe Bay. The terminus of Blackpool-Fleetwood tram line, the lifeboat station and two Burton-designed lighthouses are nearby. Speciality fish and chip lunches are served. Evening meals are only available in the hotel. A traditional jazz band, Wyre Levee Stompers, plays on the first Sunday afternoon of each month. A quiz is held weekly (Sun). The regularly changing guest beers usually include a bitter from Moorhouses. There is a no-smoking area until 8pm. ♨⇄◐◑♿⊖(Tram/Ferry) P⍻

Prince Arthur

46-48 Lord Street
✪ 11-11; 12-10.30 Sun
☎ (01253) 778659
Boddingtons Bitter; Whitbread Trophy Bitter; guest beer 🄷
Solidly-built Victorian town-centre local. Situated where East Street met West Street before it became Lord Street in 1911, as Fleetwood attempted to upgrade its status as a seaside resort. Known locally as the 'Bug' to recognise its legendary cosiness being 'as snug as a bug in a rug'. The Prince Arthur was a steamboat, one of a fleet operating between Fleetwood and Belfast in the mid-19th century, under the auspices of the North Lancashire Steam Navigation Company. An interesting collection of old photographs is displayed. Darts and dominoes are played.
◐⊖(Tram/Church St) ♣

Queen's Hotel

Beach Road
✪ 12-11; 12-10.30 Sun
☎ (01253) 876740
Thwaites Bitter 🄷
Suburban local serving a large residential area; a traditional community pub in every sense, with a pronounced bias towards sport. There are thriving football, cricket, golf, angling and gun clubs, while major televised sporting events are shown. A general knowledge quiz, often on a themed basis, is held on Thursday evening and a sports quiz on Sunday afternoon. Meeting room facilities are available. Although meals are not normally served, food can be provided for special functions.
❀♿♣P

Thomas Drummond

London Street (between Lord St and Dock St)
✪ 11-11; 12-10.30 Sun
☎ (01253) 775020
Boddingtons Bitter; Greene King Abbot; Hop Back Summer Lightning; Shepherd Neame Spitfire; Theakston Mild, Best Bitter; guest beers 🄷
Named after the architect who designed many of Victorian Fleetwood's public buildings, including the former church which is now this pub. This is arguably the best Wetherspoon's house on the Fylde coast, largely due to the enthusiasm and cellar skills of the licensees. They deliberately stock a mild and lighter session beer among their four changing guest beers. This pub reputedly sells more meals on its regular Thursday Curry Club than any

Wetherspoon's in the country. A heated patio is available.
Q❀◐◑♿▲⊖(Preston St)⚡✔

Wyre Lounge Bar

Marine Hall, The Esplanade
⏲ 11 (12 Fri, Sat & summer)-4, 7-11; 12-4, 7-10.30 Sun
☎ (01253) 771141
Courage Directors; Moorhouses Pendle Witches Brew; guest beers Ⓗ
Council-owned lounge bar, locally known as the Municipal Arms. It is part of the Marine Hall entertainment complex, the home of Fleetwood beer festival. Enjoy the spectacular views across Morecambe Bay to the mountains of the Lake District, the Isle of Man can often be seen on clear summer evenings. It is convenient for outdoor activities at the adjacent Marine Gardens where crown green bowling, crazy golf and pitch and putt are played.
♉❀♿⊖(Tram/Ferry) P

FOULRIDGE

Hare & Hounds

Skipton Old Road (A56 Colne-Skipton road)
⏲ 12-11; 12-10.30 Sun
☎ (01282) 864235
Tetley Bitter, seasonal beers; guest beers Ⓗ
Once voted the worst pub in England (1993), now a completely refurbished free house, popular with locals and visitors. It offers good food and has a model train running round the dining room. Bar snacks and bed and breakfast are available. A cash machine in the bar is handy as there are no banks in the village. It is very convenient for boaters on the nearby Leeds-Liverpool Canal. The house beer and seasonal beers are from Moorhouses. 🛏◐◑P

GARSTANG

Royal Oak

Market Place
⏲ 11-3 (4 Thu), 6-11; 11-11 Fri & Sat; 12-10.30 Sun
☎ (01995) 603318
Robinson's Hatters Mild, Hartleys XB, Best Bitter Ⓗ
17th-century coaching inn which has been sympathetically renovated. It retains three small rooms (one is a games area) alongside the main bar and restaurant. The pub has seats on the old cobbled market square – markets now take place elsewhere.
♨Q♉❀🛏◐◑▲♣P

GOOSNARGH

Grapes

Church Lane (off B5269)
⏲ 11.30-3, 5.30 (7 Mon)-11; 11.30-11 Thu & Fri; 12-11 Sat; 12-10.30 Sun
☎ (01772) 865234
Black Sheep Best Bitter; Boddingtons Bitter; Tetley Dark Mild; guest beers Ⓗ
Charming, low beamed community pub with a splendid large open fire in the centre of the main drinking area. Three guest beers are stocked at a time, usually from micros. Food is served every lunchtime and Wed-Sat evenings (all day until 7pm Sun). Specialities on the menu are often made with local produce, such as Goosnargh duck. A bowling green and function room are available. The pub is near the village green and next to the historic church and Bushell's House, which caters for 'distressed gentlefolk'. Bus No. 44 runs from Preston to the village green hourly (two-hourly on Sun); there are only two buses in the evening. ♨Q♉❀◐◑⊟♣✔

GREAT HARWOOD ❄

Royal Hotel

2 Station Road
⏲ 12-11; 12-10.30 Sun
☎ (01254) 883541 website: www.royalblues.co.uk
Beer range varies Ⓗ
A Guide entry for 11 years, this pub has won several CAMRA awards. Six ever-changing beers, mainly from small independent breweries, and a range of foreign beers can be enjoyed, together with excellent home-cooked food (no meals served Mon and Tue). The pub has an open-plan layout with a dining area. The old coach house has been renovated and is now the venue for regular live music events (contact the pub for details). ❀🛏◐◑▲♣

GRIMEHILLS (DARWEN)

Crown & Thistle

Roman Road (old Darwen-Edgworth road)
⏲ 12-2 (not Mon), 6-11; 12-11 Fri & Sat; 12-10.30 Sun
☎ (01254) 702624
Everards Tiger; Thwaites Bitter; guest beers Ⓗ
Traditional country roadside pub with wooden beams decorated with horse brasses. There is a wonderful, homely atmosphere, a piano, real fire, wooden pew seating and interesting whisky jars, Russian dolls and breweriana. The award-winning restaurant serves an international menu with daily and monthly specials, vegetarian dishes and a fine wine list. The good value, tasty food is complemented by great guest beers. ♨❀◐◑P

HASLINGDEN

Griffin

86 Hudrake (off A680 from Accrington, follow sign for ski slope)
⏲ 12-11; 12-10.30 Sun
☎ (01706) 214021
Porter Dark Mild, Bitter, Rossendale Ale, Porter, Sunshine, seasonal beer Ⓗ
The tap of the Porter Brewing Co is a haven for those who enjoy lively conversation with excellent ale. A Bud and nitro-free zone, the bar area retains its charm. Good views can be enjoyed from the lounge, there is a separate games area to the left as you enter the pub. The Porter brewing plant is downstairs and the excellent ale upstairs suggests regular quality control checks are made. ♨♣

HELMSHORE

Robin Hood

280 Holcombe Road (B6214)
⏲ 4 (1 Sat)-11; 1-10.30 Sun
☎ (01706) 213180
Tetley Bitter; guest beer Ⓗ
Small, friendly community pub. The front windows are etched with the name of the Glen Top Brewery of Waterfoot. Framed cigarette card collections cover the front

room walls, and there are ornamental ducks throughout the pub – the landlord is a fanatical collector. Real ducks can be spotted from the beer garden, overlooking the old mill lodges. If it is too cold out, there is a superb log fire inside. Visit the nearby Helmshore Textile Museum. The guest beer is usually from Phoenix. ⚠❀♣

HESKIN

Farmers Arms

Wood Lane (B5250, near M6 jct 27)
⌚ 12-11; 12-10.30 Sun
☎ (01257) 451276 website: www.farmersarms.co.uk
Boddingtons Bitter; Castle Eden Ale; Flowers IPA; Taylor Landlord 🄷

18th-century coaching inn, originally called the Pleasant Retreat, only acquiring its present name in 1902. Family-run, this pub enjoys a local reputation for its food. Unlike many country pubs of this sort, the Farmers has retained a public bar for drinkers. Upstairs there are five en-suite guest rooms, one of which has a four-poster bed. The pub is about a mile from the Park Hall conference centre and the Camelot amusement park. It is well-served by bus routes 111 and 113 (both Preston/Wigan). No. 111 runs once an hour during the day, and No. 113 every two hours (day and eve). ❀⛟◑◗⊟♣P

HEST BANK

Hest Bank

2 Hest Bank Lane (take bridge 116 on canal)
⌚ 11.30-11; 12-10.30 Sun
☎ (01524) 824339
Boddingtons Bitter; Cains Bitter; Taylor Landlord; guest beer 🄷

Over a pint you can read about the history of this pub. It was once the last stop for travellers beginning the perilous crossing of the sands. Transportation developments and surburban sprawl have cut it off from the sea, but have left it with a pleasant canalside garden. The licensed area has been greatly extended for the benefit of car-borne diners, but two older rooms remain unaltered. It is successful as a local and as an eating house and has an attractive no-smoking conservatory. Take bus 55a, or No. 5 that runs along the A5109, walk up Station Road and over the canal. ⚠Q❀◑◗⛺♣P

HEYSHAM

Royal

7 Main Street
⌚ 11-11; 12-10.30 Sun
☎ (01524) 859298
Boddingtons Bitter; Everards Beacon; Tetley Bitter; guest beers 🄷

Heysham village is a little area set apart from most of Heysham, and this rambling, multi-roomed pub (dating back to 1502), fits in well. It has a restaurant, oak-beamed lounge and pleasant garden and patio. The pub was reputedly patronised by JMW Turner, who painted some local scenes. Popular with locals and holidaymakers alike, it is close to the historic sites of Heysham. A weekly quiz is held (Tue). Bus routes 3 and 3a pass close by. ⚠❀◑◗⊟♿♣P

HOGHTON

Royal Oak

Blackburn Old Road, Riley Green (A675/A674 jct)
⌚ 11.30-3, 5.30-11; 12-10.30 Sun
☎ (01254) 201445
Thwaites Mild, Bitter, seasonal beers 🄷

Traditional, stone-built pub on the old road between Preston and Blackburn. Close to the Riley Green Basin on the Leeds-Liverpool Canal, the Royal Oak is popular with diners and drinkers. Rooms and alcoves radiate from the central bar and there is a separate dining room. The pub has low beamed ceilings and numerous brasses adorning the walls. This Thwaites tied house is a regular outlet for the brewery's seasonal beers. Visitors may want to visit the local attraction, Hoghton Tower. ⚠Q❀◑◗P⚟

LANCASTER ❄

Bowerham

Bowerham Road
⌚ 12-5, 6-11; 12-5.30, 7-10.30 Sun
☎ (01524) 65050
Boddingtons Bitter; Everards Beacon, Tiger; Jennings Bitter, Cumberland Ale; Tetley Mild, Bitter 🄷

Old, characterful local, the exterior intentionally, but misleadingly, resembles a hotel. Inside, one of the original small rooms has been retained as a games room; the rest have been turned into a huge lounge with a small stage for the many live performances (Tue, Wed, Sat and Sun). A quiz is held on Monday evening. The nearest pub to Williamson Park and the leisure park, but few visitors come here – the numerous customers nearly all live within walking distance. The bowling green is pleasant for summer drinking. ❀⊟♿♣

John O'Gaunt

53 Market Street (off A6)
⌚ 11-3 (5 Sat), 6 (7 Sat)-11; 11-11 Thu & Fri; 12-4, 7-10.30 Sun
☎ (01524) 65356
Boddingtons Bitter; Jennings Bitter; Tetley Bitter, Burton Ale; guest beers 🄷

A handsome, original frontage hides a narrow pub. The walls are crammed with a variety of objects collected by the licensee: beer mats, jazz posters and photos of musicians (reflecting one of his enthusiasms) and a growing array of awards from a number of organisations. An extremely busy pub at most times: at lunchtime, most of the customers are from nearby banks and offices; in the evening they are mostly regulars. Live music in a variety of styles is played Mon-Thu eves, 'jazz dogs and sausages' Sunday lunchtime. A small, but perfectly formed, beer 'garden' is available. ❀◑⇌

Yorkshire House

2 Parliament Street
⌚ 7-11; 7-10.30 Sun
☎ (01524) 64679
website: www.yorkshirehouse.enta.net
Everards Beacon, Tiger; guest beer 🄷

On the fringe of the town centre, this pub has pictures of old rock stars, film posters, table football and bare boards. Upstairs, a spacious room is used for live music performances on Friday and Saturday, and a jazz club on Thursday. There is a patio for summer drinking.

Graduate College Bar

Barker House Village, Ellel

12-2 (term-time only; not Sat), 7-11; 4-10.30 Sun

(01524) 65201 ext 92824

Beer range varies H

Apart from the beer, a typical, modern student bar except that (as the name suggests) the age range is slightly higher. Some undergraduates drink here too, as the choice of beer is so much better than the other campus bars. Only university members, guests, staff and people carrying a copy of this Guide are served. Two beer festivals are held each term. Take bus 4, from the main campus (buses 2, 2a, 3), walk south to Grizedale College, cross the perimeter road and Green Lane and continue through a covered walkway. The bar has no sign but is easy to spot on the main college quadrangle. Up to four of the beers are on tap, with a local bias. P

LATHOM

Briars Hall Hotel

Briars Lane (off A5209 E of Burscough)

11.30-11; 12-10.30 Sun

(01704) 892368 website: www.briarshallhotel.co.uk

Tetley Dark Mild, Bitter; Thwaites Bitter; guest beers H

The Briars Hall Hotel is a handsome, imposing premises set in its own landscaped grounds. The hotel was built in the 19th century as a private residence for a wealthy local corn-milling family. Some original features have been retained and the stable block is particularly impressive. The style is that of a residential hotel and restaurant. Nevertheless, the areas set aside for drinkers are comfortable and well-appointed. Enjoy a beer and an excellent value three course bar lunch.

Q (Burscough Jct) P

Ship Inn

4 Wheat Lane (off A5209, over canal swing bridge) OS451115

11.30-11; 12-10.30 Sun

(01704) 893117

Moorhouses Black Cat, Pendle Witches Brew; John Smith's Bitter; Theakston Best Bitter, Old Peculier; guest beers H

Situated in a conservation area at the junction of the Rufford Branch and the Leeds-Liverpool Canal, the pub is at the heart of the canal community with early boatmans' cottages, locks and a dry dock nearby. Locally known as the 'Blood Tub', the name dates back to the time canal boats delivered ingredients for the famous Lancashire black pudding, still available today. This superb free house offers traditional home-cooked food in pleasant surroundings (12-2 and 5-8 daily). Up to six guests are stocked.

Q (Burscough Jct) P

LEA TOWN

Smiths Arms

Lea Lane OS476312

12-2, 4.30-11; 12-10.30 Sun

(01772) 726906

Thwaites Bitter, seasonal beers H

Homely country pub with a hunting theme. It is known locally as the 'Slip Inn' and is located behind the nuclear plant. Food does not dominate but good value meals are prepared on the premises and are available 12-2 daily, 5-7.30 Thu-Sat, and all day Sunday. Watch out for the really ruthless chillis. The pub is within walking distance of the Lancaster Canal and an infrequent bus service (No. 185) runs between Preston and Blackpool (not Sun). Camping facilities are provided in an adjacent field. The pub has a pleasant patio for outdoor drinking.

P

LEYLAND

Dunkirk Hall

Dunkirk Lane (B5253)

11.30-3, 5-11; 11-11 Fri & Sat; 12-10.30 Sun

(01772) 422102

Courage Directors; John Smith's Bitter; guest beers H

Despite the date 1628 being carved in stone above the pub's entrance, this former 17th-century manor house became a pub less than 20 years ago. It served as offices for most of the 20th century. The area has been extensively developed over the last 30 years and the Dunkirk is an excellent community local. Two guest beers are always on tap. Bus No. 111 (Fishwick) Preston-Leyland runs every 10 minutes (day), 30 minutes (eves and Sun).

P

Eagle & Child

Church Road (B5248)

11.45-11; 12-10.30 Sun

(01772) 433531

Burtonwood Bitter, seasonal beers; guest beers H

Ancient inn nestling snugly behind the 1,000-year-old parish church, to which it is said to be connected by a secret tunnel. Next door, the old grammar school now serves as South Ribble's Museum. Inside, the original separate rooms have been opened out and the low-ceilinged bar has been sympathetically restored. All ages are catered for, but younger people tend to head towards the right of the bar. The pub bowling green is across the road and southerners should note that this is of the superior crown green variety! Bus No. 111 (Fishwick) Preston-Leyland runs every 10 minutes (day), 30 minutes (eves and Sun). No meals are available at the weekend.

P

LITTLE ECCLESTON

Cartford Hotel

Cartford Lane (by the toll bridge, 1/2 mile from A586)

12 (11.30 Sat)-3, 7 (6.30 Fri)-11; 12-10.30 Sun

(01995) 670166

Boddingtons Bitter; Fuller's London Pride; guest beers H

Converted 17th-century farmhouse set on the banks of the River Wyre. A genuine free house, with a range of ever-changing guests it usually stocks beer from Hart brewed at the rear. It is popular with walkers, cyclists and caravanners in summer. It is a frequent winner of CAMRA West Pennine's Pub of the Year. A comprehensive menu features curries, vegetarian dishes and children's meals. A play area for small children is provided. A number of guest rooms with en-suite facilities are available.

LONGRIDGE

Old Oak

111 Preston Road (B6243/B6244 jct)
12-11; 12-10.30 Sun
(01772) 783648
Theakston Mild, Bitter; guest beers

Welcoming, community local with wood settles and a real fire in the comfortable lounge. The large games room has big-screen TV for sport. A pet rabbit often wanders around the pub. The two guest beers change regularly. A singalong piano player and waiter service are provided on Sunday evening. A large array of pump clips and various stuffed cartoon characters are on display. The pub has its own beer appreciation society and runs competitions such as big onion, pie-making and alcoholic jelly contests. There is a no-smoking area at lunchtime where meals are served. Wooden tables outside the pub are ideal on summer evenings.

White Bull Hotel

1A Higher Road (at B6243/B6245 jct)
5 (12 Thu-Sat)-11; 12-10.30 Sun
(01772) 783198
M&B Mild; Worthington Bitter; guest beers

18th-century stone-built local that tends to be lively at weekends with a disco, but is quieter on weekdays. It offers four areas for different activities, including pool tables, bar football, darts and dominoes. The snug has an open fire in winter and doubles as a dining room (food is served Thu-Sun 12-7). There is a separate bottle bar. The policy is to provide two guest beers. The history of the pub is shown on a signboard at the front entrance and in a local guide-book entitled The History Of Longridge. An unusual architectural feature on the front elevation is a stained glass leaded light window uncovered a few years ago when the cement rendering was stripped off. It is on a local bus route, so it is easily accessible.

LOSTOCK HALL

Railway

69 Watkin Lane (B5254)
11-11; 12-10.30 Sun
(01772) 697233
Fuller's London Pride; John Smith's Bitter; Taylor Landlord; guest beers

A much improved pub. After being closed for several months, it has been revitalised by new tenants who have steadily changed things around so that it now stocks six real ales – the widest range for miles. Partially hidden from the main road, and with its own bowling green, it is situated just yards from waste land where the large Lostock Hall railway shed once stood. Convenient for public transport, regular bus services run to Preston and Leyland.

LYTHAM ST ANNE'S

Hole in One

Forest Drive (off B5261, in Hall Park Estate)
11.30-3, 5-11; 11.30-11 Fri & Sat; 12-10.30 Sun
(01253) 730598
Thwaites Bitter

Large, modern pub that is particularly popular in the early evening. The decor of the spacious public bar/games room reflects the local golfing amenities. Delicious home-cooked food is served daily in the new extension built for dining. Wednesday is live folk night with some well-known artistes appearing. The pub is easily accessible from Blackpool; bus No. 11 stops ouside.

Station Tavern

Station Square
11-11; 12-10.30 Sun
(01253) 734252
Theakston Cool Cask; guest beers

Large pub next to the railway station, it used to be the waiting room and ticket office. The front of the building is original and is listed. Moorhouses Dr Beeching is the house beer. A patio at the front is available for outdoor drinking. Thursday is jazz night with a live band performing.

Taps

12 Henry Street (behind Clifton Arms Hotel)
11-11; 12-10.30 Sun
(01253) 736226 website: www.thetaps.com
Beer range varies

Very busy ex-Hogshead pub. The building was converted from old ostlers' cottages. This basic but cosy ale house offers a frequently changing range of nine beers and always includes a mild. The house beer is brewed by Titanic and a real cider is stocked. Taps was the local CAMRA Pub of the Year 2002, the landlord is the only person in the area to win with two different pubs. Note the bottled beer collection and the bust of the landlord's father who was landlord of the infamous 'Tommy Ducks' in Manchester. The patio is heated, allowing outdoor drinking on chilly days. No food Sun.

MAWDESLEY

Black Bull

Hall Lane (off B5246) OS499151
12-11; 12-10.30 Sun
(01704) 822202
Greenalls Bitter; Greene King Old Speckled Hen, Marston's Pedigree; Taylor Landlord; Tetley Dark Mild

This stone-built inn dates from 1580 and, according to records, has been a pub since 1610. The structure of the low-ceilinged building follows Elizabethan lines with some magnificent oak beams. The older residents of the village know the pub as 'Ell 'Ob', which is a reference to a coal-fired cooking range. There is a games room upstairs and many certificates are displayed in the bar listing the pub's success in the Lancashire Best-Kept Village competition. In summer, the splendid hanging baskets almost completely cover the Black Bull. The beer range occasionally varies. Bus No. 347 Chorley-Southport passes (four per day, not Sun).

Robin Hood Inn

Bluestone Lane (off B5250) OS506163
12-11; 12-10.30 Sun

☎ (01704) 822275

Boddingtons Bitter; Taylor Landlord; guest beers Ⓗ

Charming, white-painted inn at the crossroads between the three old villages of Mawdesley, Croston and Eccleston. The 15th-century building was substantially altered in the 19th century. The connection with Robin Hood is a tenuous one, but he was much admired by the yeomen of the Middle Ages, who often named their properties in his honour. The pub has been in the same family for over 30 years, it has a reputation for good food but still finds room for the drinker. Six ales are always on tap. Bus No. 347 Chorley-Southport (four per day, not Sun) serves the pub. ⛬⛾◑◐P⊬

MERE BROW

Legh Arms

82 The Gravel (off A565)

⚙ 11-11; 12-10.30 Sun

☎ (01772) 812359

Boddingtons Bitter; Courage Directors; Taylor Landlord; Tetley Bitter Ⓗ

Ex-Higsons house situated close to the leisure lakes complex. A friendly local in a peaceful village just off the Preston to Southport bypass, the pub has a quiet lounge with a popular public bar for dominoes and darts. A small snug at the rear has a TV. Coal fires throughout the pub prove very welcome in winter.
⛬Q❀◑⊟♣P

MORECAMBE

Smugglers' Den

56 Poulton Road

⚙ 11-3, 7-11; 12-10.30 Sun

☎ (01524) 421684

Boddingtons Bitter; Tetley Bitter; guest beers Ⓗ

At the heart of the old fishing village of Poulton, the current name and decor – dark, low beamed, stone-flagged floors, tables shaped like casks – date from 1960. Since then there has been a single change of licensee, from father to son. The pair have accumulated a vast collection of mainly nautical artefacts. Impressive stained glass windows and a small garden with caged birds are unusual features. P

ORMSKIRK

Hayfield

County Road (500 yds from A59/A570 jct)

⚙ 12-11, 12-10.30 Sun

☎ (01695) 571157

Eccleshall Monkey Magic; Fuller's London Pride; John Smith's Bitter; Theakston Best Bitter; Old Peculier Ⓗ

Well-known pub with up to eight real ales regularly on tap. Saxon cider is available. The spacious, comfortable interior has a raised floor at the side for diners and plenty of seating. An extensive menu offers reasonably-priced meals. It is very popular at weekends with younger people when the place buzzes with a lively atmosphere. Well worth a visit. ◑◐♿⇌●P⊡

Yew Tree

Grimshaw Lane (N of town centre off A59)

⚙ 11.30-3; 6-11; 12-11 Sat; 12-4, 7-10.30 Sun

☎ (01695) 573381

Cains Bitter; Robinson's Hatters Mild; guest beers Ⓗ

Delightful, time warp 1950s-style pub in a pleasant suburb of this historic market town. Although it is some 15 minutes' walk north of the town centre, this pub is well worth seeking out. It boasts a quintessentially post-war lounge, and retains a traditional tap room (next to the no-smoking area). The internal accommodation is complemented by a small but charming walled beer garden. This was one of the last pubs to be built as part of the estate of the renowned, but now sadly defunct, Liverpool Higsons Brewery. Q❀◑◐⊟♿♣P⊬

PENDLETON

Swan with Two Necks

OS755396

⚙ 12-2 (not Mon & Tue), 7 (6 Sat)-11; 12-10.30 Sun

☎ (01200) 423112

Moorhouses Premier; Phoenix Arizona; guest beer Ⓗ

Traditional village local which now incorporates a post office in the back bar. The long main room has two attractive coal fires in winter. There is a pleasant beer garden and an upstairs restaurant where an extensive menu is served (Thu-Sun). The pub faces a long village street with a stream running down the middle. It makes an excellent starting (and finishing) point for walks which explore the Pendle Hill countryside. ⛬Q❀◑◐P

POULTON-LE-FYLDE

Thatched House

12 Ball Street (next to parish church)

⚙ 11-11; 12-10.30 Sun

Boddingtons Bitter; Theakston Cool Cask; guest beers Ⓗ

This 100-year-old pub replaced an earlier beer house and is the oldest continuously licensed premises on the Fylde. It stands in the graveyard of the parish church in the town centre. The landlord is a skilled cellarman who invariably serves his beers in immaculate condition. With a mature clientele relying on the excellence of his real ales, he refuses to stock alcopops. Awarded local CAMRA Pub of the Season, this busy, picturesque pub is a local institution. ⛬Q⊟♿⛺⇌

PREESALL

Black Bull

192 Park Lane (B5377)

⚙ 12-3, 6-11; 12-3, 5-10.30 Sun

☎ (01253) 810294

Jennings Bitter; Tetley Mild, Bitter; guest beer Ⓗ

Originally three separate single-storey thatched dwellings with pebble walls, the upper floors were added to create the 17th-century coaching inn. This cosy, multi-roomed, village local has low beams, alcoves and a small dining room serving delicious home-cooked meals. A list of licensees since 1776 hangs near the bar. An upstairs function room accommodates 60 people. It is one of the few pubs in the area to serve cask mild. There is an outside drinking area with tables. Q❀◑◐♣P⊬

PRESTON ✻

Ashton Institute

10-12 Wellington Road, Ashton

⚙ 7 (4 Fri & Sat)-11; 12-10.30 Sun
☎ (01772) 726582
website: www.drink.to/ashtoninstitute
Boddingtons Bitter; Worthington Bitter; guest beers Ⓗ
Enterprising club comprising two terraced houses that have been knocked through. It is Preston's oldest club to remain on its original site and dates from 1944. The main room has snooker, pool, table football and card tables. The club has been freed of tie for its cask ale, so guests often feature micro-breweries and milds. There is a function room for hire. The pub hosts a popular beer festival (late Oct) and is a local CAMRA award-winner, as can be seen from various press cuttings on the walls. Show this Guide or a CAMRA membership card to be signed in. A large-screen TV shows sporting events. ♣

Black Horse ☆
166 Friargate (near market)
⚙ 10.30-11 (often closes early Mon, Tue & Wed); 12-3.30 (closed eve) Sun
☎ (01772) 204855
Robinson's Hatter's Mild; Best Bitter, Frederics, Old Tom, seasonal beers Ⓗ
Classic, Grade II listed pub in the main shopping area and close to the historic open market. It is deservedly on CAMRA's national inventory. With its exquisite tiled bar and walls and superb mosaic floor, it is an English Heritage/CAMRA award-winner. There are two separate front rooms with photos of old Preston and the famed 'Hall of Mirrors' seating area to the rear. An interesting collection of memorabilia (from a previous landlord) is set in a glass partition. The modern upstairs bar (no real ale) is usually open at weekends. ⇌

Limekiln
288 Aqueduct Street (off Fylde Road, A583)
⚙ 11-11; 12-10.30 Sun
☎ (01772) 493247
Banks's Original, Bitter, seasonal beers Ⓗ
Tile-fronted locals' pub welcoming visitors as well as regulars. It has a central bar serving four drinking areas including pool and darts rooms. It is unusual in serving both mild and bitter. Entertainment includes karaoke night (Sat) and an organ singalong (Sun). The aqueduct which carried the Lancaster Canal into Preston centre was removed in the 1960s, so the terminus is now only 200 yards from the pub. In summer tables are set up outside the pub. ♣P

Market Tavern
33 Market Street
⚙ 10.30-11; closed Sun
☎ (01772) 254425
Beer range varies Ⓗ
Overlooking Preston's impressive Victorian outdoor covered market, this small pub was totally rebuilt internally and now consists of a range of seated areas around the bar, including some intimate booths. Some fascinating prints of old Preston adorn the walls. There is a jam night every Monday and live bands on the last Thursday of every month. Of the three ever-changing guests beers, one is usually from the Pictish Brewery, also a good selection of German and Belgian bottled beers is stocked. It is quite close to the second largest bus station in Europe. ⇌

New Britannia
6 Heatley Street (off Friargate)
⚙ 11-3, 6-11; 11-11 Sat; 7-10.30 Sun
☎ (01772) 253424
Boddingtons Bitter; Castle Eden Ale; Goose Eye Brontë; Marston's Pedigree; guest beers Ⓗ
This single-bar town-centre pub is very popular and attracts real ale enthusiasts from far and wide. It enjoys a reputation for the superb quality of the beers served. The pub is comfortably furnished with an attractive exterior decorated with hanging baskets and a clock. Note the splendid Britannia windows. Replica Britannia locomotive name, number and shed plates adorn the lounge wall. There is a yard for outdoor drinking. All the food is home made and is excellent quality and value, served 11-2 weekdays and 12-4 Sat. In 2002 the pub was voted CAMRA Lancashire Pub of the Year. ❀◖⇌♠

Old Black Bull
35 Friargate (Ringway jct)
⚙ 10.30-11; 12-10.30 Sun
☎ (01772) 823397
Boddingtons Bitter; Cains Bitter; guest beers Ⓗ
Town-centre pub with mock-Tudor frontage, tilework and its name spelt out in large ceramic letters. A small front vault, main bar with distinctive black and white floor tiles, two comfortable lounge areas and pool table make it a popular venue, along with the rear courtyard. A big-screen TV for sports and live music on Saturday night also help to keep the pub busy. There are usually eight beers on tap, mostly from micros or small independents. ❀◖⊟⇌♣

Old Blue Bell
114 Church Street (near bus station)
⚙ 11-11; 12-10.30 Sun
☎ (01772) 251280
Samuel Smith OBB Ⓗ
Small blue-and-white-fronted pub set back from the main road and just off the main shopping areas. The wood-lined bar counter has an overhead gantry for glasses. There is a small lounge off the main room and a snug at the rear. An extensive array of prints covers the walls. The pub is a listed building, dating from 1722, and has the remains of an old passageway to the parish church in the cellar. It offers the cheapest beer in a brewery-owned pub in town. There is a popular quiz (Tue eve). It is peaceful (with no juke box), an excellent place for conversation and relaxation. Q◖

Olde Dog & Partridge
44 Friargate (NW of Ringway)
⚙ 11-2, 6-11; 12-3, 7-10.30 Sun
☎ (01772) 252217 website: www.drink.to/dandp
Fuller's London Pride; Highgate Dark; Marston's Pedigree; guest beers Ⓗ
Well-known (internationally) as a bikers' pub but welcoming to real ale drinkers however they arrive. An impressive array of motorcycles is parked outside in summer. Music from the DJ and juke box is predominantly rock. It tends to be busy and loud during weekend evenings. A rare town-centre outlet for both real mild and real cider (Addlestone's Cloudy), it has been run

by the same landlord for over 20 years. Two guests are served weekly from the Punch Tavern's list. Basic lunchtime food is available (not served Sun). ◐⇌♣●

Stanley Arms

24 Lancaster Road (next door to Guild Hall)

✪ 10.30-11; 12-10.30 Sun

☎ (01772) 254004 website: www.stanleyarms.com

Courage Directors; Greene King Ruddles County; Theakston Best Bitter; guest beers Ⓗ

Town-centre local, close to but not part of the 'circuit'. Three guest beers are normally available, including a mild and a 'landlord's choice' which may come from anywhere in the country. There is a single lounge bar which tends to be busy and evening meals are served Wed-Sun upstairs in the recently refurbished Knowsley suite. Bar meals are served 12-6 daily. An impressive ornate listed building, the pub name refers to the Earls of Derby, once major landowners in the area. ◐◑⇌

RISHTON

Rishton Arms

Station Road

✪ 7 (12 Sat)-11; 12-10.30 Sun

☎ (01254) 886396

Thwaites Mild, Bitter, seasonal beers Ⓗ

Large, comfortable local next to the railway station. There are two rooms, a large lounge and a separate games room for darts and pool. There is also a wide-screen Sky TV. When available a Thwaites seasonal beer is served as well as the mild and bitter. This is one of the best Thwaites outlets that can be found and is why the pub is in the Guide for the tenth consecutive year. ⇌♣P

ST ANNE'S ON SEA

Trawl Boat Inn

36 Wood Street

✪ 11-11; 12-10.30 Sun

☎ (01253) 783080

Theakston Best Bitter; guest beers Ⓗ

Located in the heart of St Anne's main shopping area, this pub features the usual Wetherspoon's decor. It was once a solicitor's office. An excellent tiered outdoor drinking area at the front of the pub is popular on balmy summer nights. One of the locally brewed Blackpool Brewery beers is usually sold. Q❀◐◑♿⇌⚡●

SAMLESBURY

New Hall Tavern

Cuerdale Lane

✪ 11.30-11; 12-10.30 Sun

☎ (01772) 877217

website: www.btinternet.com/~newhall

Boddingtons Bitter; guest beers Ⓗ

This welcoming country pub is located at a rural crossroads. It is an ex-Matthew Brown house acquired by Whitbread when the nearby large brewery (now Interbrew) was built. The single bar is comfortably furnished with a large central bar area and side section for eating. Traditional home-cooked food is very popular and reasonably priced (served all day Sun). The varied beer range is popular with locals and visitors. There are usually beers from local breweries available. Live music is performed (Thu eve). The infrequent 217 Preston-Mellor bus service passes the pub. ♨❋❀◐◑♿▲♣P⚡

SILVERDALE

Woodlands

Woodlands Drive

✪ 7 (12 Sat)-11; 12-10.30 Sun

☎ (01524) 701655

Beer range varies Ⓗ

Large country house, circa 1878, on the edge of the village with its back to Eaves Wood, hence the name. The current owner is restoring it to its former glory. Easily overlooked by the casual visitor to Silverdale, most of the trade is local. Even when you find it, it does not look much like a pub. Open the large front door and you find yourself in an impressive entrance hall with no sign of a bar, take the first door on the left, pass through a lounge, and there it is, with a vast fireplace (as big as the counter). Look to your left for a beer list. Catch bus 33 from the station; 55 or 55a (infrequent). Three beers are on tap.

♨Q❋❀▲♣P▯

SNATCHEMS

Golden Ball

Lancaster Road (signed, off A683) OS449616

✪ 12-3, 5-11; 12-11 Sat; 12-10.30 Sun

☎ (01524) 63117

Beer range varies Ⓗ

Superbly located on the Lune Estuary, the road in front floods regularly, but the pub is sufficiently high to avoid the tides (the car park is even higher, at first-floor level). Customers sitting at the front can watch the birds, gaze to the hills or occasionally have a grandstand view of water-skiers. Inside the 16th-century building the three low-beamed rooms have an olde-worlde atmosphere; the largest is used as the dining room. Up to five independent brews are offered from the tiny servery. There is a garden and seats set out at the front of the pub. ♨Q❀◐◑▲♣P

TOWN GREEN

Stanley Arms

St Michaels Road, Aughton (off A59 Liverpool-Ormskirk road)

✪ 11.30-3, 5-11; 12-10.30 Sun

☎ (01695) 423241

Marston's Pedigree; Taylor Landlord Ⓗ

Traditional 'country cottage' pub with a friendly atmosphere, catering for locals and passing trade from the A59. The main features are the wooden bar and beamed ceilings. The front room is on a lower level, as is 'the well' area, the rest of the pub is L-shaped. Live music is held on Friday evening, a quiz night (Tue) and impromptu choir singing sessions (Mon). Other amenities are the bowling green and outdoor children's play area. Finally, don't forget Ollie, the friendly Cromwellian ghost.

❀◐◑⇌(Aughton) P

Town Green Inn

17 Town Green Lane

✪ 12 (5 Mon)-11; 12-10.30 Sun

☎ (01695) 422165

Beer range varies Ⓗ

Originally a tied farmhouse (dating from 1798) and built of locally quarried Aughton stone, the pub became the Town Green Inn in 1901, having previously been known as the Butcher's Arms. It is a cosy pub with a relaxing atmosphere. A central bar serves the public bar and the lounge; there are real fires in both areas. Two ever-changing guest beers are available. Food is served until 7.15pm Tue-Sat and until 4pm on Sun. (Town Green/Aughton) ♣P

UPHOLLAND

Old Dog

6 Alma Hill (off A577, between parish church and Hall Green)

5 (12 Sat)-11; 12-10.30 Sun

☎ (01695) 623487

Draught Bass; Boddingtons Bitter; guest beers Ⓗ

Found halfway up the steep Alma Hill, this small stone-built pub is worth the short climb from Upholland village. It retains an original Greenall Whitley (St Helens) etched window and one displaying the pub name. Due to its hillside location, the three small rooms are all on different levels and there is a compact bar area. Wooden beams throughout the building add character and in the lower lounge there is a large collection of decorative plates and many paintings. The rear rooms give wonderful views across Wigan to the Pennine Hills. Q♣

White Lion Hotel

10 Church Street

5 (12 Sat)-11; 12-10.30 Sun

☎ (01695) 622727

Thwaites Bitter Ⓗ

Multi-level pub built on the hillside facing Upholland parish church. Inside there are four public rooms comprising two lounges, a games room and a small snug. Photographs of old Upholland line the walls of the front lounge, it also has a TV. High on the outside front wall can be seen the pub name with the date 1921, although the building appears to be much older. The graveyard opposite the pub is the burial place of the local highwayman, George Lyon. ♣P

WALMER BRIDGE

Longton Arms

2 Liverpool Old Road (off A59)

12.30 (1 Sat; 2 Mon & Tue; 3 Thu)-11; 12-10.30 Sun

☎ (01772) 612335

Greenalls Bitter Ⓗ

White-painted, brick-built end-of-terrace village pub; a fine community local with a warm welcome. There are benches outside with colourful hanging baskets and window boxes. The pub offers a splendid small front snug, side main bar and rear lounge with a serving hatch and big-screen TV. Note the duck frieze over the snug bar. It is the haunt of wildfowlers from nearby Longton Marsh and home to a golf society and a football team. Longton Picnic Club organise days out and raise money for charity; a board listing all the presidents since 1980 is on display. Stagecoach buses on the Preston-Southport route pass the pub. ♣P

WATERFOOT

Jolly Sailor

Booth Place

5 (12 Fri & Sat)-11; 12-10.30 Sun

☎ (01706) 226340

Hancock's HB; Jennings Cumberland Ale; Taylor Landlord; guest beer Ⓗ

Built in 1825, the pub's name may commemorate the first landlord's seafaring life. Rebuilt once, and extended, the Jolly Sailor is now a friendly, open-plan pub. There is a separate games room, with convenient hatch access to the bar. A slightly raised wooden stage area is used for live music (folk, occasional Sun) and karaoke (one Sat per month), it has seats for drinkers and diners at other times. Freshly prepared hot or cold snacks and main meals are available (5-8 Mon-Thu, 12-8 Fri-Sun), with a roast lunch on Sunday. ♣

An Ode in Honour of Opening Time

In praise of Bacchus let the boozers sing,
And celebrate the hour of opening:
The god of sweet oblivion comes!
Pace the pavement, bite your thumbs,
Till unlocked doors swing wide
And you are safe inside.
Over the teeth and past the gums
Let the liquor laughter bring,
Till the strains of life are gone.
Pour it forth in double measure,
Drinking is the door to pleasure:
Let it widen,
Drink to Dryden
Who is puking in the john.

Roger Woddis in *The New Compleat Imbiber*, Collins 1986.

WENNINGTON

Bridge

Tatham (on B6480, S of station)

✪ 12-3, 6-11; 11-11 Fri & Sat; 12-10.30 Sun

☎ (015242) 21326

Boddingtons Bitter; Taylor Landlord; Tetley Bitter 🄷

The old tiny rooms have been opened out to form a single bar which is still small enough for there to be only one conversation. There is a restaurant, also small and intimate. Located in a pretty isolated spot, but with a surprisingly large number of local customers, the pub features in a Turner painting. There are plans to extend the pub into the property next door. Camping facilities (including caravans) are available nearby. ♨❀⌂◐◑♿▲⇌P

WHALLEY

Dog Inn

35 King Street

✪ 11-11; 12-10.30 Sun

☎ (01254) 823009

Theakston Best Bitter; guest beers 🄷

Originally a village stable, in 1877 the Dog was first licensed as a one-roomed ale house. It has since expanded into a multi-area pub with a pleasantly 'organic' feel. The rear of the pub is considerably lower than the front, requiring a step in the L-shaped bar. Very lively on weekend evenings, this is a true local. When the local church was being refurbished, the original ale house was consecrated and used for Thursday morning services. The pub newspaper (Boring Old Farts Herald & Chronicle) keeps patrons abreast of the many activities organised. ❀◐⇌♣

WHARLES

Eagle & Child

1 Church Road (3 miles NE of Kirkham) OS448356

✪ 12-3 (not Mon-Fri); 7-11; 12-4, 7-10.30 Sun

☎ (01772) 690312

website: www.yell.co.uk/sites/eagle-child

Beer range varies 🄷

Pleasant, relaxing atmosphere in this thatched, 17th-century ex-farmhouse which stands clear of the village. This unspoilt rural free house has been in the same ownership for many years. The long, beamed lounge is heated by a cast-iron stove, it features wooden settles, farm implements and old brewery mirrors. The absence of music, food and children creates a peaceful environment where conversation and the enjoyment of well-kept beers are paramount. The extensive pump clip collection indicates the range of beer sold over the years. ♨Q❀♣P

WHEELTON

Dressers Arms

Briers Brow (near A674)

✪ 11-11; 12-10.30 Sun

☎ (01254) 830041

Boddingtons Bitter; Old Wheelton Big Frank's Bitter; Taylor Landlord; Tetley Bitter; Worthington Bitter; guest beers 🄷

Home to the Old Wheelton Brewery, this pub has been converted in recent years from a number of terraced cottages into a spacious, multi-roomed establishment. The bar is complemented by a lounge, games room and snug. A no-smoking lounge behind the bar looks on to the brewery. Tasty food is served downstairs and there is the added attraction of an authentic Chinese restaurant upstairs. Up to three changing guest beers are on sale, mostly from micro-breweries. It is a former winner of the Real Fire Pub of the Year. Meals are served downstairs all day Saturday and Sunday until 9pm.

♨☺❀◐◑♿P⍁

Top Lock

Copthurst Lane (alongside canal at Johnsons Hillock)

✪ 11-11; 12-10.30 Sun

☎ (01257) 263376

Black Sheep Best Bitter; Coniston Bluebird; guest beers 🄷

A recent convert to real ale after many years as a keg-only pub, the Top Lock sits beside the Leeds-Liverpool Canal at the series of locks known as Johnsons Hillock. A fine example of a country pub with a single bar downstairs and an upstairs dining area. There is an authentic Indian menu alongside the more traditional pub fare. It is popular with walkers and narrow boat owners due to its close proximity to the canal. At least four guests are usually on sale, including an ever-changing dark mild.

❀◐◑P

WHITTLE-LE-WOODS

Royal Oak

216 Chorley Old Road (off A6)

✪ 2.30-11; 12-10.30 Sun

☎ (01257) 276485

Boddingtons Bitter; Jennings Cumberland Ale; guest beer 🄷

Small, single-bar, terraced village local, built in 1820 to serve the adjacent branch of the Leeds-Liverpool Canal, the tramway to Preston and the Lancaster Canal. In 1969 the canal was filled in for the M61 construction but the bridge is still visible. This local CAMRA award-winning pub has been in the Guide for 26 years consecutively. Long and narrow, with a small bar and separate games room, it is very much a community pub and a haunt of mature motorcycle enthusiasts. Note the fine Nuttalls windows and try the range of malt whiskies and pickled eggs. Infrequent No. 114 Chorley-Bamber Bridge buses pass the door; regular Preston-Chorley buses stop on the A6. ♨❀♣

WORSTHORNE

Crooked Billet

1-3 Smith Street

✪ 5 (2 Thu & Fri; 12 Sat)-11; 12-10.30 Sun

☎ (01282) 429040

Tetley Bitter; guest beers 🄷

A real gem of a pub just outside the village centre. A popular community local, but also drawing people from a wider area, the pub can get busy anytime, so it is best to arrive early. The standard beers are always on tap and the guests at weekends. The outside is a riot of colour in summer, it has won awards for the Best Pub in Bloom. The interior is all light oak panelling, setting off a glass and tiled bar area. A small patio is available for summer drinking. ♨Q❀P

CAMRA's Beers of the Year

The beers listed below are CAMRA's Beers of the Year. They were short-listed for the Champion Beer of Britain competition in August 2002, and the Champion Winter Beer of Britain competition in January 2002. The August competition judged Dark and Light Milds, Bitters, Best Bitters, Strong Bitters, Speciality Beers, and Bottle-conditioned beers, while the winter competition judged Old Ales and Strong Milds, Porters, Stouts and Barley Wines. Each beer was found by panels of trained CAMRA judges to be consistently outstanding in its category, and they all receive a 'full tankard' symbol in the Breweries section.

DARK AND LIGHT MILDS
Batemans Dark Mild
Boat Man in a Boat
Brain Dark
Hydes Dark Mild
Mighty Oak Oscar Wilde
Moorhouses Black Cat
Triple fff Pressed Rat & Warthog

BITTERS
Bullmastiff Gold
Caledonian Deuchar's IPA
Goose Eye Barmpot
Hambleton Bitter
Harviestoun Bitter & Twisted
Lees Bitter
Mighty Oak IPA
Oakham JHB
Rebellion IPA
RCH Hewish IPA
Rudgate Viking
Triple fff Alton Pride
Woodforde's Wherry
Young's Bitter

BEST BITTERS
Becketts Stoke Ale
Crouch Vale Brewers Gold
Frog Island Shoemaker
Fuller's London Pride
Harvey's Sussex
Isle of Skye Red Cuillin
Mighty Oak Burntwood
Orkney Red MacGregor
RCH Pitchfork
Reepham Rapier
Skinners Betty Stogs
Taylor's Landlord
Triple fff Moondance
Woodforde's Nelson's Revenge

STRONG BITTERS
Frog Island Fire Bellied Toad
Hogs Back Hop Garden Gold
Hop Back Summer Lightning
Fuller's ESB
Mordue Radgie Gadgie
RCH East Street Cream
Ridley's Old Bob

OLD ALES AND STRONG MILDS
Bath Festivity
Beartown Black Bear
Brakspear 4X Mild
Harvey's Sussex Old Ale
Rudgate Ruby Mild
Sarah Hughes Dark Ruby Mild
Young's Winter Warmer

PORTERS AND STOUTS
B&T Edwin Taylor's Extra Stout
Cropton Scoresby Stout
Hogs Back Blackwater Porter
Orkney Dragon Head Stout
Ringwood 4X Porter
Tomos Watkin Merlin's Double Stout
Wye Valley Dorothy Goodbody's Wholesome Stout

BARLEY WINES
Adnams Tally Ho!
Big Lamp Blackout
Burton Bridge Old Expensive
Goachers Old
Lees Moonraker
Robinson's Old Tom
Woodforde's Headcracker

SPECIALITY BEERS
Daleside Morocco
Harviestoun Schiehallion
Isle of Arran Blonde
Oakham White Dwarf
Mighty Oak Spice
Nethergate Umbel Magna
Wylam Bohemia Pilsner

BOTTLE-CONDITIONED BEERS
Brakspear Live Organic
Burton Bridge Bramble Stout
Fuller's 1845
Hop Back Summer Lightning
RCH Pitchfork
Worthington's White Shield
Young's Special London Ale

CHAMPION WINTER BEER OF BRITAIN
Wye Valley Dorothy Goodbody's Wholesome Stout

CHAMPION BEER OF BRITAIN
Caledonian Deuchar's IPA

LEICESTERSHIRE & RUTLAND

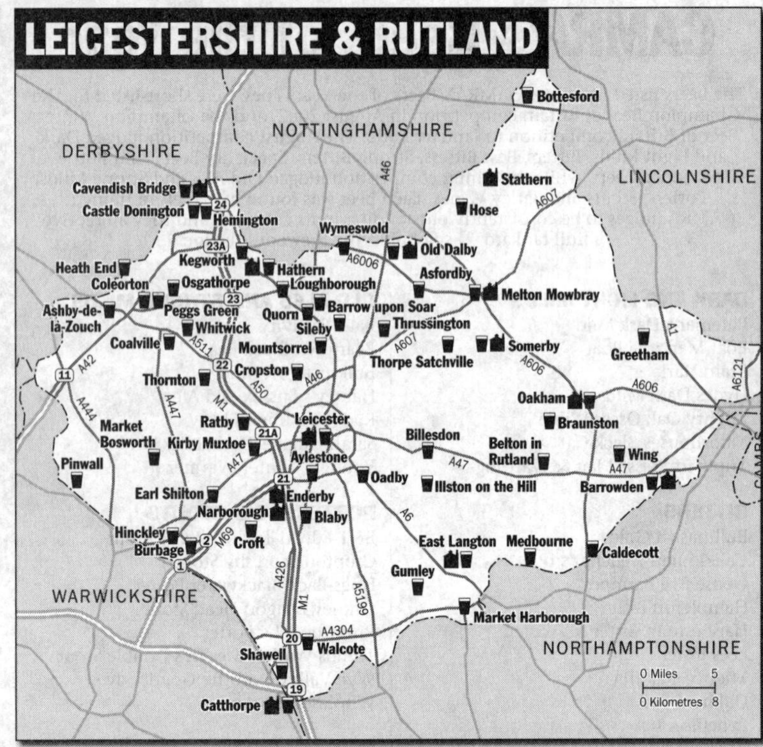

ASFORDBY

Crown Inn

106 Main Street

6.30 (12 Fri & Sat)-11; 12-10.30 Sun

(01664) 812175

Beer range varies

18th-century, friendly local, with low, beamed ceilings, and nooks to sit in. Local stone has been used for the bar – beware of its sloping top. A renovation six years ago has added character to the place. It was saved from becoming a private residence by locals persuading the landlord to reopen. As a free house, the range of beers is constantly changing: Belvoir, Brewster's and other local micros' products often feature. Popular for Sunday lunches, it is on many bus routes.

ASHBY-DE-LA-ZOUCH ❊

Plough

The Green, North Street

11-11; 12-10.30 Sun

(01530) 412817

Draught Bass; Marston's Pedigree; guest beers

Parts of this pub date back to the 1580s and, although modernised into a single bar, it has been split into various cosy areas. A friendly local, it fields darts, dominoes and cribbage teams; major rugby matches are screened. It has a rural feel, despite being in the centre of a small historic town. The guest beers are constantly changing and a cider is sometimes sold. Food is home cooked, representing excellent quality and value. Daytime buses run from Leicester via Coalville and also from Nuneaton.

AYLESTONE

Black Horse

65 Narrow Lane

11-2.30, 5-11; 11-11 Fri & Sat; 12-4, 7-10.30 Sun

(0116) 283 2811

Everards Beacon, Tiger

Tucked away in Aylestone village on the outskirts of Leicester, a pub has stood here for over 200 years. Popular and always busy, it has three rooms downstairs, plus a games room upstairs. A long skittles alley is available. Although recently refurbished, much of the pub's character has been retained.

BARROW UPON SOAR

Navigation

87 Mill Lane

11-3, 5.30-11; 11-11 Sat; 12-3, 7-10.30 Sun

(01509) 412842 website: www.countryfocus.co.uk/barrowuponsoar/navigation

Adnams Bitter; Banks's Bitter; Belvoir Star Bitter; Marston's Pedigree; guest beers

Thriving free house by the side of the Grand Union Canal and built at the same time in the 1760s. This waterside pub is popular with the locals and passing summer boat trade (moorings available nearby). The main bar boasts a bar top inlaid with old pennies, plus much brass and bric-à-brac. The cosy snug has its own bar. The outdoor seating area affords a rural view across the canal. Regular buses run to Leicester and Loughborough and the station is just a short walk away.

BILLESDON

New Greyhound

2 Market Place

✪ 12-2, 5.30-11; 12-11 Sat; 12-10.30 Sun

☎ (0116) 259 6226

Banks's Original; Marston's Bitter, Pedigree Ⓗ

Overlooking the old village's former market square (the market is long gone), this 17th-century building has been a pub for over a century. It consists of a traditional public bar with a pool table and a one-arm bandit, and a music-free lounge that has been harmoniously extended to accommodate functions. A warm, friendly welcome awaits locals and travellers alike. For the peckish, filled cobs are available.

Q ❀ ⊟ ♣ P

BLABY

Black Horse

Sycamore Street

✪ 12-11; 11-4, 6-11 Sat; 12-4, 7-10.30 Sun

☎ (0116) 277 1209

Greenalls Bitter; Marston's Pedigree; Tetley Bitter Ⓗ

This three-roomed pub, comprising a bar, lounge and vaults is situated at the centre of the village. The TV in the vaults is popular on sporting occasions, otherwise the sound is muted. Children (and dogs) are welcome. Regular quiz nights are held in the lounge.

❀ ☾ ♣

BOTTESFORD

Rutland Arms

2 High Street OS805389

✪ 12-2.30, 6.30-9.30; 12-3, 7-10.30 Sun

☎ (01949) 843031

Draught Bass; Courage Directors; Greenalls Bitter Ⓗ

This village-centre pub has two rooms, plus a restaurant. A comfortable carpeted lounge displays a menu board in a disused fireplace. A corner fish tank aids relaxation, while pictures adorn the walls. Upholstered seats complement wooden tables. The horseshoe-shaped bar is beamed and contains a pool table, games machines, darts and dominoes. The panelled restaurant serves good value English food, with inexpensive curries on Tuesday.

❀ ☾ ☽ ⊟ ♿ ≠ ♣ P

BURBAGE

Sycamores

60 Windsor Street

✪ 11-11; 12-10.30 Sun

☎ (01455) 239268

website: www.thesycamoresinn@aol.com

Marston's Bitter, Pedigree Ⓗ

Named after the two trees that stood on this site until the pub was built in 1925, the Sycamores has two rooms, one of which is a basic tile-floored bar, and a lounge where children are admitted. The garden also includes a play area. The landlord here founded the successful campaign to save the threatened Marston's Bitter in 1998 – Marston's Bitter outsells Pedigree in this area. Note the Banks's Original is nitro-keg.

❀ ♣ P

CASTLE DONINGTON ❄

Cross Keys

90 Bondgate

✪ 12-2.30, 5-11; 12-11 Sat; 12-10.30 Sun

☎ (01332) 812214 website: www.midlandspubs.co.uk/leicestershire/crosskeys

Draught Bass; Marston's Pedigree; Theakston Best Bitter; guest beers Ⓗ

Spacious local where the single bar is divided into three areas. The pub sponsors local rugby and cricket teams, as well as hosting an annual beer festival. Note the carved cross keys sign in the bar and the original etched glass windows. The pub's name indicates that a close relationship existed with the medieval church that overlooks it. A pub of great character, it serves home-cooked food weekdays. Regular buses run from Loughborough, Long Eaton and Derby; East Midlands Airport is close by. ♔ Q ❀ ☾ ♣ P

CATTHORPE

Cherry Tree

Main Street

✪ 5 (12 Sat)-11; 12-10.30 Sun

☎ (01788) 860430

Ansells Best Bitter; Draught Bass; Hook Norton Best Bitter; guest beers Ⓗ

The village of Catthorpe can now boast its own brewery – Dowbridge beers are brewed just down the road and often guest in this small, popular free house. Once a Phipp's Brewery house, it is very much a local. The cosy bar is often full; a second, smaller room has table skittles. It stages occasional live music. Usually two guest ales are on tap. A small outdoor drinking area is behind the pub. ♔ Q ❀ ♣ P

CAVENDISH BRIDGE

Old Crown

400 yds off A6 at Trent Bridge

✪ 11.30-3, 5-11; 12-5, 7-10.30 Sun

☎ (01332) 792392

Draught Bass; Marston's Pedigree; guest beers Ⓗ

Once a 17th-century coaching inn, now a cosy, atmospheric village pub on the southern side of the River Trent. Several hundred water jugs hang from the lounge ceiling while the walls are crammed full of brewery and railway memorabilia; the display even extends into the lavatories. Up to four guests beers are on tap, often featuring beers from the Shardlow Brewery, just across the river. Lunches are home

INDEPENDENT BREWERIES

Belvoir Old Dalby
Blencowe Barrowden
Brewster's Stathern
Dowbridge Catthorpe
Everards Narborough
Featherstone Enderby
Grainstore Oakham
Hoskins & Oldfield Leicester
John O'Gaunt Melton Mowbray
Langton East Langton
Parish Somerby
Shardlow Cavendish Bridge
Wicked Hathern Hathern

cooked. Daytime buses run from Derby and Loughborough, but the service is limited. ♛Q✿◐♿⅄P

COALVILLE

Bull's Head

Warren Hills Road (B587, between Copt Oak and Whitwick)
⏲ 11-2.30, 7-11; 12-3, 7-10.30 Sun
☎ (01530) 810511
Draught Bass; Marston's Pedigree; Tetley Bitter, Burton Ale; Ⓗ
Leicestershire's highest pub, at 787 feet above sea level, it dates from the 18th century. Although a single bar, it is very cosy. Note the bar built from the local granite with the odd Whitwick red brick incorporated. Around the walls hang original paintings, while attached to the beams is a collection of brass blow lamps and horse brasses. A large garden and children's play area at the rear overlooks Charnwood Forest. High quality home-cooked food is served at lunchtime in this friendly local. ♛Q✿◐♿P

CROFT

Heathcote Arms

Hill Street
⏲ 11.30-11; 12-10.30 Sun
☎ (01455) 282439
Everards Tiger, Original, seasonal beers; guest beers Ⓗ
Whitewashed pub in a prominent position overlooking the village war memorial. The heart of the pub is the public bar, where the beamed ceiling and leather upholstered settles give the room a timeless feel, accentuated by old photos of Croft. The small lounge is nicely decorated, with wooden-backed benches; it has a large games room. Outside is a split-level garden and a skittle alley. The pub is close to Croft Hill SSSI. ♛Q✿◐⊟♣P

CROPSTON

Bradgate Arms

15 Station Road
⏲ 11.30-11; 12-10.30 Sun
☎ (0116) 234 0336
Banks's Bitter; Marston's Pedigree; guest beer Ⓗ
Comfortable village pub, popular with locals and tourists alike. At the front are two small rooms whose wooden-backed bench seating and beamed ceilings give a traditional feel. At the rear, the former back wall separates the main pub from the sunken dining area (note the old bay window). Outside is a large garden with picnic tables and a skittle alley. The pub is handy for Bradgate Country Park and the Great Central Steam Railway at Rothley. ♉✿◐◑♣P⊡

EARL SHILTON

Dog & Gun

72 Keats Lane
⏲ 12-2.30 (not Mon-Thu), 5.30-11; 11.30-3.30, 5.30-11 Sat; 12-3, 7-10.30 Sun
☎ (01455) 842338
Banks's Original; Marston's Bitter, Pedigree Ⓗ
Just a short way down Keats Lane off the main A47 through the village, the pub is set back from the rest of the buildings, as it was built behind the original pub after its demolition in 1932. It has three rooms, including a snug. The bar has a tiled floor and a large log fire. With a number of walking routes in the area, the pub runs its own rambling club and participates in many local charity events. ♛✿◐♣P

EAST LANGTON

Bell Inn

Main Street
⏲ 11.30-2.30, 7 (6 Fri & Sat)-11; 12-4, 7-10.30 Sun
☎ (01858) 545278
Greene King IPA, Abbot; Langton Caudle Bitter, Bowler, seasonal beers; Ⓗ **guest beers** Ⓖ
This 17th-century listed building is at the heart of Leicestershire's hunting country. A pretty walled garden, low beams and an open log fire all add to its appeal. Quality food, produced from local ingredients, is freshly prepared each session, offering anything from a light bite to a banquet. Should you wish to extend your stay, accommodation is provided in en-suite bedrooms. Langton Brewery, which started

INN BRIEF

Leicestershire

ASHBY-DE-LA-ZOUCH

Ashby Court
35 Wood Street
11-2.30, 5-11; 11-11 Fri & Sat; 12-3, 6-9.30 Sun
(01530) 415176
Shardlow Reverend Eaton's Ⓗ
Former coaching inn, with a French restaurant, serving a local micro-brewery's beers. Ten guest rooms.

CASTLE DONINGTON

Jolly Potter
36 Hillside
11-11; 12-10.30 Sun
Draught Bass; Marston's Pedigree Ⓗ
Built at the turn of the 20th century, this characterful pub has two rooms, the front one split into two distinct areas. A cosy local.

COLEORTON

King's Arms
187 The Moor
11.30-3, 5.30-11; 12-10.30 Sun
(01530) 815435
Hook Norton Bitter, Generation, Old Hooky; Marston's Pedigree; guest beers Ⓗ
Village pub built as a miners' hostel, now extended into the next cottage. Lunches and evening meals served.

HINCKLEY

Prince of Wales Inn
Coventry Road
11-11; 12-10.30 Sun
(01455) 615020
Mansfield Dark Mild; Marston's Bitter, Pedigree Ⓗ
Former coaching inn: a large bar with projection TV and a no-smoking lounge. Lunches served Mon-Sat.

KEGWORTH

Cap & Stocking
20 Borough Street
11.30-2.30 (3 Sat), 6.30-11; 12-3, 7-10.30 Sun
Draught Bass; Ⓖ **Hancock's HB; guest beer** Ⓗ
Classic, back-street pub, with a garden, popular with the locals, where the Bass is served from the jug. Home-cooked food.

KIRBY MUXLOE

Royal Oak
35 Main Street
11-2.30, 5.30-11; 11-3, 6-11 Sat; 12-3, 6.30-10.30 Sun
(0116) 239 3166
Adnams Bitter; Everards Beacon, Tiger; guest beer Ⓗ
Modern-styled pub that replaced the original Royal Oak in the 1970s. Excellent food in pub and restaurant.

up in 1999, is situated in buildings behind the inn.
⛫Q❀⇌◐◑P

GUMLEY

Bell Inn
2 Main Street
12-3, 6-11; 12-3 (closed eve) Sun
(0116) 279 2476
Boddingtons Bitter; Everards Tiger; Greene King IPA; guest beers Ⓗ
Early 19th-century free house, popular with local rural and commuting urban clientele. Cricketing memorabilia hangs in the entrance hall, while pictures of fox hunting scenes decorate the bar and restaurant. The beamed interior comprises an L-shaped bar and a no-smoking restaurant, serving a varied menu (no food Mon eve). Behind the pub lies an extensive patio garden, but please note this is not for the use of children or dogs. ⛫Q❀◐◑♣P

HATHERN

Dew Drop
49 Loughborough Road
12-2, 6-11; 12-3, 7-11 Sat; 12-3, 7-10.30 Sun
(01509) 842438
Hardys & Hansons Best Mild, Best Bitter, seasonal beers Ⓗ
Long-established, traditional, two-roomed pub on the main A6 through Hathern. A friendly local, it stocks a good selection of malt whiskies. It fields dominoes and darts teams. Regular bus services run from Loughborough. ⛫Q❀⊟♣P

HEATH END

Saracen's Head
Heath End Lane (minor road, linking B587 and B5006) OS368214
11-2.30, 7-11; 12-2.30, 7-10.30 Sun
(01332) 862323
Draught Bass Ⓖ
Two-roomed Victorian pub, run by the same family since 1937. The brightly-lit bar has a quarry-tiled floor and scrubbed tables, while the lounge is comfortably furnished with more atmospheric lighting. Situated near Calke Abbey and Staunton Harold Church, it makes an ideal stop for walkers. This is one of the few places where gravity Bass is served from a jug. Note this place is not marked on most maps and there is no public transport available. ⛫Q❀⊟♣P

HEMINGTON

Jolly Sailor
21 Main Street
11-2.30, 4-11; 11-11 Sat; 12-10.30 Sun
website: www.midlandspubs.co.uk/leicestershire/jollysailor
Draught Bass; Greene King Abbot; M&B Mild; Marston's Pedigree; guest beers Ⓗ
Small, friendly, village pub that started life as a farmhouse, before being converted some time around the mid-19th century. Both of the heavily timbered rooms are warmed by real fires in winter, exposed beams are festooned with an extensive collection of brass blow lamps. As well as two changing guest beers and a real cider (in summer), there is an extensive range of malt whiskies. Meals are served lunchtime (Tue-Sat) and evenings (Fri & Sat); a restaurant has been created from a former sitting room. ⛫Q❀◐◑♿♣●P

HINCKLEY ✻

Railway Hotel
Station Road
12-11; 11-3.30, 7-11 Sat; 12-3.30, 7-10.30 Sun
(01455) 615285
Banks's Original; Marston's Bitter, Pedigree Ⓗ
Spacious, two-roomed local, where the basic bar is aptly adorned with railway pictures. The comfortable lounge hosts regular live music, while a conservatory houses a pool table and doubles as the family area. A function room can be booked. Bed and breakfast is also available. Q❀⇌◐≋♣P

HOSE

Black Horse
21 Bolton Lane OS734294
12-2 (not Tue), 7-11; 12-4, 7-10.30 Sun
(01949) 860336
Castle Rock Farriers Gold; guest beers Ⓗ
Traditional pub where a carpeted lounge

LOUGHBOROUGH

Beacon Inn
Beacon Road
12-3, 6-11; 12-11 Sat; 12-10.30 Sun
Marston's Pedigree; Theakston XB; guest beer Ⓗ
1960s local, off Epinal Way. It has a large lounge, a bar with a pool table and TV, a skittle alley and pétanque pitch.

Gate
99 Meadow Lane
12-11; 12-10.30 Sun
(01509) 263779
Banks's Original; Marston's Pedigree Ⓗ
One of the oldest pubs in Loughborough, Grade II listed: a front bar and a quieter lounge.

MELTON MOWBRAY

Boat
57 Burton Road
12-2 (not winter Mon-Thu), 5-11; 12-3, 7-10.30 Sun
Burtonwood Bitter, Top Hat; guest beer Ⓗ
One-roomed traditional pub, warmed by open fires, very near the station.

MOUNTSORREL

Waterside
Sileby Road
11-3, 6-11; 12-10.30 Sun
(0116) 230 2758
Everards Beacon, Tiger, Original; guest beer Ⓗ
Built in 1791, contemporary with the canal, situated by Mountsorrel Lock (moorings nearby). Food available.

OLD DALBY

Crown
7 Debdale Hill
12-3 (not Mon; 2.30 winter Tue-Thu), 6 (6.30 winter Mon-Thu)-11; 12-3, 7.30-10.30 Sun
(01664) 823134
Banks's Bitter; Ⓗ **guest beers** Ⓗ/Ⓖ
Creeper-covered pub; a tiny bar, myriad of small rooms and large garden. Popular in all seasons. Good food.

OSGATHORPE

Storey Arms
41 Main Street
12-3, 7.30-11; 12-3, 7.30-10.30 Sun
(01530) 224166
Banks's Original; Draught Bass; Mansfield Cask Ale; Marston's Pedigree; guest beer (occasional) Ⓗ
Traditional country pub, with a 1960s-style lounge. Hosts an autumn beer festival and occasional live music (Sat eve).

features a brass ornamental brick fireplace; pictures and blackboard menus surround a wooden corner bar. The unspoilt public bar has a tiled floor, wood furniture and a brick fireplace; current ales are shown on a blackboard – five guest beers usually include a mild. A wood-panelled restaurant serves a menu based on local produce (Wed-Sat, plus Sun lunch). Local CAMRA Pub of the Year 2002.

Rose & Crown
43 Bolton Lane OS734295
12-2.30 (not Mon-Wed), 7 (5 Fri; 6.30 Sat)-11; 12-3, 7.30-10.30 Sun
(01949) 60424
Greene King IPA, Abbot; guest beers H
The stone bar, with tiled floor, divides two distinct areas. The lounge, originally three rooms, is beamed and carpeted with wall decoration of Tudor struts and rural artefacts; a raised area has a stone fireplace. The bar has comfortable seats, copper-topped tables made from barrels, a stone fireplace, dartboard, pool table and quiet juke box. A patio and garden are popular in summer, when a third guest beer is stocked. Eve meals are served Wed-Sat.

ILLSTON ON THE HILL

Fox & Goose
Main Street (off B6047, near Billesdon)
12-2.30 (not Mon or Tue), 5.30 (7 Mon)-11; 12-2.30, 7-10.30 Sun
(0116) 259 6340
Everards Beacon, Tiger, Original; guest beer H
A gem: a cosy village pub with a timeless feel, displaying a fascinating collection of local mementos and hunting memorabilia. In 1997, when structural work was needed, every item on the walls was photographed and later returned to its exact place. That's how unchanged it is! Popular annual events include a conker championship, onion-growing competition and fund-raising auction for local charities. The pub is tucked away, but well worth seeking out.

KEGWORTH ❊

Red Lion
24 High Street
11-11; 12-10.30 Sun
(01509) 672466
Adnams Bitter; Banks's Original; Courage Directors; Shepherd Neame Spitfire; guest beers H
Partly dating from the 15th century, this central pub has three bars and a no-smoking children's room. A special feature at the bar is a range of Polish and Ukrainian vodkas, as well as a good selection of malt whiskies and four guest beers. Pétanque is a popular game, played on five courts; the pub also boasts a skittle alley and two darts rooms. The large garden, with a children's play area, makes a good vantage point for viewing aircraft approaching East Midlands Airport. Evening meals are served weekdays (5.30-8); no food Sun.

LEICESTER

Ale Wagon
27 Rutland Street
11-11; 12-10.30 Sun
(0116) 262 3330
websites: www.alewagon.co.uk & www.alewagon.com
Hoskins & Oldfield Mild, Bitter, White Dolphin, Supreme, EXS Bitter H
A real local atmosphere pervades the 1930s interior of this pub run by the Hoskins family. It boasts an original oak staircase, and tiled and parquet floors in its two rooms, with a central bar. A selection of home-cooked meals is served in the bar, lounge and upstairs dining room; vegetarian choices are available. It always has six Hoskins ales on tap, and is popular with rugby fans and ale drinkers visiting Leicester.

Black Horse
1 Foxon Street (on Braunstone Gate)
5 (3 Mon; 12 Fri & Sat)-11; 12-10.30 Sun
(0116) 254 0030
Everards Beacon, Tiger, seasonal beers; guest beer H
Small, traditional, street-corner pub with two rooms and a central bar, completely untouched by refurbishment. A general knowledge quiz is staged on Sunday nights; darts and dominoes are played. This is the

INN BRIEF

QUORN

Apple Tree
2 Stoop Lane
12-3.30, 5.30-11; 12-3, 7-10.30 Sun
(01509) 412296
Draught Bass; M&B Mild H
Traditional, two-roomed, unspoilt village local; only pub in Quorn serving cask mild.

SOMERBY

Old Brewery Inn
39 High Street
12-2.30, 6.30-11; 12-10.30 Sun
(01664) 454777
Draught Bass; Fuller's London Pride; Parish Special, Poachers, Baz's Bonce Blower H
15th-century, cosy pub whose outbuildings are used by Parish Brewery. No food Sun eve.

THRUSSINGTON

Blue Lion
5 Rearsby Road
12-3 (4 Sat), 6-11; 12-4, 7-10.30 Sun
(01664) 424266
Mansfield Dark Mild; Marston's Bitter, Pedigree; W&D seasonal beers H
Traditional village local, built 1785 and extended. The garden is home to various species of poultry. Food available.

WHITWICK

Lady Jane
Hall Lane
12-3, 6-11; 12-3, 6-10.30 Sun
(01530) 836889
Mansfield Dark Mild; Marston's Pedigree; guest beer H
1960s estate pub that supports many games and teams. Frequent live entertainment in lounge. Cask Marque accredited.

Rutland

OAKHAM

White Lion
30 Melton Road
11.30-3 (not Mon), 6-11; 12-3, 7-10.30 Sun
(01572) 724844
Draught Bass; Jennings Bitter; guest beers H
18th-century inn: one large room which includes a dining section and main drinking area. Near station.

❊ symbol next to a main entry place name indicates there are Inn Brief entries as well.

only pub in Leicester with two swingboards. The guest beers are from Everards Old English Ale Club. Q ♣

Globe

43 Silver Street (near clock tower)
11-11; 12-10.30 Sun
☎ (0116) 262 9819
Everards Beacon, Tiger, Original, seasonal beers; guest beers H
This city-centre pub is probably Everards' town flagship. In 1977 local CAMRA rewarded it as Pub of the Year, for being Everards first pub to sell the full range as real ale since keg dominated in 1970. Extensive renovations took place in 2001, moving the bar to the centre and incorporating the yard area into the pub. It still has four drinking areas, including the unspoilt snug. Local CAMRA's 25th anniversary was celebrated here. Guest beers are from Everards Old English Ale Club. Meals are served 12-7.

Hat & Beaver

60 Highcross Street
12-11; 12-6 Sun
☎ (0116) 262 2157
Hardys & Hansons Best Mild, Best Bitter, Classic H
Basic, two-roomed local with a relaxed atmosphere, one of Leicester's few remaining traditional pubs; it has a TV in the bar, well-filled, good value cobs are usually available at lunchtime and early evening. It is handy for the Shires shopping centre. Cribbage and darts teams represent the pub. It closes on Sunday after the last customer leaves, but it stays open at least until 6pm. ♣

Leicester Gateway

52 Gateway Street (near university and Royal Infirmary)
11-11; 12-10.30 Sun
☎ (0116) 255 7319
Castle Rock Gold; guest beers H
Friendly, air-conditioned local, a converted hosiery factory, frequented by nearby infirmary and university staff. Close to both Leicester City football and rugby grounds, it supports sporting fixtures. It stocks four or five constantly changing guest beers, plus a good range of British and continental bottled beers, and an occasional cider. Home-cooked food, on a varied menu, including vegetarian choices, is available 12-9 (6 Sat & Sun); a Sunday carvery is offered, too.
♣

Old Horse

198 London Road (opp. Victoria Park)
11-11; 12-10.30 Sun
☎ (0116) 254 8384
Everards Beacon, Tiger, Original H
Large, open-plan pub with two smaller adjoining rooms, one with a log fire. A 10-minute uphill walk along London Road from the station, it stands opposite Leicester's major open space, Victoria Park. A courtyard to the rear houses an aviary with four owls and leads to a substantial garden. A large dining area and airy conservatory with blackboard menus complete the facilities here. Meals are served 12-9 (8 Sat; 4 Sun).
♣ P

Swan & Rushes

19 Infirmary Square (by Royal Infirmary)
12-11; 12-10.30 Sun
☎ (0116) 233 9167
website: www.swanandrushes.co.uk
Hardys & Hansons Best Bitter, seasonal beers; Oakham JHB; guest beers H
Triangular, two-bar 1930s boozer, refurbished to a high standard, it is a shrine to great beer from Britain and beyond. Five real ales usually include mild. Four imported draughts and around 140 top-rated bottled beers, mainly from Belgium and Germany also feature, with probably the best range of Belgian Lambics found in any UK pub. Occasional beer festivals and interesting breweriana add to its appeal. Close to Leicester football and rugby grounds, it can be crowded before major games.
♣

Talbot

4 Thurcaston Road (vehicle access from Loughborough Rd only)
11.30-3, 6-11; 11.30-4, 6.30-11 Sat; 12-4, 7-10.30 Sun
☎ (0116) 266 2280
Ansells Mild, Best Bitter; Marston's Pedigree; guest beer H
A pub has stood on this site since the 15th century, while the cellars date back to the 12th century. Owned by the church until the 19th century, this friendly, two-roomed local is in the heart of old Belgrave, and is handy for the historic Belgrave Hall, Abbey Pumping Station and the National Space Centre. It is five minutes' walk from Leicester North Station on the Great Central Steam Railway which connects with Rothley, Quorn and Loughborough. No food Sun.
(North) ♣ P

Vaults

1 Wellington Street (near Fenwicks' store)
5 (12 Fri & Sat)-11 (10.30 Mon); 12-3, 7-10.30 Sun
☎ (0116) 255 5506 website: www.the-vaults.co.uk
Old Laxey Bosun Bitter; guest beers H
Small, friendly cellar bar. A genuine free house, it only sells beers from micro-brewers, an ever-changing variety on seven handpumps. Sales exceed 18 different cask beers weekly, approaching 3,000 different real ales since 1997. House beers come from the Isle of Man, Steamin' Billy and Brewster's. Leicester CAMRA's Pub of the Year 2002, it is a rare outlet for traditional ciders (always three). Live music Saturday afternoons means it can get very busy. An entry charge is sometimes imposed on Sunday evening for live music.
(Midland) ♣

LOUGHBOROUGH

Albion

Canal Bank
11-3 (4 Sat), 6-11; 12-3, 7-10.30 Sun
☎ (01509) 213952
Mansfield Dark Mild; Robinson's Best Bitter; Shepherd Neame seasonal beers; guest beers H
Tranquil canalside pub, with a bar, darts room and a quiet lounge, serving good value beer and home-cooked food. Outside drinking is on the canal bank or patio,

which houses an aviary. The lounge is designated a no-smoking area until 8pm. ♨Q❀◑◧♿⇌♣⅟

Swan in the Rushes

21 The Rushes

☉ 11-11; 12-10.30 Sun

☎ (01509) 217014

Archers Golden; Tetley Bitter; guest beers Ⓗ

This traditional pub (owned by Tynemill) has three rooms (one no-smoking) and is popular with the locals for its constantly changing range of six guest beers which always includes a mild. You can be entertained by musicians in the function room most weeks. Two beer festivals are staged each year, one during the spring and the other in autumn when 30-plus beers are available. A limited range of continental beers is stocked, both draught and bottled, plus a good selection of malt whiskies. All food is freshly cooked; evening meals are served Mon-Fri. ♨Q❀⇋◑◧♿⇌♣●P⅟

Tap & Mallet

36 Nottingham Road

☉ 12-2.30, 5-11; 11.30-11 Sat; 12-10.30 Sun

☎ (01509) 210028

Courage Best Bitter; Marston's Pedigree; Theakston Mild; guest beer Ⓗ

Genuine free house, between the town centre and the station. Up to five guest beers are usually available, most of them from micro-breweries, often local. The Theakston Mild is sometimes replaced by a micro's mild, and Hoegaarden beer is available on draught. There is only one bar/lounge, however the lounge can be partitioned off for private functions. The pub fields several darts teams, and the bar area also has a pool table. At the rear is a pleasant walled garden with an extensive lawn, plus a children's play area and a pets' corner. ♨Q❀⇌♣●

MARKET BOSWORTH

Olde Red Lion Hotel

1 Park Street

☉ 11-2.30, 5.30-11; 11-11 Sat; 11-3, 7-10.30 Sun

☎ (01455) 291713

website: www.theredlion.dabsol.co.uk

Banks's Original, Bitter; Camerons Bitter; Greene King Abbot; Marston's Pedigree; Theakston XB; guest beers Ⓗ

Popular, friendly pub, near the market square, with a large beamed bar and dining area displaying many horse brasses. In winter you can warm by an open fire. The range of beers, including several guests, is extensive. The choice of food is varied (eve meals Tue-Sat), and the accommodation is reasonably priced. A good base for exploring the nearby site of the Battle of Bosworth where Richard III was killed in 1485. ♨Q❀⇋◑◐♣P⅟

MKT HARBOROUGH (Little Bowden)

Cherry Tree

Church Walk, Kettering Road

☉ 12-2.30, 5-11; 12-11 Fri & Sat; 12-10.30 Sun

☎ (01858) 463525

Everards Beacon, Tiger, Original Ⓗ

This spacious pub is characterised by low beams and a thatched roof. Drinkers and diners can choose from many small alcoves and seating areas. The pub is actually situated in Little Bowden, but is very much part of the Market Harborough community. Meals are served at lunchtime (except Mon) and evenings (7-9, Tue-Sat). ❀◑⇌♣⅟

MEDBOURNE

Nevill Arms

12 Waterfall Way

☉ 12-2.30, 6-11; 12-3, 7-10.30 Sun

☎ (01858) 565288

Adnams Bitter; Fuller's London Pride; Greene King Abbot; guest beers Ⓗ

The initials MGN over the door are those of Captain Nevill who was heir to the nearby Holt estate when this former coaching inn was rebuilt in 1863 after the original building was destroyed by fire in 1856. Folklore suggests that a spark caused the fire after the village blacksmith wagered he could support an anvil on his chest while a horseshoe was forged upon it. A warm welcome awaits in the heavily beamed bar with its large inglenook. ♨❀⇋◑◐♣P

MELTON MOWBRAY ❄

Crown

10 Burton Street

☉ 11-3, 7-11; 11-11 Sat; 12-4, 7-10.30 Sun

☎ (01664) 564682

Everards Beacon, Tiger, Original; guest beers Ⓗ

Friendly, two-roomed town pub, run by a long-serving landlord. The lounge is designated a no-smoking area when lunches are being served. Popular with office workers and shoppers at lunchtime, it attracts all ages in the evening. Note the old photographs of Melton Mowbray around the walls. Close to the station and town centre, regular bus services run from Leicester, Loughborough, Grantham, Nottingham and Stamford. ♨Q♉❀◑◧⇌♣⅟

Mash Tub

58 Nottingham Road

☉ 11-11; 12-10.30 Sun

☎ (01664) 410051

Banks's Original, Bitter; guest beer Ⓗ

This pub has a single room, with a split-level bar, and several well-defined seating areas. It has a local image during the week, but attracts younger folk at weekends. It fields two well-established darts teams. The guest beer changes monthly; the cider is the award-winning Weston's Old Rosie. ◑⇌♣●

MOUNTSORREL ❄

Swan

10 Loughborough Road

☉ 12-2.30, 5.30-11; 12-11 Sat; 12-3, 7-10.30 Sun

☎ (0116) 230 2340 website: www.jvf.co.uk/swan

Greene King Ruddles County; Theakston Best Bitter, BB, Old Peculier; guest beer Ⓗ

On the old A6, this pub dates back to the 1700s. It has a split-level bar with a stone floor, while the dining area has a polished wood floor. The secluded gardens reach down to the River Soar; no moorings are available here, but moorings for narrow boats are not far away. Low ceilings make it very cosy. The restaurant serves top quality

BARROWBY

White Swan

High Road (1/2 mile from A1 and A52)
11.30-11; 12-10.30 Sun
(01476) 562375
Adnams Bitter, Broadside; guest beers H

On the main road, this pleasant village local is the only pub in Barrowby. It always keeps four real ales, usually two from Adnams. The pub appeals to all tastes, having two distinctly separate bars: the comfortable lounge is quiet, but in the larger public bar there is music and a pool table plus traditional pub games (darts, cribbage and dominoes).

Q❀◐⊟♣P✔

BELTON

Crown Inn

Stocks Hill, Churchtown
4 (12 Sat)-11; 12-10.30 Sun
(01427) 872834
Greene King Ruddles County; John Smith's Bitter; Theakston Best Bitter; guest beer H

Hard to find but worth the effort, this is consistently the most popular of many pubs serving real ale in the south of the Isle of Axholme. Look for an old brick building at the end of the lane behind the historic All Saints Church. This simple rural pub has an open-plan bar/lounge, a games room and garden, with play frame for children. Free of tie, the landlord believes in offering quality and value. The guest beer comes from the 'brewery of the month'.

♨❀♣P⊓

BILLINGBOROUGH

Fortescue Arms

27 High Street
12-2.30, 6-11; 12-3, 7-10.30 Sun
(01529) 240228
Greene King IPA; Tetley Burton Ale; guest beers H

Fine country inn with olde-worlde charm set in a village with spring wells and grand old buildings. It has a friendly, comfortable feel, and two restaurants serve excellent home-made food (booking advisable). Nearby is the site of Sempringham Abbey which includes a monument to Gwenllian, daughter of the Prince of Wales, who was confined to the priory in the 12th century. Stone from the abbey was used to build parts of the inn.

♨Q❀◐◑⊟♣P

BLYTON

White Hart Inn

66 High Street (A159)
12-3 (not Mon), 7-11; 11-11 Sat; 12-10.30 Sun
(01427) 628683
Beer range varies H

Three-roomed village pub; it comprises a small, cosy bar, warmed by a fire, a spacious lounge and a games room with pool and large-screen TV. The pub hosts ladies darts and dominoes matches. Two guest beers are kept. A pleasant patio area is available for outdoor drinking. Lunches are served on Sunday, but no other food is offered.

♨❀♣P

BOSTON ❄

Ball House

Wainfleet Road (A52, 1 mile from centre)
11.30-3, 6.30-11; 12-3, 7-10.30 Sun
(01205) 364478 website: www.theballhouse.co.uk
Draught Bass; Bateman XB, XXXB; guest beer H

Ten years in this Guide, this mock-Tudor pub is very friendly and welcoming. It stands on the site of a former cannonball store – hence the name. The pub boasts award-winning floral displays in summer as testified by the certificates that adorn the walls. Freshly-cooked food is served and barbecues are held in the summer.

♨Q❀◐◑P✔

Coach & Horses

86 Main Ridge (100 yds E of John Adams Way)
5 (6 Fri)-11; 11-3, 7-11 Sat; 12-3, 7-10.30 Sun
(01205) 362301
Bateman XB, XXXB H

A warm welcome is assured from the long-standing, friendly landlord and regulars, at this cosy, traditional one-roomed pub. It fields thriving teams in local dominoes, pool and darts leagues. Very handy for the Boston United ground, you need to get in early on match days. The pub is well worth the short walk from the centre to seek out the XXXB. ♨♣⊓

Cowbridge

Horncastle Road (B1183, N of town)
11-3, 6-11; 12-4, 7-10.30 Sun
(01205) 362597
Theakston Mild; guest beers H

Just out of town, this pub is popular with drinkers and diners. It separates into three main areas: the public bar is a no-nonsense drinking and darts environment, with a large display of football scarves; the smaller lounge is cosy, with an open fire, and opens out into the restaurant which serves excellent freshly-cooked food. The pub is handy for Boston golf club. ♨❀◐◑⊟♿♣P

Eagle

West Street (near station)
11-3, 5-11; 11-11 Fri & Sat; 12-10.30 Sun
(01205) 361116
Adnams Broadside; Banks's Bitter; Taylor Landlord; guest beers H

Back in the early 1980s this was the first pub in Boston to have a good selection of beers. This Tynemill house is a delight. Recently refurbished, the small, comfortable lounge has an open fire in winter, and the bar enjoys a very friendly atmosphere. It stocks an ever-changing range of guest beers

INDEPENDENT BREWERIES

Bateman Wainfleet
Blue Bell Whaplode St Catherine
Blue Cow South Witham
DarkTribe Gunness
Donoghue Grainthorpe
Faint Hope Scawby Brook
Happy Hooker Sleaford
Highwood Melton Highwood
Newby Wyke Little Bytham
Oldershaw Grantham
Poachers Swinderby
Willy's Cleethorpes

and food may be available by the time the Guide is published.
⛬❀⊟⥱♣●

New England Hotel

Wide Bargate
11-11; 12-10.30 Sun
☎ (01205) 365255
website: www.newenglandboston.co.uk
Beer range varies Ⓗ
Built in 1830, on the site of the Cross Keys, a name it kept until becoming an hotel. The car park was once the poultry market. The foyer/Imperial Bar boasts decorative plaster ceilings. The bar sells a good selection of British and foreign bottled beers, over 80 vodkas, and 30-plus whiskies. Both the bar and restaurant meals are recommended. Comfy seats and sofas complete the pleasant atmosphere. ⇔◐◑

Ship Tavern

Custom House Lane (off South Sq)
11-11; 12-10.30 Sun
☎ (01205) 358156
Bateman Mild, XB; Greene King IPA; guest beer Ⓗ
Spacious, one-roomed pub with distinct areas for pool and darts. A mixture of comfortable upholstered seating, wooden pews, a farmhouse table and benches create a traditional feel. Breweriana adorn the walls and corridors of this popular town-centre pub. The small patio is ideal for summer days. Sandwiches are available, but no hot food. ❀⥱♣

BRIGG ❊

Black Bull

3 Wrawby Street (near tourist information centre)
11-3 (4 Thu), 7-11; 11-11 Sat; 12-3, 7-10.30 Sun
☎ (01652) 652153
John Smith's Bitter; guest beers Ⓗ
Popular, town-centre pub with a homely feel, busy on market days (Thu and Sat). It stocks a regular beer from Highwood, usually Harvest, and an additional guest that constantly changes. The garden and car park are behind the pub, which is centrally situated for shoppers. Brigg is on the 909 bus route serving Doncaster, Sheffield, Grimsby and Hull.
❀◐⥱(Sat only) ♣P

BURTON UPON STATHER

Ferry House

Stather Road
12-5 (not Mon-Fri), 7 (6 summer)-11; 12-10.30 Sun
☎ (01724) 721783
Beer range varies Ⓗ
On the Trent bank, this popular pub has a central bar serving two drinking areas and a pool room. The large garden, ideal for watching ships, is served by a chuck wagon; barbecues are held in summer. Live music is performed (either indoors or outside) on Saturday evenings in summer; a bouncy castle is provided to amuse children. Changing guest beers are always available.
❀♿⛺♣P

CLEETHORPES

Crow's Nest Hotel

Balmoral Road
11-3, 6-11; 12-4, 7-10.30 Sun
☎ (01472) 698867
Samuel Smith OBB Ⓗ
Largely unaltered example of 1950s pub architecture, this is a focal point for the surrounding estate. The lounge is quiet, comfortable and spacious, while the bar tends to be more lively. The only pub to have received two merit awards from local CAMRA, it is the only Sam Smith's outlet for miles and sells the cheapest pint in the area. It can be hard to find, however, the No. 4 bus from Grimsby bus station to Cleethorpes Pier stops close by.
Q❀⇔◐◑⊟♿P⊬

Nottingham House

5 Seaview Street
12-11; 12-10.30 Sun
☎ (01472) 505150
Tetley Mild, Bitter Ⓗ
Traditional, three-roomed pub, it is situated in the quieter, yet still lively, part of the resort. It comprises an excellent lounge, comfortable snug and a lively bar which is very popular for football and other televised sports. ⊟⥱♣

Willy's

17 Highcliff Road
11-11; 12-10.30 Sun

INN BRIEF

BOSTON

Goodbarns Yard
8 Wormgate
11.30-11; 12-10.30 Sun
(01205) 355717
Courage Directors; Greene King Old Speckled Hen; Theakston XB; guest beers Ⓗ
Close to the Boston Stump, near the town centre, well known for its food. Garden overlooks the Haven River.

BRIGG

Lord Nelson
24-25 Market Place
11-11; 12-10.30 Sun
(01652) 652127
Old Mill Bitter, Bullion, seasonal beers Ⓗ
Refurbished hotel in the town centre. An original stained glass window depicts Nelson. Meals available most of the day.

CLAYPOLE

Five Bells
95 Main Street
11-3 (not Mon), 5.30-11; 11-11 Fri & Sat; 12-10.30 Sun
(01636) 626561
Tetley Bitter; guest beers Ⓗ
Welcoming village pub, just off the A1. Guest beers are often sourced from local micros. Attractive outdoor area.

GAINSBOROUGH

Sweyn Forkbeard
21-22 Silver Street
11-11; 12-10.30 Sun
(01427) 675000
Courage Directors; Greene King Abbot; Hop Back Summer Lightning; Theakston Best Bitter; Shepherd Neame Spitfire; guest beers Ⓗ
Comfortable, airy Wetherspoon's with friendly staff. Wheelchair WC. Meals are served all day. Cask Marque accredited.

GRANTHAM

Chequers
25 Market Place
11-11; 12-10.30 Sun
(01476) 401633
Marston's Pedigree; guest beers Ⓗ
Small Victorian pub converted into one room but retains original decor. Attracts locals but can be noisy on Sat eve.

Shirley Croft Hotel
Harrowby Road
11-11; 12-10.30 Sun
(01476) 563260
Draught Bass; Bateman XB; guest beers Ⓗ
Former Victorian gentleman's residence, retaining many fine features, near town centre. Good food.

☎ (01472) 602145
Bateman XB; Willy's Original Bitter Ⓗ
This cosmopolitan seaside bar is the home of Willy's Brewery. The brewhouse can be viewed from the bar area. As well as five real ales, the pub serves a small range of quality continental beers and enjoys a reputation for good home-cooked food. The upstairs bar, available for private functions, offers panoramic views of the shipping in the River Humber. A new feature is the Supper Club on Monday and Tuesday evenings (until 8pm); no meals are served on other evenings. ❀◑⇌

CORRINGHAM

Beckett Arms
25 High Street (A631)
⏲ 12-2, 5.30-11; 12-3, 6-11 Sat; 12-4, 7-10.30 Sun
☎ (01427) 838201
Barnsley Bitter; guest beers Ⓗ
This converted farmhouse has been a pub for the last hundred years. The open-plan layout encompasses a lounge with a bar, snug, pool room and another lower-level bar. The restaurant menu offers vegetarian and children's choices. Guest accommodation (four rooms) includes a family room. ♨❀⇌◑◑⊟♿♣P⁄

DRY DODDINGTON

Wheatsheaf Inn
Main Street (1½ miles off A1, S of Newark)
⏲ 12-3 (not Tue), 7-11; 12-10.30 Sun
☎ (01400) 281458
Marston's Pedigree; John Smith's Magnet; Theakston Mild; guest beers Ⓗ
The Wheatsheaf overlooks an unusual Norman church with a leaning tower, but no cemetery, as it stands on the village green rather than in its own grounds. The pub's traditional layout comprises a popular, small public bar, pool room and a 17th-century lounge with genuine beams and original horse brasses. Local and national newspapers are available. Guest ales, sometimes including micro-breweries' products, are on handpump. Camping and caravan spaces are available in the pub grounds; note the second hanging post sign. Q❀⊟▲♣P

EAST BUTTERWICK

Dog & Gun
High Street (off A18 at Keadby Bridge)
⏲ 6 (5 Thu & Fri; 12 Sat)-11; 12-10.30 Sun
☎ (01724) 783419
Beer range varies Ⓗ
Basic, but welcoming, unspoilt local by the River Trent. Three rooms are served by the central bar. Renowned for its real fires, it has been the main outlet for local micro, DarkTribe, ever since it began brewing. Other guest beers, such as Daleside, feature occasionally and John Smith's Bitter is a regular. The pub enjoys a strong local following and attracts many visitors to its pleasant location. The Hewitts Brewery mirror indicates its former pedigree. ♨❀♣P

EAST KIRKBY

Red Lion
Main Road
⏲ 12-2.30, 7-11; 12-3, 7-10.30 Sun
☎ (01790) 763406
Draught Bass; Broadstone Best Bitter; guest beers Ⓗ
Typical village pub frequented extensively by locals and visitors alike. It is close to a WWII airfield, once fully operational, now a museum. This three-roomed inn is full of old clocks, old tools, breweriana and antiques. The Red Lion offers a warm welcome and good home-cooked food. ♨Q❀◑◑▲♣P

EASTOFT

River Don Tavern
Sampson Street (A161, Gainsborough-Goole road)
⏲ 12-2, 6 -11; 12-11 Sat; 12-10.30 Sun
☎ (01724) 798040
John Smith's Bitter; Taylor Landlord; guest beers Ⓗ
Village local in the Isle of Axholme, CAMRA's Pub of the Isle for the last two years. A single room is divided into distinct drinking areas. Popular for good value food, particularly the hot skillet meals, it also has a restaurant (no lunches Tue). Three rotating guest beers mainly come from Yorkshire and Lincolnshire independents. It hosts an annual beer festival in summer, regular theme and party nights, and ferret racing in season (Oct-Jan). ♨❀◑◑♿▲♣P

GRIMSBY

Royal Oak
190 Victoria Street
11.30-11; 12-10.30 Sun
(01472) 354562
Draught Bass; Theakston Mild; guest beers Ⓗ
Attractive Tudor-style front and leaded lights suggest a traditional interior; a pleasant lounge plus a bar where games are played.

HORNCASTLE

Black Swan Inn
South Street
11-3, 6.30-11; 11-11.30 Sat (supper licence); 12-3, 7-10.30 Sun
(01507) 522378
John Smith's Bitter; Taylor Landlord; Tetley Bitter; guest beer (occasional) Ⓗ
Large renovated old pub, aimed at the younger generation, with one cosy snug for more mature customers.

LEADENHAM

Willoughby Arms
5 High Street
12-3 (not Mon-Wed), 5 (6 Sat)-11; 12-3, 7-10.30 Sun
(01400) 272432
Adnams Bitter; Draught Bass; Greene King IPA; Marston's Bitter Ⓗ
Comfortable inn, with an emphasis on food. The oak-panelled bar area has armchairs and occasional tables.

LINCOLN

Post Office Sports & Social Club
Maitland Block, Dunkirk Road
11-3 (4 Sat), 7-11; 12-10.30 Sun
(01522) 524050
John Smith's Bitter; guest beer Ⓗ
No-frills club, off Burton Road. Show a CAMRA membership card or this Guide to gain entry.

Pyewipe Inn
Fosse Bank, Saxilby Road
11-11; 12-10.30 Sun
(01522) 528708
Draught Bass; Greene King Abbot; Flowers Original; guest beers Ⓗ
Large pub, restaurant and hotel on the banks of the Fossdyke Roman Canal; access is via the A57.

LOUTH

White Horse
Kenwick Road
12-2.30, 6-11 (5.30-midnight Fri); 12-midnight Sat; 12-4, 6-10.30 Sun
(01507) 603331
Adnams Bitter; Draught Bass; Fuller's London Pride; Greene King Old Speckled Hen Ⓗ
Enjoying a strong local following, it offers a cosy, friendly atmosphere. Excellent reputation for food. Large outdoor area.

EAST STOCKWITH

Ferry House
27 Front Street
11.30-3, 6.30-11; closed Mon; 12-10.30 Sun
☎ (01427) 615276
John Smith's Bitter; Webster's Yorkshire Bitter; guest beers Ⓗ
Trentside, family-run free house catering for a wide mix of customers. Quality home-cooked food is served at all times and represents excellent value for money. The pub boasts a large function room and three guest rooms with river views (£20 per person per night including breakfast). Two guest beers are always stocked. A quiz is staged on alternate Wednesday evenings.
⌂❀⊨◑♣P

EPWORTH

Red Lion
Market Place
11-11; 11-10.30 Sun
☎ (01427) 872208
Tetley Bitter, Burton Ale; guest beers Ⓗ
Epworth, home of John and Charles Wesley, is the capital of the Isle of Axholme. Adjacent to the market cross stands this old coaching inn, a prime example of a modern village pub, offering a wide choice of activities, and drinking areas to cater for visitors and locals alike. The restaurant's extensive menu specialises in steaks. Reasonably-priced accommodation includes a four-poster bed, but the beer is rather expensive. Monthly folk music is staged (first Mon).
⌂⊨◑♿♣P⊭

EWERBY

Finch Hatton Arms
Main Street
12-3, 6-11; 12-3, 6-10.30 Sun
☎ (01529) 460363
Black Sheep Best Bitter; Everards Tiger; guest beer Ⓗ
Built in the early 1870s as the Angel Inn, it was bought by Lord Winchelsea in 1875 and given his family name until the mid-1960s. From a traditionally brewery-owned village pub, it then started the transition into the free house it is today. Now a fully-equipped small hotel, its extensive menu is varied, both in taste and price.
Q❀⊨◑P

FISHTOFT

Red Cow Inn
Gaysfield Road
12-3 (not Wed), 7-11; 11-11 Sat; 11-10.30 Sun
☎ (01205) 367552
Bateman Mild, XB Ⓗ
Well-established, one-roomed village local where friendly staff and customers quickly make strangers welcome. It fields many teams – for darts, pool, dominoes and quizzes. It also hosts occasional entertainment, such as local bands and race nights. About a mile from the Pilgrim Fathers' memorial, it is handy for anglers on nearby waters or ramblers and twitchers on the Wash banks. A good place to relax after the exercise, with a pint by the log fire.
⌂❀▲♣P

FLEET HARGATE

Bull Inn
Old Main Road (just off A17)
12-11; 12-10.30 Sun
☎ (01406) 426866
Bateman XB; guest beer Ⓗ
Ideally situated, just off the A17, the interior of the pub is decorated with pump clips of the many guest beers it has sold, including a good number of milds and stouts. It is home to darts, crib and dominoes teams, and hosts quiz nights. Midweek (Tue-Thu), the beer price is reduced – currently £1.60 a pint. The pub is convenient for the caravan park in the village. Evening meals are served Wed-Sat. ❀⊨◑▲♣P

FRAMPTON

Moores Arms
Church End (turn E at Kirton roundabout on A16, 1 mile)
11.30-3, 6-11; 11.30-11 Fri & Sat; 12-10.30 Sun
☎ (01205) 722408
Draught Bass; Bateman XB; guest beers Ⓗ
Dating from 1690, this village pub is well situated for walks and cycle rides to the marshes and RSPB nature reserve. It features bare brick walls and a large log fire. An extensive home-cooked menu is served in the bar and restaurant. Families are welcome, and it gets very busy Sunday lunchtime. The pub now offers a wider range of guest beers (usually two at a time).
⌂❀◑P⊭

FROGNALL

Goat
155 Spalding Road (B1525, Deeping road – old A16)
11.30-2.30, 6-11; 12-3, 6.30-10.30 Sun
☎ (01778) 347629
website: www.goat.frognall@virgin.net
Beer range varies Ⓗ
Dated 1647 and set back from the main road, this pub consists of a bar and two dining areas, where families are made welcome. Excellent food is cooked to order, and the beer range is sourced only from small regional or micro-breweries. The spacious garden has a play area for children and caters for under-fives with a variety of toys. Many awards are held by this family-run pub. ⌂Q❀◑▲P

GAINSBOROUGH ✻

Eight Jolly Brewers
Ship Court, Silver Street (off market place)
11-11; 12-10.30 Sun
☎ (01427) 677128
Broadstone Best Bitter; Highwood Tom Wood's Best Bitter; Holt Mild; Taylor Landlord; guest beers Ⓗ
An oasis which serves up to five guest ales, all from small breweries – one or two are always very cheap. Leffe, and a real cider or perry are also on draught; several foreign bottled beers (mostly Belgian) are stocked, too. The busy downstairs bar has two TVs showing sport, while upstairs is a quiet bar, except alternate Fridays, when the folk club meets. Good cheap food is served upstairs (not weekends), where much beer and brewery memorabilia is displayed.
Q❀◑♣P⊭

GOSBERTON

Bell Inn

High Street (A52)
11.30-3, 6-11; 11.30-11 Sat; 12-3, 7-10.30 Sun
(01775) 840186
Beer range varies H
Family-run pub of two bars, in the centre of the village. It has no regular beer, but offers a changing selection of one or two real ales, mainly from micro-breweries. The upstairs restaurant serves lunches and evening meals. The pub is very popular with locals and fields darts and quiz teams.
Q P

GOSBERTON RISEGATE

Duke of York

106 Risegate Road
12-11; 12-4, 7-11 Sun
(01775) 840193
Bateman XB; guest beers H
Bustling pub at the centre of village life, supporting local fund-raising efforts. It enjoys a justified reputation for beer and food at reasonable prices. The multi-roomed interior includes a no-smoking dining room and a games room. The guest beers change frequently to ensure every taste is catered for. A large garden with children's play area, goats and other animals provides additional attraction – no food Monday lunchtime.
P

GRANTHAM

Nobody Inn

9 North Street
11-11; 12-10.30 Sun
(01476) 565288 website: www.nobodyinn.com
Samuel Smith OBB; Theakston Cool Cask; guest beers H
This award-winning pub attracts a cross-section of locals. A basic boozer, it features pool, darts and sports TV. Often busy on Friday and Saturday nights, the Nobody Inn is what a good pub should be. Beware the toilet doors which often catch out strangers. The four guest beers are usually from Oakham and Newby Wyke breweries.

Lord Harrowby

65 Dudley Road
4-11; 12-10.30 Sun
(01476) 402121
Draught Bass; Worthington Bitter; guest beer H
Situated in a built-up area, this local always offers a friendly welcome. The 1930s style remains in this back-street boozer, with a bar and a lounge; note the jug and bottle entrance. The prices, in this independent, family-run pub, are low for the area. The piano in the lounge is used most Saturday nights for a regular singalong. This room is decorated with aviation pictures, capturing the spirit of Grantham's links with the RAF.

GRIMSBY

Rutland Arms

26-30 Rutland Street (behind Ramsdens store)
11-11; 7-10.30 Sun
(01472) 268732
Old Mill Mild, Bitter H
Converted from a derelict social club in 1988, this local has been a regular in this Guide since opening, and was a former local CAMRA Pub of the Year. It bears exposed brickwork and wood panelling throughout the interior; the games area is separate from the main lounge. Occasional karaoke sessions take place. On Sunday lunchtimes free snacks are available to all customers. The outdoor drinking area is simply the street. (New Clee)

Swigs

21 Osborne Street
11-11; 12-10.30 Sun
(01472) 354773
Bateman XB; Willy's Original Bitter; guest beers H
Second outlet for Willy's Brewery of Cleethorpes, it has a continental café atmosphere and offers excellent home-made food. It gets busy with shoppers and local office workers at lunchtime and opens at 9am for coffee and snacks. Some evenings can be boisterous, when it is popular with students. It has appeared in this Guide for the last 11 years. (Town)

Yarborough Hotel

29 Bethlehem Street (next to station)
11-11; 12-10.30 Sun
(01472) 268283
Bateman Mild; Courage Directors; Theakston Best Bitter, Cool Cask; guest beers H
Wetherspoon's first outlet in Grimsby, this pub has twice been CAMRA winner of the local Pub of the Year award. As is usual with this chain, the sympathetic renovation of this former railway hotel provides the drinker with an impressive venue to enjoy a pint. The cider is Addlestone's.
Q (Town)

HAXEY

Loco

31-33 Church Street
2 (12 Sat)-11; 12-10.30 Sun
(01427) 752879
John Smith's Bitter; guest beers H
Beautifully converted from a former Co-op store, the bar boasts carved woodwork, a flagged floor, old tools, taps, brass and the front end of a steam loco – hence the name! It caters for all tastes by the recent addition of a restaurant, specialising in Indian food, and Ziggy's bar, with a modern entertainment system, aimed at younger customers. The enterprising landlord is keen to promote local brewers.
P

HEIGHINGTON

Butcher & Beast

High Street
11-4, 7-11; 11-11 Fri & Sat ; 12-10.30 Sun
(01522) 790386
Draught Bass; Bateman XB, XXXB H
Pleasant local in a commuter village to the south of Lincoln. It is popular with games teams, and for a variety of village functions. The hanging baskets outside have previously won awards. Note the remote handpumps behind the bar; two guest beers are always available at a competitive price. Try the restaurant for good quality food (eve meals served Tue-Sat).
P

HEMINGBY

Coach & Horses

Church Lane (1 mile from A158)

12-2 (not Mon or Tue), 7 (6 Wed-Fri)-11; 12-3, 7-10.30 Sun

(01507) 578280

website: www.coach-horses.sagenet.co.uk

Bateman Mild, XB; guest beer H

Proper country pub that is well worth finding – real ale, good, plain home-cooked food at sensible prices, low beams, an open log fire and a warm welcome – who could ask for more? A regular outlet for Bateman Mild, the guest beer is often from a Yorkshire brewery, reflecting the landlord's origins. A bonfire and fireworks display, in aid of a village charity, is held on November 5. Meals are served Wed-Sun (but not Sun eve). Q P

HORNCASTLE

Crown Inn

28 West Street

11-11; 12-10.30 Sun

(01507) 526006

Draught Bass; Bateman XB H

Renovated, comfortable and friendly old pub in an attractive market town full of antique shops. Once owned by Hewitts of Grimsby and then a Bateman house, it was bought in 1987 by the present real ale-drinking landlord. See the pictures of old pubs in Horncastle (many now closed) and one of West Street circa 1900. The bar, and much of the seating, are made from old church pews. Note the attractive old glass etched mirrors behind the bar. An active games pub, it has a pool table. P

HUMBERSTON

Trading Post

Grimsby Road

11-11; 12-10.30 Sun

Marston's Pedigree H

The American log cabin style gives this pub a distinctly colonial feel. A large outdoor play area, coupled with a similar indoor facility, makes it an ideal venue to take children of all ages. A wide-ranging menu offers generous portions, guaranteed to satisfy most appetites. Q P

KIRKBY ON BAIN

Ebrington Arms

Main Street

12-2.30 (3 Sat; not Mon), 7-11; 12-3, 7-10.30 Sun

(01526) 354560

Bateman XB; guest beers H

Lively village local, dating back to the 16th century. This two-roomed pub boasts exposed timber ceilings. Normally between three to four guest ales are served, but this may vary during the winter months. Bar snacks are available at most times.

Q P

LINCOLN

Grand Hotel

St Mary's Street (opp. station)

11-3, 5.30-11; 12-10.30 Sun

(01522) 524211

Draught Bass; guest beers H

Drink in the Tudor Bar of this plush hotel to try a good range of guest beers, lovingly cared for by the bar team. The hotel has 46 rooms which include executive suites and four-poster beds. The renowned restaurant serves a wide variety of meals, including vegetarian options and Sunday lunch. Real ale may not be available on Sunday afternoon.

P

Lord Tennyson

72 Rasen Lane

11-2.30, 5.30-11; 12-2.30, 7-10.30 Sun

(01522) 889262

Draught Bass; Greene King IPA; Tetley Bitter; guest beer H

This city pub retains a local feel, while being close to the tourist area of Bailgate. It is named after the Lincolnshire Poet Laureate, commemorated on a front wall plaque. The comfortable open-plan interior splits into several drinking areas, with space in the larger back room for pool. The pub offers good value food; the guest beer is from the Pubmaster list.

P

Morning Star

11 Greetwell Gate (near cathedral)

11-11; 12-10.30 Sun

(01522) 527079

INN BRIEF

MARKET DEEPING

Vine
19 Church Street
11.30-2, 5.30-11; 11.30-3, 6.30-11 Sat; 12-3, 7-10.30 Sun
(01778) 342387
Wells Eagle, Bombardier; guest beer H
Small local, formerly a Victorian prep school; small bar and a cosy lounge. Cask Marque accredited.

NORTH KELSEY

Butcher's Arms
Middle Street
4-11; 12-11 Sat; 12-10.30 Sun
(01652) 678002
Highwood Tom Wood's Best Bitter, Tom Wood's Harvest Bitter; guest beer H
Small, refurbished traditional pub owned by Highwood. A lounge bar decorated in farmhouse style with a splendid fire.

Royal Oak
High Street
12-2 (4 Sat), 7-11; 12-2, 7-10.30 Sun
(01652) 678544
Barnsley Bitter; Marston's Pedigree H
Old pub in a quiet village. Comfortable lounge with open fire and wood-burning stove. Meals served Tue-Sun (not Sun eve).

SANDTOFT

Reindeer
Thorne Road
12-2 (not Mon), 5 (7 Fri & Sat)-11; 12-4, 7-10.30 Sun
(01724) 710774
John Smith's Bitter; Worthington Bitter H
Friendly pub near the local Trolley Bus Museum. Accent on food, busy at weekends. Now owned by Enterprise Inns. Children's certificate.

SCAWBY BROOK

King William IV
177 Scawby Road
12-2, 6-11; 12-3, 7-10.30 Sun
(01652) 653147
Theakston Best Bitter; Worthington Bitter; guest beers H
Friendly 18th-century pub, displaying royal and football memorabilia. Different guest beer each week. Sun lunch served.

SCOTTON

Three Horseshoes
Westgate
12-3 (not Mon-Fri), 7-11; 12-3, 7-10.30 Sun
(01724) 763129
John Smith's Bitter; guest beer H
Traditional village local; serves no food.

Greene King Ruddles Best Bitter, Abbot; Marston's Pedigree; Tetley Bitter; Wells Bombardier; guest beer Ⓗ

Opened in 1791 as the Fighting Cocks and renamed in 1841, the pub stands 200 yards east of the cathedral, near the major tourist sights. The main bar, with tiled floor, features pictures of bygone city days, while the smaller, rear bar is a cosy lounge. Saturday evenings are enlivened by a splendidly 'Les Dawsonesque' pianist; a popular quiz night is held each Tuesday. Jazz or Irish music accompanies occasional spring and summer barbecues in the garden. No lunches served Sun. ⛫Q❀◐⊟P

Peacock Inn

23 Wragby Road

⏲ 11-11; 12-10.30 Sun

☎ (01522) 524703

Hardys & Hansons Best Mild, Best Bitter, Classic, seasonal beers Ⓗ

Traditional corner-sited friendly pub; one room, plus a restaurant, serving excellent home-cooked food. Within sight of the cathedral, in the 'uphill' area of the city, it is an easy walk from the centre, and not far from the hospital. Outdoor drinking is on the patio.

⛫❀◐▶♣P

Queen in the West

12 Moor Street (off A57)

⏲ 12-3, 5.30-11; 12-11 Fri & Sat; 12-10.30 Sun

☎ (01522) 880123

Greene King Old Speckled Hen; Shepherd Neame Spitfire; John Smith's Bitter; Theakston XB; Wells Bombardier; guest beers Ⓗ

Once again a deserved entry in this Guide. Fully committed to serving quality real ale, this friendly pub is well worth seeking out. Good value food is served weekday lunchtimes when the pub is quiet. It can be bustling in the evening, living up to its claim to be a village pub in the West End. Usually a minimum of seven real ales include well-chosen guest beers. Highly recommended. ◐⊟♣

Reindeer Hotel

8 High Street (1 mile S of centre)

⏲ 12-11; 12-3, 7-10.30 Sun

☎ (01522) 520024

John Smith's Bitter; Tetley Dark Mild; guest beer Ⓗ

More of a pub than an hotel, situated at the bottom end of a long High Street. A comfortable lounge at the front contrasts with a more basic bar to the rear. Games are popular in the bar, and there is a quiz on Sunday evening. It is very convenient for the twice-yearly funfair on South Common. ⇄◐⊟♿♣P

Sippers Free House

26 Melville Street (near bus and rail stations)

⏲ 11-2, 5 (4 Fri; 7 Sat)-11; 7-10.30 (closed lunch) Sun

☎ (01522) 527612

Courage Directors; Greene King Old Speckled Hen; Marston's Pedigree; John Smith's Bitter; Wells Bombardier; guest beer Ⓗ

Comfortable, two-roomed corner pub, with various alcoved seating areas. A display of nautical items and paintings, includes a model sailing ship; look for the portholes set into one of the walls. The guest beer is usually from an independent brewer. It serves a good range of pub grub – the home-cooked ham is worth a try. This regular Guide entry gets busy weekday lunchtimes. ◐▶⇄

Strugglers Inn

83 Westgate (by castle)

⏲ 11.30-11; 12-10.30 Sun

☎ (01522) 535023

Draught Bass; Fuller's London Pride; Greene King Abbot; Hardys & Hansons Best Mild Ⓗ

First registered as an ale house in 1863, as the Struggler in the Globe, the present sign depicts a hanging – the public gallows once stood nearby. There are two bars – the bustling public bar contrasts well with the cosy snug. The patio offers a sheltered spot that is popular with families, and has barbecue facilities; during the summer the display of flowers is magnificent. Good value home-cooked lunches are served weekdays.

⛫Q❀◐⊟

Victoria

6 Union Road (behind castle)

⏲ 11-11; 12-10.30 Sun

☎ (01522) 536048

Bateman XB; Everards Original; Taylor Landlord; guest beers Ⓗ

Part of the Tynemill chain, this imposing pub lies between the castle and the Lawns tourism centre. There is always a mild among the five guest beers, and normally one from Castle Rock. Cooked breakfast is available on Saturday, and Sunday lunch can be booked in the upstairs restaurant or eaten downstairs. Beer festivals are held in June and at Christmas, but unfortunately some of the beers can be expensive.

Q❀◐⊟♿♣●

LOUTH ❄

Mason's Arms Hotel

Cornmarket

⏲ 11 (10am for coffee)-11; 11-3, 7-10.30 Sun

☎ (01507) 609525 website: www.themasons.co.uk

Bateman XB, XXXB; Marston's Pedigree; Samuel Smith OBB; Taylor Landlord; guest beer Ⓗ

Early 18th-century posting inn on the market square, formerly a meeting place for the Louth Masonic Lodge, it is now Grade II listed. Recognisable Masonic symbols can be seen on fireplaces, doors and windows. The friendly, family-run hotel bar offers excellent home-made fare (children are welcome while food is being served); the upstairs restaurant is open Friday and Saturday evenings, and Sunday lunchtime.

⇄◐▶

Newmarket Inn

600 yards E of cattle market

⏲ 7-11; 12-3, 7-10.30 Sun

☎ (01507) 605146

Adnams Bitter; Black Sheep Best Bitter; Robinson's Hartleys XB Ⓗ

This warm, welcoming free house is cosy, well furnished and comfortable. The relaxed landlord is most friendly, and attracts a middle-class clientele. Close to the theatre, it is frequented by audience members, actors and singers from local choirs. An evening venue, it serves no food, except sandwiches for the male voice choir on Tuesday – when they come to lubricate their vocal chords. Q♿

Wheatsheaf Inn

62 Westgate (near St James Church)

11-3, 5-11; 11-11 Sat; 12-4, 7-10.30 Sun

(01507) 603159

Boddingtons Bitter; Flowers Original; Taylor Landlord; guest beers H

Tucked away in the conservation area of a thriving market town, this 17th-century inn has three bars – all with coal fires and low, beamed ceilings. A 'beer and bangers' festival, held in May/June, is a popular annual event. The magnificent St James Church spire is a wonderful sight from the garden, as are the pub's large hanging baskets. A house beer, Tipsy Toad, comes from an undisclosed source. Lunches are served Mon-Sat.

Woodman

134 Eastgate

11-4, 7-11; 11-11 Fri & Sat; 12-3, 7-10.30 Sun

(01507) 602100

Banks's Original; Greene King Abbot; John Smith's Bitter; guest beers H

19th-century, town-centre pub, attracting a good mix of customers to its large lounge bar with several different areas. The public bar, to the rear, has a pool table. Two rotating guest beers are always available. Lunchtime food is served Mon-Sat.

MESSINGHAM

Horn Inn

High Street

11-11; 12-10.30 Sun

(01724) 762426

John Smith's Bitter; guest beers H

This friendly, well-appointed village pub is situated on a main road. It has an open-plan design around a central bar, with discrete areas for drinking and eating. It enjoys a good reputation for its range of tasty home-cooked meals. The rural atmosphere is enhanced by framed pictures, wooden furniture and exposed beams (remember to duck). Live music is popular (Wed eve). The two guest beers usually come from independent brewers. Well worth a visit. Wheelchair WC.

MORTON

Crooked Billet

1 Crooked Billet Street

12-11; 12-10.30 Sun

(01427) 612584

Beer range varies H

A central bar serves the three rooms of this large Victorian pub. The games room, to the rear, has table football, a juke box, pinball machine and Sky TV; it hosts occasional live music. The quiet smoke room displays local pre-war photos. The middle room stages events such as bingo and quizzes. The pub is used by the local sports teams and has a solid regular following. The two beers come from a wide range of breweries.

NETTLEHAM

Black Horse

Chapple Lane

11.30-3 (4.30 Sat), 6 (5.30 Fri)-11; 12-5.30, 7-10.30 Sun

(01522) 750702

Bateman XB; Brains Dark; Highwood Tom Wood's Harvest Bitter; Tetley Bitter; guest beers H

This village pub circa 1800, was enlarged to incorporate the workhouse in 1833. Refurbished some years ago, it retained the stone and beams and 'loads of ghosts', of the original L-shaped pub. Good wholesome food is served in the lounge, billed as 'the place to go if you do not want to cook at home' (evening meals finish at 8pm). Note the Bavarian hand-carved wood panels on the bar. Well-known blues or folk musicians play regularly. Three guest beers are sold.

Plough

1 The Green

3.30-11; 12-3, 7-10.30 Sun

(01522) 750275

Draught Bass; Bateman XB, seasonal beers; guest beer H

Of the four pubs in the village, this stone local on the green caters mainly for drinkers and serves no food apart from nuts and crisps. The opening hours are aimed at locals having a drink after work and in the evening. Most pub games are played. The low beams and pillars give the place a multi-room feel, even though it is mainly opened out.

NETTLETON

Salutation Inn

Church Street (A46)

12-3, 6-11; 12-3, 7-10.30 Sun

(01472) 851228

Highwood Tom Wood's Best Bitter; Taylor Landlord; Wadworth 6X; guest beers H

Cosy, friendly pub, situated on the edge of the Lincolnshire Wolds, it was the recipient of local CAMRA's first award for Country Pub of the Year. A good stop for walkers, food is served lunchtime and evening. The L-shaped bar has a dining area at one end, with local scenes of yesteryear adorning the walls.

NORTH KELSEY MOOR

Queen's Head

Station Road, North Kelsey (near disused station)

OS070018

12-2 (4 Sat; not Mon, Wed or Thu); 7-11; 12-4, 7-10.30 Sun

(01652) 678055

Theakston Best Bitter; guest beer H

Well-appointed, old free house, with a sympathetic modern extension. In a rural setting, the pub is enhanced by a well-kept garden. A cosy public bar, with coal fire, is decorated with beer mats and bottles; the comfortable lounge, with solid fuel stove, has two seating areas, and there is a smart dining room. Pensioners are offered special lunches (Tue and Fri); no food Sun eve.

NORTH THORESBY

New Inn

Station Road

⏲ 12-3, 6-10.30; 12-11 Sat; 12-10.30 Sun

☎ (01472) 840270

Mansfield Dark Mild; Marston's Bitter, Pedigree; guest beers 🄷

Family-run free house, a community-centred pub, with an excellent, busy restaurant area. The pub fields the usual teams (darts, dominoes and pool); Sunday is quiz night. An annual beer festival is held on August bank holiday. There is an outside play area; barbecues are a regular weekend event during the summer.
⩕❀◖♿♣P

ROPSLEY

Green Man

24 High Street

⏲ 7 (12 Sat)-11; 12-10.30 Sun

☎ (01476) 585223

John Smith's Magnet; Theakston XB; guest beers 🄷

Popular with locals, this down-to-earth, family-run pub is in the centre of Ropsley. It has a split-level layout; the bar supports village darts and pool teams, while the cosy lounge has recently been refurbished. The rare John Smith's Magnet is always on offer, and the pub features ales from local micros. On cold winter nights the real log fire is a welcome sight. In summer, sit in the small, pretty garden and enjoy the tranquil countryside or, for the more energetic, join in a game of boules.
⩕Q❀⊟♣P

ROTHWELL

Blacksmith's Arms

Hillrise

⏲ 11-11; 12-10.30 Sun

☎ (01472) 371300

Courage Directors; guest beers 🄷

Nestling in the heart of the Lincolnshire Wolds, this comfortable pub used to be the favourite haunt of RAF personnel from the now-defunct Binbrook air base. The dining room menu offers some unusual dishes – from bison to kangaroo and guinea-fowl to ostrich. Jazz sessions take place in the large function room attached to the pub. You can expect a warm, friendly welcome here.
⩕Q❀◖◗P

SAXILBY

Anglers

65 High Street

⏲ 11.30-2.30, 6 (5 Fri; 7 Sat)-11; 12-3, 7-10.30 Sun

☎ (01522) 702200

Theakston Best Bitter; guest beer 🄷

Genuine village local run by a local man, it is always busy. Games are an essential element here – with teams for darts, pool, cribbage and dominoes; match evenings can be lively. Lunchtimes are usually quieter when table skittles is sometimes played. The lounge bar, displaying old village photos, is the monthly meeting place of the local history group. The pub name refers to the hordes of anglers who once flocked to the nearby Foss Dyke, the country's oldest canal.
❀⊟⥂♣P

SCAMBLESBY

Green Man

Old Main Road (near A153)

⏲ 12-11; 12-10.30 Sun

☎ (01507) 343282

Black Sheep Best Bitter; guest beers 🄷

200-year-old South Wold village local, run by friendly, real ale-loving licensees. A roaring fire, a fine view, Harry (the pub's dog) and a pool table are features of the bar. The smaller, comfortable lounge has beams, rocking chairs, and, reputedly, a ghost. The Viking Way footpath and Cadwell Motorcycle racing circuit are nearby (motorcyclists are welcome and motorcycle prints are for sale). Good value food is served 12-9. ⩕Q☕❀⛟◖◗⊟⛺♣P

SCAMPTON

Dambusters Inn

High Street

⏲ 12-2.30 (3 Sat), 5-11; 12-4, 7-10.30 Sun

☎ (01522) 731333

Greene King IPA, Abbot; guest beer (summer) 🄷

Excellent example of a rural combination of pub and post office. Here the PO was already in situ, and the landlord turned part of his 17th-century house into a pub. It is bursting with memorabilia from the nearby airbase (currently home to the Red Arrows and previously the famous 617 Dambusters Squadron). The atmosphere is often enhanced by unobtrusive period background music. There is a sheltered no-smoking restaurant area to the rear; evening meals served Tue-Sat. ⩕❀◖◗P

SCAWBY BROOK ❄

Horse & Cart

185 Scawby Road (B1206, 1 mile W of Brigg)

⏲ 12-2.30, 5-11; 12-11 Sat; 12-10.30 Sun

☎ (01652) 652150

Daleside Bitter; Faint Hope Lazy Drayman; guest beers 🄷

Large free house, built on the site of previous pubs of the same name, with a large garden. The landlord recently started an on-site micro-brewery, Faint Hope, whose beers are finding favour both locally and at CAMRA festivals across the country. A wide range of guest beers also feature. The chef has won prizes for his pies; the special steak and mushroom pie with sherry gravy is especially recommended (eve meals Tue-Sat). It hosts twice-yearly beer festivals (Easter and Aug). ◖◗⊟⛺♣P

SCOTTER

White Swan

9 The Green

⏲ 11.30-3, 6.30-11; 11.30-11 Fri & Sat; 12-10.30 Sun

☎ (01724) 762342

John Smith's Bitter; Webster's Yorkshire Bitter; guest beers 🄷

Smart village local, decorated in country style. Very popular for food, both in the bar and in the adjoining restaurant area; the latter overlooks the garden and the River Eau. A good beer range always includes two or three guest beers. Good quality accommodation (15 rooms) completes the amenities here. ❀⛟◖◗P

SCUNTHORPE

Blue Bell Inn

1-7 Oswald Road (near station)
⊙ 11-11; 12-10.30 Sun
☎ (01724) 863921
Courage Directors; Shepherd Neame Spitfire; Theakston Best Bitter; guest beers 🄷
Wetherspoon's Blue Bell is named after a town-centre pub which closed long ago. An L-shaped, ground-floor bar is complemented by a raised no-smoking area for diners. Very popular at weekends with drinkers on the pub circuit, it holds regular beer festivals through the year. The patio is used by drinkers and diners in summer. A braille menu is available. Families with children are welcome to dine until 7pm Mon-Thu, 6pm Fri-Sun. Q❀◐◑♿⇌⊬

Honest Lawyer

70 Oswald Road (near station)
⊙ 11-11; 12-10.30 Sun
☎ (01724) 849906
Daleside Bitter; guest beers 🄷
A long, narrow bar area is fitted out in old-style dark wood decor on a legal theme. A drinking area upstairs has a large-screen TV. It is very popular among real ale drinkers due to it having a regular bitter, a real cider (Addlestone's) and five guest ales. An outdoor drinking area is set up in front of the pub during summer. ⇌🍎

Malt Shovel

219 Ashby High Street
⊙ 11-11; 12-10.30 Sun
☎ (01724) 843318
Barnsley Bitter; Courage Directors; Theakston Old Peculier; guest beers 🄷
Quiet and welcoming town pub, in a busy shopping area. A low, beamed ceiling, chintz furnishings and dark wood fittings give a country atmosphere. It is popular for meals at lunchtime and early evening. Two or three guest beers showcase independent brewers such as Abbeydale, Glentworth, Highwood and Rudgate. Its adjoining licensed snooker club also offers real ales (full and social membership available; guests can be signed in).
Q❀◐◑

Queen Bess

Derwent Road, Ashby (near A18, at Grange Lane N jct)
⊙ 11.30-3.30 (4 Sat), 6-11; 12-3, 7-10.30 Sun
☎ (01724) 840827
Samuel Smith OBB 🄷
Estate pub, named after a local ironmaking furnace, comprising a comfortable lounge with real fire, a public bar and a large function room which stages occasional live music. It draws a lively local trade and is always welcoming. The longest-serving licensee in the area deserves his reputation for the quality of his real ale. It has an active sports following and fields pub games teams. Hot snack meals are always available; the pub has a children's certificate.
⛼❀⊟♣P

SKEGNESS

Vine Hotel

Vine Road, Seacroft (1 mile S of centre)
⊙ 10-11; 10-10.30 Sun
☎ (01754) 763018 website: www.thevinehotel.com
Bateman Mild, XB, XXXB 🄷
Country-style hotel in a delightful, secluded setting, offering a complete contrast to the noise and bustle of the resort. One of the town's oldest buildings, with tales of smugglers and revenue men, Tennyson knew this part of Lincolnshire well and may have visited the Vine – his boyhood home is only a few miles away. Today's visitors will discover the perfect antidote to the razzmatazz of Skegness in summer or the biting east wind of the winter.
⛼♉❀⇆◐◑⊟♣P

SKILLINGTON

Cross Swords

The Square
⊙ 12-2 (not Mon), 7-11; 12-3, 7-10.30 Sun
☎ (01476) 861132 website: www.xswords.demon.co.uk
Highwood Tom Wood's Best Bitter; guest beers 🄷
Small, but homely, family-run pub in the middle of the village, very popular with walkers. Guest beers usually come from the Beer Seller list. The licensees are renowned for their excellent home-cooked food, using

INN BRIEF

SOUTH THORESBY

Vine
12 (7 Mon)-11; 12-10.30 Sun
(01507) 480273
Bateman XB; guest beer 🄷
Walkers' pub: wellies, boots and dogs welcome. Primitive in decor and furnishings, but a good free house in a lonely spot. Monthly guest beer.

SPALDING

Birds
108 Halmergate
11-11; 12-10.30 Sun
(01775) 732239
Greene King IPA; guest beer 🄷
Large, modern pub, just off A16 bypass. Recently refurbished as part of the Hungry Horse chain. Large outdoor area for children.

SPILSBY

Shades
24 Church Street
12-2 (not Wed), 6.30-11 (may vary summer); 12-2, 6.30-10.30 Sun
(01790) 752200
Bateman XB, seasonal beers; guest beer (occasional) 🄷
Spacious, airy, pleasantly modernised pub. Garden houses four aviaries. Accommodation; no food Sun eve.

SWINHOPE

Click'em Inn
On B1203
12-3, 7-11; 11-11 Sat; 12-3, 7-10.30 Sun
(01472) 398253
Theakston XB; guest beers 🄷
Homely atmosphere in a multi-roomed pub. Restaurant has a no-smoking policy. House beer is Click'em Inn Bitter.

WELBOURN

Joiner's Inn
21 High Street
12-3 (not Mon or Tue), 6-11; 12-3, 7-10.30 Sun
(01400) 272430
Everards Tiger, Original; Woodforde's Wherry; 🄷 **guest beer** 🄷/🄶
Atmospheric bar with fires at either end. One guest beer is usually served on gravity dispense March-Oct.

WHAPLODE ST CATHERINE

Blue Bell
Cranesgate
7-11; 12-3, 7-11 Sat; closed Mon; 12-3, 7-10.30 Sun
(01406) 540300
Blue Bell Olde Session, Olde Honesty, Olde Fashioned 🄷
Popular Fenland gem, home of the Blue Bell Brewery. Busy restaurant – booking advisable. The same landlord for 30 years.

mostly local produce, including game in season, and well-kept ales. The bar is small but comfortable, decorated with prints of the local hunting scenes. Booking is essential for the wonderful Sunday lunches.

SLEAFORD

Marquis of Granby

Westgate

4-11; 12-11 Sat & summer; 12-10.30 Sun

(01529) 303223

Flowers Original; Tetley Bitter; guest beer H

No-frills pub, just away from the centre of this market town. A former home-brew house, it was licensed under the Beer House Act of 1830 which allowed a householder or rate payer, on the payment of two guineas, to turn a private house into a public house. It is now a single-bar back-street local. Its teams enter all the traditional pub games in local leagues. This cosy pub extends a warm welcome to visitors.

SOUTH ORMSBY

Massingberd Arms

Brinkhill Road (1 1/2 miles from A16 turn at Swaby)

12-3 (not winter Mon), 5.30-11; 12-5, 7-10.30 Sun

(01507) 480492

John Smith's Bitter; guest beers H

Rural pub set in the heart of the Lincolnshire Wolds, a designated area of outstanding natural beauty. The unusual pub name comes from local landowners. The pub dates back over 200 years and is filled with old photos and curios; look out for the selection of old wooden model planes. It is ideal for walkers, daytrippers and locals alike; children, kept under adult supervision, are welcome for meals.

SPALDING

Lincoln Arms

4 Bridge Street

11-3 (3.30 Sat), 7-11; 12-4, 7.30-10.30 Sun

(01775) 722691

Banks's Original; Mansfield Dark Mild, Riding Bitter, Cask Ale, seasonal beers H

Traditional, 18th-century riverside local, overlooking the River Welland by the town bridge. It is very popular with locals and is the meeting place for various clubs, including the local branch of CAMRA. The Spalding Folk Club holds monthly gigs (first Wed). The pub has now appeared in this Guide for nine consecutive years, a testament to the landlord's pursuit of quality.

Olde White Horse

Churchgate

11.30-2.30, 5-11; 11-4, 7-11 Sat; 12-4, 7-10.30 Sun

(01775) 766740

Samuel Smith OBB H

Imposing, 14th-century thatched building by the town bridge, overlooking the River Welland. Recently renovated, it boasts stone-flagged floors in the bar with oak beams and posts throughout. Very popular with both travellers and locals, it provides a relaxed atmosphere and friendly service. The lounge is very comfortable, but can get a little smoky. The conservatory opens on to a patio.

Red Lion Hotel

Market Place

11-11; 12-10.30 Sun

(01775) 722869

website: www.redlionhotel-spalding.co.uk

Draught Bass; Blue Bell Olde Honesty; Fuller's London Pride; Greene King Abbot; Marston's Pedigree H

Attractive hotel bar on the corner of the market place looking a little like a French villa. It has been richly refurbished to provide a warm, welcoming atmosphere. Popular with the locals and visitors to the Fens, it is home to the Spalding Blues Club which puts on fortnightly live bands (Sun eve). The market place is closed to vehicles until 4pm weekdays, so tables have been set up outside. No food is served Sun eve.

SPILSBY

Nelson Butt

10 Market Street (off A16)

11-3, 7-11; 11-11 Sat; 12-3, 7-10.30 Sun

(01790) 752258

Bateman Mild, XB, XXXB; guest beers H

Homely pub, with a good ambience, enhanced by a real fire, run by welcoming hosts. There are always two guest beers on tap. Good home-cooked food includes fish, steaks and vegetarian food; on Mondays special meals are only £2.95. Lunches are served Wed-Mon; eve meals Mon-Sat. Wheelchair access is via the back door. It has a courtyard garden.

STAMFORD

Crown Hotel

6 All Saints Place

11-11; 12-10.30 Sun

(01780) 763136

website: www.crownhotelstamford.co.uk

Adnams Bitter; Draught Bass; Taylor Landlord; guest beer H

Imposing, multi-roomed hotel; in the entrance lobby the mosaic floor and array of plants set the tone for this mobile-free gem. Smoking is permitted in the main bar area only; meals may be eaten here, or in the two dining areas. Note the impressive collection of antique furnishings, mainly connected with local hunting and farming pursuits, and the original painted Bass barrel-end displays in the bar. An extensive wine list is available.

Green Man

29 Scotgate (B1081, N of town)

11-11; 12-10.30 Sun

(01780) 753598

website: www.stamfordonline.co.uk/customers/greenman

Theakston Best Bitter; guest beers H

Lively pub, a short walk from the town centre, Peterborough CAMRA's Pub of the Year 2000. It caters for all ages and tastes. Circa 1796, the pub has an L-shaped, split-level bar and secluded patio garden where successful beer festivals are held. An eclectic range of ever-changing guest beers mostly come from local micros; Newby Wyke brews Stamford Gold especially for the pub. At least three ciders or perries are usually available, plus an extensive range of Belgian bottled beers. Note the push-penny board, from which shove-ha'penny originated. Lunches are served Mon-Sat. ⛺❀⇌◖≉♣🍎

Periwig

7 All Saints Place

✪ 11-11; 12-10.30 Sun

☎ (01780) 762169

Adnams Bitter; Hop Back Summer Lightning; Marston's Pedigree; Oakham JHB; guest beers Ⓗ

Originally the Marsh Harrier, this multi-level bar has been refurbished in continental bistro-style, and is particularly popular with the younger element at weekends. It serves excellent lunches (Mon-Sat), when you can also take advantage of one of the pub's 'happy hours', 11-12 and 5-7. Four or five guests per week complement the regular beers and mini-beer festivals take place in May and October. Handy for bus and train stations. ◖≉

SURFLEET

Mermaid

2 Gosberton Road (B1356)

✪ 11-3, 6.30-11; 12-3, 7-10.30 Sun

☎ (01775) 680275

Adnams Broadside; John Smith's Bitter; guest beers Ⓗ

This good-sized pub stands on the bank of the River Glen, once the site of a brewery. It has a large garden with a play area, well used by children in summer. Excellent value meals make this a popular eating place, to the extent that much of the bar area is often given over to diners. This can be a problem, especially at weekends. A varied selection of guest ales features throughout the year. ⛺Q❀⇌◖◗P

TATTERSHALL THORPE

Blue Bell Inn

Thorpe Road

✪ 12-2.30, 7-11; 12-2.30, 7-10.30 Sun

☎ (01526) 342206

Beer range varies Ⓗ

Delightful inn, one of Lincolnshire's oldest, it dates back to the 13th century. The inn comes complete with beamed ceilings and a wealth of historical charm. During WWII the pub was the watering-hole of the famous 617 RAF Squadron, better known as the Dambusters. Numerous photographs of the era adorn the walls, and the low ceilings have been signed by many service personnel. ⛺Q❀◖◗⊟P

TETFORD

White Hart Inn

East Road

✪ 12-3, 7-11; closed Mon; 12-4, 7-10.30 Sun

☎ (01507) 533255

Adnams Bitter; Fuller's London Pride; Greene King Abbot; guest beer Ⓗ

Dating from the early 16th century, this reputedly haunted Wolds village inn, with three bars and a restaurant, was once a butcher's; meat hooks can still be spotted. Tennyson is said to have sat on the large oak settle in the public bar. The lounge/games room has a pool table and TV. It stands close to the Viking Way and six miles from Cadwell Park. A seasonal blackboard menu includes sausages made in the village (no food Sun eve). ⛺❀⇌◖◗⊟⛺♣P

THORNTON CURTIS

Thornton Hunt Inn

Main Street (A1077, between Wooton and Barton)

✪ 12-3, 6-11; 12-3, 7-10.30 Sun

☎ (01469) 531252 website: www.thornton-inn.co.uk

Taylor Landlord; Tetley Bitter; guest beer Ⓗ

Splendid, welcoming village local whose rustic charm is enhanced by wood panelling, beams, brasses and prints of rural life. Very popular for meals, the pub has its own bistro. Two draught beers are supplemented by a regular changing guest. The garden has a children's play area and a fun trail. Close by are the ruins of Thornton Abbey with its magnificent gatehouse; a visit is recommended. Q❀⇌◖◗♿P

WELBY

Crown & Anchor

Main Street (3/4 mile from B6403)

✪ 12-2.30, 7-11; closed Mon; 12-2.30, 7-10.30 Sun

☎ (01400) 230307

Draught Bass; Fuller's London Pride Ⓗ

Popular village pub, where a U-shaped room surrounds the central bar, with a dining area on one side. The remaining bar area has an effective extractor to expel unwanted cigarette smoke. Diners come from far afield to sample the pub's greatest attraction – its fish and chips on a Friday night. Jazz is played on alternate Thursdays – phone to check dates. It has one guest bedroom and a small garden. Q❀⇌◖◗P

WILLINGHAM BY STOW

Half Moon

23 High Street (off B1241)

✪ 7-11; 12-2, 5-11 Thu & Fri; 12-11 Sat; 12-10.30 Sun

☎ (01427) 788340

Wells Bombardier; guest beers Ⓗ

Traditional, two-roomed free house where real fires, beamed ceilings and brass and copper ornaments feature. The L-shaped lounge includes a dining area, noted for its fish and chip suppers. Home to darts, dominoes and football teams, it hosts a quiz night (Thu); bar skittles and shove-ha'penny are played. A past winner of local CAMRA's Pub of the Season award, a summer beer festival is planned. Two guest beers are normally on tap. ⛺Q❀◖◗⊟♣

WILLOUGHTON

Stirrup Inn

1 Templefield Road (off B1398)

✪ 7.30-11; 12-11 Sat; 12-3, 7.30-10.30 Sun

☎ (01427) 668270

John Smith's Bitter; guest beers Ⓗ

Family-run free house for the last 12 years, it was local CAMRA Pub of Season, winter 2001. A base for local football teams; darts and dominoes are popular. It is unusual for a village pub not to have to provide meals to attract visiting trade – it can rely on the quality of its beer and warm welcome to do the job. The guest beers change weekly. ⛺Q❀⊟♣P

WINTERINGHAM

Bay Horse

2-6 West End

12-11; 12-10.30 Sun

☎ (01724) 732865

Tetley Bitter; guest beers H

Traditional decor, replete with exposed beams, brasses and rural pictures, characterises this welcoming village local. An interesting range of home-cooked food from an extensive menu is offered at all times, except Monday. Two guest beers are usually available. A function room, four twin en-suite guest rooms, good wheelchair access and WC complete the facilities here.

♿♣P

WINTERTON

Lion's Head

55 Park Street

5-11; 11.30-11 Fri & Sat; 12-10.30 Sun

☎ (01724) 733343

Black Sheep Best Bitter; guest beer H

Friendly village local built in 1906. The L-shaped lounge bar has an adjoining section for darts, which along with dominoes is very popular here. There is a comfortable snug. It hosts regular weekend entertainment and a weekly quiz. The pub fields its own football and cricket teams, and a vintage motorcycle club holds its meetings here. Pleasant gardens and a patio are added attractions.

Q♿♣P

WRAGBY

Turnor Arms

Market Place (A158)

5-11; 12-11 Fri & Sat; 12-10.30 Sun

☎ (01673) 858205

Highwood Tom Wood's Best Bitter, Bomber County, seasonal beers; guest beer H

Formerly an hotel on the main A158 East Coast road, now a friendly pub. Quiz nights are held on Sun (music) and Wed (general knowledge). The wood-panelled lounge is a good size, with a stone fireplace; children are allowed in the games room. The bar is quite lively, and caters for the younger generation. Wheelchair access is via the car park entrance. Food is available in the evenings (6-9.30); the restaurant is no-smoking and free from music.

♿♣P

WRAWBY

Jolly Miller

Brigg Road (A18)

12-2, 5-11; 12-11 Sat; 12-10.30 Sun

☎ (01652) 655658

Beer range varies H

Pleasant village pub on the main road through Wrawby. Fitted out in country pub style, the walls are adorned with old village photos, and some show the last surviving post mill in the area, located nearby. Accommodation is offered in en-suite rooms or on the adjacent camping/caravan site, with full facilities. Only four miles from Humberside Airport and a mile from the busy market town of Brigg, the pub is on the 909 bus route, serving Doncaster, Sheffield, Grimsby and Hull.

♣P

Ale conner

The official ale-tester wore leather breeches. He would enter an inn without warning, draw a glass of ale, pour it on a wooden bench, and then sit down in the puddle he had made. He would sit for half an hour and would not change his position. At the end of the half hour, he would make as if to rise, and this was the test of the ale; for if the ale was impure, if it had sugar in it, the tester's leather breeches would stick fast to the bench, but if there was no sugar in the liquor, no impression would be present – in other words, the tester would not stick to the seat.

17th-century description of the work of the ale conner, a public official who inspected inns, taverns and ale houses to test the quality of the beer. William Shakespeare's father was an ale conner.

CAMRA's National Inventory

of Pub Interiors of Outstanding Historic Interest

The pubs listed here have interiors that are of national historic significance. The listing details pubs whose internal arrangements have remained more or less intact since World War Two. They are a diverse group ranging from basic street-corner locals to some of the most ornate pubs in the land. Further details about NI pubs may be found on the CAMRA website – www.camra.org.uk – and in a booklet. Most, but by no means all, the pubs sell real ale.

ENGLAND

Bedfordshire
Broom: Cock.
Luton: Painters Arms.

Berkshire
Aldworth: Bell.

Buckinghamshire
West Wycombe: Swan.

Cambridgeshire
Peterborough: Hand & Heart

Cheshire
Alpraham: Travellers Rest.
Barthomley: White Lion.
Bollington: Holly Bush
Gawsworth: Harrington Arms.
Macclesfield: Castle.
Wheelock: Commercial.

Cornwall
Falmouth: Seven Stars.

Cumbria
Broughton Mills: Blacksmiths Arms.
Carlisle: Cumberland Inn.

Derbyshire
Brassington: Olde Gate Inne.
Derby: Old Dolphin.
Elton: Duke of York.
Kirk Ireton: Barley Mow.
Wardlow Mires: Three Stags Heads.

Devon
Drewsteignton: Drewe Arms.
Holsworthy: Kings Arms.
Luppitt: Luppitt Inn.
Topsham: Bridge.

Dorset
Pamphill: Vine.
Worth Matravers: Square & Compass.

Co. Durham
Durham: Shakespeare; Victoria.

Gloucs & Bristol
Ampney St Peter: Red Lion.
Bristol: Kings Head.
Duntisbourne Abbots: Five Mile House.
Purton: Berkeley Arms.
Willsbridge: Queens Head.

Hampshire
Steep: Harrow.

Herefordshire
Kington: Olde Tavern.
Leintwardine: Sun Inn.
Leysters: Duke of York.

Kent
Broadstairs: Neptune's Hall.
Ightham Common: Old House.
Snargate: Red Lion.

Lancashire
Great Harwood: Victoria.
Preston: Black Horse

Leicestershire
Hinckley: Holly Bush
Whitwick: Three Horseshoes,

Greater London
Central: EC1: Olde Mitre.
EC4: Black Friar.
WC1: Cittie of York; Princess Louise.
WC2: Salisbury.
North. N4: Salisbury.
North-West. NW6: Black Lion.
Harrow-on-the-Hill: Castle.
South-West. SW1: Red Lion.
SW10: Fox & Pheasant
West. W1: Argyll Arms.
W8: Windsor Castle.
W9: Warrington Hotel.

Greater Manchester
Altrincham: Railway.
Eccles: Lamb; Royal Oak; Stanley Arms
Farnworth: Shakespeare.
Gorton: Plough.
Heaton Norris: Nursery Inn.
Manchester: Briton's Protection; Circus Tavern; Hare & Hounds; Mr Thomas's; Peveril of the Peak.
Rochdale: Cemetery.
Salford: Coach & Horses.
Stalybridge: Grosvenor.
Stockport: Alexandra; Arden Arms; Bishop Blaize; Swan with Two Necks.
Westhoughton: White Lion.

Merseyside
Birkenhead: Stork Hotel.
Liverpool: Belvedere; Lion; Peter Kavanagh's; Philharmonic; Prince Arthur; Vines.
Lydiate: Scotch Piper.

Norfolk
Warham: Three Horseshoes.

Northumberland
Berwick upon Tweed: Free Trade.
Netherton: Star Inn.

Nottinghamshire
Nottingham: Five Ways; Olde Trip to Jerusalem

Oxfordshire
Bix: Fox.
Steventon: North Star.
Stoke Lyne: Peyton Arms.
Stoke Talmage: Red Lion.

Shropshire
Edgerley: Royal Hill.
Halfway House: Seven Stars.
Selattyn: Cross Keys.

Shrewsbury: Loggerheads.
Whitchurch: Plume of Feathers.

Somerset
Appley: Globe.
Bath: Old Green Tree; Star.
Crowcombe: Carew Arms.
Faulkland: Tucker's Grave Inn.
Midsomer Norton: White Hart.
Witham Friary: Seymour Arms.

Staffordshire
Tunstall: Vine.

Suffolk
Brent Eleigh: Cock.
Bury St Edmunds: Nutshell.
Ipswich: Margaret Catchpole.
Laxfield: King's Head.
Pin Mill: Butt & Oyster.

East Sussex
Firle: Ram.
Hadlow Down: New Inn.

West Sussex
The Haven: Blue Ship.

Tyne & Wear
Newcastle upon Tyne: Crown Posada.

Warwickshire
Five Ways: Case is Altered.
Long Itchington: Buck & Bell (closed).

West Midlands
Birmingham: Anchor; Bartons Arms; Bellefield; Britannia; British Oak; Market Tavern; Red Lion; Rose Villa Tavern; Samson & Lion; Villa Tavern; White Swan.
Bloxwich: Romping Cat; Turf Tavern.
Dudley: Shakespeare.
Netherton: Old Swan ('Ma Pardoe's).
Oldbury: Waggon & Horses.
Rushall: Manor Arms.
Sedgley: Beacon.
Smethwick: Waterloo Hotel.
Wednesfield: Vine.

Wiltshire
Easton Royal: Bruce Arms.
Salisbury: Haunch of Venison.

Worcestershire
Bretforton: Fleece.
Clent: Bell & Cross.
Defford: Cider House.
Hanley Castle: Three Kings.
Worcester: Paul Pry Inn.

Yorkshire: East Yorks
Beverley: White Horse ('Nellie's').
Hull: Olde Black Boy; Olde White Hart.
Skerne: Eagle Inn.

North Yorks
Beck Hole: Birch Hall Inn.
Boroughbridge: Three Horse Shoes.
Harrogate: Gardeners Arms.
York: Blue Bell; Golden Ball; Swan.

South Yorks
Barnburgh: Coach & Horses.
Sheffield: Bath Hotel; Stumble Inn.

West Yorks
Bradford: Cock & Bottle; New Beehive.
Leeds: Adelphi; Beech; Cardigan Arms; Garden Gate; Rising Sun; Whitelocks.

WALES

Mid-Wales
Hay-on-Wye: Three Tuns.
Llanfihangel-yng-Ngwynfa: Goat.
Rhayader: Royal Oak.
Welshpool: Grapes.

North-east Wales
Ysceifiog: Fox.

North-west Wales
Bethesda: Douglas Arms.

West Wales
Llandovery: Red Lion.
Pontfaen: Dyffryn Arms.

SCOTLAND

Fife
Kincardine: Railway Tavern.
Kirkcaldy: Feuars Arms.

Grampian
Aberdeen: Grill.

The Lothians
Edinburgh: Abbotsford; Bennet's Bar; Café Royal; Leslie's Bar; Oxford Bar;
Leith: Central Bar.

Strathclyde
Glasgow: Horseshoe Bar; Old Toll Bar; Rigg's Bar; Steps Bar.
Larkhall: Village Tavern.
Lochgilphead: Commercial.
Paisley: Bull.
Renton: Central Bar.
Shettleston: Portland Arms.
Shotts: Old Wine Store.

Tayside
Dundee: Athletic; Clep; Speedwell; Tay Bridge.

NORTHERN IRELAND

Co Antrim
Ahoghill: Gillistown House.
Ballycastle: House of McDonnell.
Ballyeaston: Carmichael's.
Bushmills: Bush House.

Co Armagh
Portadown: Mandeville Arms (McConville's).

Belfast
Crown; Fort Bar (Gilmartin's).

Co Fermanagh
Enniskillen: Blake's Bar.
Irvinestown: Central Bar.
Tempo: J. McCormick's.

More information about National Inventory pubs and the National Inventory itself can be found in a booklet pice £2.50 from CAMRA, 230 Hatfield Road, St Albans AL1 4LW, and by visiting the CAMRA website www.camra.org.uk

Compiled by Geoff Brandwood, Dave Gamston and Mick Slaughter

GREATER LONDON

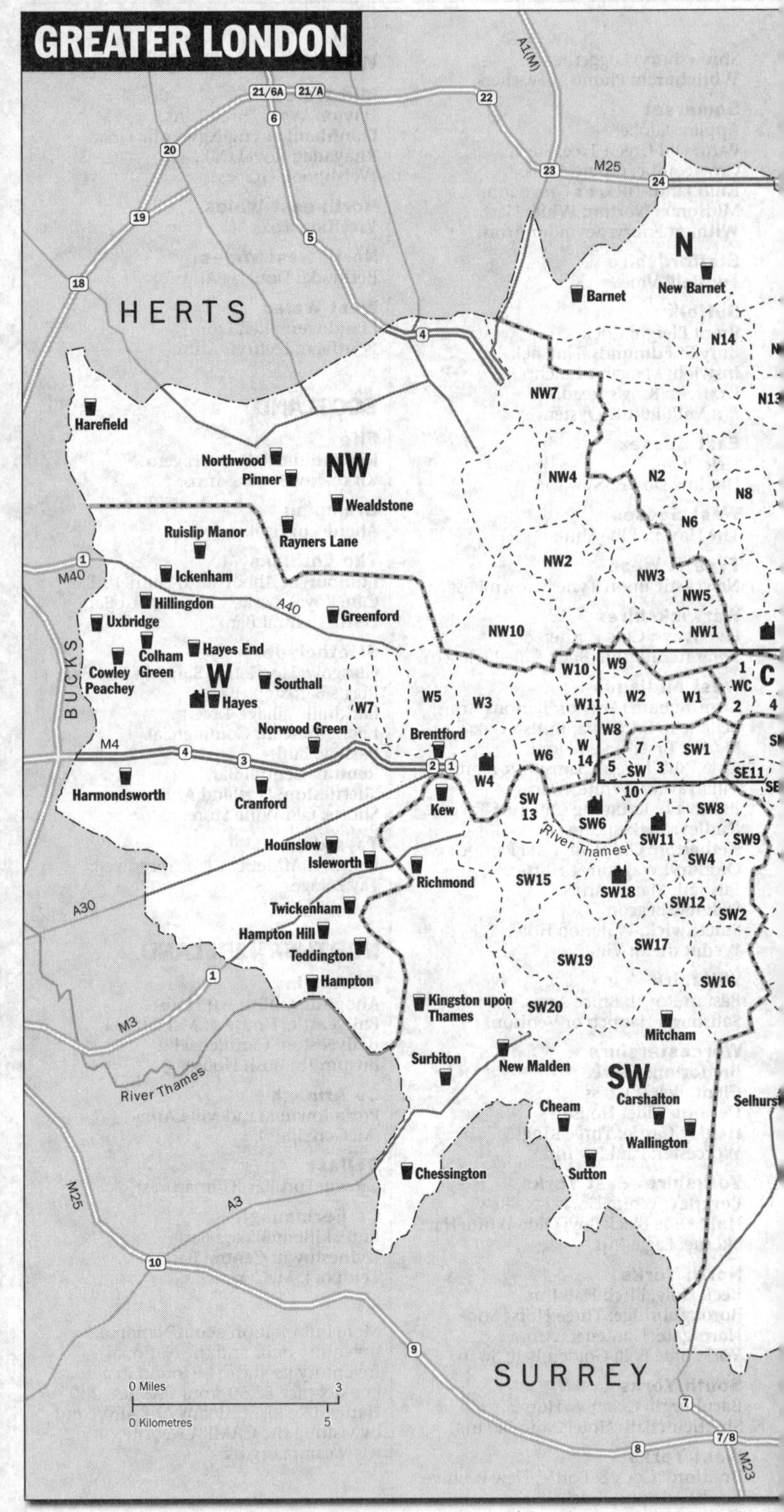

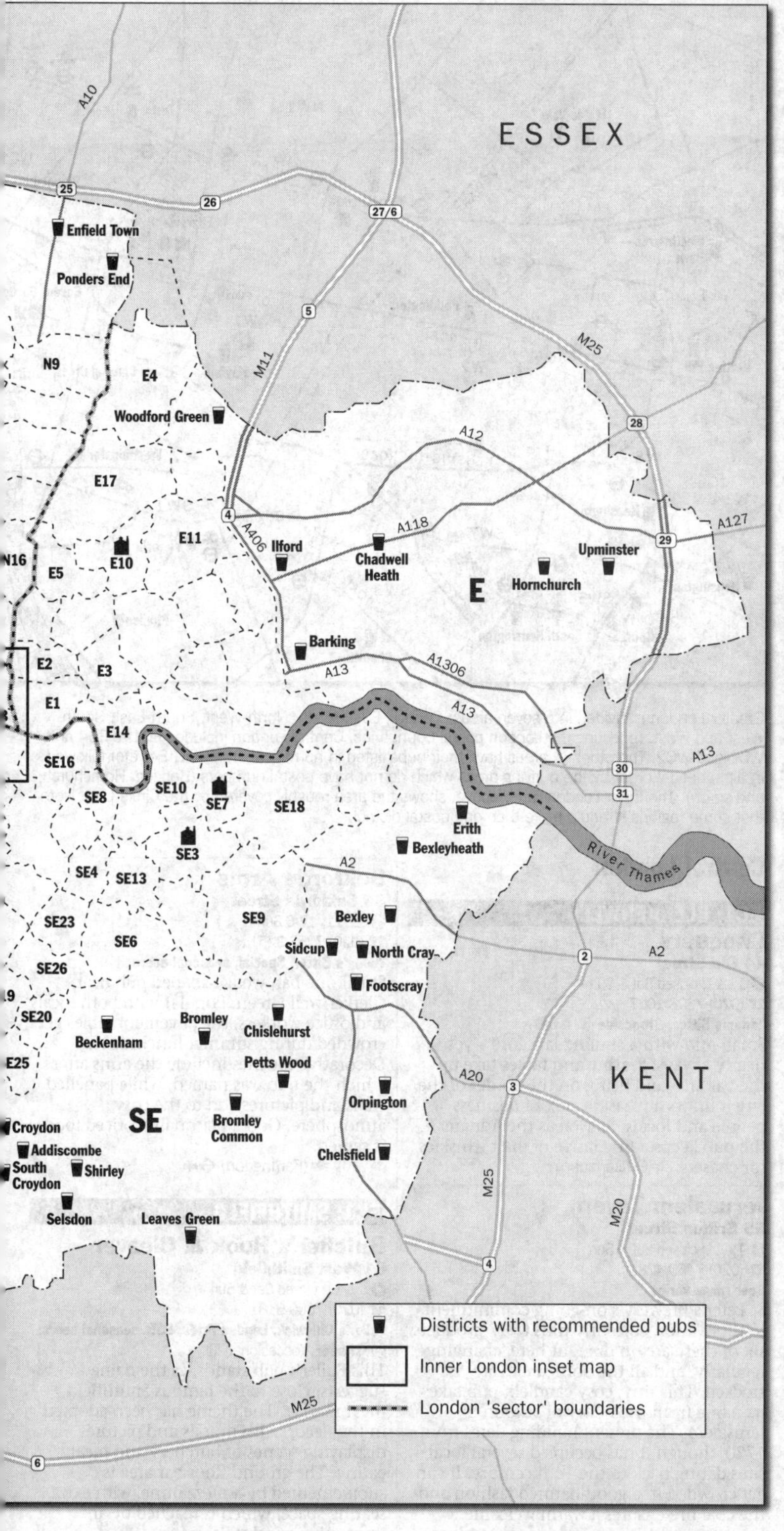
ESSEX
KENT
Enfield Town
Ponders End
N9
E4
Woodford Green
E17
E11
E10
N16
E5
Ilford
Chadwell Heath
Upminster
Hornchurch
E
Barking
E2
E3
E1
E14
SE16
SE8
SE10
SE7
SE18
Erith
Bexleyheath
SE3
SE4
SE13
SE23
SE9
Bexley
SE6
Sidcup
North Cray
SE26
Footscray
SE20
Bromley
Beckenham
Chislehurst
E25
Petts Wood
Orpington
SE
Croydon
Addiscombe
Bromley Common
South Croydon
Shirley
Chelsfield
Selsdon
Leaves Green
River Thames
A10
A12
A127
A118
A406
A13
A1306
A2
A20
M11
M25
M20
Districts with recommended pubs
Inner London inset map
London 'sector' boundaries

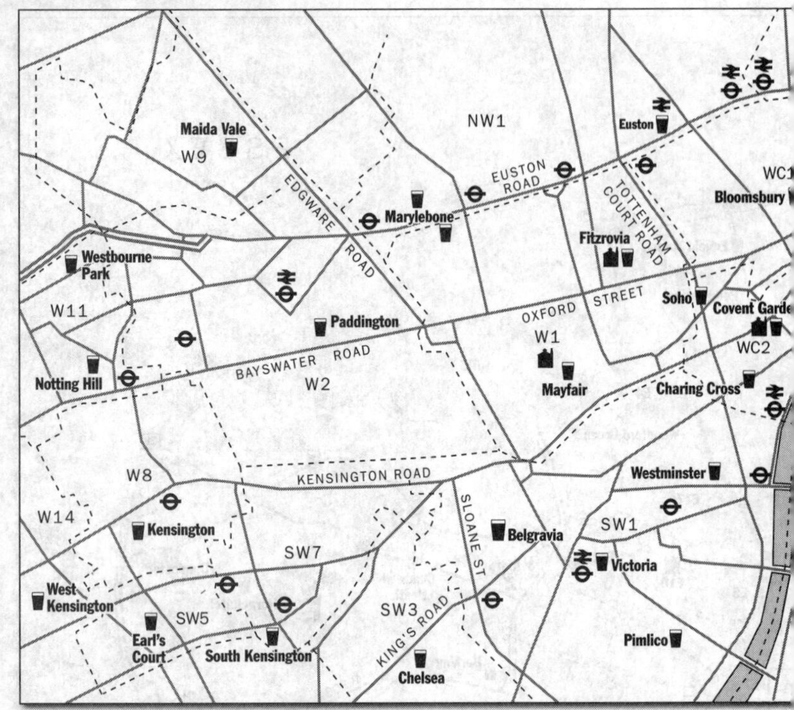

Greater London is divided into seven areas: Central, East, North, North-West, South-East, South-West and West, reflecting the London postal boundaries. Central London includes EC1 to EC4 and WC1 and WC2. The other six areas have their pubs listed in numerical order (E1, E4, etc) followed in alphabetical order by the outlying areas which do not have postal numbers (Barking, Hornchurch, and so on). The Inner London map, above, shows the area roughly covered by the Circle Line. Note that some regions straddle more than one postal district.

Central London

EC1: CLERKENWELL

Chequers
44 Old Street
⏲ 11-11; closed Sat & Sun
☎ (020) 7608 1017
Adnams Bitter, Broadside Ⓗ
Small pub with a smiling landlord – yes nearly always! Seating and tables take up the bar area and being on the border of the city it draws a pleasant mix of business people and locals. As well as the Adnams, the pub keeps a fine range of malt whiskies for chasers. ⇌⊖ (Barbican)

Jerusalem Tavern
55 Britton Street
⏲ 11-11; closed Sat & Sun
☎ (020) 7450 4281
Beer range varies Ⓗ
St Peter's Brewery's on-going commitment to innovation currently runs to 17 products, six of these are on draught here, changing regularly, and all the bottled ales are stocked. This tiny, cosy candlelit pub takes its name from the Priory of St John in Jerusalem. The present building dates from 1720, though it has occupied several local sites dating back to the 14th century. It can get crowded in a good-natured fashion and the coal fire ensures a warm welcome. Pavement tables are provided for outdoor drinking. ♨Q❀◖⇌ (Farringdon) ⊖

Sekforde Arms
34 Sekforde Street
⏲ 11-11; 12-6 Sun
☎ (020) 7253 3251
Young's Bitter, Special, seasonal beers Ⓗ
Small one-bar, wedge-shaped pub near Clerkenwell Green. Popular with both locals and office workers, the pavement tables get crowded during summer lunchtimes. Decorative touches include the arms after which the pub was named, while panelled walls and pictures add to the cosy atmosphere. Good, reasonably-priced food is served.
♨❀◖◗⇌ (Farringdon) ⊖♣

EC1: SMITHFIELD

Butcher's Hook & Cleaver
61 West Smithfield
⏲ 11-11; closed Sat & Sun
☎ (020) 7600 9181
Fuller's Chiswick, London Pride, ESB, seasonal beers; guest beers (occasional) Ⓗ
This Fuller's pub stands, as the name suggests, close to the famous Smithfield meat market. The theme has been adopted in the decor, with murals and pictures displaying scenes of butchery and meat eating. The ground-floor bar area is supplemented by a mezzanine, with extra seating space, which is reached by an impressive spiral staircase.
◖♿⇌ (Farringdon) ⊖ (Barbican) ✔

East London

E1: ALDGATE

Castle
44 Commercial Road
⊙ 11-11; closed Sat & Sun
☎ (020) 7481 2361
Courage Best Bitter, Directors; guest beer Ⓗ
Triangular pub, situated on the corner of Commercial Road and Goodmans Stile. It is divided into two areas, served from a horseshoe-shaped bar: the smaller part has a dartboard and the other is a comfortably furnished lounge with plenty of seating. The walls are covered with Dickensian prints by Anton Pieck. The pub has existed since the mid-1800s and you will find a friendly, relaxed atmosphere and a warm welcome here. ◖⊖ (East) ♣

E1: SPITALFIELDS

Pride of Spitalfields
3 Heneage Street
⊙ 11-11; 12-10.30 Sun
☎ (020) 7247 8933
Crouch Vale Essex Boys Bitter; Fuller's London Pride, ESB; guest beers Ⓗ
Small, cosy, friendly, East End pub, situated off Brick Lane in the midst of many excellent curry restaurants. It has an interesting collection of stone jugs and mugs and a vast array of pump clips mounted above the bar. The walls are covered with framed prints of local people and bustling canals, from before World War II. For excellent beers at reasonable prices, this pub is second to none.
◖≠ (Liverpool St) ⊖ (Aldgate East)

E1: WHITECHAPEL

Black Bull
199 Whitechapel Road
⊙ 11-11; 12-10.30 Sun
☎ (020) 7247 6707
Nethergate Suffolk County, Old Growler; guest beers Ⓗ
East End free house, frequented by locals, hospital staff and stallholders from Whitechapel Street market. The large single bar has comfortable seating, and you will always find a friendly welcome and excellent beer at this pub. Copies of old inn notices and 3D pictures of Dickens' characters adorn the walls. A big-screen TV shows major sporting events. ◖⊖

E2: BETHNAL GREEN

Camden's Head
456 Bethnal Green Road
⊙ 11-11; 12-10.30 Sun
☎ (020) 7613 4263
Courage Best Bitter, Directors; Greene King Abbot; Hop Back Summer Lightning; guest beers Ⓗ
Conveniently situated in the centre of Bethnal Green, this Wetherspoon's pub has a friendly, welcoming atmosphere. The cool and shady courtyard at the rear is especially popular with locals in summer. The pub is named after Lord Camden who owned property in the area; items relating to local history are displayed around the walls.
Q❀◖◗≠⊖⊬✔

E3: BOW

Coborn Arms
8 Coborn Road
⊙ 11-11; 12-10.30 Sun
☎ (020) 8980 3793
Young's Bitter, Special, seasonal beers Ⓗ
This single-bar pub just off the busy Mile End Road is divided into two distinct areas by the large horseshoe-shaped bar counter. This is a real local, with a pleasant atmosphere. More seating is provided in a larger side room which also houses one of the pub's two dartboards. Sunday meals are served 1-9. ❀◖◗♿⊖ (Mile End/Bow Rd) ♣

E4: SOUTH CHINGFORD

King's Ford
250-252 Chingford Mount Road
⊙ 11-11; 12-10.30 Sun
☎ (020) 8523 9365
Courage Directors; Greene King Abbot; Hop Back Summer Lightning; Shepherd Neame Spitfire; guest beers Ⓗ
Long, narrow pub which, while small for a Wetherspoon's, has a deceptively spacious

South-West London

SW1: BELGRAVIA

Nag's Head
53 Kinnerton Street
11-11; 12-10.30 Sun
(020) 7235 1135
Adnams Bitter, Broadside, seasonal beers Ⓗ
Small, unchanging pub of considerable character and full of nostalgia with a very low bar counter and antique handpumps.

SW8: SOUTH LAMBETH

Mawbey Arms
7 Mawbey Street
11-11; 12-10.30 Sun
(020) 7622 1936
Shepherd Neame Master Brew Bitter; Young's Bitter, Special Ⓗ
Friendly, back-street local, this listed building is attractively decorated and comfortably furnished. Food by arrangement.

SW12: BALHAM

Grove
39 Oldridge Road
11-11; 12-10.30 Sun
(020) 8673 6531
Young's Bitter, Triple A, Special, seasonal beers Ⓗ
Large pub sensitively renovated to retain a traditional bar counter and ornate ceilings. Good quality food.

SW15: PUTNEY

Railway
202 Upper Richmond Road
11-11; 12-10.30 Sun
(020) 8788 8190
Courage Best Bitter, Directors; Greene King Abbot; Hop Back Summer Lightning; Shepherd Neame Spitfire; guest beers Ⓗ
Spacious Wetherspoon's opposite the station, in an original pub on two levels. Note the figurines on the outside. Cask Marque accredited.

SW15: ROEHAMPTON

Angel
11 High Street
11-11; 12-10.30 Sun
(020) 8788 1997
Young's Bitter, Special, Winter Warmer Ⓗ
Traditional, late Victorian two-bar community local; sports-oriented public bar and a quieter lounge.

SW18: WANDSWORTH

Spread Eagle
71 Wandsworth High Street
11-11; 12-10.30 Sun
(020) 8877 9809
Young's Bitter, Special, seasonal beers Ⓗ
Large, town-centre pub where many original features include ornate glass and mahogany partitions. Also has a public bar.

air thanks to its open layout. It is popular with young and old alike, from singles wanting a quick meal and a pint, to groups going on to clubs. The pub is easily accessible from the many bus routes between Walthamstow, Chingford and further afield. Q◑♿⚟✔

E5: CLAPTON

Anchor & Hope

15 High Hill Ferry

11-3, 5.30-11; 11-11 Sat; 12-10.30 Sun

(020) 8806 1730

Fuller's London Pride, ESB H

Small, one-bar, riverside pub, it can get very crowded on hot summer days. No need to worry though, as there is plenty of space outside on the towpath – just watch out for the cyclists. This long-standing Guide entry remains popular with users of the canal, and is now open all day Saturday and Sunday. It is difficult to find. ❀≹

Princess of Wales

146 Lea Bridge Road

11-11; 12-10.30 Sun

(020) 8533 3463

Young's Bitter, Special, seasonal beers H

Spacious, popular riverside pub, it was formerly known as the Prince of Wales, but renamed after the death of Diana in 1997. The outside drinking area gets very busy during the summer months, particularly with passing boaters. The pub also picks up trade from the ice rink across the road. Q❀◑⊟≹♣P

E11: LEYTONSTONE

Birkbeck Tavern

45 Langthorne Road

11-11; 12-10.30 Sun

(020) 8539 2584

Beer range varies H

Large, two-bar Victorian corner pub with a strong local following. Recent changes of management have left the pub in good hands. The rotating beer range is chosen by the widely travelling landlord, with ales from all over the country, as well as the house beer, Rita's. It stages regular themed beer festivals. The pub fields a darts team and boasts two well-used boards. ⊟⊖ (Leyton) ♣

E11: WANSTEAD

Duke of Edinburgh

79 Nightingale Lane

11-11; 12-10.30 Sun

(020) 8989 0014

Draught Bass; Tetley Burton Ale; Young's Bitter H

Back-street local with a quiet atmosphere; although music plays quietly in the background there is no juke box. A large-screen TV is switched on for major sports events. Traditional games, such as shove-ha'penny, pool and darts are played in this wood-panelled pub. Meals are served 12-6.30. ⛼❀◐⊖ (Snaresbrook) ♣

George

159 High Street

11-11; 12-10.30 Sun

(020) 8989 2921

Courage Directors; Greene King Abbot; Shepherd Neame Spitfire; Theakston Best Bitter, Old Peculier; guest beers H

Ex-Grand Met/Truman's pub, now a Wetherspoon's. Photos of famous celebrities bearing the name George are displayed all around the bar area. Comfortably furnished, with a no-smoking area, it is somewhat different from the normal identikit Wetherspoon's outlet. ⛼Q❀◑⊖P⚟

E14: LIMEHOUSE

Barley Mow

44 Narrow Street

12-11; 12-10.30 Sun

(020) 7265 8931

Draught Bass; Greene King IPA H

Friendly, comfortable pub where one large bar is divided by small screens into cosy alcoves. Originally the dockmaster's house, it became a pub in 1905, and bears a collection of nautical memorabilia. Situated at the entrance to Limehouse Basin, a large patio with ample seating overlooks the Thames. Food is served Mon-Fri, plus weekends in the summer when barbecues are an added attraction. ❀◑⊖ (DLR Westferry/Limehouse) ♣

Grapes

76 Narrow Street

12-3.30, 5.30-11; 12-11 Sat; 12-10.30 Sun

(020) 7987 4396

Adnams Bitter; Draught Bass; Tetley Burton Ale H

This friendly pub, with its outstanding ornate frontage, boasts award-winning seafood in its upstairs restaurant. A selection of pub meals is also served in the bar (except Sun eve). A pub has stood on this site since 1583 and was visited by Charles Dickens in the mid-19th century. You can enjoy the scenic views over the Thames from the small deck area at the rear of the pub, but it gets very popular and crowded in summer. ⛼Q❀◑⊖ (DLR Westferry/Limehouse) ♣

E17: WALTHAMSTOW

Flower Pot

128 Wood Street

12-11; 12-10.30 Sun

(020) 8520 3600

Draught Bass; guest beer H

Welcoming local with one bar and two Bass handpumps. Locals come to enjoy the beer and the Sky Sport on TV; join in the team followers' lively banter when matches are on. Recently refurbished, meals are planned from the new kitchen, to accompany the acclaimed beers – is this the best Bass in town? People are prepared to travel to enjoy it. ❀≹ (Wood St)

Village

31 Orford Road

11-11; 12-10.30 Sun

(020) 8521 9982

Fuller's London Pride; guest beers H

Situated in Walthamstow village, this pub attracts a large local following, and gets crowded in the evenings. The long bar room is supplemented by a snug at the back of the pub. A sizeable back yard provides plenty of seating. The pub usually offers four guest ales, generally including a dark mild. ❀◐≹ (Central) ⊖

BARKING

Britannia

1 Church Road

⌚ 11-3, 5-11; 12-11 Sat; 12-10.30 Sun

☎ (020) 8594 1305

Young's Bitter, Special, Winter Warmer, seasonal beers (occasional) Ⓗ

Young's only tied house in the area, a long-standing entry in this Guide and local CAMRA Pub of the Year on several occasions. A roomy, comfortable saloon bar contrasts with a proper public bar where games are played. The caryatids on the pub's external fascia are a rare (and possibly only remaining) example in East London. Food is available lunchtimes and early evenings. ❀ⒹⒺ ⊟ ≋ ⊖ ♣ P

CHADWELL HEATH

Eva Hart

1128 High Road (A118)

⌚ 11-11; 12-10.30 Sun

☎ (020) 8597 1069

Courage Best Bitter, Directors; Greene King Abbot, Old Speckled Hen; Hop Back Summer Lightning; Shepherd Neame Spitfire; guest beers Ⓗ

Large and comfortable, this pub is a good Wetherspoon's conversion from what was the local police station (and subsequently a builders' merchants) on the site of the old village stocks. Eva Hart, a local music teacher and singer, was the oldest Titanic survivor; much memorabilia is displayed in the pub. It normally stocks three guest beers and Weston's Old Rosie cider is now featured regularly. The no-smoking gallery has a children's licence (until 7pm). The usual good value food range is available all day with a curry club Thu eve.

♉ ❀ⒹⒺ ♿ ≋ ● P ⊁ ⊘

HORNCHURCH

Chequers

North Street

⌚ 11-11; 12-10.30 Sun

☎ (01708) 442094

Ansells Best Bitter; Draught Bass; Tetley Bitter; Young's Bitter Ⓗ

Small, traditional, unspoilt boozer on a traffic island. It sells good value beers and is definitely a drinkers' pub. A very busy local, especially early evening when people pop in on their way home from work, it enjoys a keen darts following and fields several teams. There is an unobtrusive TV in one corner for sports fans, away from the main seating area. It was a well-deserved local CAMRA Pub of the Year in 1997-1999, and again in 2001. Lunchtime meals are served Wed-Fri. Ⓓ ≋ (Emerson Pk) ♣ P

ILFORD

Prince of Wales

63 Green Lane

⌚ 11-11; 12-10.30 Sun

☎ (020) 8478 1326

Adnams Broadside; Tetley Bitter, Burton Ale; guest beers Ⓗ

Pleasant, traditional pub, where both locals and office workers congregate. A cosy saloon bar contrasts with a usually more boisterous public bar. A small secluded garden is used when weather permits. The beer range has increased in recent years, but those listed may vary, and include others from established regional breweries. A limited lunchtime menu is served. ❀Ⓓ ⊟ ♣ P

UPMINSTER

Crumpled Horn

33-37 Corbets Tey Road (B1421)

⌚ 11-11; 12-10.30 Sun

☎ (01708) 226698 website: www.wizardinns.co.uk

Crouch Vale Brewers Gold; Mauldons Dickens, seasonal beer; Wadworth 6X; Wells Bombardier; guest beers (occasional) Ⓗ

Opened in September 2000, this is an attractive conversion of three shop units. There are normally three or four real ales on tap, supplemented by occasional beer festivals. The beers are rather expensive, but the pub provides a welcome boost to the limited local real ale scene. Food is available for most of the day. A quiz is held Tuesday evening. The pub's name was suggested in a competition and was taken from a nearby (now defunct) dairy. ⒹⒺ ♿ ≋ ⊖ ⊁ ⊘

WOODFORD GREEN

Cricketers

299-301 High Road (A1199, old A11)

⌚ 11-11; 11.30-11 Sat; 12-10.30 Sun

☎ (020) 8504 2734

McMullen AK, Country, seasonal beers, guest beer Ⓗ

Pleasant, comfortable, suburban pub on a main road, almost opposite the well-known statue of Sir Winston Churchill on the corner of the green. The pub has two bars, the saloon being fairly plush and cosy and the public, where darts is played, being a little more basic. The pub has its own golf society and supports the Guide Dogs for the Blind Association. The panelled walls are adorned with wooden plaques of various county cricket clubs. The front patio has space for three or four tables. Good value lunches include pensioners' specials (weekdays). ❀Ⓓ ⊟ ♿ P ⊘

Traveller's Friend

496-498 High Road (A104)

⌚ 11.30-11; 12-4, 7-10.30 Sun

☎ (020) 8504 2435

Courage Best Bitter, Directors; Greene King Abbot; Ridleys IPA; guest beer Ⓗ

Small, one-bar pub lying just back from the busy High Road. As far as can be ascertained the pub has never sold any keg bitter; Draught Bass was sold for many years when nearly every pub was keg-only. The single horseshoe-shaped bar is oak-panelled throughout and the original snob screens are still extant on one side. The couple who run the pub have been here many years and maintain a very sociable house. A beer festival is held annually in April. This splendid local is well worth a visit. Eve meals are only served Wed – curry night. Limited parking. Q ❀ⒹⒺ ♿ P

North London

N1: HOXTON

Beershop

14b Pitfield Street

⌚ 11-7; 10-4 Sat; closed Sun

☎ (020) 7739 3701

website: www.pitfieldbeershop.co.uk
Beer range varies
The best specialist beer off-licence in North London. Many shop here because it stocks more than 500 different bottled beers from around the world, with an emphasis on British and Belgian ales. Others are attracted by the home-brewing and wine-making supplies, the beer books or the breweriana. The highlights, however, are the organic beers from the neighbouring Pitfield Brewery. The full range is available bottle-conditioned, or alternatively they can be ordered by the polypin or firkin.
⇌ (Old St) ⊖

Prince Arthur
49 Brunswick Place
11-11; 12-10.30 Sun
☎ (020) 7253 3187
Shepherd Neame Master Brew Bitter, Best Bitter, Spitfire Ⓗ
Situated between City Road and Hoxton Square, this is a pleasant back-street pub, attracting drinkers from the City as well as local estates. A separate, sunken area towards the rear of this single bar houses a dartboard. Outside seating is available during summer. ⊖ (Old St) ♣

Wenlock Arms
26 Wenlock Road
11-11; 12-10.30 Sun
☎ (020) 7608 3406 website: www.wenlock-arms.co.uk
Adnams Bitter; Crouch Vale Brewers Gold; guest beers Ⓗ
Rescued from oblivion in 1994, this compact, lively street-corner pub near the Regent's Canal, has been North London CAMRA Pub of the Year three times. An island bar with alcove seating attracts locals and visitors from afar who come to sample an ever-changing range of beers including mild, plus cider or perry. Jazz is performed Friday and Saturday evenings and Sunday lunchtime. Bar food includes its famous salt beef 'sandwedges'. A meeting room is available. ⇌ (Old St) ⊖♣

N1: ISLINGTON

Duke of Cambridge
30 St Peter's Street
12-11; 12-10.30 Sun
☎ (020) 7359 3066 website: www.singhboulton.co.uk
Pitfield Eco Warrior; St Peter's Best Bitter Ⓗ
One of a new breed of gastro-pubs. What makes this different is that it is also run on organic, environmentally friendly lines. Taken over in 1998, it had been closed for two years, squatted in, and vandalised. Although originally several bars, it is now open plan with large wooden tables. The outbuildings have been joined on to the pub to create a restaurant (waiter service), you can eat in the main bar as well (no food Mon lunch). It can be very crowded with diners in the evenings, but you do not feel out of place just having a beer. Organic produce does not come cheap and this is reflected in the prices. Q ⊖ (Angel) ⅟

N2: EAST FINCHLEY

Madden's
130 High Road
11-11; 12-10.30 Sun
☎ (020) 8444 7444
Fuller's London Pride; Greene King Abbot; guest beers Ⓗ
Look out for an ivy-clad frontage and floral display on a converted shop. Two regular ales are on tap here, and usually four changing beers. Curries, chow meins and other Chinese food are brought in from the restaurant next door. The long, dimly-lit interior, with the bar at the side, provides an intimate setting. Jazz figurines are featured as well as the 1999 Grand National winning jockey's shirt, complemented by football and racing pictures. Chess and backgammon are played here.
♿ ⊖

N8: CROUCH END

Harringay Arms
153 Crouch Hill
12-11; 12-10.30 Sun
☎ (020) 8340 4243
Courage Best Bitter, Directors Ⓗ
At the centre of Crouch End is this welcoming single-bar local, frequented by a devoted clientele. The interior is all dark wood and red plush, with two walls given over to old photos of the area and copies of historical documents relating to this former beer house. A TV sometimes shows sport but conversation rules here. At the rear is a walled courtyard with seating. Filled rolls are served lunchtimes. Quiz night Tuesday.
⇌ (Crouch Hill) ♣

N8: HORNSEY

Toll Gate
26-30 Turnpike Lane
11-11; 12-10.30 Sun
☎ (020) 8889 9085
Courage Directors; Greene King Abbot; Shepherd Neame Spitfire; Theakston Best Bitter; guest beers Ⓗ
This spacious pub, converted from several shops, is decorated in Wetherspoon's old house style of dark wood and bright upholstery. Old black and white photos show Wood Green and Hornsey a century ago. Usually at least four handpumps are devoted to the guest beers, which come from the company's seasonal lists. The good value food is served until an hour before closing time. It can be very noisy weekend evenings.
Q ⇌ ⊖ (Turnpike Lane) ⅟

N9: EDMONTON

Beehive
24 Little Bury Street
11-11; 12-10.30 Sun
☎ (020) 8360 4358
Adnams Bitter; Draught Bass; Marston's Pedigree; Tetley Bitter Ⓗ
Typical 1930s pub, opened out to one bar with a central bar area. Situated in a residential area, it attracts a local clientele. A games area has a pool table, noted for its purple cloth, darts and a big-screen TV for sporting events. It hosts occasional quiz nights and other 'speciality' nights. The coat and umbrella stand with a mirror is unusual. Evening meals are served 5-8.30 Mon-Fri.
♣P

N13: PALMERS GREEN

Whole Hog

430-434 Green Lanes

11-11; 12-10.30 Sun

☎ (020) 8882 3597

Courage Directors; Greene King Abbot or Hop Back Summer Lightning; Shepherd Neame Spitfire; Theakston Best Bitter; guest beer Ⓗ

Typical Wetherspoon's shop conversion at the quieter (northern) end of this busy suburb. Do not be put off by the external colour scheme; the comfortable split-level interior includes a larger seating area downstairs with a children's licence until 9pm (7pm Fri/Sat). A special children's menu is available. The lower bar is only staffed at busy times. Old pictures of the area and illustrations of local historical characters adorn the walls. Quiz night is Wed. Q◑◐♿⇌⚟✔

N14: SOUTHGATE

New Crown

80-84 Chase Side

11-11; 12-10.30 Sun

☎ (020) 8882 8758

Courage Best Bitter, Directors; Greene King Abbot; Hop Back Summer Lightning; Shepherd Neame Spitfire; guest beers Ⓗ

Large one-bar Wetherspoon's conversion; it has been established for about five years and is located on the main road, a few minutes' walk from the tube station. It is a welcome addition to an area now sadly lacking in outlets for real ale, and is popular with a variety of age groups. The beer is from the usual Wetherspoon's range, but up to four additional guest beers may be available. Q◑◐⊖⚟✔

N16: STOKE NEWINGTON

Rochester Castle

145 Stoke Newington High Street

11-11; 12-10.30 Sun

☎ (020) 7249 6016

Courage Best Bitter, Directors; Fuller's London Pride; Greene King Abbot; Hop Back Summer Lightning; Shepherd Neame Spitfire; guest beers Ⓗ

On entering, stop to look at the original tiled mosaic doorstep, complementing the decorative tiled entrance walls; both are listed features. The front area is often busy with animated conversation; the central area is generally quieter. The natural light from the vaulted skylight allows for a relaxing read or enjoy a convivial chat in the side alcoves. The rear conservatory is no-smoking, and is popular with chess players. Leading off this, is the tree-shaded patio, which closes at 8pm.
Q❀◑◐⇌(Kingsland Rd)⚟✔

N21: WINCHMORE HILL

Orange Tree

18 Highfield Road

11-11; 12-10.30 Sun

☎ (020) 8360 4853

Greene King IPA; guest beers Ⓗ

This pub, popular with locals, is hidden away, but signposted off Green Lanes. The large single bar is decorated with horse brasses and sports trophies. It has a pool table, dartboard, and a large-screen TV for sporting events. The large garden and patio area has a barbecue and children's play area with swings, climbing frame and slide. The guest beers are varied and good value, as are the popular meals (booking is advised). Local CAMRA Pub of the Year 1999, 2000 and 2002. ❀◑⇌♣

BARNET

Albion

74 Union Street

12 (11 Sat)-11; 12-10.30 Sun

☎ (020) 8441 2841

Greene King IPA, Abbot; Tetley Burton Ale Ⓗ

Archetypal back-street boozer, tucked away off the High Street, still a proud possessor of outdoor gents' toilets. One bar serves two distinct areas: the smaller 'public' side has a dartboard and games set into table tops; the 'lounge' area has a TV for sport watched by a strong rugby following. The surprisingly large garden has a children's play area. Addlestone's cider is available.
❀⊖(High Barnet)♣●P

King William IV

18 Hadley Highstone

11-3, 5.30-11; 11-11 Fri, Sat & summer; 12-10.30 Sun

☎ (020) 8449 6728

Greene King IPA, Ruddles Best Bitter; Tetley Burton Ale; guest beer Ⓗ

This 17th-century pub stands near Hadley Common and the site of the Battle of Barnet which took place in 1471. The small and cosy drinking areas are all free of gaming machines. Known to the locals as the 'Willy' it boasts two real fires. Excluding Sundays, a full menu is served in the evenings in the restaurant to the rear. The house beer is an Usher's beer brewed by the Thomas Hardy Brewery. ⛫Q❀◑◐

Lord Nelson

14 West End Lane

11-2.30, 6.30-11; 11-3, 6-11 Sat; 12-4, 7-10.30 Sun

☎ (020) 8449 7249

Adnams Bitter; Fuller's London Pride; Greene King IPA, Abbot; Tetley Dark Mild Ⓗ

Welcoming, friendly back-street local; the original pub was the circa 1800 house next door, now a private residence. The present building dates from the 1930s. There is a framed poem written on the wall by Richard Burton, as he and Liz Taylor frequented this pub when filming at Elstree in the 1960s. Meals include fish and chips evening (Mon) and steak evening (Wed); no other evening meals are served and there is no food Sun. Ask for games if you wish to play. ❀◑♣

Mitre Inn

58 High Street

11-11; 12-10.30 Sun

☎ (020) 8449 6582

Adnams Bitter; Ansells Mild; Tetley Bitter; guest beers Ⓗ

Once a famous coaching inn, where rival companies literally fought for custom, the pub's character has changed very little since the days of celebrated visitors General Monk and Dr Johnson. Lively in the evenings, it is quieter in the afternoon when you can peruse the pub's own news-

sheet (edited by the landlord) and smile at the wonderful inscriptions on the walls, a favourite being 'appetite comes with eating, but the thirst goes away with drinking'. Local CAMRA Pub of the Year 2001.
(High Barnet) P

Sebright Arms
9 Alston Road
12 (5 Mon)-11 (midnight Wed & Sat); 12-10.30 Sun
(020) 8449 6869
McMullen AK, Country, seasonal or guest beer H
Located in a residential area, the saloon bar is free of gaming machines and has pictures of old Barnet adorning the walls. The public bar has a TV and a photographic display dedicated to Barnet FC; it also boasts a hand-painted sporting mural. On Wednesday and Saturday evenings there is live jazz in the saloon bar and the pub is open until midnight (no admission after 10.30pm). A quiz is held on Tuesday evening. Lunches are served Tue-Fri.

ENFIELD TOWN

George
5 The Town
11-11; 12-10.30 Sun
(020) 8363 0074
Adnams Bitter; Draught Bass; Greene King Old Speckled Hen; Highgate Bitter H
Old coaching inn, now one large, split-level bar. Its decor is 1980s-style, with library shelves and alcove seats in a raised area. Promotional posters, old adverts, and historic pictures of Enfield decorate the walls. There are fruit machines, but no music. Part of the Goose and Granite chain, its prices are set to compete with Wetherspoon's. It makes an ideal refuge after shopping in Enfield Town. Meals are served all day until 9pm.

Old Wheatsheaf
3 Windmill Hill
11-11; 12-10.30 Sun
(020) 8363 0516
Adnams Bitter; Greene King IPA; Tetley Bitter; guest beers H
This traditional, two-bar pub, near the station, is noted for its floral displays. Comfortable, and popular with locals, the saloon bar is decorated with pictures of old Enfield, and offers a TV and fruit machines by way of amusement. There is a body-building gym, with weights, at the rear of the pub; bar meals are served weekday lunchtimes. It hosts regular quiz nights and a folk club. (Enfield Chase)

NEW BARNET

Hadley Hotel
113 Hadley Road
11-11; 12-10.30 Sun
(020) 8449 0161
Adnams Broadside; Fuller's London Pride; Greene King IPA; Young's Bitter H
This pub is located 10 minutes' walk from New Barnet railway station, in a residential area near Hadley Woods. It has recently become a free house, offering a range of real ales. It also provides B&B, with seven bedrooms. The bar is split into three areas: the right-hand part has a mural of the 1471 Battle of Barnet; the other two are traditionally decora.ted and display paintings for sale by a local artist. Evening meals are served Thu-Sat; no food Sun.
P

Railway Bell
13 East Barnet Road
11-11; 12-10.30 Sun
(020) 8449 1369
Courage Best Bitter, Directors; Greene King Abbot; Shepherd Neame Spitfire; Theakston Best Bitter; guest beers H
Large, split-level Wetherspoon's, decorated with railway memorabilia and old photos of the area. Recent refurbishments have created a no-smoking conservatory and a cosier atmosphere. Up to four guest beers are normally on tap, usually from micro-breweries. It hosts occasional beer festivals and offers the usual JD value for money.
Q P

PONDERS END

Picture Palace
Lincoln Road
11-11; 12-10.30 Sun
(020) 8344 9690
Courage Best Bitter, Directors; Greene King Abbot; Shepherd Neame Spitfire; Theakston Best Bitter; guest beers H
Built as a cinema which opened in 1913, it carried on as such until the outbreak of World War II. During its later life it became Howard Hall and served as a dance hall, and latterly a community centre until closed by the council. Ten years of local authority neglect followed until it was rescued by Wetherspoon's and transformed into a rather magnificent pub. The upper walls and high ceiling are adorned with impressive plaster mouldings and two large comfortable-looking chesterfield settees break up the rather regimented seating. The car park contains bicycle racks and two dedicated disabled parking spaces. The bar is also lowered in two places to allow wheelchair access. Q (Southbury/ Ponders End) P

North-West London

NW1: CAMDEN TOWN

Spread Eagle
141 Albert Street
11-11; 12-10.30 Sun
(020) 7267 1410
Young's Bitter, Triple A, Special, Waggle Dance, Winter Warmer, seasonal beers; guest beer H
Elegantly decorated pub, divided into two rooms, featuring old framed prints and extensive dark wood panelling. The elongated bar is carpeted and furnished with benches and stools. The other room boasts a panoramic window and is filled with tables and chairs. The guest beer is usually Smiles Bitter or a Smiles seasonal brew. Food is served 12-7 daily. There is an outside drinking area with benches and tables alongside the quieter side road.
(Camden Rd)

NW1: EUSTON

Head of Steam

1 Eversholt Street

11-11; 12-10.30 Sun

(020) 7388 2221

Holt Bitter; Hop Back Summer Lightning; guest beers H

Previously called Rails, this pub is now the only London house of a small chain. Of the seven changing guest beers one is always a mild; Budvar and Hoegaarden are also stocked. It hosts regular beer festivals, often themed geographically. The pub is full of railway memorabilia and transport models, most of which are for sale. The bar billiards table is a rarity in London these days. Evening meals are served 5-8 Mon-Fri; no food Sun. Ask at the bar for the code to use the toilets. Local CAMRA Pub of the Year 1999. (Euston Sq)

NW1: MARYLEBONE

Perseverence

11 Shroton Street

11-11; 12-10.30 Sun

(020) 7723 7469

Draught Bass; Greene King IPA H

Former inn, which was a stop for stagecoaches. Previously a regular in this Guide, it now has new owners. Originally two bars, it was knocked through into one in the early 1990s, but then suffered two major floods in the space of a year when a waterpipe burst in nearby Lisson Grove, filling the cellar and rising into the bar itself. This friendly pub is a genuine central London local. A patio is available for warm weather. (Marylebone) (Baker St/Edgware Rd)

NW2: CRICKLEWOOD

Beaten Docket

50-56 Cricklewood Broadway

11-11; 12-10.30 Sun

(020) 8450 2972

Courage Directors; Greene King Abbot; Shepherd Neame Spitfire; Theakston Best Bitter; guest beer H

This is the place for real ale in Cricklewood, an area made famous by Alan Coren; a fairly typical Wetherspoon's conversion, which, with the passage of time, has become very comfortably worn in. A series of well-defined drinking areas disguise the vastness of the place. The pub's name refers to a losing betting slip; plenty of prints and paraphernalia reinforce the theme. There is a good choice of excellent value restaurants nearby (try the Khana). Benches are set outside for summer drinking.

Q

NW3: HAMPSTEAD

Duke of Hamilton

23-25 New End

12-11; 12-10.30 Sun

(020) 7794 0258

Fuller's London Pride, ESB; guest beers H

Visitors always receive a warm welcome in this Hampstead community local. The single bar displays an extensive collection of sporting, brewing and local history posters and photographs. Over 200 years old, with stables to the rear and a cobbled courtyard, the pub is named after a prominent Civil War Royalist. Eleven consecutive years in this Guide and local CAMRA Pub of the Year 2002, it stocks draught Gambrinus Czech lager and a range of 15 malt whiskies. It has an outside terrace, and a cellar bar, available for meetings. Q

NW4: HENDON

Greyhound

52 Church End

11-11; 12-10.30 Sun

(020) 8457 9730

Young's Bitter, Triple A, Special, seasonal beers H

Set atop a hill, between an idyllic 18th-century church and the Charles II period church farmhouse museum, the pub is a rare local outlet for Young's. The bar area, adorned with pictures of former Hendon Aerodrome, is flanked by two lounge areas: the larger one has wood panelling, while the other displays church boards, due to its link with the church. Handy for Middlesex University and the Town Hall, the current building dates from 1845.

NW5: TUFNELL PARK

Dartmouth Arms

35 York Rise

11 (10 Sat)-11; 10-10.30 Sun

(020) 7485 3267

Adnams Bitter; guest beers H

This excellent, two-roomed pub effortlessly combines the functions of a community local and a gastro-pub. The back room is hung with artwork for sale. There is a TV in the front bar, and, more unusually, a secondhand bookshop. One of the two guest beers often comes from a micro-brewery such as Mighty Oak or Cottage. The food (served all day) is imaginative and well priced; daily specials are written on copper boards. Frequent wine tastings are arranged and a quiz night is held (Tue). Outside seating is on the pavement.

NW7: MILL HILL

Rising Sun

137 Marsh Lane, Highwood Hill

12-11; 12-10.30 Sun

(020) 8959 1357

Adnams Bitter; Greene King Abbot; Young's Bitter H

Attractive, former drovers' inn, dating from the 1600s, it was once owned by Sir Stamford Raffles, founder of Singapore. Reputedly haunted by Nan Clarke, a local licensee murdered in 1702, it made the news more recently when a bus crashed through the front door, almost demolishing the pub. One small bar serves three distinct areas, one of which is an unusual raised snug. The excellent, home-cooked food is available in the bar and the adjoining Stables restaurant. A family room is available until 5.30pm. P

NW10: HARLESDEN

Grand Junction Arms

Acton Lane

11-11 (1am Fri; midnight Sat); 12-10.30 Sun

(020) 8965 5670

Young's Bitter, Special, seasonal beers H

Imposing pub, alongside the Grand Union

Canal (moorings available), offering three contrasting bars, together with extensive gardens, a patio and children's amusements. The front bar has pool tables and a large sports screen; the middle bar is smaller and may also feature TV sports. The beamed back bar opens on to the canal and has a children's certificate until 7pm at weekends. Live music is performed Fri eve. Food is served all day until 9pm (cold snacks 3-6; hot snacks on late night extensions when there is no admission after 10.30).
❀ⒸⒹ⊟⇌⊖♣P

HAREFIELD

Spotted Dog

Breakspear Road North

✪ 12-11; 12-10.30 Sun

☎ (01895) 822190

Courage Best Bitter; Wells Bombardier Ⓗ

Formerly a two-bar pub, with a fine garden, the building has fallen to the ubiquitous single counter conversion. Located at the far eastern end of the village, practically opposite Harefield United FC, it offers a warm welcome and is the area's only known outlet using oversized glasses throughout. Alight at the pond as the 331 bus route from Ruislip and Uxbridge does not pass outside. Weekday lunches are served. ❀Ⓒ♣▽

White Horse

Church Hill

✪ 12-11; 12-10.30 Sun

Adnams Bitter; Flowers Original; Fuller's London Pride; Marston's Pedigree; Theakston Best Bitter; guest beer Ⓗ

Excellent, lively, traditional local on the south side of the village, a Grade II listed, 17th-century watering-hole. It is one of the few pubs to retain an active public bar; the saloon is a very much cosier bar with a raised floor to one side which serves as the dining room, where children are admitted.
Q⊱ⒸⒹ⊟♣P

NORTHWOOD

Olde Northwood

142 Pinner Road

✪ 12-11; 12-7 Sun

☎ (01923) 840862

Beer range varies Ⓗ

Grade II listed, corner local with newly-painted signage adorning its somewhat jaded frontage. This pub started life in 1901 as the Clifton, then changed to the Ironbridge before adopting its current name. A warm welcome awaits within this local, but beware the 'exotic' dancers performing 2-10 Mon-Sat. The guest beer is always from the Nethergate Brewery, very unusual for the area. A couple of benches are provided out at the front for fine weather. Q❀P

Sylvan Moon

27 Green Lane

✪ 11-11; 12-10.30 Sun

☎ (01923) 820760

Courage Directors; Fuller's London Pride; Shepherd Neame Spitfire; Theakston Best Bitter; guest beers Ⓗ

The frontage of this corner Wetherspoon's house, is hung with attractive hanging baskets in summer. Framed photos of Northwood village in days gone by decorate the walls of the interior. A good mix of all ages frequents this busy local, especially Thu and Fri eves when students from the nearby college join the throng. At least two guest beers are on tap at any one time.
QⒸⒹ♿⊖⚟✔

PINNER

Oddfellows

2 Waxwell Lane

✪ 11-3, 5.30 (6 Sat)-11; 12-3, 7-10.30 Sun

☎ (020) 8866 7372

Fuller's London Pride; Greene King IPA; Young's Special Ⓗ

Grade II listed building. A local, well-respected gentleman, Mr Ellement, belonged to the local Oddfellows Society; he borrowed money from them to build the pub in 1853 and named it in recognition. A very comfortable 'village' local at the end of the High Street, it boasts a collection of prints and memorabilia, including old '78' records. The large garden is an asset in summer. ❀Ⓒ⊖

Queen's Head

31 High Street

✪ 11-11; 12-10.30 Sun

☎ (020) 8868 9844

Adnams Bitter; Ansells Best Bitter; Draught Bass; Greene King Abbot; Tetley Bitter; Young's Special Ⓗ

This Grade II listed building is the oldest pub in Pinner, partly dating back to 1540, although an ale house is believed to have been on this site since the first Pinner Fair in 1336. Exposed beams, attractive decor and an open fire make this well worth a visit. A no-smoking area is available at lunchtime. ♨Q❀Ⓒ⊖P⚟

RAYNERS LANE

Village Inn

402-408 Rayners Lane (lower end of one-way system)

✪ 11-11; 12-10.30 Sun

☎ (020) 8868 8551

Courage Best Bitter, Directors; Greene King Abbot; Hop Back Summer Lightning; Shepherd Neame Spitfire; Theakston XB; guest beers Ⓗ

Standard Wetherspoon's shop conversion, next to Spencers excellent home-brew shop, it lies on the inside of the one-way system, where Rayners Lane crosses Village Way – hence the pub's name. It usually has two guest beers on tap and more during the two annual beer festivals. Parking at the rear via an alley is very limited and difficult; the pay and display opposite is an alternative. A mix of booths and stools provide seating; a pleasant sunny aspect is enhanced by open doors at the front in summer. It is rarely overcrowded, so you can inspect the abundance of 'Metroland' and other local photographs and panels.
Q❀ⒸⒹ♿⊖ (Rayners Lane) P⚟

WEALDSTONE

Royal Oak

60 Peel Road

✪ 12-11; 12-10.30 Sun

☎ (020) 8427 3122

Adnams Bitter; Tetley Bitter, Burton Ale Ⓗ

The several distinct areas betray the origins

of this 1930s 'Metroland' local as a multi-bar pub – the public bar having been lost, but a conservatory gained during a recent refurbishment. Good value beer and food is offered, the latter until 9pm weekdays, with roasts on Sundays until 4pm, although, according to a sign behind the bar, 'prices are liable to change according to customers' attitudes'. The long-standing landlord presides over an establishment entering its 11th consecutive year as an entry in this Guide. ❀◑◗ ⇌ (Harrow & Wealdstone) ⊖P

South-East London

SE1: THE BOROUGH

George Inn

77 Borough High Street

11-11; 12-10.30 Sun

☎ (020) 7407 2056

website: www.georgeinn-southwark.co.uk

Flowers Original; Fuller's London Pride; Greene King Abbot; guest beers H

First mentioned in Stow's Survey of London in 1598, the building dates from 1677, the earlier inn being destroyed in the Southwark fire of 1676. Until the late 19th century there were a number of galleried coaching inns in The Borough, but most were demolished for rail or road schemes. In 1889 the George itself had two of its three galleried wings destroyed by its then owners, the Great Northern Railway Company. Today the NT-owned George is London's only galleried inn. The nearest room as you approach from the street is the most original of the five on the ground floor. The house beer is brewed by Adnams. No food Sun eve.

Q❀◑◗ ⇌ (London Bridge) ⊖⅟

Lord Clyde

27 Clennam Street

11-11; 12-4, 8-11 Sat; 12-4, 8-10.30 Sun

☎ (020) 7407 3397

Courage Best Bitter; Fuller's London Pride; Greene King IPA; Shepherd Neame Spitfire; Young's Bitter H

Hidden gem, well worth seeking out, this is a family pub in every sense, because the pub has been in the same family since 1956. The superb tiled exterior remains exactly as when this 300-year-old pub was rebuilt in 1913. Inside are two cosy, welcoming rooms, one housing a large, brilliant-etched brewery mirror. All the food (served weekdays) is home cooked. The pub is handy for the rebuilt Globe Theatre and Tate Modern. Q◑◗ ⇌ (London Bridge) ⊖♣

Royal Oak

44 Tabard Street

11-11; closed Sat & Sun

☎ (020) 7357 7173

Harveys XX Mild, Pale Ale, BB, seasonal beers H

Harveys only tied house in London. Although well hidden, the pub is in fact only a couple of hundred yards from the tube station. The original Tabard Inn, destroyed by fire in 1676, was rebuilt, renamed the Talbot and eventually demolished in 1873. It was located in the present Talbot Yard and not in Tabard Street. A tabard was a sleeveless coat worn by heralds and knights and gave its name to the famous inn from which Chaucer's pilgrims started their journey in his Canterbury Tales. The Royal Oak has two rooms and is a warm, friendly inn where today's pilgrims in search of Harveys' full range of beers will enjoy a ready welcome.

Q◑◗ ⇌ (London Bridge) ⊖✔

Shipwright's Arms

88 Tooley Street

11-11; 12-10.30 Sun

☎ (020) 7378 1486

Beer range varies H

Always three cask beers, with at least one from a new micro-brewery, are on tap here. One large room, dominated by its central island bar, the pub has a very traditional feel. Note the superb interior tilework depicting a scene from the Pool of London by Charles Evans Ltd. HMS Belfast is now permanently moored in the Pool, which until the 1950s was busy with shipping. Other tourist attractions near the pub are the London Dungeon and the Britain at War Experience. Hay's Galleria and Tower Bridge are also quite close.

◑ ⇌ (London Bridge) ⊖♣

SE1: TOWER BRIDGE

Pommelers Rest

196-198 Tower Bridge Road

11-11; 12-10.30 Sun

☎ (020) 7378 1399

Courage Directors; Fuller's London Pride; Greene King Abbot; Shepherd Neame Spitfire; Theakston Best Bitter; guest beers H

Wetherspoon's pub, divided into two sections, one of which is a designated family area (until 9pm), which makes the pub handy for tourists visiting nearby Tower Bridge and the Tower of London. The Courage Anchor Brewery (now luxury flats) stood next to the river in Horselydown Lane. Apart from breweries, Bermondsey was the centre of the leather workers' trades; the pub's name refers to a tool used by saddlers. Nearby Tanner Street has the dealers' own antique market (Sat) but you must be there at 5am to pick up any bargains!

Q◑◑♿ ⇌ (London Bridge) ⊖ (Tower Hill) ⅟✔

SE1: WATERLOO

Film Café

National Film Theatre, South Bank Centre, Belvedere Road

11-11; 12-10.30 Sun

☎ (020) 7928 5362 website: www.bfi.org.uk

Young's Bitter, Special P

This Thameside café is close to the theatres and attractions of the South Bank. A short walk across Waterloo Bridge brings you to Somerset House, home of the Courtauld Gallery. The café serves food from opening until 9pm, and is open to the general public. Every Sunday a secondhand book fair takes place in front of the café.

❀◑♿ ⇌ (Waterloo) ⊖

SE4: BROCKLEY

Brockley Barge

184 Brockley Road

11-11; 12-10.30 Sun

☎ (020) 8694 7690

Courage Best Bitter, Directors; Greene King Abbot; Hop Back Summer Lightning; Shepherd Neame

Spitfire; guest beers Ⓗ

The former Breakspeare Arms had been closed for many years before it was extensively refurbished by Wetherspoon's and reopened in October 2000. The new name recalls the pub's proximity to the former Croydon Canal which was filled in during the 1830s, to make way for the railway from New Cross Gate to West Croydon. The usual good value Wetherspoon's range of food and drinks attracts a very cosmopolitan crowd. The pub is a very welcome addition to an area where good real ale is scarce.

Q ❀ ◐ ◑ ♿ ≹ ⚡ ⊘

SE6: CATFORD

Catford Ram

9 Winslade Way

11-11; 12-10.30 Sun

☎ (020) 8690 6206

Young's Bitter, Special, Winter Warmer Ⓗ

Comfortable, air-conditioned pub, with a large raised seating area, it is situated at the Broadway entrance to Catford shopping precinct. Popular with lunchtime shoppers from the Broadway street market, it is also handy for the renamed Broadway Theatre, home of the Catford Real Ale Festival in June. Sporting events are shown on a large-screen TV. The Ram has appeared in many editions of this Guide over the last 20 years.

◐ ♿ ≹

London & Rye

109 Rushey Green (A21)

11-11; 12-10.30 Sun

☎ (020) 8697 5028

Beer range varies Ⓗ

This café-style Wetherspoon's pub, takes its name from the road outside, which runs from London to Rye and Hastings (alias the A21). With a small, no-smoking area at the rear, it has all the usual Wetherspoon's features, plus a patio at the front. It is convenient for the local shops in Rushey Green and the Catford Real Ale Festival in June. ❀ ◐ ◑ ♿ ≹ (Catford Bridge/Catford) ⚡ ⊘

Rutland Arms

55 Perry Hill

11-11; 12-10.30 Sun

☎ (020) 8291 9426

Adnams Bitter, Broadside; Draught Bass; Fuller's London Pride, ESB; Young's Bitter, Special Ⓗ

Very friendly, if slightly out of the way, the Rutland Arms is well known for its jazz and R&B evenings. Serving good beer, with seven ales always available, it also offers tasty food: bar snacks at lunchtime and traditional roasts on Sunday. ◑

SE8: DEPTFORD

Dog & Bell

116 Prince Street

12-11; 12-3.30, 7.30-10.30 Sun

☎ (020) 8692 5664

Fuller's London Pride, ESB; guest beers Ⓗ

This genuine free house, on the Thames path national trail, has twice been CAMRA national Pub of the Year. Guest beers from micro-breweries vary from week to week; 20 malt whiskies are stocked. It hosts a pickles contest each winter. Pub games include bar billiards and shove-ha'penny; a weekly quiz is held (Sun). The secluded garden at the rear is a bonus; there is storage space for bicycles, too. ♨ Q ❀ ◐ ≹ (New Cross) ⊖ ♣ ⊘

SE9: ELTHAM

Howerd Club

447 Rochester Way

12-3 (not Mon-Fri), 7.30-11; 12-3, 7.30-10.30 Sun

☎ (020) 8856 7212

Fuller's London Pride; Shepherd Neame Master Brew Bitter; guest beer Ⓗ

This small, friendly club is situated at the rear of St Barnabas church hall. Winner of the CAMRA national Club of the Year 1997, it has appeared in every edition of this Guide since 1998. The idea for this club came from a former vicar, who found it difficult to find a decent pint of real ale in the area. The club takes its name from comedian Frankie Howerd, who was born locally. Open to card-carrying CAMRA members, a warm welcome awaits. ≹

SE10: GREENWICH

Admiral Hardy

7 College Approach

11-11; 12-10.30 Sun

☎ (020) 8858 6452

Beer range varies Ⓗ

This recently refurbished pub dates from 1830. It backs on to Greenwich market where a covered outdoor drinking area can be found. Evening meals (served Mon-Fri) include seafood specials. It also incorporates a shop, selling fish, cheeses and charcuterie. The pub is named after the Captain of Nelson's Victory, who was Governor of the Royal Naval Hospital at the time the pub was built. It is convenient for tourist attractions such as the Cutty Sark and the National Maritime Museum.

❀ ◐ ◑ ⊖ (DLR Cutty Sark)

Ashburnham Arms

25 Ashburnham Grove

12-3, 6-11; 12-3, 7-10.30 Sun

☎ (020) 8692 2007

Shepherd Neame Best Bitter, Spitfire, seasonal beers Ⓗ

Popular community pub, dating from the mid-19th century, it was acquired by Shepherd Neame in 1975. The bar area is adorned with scenes of Greenwich by local artists. It boasts a patio, conservatory and garden area. This CAMRA Pub of the Year, houses a bar billiards table. No food is available Mon; evening meals are served Tue-Fri. ❀ ◐ ◑ ≹ ⊖ (DLR) ♣

Greenwich Union

56 Royal Hill

11-11; 12-10.30 sun

☎ (020) 8692 6258

Meantime Blonde Ⓗ

Stylish comfortable bar, run by the Meantime Brewery. Decorated in a bright, modern style, beer lovers should not be put off by the decor. It also stocks a number of the brewery's draught beers dispensed under pressure, such as raspberry, chocolate stout pilsner, and wheat beer. The cask Meantime Blonde is brewed by Rooster's, as a house beer. Friendly service includes the offer of beer samples. A contemporary menu is featured. Some background, laid-back music played and a selection of board games is available. ❀◑ ⇌ ⊖ (DLR) 🍺

Plume of Feathers

19 Park Vista

⏲ 11-11; 12-10.30 Sun

☎ (020) 8858 0533

Adnams Bitter; Fuller's London Pride; Webster's Yorkshire Bitter; guest beers Ⓗ

This pub dates back to 1691, in keeping with the other historic buildings of Greenwich. Its comfortable, homely atmosphere, with candlelit tables, suits its mature clientele. A good menu offers a better than average selection for vegetarians; a dining area is to the rear of the pub. Unobtrusive background music is played, and major sporting events are shown on TV. ❀ ⇌ (Maze Hill)

Richard I (Tolly's)

52-54 Royal Hill

⏲ 11-11; 12-10.30 Sun

☎ (020) 8692 2996

Young's Bitter, Special, seasonal beers Ⓗ

Plain and simple pub where you will find a friendly welcome. Popular with all ages of drinkers, it stocks a good range of Young's beers, including bottled varieties. The large rear garden is popular in summer, and its use is extended by a number of outdoor heaters. Barbecues are held on summer weekends. Q ❀◑ ⇌ ⊖ (DLR)

Trafalgar Tavern

Park Row

⏲ 11-11; 12-10.30 Sun

☎ (020) 8858 2437 website: www.trafalgartavern.co.uk

Courage Best Bitter Ⓗ

Famous old riverside pub with Georgian decor. Its large windows afford fine views of the river. Due to its lovely location, it can get very busy at times. The Trafalgar Bitter comes from the Flagship Brewery of Chatham. An upstairs banqueting suite caters for up to 200 people. Children are allowed in the restaurant area; evening meals are served 5-9 weekdays. Piped background music is played and photographs of some of its visitors provide amusement. ◑ ⇌ (Maze Hill) ⊖ (DLR)

SE11: KENNINGTON

Prince of Wales

48 Cleaver Square

⏲ 12-11; 12-10.30 Sun

☎ (020) 7735 9916

Shepherd Neame Best Bitter, Spitfire, seasonal beers Ⓗ

Cosy local, situated in a tree-lined square, set back from the noise and traffic of the main road. Many locals are attracted to this pub, which has escaped the excesses of refurbishment. Old pictures decorate the back bar, including a couple of Lord Lucan. Evening meals are served 6-8.30 Mon-Thu. ◑ ⊖

SE13: LEWISHAM

Dacre Arms

11 Kingswood Place

⏲ 12-11; 12-10.30 Sun

☎ (020) 8244 2404

Courage Best Bitter; guest beers Ⓗ

This little gem is situated in the back streets, not far from Lee High Road. The pub is decorated with china plates, and a collection of steins and tankards is arranged behind the bar. A well-kept garden (access through the bar) is an added attraction. Major sporting events are shown on satellite TV, but this does not interfere with conversation as the volume is kept low. ❀ ⇌ (Blackheath)

Jordan

354 Lewisham High Street

⏲ 11-11; 12-10.30 Sun

Beer range varies Ⓗ/Ⓖ

Formerly part of the Hogshead chain, this pub has been renamed, using the surname of the tenant. A constantly changing beer range is available, mainly on handpump, but two are served by gravity. Although the exterior has been altered slightly there are no immediate plans to change the interior, which boasts bare boards, beams and barrels. Check times of food service. ❀◐ ⇌ (Ladywell)

Watch House

198-204 Lewisham High Street

⏲ 11-11; 12-10.30 Sun

☎ (020) 8318 3136

Courage Best Bitter, Directors; Shepherd Neame Spitfire; Theakston Best Bitter; guest beers Ⓗ

This Wetherspoon's pub is named after an old village green. It bears all the company's hallmarks, such as bookcases, stained glass alcoves, prints and photographs. It hosts two beer festivals a year, as is the norm. Although the pub can get very crowded you will usually find a seat. Q ◐◑ ♿ ⇌ ⊖ (DLR) 🍏 ⊬ ⊘

SE16: ROTHERHITHE

Ship & Whale

2 Gulliver Street

⏲ 12-3, 6-11; 11-11 Sat; 12-10.30 Sun

☎ (020) 7237 7072

Shepherd Neame Master Brew Bitter, Spitfire Ⓗ

Old Docklands pub, refurbished to a high standard. It offers a seasonal menu, with food freshly produced. Sofas, chairs and pews create a comfortable atmosphere. Board games and newspapers are provided and occasional live music is performed. Children are welcome and have their own menu to choose from. ❀◑ ⊖ (Surrey Quays/Canada Water) ♣

SE17: WALWORTH

Beehive

60-62 Carter Street

⏲ 11-11; 12-10.30 Sun

☎ (020) 7703 4992

Courage Directors; Fuller's London Pride; Greene King Old Speckled Hen; Wadworth 6X Ⓗ

Just a few minutes' walk from the brashness of Walworth Road is this haven of relative tranquillity, but is it a pub, a bar, or a restaurant? Within its simple interior, the Beehive manages to combine all three with ease. The friendly staff, sporting white aprons and bow-ties, help to create a warm atmosphere where the burble of conversation makes the piped music superfluous. Repair to the outside patio when the sun shines. ❀◑ ⊖ (Kennington)

SE18: WOOLWICH

Elephant & Castle

18 Greens End

7am-7pm; 10-3 Sun

Brains Bitter; guest beers H

Large pub, situated near a thriving market, hence the unusual opening hours. This pub is decorated with murals depicting scenes of London, and sporting memorabilia, particularly from Charlton FC. Note the collection of different coloured elephants behind the bar. At the time of survey the Brains Bitter was available at the regular price of £1.30. Breakfast is served from 7-11. Sky TV is shown. ≋(Arsenal)

Prince Albert (Rose's)

49 Hare Street

11-11; 12-3 (closed eve) Sun

☎ (020) 8854 1538

Beer range varies H

This pub is known locally as Rose's so do not ask for directions to the Prince Albert. Until 1985 this genuine free house was owned by GJ Rose and Co whose sign still hangs in the pub, hence the nickname. At least three ales are always on tap, and cider is served at weekends. Filled rolls and hot snacks are available at most times. Bed and breakfast accommodation is reasonably priced. ≋(Arsenal) ♣

SE19: GIPSY HILL

Railway Bell

14 Cawnpore Street

12-11 (weekend extensions); 12-10.30 Sun

☎ (020) 8670 2844

Young's Bitter, Special; guest beers H

This small Young's pub, near Crystal Palace Park boasts a good collection of railway pictures. Many miniature bottles and teapots also decorate the bar area. A pleasant atmosphere prevails here, and children are welcome until 7pm every day. 1970s music is played on Friday evenings. The pub has recently won an award for its menu; lunches are served until 4.30 on Sunday. The garden has also won two awards. ≋♣

SE20: PENGE

Moon & Stars

164-166 High Street

11-11; 12-10.30 Sun

☎ (020) 8776 5680

Courage Best Bitter, Directors; Shepherd Neame Spitfire; Theakston Best Bitter; Wadworth 6X; guest beers H

It was originally planned to convert the cinema on this site, but this proved impossible, so this purpose-built pub was put up instead in 1994. The usual Wetherspoon's menu is available, together with the chain's regular offers and beer festivals. A well-designed pub, it features superb woodwork throughout and many partitioned alcoves, in a very pleasant atmosphere. Q ≋(East/Kent House) ⊖(Beckenham Rd Tramlink) P

SE23: CATFORD

Blythe Hill Tavern

319 Stanstead Road (A205)

11-11; 12-10.30 Sun

☎ (020) 8690 5176

Courage Best Bitter; Fuller's London Pride H

Lying on the South Circular between Forest Hill and Catford, a small frontage hides a busy, three-bar boozer. All the bars have dark wood panelling and combine the essence of an early 20th-century pub with more modern additions, such as wide-screen TV. At the rear the garden has a children's play area. Parking space is limited. ≋(Catford/Catford Bridge) ♣P

SE25: SOUTH NORWOOD

Portmanor

Portland Road

11-11; 12-10.30 Sun

☎ (020) 8655 1308

Courage Best Bitter; Fuller's London Pride; Greene King Abbot; guest beers H

Heavily modernised inside and out, this single-bar free house has a strong commitment to traditional beer, if not to architecture. Handy for Norwood Junction Station, it is liable to be very busy on Selhurst Park match days. Mini-beer festivals are held in spring and autumn. The restaurant upstairs is open weekend evenings and all day Sunday; good bar meals at other times. A small patio allows for outdoor drinking.

≋(Norwood Jct) ⊖(Harrington Rd Tramlink)

SE26: UPPER SYDENHAM

Dulwich Wood House

39 Sydenham Hill

11-11; 12-10.30 Sun

☎ (020) 8693 5666

Young's Bitter, Special, seasonal beers H

This deservedly popular pub was designed as a private residence in 1857 by Sir Joseph Paxton, the architect of the Crystal Palace for the Great Exhibition in 1851. The pub has recently been extended into the garden to provide a large dining area. The garden itself has also been substantially altered to provide more seating and outdoor heating. Near Dulwich and Sydenham Hill golf course, the pub has a long-standing golf society. Award-winning Special London Ale is available.

Q ≋(Sydenham Hill)

ADDISCOMBE

Claret Free House

5a Bingham Corner, Lower Addiscombe Road (A222)

11.30-11; 12-10.30 Sun

☎ (020) 8656 7452

Palmer IPA; Shepherd Neame Spitfire; guest beers H

This excellent local has featured in this Guide each year since 1989. Note the old brewery mirrors, posters and historical photographs of the area. Independent of any brewery, the four ever-changing guests come from a wide range of micro-breweries – see the beer menu on the wall. Meals are served 12-2 weekdays, filled rolls are available Saturday lunchtime. The tram stop is a two-minute walk, while the bus stop for routes 289, 312 and 494 is nearby.

⊖(Tramlink)

BECKENHAM

Jolly Woodman

9 Chancery Lane (between A222 and B230)
11.30-2.30, 4.30-11; 11.30-11 Fri & Sat; 12-10.30 Sun
(020) 8663 1031
Draught Bass; Harveys BB H

Very pleasant and popular back-street former beer house. Only one bar but a partition separates the pub into two, so if the TV is on in one bar it does not intrude too much into the other half of the pub. The house bitter is M&B Brew XI rebadged. A nice courtyard at the rear complements the homely atmosphere and comfortable furniture. The pub fields a darts team.
Q ❀ (Jct) (Tramlink) ♣

BEXLEY

Black Horse

63 Albert Road
11.30 (12 Sat)-11; 12-4, 7-10.30 Sun
(01322) 523371
Beer range varies H

Friendly, back-street local, offering affordable lunchtime food in comfortable uncrowded surroundings. The bar area is split into two, with the front and left-hand side providing open space and a dartboard, while the right-hand side offers a small, more intimate drinking area, and leads to the garden. Unusually, the pub supports a golf society. The beers vary: the publican's aim is to ensure a different beer each time a barrel runs dry – a noble ambition.
❀ ♣

Cork & Cask (off-licence)

3 Bourne Parade, Bourne Road
12-2, 4-10; 10-10 Sat; 12-3, 7-10 Sun
(01322) 528884
Beer range varies G

A welcome oasis of take-home real ale. Over 800 different real ales, mostly from independent breweries, have been offered in the seven years since opening. Draught ciders are also regularly available, plus a good selection of bottled beers and ciders from independent producers, as well as imported bottled beers, particularly from Belgium, and a range of wines and spirits. Carry-out containers are sold. Larger quantities, such as polypins, can be supplied if ordered in advance.

King's Head

65 Bexley High Street
11-11; 11-4, 6-11 Sat; 12-4, 7-10.30 Sun
(01322) 526112
Courage Best Bitter; Greene King IPA, Abbot H

Very popular pub which is particularly busy in early evenings with commuters. Dating from the 16th century, this is one of the oldest buildings in Bexley village, and has been used as a pub for around 300 years. The picturesque, weatherboarded exterior makes it a local landmark. The interior boasts many original oak beams, and a few not so genuine ones following Victorian alterations. To the rear, the function room is used for Sunday lunches and for live jazz (Mon eve). A forecourt drinking area has picnic tables.
❀ P

BEXLEYHEATH

Robin Hood & Little John

78 Lion Road
11-3, 5.30 (7 Sat)-11; 12-4, 7-10.30 Sun
(020) 8303 1128
Brains Rev James; Brakspear Bitter; Flagship Futtock; Fuller's London Pride; Harveys BB; guest beers H

Dating from 1854, when it sat amid fields, this friendly back-street local is now surrounded by suburbia. It enjoys a well-deserved reputation for its beers and excellent lunches (Mon-Sat) – an extensive menu is supplemented by daily themed home-made specials and Italian pasta dishes. Meals can be eaten at tables made from old Singer sewing machines. Winner of CAMRA Greater London Pub of the Year 2000 and 2001, it was the local Pub of the Year 2002. Over 21s only are admitted. ❀

Royal Oak (Polly Clean Stairs)

Mount Road
11-3, 6-11; 11-11 Sat; 12-3, 7-10.30 Sun
(020) 8303 4454
Courage Best Bitter; guest beers H

This attractive brick and weatherboarded pub has a very rural look about it, overtaken as it was by 1930s housing. Its nickname is derived from a house-proud landlady who washed the front steps every day. Mind the cribbage players just inside the door; for this is a very cosy pub with lots of different seating areas. Plates and tankards adorn the walls and ceiling. Sandwiches and rolls are available lunchtime (not Sun). Children are allowed in the garden, not inside the pub. Q ❀ P

BROMLEY

Bitter End (off-licence)

139 Masons Hill
12-3 (not Mon), 5-10 (9 Mon); 11-10 Sat; 12-2, 7-9 Sun
(020) 8466 6083 website: www.thebitterend.biz
Beer range varies G

A beer festival in a shop is the best description of this off-licence. With reasonable notice, most beers can be obtained in polypins or firkins; samples may be available to try. A large range of bottle beers (some bottle-conditioned) is also stocked alongside a small number of imported bottled beers. Glass hire can be arranged for parties. A second shop is now open in Tunbridge Wells.

Bricklayer's Arms

141-143 Masons Hill
11-3.30, 5.30-11; 11-3, 7-11 Sat; 12-3, 7-10.30 Sun
(020) 8460 4552
Shepherd Neame Master Brew Bitter, Best Bitter, Spitfire, Bishops Finger H

This spacious, traditional pub is enhanced by chandeliers, oak tables and chairs, and is decorated by pictures throughout, including some framed cartoons. Background music is played. The bar is divided into three areas connected by arches and doorways. There is a small patio. This pub is set on the main A21 just outside the town centre. The lunch menu changes daily.
❀ (South)

Bromley Labour Club

HG Wells Centre, St Marks Road

11-11, 12-10.30 Sun

(020) 8460 7409

Shepherd Neame Master Brew Bitter; guest beers H

CAMRA members carrying a current card will be signed in to this friendly club, close to Bromley South Station. The main bar is mahogany-effect and the room is lit by three large windows. Pool and Sky TV are available. Cosy alcove seating and a number of upholstered chairs make this a comfortable place to enjoy a pint. ❀≠(South) ♣P⅟

Red Lion

10 North Road

11-11, 12-10.30 Sun

(020) 8460 2691

Greene King IPA, Abbot; Harveys BB; guest beers H

This pub was deservedly voted SE London CAMRA Pub of the Year 1997. Its original tiling and fireplace are still intact, and the jug and bottle sign has been preserved from an old door. A large pump clip collection around the bar indicates the vast range of guest beers sold. An extensive array of books adorns one wall of the pub. Evening meals finish at 7pm. ⛰Q❀◑≠(North) ♣

BROMLEY COMMON

Bird in Hand

82 Gravel Road

11-11; 12-10.30 Sun

(020) 8462 1083

Courage Best Bitter; guest beers H

This pub dates from 1830 and was built by a local firm. The main bar is decorated by bric-à-brac, hops and hanging baskets. There is also an old clocking-in machine behind the bar. A function room, with its own bar holds 45 people. Summer barbecues are held in the garden. There is no access to Gravel Road from the A21; cars should approach via Oakley Road. Bus 320 stops in Oakley Road, and routes 61, 358 and 402 on the A21. ❀◑♿♣

Two Doves

37 Oakley Road

12-3, 5.30 (5 Mon & Fri; 6 Sat)-11; 12-3, 7-10.30 Sun

(020) 8462 1627

Courage Best Bitter; Young's Bitter; guest beers H

Friendly local that offers three regularly changing guest ales to complement the regular beers. Recent refurbishments have not reduced its character and the original leaded windows are still in place. The bar is decorated by hops and various paintings. The conservatory is designated as the no-smoking area. Bus route 320, Bromley-Biggin Hill, stops outside. It was voted SE London CAMRA Pub of the Year 2000. Q❀⅟

CHELSFIELD

Five Bells

Church Road

11-11; 12-10.30 Sun

(01689) 821044

Courage Best Bitter; Greene King IPA, Old Speckled Hen; guest beer H

Welcoming, two-bar village pub, dating back to the 17th century. After many decades in the same family, the pub now has a new landlord who has enhanced the food operation, while maintaining the excellent beer quality. Evening meals (Wed-Sat) specialise in seafood. Traditional games include shove-ha'penny and shut the box. A regular Guide entry in recent years, the pub is now open all day. ❀◑◑♣P

CHISLEHURST

Bull's Head

Royal Parade

11-11; 12-10.30 Sun

(020) 8467 1727

Young's Bitter, Special, Winter Warmer H

Hotel with five guest rooms, it also has a large, wood-panelled main bar. The newly refurbished back area is suitable for children. There is an extensive garden and car park. The cocktail bar has wheelchair access. It was voted Kent CAMRA Town Pub of the Year 1999. Snacks are available in the bar Mon-Sat lunchtimes. ⛰Q❀❀⛿♿≠♣P

CROYDON

Dog & Bull

24 Surrey Street

11-11; 12-10.30 Sun

(020) 8667 9718

Young's Bitter, Triple A, Special, seasonal beers H

Grade II listed building, where a pub has stood since 1431. Situated on Croydon's famous street market, the pub has a large rear garden with a bar that opens in summer. Inside the pub the island bar is surrounded by wood-panelled walls and bare boards; prints of old Croydon are displayed. The building has been extended into the adjoining property, where additional seating is provided. An excellent, traditional market pub, it serves good value food, and hosts barbecues in summer. Q❀◑≠(East/West) ⊖(Church St/George St Tramlink)

Fisherman's Arms

78 Windmill Road (A213)

12 (11 Sat)-11; 12-10.30 Sun

(020) 8689 7887

Fuller's Summer Ale, London Pride, ESB H

Popular Fuller's pub where the original lower level part is Grade II listed. The Croydon Canal used to flow past the end of the new child-friendly garden which features a lawn, patio seating, vegetable and herb garden, two rockeries and pétanque and croquet pitches; summer weekend barbecues are held. Home-cooked food is served: Sunday roast lunches include game in season; evening meals are on request. The pub fields a pool team; dominoes, bridge, darts and cribbage are played, and the Selhurst pigeon racing club meets here. ❀◑♣

Royal Standard

1 Sheldon Street

12-11; 12-10.30 sun

(020) 8688 9749

Fuller's Chiswick, London Pride, ESB, seasonal beers H

Popular corner local, and a regular Guide entry, this Fuller's house, dating back to the

1860s, was sensitively extended in the 1990s to give three distinctive drinking areas, without losing the feel of a traditional back-street pub. The garden across the road, tucked under the Croydon flyover and adjacent to a multi-storey car park, is nevertheless pleasant. Food is served 7-9 in the evenings. It was CAMRA's Greater London Pub of the Year in 1996.
Q❀◑◐ ≈ (East/West) ⊖ (Church St/George St Tramlink) ♣✓

FOOTSCRAY

Seven Stars
Footscray High Street
11.30-11; 12-6 (closed eve) Sun
☎ (020) 8300 2057
Adnams Bitter; Draught Bass; Greene King IPA H
16th-century local in what was once a quaint village, now rather over-developed. It comprises three main drinking areas and a dining area. The decor combines a mix of old and new, where many original features contrast with gaming machines. See if you can spot the carving above one of the fireplaces. Live music is staged Friday and Saturday evenings.
❀◑P

LEAVES GREEN

King's Arms
Leaves Green Road (A223)
11-11; 12-10.30 Sun
☎ (01959) 572514
Courage Best Bitter; guest beers H
This deceptively large pub is situated on the green. Bus 320, Bromley-Biggin Hill stops outside. A patio area, with benches, is on the green itself, while a garden at the rear has a play area. Children are not allowed in the restaurant. This 400-year-old pub boasts a weatherboarded exterior and low beams inside. Occasional live music is performed. There is a campsite in Downe village nearby, where Darwin's home, Downe House, can be visited.
Q❀◑◐ ▲♣P

NORTH CRAY

White Cross
146 North Cray Road
11-11; 12-10.30 Sun
☎ (020) 8300 2590
Courage Best Bitter, Directors; guest beers H
One of the few old buildings to survive when the dual carriageway was cut through the historic village in the 1960s, the pub was known as the Red Cross from 1730 until 1935, when the War Office decreed the name contravened the Geneva Convention. Its comfortably-appointed interior boasts copper and brass utensils hanging in the front bar. Very popular for meals, particularly at lunchtime, food is served all day Saturday and Sunday. Vehicle access is from the northbound carriageway of the road. It is on the 492 bus route.
❀◑◐P

ORPINGTON

Cricketers
93 Chislehurst Road
12-3, 5-11; 12-11 Sat; 12-10.30 Sun
☎ (01689) 812648
Adnams Bitter, Broadside; Wadworth 6X; guest beer H
Tucked away just a few hundred yards from the High Street, a rather austere frontage hides a friendly, one-bar, basic boozer, where dogs are welcome. There is a large no-smoking family room with access to the garden. The bar, with a large-screen TV, displays trophies and photographs of the local cricket team. Adnams beers are now stocked on a regular basis. Parking is limited.
❀P⚟

Harvest Moon
141-143 High Street
11-11; 12-10.30 Sun
☎ (01689) 876931
Courage Best Bitter, Directors; Greene King Abbot; guest beers H
Typical Wetherspoon's town-centre pub, handy for the Walnuts shopping precinct and leisure centre. A comfortable one-bar pub, it is free from intrusive music or games machines. Families are welcome on Sundays until 6pm; food is served all day.
Q◑◐ ♿ ≈⚟✓

PETTS WOOD

Sovereign of the Seas
109-111 Queensway
11-11; 12-10.30 Sun
☎ (01689) 891606
Courage Best Bitter, Directors; Greene King Abbot; Shepherd Neame Spitfire; Wadworth 6X; guest beers H
Wetherspoon's pub, opened in 1995, on the site of a supermarket. Petts Wood was built virtually from scratch in the two decades before the Second World War, and several photographs are displayed illustrating its development. The clientele cover a wide range of ages, a surprisingly high proportion attracted from outside the local area. A children's certificate has been granted, under which the no-smoking area (not a separate room) serves as a family area until 9pm. The pub is well served by local bus routes. Q❀◑◐ ♿ ≈♣⚟✓

SELSDON

Sir Julian Huxley
152-154 Addington Road (A2022)
11-11; 12-10.30 Sun
☎ (020) 8657 9457
Courage Best Bitter, Directors; Hop Back Summer Lightning; Shepherd Neame Spitfire; Theakston Best Bitter; guest beers H
Attractive Wetherspoon's in former supermarket premises. The posh Selsdon Park Hotel and golf course is just up the road. It is tricky to reach by public transport (buses 64, 409 and 412 all stop nearby, but at different stops). It is always busy at weekends with both diners and drinkers. The pleasant garden is a suntrap in the summer. Usually three to four guest ales are available here.
Q❀◑◐ ♿⚟✓

SHIRLEY ❊

Orchard
116 Orchard Way (off A232)

⌚ 12-11; 12-10.30 Sun
☎ (020) 8777 9011
Greene King IPA; Harveys BB; guest beers Ⓗ
Modern urban retreat with a good loyal local following. Well away from public transport routes, the nearest station (Eden Park) is well over a mile away; a bus route (367) runs within half a mile, otherwise it is a fair walk from the nearest main road, but well worth finding. Several guest ales are sold each month in this rare Croydon outlet for Harveys. Sky sports is switched on for big matches; darts is played. Do not miss the big oak tree standing outside. No food Sun. ❀◐♣P

SIDCUP

Alma
10 Alma Road
⌚ 11-2.30, 5.30-11; 11-11 Fri; 11-3, 6-11 Sat; 12-3, 7-10.30 Sun
☎ (020) 8300 3208
Courage Best Bitter; Fuller's London Pride; Shepherd Neame Spitfire; guest beers Ⓗ
Back-street local, just south of Sidcup Station, so early evenings are busy with commuters recovering from travelling on crowded trains. The building dates from 1868, when it was known as the Railway Tavern. It was extended in 1897 by the addition of a large billiard room, which is now used for functions. The pub was extended again in 1934 but still left a sizeable garden which is popular in summer. The interior retains some of its Victorian character despite recent decoration in pale colours. Lunches are served weekdays. Tiny car park. Q❀◐⇌♣P

SOUTH CROYDON

Rail View
188 Selsdon Road (off A235)
⌚ 11-11; 12-10.30 Sun
☎ (020) 8688 2315
Adnams Bitter; Fuller's London Pride; Hancock's HB; Young's Special; guest beers Ⓗ
This friendly corner local was an undertaker's premises back in 1851; the hearse was kept in the pub building and the horses in stables at the back. In the 1860s it became a beer shop to provide refreshment for the mourners. Sunday roast lunches are a speciality (booking advised); afterwards you can test your wits at the Sunday evening pub quiz. Happy hours (Mon-Sat, 5.30-8pm) offer discounts on selected drinks. It hosts occasional barbecues in summer. ◐⊟⇌♣P

South-West London

SW1: BELGRAVIA ❄

Star Tavern
6 Belgrave Mews West
⌚ 11.30-11; 11.30-3, 6.30-11 Sat; 12-3, 7-10.30 Sun
☎ (020) 7235 3019
Fuller's Chiswick, London Pride, ESB, seasonal beers Ⓗ
Cracker of a public house, not easy to find, but can be accessed from the German Embassy one end and Knightsbridge at the other. In every edition of this Guide, it was West London CAMRA Pub of the Year 2001. This Grade II listed building caters for a regular clientele as well as tourists. A large function room upstairs can be booked for meetings and dinner parties. It is home to members of the Caledonian Club near Belgrave Square.
⩓Q◐◑⊖(Knightsbridge/Hyde Pk Cnr) ⊘

SW1: PIMLICO

Morpeth Arms
58 Millbank
⌚ 11-11; 12-10.30 Sun
☎ (020) 7834 6442
Young's Bitter, Special, seasonal beers Ⓗ
This very grand and imposing Victorian building faces the MI6 HQ on the other side of the Thames. Tate Britain is only a few minutes' walk towards Westminster. The pub is very well served by frequent 77 and 88 buses from the West End. There is a rather attractive snug towards the rear and the large saloon is partly wood-panelled. The landlord's dog is often encountered. Good food is served at all times.
Q❀◐◑⇌(Vauxhall) ⊖

Pimlico Tram
6 Charlwood Street
⌚ 11-11; 12-10.30 Sun
☎ (020) 7828 0448
Greene King IPA, Abbot, seasonal beers Ⓗ
Real ale conversion thanks to Greene King. A pool table and juke box grace the main bar area. There is also a raised seating area toward the front of the pub, with a few tables. The walls depict local scenes and, of course, trams. Happy hour (5-7 Sun-Thu) applies to a selected cask ale. Meals are served all day until 9pm. ◐◑⇌(Victoria) ⊖

SW1: VICTORIA

Cask & Glass
39 Palace Street
⌚ 11-11; closed Sun
☎ (020) 7834 7630
Shepherd Neame Master Brew Bitter, Best Bitter, Spitfire, seasonal beers Ⓗ
Just a few hundred yards from where the passport office used to be, this is a lovely little pub, serving fine Shep's ales. Wood-panelled throughout, it was a Watney house, and still displays lots of old prints from its previous ownership. The bar also boasts a fine display of model aeroplanes, and MPs are to be found here too – pictorially at least. An extensive menu of home-cooked snacks is served weekday lunchtimes; sandwiches on Saturdays.
Q⇌⊖(St James's Pk)

Jugged Hare
172 Vauxhall Bridge Road
⌚ 11-11; 12-10.30 Sun
☎ (020) 7828 1543
Fuller's Chiswick, London Pride, ESB, seasonal beers; guest beers Ⓗ
Classic 'ale and pie' style pub, it can be very busy in the evenings, drawing a lot of its trade from the Warwick Way and Tachbrook Street areas. There is an upstairs balcony that can be used as a function room. Before Fuller's bought the site, it traded as a bank; what used to be the bank manager's office is now a no-smoking area. It is quite different from some of the other

pubs nearby, but worth seeking out all the same; good food too. Q ◐ ⇌ ⊖ (Pimlico) ⊬ ✔

Wetherspoon's

Victoria Island, Victoria Concourse
11-11; 12-10.30 Sun
☎ (020) 7931 0445
Courage Directors; Fuller's London Pride; Shepherd Neame Spitfire; Theakston Best Bitter; guest beers Ⓗ
This pub is situated above the WH Smith's bookshop, between platforms 7 and 9 in Victoria Station. Most of the guest beers are dispensed from kilderkins, such is the demand. There are two bars: the left-hand one is no-smoking, and the other overlooks the train indicators. Regular beer festivals are held, and it is a very good meeting point. The menu, served all day, changes regularly. Q ❀ ◐ ♿ ⇌ ⊖ ⊬ ✔

SW1: WESTMINSTER

Buckingham Arms

62 Petty France
11-11 (5.30 Sat); 12-5.30 Sun
☎ (020) 7222 3386
Smiles seasonal beers; Young's Bitter, Special, Winter Warmer Ⓗ
Still a lovely pub, even though some of its custom (from the passport office that used to be down the road) has gone. The Buckingham has, to date, featured in every edition of this Guide, and a couple of years ago a grand presentation was held to mark the achievement. A side corridor drinking area and many leaded windows contribute to its Grade II listed status. It now serves Smiles seasonal beers alongside Young's Winter Warmer.
◐ ⇌ (Victoria) ⊖ (St James's Pk)

Lord Moon of the Mall

16-18 Whitehall
11-11; 12-10.30 Sun
Courage Best Bitter; Fuller's London Pride; Greene King Abbot; Shepherd Neame Spitfire; guest beers Ⓗ
The Lord Moon was not always a pub. The building started life in recent times as a bank, and retains a cash dispenser from its former days. The walls are decorated with prints of local sights and monuments. Theatreland is right on the doorstep, with the Whitehall, next door. The National Gallery and St Martin in the Fields are just moments away. Unusually for Wetherspoon's, the pub has a children's certificate, so it is handy for tourists with offspring in tow. It can be very crowded at the weekends. Food is available all day.
Q ◐ ♿ ⇌ (Charing Cross) ⊖ ✔

Royal Oak

2 Regency Street
11-11; closed Sat; 12-4 Sun
☎ (020) 7834 7046
Young's Bitter, Special, seasonal beers Ⓗ
The Royal Oak was first licensed in 1831. It was saved from destruction by a campaign of locals and CAMRA members. It belonged to Watneys at one time, later to be acquired by Young's. Quiet during the afternoons, it is situated just off the Horseferry Road. The Horticultural Halls are nearby, and it is handy for the shops on Victoria Street. The pub has an extensive menu, displayed on seven blackboards. Clear glass windows and an open-plan layout with a polished wood floor create a light, airy atmosphere.
◐ ⇌ (Victoria) ⊖ (Pimlico/St James's Pk)

Westminster Arms

9 Storeys Gate
11-11 (8 Sat); 12-6 Sun
☎ (020) 7222 8520
Adnams Bitter, Broadside; Brakspear Bitter; Greene Abbot; guest beers Ⓗ
The Westminster Arms is just over the road from the Queen Elizabeth Centre and a few minutes' walk from the Houses of Parliament. Like one or two other pubs and numerous political clubs in the area, it comes complete with a division bell. Up until 1969 it was named the Red Lion. Good food is served in an attached restaurant and wine bar until 8pm. Very busy at lunchtime, so arrive early to eat. The pub is frequented by MPs and members of the Royal Family. ❀ ◐ ⊖ ✔

SW2: BRIXTON

Crown & Sceptre

2 Streatham Hill
11-11; 12-10.30 Sun
☎ (020) 8671 0843
Draught Bass; Courage Directors; Greene King Abbot; Hop Back Summer Lightning; Shepherd Neame Spitfire; guest beers Ⓗ
Transformed from a notorious pub in 1990, this is the finest (and earliest) Wetherspoon's in south-west London. First named JJ Moon's, the change back to the original was requested by the Streatham Society. The fascia was cleaned to reveal its old identity and that of its former owners, Truman. Different levels give it great character and allow for easy conversation. A children's certificate is held for the no-smoking area. There is a very high turnover of cask beer here.
Q ❀ ◐ ⇌ (Streatham Hill) P ⊬ ✔

SW3: CHELSEA

Cooper's Arms

87 Flood Street
11-11; 12-10.30 Sun
☎ (020) 7376 3120 website: www.thecoopers.co.uk
Young's Bitter, Triple A, Special, seasonal beers Ⓗ
On a corner close to the King's Road, food is a big feature here, served both in the bar and the upstairs dining room (no meals Sun eve). The decor is modern and basic with a wood floor and pale yellow walls and ceiling, displaying lots of pictures, two interesting clocks, an elk's head and a boar's head. Quality newspapers are available, as one might expect in such an affluent area.
♛ Q ◐ ⊖ (Sloane Sq)

Crown (at Chelsea) Surprise

153 Dovehouse Street
11-11; 12-10.30 Sun
☎ (020) 7352 9505
Adnams Bitter; Fuller's London Pride Ⓗ
Long, narrow pub close to the Fulham Road and the Royal Marsden Hospital. At the front there is a small bar area. Towards the rear the accent is more on dining; evening meals are available Tue-Thu. The decor is modern, in pale green and yellow. Newspapers are available and quiet background music is often played.
◐ ⊖ (Sth Kensington)

Surprise (in Chelsea)

6 Christchurch Terrace
12-11; 12-10.30 Sun
(020) 7349 1821
Adnams Bitter; Draught Bass; Fuller's London Pride H
This traditional pub, dating back to 1853, lies at the heart of Chelsea. The ceiling is very high and the magnificent bar boasts a painted frieze. The floor is wood, strewn with large rugs. There is an assortment of stools, tables and chairs including some sofas and padded chairs. The TV is used for sporting events, and there is a dartboard. Christchurch Terrace is not shown on most street atlases – it lies at the eastern end of Caversham Street. In summer, tables and benches are put out in front of the pub.
Q ❀ ⊖ (Sloane Sq) ✔

SW4: CLAPHAM

Bread & Roses

68a Clapham Manor Street
12-11; 12-10.30 Sun
(020) 7498 1779
Adnams Bitter; guest beer (summer) H
The name comes from the banner above the bar which sets the tone for this award-winning modern pub owned by the local workers' co-operatives and trade councils. It is very busy at weekends, hosting a West African day on Sundays with food and music. There is a fine children's room at the rear; the pub draws families for its excellent food. Three good foreign beers are served, while the guest ale is usually from Wolf Brewery.
❀ ◑ ⊖ (North)

Rose & Crown

2 The Polygon
12-11; 12-10.30 Sun
(020) 7720 8265
Greene King IPA, Abbot; guest beers H
Near the other Polygon pubs, this one is easily the best. The 'Noted Simonds Ales' fascia reminds more seasoned drinkers of that wonderful ale range. This is still a traditional beer house which draws a strong regular trade, mostly for the unusual range of guest beers. The pub's one bar is split into different areas by pillars and wood partitions. The landlord is justly proud of his beer which is served by helpful bar staff. Weekend lunches are available until 5pm. ◑ ⊖ (Common)

SW5: EARL'S COURT

Blackbird

209 Earl's Court Road
11-11; 12-10.30 Sun
(020) 7835 1855
Fuller's Chiswick, London Pride, ESB H
Typical, though small, Fuller's Ale & Pie house, it was converted from a bank in 1993 and manages to convey something of the air of a 'gin palace'. The TV is used for major sporting events and quiet background music is often played. The tables and chairs are simple; it is partly-carpeted, giving distinctly different areas and some interesting pictures are hung on the walls.
◑ ⊖

SW6: PARSONS GREEN

Duke of Cumberland

235 New Kings Road
11-11; 12-10.30 Sun
(020) 7736 2777
Young's Bitter, Triple A, Special H
Once a fine old 'gin palace', it won the 1971 Evening Standard Pub of the Year award, but has been much altered and loud music is played at all times. See the biography of the Duke of Cumberland and a magnificent tiled panel; other features include two real fires and a table football game. To the rear is a carpeted dining area. It gets packed if Chelsea or Fulham are playing at home.
◑ ⊖

White Horse

1-3 Parsons Green
11-11; 12-10.30 Sun
(020) 7736 2115 website: www.whitehorsesw6.com
Adnams Broadside; Draught Bass; Harveys BB; Highgate Dark; guest beers H
This justly famous, upmarket pub was originally two properties. The beer is reasonably priced but the food is expensive by pub standards. Seating consists of chairs and sumptuous leather sofas. The decor features much breweriana. Barbecues are held throughout the year, but particularly in summer, on the large patio. It is packed when Chelsea or Fulham are playing at home. Regular beer festivals are held. There is a large dining area at the rear. Local CAMRA Branch Pub of the Year 2001.
Q ❀ ◑ ⊖ ✔

SW7: SOUTH KENSINGTON

Anglesea Arms

15 Selwood Terrace
11-11; 12-10.30 Sun
(020) 7373 7960
Adnams Bitter, Broadside; Brakspear Bitter, Special; guest beers H
Regular Guide entry offering a high standard of service in a smart, fashionable area. Built in 1827 and it has been maintained as a basic, but comfortable, pub with wood panelling, bare floorboards and green leather upholstered seats. The rear bar now serves as the restaurant, but more seating is available on the raised front patio. The customers can get quite animated during the televised rugby or cricket.
Q ❀ ◑ ⊖

SW8: SOUTH LAMBETH ❄

Priory Arms

83 Lansdowne Way
11-11; 12-10.30 Sun
(020) 7622 1884
Adnams Bitter, Broadside; Harveys BB; guest beers H
True free house with a strong commitment to real ale, normally offering three guest beers from independents. A regular winner of the local CAMRA Pub of the Year award, this Grade II listed building has a single bright bar. It stocks a range of continental bottled beers, and hosts a German beer festival each October. Good food; Sunday lunches are especially popular.
❀ ◑ ⊖ ✔

SW9: BRIXTON

Trinity Arms

45 Trinity Gardens

11-11; 12-10.30 Sun

(020) 7274 4544

Young's Bitter, Special, seasonal beers H

Single-bar retreat, a few yards from Brixton's busy town centre. Locals vary from Town Hall staff to regulars who come for the fine beers. Built in 1850, the pub stands in Trinity Gardens, named after the Trinity Asylum that stood in nearby Acre Lane, founded in 1824 by Thomas Bailey for 12 poor women who affirmed belief in the Holy Trinity. Weekday lunches are served.

Q

SW9: CLAPHAM

Landor

70 Landor Road

12-11; 12-10.30 Sun

(020) 7274 4386 website: www.landor.com

Greene King IPA; Shepherd Neame Spitfire; guest beer H

Vibrant pub, which is highly decorated with various artefacts. It is particularly busy when the highly-regarded upstairs theatre is in action (Tue-Sat eve). The service is always excellent and the home-cooked food represents good quality and value (no food Mon; Sat meals served 3-9; Sun 1.30-5). Sports events are shown on a large-screen TV at the locals' request. The pub boasts three pool tables which are always in use. Good coffee is a speciality.

(High St) (North)

SW10: WEST BROMPTON

Chelsea Ram

32 Burnaby Street

11-3, 5 (6 Sat)-11; 11-11 Fri; 12-10.30 Sun

(020) 7351 4008

Young's Bitter, Triple A, Special H

Occupying a corner site in the affluent Lots Road area, the pub is furnished in modern style. Towards the rear it manages to be cosy, despite a skylight in the ceiling. The chairs are simple, but the tables are real oak. The opening hours seem strange by today's standards in London and change when local football matches are played.

Q

SW12: BALHAM

Moon under Water

194 Balham High Street

11-11; 12-10.30 Sun

(020) 8673 0535

Courage Directors; Hop Back Summer Lightning; Shepherd Neame Spitfire; Theakston Best Bitter; guest beers H

Thriving, single bar in a former gas showroom, this vibrant pub truly reflects the local community. Quality beer and conversation are guaranteed in this typical Wetherspoon's outlet. Rock-bottom prices ensure a big turnover for cask beer, especially the Summer Lightning; usually two guest beers are on tap. The front area is very lively at times but the rear no-smoking section provides a quieter haven.

Q

SW13: BARNES

Rose of Denmark

28 Cross Street

11-11; 12-10.30 Sun

(020) 8392 1761

Brakspear Bitter; Taylor Landlord; Woodforde's Wherry H

Street-corner local, tucked away, but well worth seeking out. It is comfortable, friendly and surprisingly roomy. The landlord listened to customers' requests, hence the regular availability of the Wherry and Landlord. Snacks and basket meals are on offer at any time, even for takeaways. Local CAMRA Pub of the Year in 2001, it is named after Queen Alexandra, wife of Edward VII. Q (Barnes Bridge)

SW15: PUTNEY

Green Man

Putney Heath

11-11; 12-10.30 Sun

(020) 8788 8096

Young's Bitter, Triple A, Special, Winter Warmer H

Ancient pub on the edge of Putney Heath. Cosy and welcoming in winter, it is busier in summer due to the large garden and patios in front of the pub. Inside, the lounge is quiet, while the public bar has TV sport and the surprisingly difficult and rare game of ring the bull. The heath opposite was once a notorious duelling spot and the (surviving) protagonists often retired to the Green Man afterwards. More peacefully, the poet Swinburne used to drink here.

Q

SW16: STREATHAM

Hogshead

68-70 Streatham High Road

11-11; 12-10.30 Sun

(020) 8696 7587

Brakspear Bitter; Fuller's London Pride; Gale's HSB; H **Harveys BB;** G **Young's Bitter; guest beer** H/G

Formerly Il Caretto Italian restaurant, this Hogshead is, unusually, split into different levels, enhancing the varied drinking areas. The excellent management team always try to make it different from others in the chain, despite all the changes in ownership. One draught beer is always sold at a reduced price. Good quality food is unobtrusively served 12-9 (7 Sat; 8 Sun). The best bet in this thriving area, the pub is busy on Wednesday evening for the weekly quiz.

Q (Hill)

SW16: STREATHAM COMMON

Pied Bull

498 Streatham High Road

11-11; 12-10.30 Sun

(020) 8764 4003

Young's Bitter, Special, Winter Warmer H

Spacious renovated pub where an island bar serves three distinct areas attracting different clientele. This vibrant pub hosts Friday night karaoke and a swing jazz band (alternate Sun). There are comfortable sofas and upholstered chairs; pictures and prints adorn every wall. A varied selection of meals and snacks is available (not Sun eve), but food does not dominate. A

large-screen TV is used for major sports events, but can be avoided in other areas.
⛰Q❀◖◗⇌P

SW17: SUMMERSTOWN

Prince of Wales
646 Garratt Lane
✪ 11-11; 12-4, 7-10.30 Sun
☎ (020) 8946 2628
Young's Bitter, Special 🄷
Welcoming, two-bar local on a corner site boasting an impressive tiled exterior. Handy for the greyhound stadium and Sunday market, it retains a public bar with lower prices. The family room, off the main bar, is also used for darts some evenings. Lunches are served weekdays. The long-serving licensee ensures consistently good beer, thus deservedly earning a regular entry in this Guide.
⛰♘❀◖⊟⇌(Earlsfield) ♣P

SW17: TOOTING

Gorringe Park
29 London Road
✪ 11-11; 12-10.30 Sun
☎ (020) 8648 4478
Young's Bitter, Triple A, Special, seasonal beers 🄷
Characterful little pub, a few doors along from Tooting Station, that attracts all sorts. The friendly public bar is at the front, while the cosy, wood-panelled lounge is entered from the side street. Figges Marsh, the common land lying between Tooting and Mitcham, is only a short stroll away. The pub takes its name from a local estate, now swallowed up by suburbia. Fans of cryptic crosswords will enjoy the pub sign.
⛰❀◖◗⊟⇌♣

SW18: WANDSWORTH ❄

Cat's Back
86-88 Point Pleasant
✪ 12-11; 12-10.30 Sun
☎ (020) 8877 0818
O'Hanlon's Blakeley's Best or Port Stout; Eccleshall Slaters Supreme 🄷
Delightful, atmospheric free house in an isolated location on the edge of a riverside development area. It keeps up to four real ales, with at least one each from O'Hanlon's and Eccleshall's range (not always the Supreme) usually available. Homely old furniture, original paintings, a modern stained glass window and sundry weird and wonderful artefacts characterise this dimly-lit pub. Added attractions are the occasional live music and unforgettable lunches (not Sat); breakfast is served weekdays 10-4.
⛰Q◖

Grapes
39 Fairfield Street
✪ 11-11; 12-10.30 Sun
☎ (020) 8877 0756
Young's Bitter, Special 🄷
Small, traditional one-bar local with notable wood panelling and mirrors along one wall. The pub may soon have a conservatory, which will enable the admission of children. The pub has a dartboard and fields a team in the local league. The Grapes dates from at least 1833 and at one time part of the pub was a smithy. The garden is an award-winner. Weekday lunches available.
❀◖⇌(Town) ♣

Old Sergeant
104 Garratt Lane
✪ 11-11; 12-10.30 Sun
☎ (020) 8874 4099
Young's Bitter, Special, seasonal beers 🄷
Two-bar Young's pub that is a regular contender in the local CAMRA Pub of the Year lists. An 18th-century pub, its coach house doors remain. Darts is played in the public bar, with the pub fielding several teams. Food is available weekdays. A short walk from the town centre, it is also served by 44 and 270 buses. ⛰◖◗♣

SW19: SOUTH WIMBLEDON

Sultan
78 Norman Road
✪ 12-11; 12-10.30 Sun
☎ (020) 8542 4532
Hop Back GFB, Summer Lightning, seasonal beers 🄷
Hop Back's London pub, situated on a residential road, is named after a 19th-century racehorse. Acquired by Hop Back in 1994, this two-bar pub has one quiet side, with darts and cards; the other side has music playing and draws a mixed crowd. Special events include an annual beer festival (Sept) with barbecue, and a Beer Club (Wed 6-9) with discounted real ale. A walled patio is used for outdoor drinking. Note Hop Back Entire Stout and Thunderstorm are served with a cask breather. Local CAMRA Pub of the Year 2001. Q❀⊟♿⇌(Haydons Rd) ⊖(Colliers Wood) P

SW19: WIMBLEDON ❄

Brewery Tap
68-69 High Street
✪ 11-11; 12-10.30 Sun
☎ (020) 8947 9331
Adnams Bitter; Castle Eden Ale or Flowers Original; Fuller's London Pride; guest beers 🄷
Pleasant, open-plan pub refurbished in a continental style that appeals to younger drinkers, but still draws a real mix of customers. Satisfying breakfasts (served from 11am Sun) and lunches every day, but apart from quality nibbles the only food available in the evening is Wednesday's excellent tapas. The landlord has a strong interest in northern micro-breweries' products as part of a frequently changing range of guest beers. A lesson for all the surrounding themed fizz bars, it makes a change from the (albeit excellent) Young's that dominates the village's choice of real ale. ◖⇌⊖✔

Hand in Hand
7 Crooked Billet
✪ 11-11; 12-10.30 Sun
☎ (020) 8946 5720
Young's Bitter, Special, seasonal beers 🄷
The pub stands on the site of a house once owned by Daniel Watney whose great-grandson founded the brewery, and began selling beer here in 1867. A small courtyard at the front, plus the large green opposite provide ample outdoor drinking space. The pub has been much altered since Young's

acquired it and gained a full licence in 1974; until then it was just a beer house.
♔Q♨❀◐◑♿♣

CARSHALTON

Greyhound Hotel
2 High Street (A232)
⏲ 11-11; 12-10.30 Sun
☎ (020) 8647 1511
Young's Bitter, Special, seasonal beers; guest beer Ⓗ
Grade II listed building opposite Carshalton ponds, it is close to the ancient parish church and the Sutton Heritage Centre. The original building dates from about 1706, while the brick and stone western end was added later. The Swan bar boasts a real fire, grandfather clock and antique artefacts. The main bar is U-shaped: part bare boards and part carpeted, displaying historical prints on the walls. An extension houses a 21-bedroom hotel. Meals in the restaurant are recommended (6.30-10; 12-7 Sun). Guest beers come from Smiles. ♔Q❀⇄◐◑⇌P

Railway Tavern
47 North Street (off A232)
⏲ 12-2.30, 5-11; 11-11 Sat; 12-10.30 Sun
☎ (020) 8669 8016
Fuller's London Pride, ESB Ⓗ
Friendly, comfortable, traditional one-bar pub on a street corner. Served by bus routes 127 and 157, it is only three minutes from the station. This small pub fields two marbles teams as well as darts; the walls are adorned with the many awards the pub has won. The patio garden is well appointed, if small. As befits the pub's name it has a station clock that keeps good time plus many railway pictures and signs.
Q❀◐⇌♣✔

Windsor Castle
378 Carshalton Road (A232/B271 jct)
⏲ 11-11; 12-10.30 Sun
☎ (020) 8669 1191
Fuller's London Pride; Hancock's HB; guest beers Ⓗ
Large, open-plan wood-panelled bar with a restaurant end. Two banks of handpumps dispense the two regular beers, plus guests. The walls are covered with pump clips showing the huge range of beers which have been sold, mainly from small micro-brewers. Additional beers are available from the cellar in four-pint jugs; the pub offers a jug discount. A beer festival is held once a year. Evening meals are served Tue-Sat.
❀◐◑⇌(Beeches) P

CHEAM

Claret Wine Bar
33 The Broadway (off A232)
⏲ 11-11; 12-10.30 Sun
☎ (020) 8715 9002
Shepherd Neame Master Brew Bitter, Spitfire; guest beers Ⓗ
Shop conversion to provide an attractive narrow bar which opens out at the rear with partitioned seating. A dark beamed ceiling contrasts with pale woodwork elsewhere. A spiral staircase leads to the first-floor restaurant. A jug discount is offered on the two regular and two guest beers. Booking is advised in the restaurant which features Chinese meals (Tue) and a curry night (Thu). ◐◑⇌

Prince of Wales
28 Malden Road (off A232)
⏲ 11-11; 12-10.30 Sun
☎ (020) 8644 4464
Adnams Bitter; Fuller's London Pride; Young's Bitter; guest beer Ⓗ
Situated just north of the main shopping area, this 19th-century detached building has a distinctive front verandah. Inside at the front is an L-shaped bar and a drinking area; two more drinking areas lead off to the rear. At the back, a quiet no-smoking section admits accompanied children. The middle drinking area is dominated by the pub golf society's trophy cabinet. A large range of food is available (evening food to 9pm Mon-Sat; all day to 9pm Sun); see the large board menu in the front bar.
Q❀◐◑⇌♣⚡

CHESSINGTON

North Star
271 Hook Road, Hook (A243)
⏲ 12-11; 11-11 Sat; 12-10.30 Sun
☎ (020) 8391 9811
Adnams Bitter; Draught Bass; Fuller's London Pride Ⓗ
Large community pub, open plan, but with several distinct areas, it lies on the main road from Kingston to Leatherhead, and is on the 71 bus route. The house policy is for background music to be just that; it sometimes shows sports events on terrestrial TV. Meals are served at lunchtimes and early evening (no food Sun eve). There is a patio for summer drinking. ❀◐◑♿P

KEW

Coach & Horses Hotel
8 Kew Green
⏲ 11-11; 12-10.30 Sun
☎ (020) 8940 1208
Young's Bitter, Triple A, Special, seasonal beers Ⓗ
A Young's house since 1831, the Coach & Horses now has a modern hotel, complete with underground car park, at the rear. Its reopening in 2001 also saw a refurbishment of the bar area, creating more space and allowing a no-smoking room to be used mainly for dining. It has a justifiably excellent reputation for home-cooked food, which now includes fish specialities (best to book for Sunday lunch). Close to Kew Gardens, it stands on bus route 65.
♔Q❀⇄◐◑⇌(Bridge) ⊖(Gardens) ⚡

KINGSTON UPON THAMES ✻

Canbury Arms
49 Canbury Park Road
⏲ 11-11; 12-10.30 Sun
☎ (020) 8288 1882
Adnams Broadside; Courage Best Bitter; Greene King Old Speckled Hen; Wychwood Hobgoblin; guest beers Ⓗ
Victorian drinkers' pub close to Kingston town centre, keeping a good range of beers; the cider varies. The comfortable interior features mock beams and a small raised seating area; a pool table and other pub games are played. Live music is performed Fri and Sat eve; a quiz is held Sun. Note the collection of 500+ pump clips around the walls at this previous local CAMRA Pub of the Year. Home to three friendly dogs,

people wishing to bring their own dog must phone ahead.
❀⇌♣●P🍷

Park Tavern
19 New Road
⊛ 11-11; 12-10.30 Sun
Brakspear Special; Young's Bitter; guest beers Ⓗ
This excellent pub is tucked away down a small side road, not far from Kingston Gate of Richmond Park. The homely single bar is adorned with old pictures, clocks and an inventive display of the many pump clips used over the years. The bar faces the doors as you enter, with comfortable bench seating around the walls on either side and an open fire. For the better weather there is a patio along the front of the pub. Some 150 years old, it was converted from three cottages to become a very popular pub.
♨❀🍷

Willoughby Arms
47 Willoughby Road
⊛ 10.30-11; 12-10.30 Sun
☎ (020) 8546 4236
Flowers IPA; Fuller's London Pride; Taylor Landlord; guest beers Ⓗ
This large two-bar local has successfully defied trends by replacing swan necks with short pipes and retaining 10.30 opening. You will find here a friendly clientele, a cat, games and local papers. The saloon features pictures of old Kingston and handpump-handle lampstands. The sports area offers pool, three dartboards and a large-screen TV. The upstairs function room was used for rehearsals by the Yardbirds in the 1960s. It hosts beer festivals for St George's Day and Hallowe'en. A cheap beer is available on Wednesday. ❀♿♣●

Wych Elm
93 Elm Road
⊛ 11-3, 5-11; 11-11 Sat; 12-10.30 Sun
☎ (020) 8547 0321
Fuller's Chiswick, London Pride, ESB Ⓗ
Very traditional, two bar-pub: a basic public bar, with lino floor and dartboard contrasts with the more comfortable and decorative lounge bar. It is run by a charismatic landlord from Spain, who looks after his pub and beers very well. Out the back is a pleasant garden. The pub is Victorian and was evidently named after a tree which grew near the pub, but has long since gone. Home-cooked food is served Mon-Sat.
❀◑⊟♣●

MITCHAM

King's Arms
260 London Road
⊛ 11-11; 12-5.30, 8-10.30 Sun
☎ (020) 8648 0896
Young's Bitter, Triple A, Special, seasonal beers Ⓗ
Large, popular pub in the pedestrianised part of the town centre; it has an island bar and old prints line the walls. There is a function room on the first floor. The outdoor drinking area overlooks Fair Green. A full menu is available weekday lunchtimes. Music and trivia quizzes are held on Thu and Sun eves; live music is performed Sat eve. Noise from the games machines is kept to a reasonable level. ❀◑♣

NEW MALDEN

Woodies
Thetford Road
⊛ 11-11; 12-10.30 Sun
☎ (020) 8949 5824
Flowers Original; Fuller's London Pride; Young's Bitter, Special; guest beers Ⓗ
Originally the sports and social club for Fyffes, this popular free house is believed to be the only pub in Britain in a wooden pavilion. Renowned for its sporting, TV, film and theatrical memorabilia covering the walls and ceiling, further additions are always welcomed. The pub runs its own football, cricket, fishing and ladies' darts teams. Two guest beers are usually available. The smoke extraction system compensates for the lack of no-smoking area. The home-cooked menu caters for children.
♨Q❀◑♿♣P

RICHMOND

Red Cow
59 Sheen Road
⊛ 11-11; 12-10.30 Sun
☎ (020) 8940 2511
Young's Bitter, Special, seasonal beers Ⓗ
Popular local, a few minutes' walk from Richmond's shops and station. There are three distinct drinking areas, where rugs on bare floorboards and period furniture create

INN BRIEF

South-West London

SW19: WIMBLEDON COMMON

Crooked Billet
15 Crooked Billet
11-11; 12-10.30 Sun
(020) 8946 4942
Young's Bitter, Triple A, Special, seasonal beers Ⓗ
Large pub on the edge of the common, with drinking on the green in the summer. Good food.

SW20: RAYNES PARK

Raynes Park Tavern
32 Coombe Lane
11-11; 12-10.30 Sun
(020) 8946 0872
Theakston Best Bitter; guest beers Ⓗ
Imposing Edwardian pub, facing the entrance to Raynes Park Station. Up to five guest beers .

KINGSTON UPON THAMES

Bricklayer's Arms
53 Hawks Road
12-11; 12-10.30 Sun
(020) 8549 7520
Greene King IPA, Abbot Ⓗ
Single-bar pub, renowned for its home-cooked food with generous portions, served from 12-4. Cask Marque accredited.

Owl & Pussycat
144 Richmond Road
11.30-11; 12-10.30 Sun
(020) 8546 9162
Adnams Bitter; Young's Bitter; guest beer Ⓗ
Recently refurbished in a modern, bright style. Food is available lunch and eve; children welcome. Pavement seating in summer.

West London

W1: FITZROVIA

One Tun
58 Goodge Street
11.30-11; 12-10.30 Sun
(020) 7409 2916
Young's Bitter, Special, seasonal beers Ⓗ
Ex-Finches pub acquired by Young's. Fully carpeted, with Bass mirrors and central island bar. Food is served lunchtime.

W1: MARYLEBONE

Beehive
7 Homer Street
11-3, 5.30-11; 11-11 Fri & Sat; 12-10.30 Sun
(020) 7262 6581
Fuller's London Pride; Young's Bitter Ⓗ
Small, friendly, side-street pub with very loyal clientele. No food eves.

a traditional atmosphere. The first floor has been converted to provide four en-suite bedrooms. Good lunches are served daily and evening meals until 8.30 on weekdays. Tuesday is quiz night, and Thursday night is for live music.

Triple Crown
15 Kew Foot Road
11-11; 12-10.30 Sun
(020) 8940 3805
Beer range varies
True free house, serving four regularly changed ales, it stands by Richmond Athletic ground, close to Old Deer Park and Kew Gardens. Convenient for Richmond Station, the pub is small and narrow but still has room for darts at the far end. It is popular for the quiz (Tue eve) and Sunday afternoon jazz. There are a couple of tables on the front pavement, and an upstairs function room has its own bar (with handpumps) and a small balcony. Lunches served Mon-Sat.

White Cross
Riverside, Water Lane
11-11; 12-10.30 Sun
(020) 8940 6844
Young's Bitter, Triple A, Special, seasonal beers
This popular pub is a prominent feature on Richmond's waterfront. It dates from 1835, but a stained glass panel in the bar reminds drinkers that it stands on the site of a former convent of the Observant Friars, whose insignia was a white cross. It is reached by steps – for good reason, as the river often floods here. Inside an island bar is flanked by two side rooms (one at mezzanine level). An unusual feature is a fireplace beneath a window. A ground-level patio bar opens at busy times; the patio boasts a rare Greek Whitebeam tree.

SURBITON

New Prince
117 Ewell Road (A240)
11-11; 12-10.30 Sun
(020) 8296 0265
Gale's Butser, GB, HSB
Locals' pub on a main road, catering for all ages. It fields a team in the local darts league and hosts a crib evening every Monday, just for fun. The pub is a recent addition to the Gale's estate. The main room houses the bar counter, a no-smoking area leads off from this. Q

Waggon & Horses
1 Surbiton Hill (A240)
11-11; 12-10.30 Sun
(020) 8390 0211
Young's Bitter, Special, seasonal beers
Built in 1888, it stands on the site of a coaching inn where an extra horse was supplied to heavy wagons for the climb up Surbiton Hill. The front bar has been brightened up with bleached pine, while the rest of the pub bears more traditional dark wood panels. Following the recent retirement of the tenant after 35 years, the pub has become a managed house, but the cellarman has stayed on. The pub hosts weekly quizzes (Tue) and a raffle (Sun). Lunch is served daily and evening meals Tue-Sat with Thai food a speciality.
Q

SUTTON

Little Windsor
13 Greyhound Road (off A232)
11.30-11; 12-10.30 Sun
(020) 8643 2574
Fuller's Chiswick, London Pride, ESB, seasonal beers; guest beer
Cosy, street-corner local in Sutton's new town. Low-ceilinged, with half-panelled walls, it is well ventilated. A friendly atmosphere is a hallmark of the split-level bar (mind the step). A good-sized extension lies to the rear. It displays a prominent price list, with a good selection of wines. It features handy coat or handbag hooks under the bar and interesting wall lights. A discount is given on four-pint jugs of ale. Games include chess and backgammon.

New Town
7 Lind Road (off A232)
12-3, 5-11; 12-11 Fri & Sat; 12-10.30 Sun
(020) 8770 2072
Young's Bitter, Triple A, Special, seasonal beers
Spacious, attractive, street-corner local in the area of Sutton known as 'new town'. The public bar prices are a little cheaper; the saloon bar is unusual as it is on three levels

---

Carpenter's Arms
12 Seymour Place
11-11; 12-10.30 Sun
(020) 7723 1050
Beer range varies
Close to Marble Arch, this real ale mecca stocks a rotating choice of six beers from regional and micro-breweries. Cask Marque accredited.

W1: SOHO

Clachan
34 Kingly Street
11-11; 12-10.30 Sun
(020) 7494 0834
Adnams Bitter; Fuller's London Pride; Greene King IPA
Recently reopened after refurbishment, it still very much bears the same impressive Victorian style.

King's Arms
23 Poland Street
11-11; 12-10.30 Sun
(020) 7734 5907
Courage Best Bitter, Directors
Unspoilt hostelry – a well-known gay pub – where clubs meet. Good food.

W5: EALING

Ealing Lawn Tennis Club
Daniel Road
6-11; 2.30-10.30 Sun
(020) 8992 0370
Draught Bass; Fuller's London Pride; guest beers
Single bar in a Tudor-style clubhouse with an ever-changing guest beer.

Rose & Crown
Church Place, St Mary's Road
11-11; 12-10.30 Sun
(020) 8567 2811
Fuller's Chiswick, London Pride, ESB, seasonal beers
Popular, two-bar local with a conservatory-style annexe, tucked away behind St Mary's Church. Cask Marque accredited.

W7: HANWELL

Dolphin
13 Lower Boston Road
12-11; 12-10.30 Sun
(020) 8840 0850
Brakspear Bitter; Fuller's London Pride; Greene King Old Speckled Hen; Marston's Pedigree; Wadworth 6X
This showcase free house is all a good pub should be.

– access to the garden is via the lower level bar area. A quiz is held on Sunday evening, when no food is served. Old photos of Sutton pubs and the surrounding area adorn the walls.

WALLINGTON

Duke's Head

6 Manor Road (off A232)
11-11; 12-10.30 Sun
(020) 8647 1595
Young's Bitter, Special, seasonal beers H

Large, listed building by the village green, which provides ample outdoor drinking space in summer. Recently extended to incorporate an hotel and restaurant. The public and saloon bars still offer a quiet, more mature drinking atmosphere (over 21s only). The building has a long history, dating back to its time as a coaching inn. The main bar is wood panelled and decorated with some local historical photographs. Q P

West London

W1: FITZROVIA

Duke of York

47 Rathbone Street
11-11 (5 Sat); closed Sun
(020) 7636 7065
Greene King IPA, Abbot H

Quiet, back-street local situated near the busy Tottenham Court Road, at the end of the paved Charlotte Place. One side of the pub has comfortable bench seating; a dartboard hangs at the other end. Food is restricted to baguettes, freshly prepared, but customers are welcome to bring food from outside to consume on the premises. The pub is available for hire on Saturday evenings. (Goodge St/Tottenham Ct Rd)

W1: MARYLEBONE

Golden Eagle

59 Marylebone Lane
11-11; 12-10.30 Sun
(020) 7935 3228
Adnams Bitter; Brakspear Bitter; Fuller's London Pride; guest beers H

Not far from Oxford Street and Marylebone High Street, this small free house is very much a local, patronised by office workers and artisans. The pub has been refurbished several times over the years, but retains some fine glass mirrors. On Thursday and Friday evenings a pianist plays from about 8.30 pm. A classic atmosphere can be enjoyed here, and the snack food is first rate – baguettes filled with Biggles sausages from a shop just a few hundred yards down the lane. (Bond St)

Wargrave Arms

40 Brendon Street
11-11; 12-10.30 Sun
(020) 7723 0559
Young's Bitter, Special, seasonal beers H

Well-kept L-shaped ex-Finch's pub, just off the busy Edgware Road, it provides a quiet haven for good conversation and the local chess club. Comfortable seats fill one area while the rest is taken up with tables and chairs, mainly used by diners. Good service and a relaxed atmosphere is excellent therapy for a hectic London life.
Q (Paddington) (Edgware Rd)

W1: MAYFAIR

Guinea

30 Bruton Place
11-11 (6.30 Sat); closed Sun
(020) 7409 1728
Young's Bitter, Special, seasonal beers H

About 60 yards off Berkeley Square in a small mews, which can be quite difficult to find, this establishment is the oldest pub in Mayfair and dates from around 1675. Very much inhabited by office workers and tourists, it is divided into two sections, and can be very crowded, particularly during the evenings. There is an excellent restaurant attached, the Guinea Grill, famous for its steak and kidney pies. Q (Bond St)

Hogshead

11 Dering Street
11 (12 Sat)-11; closed Sun
(020) 7629 0531
Adnams Bitter; Fuller's London Pride; H **guest beers** H/G

The Hogshead was at some time in the past Wethered's Bunch of Grapes, and maintains the original ale house concept, offering several different cask beers. It also stocks a small line in Belgian bottled beers, and firkins are kept on a stillage behind the bar. Meals, from an ever-changing menu, are served all day. It gets very busy in the evenings towards the end of the week, but afternoons can be quieter. Wheelchair access is restricted to the ground floor.
(Bond St)

W1: SOHO

Ain't Nothin' But...

20 Kingly Street
6-1am (2am Thu; 2.30am Fri & Sat); 7.30-midnight Sun
(020) 7287 0514 website: www.aintnothinbut.co.uk
Adnams Bitter, Broadside; Fuller's London Pride; guest beers H

There has been a blues club at the Ain't Nothin' But for a few years now, but Adnams beers are a recent innovation. Prices are considerably higher (20%) than elsewhere in the locality, but then there is live music and a late licence. An extensive programme of live gigs is published weeks in advance. Four-pint pitchers, with £2 off normal prices, are sold between 6 and 8pm. An entry charge of £5 is levied from 8.30pm Friday and Saturday. The club can get very crowded indeed.
(Oxford Circus/Piccadilly Circus)

Coach & Horses

29 Greek Street
11-11; 12-10.30 Sun
(020) 7437 5920
Fuller's London Pride; Marston's Pedigree; Tetley Burton Ale H

Landlord Norman Balon has been at the Coach & Horses for many years now, and the pub has been considered a local institution since the 1960s. It displays cartoons galore by Heath. Partitions divide three distinct drinking areas, all complemented by comfortable old

furniture. Happy hour offers good value (Sun and Fri 11-4pm pints £2.20, half-pints £1.10) but at other times it can be expensive. Sandwiches (served all day), however, are just £1. It can be very crowded Friday and Saturday.
Q ⊖ (Piccadilly Circus/Leicester Sq)

Ship
116 Wardour Street
11-11; closed Sun
☎ (020) 7437 8446
Fuller's London Pride, ESB, guest beers H
This is indeed a rare Fuller's outlet in Soho, the only one with real ale in this cosmopolitan area. Popular music, from the 1960s-1990s, is played throughout the day, and can be quite loud, especially during the evenings. The pub suffered serious damage in the 1950s due to a gas explosion, destroying many original fittings, but the subsequent restoration is very attractive. Good food is served Mon-Sat.
⊖ (Piccadilly Circus)

Star & Garter
62 Poland Street
11-11; closed Sun
☎ (020) 7439 0218
Courage Best Bitter; Fuller's London Pride; Shepherd Neame Spitfire; guest beers H
This very well known Soho institution has two private bars available upstairs (enquire at the bar). A lot of media and film folk based in the Wardour Street area drink here. Dating from about 1825, the pub's interior is wood-panelled in shades of brown, with comfortable benches and other seating. There is a plain wood floor throughout. It is hung with much brass, copper and ceramic breweriana and many old photos and drawings, but pride of place is given to a large mirror depicting a Star & Garter. The landlord's choice of music is blues. Snacks available.
⊖ (Oxford Circus/Leicester Sq/Piccadilly Circus)

W2: PADDINGTON

Archery Tavern
4 Bathurst Street
11-11; 12-10.30 Sun
☎ (020) 7402 4916
Badger K&B Sussex, Best, Tanglefoot, seasonal beers H
Small pub, dating from 1840, located next to a mews with stables. The pub is well furnished, with plates and dry hops above the bar. This Badger outlet offers the full range from Blandford Forum and a seasonal King & Barnes beer, brewed in Dorset. The pub is always popular with locals and tourists staying in the nearby hotels. The rear of the pub, where the TV is also located, has a separate serving hatch.
❀ ≉ ⊖

Mad Bishop & Bear
First Floor, The Lawn, Paddington Station
11-11; 12-10.30 Sun
☎ (020) 7402 2441
Fuller's Chiswick, London Pride, ESB, seasonal beers; guest beer H
Newly-built Fuller's pub in Paddington Station, situated at the top of two escalators near the airline check-in desks and sharing the area with coffee and sandwich outlets. The pub is a good place to wait for your train to take you home or, after checking your baggage with the airline, a good excuse to have a pint of beer before taking the next Heathrow Express train to the airport. The pub has the new plasma train information screens, which at the time of survey were not functioning.
❀ ≉ ⊖

Royal Exchange
26 Sale Place
11-11; 11-4, 7-11 Sat; 12-4, 7-10.30 Sun
☎ (020) 7723 3781
Boddingtons Bitter; Brakspear Bitter H
Popular, friendly Irish pub, situated just off Praed Street, close to St Mary's Hospital, it was first licensed in 1841, prior to the arrival of the Great Western railway. The name dates back to the days when letters were exchanged between horse-drawn Royal Mail coaches. The pub is a well-preserved gem, run by the same landlord for 23 years, a keen follower of racehorses.
≉ ⊖ (Paddington/Edgware Rd)

Victoria
10a Stathearn Place
11 (12 Sat)-11; 12-10.30 Sun
☎ (020) 7724 1191
Fuller's Chiswick, London Pride, ESB, seasonal beers H
Ornate, street-corner local, with a single bar displaying etched mirrors and old prints. The pub is always popular as the beers are in good condition and the welcome friendly. One side of the pub has Sky TV for sport, but never too loud, and outside benches nestle behind plants which act as a screen from the traffic. It is rumoured that Queen Victoria visited the pub prior to opening Paddington Station, hence the name of the pub.
❀ ≉ ⊖

W3: ACTON

Duke of York
86 Steyne Road
11-11; 12-10.30 Sun
☎ (020) 8992 0463
Brakspear Bitter; Courage Best Bitter; Fuller's London Pride H
Friendly free house, it comprises a single dog-leg bar, a dining area, pool room and a function room upstairs for hire. Its regular clientele is occasionally augmented by local celebrities. The garden has heaters to extend its use. Meals are served all day Sun.
❀ ≉ (Central) ⊖ ♣

King's Head
214 High Street
11-11; 12-10.30 Sun
☎ (020) 8992 0282
Fuller's Chiswick, London Pride, ESB H
This large, comfortable single-bar pub offers distinct areas for drinking and dining. The pub occupies a prominent position towards the western end of central Acton, near Safeway's supermarket. A paved frontage provides space for benches for outdoor drinking. No evening meals are served Sun.
❀ ≉ (Central)

W4: CHISWICK

Bell & Crown

11-13 Thames Road, Strand on the Green

11-11; 12-10.30 Sun

(020) 8994 4164

Fuller's Chiswick, London Pride, ESB, seasonal beers H

Riverside pub located near Kew Bridge and the Steam Museum. During the summer the pub can get busy as it nestles on a quiet stretch of the Thames. However the pub is popular in all weathers as there is an indoor conservatory which overlooks the river. It has one main bar, with a separate street entrance, and ample seating for diners and drinkers alike. Food is always good as the pub employs its own chef.

(Kew Bridge)

George & Devonshire

8 Burlington Lane

11-11; 12-10.30 Sun

(020) 8994 1859

Fuller's Chiswick, London Pride, ESB, seasonal beers H

Situated next door to Fuller's Brewery, opposite the Hogarth roundabout on the A4, this pub is an unspoilt local with an uncarpeted public bar and a carpeted saloon bar with a real fire. As its location suggests, the Fuller's beers are always in good condition as this pub acts as the unofficial brewery tap, with staff coming in after the brewery closes for the day. The function room resembles a director's room with a central table and old prints on the wall. Food is served lunchtime and evenings until 9pm.

P

Old Pack Horse

434 Chiswick High Road

11-11; 12-10.30 Sun

(020) 8994 2872

Fuller's London Pride, ESB, seasonal beers H

Spacious, ornate wood-panelled street-corner pub located close to Chiswick Park Station. The pub is divided into five areas with a Thai restaurant and a small snug with real fire for cold nights. The pub is popular during the evenings with younger up-and-coming locals chilling out after a hard day's work in the office. No food Sun eve.

(Gunnersbury) (Park)

Tabard

2 Bath Road

11-11; 12-10.30 Sun

(020) 8994 3492

Adnams Broadside; Draught Bass; Greene King IPA; Marston's Pedigree; Tetley Bitter H

Sympathetically refurbished pub; dating back to 1880, the building was designed by Norman Shaw as part of Bedford Park. The renovation has preserved the original frieze and the upstairs theatre. The pub is divided into four areas with a second small bar by the front door. A modern side room, added during previous work doubles as a function room. The pub is popular with locals and the younger set, creating a good atmosphere. Food is served all day until 9pm.

W5: EALING

Castle

36 St Mary's Road

11-11; 12-10.30 Sun

(020) 8567 3285

Fuller's Chiswick, London Pride, ESB, seasonal beers H

Traditional local endowed with a particularly striking exterior, standing opposite Thames Valley University. Inside, a sympathetic refurbishment has left much of the pub open plan, but a wooden partition to the right of the door has been retained and encloses a small snug bar. The scene is completed by a genuine stone-flagged floor in the main bar. Thai food is a speciality.

(South)

Duffy's

124 Pitshanger Lane

11-11; 12-10.30 Sun

(020) 8998 6810

Draught Bass; Fuller's London Pride; Greene King Abbot; Young's Bitter; guest beers H

Welcome oasis in the severely under-pubbed Pitshanger area, north of Ealing town centre. Built as a shop for United Dairies in 1910, Duffy's then became a wine bar before emerging as a pub in 1985. Inside, a single bar serves two distinct areas: the front is fairly basic and houses the TV; behind is a more comfortable section which leads to a downstairs restaurant area. It hosts live music most Sunday evenings, and an annual beer festival.

Red Lion

13 St Mary's Road

11-11; 12-10.30 sun

(020) 8567 2541

Fuller's Chiswick, London Pride, ESB, seasonal beers H

Single-bar institution, opposite Ealing Film Studios, hence its alternative name of Stage Six. The walls of this traditional pub are covered in pictures from the many films and BBC TV programmes that originated over the road. Although dating from at least the early 18th century, the attractive courtyard style garden at the rear is much more recent. The pub will have undergone a minor sympathetic refurbishment by the time you read this.

Q (Broadway) (South)

Wheatsheaf

41 Haven Lane

11-11; 12-10.30 Sun

(020) 8997 5240

Fuller's Chiswick, London Pride, ESB, seasonal beers H

Welcome return to the Guide for this former stalwart. The Wheatsheaf lies just north of Ealing town centre and is a deceptively large pub with much wood in evidence. An early 1990s refurbishment led to it actually gaining a public bar at the front. Alongside this is a comfortable saloon, which leads to a large open area at the rear. It is gaining a deservedly good local reputation for its food.

(Broadway)

W6: HAMMERSMITH

Andover Arms
57 Aldensley Road
11-11; 12-3.30, 7-10.30 Sun
☎ (020) 8741 9794
Fuller's Chiswick, London Pride, ESB, seasonal beers Ⓗ
Located in Brackenbury village to the north-west of Hammersmith, this pub is a well-hidden gem. Fully carpeted, it displays period prints in the single central bar which boasts all too rare snob screens. It provides a contrast to the usual hectic pace of life experienced in this area of London. The pub is popular with locals and diners who come for the Thai food during lunchtime and evenings (Mon-Fri). ⊖ (Ravenscourt Pk)

Brook Green Hotel
170 Shepherd's Bush Road
11-11; 12-10.30 Sun
☎ (020) 7603 6827
Young's Bitter, Special, seasonal beers Ⓗ
Imposing Victorian pub, located between Shepherd's Bush and Hammersmith, overlooking Bush Green. Ornate Victorian mirrors and woodwork have been preserved in the spacious main bar. The hotel has 14 rooms at reasonable rates for the capital. Entertainment is provided by morris dancers on Tuesday evening, and a Comedy Night held in the basement bar (Thu).
⊖

Cross Keys
57 Black Lion Lane
11-11; 12-10.30 Sun
☎ (020) 8748 3541
Fuller's London Pride, ESB, seasonal beers Ⓗ
Situated in Black Lion Lane, just off King Street, this quiet, back-street pub has been recently refurbished, with alcove seating towards the rear and a patio for alfresco drinking. The front of the pub comprises the main bar area, where Sky TV allows locals to catch up with the sporting action. The welcome is friendly and real ale enjoys good local support. ⊖ (Stamford Brook)

Dove ☆
19 Upper Mall
11-11; 12-10.30 Sun
☎ (020) 8748 5405
Fuller's London Pride, ESB Ⓗ
Famous 17th-century pub, accessible from the Thames path from Hammersmith Bridge, it boasts historical connections with Charles II and Nell Gwyn. Thomas Arne composed Rule Britannia here. The pub has a small bar, with a smaller public bar towards the front and a saloon bar with original fireplace (sadly gas-fired). The rear of the pub is more modern with an outdoor terrace and a seating area for diners.
Q ⊖ (Ravenscourt Pk)

Salutation
154 King Street
11-11; 12-10.30 Sun
☎ (020) 8748 3668
Fuller's Chiswick, London Pride, ESB, seasonal beers Ⓗ
Former coaching inn with an eye-catching purple tiled exterior and passageway. The pub is located towards the end of King Street which means it can attract younger drinkers on Friday nights. However most of the time the pub is popular with a mixed clientele, which makes the atmosphere relaxing, unlike most circuit bars nearby. The pub offers food all day and a quiz on Tuesday evening. ⊖ (Ravenscourt Pk)

W7: HANWELL

Fox
Green Lane
11-11; 12-10.30 Sun
☎ (020) 8567 4021
Brakspear Bitter; Fuller's London Pride; Taylor Landlord; guest beers Ⓗ
Dating from the early 19th century, this building stands at the confluence of the River Brent and Grand Union Canal. In the last couple of years the new management has firmly established this family-centred pub in the local community. It now hosts regular beer festivals and dispenses guest ales at all times. Sunday lunches are always popular, and occasional barbecues are held during summer months. Accompanied children (and dogs) are always welcome.
P

W8: KENSINGTON

Britannia
1 Allen Street
11-11; 12-10.30 Sun
☎ (020) 7937 6905
Young's Bitter, Special; guest beer Ⓗ
This pub has three main areas: the top bar, which is wood-panelled and has some seating, leads down a few steps to the back bar, which has comfortable seating and a conservatory at the rear, reached by the side passage. The conservatory, which doubles as a family function room, is no-smoking until 8pm. Close to Kensington High Street shopping area, it has appeared in all editions of this Guide. Q ⊖ (High St)

Churchill Arms
119 Kensington Church Street
11-11; 12-10.30 Sun
☎ (020) 7727 4242
Fuller's Chiswick, London Pride, ESB, seasonal beers Ⓗ
This popular Fuller's pub is run by an Irishman, who displays various items of memorabilia from Gaelic football, hurling and rugby, plus other bric-à-brac. Awards hang from the ceiling and cover the walls. Food is available in the Thai restaurant and the bar area. The TV sets show sporting events. Q ⊖ (Notting Hill Gate)

W9: MAIDA VALE

Warrington Hotel ☆
93 Warrington Crescent
11-11; 12-10.30 Sun
☎ (020) 7286 0310
Brakspear Special; Fuller's London Pride; Young's Special; guest beer Ⓗ
It is rumoured that the Warrington was once a house of ill-repute. There is a hint of joys to come in the naked, Art Nouveau nymphs that adorn the fascia above the marble bar. They may entice you upstairs, where there are Epicurean delights to be savoured; today they come in the form of Thai food. For the less dissipated, there is a

quiet public bar where an unerotic game of darts can be enjoyed.
(Warwick Ave)

Warwick Castle
6 Warwick Place
12-2.30, 5-11; 12-11 Fri & Sat; 12-10.30 Sun
(020) 7432 1331
Draught Bass; Fuller's London Pride
This pub is named after Jane Warwick of Warwick Hall who married into the family of the lessee of much of this area. The pub, a genuine local where strangers are made welcome, is furnished with memorabilia from a bygone era, especially the snug bar at the back which boasts a magnificent chandelier and a genuine coal fire. The archaic atmosphere is slightly marred by the incongruous intrusion of the 20th century, in the form of a television.
(Warwick Ave)

W11: NOTTING HILL

Cock & Bottle
17 Needham Road
12-11; 12-10.30 Sun
(020) 7229 1550
Brakspear Bitter; Fuller's London Pride
Corner pub, set in a side street off Bayswater, it differs from other pubs and bars in the area by remaining traditional. The main bar has a high ceiling, comfortable seating, and a TV which shows various sports (mainly football and rugby). Through a set of swing doors you will find the lounge bar where food is served at lunchtimes. (Gate)

Ladbroke Arms
54 Ladbroke Road
11-3, 5.30-11; 11-11 Sat; 12-10.30 Sun
(020) 7727 6648
Courage Directors; Greene King Abbot; guest beer
Rare in an area where the majority of pubs are either tied, managed, converted into restaurants or housing, this is a genuine free house. A Victorian pub, it was refurbished to a high standard in 1999 when an additional seating area was built. Two guest beers are normally available. The evenings can be very busy. Outside the front of the pub is a raised patio area with bench seating. Q (Holland Park/Gate)

W11: WESTBOURNE PARK

Pelican
45 All Saints Road
12 (5.30 Mon)-11; 12-10.30 Sun
(020) 7792 3073
Pitfield Shoreditch Stout, Eco Warrior; St Peter's Best Bitter; guest beer
Situated near the bustling Portobello market, the pub was purchased by Singhboulton in May 2001. After refurbishment, it opened in August and was the venue for the launch of the 2002 Good Beer Guide. Upstairs is a no-smoking restaurant (open Wed-Fri eves, all day Sat, lunchtime and eve Sun). Food is also served (Tue-Sat) in the bar which has a no-smoking area. All food is home-made and certified organic by the Soil Association. The house beer, Singhboulton, is brewed by Pitfield.
Q

W14: WEST KENSINGTON

Radnor Arms
247 Warwick Road
11-11; 12-10.30 Sun
(020) 7602 7708
Everards Tiger
Small one-bar, back-street local, it is part wood-panelled with a polished wood floor, the small rear raised seating area is carpeted. There are two TVs so you need never miss a goal. Located off Kensington High Street, this pub is handy for exhibitions at Olympia including the Great British Beer Festival, when the pub's own beer range expands. The Tiger, served with or without a tight sparkler, is locally referred to as Flat or Fluffy. It may close early at weekends.
(Olympia)

BRENTFORD

Brewery Tap
47 Catherine Wheel Road
11-11; 12-10.30 Sun
(020) 8560 5200
Fuller's Chiswick, London Pride, ESB, seasonal beers
Originally the tap of the William Gomm Brewery, which was purchased by Fuller's in 1908, but subsequently closed. Of Victorian origin, the pub is reached by steps from

INN BRIEF

West London

W10: KENSAL GREEN

Paradise (by way of Kensal Green)
19 Kilburn Lane
12-11; 12-10.30 Sun
(020) 8969 0098
Shepherd Neame Spitfire
Victorian pub with a Bohemian atmosphere and an upstairs bar. Lunches and evening meals served daily.

COLHAM GREEN

Crown
Colham Green Road
11-11; 12-10.30 Sun
(01895) 442303
Fuller's London Pride, ESB
The rejuvenation of the 'Hut' nearby was just what this pub needed! Offers an extensive food menu, virtually non-stop.

CRANFORD

Queen's Head
123 High Street
11-11; 12-10.30 Sun
(020) 8897 0722
Fuller's Chiswick, London Pride, ESB
A Trivial Pursuit question records this 1930s pub as the first to acquire a full liquor licence; but visit for the beer.

GREENFORD

Black Horse
425 Oldfield Lane, North Greenford Road
11-11; 12-10.30 Sun
(020) 8578 1384
Fuller's London Pride, ESB, seasonal beers
English Inns pub in a superb canalside location with a garden, in the middle of an industrial estate.

HAYES END

Crown
1090 Uxbridge Road
11-11; 12-10.30 Sun
(020) 8573 2589
Courage Best Bitter, Directors
Single-bar, comfortable roadside local, still sporting Watney livery.

HILLINGDON

Star
Uxbridge Road
12-11; 12-10.30 Sun
(020) 8573 1096
Draught Bass; Boddingtons Bitter
Comfortable roadside local housing a pool table in the public and a TV in the narrow saloon bar.

road level, as the river used to flood here. It was recently saved from demolition under area development plans, following vigorous campaigning by the landlord and locals. In recent years the pub has become well known for its regular jazz (Tue & Thu eves), plus other live music at weekends. Lunches are popular; booking is necessary on Sunday. ❀◖⇌♣

Magpie & Crown

128 High Street

✪ 11-11; 12-10.30 Sun

☎ (020) 8560 5658

Brakspear Bitter; guest beers 🄷

Mock-Tudor pub, opposite the Magistrate's Court, set back from the road, so providing an outside drinking area. Three constantly changing guest beers, mainly from regional and micro-breweries, have made it a magnet for ale-lovers. A varying cider (or occasionally perry) is available, plus draught Budvar and Hoegaarden, and a selection of continental bottled beers. Weekday lunches are served. Friday is karaoke night; major sports events are shown on TV. Local CAMRA Pub of the Year 1999 and 2000. ❀◖⇌♣🍎

COLHAM GREEN ❊

Hut

2 Old Orchard Close

✪ 11-11; 12-10.30 Sun

☎ (01895) 437935

Greene King Old Speckled Hen; guest beer 🄷

Following its transformation from a pub which faced closure and demolition just a couple of years ago, to a community local, the beer range has settled down to one regular plus a guest – often unusual for the area such as Castle Eden Ale. Exceptionally good value food is available until 9pm most days, except Sunday. Also rare for the area is the bar billiards table and the pool table, consigned to a bar of its own. Cut off from a staggered junction location by road closures, it is best approached by heading south and east from Hillingdon Hospital. ❀◖◗♣P

COWLEY PEACHEY

Paddington Packet Boat

High Road

✪ 12-11; 12-10.30 Sun

☎ (01895) 442392

Fuller's Chiswick, London Pride, ESB 🄷

Large, friendly pub which, despite having been completely modernised, retains some old fittings and mirrors, and displays memorabilia relating to the old packet boat service to Paddington. It draws a good passing trade, although most of its customers are local, and include workers from the almost adjacent Grand Union Canal. No meals Sun eve. ❀⇆◖◗♿♣P

CRANFORD ❊

Jolly Gardeners

144 High Street

✪ 11-11; 12-10.30 Sun

☎ (020) 8897 6996

Tetley Bitter; guest beer 🄷

Small local on a 'High Street', famed for its complete lack of shops. Strangely, the public bar attracts greater patronage than the cosy lounge. The landlord marks the advent of guest ales with a chalkboard cartoon and serves ample portions of traditional English food most days, with roasts on Sunday. The large garden is well-equipped for families, although off-street parking is limited. Live music on Saturday night occasionally stages the 'world-famous' (for Cranford) Vortons '60s revival band. Guest accommodation is available during the week, not at weekends. ♛❀⇆◖♣P

GREENFORD ❊

Bridge Hotel

Western Avenue (A40/A4127 jct)

✪ 11-11; 12-10.30 Sun

☎ (020) 8566 6246

website: www.bridgehotel@youngs.co.uk

Young's Bitter, Special, seasonal beers 🄷

Locals and hotel residents mix in this 1937 development. In 1989 a 68-bedroom hotel was added. Originally one of a pair, the other (the Greenford) is currently no longer a pub. The names were transposed by clerical error, but the 1979 flyover now gives meaning to the name. The main bar retains a traditional style. Food is served in the bar and the high quality restaurant. ❀⇆◖◗♿⇌⊖P

HAMPTON

Jolly Coopers

16 High Street

✪ 11-3, 5-11; 11-11 Sat; 12-10.30 Sun

☎ (020) 8979 3384

Brakspear Bitter; Courage Best Bitter; Hop Back Summer Lightning; Marston's Pedigree 🄷

Popular bar, dating back to the early 1700s. Over the years it has accumulated some interesting paraphernalia, much of it drinks-related. A recent refurbishment has created a restaurant area and a small patio at the rear, from which there is wheelchair access. The restaurant offers an à la carte menu and opens 7-9.30 Tue-Sat eves. Food at the bar is offered weekday lunchtimes. ❀◖◗♿⇌

White Hart

70 High Street

✪ 11.30-3, 5.30-11; 11.30-11 Sat; 12-10.30 Sun

☎ (020) 8979 5352

Greene King Abbot; guest beers 🄷

This imposing, but attractive, pub stands back from the pavement behind a large patio, surrounded by neatly trimmed conifers. It was rebuilt in 1898 on the site of an earlier pub, once owned by the actor David Garrick, and was mentioned by Dickens in Oliver Twist. The comfortable, chintzy bar area wraps around the brick-fronted counter with its array of eight handpumps. The Thai restaurant upstairs is open Tue-Fri eves and all day Sat and Sun. Beers from Hogs Back, Hop Back and Ringwood feature regularly. ♛❀◖◗⇌

HAMPTON HILL

Roebuck

72 Hampton Road

✪ 11-11; 12-10.30 Sun

☎ (020) 8255 8133

Badger Best, Tanglefoot; guest beer 🄷

This pub is technically in Teddington but is

much closer to Hampton Hill's main street. The owners have created a very welcoming, comfortable establishment. Ships, trains, traffic lights, bank notes and other bric-à-brac adorn the walls and alcoves. Bus routes 285 and R68 pass by. Weekday lunches are served. Three single and one twin-bedded room are available for bed and breakfast. The guest beer changes monthly.
⛫❀🛏◐⇌ (Fulwell)

HARMONDSWORTH

Five Bells

High Street

11-11; 12-10.30 Sun

☎ (020) 8579 4713

Adnams Bitter, Broadside; guest beers Ⓗ

At the back of BA's waterside office complex (but not directly accessible from it), this thriving pub is deceptively large. The small public bar continues its all-keg policy, but the larger saloon, reached via the lane between the pub and the church, is a veritable real ale oasis. The guests include nationals, other regionals and micro-breweries, with at least two on tap at most times, occasionally more. Enjoy before the inevitable third runway gets the go-ahead, now that a fifth Heathrow terminal is to be built nearby. Evening meals served Mon-Fri until 9pm. Q❀◐◑⊟♣

HAYES

Botwell Inn

25-29 Coldharbour Lane

11-11; 12-10.30 Sun

☎ (020) 8848 3112

Courage Best Bitter, Directors; Greene King Abbot; Hop Back Summer Lightning; Shepherd Neame Spitfire; guest beers Ⓗ

Large Wetherspoon's, sporting much Art Nouveau decor throughout. It is almost verging on a young person's bar, however, the beer quality is such that the clientele is drawn from a mixed age group. In summer months, part of the pavement is used for outside seating. ◐◑⊁✔

HILLINGDON ❄

Oak Tree

132 Ryefield Avenue

11-11; 12-10.30 Sun

☎ (01895) 238085

Fuller's London Pride, ESB Ⓗ

Built in 1956, to serve a new estate, the Oak Tree is tucked away. A well-used, traditional back-street local where almost everyone is on first name terms, it has an unusually small private bar, accessed through the central door of the pub. Children are welcome in the lounge bar (when open).
⛫Q❀P

HOUNSLOW

Cross Lances

236 Hanworth Road (A314)

11-11; 12-10.30 Sun

☎ (020) 8570 4174

Fuller's London Pride, ESB, seasonal beers Ⓗ

Dark red-tiled Victorian local, the Cross Lances, now run by a Master Cellarman landlord, was extended in 2001 to give more bar space and better access to the garden. The new extension provides wheelchair access. Huge lunches, including popular Sunday roasts, are served, with senior citizens' discount on Tuesday. There is frequently something going on here: crib on Mon, quiz Thu, live music Wed (and occasional Sat), and pool and darts matches.
❀◐⊟♿⇌♣P✔

Moon under Water

84-88 Staines Road

11-11; 12-10.30 Sun

☎ (020) 8572 7506

Courage Best Bitter, Directors; Greene King Abbot; Hop Back Summer Lightning; guest beers Ⓗ

Local history panels adorn the walls of this early Wetherspoon's outlet, now enlarged. It has become a popular local with many regular customers, not just because of the keen prices, but also because its guest ale range is more extensive than most – usually two or three, with more at festival times. Just past Safeway's, it stands at the western end of Hounslow's High Street.
Q❀◐◑♿⇌⊖ (Central) ⊁✔

ICKENHAM

Tichenham Inn

11 Swakeleys Road

11-11; 12-10.30 Sun

☎ (01895) 678916

Courage Best Bitter, Directors; Fuller's London Pride; Greene King Abbot; Hop Back Summer Lightning; Shepherd Neame Spitfire; guest beers Ⓗ

Smallish Wetherspoon's on a former garage site. Tichenham derives from the 1086 Domesday survey of the village. CCTV is in operation here. It is too dark in some areas for reading, but staff will adjust lighting on request. It gets very busy on Thursday – curry night; food prices are now reduced to two for £5.00 'all day, every day', with nine choices. Situated opposite the pretty St Giles Church, parking is difficult at most times. A sampling scheme is available on real ales.
Q❀◐◑♿⊖⊁

INN BRIEF

West London

NORWOOD GREEN

Plough

Tentelow Lane

11-11; 12-10.30 Sun

(020) 8574 1945

Fuller's Chiswick, London Pride, ESB Ⓗ

Old inn, at the heart of the village; a pub to linger in and perhaps enjoy food from an expanding menu.

TEDDINGTON

Builder's Arms

38 Field Lane

11-11; 12-10.30 Sun

(020) 8255 4220

Badger Tanglefoot; Brakspear Bitter; Courage Best Bitter Ⓗ

Popular, side-street local with saloon and public bars. Thai food is always available; occasional live music.

❄ symbol next to a main entry place name indicates there are Inn Brief entries as well.

ISLEWORTH

Coach & Horses

183 London Road (A315)
11-11; 12-10.30 Sun
☎ (020) 8560 1447
Young's Bitter, Triple A, Special, seasonal beers Ⓗ
First leased by Young's in 1831, this is one of the few remaining coaching houses that were once abundant on this road. There have been a few changes since it was mentioned by Dickens in Oliver Twist, including the removal of bar partitions, but it remains a pub of great character. Music eves, with a midnight extension, are now a feature – usually jazz Mon, folk or blues Tue, and various bands Fri and Sat. Meals (except Sun eve) are served in the bar or the Thai-based restaurant. A family-oriented garden is at the rear.
⚘(Syon Lane) ♣P

Red Lion

92-94 Linkfield Road
11-11; 12-10.30 Sun
☎ (020) 8560 1460 website: www.red-lion.info
Brakspear Bitter, Special; guest beers Ⓗ
Spacious, two-bar free house with a very strong community focus. There is always something going on; it might be a pantomime, or a summer production in the garden, by their own theatre group, the Hiss and Boo Co., or live music (weekends), or the monthly 'retro' nights (last Fri). Regular theme nights, darts and pool competitions, summer barbecues and occasional beer festivals complete the picture. Weekday lunches served. ⚘♣

Royal Oak

128 Worton Road
12-11; 12-10.30 Sun
☎ (020) 8560 2906
Fuller's Chiswick, London Pride, ESB, seasonal beers; guest beer Ⓗ
Built in 1843, the Royal Oak is in an entirely residential area, served by bus route H20, by the Duke of Northumberland's River. It is totally traditional, with dark wood partitions, etched glass, upholstered seating and bric-à-brac. Old photos of local interest hang on the walls and ceilings, alongside the long-serving landlord's many awards and cellarmanship certificates. With a riverside patio, food from a comprehensive menu served all day, and TV at the back for sports, it is the perfect local.
⚘

RUISLIP MANOR

JJ Moon's

12 Victoria Road
11-11; 12-10.30 Sun
☎ (01895) 622373
Courage Best Bitter, Directors; Fuller's London Pride; Greene King Abbot; Hop Back Summer Lightning; guest beer Ⓗ
Usually busy Wetherspoon's outlet, formerly a Woolworths. It is run by one of the company's longest-serving managers. A marquee is erected at the rear for the two annual beer fests, when some 25 ales are available on gravity. No pub car park, but there is a large pay and display next door (approached from Pembroke Road). Only part of the bar area is no-smoking; steps at the rear lead to an area preferred by most diners, which is available for private functions. Extractors can cause draughts in some areas, but are necessary due to the number of smokers who drink here.
Q♣✓

SOUTHALL

Beaconsfield Arms

63-67 West End Road (off A4020)
11-11; 12-10.30 Sun
☎ (020) 8574 8135

Choosing Pubs

CAMRA members and branches choose the pubs listed in the Good Beer Guide. There is no payment for entry, and pubs are inspected on a regular basis by personal visits; publicans are not sent a questionnaire once a year, as is the case with some pub guides. CAMRA branches monitor all the pubs in their areas, and the choice of pubs for the guide is often the result of democratic vote at branch meetings. However, recommendations from readers are welcomed and will be passed on to the relevant branch: write to Good Beer Guide, CAMRA, 230 Hatfield Road, St Albans, AL1 4LW; or send an e-mail to camra@camra.org.uk.

Draught Bass; Scanlon's Spike; guest beers Ⓗ
Prominent pub, halfway along a residential street. Originally three bars, it has been long converted into a traditional horseshoe shape. The landlord was a recent recipient of a joint award from the local branch, and CAMRA's Light & Dark Ale support group in recognition of his commitment to serving a real dark mild over the last decade. Currently, this is invariably Ansells Mild, with guest beers often from the Rebellion stable; perfect for imbibing before (or after) a curry on the Broadway.
❀≠♣P▯

Southall Conservative & Unionist Club

Fairlawn, High Street
11.30-2.30, 6-11; 12-2, 7-10.30 Sun
☎ (020) 8574 0261
Rebellion IPA; guest beer Ⓗ
You do not need to be 'blue' to take advantage of the many facilities this superb club offers but without a CAMRA membership card or a copy of this edition of the Guide, you will not gain admittance. Inexpensive weekday lunches, four snooker tables and an outdoor bowling green feature among its attractions. Most evenings are usually themed, with Monday the regular quiz night and live bands appearing at weekends. A complete cross-section of the local community can be found here.
Q❀◐≠♣P

TEDDINGTON

Lion

27 Wick Road
12-11; 12-10.30 Sun
☎ (020) 8977 6631
Fuller's London Pride; Greene King Abbot; Young's Bitter; guest beer Ⓗ
Single-bar pub that has been totally transformed by CAMRA award-winning tenants, now attracting custom from further afield. In a side street, a short walk from Hampton Wick Station, an excellent reputation has already been established for the food (not served Sun eve) with an imaginative modern menu. There is a function room and an attractive garden for summer barbecues. It hosts live music (Sat eve) and a monthly comedy night. An annual beer festival is held.
❀◐◑≠(Hampton Wick) ♣●✓

Queen Dowager

49 North Lane
11-11; 12-10.30 Sun
☎ (020) 8977 2583
Young's Bitter, Special, seasonal beers Ⓗ
Tucked away past the town car parks off Broad Street (handy for Tesco's), this red-brick and pebble-dashed pub was built in 1906, although there was a pub here from 1747. It commemorates Queen Adelaide, widow of William IV, who was also the ranger of Bushy Park, and lived in nearby Bushy House. Comfortable, rather than trendy, the pub is still awaiting refurbishment following a change of landlord in 2000. No food Sun.
❀◐≠♣

TWICKENHAM

Eel Pie

9-11 Church Street
11-11; 12-10.30 Sun
☎ (020) 8891 1717
Badger K&B Sussex, IPA, Best, Tanglefoot, seasonal beers; Gribble Inn Fursty Ferret Ⓗ
Perhaps surprisingly, the Eel Pie has been a pub for less than 20 years – it was previously a wine bar. It has all the feel of a traditional pub, with a choice of drinking areas, a distinctly 'historic' look, and much rugby-oriented paraphernalia. The beers are complemented by Inch's Stonehouse cider. All the food is home made, with lunches daily (Sunday roasts are popular) and light evening meals until 10pm (except Sun). A bar billiards table is available. ◐◑≠●✓

Old Anchor

71 Richmond Road
11-11; 12-10.30 Sun
☎ (020) 8891 2117
Young's Bitter, Special, seasonal beers Ⓗ
This long-established Young's local (acquired 1897) has recently been refurbished in a modern rustic style. Food is an increasingly important feature, and an eclectic menu might have tapas and taramasalata alongside bangers and mash. The prices perhaps reflect an upmarket shift, but the clientele still includes loyal regulars as well as an increasing number of young professionals. Live weekend entertainment covers various musical styles.
❀◐◑≠

UXBRIDGE

Load of Hay

33 Villier Street
11-3, 5.30 (7 Sat)-11; 12-3, 7-10.30 Sun
☎ (01895) 234676
website: www.loadofhay-uxbridge.co.uk
Brains Bitter, Buckley's Best Bitter; guest beers Ⓗ
Originally the officers' mess of the Elthorne Light Militia, it became a pub in the late 1870s. Situated in the Greenway conservation area, not far from Brunel University, this establishment serves traditional pub food (no meals Sun eve) and an ever-changing range of guest beers. The cosy front lounge can be used as a family room or for private functions. It has deservedly won several local CAMRA Pub of the Year awards. Q❀◐◑♣P

Pipemaker's Arms

57 St John's Road
12-11; 12-10.30 Sun
☎ (01895) 251150
Adnams Bitter; Fuller's London Pride; Marston's Pedigree; Tetley Bitter Ⓗ
Enjoy the recently extended patio alongside a sylvan link between the Fray's River and the Colne Brook and seek out the eulogy to Phipps' (of Northampton) and Dulley's (of Wellingborough) which slates Bedford & Praed's (also of Wellingborough) beers at the same time. Thai food is served until 10.30pm weekdays with lunchtime roasts taking over on Sunday. It is accessible from the nearby Grand Union Canal. The name refers to the old local cottage industry of clay pipe manufacturing. Other beers are occasionally available. ❀◐◑

Draught Bass; Boddingtons Bitter; Taylor Best Bitter; Tetley Dark Mild, Bitter; guest beers H
Cosy, stone hostelry on the edge of the moors, handy for walkers and visitors to the Reebok Stadium. A genuine free house, run by friendly, enterprising owners, the pub has been in existence for around 200 years and is named after a regular, Bob the blacksmith, who used to work across the road. Guest beers are usually sourced from small independent breweries. Lunches are served Tue-Fri. ♨❀☾P

Dog & Partridge
22 Manor Street (A676)
✪ 6.30 (12 Sat)-11; 7-10.30 Sun
☎ (01204) 388596
Thwaites Bitter H
Unspoilt, three-roomed local situated on the edge of the town centre. The pub dates from the 18th century and features a traditional vault with a curved bar. The small games room at the back has an acid etched Cornbrook Ales window; the larger side room has a pool table and hosts weekend discos. The pub is home to pool and quiz teams. Public car parks are at the side and across the road. ⊡⇌♣

Hen & Chickens
143 Deansgate (near bus station, off A676)
✪ 11.30-11; 7.30-10.30 Sun
☎ (01204) 389836
Cains Mild; Greenalls Bitter; guest beers H
Busy, friendly, town-centre local with a central bar, standing opposite the post office, known as the higher Hen & Chickens until 1888 (see over door). A painting over the fireplace shows a Crimean battle in which a former landlord's son fought. Good value lunches are supplemented by sandwiches available all day. Three ever-changing guest beers are always available (details on the blackboards near the front door). ☾⇌

Hope & Anchor
747 Chorley Old Road (B6226)
✪ 3 (12 Sat)-11; 12-10.30 Sun
☎ (01204) 842650
Lees Bitter; Taylor Landlord; Tetley Mild, Bitter H
Compact local where a central bar serves two distinct snugs, used for different functions, including quizzes, darts, dominoes and family gatherings. It is known by the locals clustered around the bar as the Little Cocker, due to the proximity of Doffcocker Lodge, a nature reserve. Less than two miles from the town centre, take bus No. 519 from the bus/rail interchange or No. 501 from the crown court to Doffcocker. ♨☕❀♣P

Howcroft Inn ☆
36 Pool Street (300 yds from Topp Way, A673)
✪ 12-11; 12-10.30 Sun
☎ (01204) 526814
Taylor Landlord; Tetley Mild, Bitter; guest beers H
Exceptional, multi-roomed local, one of a dying breed. A 1980s refurbishment won CAMRA's Joe Goodwin award for Best Pub Conservation. It stages regular folk/acoustic nights and a well-kept bowling green is available for hire. The green is covered by a marquee for the October Bolton beer festival. The lunchtime menu is good value. The unofficial tap for nearby Bank Top Brewery, one of its beers is always stocked. Take bus No. 501 from the crown court to Vernon Street. ♨❀☾♣P

King's Head
52-54 Junction Road, Deane (off A676, Wigan road)
✪ 12 (3.30 winter)-11; 12-10.30 Sun
☎ (01204) 62609
Moorhouses Pride of Pendle; Taylor Landlord; Tetley Mild, Bitter; guest beers H
300-year-old Grade II listed pub, adjacent to the Deane Clough nature trail. It was refurbished in 1991 to provide three distinct drinking areas, the largest of which has York stone flooring and an authentic-looking range. A well-used crown bowling green at the rear is available for hire, and supports five teams. No juke box, but piped music and TV underlie the buzz of conversation. A Bank Top beer is often available. Sunday lunch is served until 6pm. Q❀☾♣P

Olde Man & Scythe
6-8 Churchgate
✪ 11-11; 12-10.30 Sun
☎ (01204) 527267 website: www.manandscythe.co.uk
Boddingtons Bitter; Flowers Original; Fuller's London Pride; Greene King Old Speckled Hen; Holt Bitter; Tetley Bitter H
Reputedly the fourth oldest pub in Britain, its barrel-vaulted cellar was probably built before 1200. The first record of the pub's existence was 1251, but the present building dates from 1636. In 1651 the seventh Earl of Derby spent his last hours here before his execution in the market place outside for his part in the 1644 Bolton Massacre. A stone-flagged floor is flanked by two side rooms (one displaying the pub's history). It hosts various events and entertainment. ❀☾☽♿⇌♣●

BREDBURY

Traveller's Call
402 Stockport Road West
✪ 12-11; 12-10.30 Sun
☎ (0161) 430 2511
Lees GB Mild, Bitter, seasonal beers H
Lee's only outlet in Stockport has gone from strength to strength. The threat of demolition to make way for a bypass has finally been lifted and the brewery has invested heavily to create a fine local that now attracts a wide age range. A warm welcome awaits all, but the same could not be said when the pub first opened in the early part of the 19th century, when travellers were frequently assaulted by highwaymen. Meals finish at 7pm. ❀☾☽♿⇌P

BROMLEY CROSS

Flag Inn
50 Hardmans Lane (off B6472, Darwen road)
✪ 12-11; 12-10.30 Sun
☎ (01204) 598267
Boddingtons Bitter; guest beers H
Enterprising management and constantly changing guest beers, sourced from small independent breweries, make this popular beer-drinkers' mecca well worth seeking out. Although not immediately apparent, the building's history has been traced back

over 300 years. The old brick arched cellars were originally stables. In a spacious open-plan interior, TV screens attract sports enthusiasts, but do not dominate, or impede conversation. It gets very busy at weekends. ♨❀⇌✔

BURY

Arthur Inn

97 Bolton Road

⏲ 12-11; 12-10.30 Sun

☎ (0161) 797 3860

Porter Dark Mild, Floral Dance, Bitter, Rossendale Ale, Sunshine Ⓗ

Community local, on the main road between Bury and Bolton. When purchased by the Porter Brewing Company, it was in need of considerable refurbishment. Since then, it has been transformed into a comfortable, friendly outlet for their excellent beers and is a very rare outlet for guest cask ciders in the area. The main lounge is complemented by a small games room and a no-smoking side room. The 471 bus is frequent and will drop you nearby. ⊖🍎⅟

Dusty Miller

87 Crostons Road (B621/B6214 jct)

⏲ 2 (12 Fri & Sat)-11; 12-10.30 Sun

☎ (0161) 764 1124

Moorhouses Black Cat, Premier, Pendle Witches Brew; guest beers Ⓗ

This is a proudly traditional local that caters for a mixed clientele. Its position at a busy road junction makes parking difficult, but it is well worth making the effort to visit. Divided into two rooms served by a central bar, there is also a covered courtyard and outdoor seating in summer. It is one of only a small number of tied Moorhouses pubs.

⊞⊖

Old Blue Bell

2 Bell Lane (B621/B622 jct)

⏲ 12-11; 12-10.30 Sun

☎ (0161) 761 3674

Holt Mild, Bitter Ⓗ

Prominent, solidly-built pub on a busy road junction. Its traditional exterior is matched by the interior where, with several rooms, there is space to be found even when the pub is busy. Comfortable and welcoming, it hosts live music Saturday afternoon, plus Thursday and Sunday evenings. Well-behaved children are welcome until 6pm at this community local.

Q⊞⊖♣

Rose & Crown

16 Manchester Old Road

⏲ 12-3, 5-11; 12-11 Thu-Sat; 12-10.30 Sun

☎ (0161) 764 6461

Black Sheep Best Bitter; guest beers Ⓗ

Attractive, traditional end-of-terrace pub, offering up to eight real ales. One large room is divided into distinct drinking areas where no juke box will distract you from the pleasures of imbibing. Look out for local Phoenix beers which feature regularly. Good value lunches are available on weekdays and Sunday. It also stocks an ever-increasing range of malt whiskies, wine and foreign bottled beer.

(⊖

CHEADLE HULME

Church

90 Ravenoak Road (A5149)

⏲ 11-11; 12-10.30 Sun

☎ (0161) 485 1897

Robinson's Hatters Mild, Old Stockport, Hartleys XB, Best Bitter, seasonal beers Ⓗ

Very attractive, cottage-style pub with a warm, traditional atmosphere and a strong local following. There are two lounges, one with a real fire and the other mainly used for dining; a small vault is located behind the main bar. Service is excellent, even during busy periods; there is no food on Sunday evening. An unusually wide range of Robinson's beers includes their seasonal brews. The car park is on the opposite side of the road. ♨Q❀()⊞⇌♣P

CHEETHAM

Queen's Arms

6 Honey Street (off A665)

⏲ 12-11; 12-10.30 Sun

☎ (0161) 834 4239

Phoenix Bantam; Taylor Landlord; guest beers Ⓗ

Well worth the walk uphill from Manchester city centre, this well-established free house doubled in size some years ago but retained its old Empress Brewery façade. An enterprising range of food is served 12-2.30 weekdays (evenings by arrangement), and 12-8 at weekends. The back garden, where supervised children are welcome, is popular for drinking and barbecues in summer. ♨❀()⇌(Victoria) ⊖♣

CHORLTON-CUM-HARDY

Beech Inn

72 Beech Road

⏲ 11-11; 12-10.30 Sun

☎ (0161) 881 1180

Boddingtons Bitter; Taylor Best Bitter, Landlord; guest beers Ⓗ

Thriving three-roomed pub, just off the village green; no food, no music, no gimmicks. Most of the hostelries in this road have been converted to café bars, but do offer food whereas the Beech is purely aimed at drinkers. Q❀⊞♣

Marble Beer House

57 Manchester Road

⏲ 12-11; 12-10.30 Sun

☎ (0161) 881 9206

Marble Chorlton-cum-Hazy, Cloudy Marble, Uncut Amber, Old Lag; guest beers Ⓗ

Continental-style café-bar with pavement seating, stocking a good range of bottled Belgian and continental beers, alongside the full range of Marble beers, brewed in Manchester. Converted from a shop, no food is sold here, but there are plenty of restaurants in the neighbourhood. Q❀

CHORLTON ON MEDLOCK

Kro Bar

325 Oxford Road (B5117, opp. Manchester University's main entrance)

⏲ 11-11; 12-10.30 Sun

☎ (0161) 274 3100 website: www.kro.co.uk

Boddingtons Bitter; Taylor Landlord; guest beers Ⓗ

A former Temperance Society building, this is now a lively Danish-style bar in the heart of Manchester's vibrant university district. Kro is Danish for a village pub. The decor and furnishings are modern and functional. In addition to the main bar area, there is a conservatory to the rear and a quiet room upstairs. The bar offers a good selection of European bottled beers. The pub opens early for coffee and food, which is served all day. Q (Oxford Rd)

COMPSTALL

Andrew Arms

George Street

11.30-11; 12-10.30 Sun

(0161) 427 2281

Robinson's Hatters Mild, Best Bitter H

Detached stone pub in a quiet village off the main road, close to the Etherow Country Park, with wildlife and river valley walks. This pub has been a continuous entry in this Guide since the mid-1970s and deservedly so. With a comfortable lounge and small traditional games room, it is a true local, catering for all tastes. P

CORNBROOK

Hope Inn

297 Chester Road

11-5, 7.30-11; 12-5, 7.30-10.30 Sun

(0161) 848 0038

Hydes Light, Bitter, P **seasonal beer** H

Rare example of a surviving stand-up, street-corner local, where you will find telly, lots of chat, and a friendly welcome. It is a 15-minute walk from both Old Trafford cricket and football grounds, and the ale justifies the 20-minute walk from the Castlefield end of Manchester's city centre.

(Deansgate) (G.Mex)

DAISY HILL

Rose Hill Tavern

321 Leigh Road, Westhoughton (B5235)

12-11; 12-10.30 Sun

(01942) 815776

Holt Mild, Bitter H

Large, welcoming pub, now opened out, but retaining the outline of the old room plan, with two rooms taken up by games of all sorts. It is often referred to by locals as the Bug since a workhouse (the bug house) was demolished to make way for the pub. It was built in 1889, the year after the railway came to the village. It was originally owned by the Oldfield Brewery of Poolstock, Wigan, whose crest can be seen over the door. P

DELPH

Royal Oak (Th' heights)

Broad Lane, Heights (1 mile above Denshaw Road) OS982090

7-11; 12-4, 7-10.30 Sun

(01457) 874460

Boddingtons Bitter; Moorhouses Black Cat; guest beers H

Isolated, 250-year-old stone pub on a packhorse route, overlooking the Tame Valley. Set in a popular walking area, it offers outstanding views. The pub, which once had its own brewhouse, now comprises a cosy bar and three rooms. The refurbished side room boasts a hand-carved stone fireplace, while the comfortable snug has exposed beams. Good home-cooked food (Fri-Sun eve) often features game and home-bred pork and beef. The house beer is brewed by Moorhouses. Q P

DENTON

Lowes Arms

301 Hyde Road (A57)

12-3, 5-11; 12-11 Sat; 12-10.30 Sun

(0161) 336 3064

The LAB Frog Bog, Wild Wood, Broomstairs, Haughton Weave H

Brewing has returned to the Lowes after a break of a century, with the opening of The LAB micro-brewery. Up to five beers from The LAB are served in this thriving local. A warm and comfortable lounge doubles as a restaurant, serving excellent food at reasonable prices. The games room is traditional and spacious. Staging occasional live music and other community events, this brew-pub is well worth a visit.

(Hyde Central) P

DIGGLE

Diggle Hotel

Station Houses (1/2 mile off A670) OS011081

12-3, 5-11; 12-11 Sat; 12-3, 5-10.30 Sun

(01457) 872741

Boddingtons Bitter; Taylor Golden Best, Landlord; guest beers H

Family-run stone pub in a pleasant hamlet, near the recently reopened Standedge canal tunnel under the Pennines. Built as a merchant's house in 1789, it became an ale house and general store during the construction of the nearby railway tunnel in 1834. In a picturesque area, affording fine views of the Saddleworth countryside, this makes a convenient base in a popular walking area. It comprises a bar and two rooms, with an accent on home-cooked food (served all day Sat). P

DOBCROSS

Swan Inn (Top House)

The Square

12-3, 5-11; 12-3, 7-10.30 Sun

(01457) 873451

Moorhouses Pendle Witches Brew; Phoenix Arizona, Wobbly Bob, seasonal beers; Theakston Mild, Best Bitter H

This village local, circa 1765, was built for the Wrigley family of chewing gum fame, but part of the building was later used as a police court. Overlooking an attractive square, the pub has been well renovated, with flagged floors and three distinct drinking areas, plus a characterful function room. It gets busy during local events, such as the Whit Friday brass band contest and the August Rushcart Festival. Good value home-cooked food includes Indian dishes (no food Sun eve). Q

ECCLES

Lamb Hotel ☆

33 Regent Street (opp. Metrolink terminus)

11.30-11; 12-10.30 Sun

(0161) 789 3882

Holt Mild, Bitter H

A Holt's house since 1865, the Lamb was

rebuilt in 1906. Although not the largest, it is perhaps the best preserved of several opulent Edwardian showpieces in Holt's Eccles estate. Enjoy the different atmospheres of its four rooms (the largest of which boasts a full-sized billiard table), or drink in the full Art Nouveau richness of mahogany, glazing and tilework while seated at the foot of the stairs. Q⊟≥⊖♣P

EGERTON

Mason's Arms

156-158 Blackburn Road (A666)
4 (3 Fri; 12 Sat)-11; 12-10.30 Sun
☎ (01204) 302043
Bank Top Brydge Bitter; Theakston Best Bitter Ⓗ
Attractive, late Victorian red-brick pub, next to stone terraced cottages at the lower end of a straggling suburban village. A genuine, small, welcoming local with a friendly atmosphere, it has a comfortable open-plan interior. Darts and dominoes are played; quiz night is Tuesday. A pleasant patio has recently been added at the back. ❀♣

FALLOWFIELD

Friendship

373 Wilmslow Road (B5093)
11.30-11; 12-10.30 Sun
☎ (0161) 224 5758
Hydes Bitter, Jekyll's Gold, seasonal beers Ⓗ
Thriving main road local, linked by frequent buses to the famous Manchester 'curry mile' and the largest student campus in Europe. An excellent refurbishment has resulted in a horseshoe-shaped bar in a smart, open-plan area and proves that it is possible to enjoy large-screen football and good beer in the same pub. A spacious front patio gives a good view of this buzzing student area of café-bars and fast food joints.
❀◐♣P

FARNWORTH

Britannia

34 King Street (opp. bus station, off A6053)
11-11; 12-10.30 Sun
☎ (01204) 571629
Moorhouses Premier; Whitbread Trophy Bitter; guest beer Ⓗ
Typical, lively, town-centre pub that has a small, recently refurbished lounge (note the brass ornaments) and a larger, basic vault; the central bar serves both areas. The pub hosts two popular mini-beer festivals (May and Aug bank holidays), with around six beers served from a specially-built (covered) outside bar. The lunches are wholesome and well-priced – worth trying. A free car park is behind the pub. ❀◐⊟≥♣

FLIXTON

Church Inn

34 Church Road (B5123, near station)
11-11; 12-10.30 Sun
☎ (0161) 748 2158
Cains Bitter; Greenalls Bitter; guest beer Ⓗ
Former school house and courtroom, now a comfortably furnished pub with various seating areas, it stands in the old part of the town, a five-minute walk from the station. Do not be put off by its external appearance, this rare outlet for mild is definitely worth a visit. ⩕❀◐▶≥♣P

GATHURST

Navigation Inn

162 Gathurst Lane (B5206, between Shevington and Orrell)
12-11; 12-10.30 Sun
☎ (01257) 252856
Taylor Landlord; Tetley Bitter; guest beers Ⓗ
Extended canalside pub, next to bridge 46 on the Leeds-Liverpool Canal, popular with boaters, walkers and cyclists. Food is

INN BRIEF

HAWKSHAW

Red Lion
81 Ramsbottom Road
12-3, 6-11; 12-10.30 Sun
Jennings Bitter, Cumberland Ale Ⓗ
Attractive stone pub in a picturesque village. Food available 12-2.30, 6-9 (all day Sun). Cask Marque accredited.

HEATON NORRIS

Silver Jubilee
21 Hamilton Square
11.30-11; 12-10.30 Sun
(0161) 480 3321
Robinson's Hatters Mild, Old Stockport, Best Bitter Ⓗ
Two-roomed estate pub with a pleasant garden where brass bands play summer Sundays.

HOLLINWOOD

Bridgewater Hotel
197 Manchester Road
11.30-11; 12-10.30 Sun
(0161) 628 8464
Holt Mild, Bitter Ⓗ
Modern, low level, two-roomed Holt's outlet. A vibrant, noisy vault is complemented by an open-plan lounge.

LEIGH

Globe
81-85 Bradshawgate
Holt Mild, Bitter Ⓗ
Good town-centre local where a central bar serves a comfortable lounge with pool and darts. Small patio.

MANCHESTER CITY CENTRE

Briton's Protection ☆
50 Great Bridgewater Street
12-11; 12-11 Sun
(0161) 236 5895
Jennings Bitter; Robinson's Best Bitter; guest beers Ⓗ
On CAMRA's National Inventory, it boasts beautifully preserved tiling, inside and out. Opposite the Bridgewater Concert Hall.

Ox
71 Liverpool Road
11-11; 12-10.30 Sun
Boddingtons Bitter; Taylor Landlord; guest beers Ⓗ
Named after a potato (Oxnoble), it is possibly Manchester's first so-called gastro-pub.

Paddy's Goose
29 Bloom Street
11-11; 12-10.30 Sun
(0161) 236 1246
Lees Bitter; Robinson's Best Bitter; Theakston Cool Cask; guest beer Ⓗ
Lively mixed clientele frequent this single-roomed pub in 'gay village'. Handy for Chorlton Street bus station.

MARPLE

Ring O' Bells
130 Church Lane
11.30-3, 5.30-11; 11.30-11 Sat; 12-10.30 Sun
(0161) 427 2300
Robinson's Hatters Mild, Best Bitter, Hartleys Cumbria Way, seasonal beers Ⓗ
Comfortable, friendly pub serving good value meals, alongside the Macclesfield/Peak Forest Canal. Cask Marque accredited.

MONTON

Drop Inn
204 Monton Road
11.30-11; 12-10.30 Sun
(07950) 559852
Boddingtons Bitter; John Smith's Bitter; guest beer Ⓗ
Comfortable H-shaped village local, hosting live jazz (Wed eve); games room.

available all day Saturday and Sunday. Named after the Douglas Navigation Company, who kept the adjacent River Douglas navigable in the 19th century, the transfer point for barges from the river to the canal is still visible alongside the nearby locks. Bulmers cider is stocked in summer. The garden houses a boules pitch.

GORTON

Waggon & Horses
736 Hyde Road
11-11; 12-10.30 Sun
(0161) 231 6262
Holt Mild, Bitter

Main road drinkers' pub, consisting of a vault and a large lounge, the latter broken up into several areas, each with its own character. Large-screen TV is switched on in the vault for major sporting events, while off the lounge is an area where pool and darts can be played (both standard and Manchester log-end boards). Live entertainment is featured most weekends. Mainly frequented by locals, keen prices ensure that it is well patronised at all times. P

GREENFIELD

Railway
11 Shaw Hall Bank Road (opp. station)
5 (12 Fri & Sat)-11; 12-10.30 Sun
(01457) 872307
John Smith's Bitter; Taylor Landlord; guest beers

Friendly, no-frills village local in a stone terrace, with a central bar and games area. The public bar displays a collection of old Saddleworth photos. In a picturesque area, close to the recently reopened Huddersfield narrow canal, it provides a good base for walking, rock climbing and other outdoor pursuits. Live music, including Cajun, R&B and jazz is performed Thu and Fri eves and Sun afternoons. Accommodation is reasonably priced; two bedrooms afford good views of the Chew Valley. P

GUIDE BRIDGE

Boundary
2 Audenshaw Road
11-11; 12-10.30 Sun
(0161) 330 1677
Webster's Green Label; guest beers

Very busy, friendly pub on a major road junction, next to Guide Bridge railway station and the Ashton canal. Good value meals are a feature at the pub which usually hosts an annual beer festival in June. All in all, it is an enterprising pub doing an extremely good job. P

HALE

Railway
128-130 Ashley Road (opp. station)
11-11; 12-10.30 Sun
(0161) 941 5367
Robinson's Hatters Mild, Old Stockport, Hartleys XB, Best Bitter, seasonal beer

Reputedly haunted, but friendly and unspoilt, this 1930s multi-roomed local retains much wood panelling and character. With a relaxed atmosphere throughout, the quiet side rooms in particular are suited to conversation. The Railway provides a focal point for the community of this small commuter village, now consumed by Altrincham. Q (Altrincham)

HEALD GREEN

Griffin
124 Finney Lane
12-11; 12-10.30 Sun
(0161) 437 1596
Holt Mild, Bitter

There has been a pub on this site for some 120 years, with this building in place since the late 1960s. This large three-roomed public house on the corner of Wilmslow Road, has one room given over to a vault, the other two being open plan, with a central L-shaped bar serving all three rooms. A thriving community local, with a warm, friendly atmosphere, it hosts live musical entertainment on Thursday and occasional Sunday evenings.

HEATON MERSEY

Griffin
552 Didsbury Road (A5145)
12-11; 12-10.30 Sun
(0161) 443 2077
Holt Mild, Bitter

Popular during the day, especially at lunchtime for its good value meals (including pensioners' specials) and in the evening for its great atmosphere, this large multi-roomed pub situated on the main road is always buzzing with conversation. Several years ago a petition from the regulars saved from destruction the superb Victorian mahogany and etched glass bar, which is the main feature of the pub; a replica of the original bar has since been built in the spacious extension. A visit is a must. (E Didsbury) P

HEATON NORRIS

Moss Rose
63 Didsbury Road (A5145)
11.30-11; 12-10.30 Sun
(0161) 432 5168
Hydes Light, Bitter,

The phrase 'don't judge a book by its cover' could have been coined for the Moss Rose. Outwardly, an unpromising example of modern pub design, inside you will find a comfortable, down-to-earth local that is popular with all ages. There is a large vault, displaying an impressive array of sports trophies, and an extensive lounge. Karaoke often features at weekends. An unusual feature is separate cellars for mild and bitter. Sandwiches are made on request. P

Nursery Inn ☆
258 Green Lane (off A6, by Dunham Jaguar)
11.30-3, 5.30-11; 11.30-11 Sat; 12-10.30 Sun
(0161) 432 2044
Hydes Mild, Bitter, Jekyll's Gold, seasonal beers

Twenty consecutive years in this Guide and CAMRA's national Pub of the Year 2001, this classic, unspoilt 1930s pub is well hidden in a pleasant suburban area. The multi-roomed interior includes a traditional vault, with its own entrance and a spacious

wood-panelled lounge which doubles as a dining room. At the rear is an immaculate, well-used bowling green. The home-made food draws customers from many miles around, the Sunday lunches being particularly popular (children are welcome if dining).
❀◑⊟♣P⊡

HEYWOOD

Wishing Well

89 York Street (A58)
⊙ 12-11; 12-10.30 Sun
☎ (01706) 620923
Tetley Bitter; guest beers Ⓗ
Popular free house in the centre of Heywood, that attracts real ale drinkers from near and far. There are several comfortable drinking areas to choose from as you ponder the extensive beer list. Unsurprisingly, local brewery Phoenix often features alongside other micro-brewers. The long-standing landlord has received many awards over the years and his efforts are reflected in the quality of the beer. The frequent 471 Bury-Rochdale bus stops outside. ◑P

HIGH LANE

Royal Oak

Buxton Road
⊙ 12-3, 6-11; 11-11 Sat & summer; 12-10.30 Sun
☎ (01663) 762380
Burtonwood Bitter; guest beer Ⓗ
This is a well-appointed pub on a busy main road. It has a pleasant exterior, with a good garden and a children's play area. Although open plan, there are three distinct drinking areas, one of which is used for games. It stages live entertainment on most Friday evenings. Burtonwood beer makes a welcome addition to the usual beer range in the area.
Q❀◑◐⊟♿P

HORWICH

Crown

1 Chorley New Road (A673/B6226 jct)
⊙ 11-11; 12-10.30 Sun
☎ (01204) 690926
Holt Mild, Bitter Ⓗ
The Crown Hotel is an imposing pub, situated towards the edge of town, though not too far from the Reebok Stadium. It has a well-furnished drinking area, with a vault and games room at the rear. The landlord manages to cater for all ages and provides good value food at lunchtime. Wednesday is quiz night, but Sunday evening is very popular when the locals provide their own entertainment with free and easy singalongs. Superb views of Rivington Pike are a bonus. ♨ᗜ❀◑⊟♿♣P

HYDE

Sportsman Inn

57 Mottram Road
⊙ 11-11; 12-10.30 Sun
☎ (0161) 368 5000
Plassey Bitter; Taylor Landlord; Whim Hartington Bitter; guest beers Ⓗ
This brilliant, spacious local has become a thriving hub of the community. Gradually renovated, with the floors stripped back to bare boards and original tiling restored, it is a pleasure to sit on the old bench seats and enjoy the beer. The pub has three pleasant main rooms, plus an upstairs room. Games features strongly, including snooker and log-end darts; a pub to feel at home in.
♨Q❀◑⊟⇌ (Central/Newton) ♣●P⊡

White Lion

7 Market Place
⊙ 11-11; 12-5 Sun
☎ (0161) 368 2948
Robinson's Hatters Mild, Best Bitter, Ⓟ **Old Tom** (winter) Ⓗ
The hub of market life in the town centre,

INN BRIEF

NORDEN

Bridge Hotel
741 Edenfield Road
12-11; 12-10.30 Sun
(01706) 648242
Jennings Bitter, Cumberland Ale Ⓗ
Friendly, one-roomed local offering good food, near the bus terminus serving Bury and Rochdale.

PATRICROFT

Queen's Arms
Green Lane
7 (5 Fri; 11 Sat)-11; 12-10.30 Sun
(0161) 789 2019
Boddingtons Bitter; guest beer Ⓗ
Grade II listed pub built in 1828 on the Manchester-Liverpool line, making it the world's first railway pub.

PENDLEBURY

Lord Nelson
653 Bolton Road
11-11; 12-10.30 Sun
(0161) 794 6348
Holt Mild, Bitter Ⓗ
Lively 1960s local: a club-like lounge with a stage, and an austere vault.

ROCHDALE

Cemetery Hotel ☆
470 Bury Road
12-11; 12-10.30 Sun
(01706) 645635
Marston's Pedigree; John Smith's Bitter; Taylor Best Bitter, Landlord; guest beers Ⓗ
Detached, 19th-century brick building: its comfortable lounge contrasts Victorian splendour with cosy corners.

ROYTON

Railway Hotel
1 Oldham Road
11-11; 12-10.30 Sun
(0161) 624 2793
Lees GB Mild, Bitter Ⓗ
Large, busy pub at the main town-centre junction, comprising a vault, central lounge and cosy snug. Home-cooked food is good value.

SALE

Volunteer
81 Cross Street
12-11; 12-10.30 Sun
(0161) 973 1537
Holt Mild, Bitter Ⓗ
Victorian roadhouse with several distinct seating areas.

SALFORD

Mark Addy
3 Stanley Street
11.30-11; 12-10.30 Sun
(0161) 832 4040
Boddingtons Bitter; guest beer Ⓗ
Set on the Irwell river bank; named after local hero. Large portions of bread and cheese. Food served until 8pm.

STALYBRIDGE

Pineapple
Kenworthy Street
4 (12 Fri & Sat)-11; 12-10.30 Sun
(0161) 338 2542
Robinson's Hatters Mild, Best Bitter, Frederics, seasonal beers Ⓗ
Thriving local, very much a community focal point; comfortable and friendly, with a large garden.

STANDISH

Horseshoe
1 Wigan Road
12-11; 12-10.30 Sun
(01257) 400716
Burtonwood Bitter; guest beer Ⓗ
Open-plan pub where TV and snob screens abound. Darts and pool available. Popular with diners, it can be busy.

this imposing establishment has recently had the first of the local council's huge outdoor information screens placed on the doorstep, a real contrast with the solid Victorian construction. Although opened up inside, this vibrant community pub retains its long central bar separating the original public saloon from the lounge. This wonderful hostelry fields several active sports teams and an organist plays at weekends, when it is always full to capacity. ◐⊟≷(Central/Newton) ♣

INCE IN MAKERFIELD

Black Diamond

243 Warrington Road, Lower Ince

⌚ 12-2 (not Mon), 5-11 (12-11 summer); 12-10.30 Sun

☎ (01942) 237846

John Smith's Bitter; Theakston Mild, Cool Cask; guest beer Ⓗ

Previously known as the Ince Hall Hotel, it has now inherited its nickname. A surprisingly large pub, with lots of nooks and crannies and a pool room on a mezzanine floor, the fire dominates the atmosphere and the bare brick decor is very effective. A well-appointed dining room, a large-screen TV (reserved for major sporting events) and an upstairs function room complete the amenities here. ⛼◐◑≷♣

LEIGH ✻

Musketeer

15 Lord Street

⌚ 11-11; 12-3, 7-10.30 Sun

☎ (01942) 701143

Tetley Mild; Boddingtons Bitter; guest beers Ⓗ

Three comfortable lounge areas are served by a central bar. The main lounge displays a collection of Lancashire pit plates. The tap room, with its own entrance on Lord Street, is served from its own bar. Regular quizzes and live entertainment are laid on during the week. ⊟♣

Nevison

96b Plank Lane (A578, W of centre)

⌚ 12-11; 12-10.30 Sun

☎ (01942) 671394

Bateman XB; Robinson's Hatters Mild, Best Bitter; Tetley Bitter; guest beers Ⓗ

Situated close to the Plank Lane swingbridge on the Leigh branch of the Leeds-Liverpool Canal, the pub takes its name from William Nevison, a highwayman. The pub boasts sizeable collections of brass, plates and water jugs in the front parlour and lounge. Pool, darts and dominoes are played in the long vault. At the rear of the pub is a large, well-kept garden with a play area; children are welcome until 9pm. ❀◐◑⊟♣P

LONGSIGHT

Sir Edwin Chadwick

587 Stockport Road (A6, near A6010 jct)

⌚ 11-11; 12-10.30 Sun

☎ (0161) 256 2806

Boddingtons Bitter; Greene King Abbot; Hop Back Summer Lightning; Shepherd Neame Spitfire; guest beers Ⓗ

Thriving community pub, a beacon of quality in an inner city real ale desert. A successful conversion from a former supermarket, it is popular with all ages. It boasts a front patio and a garden to the rear. The licensee endeavours to keep guest beers available and takes part in all Wetherspoon's beer festivals. The name comes from a local man who rose to prominence by introducing some of Britain's earliest public health legislation. This is not a circuit bar. Q❀◐◑♿⅟✔

LOWTON (LANE HEAD)

Red Lion

324 Newton Road

⌚ 12-3.30, 6-11; 12-11 Fri & Sat; 12-10.30 Sun

☎ (01942) 671429

Greenalls Bitter; Marston's Pedigree; Tetley Mild, Bitter; guest beers Ⓗ

Situated between Manchester and Liverpool, just off the East Lancs road (A580), this large, popular local makes a handy base for touring the area, where local attractions include Haydock Park and Pennington Country Park. The pub has three lounge areas and a tap room. At the rear is a large garden and bowling green. It hosts a friendly quiz every Tuesday. Sport tends to dominate the conversations here. ❀⇌◐◑⊟♣P

LOWTON (ST LUKES)

Hare & Hounds

1 Golborne Road

⌚ 11-11; 12-10.30 Sun

☎ (01942) 728387

Tetley Bitter; guest beers Ⓗ

Large, popular, one-roomed local, where various areas are spread around a central horseshoe-shaped bar. A low-ceilinged lounge and tap room are at the front of the pub, with a sunken lounge, no-smoking area and children's play room at the rear. There is plenty of room around the bar for standing. Outside is a large car park, and garden with children's play area. ❀◐◑⊟♣P

LYDGATE

White Hart

51 Stockport Road (A669/A6050 jct)

⌚ 12-11; 12-10.30 Sun

☎ (01457) 872566 website: www.thewhitehart.co.uk

Boddingtons Bitter; Holt Bitter; Lees Bitter; Tetley Bitter; guest beers Ⓗ

Detached stone pub and restaurant, commanding impressive views over the hills of Oldham. It has four rooms, two are used for dining, each with an open fire. A small snug has its own bar servery and is complete with Victorian gothic backpanels and high-backed wooden seats. The popular bar boasts eight handpumps, and a new extension, with a bar area provides a brasserie-style restaurant. A good base for visiting Saddleworth Moors; accommodation is in 12 en-suite rooms. ⛼Q❀⇌◐◑♿P

MANCHESTER CITY CENTRE ✻

Bar Fringe

8 Swan Street (30 yds from A665/A62 jct)

⌚ 12-11; 12-10.30 Sun

☎ (0161) 835 3815 website: www.barfringe.co.uk

Beer range varies Ⓗ

This Belgian-style bar would not look out of place in Bruges or Brussels, with its choice of continental beers, wall posters and sawdust on bare floorboards. The four handpumps dispense a changing range of beers from Bank Top, Boggart Hole Clough and other small brewers. As a lively part of the Northern Quarter scene, it is often busy and noisy. Hot and cold food is available 12-7pm. ❀◑≠(Victoria) ⊖(Market St)

Castle

66 Oldham Street (near A62/A665 jct)

⏲ 12-11; 12-10.30 Sun

☎ (0161) 236 2945

Robinson's Hatters Mild, Old Stockport, Hartleys XB, Best Bitter, Old Tom, seasonal beers Ⓗ

Robinson's only city-centre pub sells all their regular beers as well as the seasonal ale. The ornate tiled façade and mosaic-floored entrance lead into a cosy front bar, behind which is a small snug. A big games room houses a pool table, pinball machine and dartboard. Most of the walls are covered in old posters, many advertising bands who have performed here. This 18th-century Grade II listed building should be included in any visit to the nearby Northern Quarter. Q⊟

Centro

74 Tib Street (off A665)

⏲ 12-12 (1am Thu-Sat); closed Sun

☎ (0161) 835 2863

Beer range varies Ⓗ

On a narrow, old street poised between decay and gentrification, Centro stands out as a café-bar with a difference: it sells real ale! Up to four, often from local micro-breweries, are supplemented by continental draught beers and American bottles. The upstairs bar is bare-boarded and subtly lit, with exhibited artworks for sale; downstairs is a smaller room with a mini-dance floor. Food is always available.

◑▶≠(Victoria/Piccadilly) ⊖(Market St)

City Arms

48 Kennedy Street

⏲ 11-11; 12-10.30 Sun

☎ (0161) 236 4610

Beer range varies Ⓗ

Deservedly popular, the City Arms is much frequented by the business community, especially on weekday lunchtimes. This listed building bears a noteworthy frontage. A range of up to eight beers constantly change.

◑≠ (Oxford Rd) ⊖ (St Peter's Sq)

Hare & Hounds ☆

46 Shudehill (near tram crossing)

⏲ 11-11; 12-10.30 Sun

☎ (0161) 832 4737

Holt Bitter; Tetley Bitter Ⓗ

Rare phenomenon: a traditional 'local' at the centre of a large city. A Grade II listed building, it bears a tiled frontage and many original features inside. A roomy lobby, with brown and cream tiling, fronts the bar which boasts much leaded glass and the old pulleys for modesty screens. There is a comfortable back lounge and a small front vault. A piano is the focus for lively singalongs, popular with older customers. Folk concerts are staged upstairs (Fri eve).

⇄≠(Victoria) ⊖(Market St) ♣P

Jolly Angler

47 Ducie Street

⏲ 12-3, 5.30-11; 12-11 Sat; 12-5, 8-10.30 Sun

☎ (0161) 236 5307

Hydes Bitter, seasonal beers Ⓗ

One of the last remaining back-street boozers in the city centre, the Angler's loyal following come from far and wide, despite its somewhat remote location. Music is provided by spontaneous sessions, mostly of an Irish flavour, especially on Thursday, Saturday and Sunday evenings. The original two-roomed layout has been opened out and is partly heated by a peat fire, but the corner bar is the hub of the pub.

♨≠(Piccadilly) ⊖

Marble Arch

73 Rochdale Road (300 yds from A664/A665 jct)

⏲ 11.30-11; 12-10.30 Sun

☎ (0161) 832 5914 website: www.marblebeers.co.uk

Marble N/4, Cloudy Marble, Uncut Amber, Old Lag, seasonal beers; guest beers Ⓗ

Home of the organic Marble Brewery, which can be observed from the rear lounge, it was built in 1888 for McKennas Harpurhey Brewery (note the mirror). This well-established free house boasts a notorious sloping mosaic floor from the impressive shap granite entrance to the corner bar at the bottom. Its brown-tiled barrel-vaulted ceiling with its frieze of various drinks, is complemented by the green-tiled walls. It hosts live music (Thu); eve meals Mon-Thu, 5-8; no food Sun. ❀◑≠(Victoria) ⊖

Old Monkey

90-92 Portland Street

⏲ 11.30-11; 12-10.30 Sun

☎ (0161) 228 7450

Holt Mild, Bitter Ⓗ

Opened in 1993, this flagship development marked the start of Holt's move into the city centre. It stands on a busy corner site handy for Chinatown, in a block containing two other pubs. Spread over two levels, it has a ground-floor public bar and a quieter upstairs lounge. High quality materials have been used throughout, with local memorabilia as decor. Low prices and high standards make it (sometimes very) busy.

◑⊟≠(Piccadilly/Oxford Rd) ⊖(St Peter's Sq)

Peveril of the Peak ☆

27 Great Bridgewater Street

⏲ 12-3 (not Sat), 5.30 (7 Sat)-11; 7-10.30 Sun

☎ (0161) 236 6364

Marston's Pedigree; Tetley Bitter; Wells Bombardier; guest beer Ⓗ

A superb tiled exterior, together with woodwork and stained glass in the bar make this a classic, worthy of its inclusion in CAMRA's National Inventory. Named after an historic coach service, the Peveril opens Saturday lunchtime when Manchester United play at home. Almost triangular in shape, this distinctive pub should not be missed.

♨❀◑⊟≠(Oxford Rd) ⊖(St Peter's Sq) ♣

Pot of Beer

36 New Mount Street (off Rochdale road, A664)

⏲ 12-11; closed Sun

☎ (0161) 834 8579

Boddingtons Bitter; Robinson's Dark Mild; guest beers Ⓗ/Ⓖ

Perhaps the hardest to find of the N/4 pubs, but one of the most rewarding, licensed since at least 1875, it passed from Marston's to become a free house in 1996. A chest-high partition separates the two bare-boarded drinking areas. On the walls are copies of documents relating to the pub's history. The guest beers are well selected from UK micros, while the food has a Polish flavour (12-2 Mon-Fri; 12-4 Sat). Moles Black Rat cider is stocked.
❀◖⇌(Victoria) ⊖●

Rain Bar

80 Great Bridgewater Street
⏲ 11-11; 12-10.30 Sun
☎ (0161) 235 6500
Lees GB Mild, Bitter, Moonraker, seasonal beers Ⓗ
This former umbrella factory was converted into a pub in 1999. The patio overlooks the Rochdale Canal, and it is surrounded by trendy flats. Weekend breakfasts are served from 9am. The pub incorporates three distinct styles over its three floors: downstairs is fairly traditional with much wood and a stone floor; on the first floor is a café-bar and above that a private room for hire. ❀◖◗♿⇌(Oxford Rd) ⊖(St Peter's Sq)

Smithfield Hotel & Bar

37 Swan Street
⏲ 12-11; 12-10.30 Sun
☎ (0161) 839 4424
Greene King XX Mild; guest beers Ⓗ
Hotel bar, very much an integral part of the Northern Quarter circuit. A single, narrow room, with a pool table at the front, opens out to the rear with more seating and a large TV, often on for football. Eight handpumps dispense rare beers from regional and micro-breweries from all over the country. The house beer comes from Phoenix. It holds regular beer festivals, when the handpumps are supplemented by jugs from the cellar. The accommodation is good value. 🛏◖⇌(Victoria) ⊖(Market St) ♣

White Lion

43 Liverpool Road
⏲ 11.30-11; 12-10.30 Sun
☎ (0161) 832 7373
Taylor Landlord; guest beers Ⓗ
Popular, busy, pub opposite the Air and Space Museum near the Castlefield basin. Food is served 12-9 (6 Fri-Sun). Not only does it offer good guest beers from local micros, but it also stocks a massive selection of whiskies, cognacs and wine.
❀◖◗⇌(Deansgate) ⊖(G.Mex)

MARPLE ❄

Railway

223 Stockport Road
⏲ 11.45-11; 12-10.30 Sun
☎ (0161) 427 2146
Robinson's Hatters Mild, Hartleys Cumbria Way, Best Bitter Ⓗ
This impressive pub opened in 1878 alongside Rose Hill Station, whose Manchester commuters still number among its customers. Replacing a former beer house (the Gun Inn), the pub was opened by Bells Brewery from Hempshaw Brook, Stockport and is little changed externally. Handy for walkers and cyclists on the nearby Middlewood Way, its two pleasant, open-plan rooms have an airy, relaxing atmosphere. The landlord recently won Robinson's Best-Kept Cellar competition. Children are welcome until 3pm.
❀◖♿⇌(Rose Hill) P

MELLOR

Oddfellows Arms

73 Moor End Road (2 miles from Marple Bridge)
⏲ 11-3, 5.30-11 (closed Mon); 12-3, 7-10.30 Sun
☎ (0161) 449 7826
Adnams Bitter; Flowers IPA; Marston's Pedigree; guest beers Ⓗ
The Oddfellows is an elegant three-storey building, totally in keeping with its picture postcard setting. Sympathetically restored internally, a good social atmosphere prevails in its comfortable bar and lounge. The upstairs restaurant enjoys an excellent reputation with a strong accent on quality food. ⚠Q❀◖◗♿P

MIDDLETON

Old Boar's Head ☆

111 Long Street
⏲ 11-11; 12-10.30 Sun
☎ (0161) 643 3520
Lees GB Mild, Bitter Ⓗ
Truly historic building on CAMRA's National Inventory of pubs with outstanding interiors. The exterior is half-timbered and the building dates back to 1632 (the date is cut into a stone lintel in the cellar). An inn since at least 1737, it was acquired by JW Lees in 1986. An extensive and sympathetic renovation three years later returned it to its former glory. Divided into a number of rooms, big and small, the whole pub is inviting and comfortable. An extensive range of meals is offered (eve meals 5-7). ⚠❀◖◗♿P⚟

Ring O' Bells

St Leonard's Square
⏲ 6 (12 Sat)-11; 12-10.30 Sun
☎ (0161) 654 9245
Lees Bitter, seasonal beers Ⓗ
Opposite Middleton's historic St Leonard's parish church, this neat, attractive pub dates from 1831. It has an odd history, once hosting entomological exhibitions which included a locally-caught giant locust. To this day the pub has a large butterfly collection, though not on public display. A central bar splits the main room into two distinct areas and a games room is hidden at the rear. Friendly and welcoming, this pub is a rare Middleton outlet for Lees seasonal beers. ❀♣

Tandle Hill Tavern

Thornham Fold, Thornham Lane (1 mile off A671 or A664, along unmetalled road) OS898091
⏲ 7 (5 summer; 12 Sat)-11; 12-10.30 Sun
☎ (01706) 345297
Lees GB Mild, Bitter Ⓗ
Delightfully unspoilt pub which is well worth the effort to find. Its two relaxing rooms are popular with the local farming community and with walkers enjoying the surrounding country park. It opened as a beer house in 1850 and was bought by Lees in 1932. It hosts many events, including the annual Tandle Hill fun run. Locally produced eggs, butter and honey can be

bought at the bar; soup and sandwiches are available at lunchtime. Evening opening hours may vary, so check before travelling. ⌂Q❀☙◐

MILNROW

Crown & Shuttle

170 Rochdale Road (A640)
⊙ 12-11; 12-10.30 Sun
☎ (01706) 648259
Lees GB Mild, Bitter ⊞

Traditional pub, popular with locals and homeward-bound workers. Usually busy, with a friendly atmosphere, the three rooms have a homely feel. The upstairs function room houses the landlord's military museum – his collection started with the acquisition of a WWI memorial board. The pub has charity collections for a local ex-servicemen's home and has even been visited by Chelsea Pensioners. An unusual 'hoop' game is played in the tap room and the pub supports cricket, netball and rounders teams. ⌂❀♣P

MOSSLEY

Church Inn

82 Stockport Road
⊙ 11-11; 12-10.30 Sun
☎ (01457) 832021
John Smith's Bitter; Theakston Cool Cask; guest beers ⊞

Formerly a Boddingtons house, the exterior of this inn is typical of so many northern town pubs; built at the end of a long, stone terrace row, giving an impression of permanence and always doing the job for which it was intended. A traditional local in every sense, catering for all ages, it has a tap room, served from a through bar, with Sky Sports on TV. The two guest beer pumps give a good choice of ales. The car park is tiny. ❀⊟⇌♣P

Rising Sun

235 Stockport Road
⊙ 6-11; 12-10.30 Sun
☎ (01457) 834436
Black Sheep Best Bitter; Taylor Landlord; Tetley Bitter; guest beers ⊞

The Rising Sun appears to be squeezed into the hillside which rises to 965 feet behind. This perhaps explains why, on entering, the interior is larger than expected. The present owners maintain a lively guest beer policy (three of the six cask ales available). A small games room allows the darts and crib teams to compete in the local league, and hosts a folk music session (Tue), notwithstanding the bridge veterans. Now 15 years in the free trade, since its Wilsons days, this house continues to improve. Q❀♣P

MOSTON

Blue Bell

493 Moston Lane
⊙ 11-11; 12-4, 7-10.30 Sun
☎ (0161) 683 4096
Holt Mild, Bitter ⊞

The Blue Bell was built in 1905 to replace a small cottage pub on an adjacent site. Four large rooms: a lounge, pool room (no pool!), back lounge, front room and a tap/vault cater mainly for a local community that has seen many changes in recent years. There are reports of a ghost having been seen around the pub. Always check the handpump when requesting mild to make sure of the real thing, or you may get smooth (cask-conditioned, but with added gas). ❀⊟♿♣P

MOTTRAM

White Hart

91 Market Street
⊙ 11-11; 12-10.30 Sun
☎ (01457) 764307
Moorhouses Black Cat; Phoenix Bantam; Plassey Bitter; John Smith's Bitter; Taylor Landlord; guest beers ⊞

Village-centre local in a conservation area, opposite the old courthouse. Its comfortable lounge, tap room and bare-boarded open area around the bar, are complemented by a Cuban, Caribbean and Tapas restaurant upstairs (open Thu-Sat, 6-10 and Sun 2-9), offering a wide vegetarian choice. Formerly an all-keg pub, it is now by far the most popular pub locally. The cider constantly changes. Regular bus services run from Hyde and Glossop. ⌂Q❀◑♿♣●

NANGREAVES

Lord Raglan

Mount Pleasant
⊙ 12-2.30, 7-11; 12-10.30 Sun
☎ (0161) 764 6680
Leyden Nanny Flyer, Black Pudding, Light Brigade, Raglan Sleeve, Heavy Brigade ⊞

This inn is the home of the Leyden Brewery and several of their beers feature on the bar. The Leyden family have run this charming country local for almost 50 years. It is decorated throughout with many items of interest, including antique glassware and pottery, old pictures and photographs. The pub is renowned for its good food; the chef is also the head brewer. Meals are served all day Sunday until 9pm. ❀◐◑P

NEW SPRINGS

Colliers Arms

192 Wigan Road (B5238)
⊙ 1.30-5.30 (not Wed or Thu), 7.30-11; 12-5, 7.30-10.30 Sun
☎ (01942) 831171
Burtonwood Bitter ⊞

Known locally as the Stone, this popular, two-roomed inn is making its 19th consecutive appearance in this Guide, a feat unrivalled by any other pub in the Wigan area. A striking mock-Tudor building, dating from 1700, it displays much memorabilia of local collieries, including a pit helmet in the lounge, used to illuminate the fireplace, as well as books on walking and rambling. It is handy for nearby attractions, Haigh Hall and the Leeds-Liverpool Canal. Tiny car park. ⌂Q❀P

OLDHAM

Black Swan

13 Bottom Th' Moor, Mumps Bridge
⊙ 11-11; 12-10.30 Sun
☎ (0161) 624 4977
Lees Bitter ⊞

Drawing a mainly mature clientele, this

detached pub is divided into three areas around a central bar, pleasantly furnished. The function room is used regularly by various naval and sea cadet brigades. It can get quite busy with postal workers from the local sorting office, and is handy for the station. Unusual features include the black and white floor tiles around the bar and the pub's name depicted in mosaic in the vestibule – now quite rare.
(Mumps) P

Gardener's Arms
Dunham Street (Millbottom), Lees
12-11; 12-10.30 Sun
☎ (0161) 624 0242
Robinson's Hatters Mild, Best Bitter H
Sitting next to the River Medlock, on one of the old roads to Yorkshire, this pub retains many of the original features from the time it was rebuilt around 1930, including the layout of separate rooms. Fireplaces, tilework and plenty of brassware are evidence of an almost unchanged pub. Lunches are served weekdays. P

Hunt Lane Tavern
754 Middleton Road, Chadderton
11.30-11; 12-10.30 Sun
☎ (0161) 627 2969
Lees GB Mild, Bitter H
Busy main road pub which appeals to locals and visitors; a friendly Lees outlet where occasional background music does not impede the convivial atmosphere. The games room has pool table, darts, dominoes and cards. The main room is divided into three sections, with beamed ceilings, leaded windows and numerous rural pictures giving the impression of a country tavern. The ivy-clad frontage and hanging baskets look wonderful in summer. Evening meals are available on Friday.
(Mills Hill) P

Royal Oak
176 Manchester Road, Werneth
12-11; 12-5, 8-11 Sat; 12-10.30 Sun
☎ (0161) 629 5795
Robinson's Hatters Mild, Best Bitter H
Traditional Robinson's pub, with four drinking areas served from a central bar. Recently refurbished to a high standard, it retains the original character of a community local, by keeping the wood panelling and old-fashioned cast-iron radiators. The mainly older regulars are keen players of traditional pub games. Unusual features include an old Gledhill cash register and a rare Robinson's Old Tom mirror in the games room. Handy for the station. (Werneth)

ORRELL

Robin Hood
117 Sandy Lane (400 yds from station)
12-11; 12-10.30 Sun
☎ (01695) 627479
Beer range varies H
Small, unspoilt two-roomed, family-run pub, themed on the well-known freedom fighter from Sherwood Forest. Pictures of Robin Hood abound and the ladies cloakroom is romantically dubbed the Damsels. It looks like the sort of place that ought to sell real ale, and now does after many years in the keg wilderness, although the Greenall's beers are still keg. Home-cooked food and a quiz night (Wed) are added attractions. Q P

PATRICROFT

Stanley Arms
295 Liverpool Road (A57, near Bridgewater Canal)
12-11; 12-10.30 Sun
☎ (0161) 788 8801
Holt Mild, Bitter H
Victorian pub, acquired by Holt's in 1909, the Stanley is proof that small is beautiful. Enter by the side door on Eliza Ann Street into a small lobby and corridor with green tiling. Beyond the small central bar is the front vault and to the left is the 'best room'. Everything sparkles like a new pin in one of Holt's last remaining tenancies. At the end of the corridor a door marked 'private' leads to a third public room, with a massive cast-iron range, used mainly at weekends.

PEEL GREEN

Grapes Hotel
439 Liverpool Road (A57, near M60 jct 11)
11-11; 12-10.30 Sun
☎ (0161) 789 6971
Holt Mild, Bitter H
This monumental Edwardian listed pub was built about 1906 on the site of a previous pub and brewhouse. Today's pub has a billiards room in place of the brewhouse, but with only a pool table at present. There are two other large, comfortable rooms, and the spacious vault is the scene of much lively banter. Most of the original features are intact, including a mosaic floor, extensive tiling and a wealth of heavy mahogany carvings and etched glass.
Q (Patricroft) P

PENDLEBURY

Newmarket
621 Bolton Road (A666)
11-11; 12-10.30 Sun
☎ (0161) 794 3650
Holt Mild, Bitter H
Very much a local, the front vault features two old photos of Swinton RLFC's champion winning teams (1927-28 and 1962-63), alongside horse-racing photos. There is also a smaller vault at the rear. A long lounge area hosts special nights, karaoke (Mon), a quiz (Wed), and a disco on Friday. Q P

RAMSBOTTOM

Hare & Hounds
400 Bolton Road West, Holcombe Brook
12-11; 12-10.30 Sun
☎ (01706) 822107
Boddingtons Bitter; Taylor Landlord; guest beers H
Basically, this is a very large, one-roomed pub, split into distinct drinking areas, including a raised no-smoking area. The abundance of TVs testify to the locals' interest in sport. It can be very busy, especially at weekends and on matchdays. In an area not renowned for choice, customers are attracted by the good service and excellent beer quality. Four interesting

guest beers complement the regulars. Food is served every day until 9.30pm.
⊭❀◐◑♿P⊬

ROCHDALE ❊

Albion

600 Whitworth Road (A671)
12-2.30, 5-11; 12-11 Sat; 12-10.30 Sun
☎ (01706) 648540
Holt Bitter; Hydes Dark; Lees Bitter; Taylor Best Bitter, Landlord; guest beers Ⓗ
One of the few remaining true free houses, this pub, with its multi-roomed layout, is built into the side of the hill; the garden is almost on the roof, such is the incline. The popular bistro offers a range of English/Afro cuisine which is reflected in the bar meals. One or two guest beers, and a selection of wines, supplement the regular beers. Popular with locals, visitors often come again. ⊭Q❀◐◑♿

Britannia Inn

4 Lomax Street (off A671, near A58 jct)
12-11; 12-10.30 Sun
☎ (01706) 646391
Lees GB Mild, Bitter, seasonal beers Ⓗ
Friendly, two-roomed pub, five minutes' walk from the town centre, run by the longest-serving landlord in the area. There is a collection of plates from around the world in the lounge, which also boasts a magnificent fireplace surround, dated 1881. This is not an original fixture, but was rescued from destruction by the landlord. The exterior features an unusual 'witch's hat' spire and a relief of Britannia. Lunches are served 12-1.30, evening meals 5-6.30.
❀◐◑♣

Cask & Feather

1 Oldham Road
11-11; 12-10.30 Sun
☎ (01706) 711476
website: www.mcguinnessbrewery.com
McGuinness Feather Plucker Mild, Best Bitter, Junction Bitter, Tommy Todd's Porter Ⓗ
On the main route to Oldham, the pub provides a welcome break at the top of a long climb from the town centre, midway between bus and rail stations. Stone-built, with one L-shaped room and the brewery at the rear, this is McGuinness's only tied outlet. The whole beer range is usually on tap at all times, and at affordable prices. Park in the pay and display car park opposite. ◐⇌

Healey Hotel

172 Shawclough Road (B6377)
12 (3 Tue & Wed)-11; 12-10.30 Sun
☎ (01706) 645453
Robinson's Best Bitter, Old Tom, seasonal beers Ⓗ
This 18th-century stone pub, at the entrance to Healey Dell nature reserve, is a gem. Many original and interesting features remain, including a splendid bar, original oak doors and tilework from the 1930s. A traditional layout consists of a quiet, no-smoking front parlour, decorated with local scenes, a rear gentlemen's room with a sporting motif and a bar/lounge displaying film star portraits. The extensive gardens boast a well-used pétanque piste.
⊭Q❀▲♣⊬

Merry Monk

234 College Road (near A6060/B6222 jct)
12-11; 12-5, 7-10.30 Sun
☎ (01706) 646919
Hydes Dark, Bitter, Jekyll's Gold; guest beers Ⓗ
Victorian, detached brick local, first licensed in 1850. A glimpse of its history can be seen in the fine pair of Phoenix (Heywood) tile sets in the entrance. The pub passed to Bass via Cornbrook, and was purchased as a free house in 1984. There are always one or two guest beers available. The open-plan layout is home to strong darts and quiz teams; ring the bull and bar billiards are also played, while outside pétanque pistes provide amusement. ❀♣P

ROYTON ❊

Dog & Partridge

148 Middleton Road
12-11; 12-10.30 Sun
☎ (0161) 620 6403
Lees GB Mild, Bitter Ⓗ
Five minutes' walk from the town centre, this is a classic, welcoming and friendly local, comprising a comfortable, spacious lounge, a vault, a games room and an outdoor drinking area. It stocks an excellent selection of malt whiskies. The pub was awarded Best-Kept Cellar by Lees Brewery for three consecutive years from 1997 to 1999. Q❀♣

INN BRIEF

STOCKPORT

Grapes
1c Castle Street, Edgeley
11-11; 12-10.30 Sun
(0161) 480 3027
Robinson's Hatter's Mild, Best Bitter Ⓗ
Excellent, down-to-earth, two-roomed boozer on a shopping precinct. Busy at lunchtime, quieter eves.

WHITEFIELD

Coach & Horses
71 Bury Old Road
12-11; 12-10.30 Sun
(0161) 798 8897
Holt Mild, Bitter Ⓗ
Built in 1830, a traditional multi-roomed local that still bears much of its original character.

WIGAN

Brocket Arms
Mesnes Road
11-11; 12-11 Sun
(01942) 820372
Courage Directors; Shepherd Neame Spitfire; Theakston Best Bitter; guest beers Ⓗ
Wetherspoon's offering comfortable surroundings, a large, no-smoking area, disabled access and accommodation. Cask Marque accredited.

Fox & Goose
37-39 Wigan Lane
11-11; 12-10.30 Sun
(01942) 517605
Holt Bitter; Tetley Bitter Ⓗ
Typical, friendly local with lounge and vault containing pool table; two large-screen TVs. Folk night (Tue); garden.

Silverwell
117 Darlington Street East
12-11; 12-10.30 Sun
Holt Mild, Bitter, seasonal beers Ⓗ
Large, multi-roomed pub on the main road; children welcome. Refurbished in 2000, it hosts live music Sat eve.

❊ symbol next to a main entry place name indicates there are Inn Brief entries as well.

SALFORD

Albert Vaults

169 Chapel Street (A6, near central station)
11-11; 12-10.30 Sun
☎ (0161) 819 1368
Phoenix Arizona; guest beer H

Literally standing in the shadow of the former Threllfalls Brewery (closed by Whitbread over a decade ago), this basic friendly pub has a large popular room to the right of the bar, a much quieter one to the left, and a vault with minimal seating at the rear. The left-hand lounge does, however, host a live artist on Sunday evening. Note the very unusual coloured glass window over the bar. (Central)

Crescent

18-20 Crescent
11.30-11; 12-10.30 Sun
☎ (0161) 736 5600
Hydes Bitter; Rooster's Special; guest beers H

Quality and value are the hallmarks of this thriving free house near Salford University. One central bar serves three rooms, plus a side games vault. Up to eight guest ales are complemented by real cider and a good range of draught and bottled foreign beers. Regular beer festivals are held, at which the cellar runs have become legendary! The food is excellent value, including curry night (Wed); no meals Sun eve. A small enclosed garden hosts occasional barbecues. (Crescent) P

Eagle Inn (Lamp Oil)

19 Collier Street (250 yards from A6041/A6042 jct)
11-11; 12-10.30 Sun
☎ (0161) 832 4919
Holt Mild, Bitter H

Wonderful, classic example of a Holt's back-street boozer with bow-fronted windows, comprising just three small rooms, a snug, tap and games room; a selection of pre-Raphaelite prints brightens the snug. For well over 50 years, the pub has been known affectionately as the Lamp Oil, due to a connection with selling that product. This name is displayed on the lamp hanging over the entrance. A little difficult to find, but once found it is never forgotten. (Central) (Victoria)

Olde Nelson

285 Chapel Street (A6, near cathedral)
12-11; 12-10.30 Sun
☎ (0161) 281 9607
Flowers IPA; Lees Bitter H

Opening as the Nelson Tavern in 1805 (the nearby Lord Nelson had opened five years earlier), the present Olde Nelson is a lofty hotel where the name is a feature of the elaborate ceramic exterior. Beyond the entrance is a lobby, with an L-shaped vault to the right. Here, a large-screen TV is used mainly for football matches. At the back is a long, comfortable lounge which is home to quiz matches and darts.

Union Tavern

105 Liverpool Street (parallel to A6 and A57)
11-11; 12-10.30 Sun
☎ (0161) 736 2885
Holt Mild, Bitter H

Popular with the locals who support five darts teams (three men's, two ladies'), this basic, traditional boozer has three rooms: best, vault and games. At the rear of the bar, the darts trophies are displayed. Located in an area that has seen many pubs fail or demolished in recent years, local CAMRA members have a soft spot for the Union, which has consistently appeared in this Guide for two decades. A warm welcome awaits the casual visitor. (Crescent) P

Welcome Inn

Robert Hall Street, Ordsall (off A5066)
12-11; 12-4, 7.30-11 Sat; 12-3, 7.30-10.30 Sun
☎ (0161) 872 6040
Lees GB Mild, Bitter P

Built in the 1970s and internally refurbished in 2001, this community local has a comfortable lounge, a well-used games room, and a function room. Hot and cold bar snacks are served 12-3 and 7.30-9.30 Mon-Sat. The lounge displays Harold Riley prints, depicting a now vanished Ordsall, while today's customers represent the best of the new era. Lees' seasonal ales may be stocked. A small yard provides space for outdoor drinking. P

STALYBRIDGE

Station Buffet Bar ☆

Platform 1, Stalybridge Station, Rassbottom Street
11-11; 12-10.30 Sun
☎ (0161) 303 0007
Boddingtons Bitter; Flowers IPA; Wadworth 6X; guest beers H

A national institution and rightly so; lovingly restored to its former glory and seamlessly extended into the former living quarters. The marble-topped bar in this Victorian gem, which has won a shelf-full of awards, is the centrepiece of the four diverse rooms. Here, or at the outside benches, you can enjoy up to five ever-changing guest beers from new and established breweries. Regular beer festivals are held throughout the year; a pub not to be missed.
Q P

STANDISH

Dog & Partridge

33 School Lane
1-11; 12-10.30 Sun
☎ (01257) 401218
Tetley Mild, Bitter; guest beers H

Popular drinkers' pub which usually offers three interesting guest beers, often including beers from the local Mayflower Brewery. One central bar serves both sides of the pub – one side is popular for football and rugby matches on TV, while the other is quieter. It hosts a beer festival in March, with proceeds going to charity. P

Globe

94 High Street (opp. police station)
11.30-11; 12-10.30 Sun
☎ (01257) 400759
website: www.theglobestandish.co.uk
Theakston Cool Cask; guest beers H

Large roadside pub, a landmark on the road from Wigan when you reach the centre of Standish. Two varied guest beers are available in the open-plan interior that displays many photographs and paintings of the pub and its surroundings over the years. Good value, home-cooked food is served. The games room houses a large-screen TV which is popular for sporting events. Buses on the main Wigan to Chorley route stop right outside. The Globe has a children's certificate. ◑♿♣P

STOCKPORT ❄

Arden Arms ☆

23 Millgate (behind Asda)
⊛ 12-11; 12-10.30 Sun
☎ (0161) 480 2185 website: www.ardenarms.com
Robinson's Hatters Mild, Hartleys Cumbria Way, Best Bitter, 🄷 **Old Tom** (winter), 🄶 **seasonal beers** 🄷
Restaurant quality food and fine ales combine to make a visit to this Grade II listed, multi-roomed gem, a very rewarding experience. Highlights include two roaring fires in the winter months and a tiny snug, only accessible through the bar. The licensees formerly ran a highly-rated restaurant and this is reflected in the imaginative menu which is gaining a reputation locally. Small car park but a public one opposite is free evenings.
♨Q❀◑P

Blossoms

2 Buxton Road, Heaviley (A6)
⊛ 12-3, 5-11; 12-11 Sat; 12-10.30 Sun
☎ (0161) 477 2397
Robinson's Hatters Mild, Best Bitter, 🄷 **Old Tom** (winter) 🄶
Multi-roomed, early Victorian gem retaining its original layout of bar, lobby and three rooms off (one is now used for pool). The best is the cosy rear smoke room with its carved fireplace and stained glass window panels. The emphasis here is on quality and tradition, epitomised by the cask of Old Tom featured on the bar in winter. Lunchtime food includes superb value pork pies made by the licensee's son. This friendly, down-to-earth pub was local CAMRA Pub of the Year 1998.
◑≹(Davenport) ♣P

Crown

154 Heaton Lane (under viaduct, 100 yds from A6)
⊛ 12-3, 6-11; 12.30-11 Fri & Sat; 7.30-10.30 Sun
☎ (0161) 429 0549
Jennings Bitter; guest beers 🄷
Stockport's top pub for choice, where 10 handpumps dispense an ever-changing range of beers – four from local micros; a mild and cider are always available. Standing right underneath Stockport's famous railway viaduct – reputed to be the largest brick structure in Europe – this early Victorian pub retains many original features including a gaslit vault and three lounge areas, with open fires. Can be very busy at weekends and evenings, particularly for music sessions, but quieter at lunchtime.
♨❀◑⊟≹♣●⚡

Olde Vic

1 Chatham Street, Edgeley (behind station)
⊛ 5 (7 Sat)-11; 7-10.30 Sun
☎ (0161) 480 2410
Greene King IPA; guest beers 🄷
The first Stockport pub to offer guest beers, and still flying the flag with four ever-changing guests, the 'pump clip ceiling' over the bar is testimony to the choice available. An easy-going atmosphere prevails in this tightly-run ship, where a no-swearing policy is strictly enforced. The pub opens Saturday lunchtime when Stockport County are at home, and welcomes well-behaved away supporters. The cider is from Weston's. Beware of the cat! ♨❀≹●

Olde Woolpack

70 Brinksway (A560)
⊛ 11.30-3, 5-11; 11.30-11 Fri; 11.30-4.30, 7.30-11 Sat; 12-10.30 Sun
☎ (0161) 476 0688
Theakston Best Bitter, Cool Cask; Wells Bombardier; guest beers 🄷
Set hard by the Mersey and standing guard over the old Brinksway bridge, the pub now appears rather incongruous against the backdrop of a busy urban motorway and a blue glass pyramid. Rescued from dereliction some 13 years ago, the original floorplan of the vault and plush rooms around the bar survives. Heavy emphasis is laid on quality, from the two guest beers to the tasty food (popular with the pyramid's workforce). Local CAMRA Pub of the Year 1999. Q❀◑♣P

Railway

1 Avenue Street (off A560, opp. Peel Centre)
⊛ 12-11; 12-10.30 Sun
☎ (0161) 429 6062
Porter Dark Mild, Floral Dance, Bitter, Rossendale Ale, Porter, Sunshine 🄷
Holding the title of CAMRA 2002 local Pub of the Year, this unpretentious, single-roomed pub is a must to visit. Bar billiards has been introduced, but no TV, juke box or games machines will spoil your enjoyment of the seven different beers (Sleeper is brewed just for this pub) permanently available, along with occasional seasonal beers. An ever-changing cider is served, together with what must be the largest range of Belgian and foreign beers in the area. Q❀◑♣●

Red Bull

14 Middle Hillgate
⊛ 11.30-11; 12-3, 7-10.30 Sun
☎ (0161) 480 2087
Robinson's Hatters Mild, Best Bitter 🄷
Although situated in the centre of Stockport, the pub exudes a warm country feel, particularly in the stone-flagged period snug with pew seating, off the main bar. Dark wood, traditional pub colours, and bric-à-brac decorate the four rooms. The fairly complex, two-bar, multi-level layout also boasts another small snug at the back, that accommodates just eight drinkers. It can be busy with diners weekday lunchtimes. Bats are often seen flying in the yard at night. Q❀◑≹P

Spread Eagle

31 Lower Hillgate
(next to Robinson's Brewery)
⊛ 12-11; 7.30-10.30 Sun
☎ (0161) 480 7057
Robinson's Hatters Mild, Best Bitter, Old Tom (winter) 🄿
Now firmly established as a Guide regular, Robinson's brewery tap has flourished in recent years with a reputation as a well-run, homely local, attracting both a loyal core of regulars and shoppers from the town centre.

The Old Tom is the landlord's pride and joy, and is also available in vintage nip glasses. Food is restricted to sandwiches plus the licensee's superb, home-made, value-for-money curries which are also available to take away.
≠♣▯

Swan with Two Necks ☆

36 Princes Street (behind Woolworth's)
✪ 11-11; closed Sun
☎ (0161) 480 2341
Robinson's Hatters Mild, Best Bitter, Hartleys Cumbria Way, Frederics, Old Tom, seasonal beers Ⓗ
Set amid the busy main street shops, this little gem is a classic Victorian pub. A multi-roomed layout is retained with a small, well-used vault at the front and superb oak-panelling in the bar and more spacious middle room. The previously unused rear room has now been decorated and is used mainly by diners – lunches are served six days a week. No TV, juke box or pool table here, only good beer and conversation.
Q☾⊟♣

Tiviot

8 Tiviot Dale (near A560/B6167 jct)
✪ 11-11; 12-3 (closed eve) Sun
☎ (0161) 480 4109
Robinson's Hatters Mild, Best Bitter, Ⓟ **Old Tom** (winter) Ⓖ
Close to the site of long-gone Tiviot Dale Station, steam loco paintings still hang in the vault. Today's bustle is provided by the Merseyway shops, when at lunchtime, regulars and shoppers are attracted by the no-nonsense, good value food (not served Sun). A set of ink drawings of town pubs adorns the front lounge, games room (with table football) and dining room. Although spartan in decor, it does not fall short on homeliness and welcome. ❀☾⊟♣P▯

STONECLOUGH

Market Street Tavern

131 Market Street, Radcliffe (A667)
✪ 12-11; 12-10.30 Sun
☎ (01204) 572985

Choosing Pubs

CAMRA members and branches choose the pubs listed in the Good Beer Guide. There is no payment for entry, and pubs are inspected on a regular basis by personal visits; publicans are not sent a questionnaire once a year, as is the case with some pub guides. CAMRA branches monitor all the pubs in their areas, and the choice of pubs for the guide is often the result of democratic vote at branch meetings. However, recommendations from readers are welcomed and will be passed on to the relevant branch: write to Good Beer Guide, CAMRA, 230 Hatfield Road, St Albans, AL1 4LW; or send an se-mail to camra@camra.org.uk.

Tetley Bitter; guest beer Ⓗ
Busy main road pub with a lounge and a vault, popular with locals. The landlord has a dedication to cask beers; Bolton's Bank Top brewery provides the regular guest beer, Flat Cap, which is the best seller and is very keenly priced. There is an outdoor drinking area at the front of the pub and a car park at the rear. ❀≠(Kearsley) ♣P

SWINTON

White Lion
242 Manchester Road (A6/A572 jct)
✪ 12-11; 12-10.30 Sun
☎ (0161) 288 0434
Robinson's Hatters Mild, Best Bitter, Hartleys Cumbria Way, seasonal beer Ⓗ
Although much of this building dates back to about 1790, many alterations and additions have been made. Most recently, a derelict cottage next door was demolished and the pub extended to provide a modern kitchen. Today there is a vault, a split-level main lounge, and a new, small room. A large rear annexe is the official 'Hall of Fame' for Swinton RL club, which has a long association with the pub. Eve meals served 5-7 (food all day Sun); children's room available until 7pm. ❀◐◑ ⊟♣P

White Swan
186 Worsley Road
✪ 12-11; 12-10.30 Sun
☎ (0161) 794 1504
Holt Mild, Bitter Ⓗ
Replacing a terraced cottage beer house from the early 19th century, the Swan was built in the 1920s. The only significant alteration was made in the early 1990s, when two rooms virtually became one, but three other rooms remain: a vault, a back lounge with wood-panelled walls and a large rear room used for functions, TV football and as a family room on Sunday afternoon. Eve meals are served 4-7; Sunday lunch available. ⌂❀◑ ⊟♣P

TIMPERLEY

Quarry Bank Inn
Bloomsbury Lane
✪ 11.30-11; 12-10.30 Sun
☎ (0161) 903 9483
Hydes Mild, Bitter, seasonal beers Ⓗ
Thriving, popular, suburban pub on the edge of the old village centre: it has a popular vault and a quieter lounge with restaurant area. It boasts a well-used bowling green, one of very few pubs still to have one nowadays. Q❀◐◑ ⊟♿♣P

TYLDESLEY

Half Moon
115-117 Elliot Street
✪ 11-11; 12-10.30 Sun
☎ (01942) 873206
Boddingtons Bitter; Holt Mild, Bitter; guest beers Ⓗ
Long-established, town-centre local where the main lounge has various seating areas, and a low ceiling. There is a second comfortable lounge, separate from the bar, which is useful for a quiet pint or two. The local landlord ensures a friendly pub. In summer the pleasant garden at the rear comes into use. ❀♣

UPPERMILL

Cross Keys
Off Running Hill Gate (off A670, up Church Rd)
✪ 11-11; 12-10.30 Sun
☎ (01457) 874626
Lees GB Mild, Bitter, Moonraker, seasonal beers Ⓗ
This attractive, beamed, 18th-century stone building overlooks Saddleworth church. The bar boasts a stone-flagged floor and a Yorkshire range. The centre for many activities, including mountain rescue, clay pigeon club, Saddleworth runners and the Garland Girls, it is busy during annual events, such as the charity beer walk (June) and the Saddleworth Rushcart Festival (Aug). It hosts folk nights (Wed and Sun) in the barn. Good value, home-cooked food is served until 7pm. Children's certificate held.
⌂Q❀◐◑ ⊟♣P

WARDLEY

Morning Star
520 Manchester Road (A6, between Swinton and Walkden)
✪ 12-11; 12-10.30 Sun
☎ (0161) 794 4927
Holt Mild, Bitter Ⓗ
Friendly community pub that runs a social club and darts and dominoes teams. The exterior is Edwardian, but the interior is more modern with a small bar lounge leading to the large main lounge. On the other side of the bar is a traditional vault. Excellent value home-made meals, available weekday lunchtimes, are served direct from the kitchen which has been awarded a Silver Merit for Hygiene and Excellence by the local area health authority.
❀◐⊟≠(Moorside) ♣P

WESTHOUGHTON

White Lion
2 Market Street (B5235, next to Town Hall)
✪ 11-11; 12-10.30 Sun
☎ (01942) 811191
Holt Mild, Bitter Ⓗ
An inn has been on this site for about 250 years, it was acquired by Holt in 1925. Today it is a totally unspoilt and unpretentious pub. Its most attractive feature is the curved, shuttered island bar serving the five distinct drinking areas: a vault (with its own entrance), a cosy bar/parlour, smoke room (used for darts), lounge and a lobby area. Most of the furniture and fittings have been restored in keeping with this old-fashioned hostelry.
❀♣P

WHITEFIELD ❄

Eagle & Child
Higher Lane (A665/A56 jct)
✪ 12-11; 12-10.30 Sun
☎ (0161) 766 3024
Holt Mild, Bitter Ⓗ
Large, black and white pub set back from the road. It has an L-shaped main bar and a cosy side room. The well-kept bowling green at the rear is very popular in summer. The building dates from 1936, replacing the original Eagle & Child (built 1802) which was the first hostelry on Higher Lane. The

other five pubs that served this lane are long gone. Once a Whitefield Brewery pub, it has been a Holt house since 1907.
❀⊖(Besses o' th' Barn) P

WIGAN ❄

Anvil
Dorning Street
(next to bus station)
11-11; 12-10.30 Sun
☎ (01942) 239444
Hydes Mild, Bitter, seasonal beers; guest beers H
A very modern feel prevails in this well-placed, town-centre pub – a former karaoke bar – with a bus station on one side, railway stations on the other, and in the shadow of Wigan parish church. Regular guest beers join the impressive Hydes' range. Wide-screen TV caters for sports fans in a separate room. A friendly haven, away from the town-centre club and wine bar scene, it is well worth a visit.
❀◑⇌(North Western/Wallgate) ✔

Beer Engine
69 Poolstock Lane
11-11; 12-10.30 Sun
☎ (01942) 321820
Beer range varies H
The former Poolstock Labour Club has been converted to a community pub. Its amenities include a bowling green to the rear and a concert room that hosts occasional beer festivals as well as music events.
❀◑♿♣P

Bowling Green
106-108 Wigan Lane
(A49, 100 yds from infirmary)
4 (3 Fri; 12 Sat)-11; 12-10.30 Sun
☎ (01942) 516004
Brains SA; Caledonian Deuchars IPA; Jennings Cumberland Ale; Robinson's Best Bitter; Tetley Dark Mild, Bitter; guest beers H
A Guide regular and frequent local CAMRA Pub of the Year, it boasts a striking, hop-strewn interior with original etched windows. There is a lively vault and two lounges, complete with log fires and waitress service. To the rear, an attractive garden hosts regular barbecues. Bank holidays see popular live music sessions, while acoustic sessions crop up from time to time. Up to 25 malt whiskies are stocked and daily newspapers are available. Euros are accepted here.
❀♣

Moon under Water
5-7a Market Place
11-11; 12-10.30 Sun
☎ (01942) 323437
Cains Mild; Courage Directors; Shepherd Neame Spitfire; guest beer H
Wigan's first, and best, Wetherspoon's, situated at the very centre of town, previously a Halifax Building Society office, tailor's shop and photography store. Large, fully opening windows create an alfresco atmosphere in sunny weather. Upstairs a side entrance opens on to the Wiend (historic shopping street). It can be busy at weekends. Meals are served all day.
Q◑♿⇌(North Western/Wallgate) ✔

Orwell
Wigan Pier, Wallgate
11-11; 12-10.30 Sun; (hours vary winter)
☎ (01942) 323034 website: www.wiganpier.co.uk
Beer range varies H
Converted Victorian cotton warehouse on the Leeds-Liverpool Canal, approximately 10 minutes' walk from the JJB Stadium (home of Wigan Athletic and the Wigan Warriors). The menu includes a good choice of home-made soups and hot and cold sandwiches. This true free house, the current local CAMRA Pub of the Year, offers the widest range of beers from micro-breweries in the area, with seasonal ales from the likes of Bank Top, Blackpool, Pictish and Phoenix.
❀◑♿⇌(North Western/Wallgate) ♣P

Swan & Railway
80 Wallgate (opp. North Western Station)
12 (11 Sat)-11; 12-10.30 Sun
☎ (01942) 495032
Banks's Original, Bitter; Camerons Strongarm; Mansfield Dark Mild; guest beer H
Classic, largely unspoilt boozer, it was saved by the local CAMRA branch from unsympathetic treatment a few years ago. The mosaic porch and tiled bar are the highlights but there are also attractive stained glass inserts in the vault, commemorating local locomotives. Prints of Victorian still life abound. Handy for both stations, there is sport on TV for those who enjoy it, and a pool table in the front snug. ◑⇌(North Western/Wallgate) ♣

WITHINGTON

Victoria
438 Wilmslow Road (B5093)
11.30-11; 12-10.30 Sun ☎ (0161) 448 1083
Hydes Mild, Bitter, Jekyll's Gold, seasonal beers H
Built in the 1800s and bought by Hydes in 1904, the period exterior, with its etched glass windows, hides a spacious interior, each room with its own identity. Situated on one of the busiest bus corridors in Europe, the pub is popular with locals at lunchtime, swelled by a large student population in the evening. Regular entertainment reflects the diversity and wide age range of its customers: a pianist (twice monthly), quiz nights (Thu) and weekly darts nights. Weekend lunches continue until 5pm. ❀◑♣✔

WOODFORD

Davenport Arms (Thief's Neck)
550 Chester Road (A5102)
11-3.30, 5.15-11; 11-11 Sat; 12-3, 7-10.30 Sun
☎ (0161) 439 2435
Robinson's Hatters Mild, Best Bitter, Old Tom (winter), **seasonal beers** H
This superb, unspoilt, multi-roomed farmhouse pub, on the edge of suburbia, has been run by the Hallworth family for over 70 years. The front rooms comprise a traditional tap and a cosy, no-smoking snug, while the larger back room houses the bar which can get very busy. All three rooms have real fires. The food is all cooked on the premises. Children are welcome at lunchtime in the snug and the large, attractive garden. Q❀◑♣P

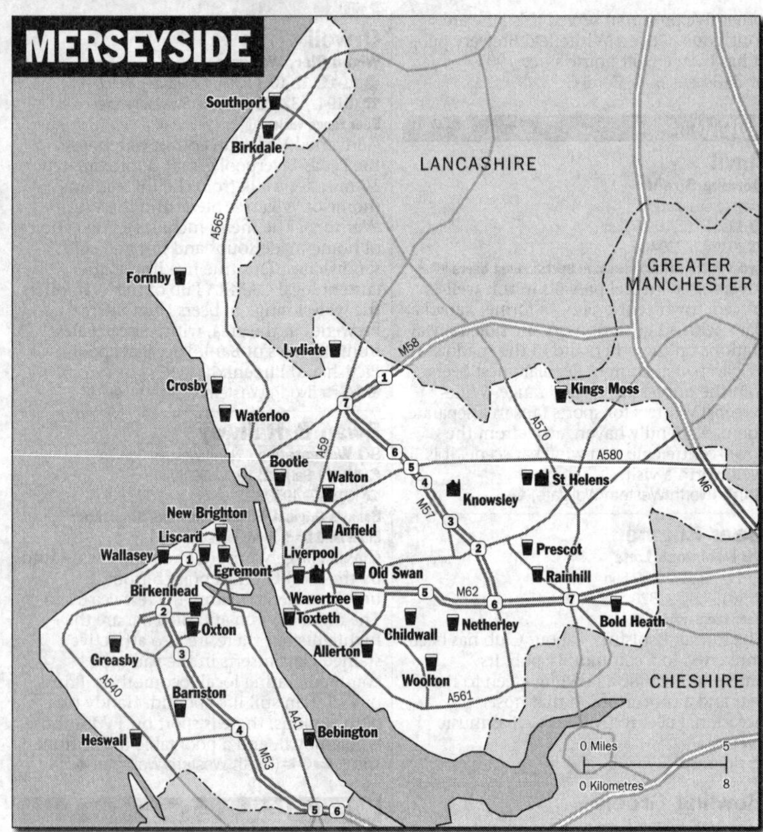

BARNSTON

Fox & Hounds

107 Barnston Road (A551)
11-11; 12-10.30 Sun
☎ (0151) 648 7685
website: www.the-fox-hounds.co.uk
Marston's Pedigree; Theakston Best Bitter, Old Peculier; Webster's Yorkshire Bitter; guest beer Ⓗ
Built in 1911 on the site of an 18th-century pub, until the 1930s the lounge was a tea room attracting country walkers. It has a fine black kitchen range and many old photos of Barnston. There is a traditional tiled bar with brasses and horse racing photos, and an adjacent snug with a penny slot machine. All rooms have welcoming real fires in winter. It offers home-cooked pub grub (12-2 daily) and a flowery courtyard as a resting point for the local CAMRA 13 Pubs Walk in summer.
Q P

BEBINGTON

Travellers Rest

169 Mount Road
12-11; 12-10.30 Sun
☎ (0151) 608 2988
Boddingtons Bitter; Cains Bitter; Flowers IPA; Greene King Abbot; Taylor Landlord; guest beers Ⓗ
Wirral CAMRA Pub of the Year 1998-99. Reputedly over 300 years old, this cosy pub is a hub of the local community and regularly supports charity events. Ales are served from a central bar area that feeds two other rooms (one no-smoking). The guest beers are usually from micro-breweries. Popular every day for its award-winning food (served lunchtime only, not Sun); there is a Monday evening quiz. Q

BIRKDALE (SOUTHPORT)

Up Steps

20 Upper Aughton Road
11.30-11; 12-10.30 Sun
☎ (01704) 569245
Coach House Coachman's Best Bitter, Gunpowder Strong Mild, seasonal beers; Theakston Mild, Best Bitter; guest beers Ⓗ
Traditional street-corner local, one of a dying breed in the town. Once three-times Grand National winner Red Rum's local pub, it was formerly a private home called Bankfield House. The only outlet for Coach House beers in Southport, it is a popular venue for all away teams in the local darts, dominoes and quiz leagues. Unfortunately not very accessible for disabled drinkers, but well worth the effort. Winner of several local CAMRA awards. Q P

BIRKENHEAD

Crown

128 Conway Street (by Warner Village cinema)
11-11; 11-10.30 Sun
☎ (0151) 647 0589 website:
www.icbirkenheadfest.co.uk
Cains Bitter; Greenalls Bitter; Tetley Mild; guest beers Ⓗ

Three-roomed listed building convenient for shops, market and buses. The fine old wooden fixtures in the bar incorporate a Higsons ornamental gold frieze. Food is served every day between noon and 6pm and orders may be phoned in advance to be ready when you arrive. Children are permitted until 7pm but not in the bar. Quiz night is Sunday, chess is played on Tuesday evening and Wednesday is acoustic music night. ❀◐⊟⇌(Conway Pk) ♣✔

Old Colonial

167 Bridge Street

12-11; 12-10.30 Sun

☎ (0151) 650 1110

Cains Mild, Bitter, FA; guest beers Ⓗ

Refurbished Cains pub adjacent to Birkenhead Tram Museum garage. Trams run from Woodside ferry and bus terminus on bank holidays and weekends and pass through the car park. A pool table and dartboard are provided. There is no juke box but a traditional jazz band play on a Thursday night. There is a compact side room with bar access. Set meals and specials are available (12-3 and 5-7 Mon-Sat). A small maritime museum with a German U-boat hulk is nearby.

❀◐◗⇌(Hamilton Sq/Conway Pk) ♣P✔

Stork Hotel ☆

41-42 Price Street

11.30-11; 12-10.30 Sun

☎ (0151) 647 7506

Beer range varies Ⓗ

Wirral Pub of the Year 2002, a superb example of extravagant but practical architecture, it rightly features in the CAMRA National Inventory of Pub Interiors. Built in 1840, it has many original interior fittings, including an ornate circular bar with leaded stained glass and lighting. This street-corner pub has a colourful ceramic exterior and wonderful mosaic floor and etched windows. The 'newsroom' with its original bell pushes, etched windows and door is a no-smoking area. A must for traditional pub lovers. Food is served daily (Mon-Fri 12-2 and 4.30-6.30). Children are welcome until 9pm.

❀◐◗⇌(Hamilton Sq/Conway Pk) ♣⅟

BOLD HEATH

Griffin

184 Warrington Road (A57 Clock Face Rd jct)

12-11; 12-10.30 Sun

☎ (0151) 424 5143

Beer range varies Ⓗ

Large, attractive pub with part-beamed ceilings. It was formerly a 19th-century coaching inn. The beer range comprises two cask ales on handpump plus a single rotating guest beer. Food is served all day, seven days a week and families are well catered for with both a family eating area, and a children's play area situated in the spacious garden to the rear. A recent extension has added a conservatory which offers pleasant views of the countryside. There is ample car parking. ❀◐◗♿P⅟

CROSBY ❄

Crow's Nest

63 Victoria Road

11.30-11; 12-10.30 Sun

☎ (0151) 924 6953

Cains Bitter; guest beer Ⓗ

Charming, small pub which is a Grade II listed building. A popular local with a cosy bar, tiny snug and comfortable lounge. The interior has several interesting features, including a tiled floor on entry and original etched windows. Friendly staff ensure a warm welcome for locals and visitors alike. A list of forthcoming beers is displayed; you are sure to want to return to this suburban gem. Q❀⊟⇌(Blundellsands/Crosby) P

Stamps Wine Bar/Bistro

4 Crown Buildings

10.30-11; 12-10.30 Sun

☎ (0151) 286 2662 website: www.stampsbistro.co.uk

Beer range varies Ⓗ

Small bistro/bar with a friendly atmosphere, building a reputation for good beer. This converted post office has bistro-style tables and a bar on the ground floor with a comfortable lounge upstairs. Three beers are on tap from local micro-breweries and further afield. A successful mini beer festival is held each year. Good food is available all day with an evening tapas menu, the Sunday roasts are particularly popular. Stamps has been nominated for a national music award in recognition of the wide variety and quality of the live performances it provides. You can even surf the CAMRA website while supping your ale.

◐◗⇌(Blundellsands/Crosby)

EGREMONT

Brighton

133 Brighton Street (opp. Wallasey Town Hall)

11.30-11; 12-10.30 Sun

☎ (0151) 638 1163

Cains Bitter; Marston's Pedigree Ⓗ

This impressive listed sandstone building is 120 years old and stands on the main route from Birkenhead to New Brighton. It offers two lounges and a public bar, all served from one main bar. There is a separate TV room. At the entrance to the middle lounge (from the main road) there are two attractive leaded coloured glass panels which are thought to be original. The pub boasts successful darts and pool teams, plus a Crown Green bowls team. ⊟●

FORMBY

Freshfield Hotel

Massams Lane

(1 mile from village centre, $1/2$ mile from station)

12-11; 12-10.30 Sun

☎ (01704) 874871 website: www.blemon.demon.co.uk

Boddingtons Bitter; Castle Eden Ale; Flowers IPA; Moorhouses Black Cat; Taylor Landlord; guest beers Ⓗ

Award-winning pub that consistently provides quality and variety. It always has 12 real ales available, including one dark

INDEPENDENT BREWERIES

Beecham's St. Helens
Cains Liverpool
Cambrinus Knowsley
Liverpool Liverpool
Wapping Liverpool

mild. Smaller brewers are favoured by the landlord of many years. A function room at the rear is used for local groups, including guitar club, and quizzes. The lounge is open-plan with a public bar at the side. Wooden floors and an inviting real fire add character. The pub is close to the National Trust area of Formby Point; this reserve leads to the beach. ⚠❀◐⇌(Freshfield) ♣P

GREASBY (WIRRAL)

Irby Mill

Mill Lane

⊙ 12-11; 12-10.30 Sun

☎ (0151) 604 0194

Boddingtons Bitter; Cains Bitter; Marston's Pedigree; Taylor Landlord; Theakston Best Bitter; Wells Bombardier; guest beers Ⓗ

Traditional sandstone country pub built in 1980 on the site of an old mill. It is popular with locals, cyclists and walkers. Two rooms are linked by a narrow bar. This warm and friendly pub is an oasis with 13 handpumps; six of these serve ever-changing guest ales. No music or fruit machines spoil the peace and the pub is filled with plenty of lively banter. The recipient of numerous CAMRA awards, it also gained Cask Marque Pub of the Year in 2001. Look for the two small Higson's windows. No food is served on Sunday evening. Q❀◐⊟P⊘

HESWALL

Johnny Pye

Pye Road (opp. bus station)

⊙ 11-11; 12-10.30 Sun

☎ (0151) 342 8215

Banks's Original, Bitter; Camerons Bitter Ⓗ

Named after a local 1920s entrepreneur who operated an omnibus company. A bustling, modern Banks's pub with a bright, open-plan interior and polished wood floor. It features a collection of pictures of historic Heswall. The raised lounge seating area is L-shaped with a similar separate area set aside for non-smokers. It has a large-screen TV for sports and can be lively during the more popular football matches. A pub quiz is held on Thursday evening. Beer is served in oversized lined glasses. No food is served on Sun.
❀◐♿♣P⚟▢

KINGS MOSS

Collier's Arms

37 Pimbo Road (off B5205, Rainford Road)

⊙ 12-11; 12-10.30 Sun

☎ (01744) 892894

Beer range varies Ⓗ

Traditional-style pub with a warm, friendly atmosphere. Good home-cooked food is served at lunchtimes and evenings and all day on Sun. The beer range includes up to three guest beers. The pub is located in the tiny hamlet of King's Moss, near Billinge. It was built in 1850 and has a stone-flagged floor and an attractive garden to the rear. There is a separate public bar which has an open fire. A row of former miners' cottages is situated opposite and during spells of bad winter weather the miners used to collect their wages from the pub; hence the name.
⚠❀◐⊟♿♣P⚟

LISCARD

Saddle

30 Withens Lane, Wallasey

⊙ 11-11; 12-10.30 Sun

☎ (0151) 639 2534

Flowers IPA; Greene King IPA; guest beer Ⓗ

Small, welcoming pub close to the local shopping area (Liscard) and even closer to the local police station! The licensee thinks that the pub was originally two cottages before it became a pub and could possibly be over 150 years old. The guest beers rotate once a week and are usually from micros. The new conservatory, built at the side of the pub, caters for the increasing number of diners the pub attracts. ❀◐♿♣P

Stanley's

83 Seaview Road, Wallasey (just outside main shopping area)

⊙ 11-11; 12-10.30 Sun

☎ (0151) 639 9736

Theakston Cool Cask; Younger IPA; guest beers Ⓗ

Celebrating its fifth birthday, this popular pub is one of Wallasey's best real ale outlets. The interior has bare brick walls and church pew seating but is comfortable nonetheless. It always has three guest beers on tap from various micro-breweries all over the UK, alongside Scottish Courage products. The food menu is an eye-opener! ❀◐♿P

LIVERPOOL: *ALLERTON*

Allerton Hall (Pub in the Park)

Springwood Avenue, Clarke Gardens

⊙ 11.30-11; 12-10.30 Sun

☎ (0151) 494 2664

Cains Bitter; Marston's Pedigree; guest beers Ⓗ

Large suburban pub set in the grounds of Clarke Gardens, next to Springwood Crematorium, it was sympathetically restored after being gutted by fire, and the interior decoration is in keeping with the elegant building. There are usually up to six real ales, four of which are guests, available from the central bar. Food is offered all day. A section is set aside for families, with an outdoor play area for children.
Q⛑❀◐♿⇌(Allerton) P⚟

Storrsdale

43-47 Storrsdale Road

⊙ 3 (12 Sat)-11; 12-10.30 Sun

☎ (0151) 724 3464

Taylor Landlord Ⓗ

Convivial two-roomed suburban local. It has a basic but comfortable bar with a well-used dartboard and a large cosy lounge. The original leaded windows are typical of the 1930s construction. It attracts a mix of locals and thirsty sportsmen from the nearby Heron-Eccles playing fields, drawn by the relaxed atmosphere and good beer. A well-attended quiz is held each Wednesday night and there is live music every Saturday evening. ⊟⇌(Mossley Hill) ♣

LIVERPOOL: *CHILDWALL*

Childwall Abbey

Score Lane (off Childwall Valley Road)

⊙ 11-11; 12-10.30 Sun

☎ (0151) 722 5293

Burtonwood Bitter, Top Hat; guest beers Ⓗ

Fine sandstone 18th-century inn, opposite

Childwall Church. The name is a misnomer as the church was never an abbey or priory. A country atmosphere prevails in Liverpool suburbia at this Grade I listed building. The guest beer is always keenly awaited and is served on Thursday. Evening meals finish at 8.15pm (Mon-Sat) and 6pm Sun. The pub also boasts seven en-suite guest bedrooms.

LIVERPOOL: *CITY CENTRE*

Baltic Fleet
33 Wapping
12 (11 Sat)-11; 12-10.30 Sun
(0151) 709 3116
Cains Mild, Bitter; Wapping Bitter, Cornhill Summer Ale, Baltic Extra; guest beers H
Close to the Albert Dock, this Grade II listed pub has an unusual 'flat-iron' shape that closely resembles a ship. The nautical theme extends into the well-decorated interior. The owners have recently acquired the brewing kit from the old Passageway Brewery and have launched the Wapping Brewery in order to produce the house beers. Two guest beers are also available. The pub serves freshly prepared, quality food (Tue-Sun); the Sunday roasts never disappoint. Local CAMRA Pub of the Year 2000.
(James St.)

Bear's Paw
62 Irvine Street
12-11; 12-10.30 Sun
(0151) 708 8749
Cains Mild, Dr Duncans IPA, Bitter, seasonal beers H
On the outer fringe of the city centre, the quality of the beers makes this pub well worth a visit. A single bar serves three separate rooms, each with its own character. Currently only Cains' products are available, but these are of such high quality that a growing band of regulars make this a very lively pub. No mention can be made of the pub without reference to the Williamson Tunnels to which it allegedly has an entrance.

Cambridge
51 Mulberry Street (near Catholic cathedral)
11.30-11; 12 (7 vacations)-11 Sat; 12-10.30 Sun
Burtonwood Bitter, Top Hat; guest beer H
Popular, busy, corner pub frequented by students, but with the atmosphere of a local. Bustling during term-time but is still friendly and cosy. A Burtonwood-managed house with a changing guest which can be the named monthly special. Lunchtime food is basic burger-type fare but try the speciality Sunday breakfast. A weekly quiz is held (Sun). Sports TV is popular here.
(Central)

Carnarvon Castle
5 Tarleton Street
11-11 (8 Mon & Tue); 12-6 Sun
(0151) 708 0516
Cains Mild, Bitter; guest beer H
Charming, intimate city-centre pub, the perfect oasis in the middle of the main shopping area. It has a narrow front bar area with a real fire and a snug rear lounge, so the pub can get quite crowded but the atmosphere is always warm and friendly. The walls of the pub are full of displays of bric-à-brac. There is a rotating guest beer.
Q (Lime St) (Central)

Crown
43 Lime Street
11-11; 12-10.30 Sun
(0151) 707 6027
Taylor Landlord; guest beers H
Built at the turn of the last century in Art Nouveau style, this impressive pub is situated within a few seconds' walk of Lime Street Station. With a small but excellently-kept range of beers, it caters for a wide range of patrons and provides good value food until evening, served by friendly and efficient staff. To the delight of customers, the original interior decoration has been retained in the two downstairs rooms and the upstairs function room. (Lime St) (Central)

Dispensary
87 Renshaw Street
11.30-11; 12-10.30 Sun
(0151) 709 2160
Cains Mild, Bitter, FA, seasonal beers; guest beers H
Traditional, Victorian corner pub which was an original Robert Cain pub. A wall-mounted display case near the 100-year-old Irish-style bar holds the many local CAMRA awards, together with the CAMRA/English Heritage Pub Refurbishment award, accumulated since the pub opened. A great pub to relax in and enjoy a pint while reading the supply of daily newspapers. This gem is a must for any real ale drinker visiting Liverpool.
(Lime St) (Central)

Doctor Duncan's
St John's House, St John's Lane
11.30-11; 12-10.30 Sun
(0151) 709 5100
Cains Mild, IPA, Bitter, FA, seasonal beers; guest beers H
Large city-centre pub, part of which is the renovated Pearl Assurance office. The pub has deservedly won many local CAMRA awards, together with regional Pub of the Year and Merseyside Tourism Pub of the Year. A central bar serves all the surrounding rooms, the pick of which is the stunning Victorian tiled room. Top quality food is served daily. Up to four guest beers supplement the Cains' range and a good selection of draught and bottled Belgian beers are available.
Q (Lime St)

Excelsior
121-123 Dale Street (5 minutes' walk from the Town Hall)
11-11; 7-10.30 Sun
(0151) 236 6486 website: www.excelsior.8m.net
Cains Bitter; guest beers H
Corner pub with a very friendly welcome and a small but excellently kept range of real ales. Situated at the edge of the city business area, it attracts a wide range of customers and is a favourite of the student population during term-time. Currently one set of pumps serves both areas which retain a quality of the traditional 'local'. Superb, low cost food is available until early evening and entertainment is provided most nights.
(Lime St) (Moorfields)

Globe
17 Cases Street (close to Central Station)
11-11; 12-10.30 Sun
(0151) 707 0067
Cains Mild, Bitter, FA; guest beer H
Small, two-roomed city-centre Victorian pub. The bar has an unusual sloping floor. The pub is popular with regulars and shoppers, being close to Central Station and next to Clayton Square shopping centre. The regular Cains' beers are supplemented by a changing guest. The Merseyside branch of CAMRA was formed in the pub in January, 1974, and the pub displays a plaque on the wall of the back room, presented by the branch to commemorate its 25th anniversary. ≠(Lime St) ⊖(Central)

Head of Steam
7 Lime Street
11-midnight (2am Fri & Sat); 12-midnight Sun
(0151) 707 9559 www.headofsteam.co.uk
Beer range varies H
Large, busy pub forming part of the Lime Street Station complex. Two of the five bars serve real ale, with the best selection being in the Grand Hall, where up to 16 real ales can be available, plus a real cider and selection of Belgian beers. There are regular themed beer festivals as well as comedy and music nights. Food is served all day, although the choice is more limited after 8pm. Q ≠(Lime St) ⊖

Lion Tavern ☆
67 Moorfields
11-11; 12-10.30 Sun
(0151) 236 1734
Lees Bitter; guest beers H
Victorian splendour lives on in this Grade II listed, traditional street-corner pub. An extravaganza of wood and tiles, the central bar serves both the public bar and the two comfortable rear lounges. Much of the original glazing survives and the amazing glass cupola in the back lounge should not be missed. This is the smallest of Liverpool's Victorian gems. Food is served daily. A rare outlet in Liverpool for the excellent Lees bitter. ⊖(Moorfields)

Ma Boyle's
Tower Buildings, Tower Gardens (off Water St)
11-11; 12-8 Sat; closed Sun
(0151) 236 1717
Hydes Bitter; guest beer H
Since 1870 Ma Boyle's has been a Liverpool institution, where many a business deal has been concluded over a pint and a plate of oysters. This splendid pub is well worth seeking out, not just for the beer, but for the great food served weekdays until 9pm and all day Saturday. If you tire of the beer, try a pint of prawns instead. A friendly welcome is guaranteed in either the upstairs or quieter downstairs bars. Jazz is played (Wed eve). Q ⊖(Moorfields/James St)

Peter Kavanagh's
2-6 Egerton Street
12-11; 12-10.30 Sun
(0151) 709 3443
Cains Bitter; Greene King Abbot; guest beers H
This excellent, back-street local is well worth seeking out. The original terraced structure dates back over 150 years. The stained glass windows are protected by wooden shutters. Period paintings adorn the walls of the two quiet snugs either side of the bar. The pub has expanded into the two adjoining properties. There are usually two guest beers, often from micro-breweries. Sunday breakfast is popular. There is Irish music Friday evenings and a Thursday quiz. Q

Philharmonic ☆
36 Hope Street
12-11; 12 (5 winter)-10.30 Sun
(0151) 707 2837
Cains Bitter; guest beers H
This architecturally stunning, Grade II listed pub, is situated near two university campuses. The front entrance is behind two Art Nouveau metal gates. Inside there is a large bar area, two smaller lounges (known as the Brahms and the Liszt) and a back room. The impressive features include bay windows, a two-storey oriel, stepped gables, turrets and a balustraded parapet. Another point of interest is the gents'; this spectacular pub is a must.

Poste House
23 Cumberland Street
11-11; 12-10.30 Sun
(0151) 236 4130
Cains Mild, Bitter H
Small, busy Victorian pub just off Dale Street. The pub was recently saved from demolition for redevelopment. A relaxed, friendly environment, the pub consists of two cosy rooms, one on either floor of the two-storey drinking area. Over the years the pub has been visited by many famous people, including Charles Dickens, James Maybrick (a Jack the Ripper suspect) and Adolf Hitler.
≠(Lime St) ⊖(Moorfields)

Railway Hotel
18 Tithebarn Street
11-11; 12.30-10.30 Sun
(0151) 236 7210
Cains Mild, Bitter; Marston's Pedigree; guest beers H
Large Victorian corner pub close to Moorfields Station. An attractive pub it still bears the black and gold Cains' livery and its original stained glass windows. A central bar serves various rooms, including two quiet snugs and a large lounge with big-screen satellite sports. A warm welcome and friendly service attracts both locals and the business community.
Q ≠(Lime St) ⊖(Moorfields)

Roscoe Head
24 Roscoe Street
11-11; 12-10.30 Sun
(0151) 709 4365
Greene King Old Speckled Hen; Jennings Bitter H
Present in this Guide since 1974 and run by the same family for 18 years, this back-street local has a friendly, cosy atmosphere. Unspoilt, the Roscoe still has a small bar leading into a front snug, a rear lounge/snug and a tiny front bar. A traditional locals' pub with a big welcome, the Roscoe is popular for its quiz night (Tue) and cribbage night (Wed). The home-cooked lunches can be ordered by phone.
≠(Lime St) ⊖(Central)

Ship & Mitre
133 Dale Street
11.30 (12.30 Sat)-11; 3.30-10.30 Sun
(0151) 236 0859
Beer range varies H
Friendly city-centre pub with gas lighting creating a warm, welcoming atmosphere. The main island bar serves the two drinking areas. A constantly changing range of real ales is supported by a large selection of foreign draught and bottled beers. A long-standing entry in the Guide, this pub has received numerous awards from the local CAMRA branch, including Pub of Excellence, and, most recently, Pub of the Year 2001. Popular quarterly beer festivals are held with beers on stillage as well as served from the bar. Lunchtime weekday food and early evening meals are served.
(Lime St) (Moorfields)

Swan Inn
86 Wood Street
11.30-11; 12-10.30 Sun
(0151) 709 5281
Cains Bitter; Marston's Pedigree; Phoenix Wobbly Bob; guest beers H
Lively, back-street, city-centre pub with a long history of serving real ales. It attracts a mixed and friendly clientele. The downstairs bar features a large stained glass window, wooden floors and a long exposed brick bar. Regular beers are supplemented by three ever-changing guest beers (over 100 different breweries a year). The pub features an extensive rock juke box and hosts live blues music on Sunday evenings. There is an upstairs bar with Sky TV. Thursday is quiz night.
(Lime St) (Central)

Vernon Arms
69 Dale Street
11.30 (12 Sat)-11; closed Sun
(0151) 236 4525
Coach House Gunpowder Strong Mild; guest beers H
Close to the business district, the Vernon serves up to six guest beers alongside a permanent mild, in a welcoming atmosphere. A single long bar services three drinking areas: a small snug, the main room and a back room that may be hired for private functions. The sloping floor may initially disorientate inebriated customers. Good value meals are available. Winner of local CAMRA Pub of Excellence awards in 2000 and 2001. (Lime St) (Moorfields)

White Star
4 Rainford Gardens
11.30-11; 12-10.30 Sun
(0151) 231 6861
Beer range varies H
Located in the famous Cavern Quarter, this pub is an oasis for real ale. A traditional Liverpool boozer with plenty of ale, banter and a warm welcome. The front bar has pictures of local boxing legends, coupled with nautical liners from the legendary White Star. The comfortable back lounge has a Beatles corner and a huge Bass mirror. The friendliness of the pub is typified by its twinning with pubs in both Norway and the Czech Republic. Three ever-changing guest beers are on offer.
(Lime St) (Moorfields/Central)

LIVERPOOL: *OLD SWAN*

Wetherspoon's
690 Queens Drive
11-11; 12-10.30 Sun
(0151) 220 2713
Beer range varies H
Very comfortable pub with a combination of drinking areas in what is essentially a single room. The clever design creates the impression of a multi-roomed pub on two levels. The designated no-smoking area is in the elevated area. The staff place great emphasis on service and value, and their enthusiasm adds to the genial atmosphere and the pub's reputation for its beer quality.

INN BRIEF

BOOTLE

Cat & Fiddle
St Martin's House, Stanley Road
11.30-11; 12-10.30 Sun
(0151) 922 9561
Cains Bitter; guest beers H
Modern bustling pub popular with local office workers lunchtimes and early eves, and locals at night.

CROSBY

Crosby
75 Liverpool Road
11-11; 12-10.30 Sun
(0151) 924 2574
Fuller's London Pride; Taylor Landlord H
Large one-roomed pub in Crosby village. Pleasant beer garden at rear and quiz night held on Wed.

LIVERPOOL: *ANFIELD*

Strawberry
Breckfield Road South
11-11; 12-10.30 Sun
Oakwell Barnsley Bitter, Old Tom H
Comfortable, spacious modern pub. An oasis of real ale in a predominantly keg area. Only Oakwell products are sold.

LIVERPOOL: *CITY CENTRE*

Augustus John
Peach Street
11.30-11; closed Sat & Sun
(0151) 794 5507
Cains Bitter; guest beer H
Modern pub in the heart of the university campus, so popular with students for loud music, pool and Wed karaoke night.

Brewery
21-23 Berry Street
12-2am; closed Sun
(0151) 709 5055
Beer range varies H
Liverpool Brewing Company's brewery tap. Popular with students for live music and large-screen TV. Brewery visible in pub window.

Cornmarket Hotel
Old Ropery
11.30 (7.30 Sat)-11; closed Sun
(0151) 236 2131
Beer range varies H
Large pub that attracts business community lunchtime and early eve, when good-quality food is available.

Everyman Bistro
5-9 Hope Street
12-midnight (1am Thu; 2am Fri & Sat); closed Sun
(0151) 708 9545
Beer range varies H
Bustling bistro close to university, particularly popular with students. Interesting food menu and late bar.

Flying Picket
24 Hardman Street
12 (7 Sat)-11; closed Sun
(0151) 709 3995
Cains Bitter; Coach House Coachman's Best Bitter, Gunpowder Strong Mild, Marston's Pedigree H
Small, comfortable bar which is part of the Trade Union Resource Centre. Excellent value Coach House mild at 99p a pint!

Pig & Whistle
12 Covent Garden
11.30-11; closed Sun
(0151) 236 4760
Cains Bitter; Taylor Landlord H
Comfortable split-level pub in business area. Upstairs bar open at lunchtime. Live music at weekends.

Good value food is served and regular beer festivals and other promotions are offered.
Q❀◑◗♿⚡●

LIVERPOOL: *TOXTETH*

Brewery Tap
35 Grafton Street (adjoining Cains Brewery)
⚙ 11-11; 12-10.30 Sun
☎ (0151) 709 2129
Cains Mild, Dr Duncans IPA, Bitter, FA, seasonal beers; guest beers Ⓗ
A deserved winner of the CAMRA English Heritage Pub Refurbishment award for 1995 for Cains' magnificent restoration of the run-down former Grapes. The tap is an original fixture of the Victorian Robert Cain Brewery. A very popular pub, especially as host to the brewery tours, with a broad mix of customers. In addition to the Cains' range, up to three guest beers are available – usually from micros. For entertainment there is an interesting collection of Merseyside breweriana, Sky Sports and cribbage.
❀◑●P

LIVERPOOL: *WAVERTREE*

Edinburgh
4 Sandown Lane
⚙ 12-11; 12-10.30 Sun
Cains Mild, Bitter, FA, seasonal beers; guest beers Ⓗ
A real gem just off the bustling Wavertree High Street, an area that until recently, offered a superb real ale crawl. A frequent Guide entry from its days as a Peter Walker tied house, it was rescued by Cains in the late 1990s from the fate of smoothflow conversion that has befallen most of the nearby pubs. The pub is tiny with a compact lounge and even smaller bar, but there is always a big welcome awaiting those who seek it out. ⊟⇌ (Wavertree Technology Pk)

Willowbank
329 Smithdown Road
⚙ 12-11; 12-10.30 Sun
☎ (0151) 733 5782
Beer range varies Ⓗ
Friendly pub with good atmosphere, which has been popular with locals and students for many years. A constantly changing range of up to 11 good quality real ales is enhanced by regular themed beer festivals. Bar food is available including several vegetarian options and a choice of very affordable specials on weekday evenings until 8pm. There is a large lounge and separate public bar and some fascinating photos of old Liverpool are displayed throughout. Enjoyable quiz held on Wed.
❀◑◗⊟♿♣P

LIVERPOOL: *WOOLTON* ❊

Gardeners Arms
101 Vale Road
⚙ 4 (12 Sat)-11; 12-10.30 Sun
☎ (0151) 428 1443
Cains Mild, Bitter Ⓗ
Well-presented local, which has a country pub feel. A large central bar serves the very comfortable lounge areas. The pub has a warm and friendly atmosphere, with the convivial buzz of conversation always in the background. It is a rare suburban outlet for the superb Cains mild. The pub is home to a number of sports teams and has its own golf society. Regular charity events are held and a popular quiz is run on Tuesday evening. ♿⚡

LYDIATE

Scotch Piper ☆
Southport Road
⚙ 12-3, 5.30-11; 12-11 Sat; 12-10.30 Sun
☎ (0151) 526 0503
Burtonwood Bitter, Top Hat Ⓗ

INN BRIEF

Wetherspoon's
1-2 Charlotte Row
11-11; 12-10.30 Sun
(0151) 709 4802
Beer range varies Ⓗ
Typical city-centre Wetherspoon's which can be very crowded. Good value food and regular beer festivals. Cask Marque accredited.

LIVERPOOL: *NETHERLEY*

Falcon
Caldway Drive
11-11; 12-10.30 Sun
(0151) 487 9994
Oakwell Barnsley Bitter, Old Tom Ⓗ
Two-roomed modern pub on edge of Netherley housing estate. Rare real ale gem in predominantly keg-only area.

LIVERPOOL: *WALTON*

Raven
72 Walton Vale
11-11; 12-10.30 Sun
(0151) 524 1255
Beer range varies Ⓗ
This large one-roomed suburban Wetherspoon's is bustling and friendly. Cask Marque accredited.

LIVERPOOL: *WOOLTON*

White Horse
2 Acrefield Road
12-11; 12-10.30 Sun
(0151) 428 1862
Cains Bitter; Marston's Pedigree Ⓗ
Cosy village atmosphere, weekday food and Sunday roasts served at lunchtime. Popular quiz on Wed.

NEW BRIGHTON

Commercial
19 Hope Street
11-11; 12-10.30 Sun
(0151) 639 2105
Cains Mild, Bitter; Ⓗ
Small, cosy corner pub, a single bar serves the two rooms. Comfortable lounge with waitress service.

PRESCOT

Old Mill
8 Mill Street
12-11; 12-10.30 Sun
(0151) 430 6826
Hydes Bitter, Jekyll's Gold, seasonal beers Ⓗ
Attractively refurbished pub just off A57, the main Liverpool to Prescot Road. Friendly welcome assured in Hydes' only tied house in Merseyside.

ST HELENS

Glasshouse
Market Street
11-11; 12-10.30 Sun
(01744) 762310
Beer range varies Ⓗ
Town-centre Wetherspoon's. Regular 'happy hours' on cask ales. Good value meals. Cask Marque accredited.

Red Lion Hotel
194 Robins Lane, Sutton
11-11; 11-10.30 Sun
(01744) 813351
Holt Mild, Bitter Ⓗ
Friendly local which has experienced a renaissance since being taken over by the Joseph Holt Group.

❊ symbol next to a main entry place name indicates there are Inn Brief entries as well.

Small, cosy three-roomed National Inventory pub on the county border, it claims to be the oldest pub in Lancashire with a date of 1320 over the front door. The atmosphere is relaxed and friendly, but mind your head on the low beams. The pub was lovingly and carefully restored by Burtonwood following a serious fire in 1985. The No. 300 bus from either Liverpool or Southport will drop you off outside the door. ⩕Q❀♣P

NEW BRIGHTON ❊

Clarence Hotel

89 Albion Street

⏲ 11-11; 12-10.30 Sun

☎ (0151) 639 3860

Cains Bitter; Caledonian Deuchars IPA; Fuller's London Pride; guest beers Ⓗ

A 10-minute walk from the resort of New Brighton, this pub has been recently refurbished and extended. It has a split-level lounge (children are restricted to the lower level) and a function room. Pub games, including darts, are played. A varied range of up to five real ales is available. Tasty, home-cooked food is served (Wed-Sun). There is a patio for summer drinking. ☕❀◐◑⊟♿⇌♣⊬

OXTON

Shrewsbury Arms

78 Claughton Firs (take B5151 off A552 then right at Queen's Hotel)

⏲ 11-11; 12-10.30 Sun

☎ (0151) 652 1775

Boddingtons Bitter; Cains Bitter, FA; Exmoor Stag; Tetley Bitter; Theakston Best Bitter Ⓗ

Local village pub, it is rather isolated from Birkenhead as the three major roads bypass Oxton. It is quite small with one long bar which can get very crowded at weekends. The staff are pleasant and service quick on even the busiest nights. Well-decorated with a split-level area, the pub's only drawback is the steps to both entrance and patio area, making it difficult for wheelchair access. ❀◐P⊬

PRESCOT ❊

Clock Face

54 Derby Street (A57)

⏲ 11-11; (11-3, 7-11 winter); 12-10.30 Sun

☎ (0151) 292 4121

Thwaites Bitter Ⓗ

Imposing former Georgian mansion, previously owned by Lord Derby. Attractively decorated and comfortably furnished, this multi-roomed pub is served by one long bar. A warm and friendly welcome will ensure that you stay for more than one pint in this rare outlet for Thwaites in Liverpool. The pub benefits from an open aspect which makes sitting at the benches and tables outside enjoyable in summer. Watch out for the two ghosts! ❀◐⇌♣P

Sun Inn

11 Derby Street (A57)

⏲ 11-11; 12-10.30 Sun

Beer range varies Ⓗ

Stone-clad, old-style local, conveniently situated on the main road into Prescot from Liverpool. It has several rooms including a comfortable lounge with a large real fire. There is also a separate public bar with dartboard. A central bar serves all areas. The pub has managed to retain a traditional Edwardian feel with several features including etched windows. One guest beer is constantly rotated and forthcoming guests are advertised with dates on a prominent chalkboard. ⩕Q⊟⇌♣

RAINHILL

Commercial

12 Station Road (off A57)

⏲ 11-11; 12-10.30 Sun

☎ (0151) 430 8473

Cains Bitter Ⓗ

Overlooking Rainhill Station, this section of the line is a significant location in railway history for the trials of 1829 in which Stephenson's Rocket emerged victorious. The event is depicted pictorially inside the pub alongside scenes of old Rainhill and Prescot. The pub is always busy. The racing channel is popular during the afternoon. Well worth breaking your journey here if travelling between Manchester Victoria and Liverpool. ⊟⇌(Rainhill) P

ST. HELENS ❊

Abbey Hotel

11 Hard Lane, Dentons Green

⏲ 12-11; 12-10.30 Sun

☎ (01744) 28609

Holt Mild, Bitter Ⓗ

Large former coaching inn, over 100 years old, located on the edge of the town approximately one mile from the town centre. The pub has one long bar which serves four separate rooms, each retaining its original name, and function rooms are available to hire. Traditional pub games are played and a quiz night is held on Thursday. A large-screen TV features popular sporting events. Q☕◐♣P⊬

Beecham's Bar & Brewery

Water Street (A58, near clock tower)

⏲ 12-11; 12-10.30 Sun

☎ (01744) 623420

Greene King Abbot; Thwaites Bitter; guest beers Ⓗ

This bar and brewery are situated in the former Beecham's Powders buildings, now part of the local college. This area of town has seen a great deal of recent investment. The bar is a small one-roomed affair, affording a good view of the attached brewhouse. This is used by the students to gain practical experience as part of the courses available on site. There is usually one of the Beecham's beers available on the bar. The availability of these dictates the number of guests stocked.

⇌(Central) ⊽

Sutton Oak

73 Bold Road (B5204)

⏲ 12-11; 12-10.30 Sun

☎ (01744) 813442 website: thesuttonoak.co.uk

Black Sheep Best Bitter; guest beers Ⓗ

Small, friendly community pub built in 1870, offering traditional pub games including dominoes, darts, pool and cribbage. It is located close to a nature trail through a wildlife conservation area. The

pub has its own angling club which meets regularly, and also holds karaoke and quiz nights. A large-screen TV features popular sporting events. It was previously known as the Boundary Vaults owing to its close proximity to the borough boundary and was renamed only three years ago.
❀⊟≋ (Jct) P ✔

SOUTHPORT

Barons Bar, Scarisbrick Hotel

239 Lord Street (opp. tourist information office)
☺ 11-11; 12-10.30 Sun
☎ (01704) 543000 website: www.scarisbrickhotel.com
Taylor Landlord; Tetley Bitter; guest beers Ⓗ
The Barons Bar is located within the historic Scarisbrick Hotel which occupies an imposing position in the centre of Lord Street. The bar is furnished, as its name suggests, in the style of a medieval baronial hall with weaponry and hatchments decorating the walls, a vaulted and arched bar, together with comfortable leather armchairs. The house beer is Flag and Turret, a session bitter. The Barons Bar can be reached through the hotel reception area or from an entrance off the pedestrianised thoroughfare next to the hotel. A beer festival is held annually during the first week in May, commencing at 6am on May Day.
⊭♿≋ (Chapel St) ✔

Berkeley Arms

19 Queens Road (near YMCA)
☺ 4-11; 12-11 Sun
☎ (01704) 500811 www.berkeley-hotel.co.uk
Adnams Bitter; Banks's Bitter; Camerons Strongarm; Fuller's London Pride; Marston's Pedigree; Moorhouses Black Cat Ⓗ
Popular with local residents, this pub is housed within an imposing Victorian semi-detached residence, formerly a seaside hotel. Bed and breakfast accommodation is available and delicious home-made pizzas are a speciality. The drinking area is divided into a small, cosy bar with a golfing theme and a lounge (part of which is no-smoking). There is a comfortable family room to the rear. Up to eight real ales are available with beers from Moorhouses of Burnley a feature. Some ales are always available at discounted prices during the pub's 'happy hour' (4-7 weekdays). ❀⊭◑⊟≋♣P⊬

Bold Arms

59-61 Botanic Road
☺ 11.30-11; 12-10.30 Sun
☎ (01704) 228192
Tetley Dark Mild, Bitter; guest beers Ⓗ
This is one of the oldest public houses in Southport, situated in the historic 18th-century Churchtown conservation area. A former coaching inn, it still has a stable block to the rear and retains a multi-roomed layout. There is a large, popular tap room and the other areas vary greatly in size. It is located next to Southport's Botanic Gardens.
⚔❀◑⊟♿P

Falstaff

68 King Street
☺ 11.30-11; 12-10.30 Sun
☎ (01704) 501116
Courage Directors; Theakston Mild, Best Bitter; Wells Bombardier; guest beers Ⓗ
Traditional town-centre pub with a reputation for good value food and beer. Popular with senior citizens, but also with people from all areas of town due to the quality and variety of the cask beers. A short walk from the railway station and the internationally famous Lord Street, it is also close to all of the town's major hotels. Awarded local CAMRA Pub of the Year for 2000/2001. Evening meals are served until 8pm. Seating is provided at the front of the pub for summer drinking.
Q❀◑♿≋♣

Guest House

16 Union Street
☺ 11-11; 12-10.30 Sun
☎ (01704) 537660
Cains Bitter; Moorhouses Black Cat; guest beers Ⓗ
This unspoilt Edwardian gem is situated just off the northern end of historic Lord Street. The double-fronted elegantly styled exterior is complemented by a traditional interior with wood-panelled walls and glazed panelling over the bar. The decoratively tiled entrance hall leads to two comfortably furnished rooms, free from piped music, one of which is reserved for non-smokers. A further equally inviting drinking area is situated to the left of the main bar, all have traditional fireplaces. A recent sympathetic refurbishment further enhances this pleasant drinking location.
Q❀≋ (Chapel St) ♣⊬

London

14 Windsor Road
☺ 12-11; 12-10.30 Sun
☎ (01704) 542885
Oakwell Barnsley Bitter Ⓗ
This pub is the only outlet in Southport for a beer brewed at the Oakwell Brewery in Barnsley, South Yorkshire. The London is a large and relaxing pub, attractively refurbished to a high standard. The main drinking area is spacious and comfortably furnished. The pub boasts a tap room as well as a separate family room. Darts, dominoes and pool are played and outside there is a bowling green and a beer garden. The pub is about 10 minutes' walk from Southport Station. Q❀❀⊟≋♣P

Wetherspoon's

93-97 Lord Street
☺ 11-11; 12-10.30 Sun
☎ (01704) 530217
Cains Mild; Courage Directors; Hop Back Summer Lightning; Shepherd Neame Spitfire; Theakston Best Bitter; guest beers Ⓗ
Typical Wetherspoon's pub in a transformed 19th-century former department store situated on the famous thoroughfare of Lord Street. Conveniently situated for the shops, the fair, the railway station and major bus routes, this is another very welcome addition to the real ale scene in Southport, and frequented by many young people en-route to the local night clubs. Good value meals and a no-smoking section result in a pub with something for everyone.
Q◑♿≋●⊬✔

WALLASEY

Farmer's Arms

225 Wallasey Village

11.30-11; 12-10.30 Sun

☎ (0151) 638 2110

Cains Mild, Bitter; Tetley Bitter; Theakston Best Bitter; guest beer Ⓗ

Originally two stone cottages, this characterful pub has three distinct drinking areas catering for all tastes. It has a traditional front bar with TV, side snug and a back lounge. A former local CAMRA Pub of the Month, Pub of the Year and regional winner, the licensee is one of only two remaining Higson's managers whose standards are exemplary. Weekday lunches include speciality Chinese stir-fries. A quiz night is held on Tuesday and the pub runs a golf society. The guest beer pump is in the bar.

(Grove Rd)

WATERLOO

La Barbacoa

49-51 Mersey View

12-3 (not Mon), 7-midnight; 12-midnight Sat; 12-11 Sun

☎ (0151) 924 0445

Beer range varies Ⓗ

Large, modern pub popular with all ages. A long central bar serves both the front lounges and the rear conservatory. The pub regularly gets busy on Tuesday and Saturday evenings for live music and for big-screen sports events. The upstairs restaurant offers an interesting menu comparable to most specialist restaurants. No real ale is served in the restaurant bar. Pub food is available in the main bar (no food Mon). Five constantly changing guest beers are on offer. (Blundellsands)

Volunteer Canteen

45 East Street

12-11; 12-10.30 Sun

☎ (0151) 928 6594

Cains Bitter; guest beer Ⓗ

Traditional Edwardian back-street pub with table service in the lounge. Beautifully maintained and furnished this classic pub is a firm favourite. The lounge has wood panelling, etched windows and a fascinating display of local photographs. Guest beers for the coming month are displayed in the two bars. Charity barbecues are held at weekends and Tuesday evenings. The Volunteer has a relaxed atmosphere where the sound of conversation and rustling newspapers take the place of a juke box – heaven. Q ♣

State of Gladness

Beer is a light, narcotic, alcoholic beverage, which charms us into a state of gladness and soft hilarity; it protects our hearts against stings of all kinds, awaiting us in this valley of misery; it diminishes the sensitiveness of our skin to the nettles and to all the bites of the numberless, detestable human insects that hum, hiss, and hop about us. The happy mortal who has selected beers as his preferred stimulant imbeds greater griefs and joys in soft pillows; surely thus being wrapped up he will be able to travel through this stormy life with less danger. Yes, I find such perfection of forms, such a softness and ductility of the tissue in the pale juice of barley, that I, to express its physiology with a few words, might say: 'It is to us in our lifetime like a wrapper which enables our fragile nature unendangered to reach the safe port'.

Paolo Montegazza MD, circa 1850.

NORFOLK

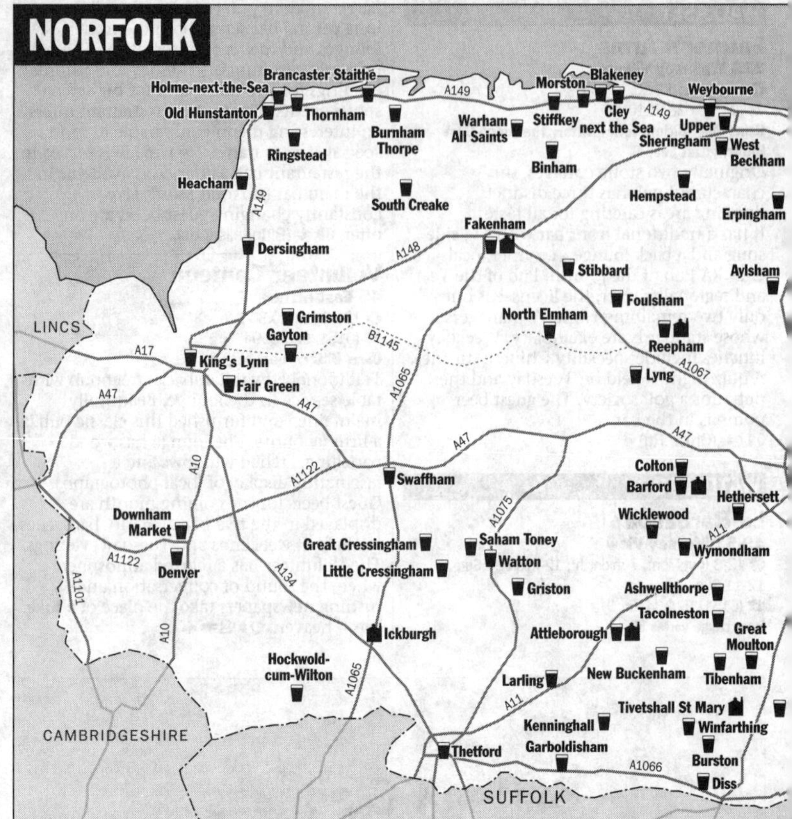

ASHWELLTHORPE

White Horse

49-55 The Street

⌚ 12-2.30 (not Mon & Tue), 5.30-11; 12-3.30, 7-10.30 Sun

☎ (01508) 489721

Adnams Bitter; Fuller's London Pride; guest beers Ⓗ

Village-centre free house featuring original beams. It has a small, reduced inglenook with an armorial fireback and a woodburner in the separate dining area. Brasses and brewery/pub artefacts enhance the friendly atmosphere. The pub holds regular charity events, midsummer balls and theme eves. There is an attractive, large beer garden at the rear and tables at the front. The woman trying to enter the pub through a bricked-up door is Maude, the resident ghost. Lunch hours are occasionally extended (check in advance); no food Sun eve. ⛰❀◐◑♣P

ATTLEBOROUGH

Bear

Exchange Street (town centre one-way system)

⌚ 11-2, 5.30-11; 11-11 Fri & Sat; 12-3, 7-10.30 Sun

☎ (01953) 454421

Fuller's London Pride; guest beers Ⓗ

Recently refurbished free house that has quickly attained a reputation for quality and service. Although the bar area is very small there is ample space in the pub: two main bars, a no-smoking, peaceful snug and a large restaurant leading to a covered patio. All the food is home cooked and excellent value for money. The house beer is brewed by Wolf and there are two other ever-changing guest beers. It is well patronised by drinkers and diners. Live music is a regular feature. Q❀◐◑⊟♿⇌

BARFORD

Cock Inn

Watton Road (B1108)

⌚ 12-2.30, 6-11; closed Mon; 12-3, 7-10.30 Sun

☎ (01603) 757646

Blue Moon Easy Life, Sea of Tranquility, Hingham High; Milk of Amnesia; guest beers Ⓗ

Home to the Blue Moon Brewery, which is clearly visible at the rear of the building. Formerly a coaching inn, it still has rings where the drovers' cattle were tethered. There are two bars, one with a wooden floor and real fire, the other is carpeted. The attractive restaurant together with the small intimate eating areas leave the bar free for drinkers. There is an extensive fish menu and the pub has gained a good reputation locally for its quality food. The bowling green has been restored.

⛰❀◐◑♣P

BINHAM

Chequers

Front Street

⌚ 11.30-3, 5.30-11; 12-3, 7-10.30 Sun

☎ (01328) 830297

Adnams Bitter; Greene King IPA, Abbot; Woodforde's Wherry Ⓗ

Imposing 17th-century inn owned by the village charity. One end of the long, narrow bar area is no-smoking, the other end has the original bar, with excellent fireplace and beams. A welcoming, friendly pub where conversation is almost obligatory, it serves good value snacks and full meals. The village is well worth walking round, and has good local shops. Binham Priory remains (English Heritage) are free to visit, and the parish church is particularly interesting. ♨⛟◐◑♣●P⊭

BLAKENEY

King's Arms

Westgate Street (just W of Blakeney Quay)

✪ 11-11, 12-10 Sun

☎ (01263) 740341

Adnams Bitter; Ⓖ **Greene King Old Speckled Hen; Marston's Pedigree; Webster's Yorkshire Bitter;** Ⓗ **Woodforde's Wherry** Ⓖ

This attractive, white-painted flint inn, a Grade II listed building, is near the village centre. The spacious interior has six rooms (three are no-smoking). Five cask beers are served, and food is available all day. Blakeney, a coastal resort, is very popular with tourists and a haven for boaters, ramblers and birdwatchers. The pub car park is small but other parking space can be found nearby. Accommodation includes en-suite guest rooms and self-contained flatlets. A daily bus service along the North Norfolk coast road between Sheringham and King's Lynn passes through the village. ♨Q☺⛟◐◑⊟♿P⊭

BRANCASTER STAITHE ❄

Jolly Sailors

Main Road (A149)

✪ 11-11 (11-3, 6-11 winter Mon-Thu); 12-10.30 Sun

☎ (01485) 210314 website: www.the-jolly-sailors.co.uk

Iceni Fine Soft Day; Woodforde's Wherry; guest beers (summer) Ⓗ

Busy, authentic village local, popular with visitors to the coast and birdwatchers. Ample room for drinkers in this spacious pub and the restaurant specialises in seafood, including Brancaster mussels. The large, sheltered garden has a well-equipped children's play area. Guest beers from local micros are served in summer and a beer festival, featuring local ales, is held each April. This marks the beginning of the high season on the Norfolk coast; the Jolly Sailors is the perfect place for the real ale drinker. ♨Q❀◐◑♿♣P

BROOKE

White Lion

49 The Street (off B1332, opp. the mere)

OS289992

✪ 12-3, 5.30-11; 12-11 Sat; 12-10.30 Sun

☎ (01508) 550443

Adnams Bitter; Tindall Best Bitter; guest beers Ⓗ

Charming thatched pub, at least 200 years old, with part clay-tiled floor and a very low ceiling in the long, narrow bar. Warmed by an open fire, this friendly local enjoys a peaceful, rural setting in a quiet, unspoilt village. There is a small dining room (no eve meals are served Sun or Tue). Enjoy a drink overlooking the mere in one of the two beer gardens. This pub is popular with locals and walkers. ♨❀◐◑♣P

BURNHAM THORPE

Lord Nelson

Walsingham Road

✪ 11-3, 6-11; 12-3.30, 7-10.30 Sun

☎ (01328) 738241 website: www.nelsonslocal.com

Greene King IPA, Abbot; Woodforde's Wherry, Nelson's Revenge Ⓖ

Historic village pub with connections to Nelson and a collection of Nelson memorabilia. The front bar, where drinks are served at your table, is almost unchanged; no food is served in here. The rest of the building has been sensitively remodelled to provide extensive eating

INDEPENDENT BREWERIES

Blanchfields Fakenham
Blue Moon Barford
Buffy's Tivetshall St. Mary
Chalk Hill Norwich
Humpty Dumpty Reedham
Iceni Ickburgh
Reepham Reepham
Tindall Seething
Winter's Norwich
Wolf Attleborough
Woodforde's Woodbastwick

areas. This is the only place in England where you can buy Nelson's Blood, made to a secret recipe but based on rum and cloves. There is a large children's play area with a wide range of equipment. ♨Q✿◑♿♣P

BURSTON

Crown Inn

Crown Green (side road 2 miles W of A140)
⏲ 12-2, 6-11; 12-6 Sun
☎ (01379) 741257
Adnams Bitter; guest beers Ⓖ
Built in 1580, this fine old inn is situated in the middle of the village, close to the famous Strike School, now a museum, which in the early part of last century was the centre of the longest strike in TUC history. The pub interior consists of three rooms: a bar with pool table (the only room where smoking is allowed), a comfortable lounge with a wonderful original brick fireplace, and a dining room. The beer range includes an ever-changing range of guest beers, many of which are supplied by local brewers, especially Old Chimneys. Outside is a bowling green complete with sets of bowls. Food served all day Sunday. Bus services run weekdays between Diss and Norwich through Burston village.
♨Q✿◑⊟▲♣P⚟

CANTLEY

Cock Tavern

Manor Road
⏲ 11-3.30, 6-11; 12-5, 7-10.30 Sun
☎ (01493) 700895
Adnams Bitter; guest beers Ⓗ
On the outskirts of the village, this pub is about a mile from Cantley Station. Its origins can be traced back to the late 1800s: note the beams, exposed brickwork and intriguing old photos on display. One bar serves several drinking areas; Addlestones cider is available and the beer range is always interesting with many ales coming from local and smaller brewers. There is a separate no-smoking restaurant.
♨Q♉✿◑▲♣●P⚟

CHEDGRAVE

White Horse

5 Norwich Road
⏲ 11-11; 12-10.30 Sun
☎ (01508) 520250
Adnams Bitter; Flowers Original; Tetley Bitter Ⓗ
The building dates back to the 1700s and has previously been a shop and a post office before becoming a pub. The single bar serves several drinking areas; the bar and snug have wood and tiled floors while the carpeted lounge has a small dining space. Original features have been retained such as an ornate Victorian fireplace with brown glazed tiles. A separate dining room doubles as a function room. The locals are friendly and knowledgeable about the history of the pub. Real cider is sometimes stocked.
♨✿◑♣●

CLEY NEXT THE SEA

Three Swallows

Newgate Green (1/2 mile S of main coast road)
⏲ 11-11; 12-10.30 Sun
☎ (01263) 740526
Adnams Bitter; Greene King IPA; guest beer (summer) Ⓗ
With the parish church behind it and the village green in front, this old pub certainly looks the part. A very cosy interior consists of three bars, many interesting old photographs of local scenes and a roaring log fire. Children are welcome in the no-smoking lounge and the dining room. Food is available lunch and eves and all day at weekends. On warm summer days one can sit outside and look across to the river, once the site of a bustling port. Daily bus services pass through the village centre along the North Norfolk coast road between Sheringham and King's Lynn.
♨Q♉✿⇆◑⊟♣⚟

COLTON

Ugly Bug Inn

High House Farm Lane
⏲ 12-3, 5.30-11; 12-3, 5.30-10.30 Sun
☎ (01603) 880794
Greene King Abbot; Ⓖ **Woodforde's Wherry; guest beers** Ⓗ
This barn conversion has an attractive brick and beamed interior. The pub offers several drinking areas, while a separate restaurant and pleasant conservatory complete the picture. Families are welcome and the extensive rear gardens enhance the relaxed

INN BRIEF

AYLSHAM

Black Boys
Market Place
11-11; 12-2.30, 7-10.30 Sun
(01263) 732122
Adnams Bitter; Draught Bass; guest beer (summer) Ⓗ
Pleasant 17th-century coaching inn where children are welcome. Food is served all day in summer.

BRANCASTER STAITHE

White Horse
Main Road
11-11; 12-10.30 Sun
(01485) 210262
Adnams Bitter; Greene King IPA; guest beer (summer) Ⓗ
Comfortable pub with superb sea views to Scolt Head island. Outdoor drinking areas and a conservatory add to the interest.

DOWNHAM MARKET

Cock
43 Lynn Road
12-2.30, 7-11; 12-2, 7-10.30 Sun
(01366) 384175
Adnams Bitter; Brakspear Bitter; guest beer Ⓗ
This local has a children's certificate and a Healthy Eating award. A spring bank holiday beer festival is held in a marquee.

FAKENHAM

Star
44 Oak Street
12-2.30 (3 Wed), 7-11; 11-2.30, 7-11 Sat; 12-3, 8-10.30 Sun
(01328) 862895
Tolly Cobbold Original; guest beer Ⓗ
Built in the 16th century, this welcoming pub offers a pool table in a separate room, and a large, secure garden.

GREAT YARMOUTH

Red Herring
24 Havelock Road
12-2.30, 6.30-11; 12-11 Sat; 12-10.30 Sun
(01493) 853384
Beer range varies Ⓗ
Corner pub serving good range of beers. Newspapers and a secondhand bookstall make this a relaxing local.

HAPPISBURGH

Hill House
Happisburgh Road
11-11; 12-10.30 Sun
(01692) 650004
Adnams Bitter; Shepherd Neame Spitfire; guest beers Ⓗ
16th-century village pub with exposed brickwork and beams. It has a restaurant.

atmosphere. Good food is available with children's portions (no meals served on Sun). Q ❀ ⇆ ◑ ♿ ♣ P ⚡

CROMER

Red Lion Hotel

Brooke Street

11-11; 12-10.30 Sun

☎ (01263) 514964

Adnams Bitter; Draught Bass; Fuller's London Pride; Greene King Abbot; guest beer Ⓗ

Victorian free house hotel offering commanding views over the promenade and sea. Enjoy a drink in the Edwardian public bar where the rich mahogany fittings complement the flint and brick interior. Cromer is a pleasant seaside town and within easy reach of attractions such as Felbrigg Hall (a National Trust property).

⇆ ◑ Å ⇌ P

DENVER

Bell

2 Ely Road (opp. church)

12-2.30 (not Mon), 6 (5 Fri)-11; 12-11 Sat; 12-10.30 Sun

☎ (01366) 382173

Greene King IPA; guest beers Ⓗ

Locals' pub with two guest pumps offering a variety of beers. The front bar has a TV for sport coverage. There is a separate pool room and restaurant, although food is also served in the bar. A small verandah overlooks a large beer garden with a children's activity centre. Close by is Denver Windmill (with its fresh baked bread) and the Denver Sluice Boating Complex.

ᗑ ❀ ◑ Å ♣ P

DERSINGHAM

Feathers Hotel

Manor Road

11-2.30, 4.30-11; 12-10.30 Sun

☎ (01485) 540207

Adnams Bitter; Draught Bass; guest beer Ⓗ

Close to the Sandringham estate, this three-bar hotel offers something for everyone. Two of the bars are wood-panelled and are in the main building with the restaurant. These areas are ideal for a peaceful drink or meal. There is a separate bar in the old stables for a lively atmosphere; it suits younger customers and hosts regular music events. In summer, the large garden, complete with toys, is popular with families. ᗑ Q ❀ ⇆ ◑ P

DISS

Cock Inn

63 Lower Denmark Street (just S of town centre)

12-3; 5-11; 11-11 Fri & Sat; 12-10.30 Sun

☎ (01379) 643633

Adnams Bitter; Black Sheep Best Bitter; Greene King Abbot Ⓗ

Fine town pub, opposite Fair Green, it offers three excellent cask ales. The interior is uncluttered and well-furnished with large comfortable chairs, a tiled floor, genuine beams and many paintings. Occasional live music is performed at weekends (look for blackboard next to the bar for programme). Diss is well served by public transport; on the main intercity railway line between Norwich and Liverpool Street (London) and numerous local bus services pass through the town linking most of the nearby towns and villages.

ᗑ P

DOWNHAM MARKET ❄

Live & Let Live

22 London Road

12-2 (not winter Mon-Thu), 7-11; 12-10.30 Sun

☎ (01366) 383933

Greene King IPA; guest beers Ⓗ

Busy town pub serving three constantly varying guest beers from independent breweries. The split-level bar has a quieter area where dominoes and cribbage are played. The lower bar has a pool table, a dartboard and a large-screen TV (for football). The pub has its own Sunday League football team. Live music is performed most weekends in the lower bar. Parking is available in Tesco's car park, access via the back gate into the garden.

❀ ⇆ ⇌ ♣

EARSHAM

Queen's Head

Station Road

12-3, 6-11; 12-3, 7-10.30 Sun

☎ (01986) 892623

Beer range varies Ⓗ

Popular local dating from 1684. The bar area has timber posts, beams and a clay-tiled floor with a central fireplace separating it from the games room. Three handpumps are in constant use; the beers are from all over Britain, and a dark ale is often available. The newly-extended restaurant has been pleasantly refurbished (no food is served on Sun eve). Close links exist with the local community and the pub doubles as the village post office. Planning permission has been given to start a brewery. The pub may stay open during weekend afternoons.

ᗑ ❀ ◑ Å ♣ P

ERPINGHAM

Spread Eagle

Eagle Road

11-3, 6.30-11; 12-3, 7-10.30 Sun

☎ (01263) 761591

Adnams Bitter, Broadside; Greene King Old Speckled Hen; Woodforde's Wherry, Nelson's Revenge, Norfolk Nog Ⓗ

Pleasant 16th-century inn situated in the heart of this small village. The barn in the car park was the second home of Woodforde's Brewery. Well-furnished, this long, open-plan pub is split into distinct areas: a traditional games room, bar/lounge and a no-smoking dining section. A wood-burning stove adds to the homely atmosphere of this family-run inn. Excellent home cooking is offered along with a choice of six cask ales. Live music is played occasionally at weekends. Large garden for summer, children and pets are welcome. Daily buses pass through the village to and from Aylsham. Several local campsites make it a good base for touring. Blickling Hall (NT), is close by.

ᗑ ❀ ◑ Å ♣ P

FAIR GREEN

Gate Inn

North off A47

12-2.30, 7-11; 12-3, 7-10.30 Sun

(01553) 840518

Greene King IPA; guest beer Ⓗ

Just east of King's Lynn, and slightly north of the A47, the Gate is a village local which offers a small dining room, comfortable bar and a games room with pool table. There is a garden for summer and a roaring fire for winter eves. The food is good value and the fresh fish is especially popular on Friday and Saturday (no meals Mon eve).

FOULSHAM

Queen's Head

2 High Street

11-3, 7-11; 12-3, 7-10.30 Sun

(01362) 683339

Adnams Bitter; Woodforde's Wherry; guest beer (summer) Ⓗ

Friendly, 17th-century free house in a central village location. The low-beamed main bar area has a wooden fronted bar and two fireplaces. The small no-smoking snug with woodburner and no-smoking dining section are cosy and gently lit with a relaxing, homely atmosphere. A varied menu uses local produce and includes vegetarian dishes. Walkers and cyclists are welcome, the pub is on the National Cycle Network Route 1. Camping facilities are available in the large garden. Afternoon hours may be extended.

GARBOLDISHAM

Fox Inn

The Street

11.30-2.30, 5-11; 11.30-11 Sat; 12-10.30 Sun

(01953) 688151

Adnams Bitter; Greene King IPA (summer); **Shepherd Neame Spitfire; guest beers** Ⓗ

Splendid 17th-century village pub, the main bar area is dominated by a huge inglenook. There is an abundance of wood including beams and an array of pine tables and pews. All the food is freshly cooked to order, and uses local produce where possible (no meals Sun eve). Dogs and well-behaved children are welcome. There is plenty of natural ventilation in the pub so it is not too smoky. Unusually, one of the pub ghosts is a black labrador.

GAYTON

Crown

Lynn Road

11.30-2.30 (3 Sat), 6 (5.30 Fri)-11; 12-3, 7-10.30 Sun

(01553) 636252

Greene King XX Mild, IPA, Abbot; Old Speckled Hen; guest beers Ⓗ

Classic pub, at the heart of village life, that seems to improve every year. The two bars are often busy, but there is also a family room, a garden and a restaurant. There are regular events, such as music and quiz nights. The food is distinctive and interesting, and the size of the portions would make it difficult to leave still hungry. Greene King beer does not come much better than this, but if that is not to your taste there are now regular guest beers.

GELDESTON

Wherry

7 The Street (off A143)

12-3, 7-11; 11.30-11 Sat; 12-10.30 Sun

(01508) 518371

Adnams Bitter, Broadside, seasonal beers Ⓗ

Cosy, brick-built, two-bar local with a friendly atmosphere. The classic public bar boasts a clay-tiled floor, with the original timbers still visible, and parts of the building date back to the early 17th century. Old pictures adorn the walls, many depicting the wherry from the nearby river from which the pub derives its name. There is a larger main bar at the rear, and both bars have open fires. The pub serves excellent home-cooked fresh food at reasonable prices. Families are welcome; there is a garden, patio and courtyard for summer drinking.

GORLESTON-ON-SEA

Dock Tavern

Dock Tavern Lane

12-11; 12-10.30 Sun

(01493) 442255

Adnams Broadside; Elgood's Black Dog Mild; Fuller's London Pride; Greene King IPA; guest beers Ⓗ

One of very few pubs to have a road named after it, this single-bar pub is close to the River Yare and the docks. An upside-down rowing boat over the bar is an unusual feature. The pub has been subject to flooding, note the flood levels on the wall by the door. Up to four guest beers are available. It is close to the main High Street which is served by many buses.

Lord Nelson

33 Trafalgar Road West

11-11; 12-10.30 Sun

(01493) 301084

Adnams Bitter, Broadside; Woodforde's Wherry; guest beers Ⓗ

Two-bar pub with extensive choice of six or seven real ales, some on gravity, quite a change from its former Pubmaster days. One bar features a collection of over 4,000 cigarette lighters and a history of Nelson and Trafalgar, the second leads to a function room with a splendid mirror collection. A replica cannon stands in the outside drinking area. The new entrance porch houses a model of HMS Victory. The house beer is brewed by Elgood's and well worth a try. Pizzas, to eat in the pub or take away, are served 7-9.

New Entertainer

80 Pier Plain

12-11; 12-10.30 Sun

(01493) 441643

Greene King IPA; guest beers Ⓗ

Built in the late 1800s as the Suffolk Hotel, this pub is completely surrounded by highway, without any pavement. It has an unusual rounded end with an original Lacons window. The open-plan interior offers a carpeted lounge and a wooden-floored bar area. Photographs of Gorleston at the turn of the century adorn the walls. A selection of bottled Belgian beers and six guest ales are stocked. It has a pool team and hosts regular quiz eves. ♣

GREAT CRESSINGHAM

Olde Windmill Inn

Water End (off A1065, between Watton and Swaffham)
⏲ 11.30-3, 6-11; 12-3.30, 6.30-10.30 Sun
☎ (01760) 756232
Adnams Bitter, Broadside; Greene King IPA; guest beers Ⓗ
Quality free house under same family ownership for the last 47 years. This spacious pub offers distinct drinking, eating and socialising areas including a conservatory. The beer range includes two regular guest ales plus the house ale Windy Miller. The main pub dates from 1650 but many areas have been sympathetically extended over the years. Live music is performed (Tue and Thu eves), but does not permeate through the whole pub. There is a large child-friendly garden with sandpit and play area. Aunt Sally can be played by arrangement. ♨Q⛾❀◐◑Λ♣P

GREAT MOULTON

Fox & Hounds

Frith Way (approx 2 miles from A140)
⏲ 11-2.30 (not Tue), 7-11; closed Mon; 12-2.30, 7-10.30 Sun
☎ (01379) 677506
Adnams Bitter; guest beers Ⓗ
This quaint village free house has been called the Fox & Hounds since 1789. The cosy, low-beamed bar has comfy settees and chairs by a large inglenook. The curtains depict hunting scenes, and an interesting mix of old pictures and plates decorates the walls. The pub is popular for food, and there is a separate restaurant area with a varied menu. Wednesday is curry night. The garden (dogs not allowed) has a large pond and children's play area with Shetland ponies. ♨❀◐◑P⊟

GREAT YARMOUTH ❊

St John's Head

58 North Quay
⏲ 11-11; 12-10.30 Sun
☎ (01493) 843443
Elgood's Cambridge; guest beers Ⓗ
Single bar, a modern-style drinking pub between the town centre and the river. Nearby see the ships moored on the quay. Trace the 'rows' or alleys which were unique to Yarmouth. There are tables set out at the front of the pub for summer drinking. The local camping facilities include caravans (static and touring). ❀Λ⇌(Vauxhall) ♣●P

Talbot

4 Howard Street North
⏲ 11-11; 12-6 Sun
☎ (01493) 843175
Greene King Abbot; guest beers Ⓗ
This mid-Victorian bar was originally called the City of London Tavern and was the scene of a gruesome murder in 1865 when the area was frequented by sailors. Nowadays it is a more cheerful, basic, back-street boozer. The single room has a wooden floor and wood panelling. The juke box is excellent with many classic hits. Regular beer festivals are hosted. Λ⇌♣⊘

GRIMSTON

Bell

1 Gatton Road
⏲ 11 (5 Mon)-11; 12-10.30 Sun
☎ (01485) 601156
Greene King IPA; Ⓗ **guest beers** Ⓖ
There have been great changes at this village local over the past couple of years. A complete refurbishment has given the lounge a café or tearoom feel, while retaining the public bar. Accommodation is offered in three well-appointed en-suite bedrooms. There have also been improvements made to the cellar to allow beers to be dispensed by gravity, except for the IPA, which the locals prefer on handpump. ♨❀⇌◐◑⊟P

GRISTON

Waggon & Horses

Caston Road (3/4 mile from A1075)
⏲ 11-3, 6.30-11; 12-3, 7-10.30 Sun
☎ (01953) 883847
Greene King IPA, Abbot; guest beers Ⓗ
Splendid 18th-century rural pub with two bars separated by an inglenook. This friendly local has an extensive traditional menu plus daily specials. No booking needed, just turn up and enjoy. There is no juke box or fruit machine, just a pool table in a separate room. Cribbage and dominoes are played. Dogs and gumboots are welcome. There are usually four real ales available and an excellent selection of malts. Q⛾❀◐◑♣P⚟

HARLESTON

Duke William

28 Redenhall Road
⏲ 11-11; 12-10.30 Sun
☎ (01379) 853183
Adnams Bitter; Courage Directors; Woodforde's Wherry; guest beer Ⓗ
An easy-going, no-frills atmosphere characterises this popular town local. The 16th-century, Grade II listed building bears a heraldic sign with the motto 'insolens negate est'. There is also an old Lacons wall plaque. The landlady concentrates on serving good quality real ale, so no food is provided other than filled rolls. Note the collection of jugs in the public bar. There is a large, pleasant garden. ❀⊟♣

HEACHAM

Fox & Hounds

22 Station Road (turn left into Heacham at Norfolk Lavender – 1/2 mile)
⏲ 12-11; 12-10.30 Sun
☎ (01485) 570345
Draught Bass; Iceni Fine Soft Day; guest beers Ⓗ
Thriving, friendly local, a real ale haven for the many visitors to the coast. The pub boasts five handpumps and specialises in beers from micro-breweries. The landlord plans to open his own brewery in summer 2002. A range of real ciders is available from Saxon and Iceni. Good food is served every day. A popular beer festival is hosted annually (mid-July). ❀◐◑Λ●P

HEDENHAM

Mermaid

Norwich Road (B1332)
⏲ 12-3, 7 (5 Fri)-11; 12-4, 7-10.30 Sun
☎ (01508) 482480
Greene King IPA; Tindall Best Bitter; guest beer Ⓗ
300-year-old former coaching inn serving a small rural village, it stands beside the main road with a regular bus service. The pub is a large, timber-framed building, and the oak beams, together with brick floors and open fires, add to its charm. The once bright yellow paint on the external walls has toned down to give a pleasing appearance in keeping with the locality. Children are welcome in the pub and there is a play area. Good food is served with a separate restaurant to meet demand. ♨❀◑◗▲♣P

HEMPSTEAD

Hare & Hounds

Baconsthorpe Road (2 miles SE of Holt)
⏲ 11-3.30, 6.30 (5.30 summer)-11; 12-10.30 Sun
☎ (01263) 712329
Adnams Bitter; Woodforde's Wherry; guest beer Ⓗ
Between Hempstead and Baconsthorpe, north of the main village, this pub reopened in 2001, after North Norfolk Council refused permission to convert it to a house. Three cask ales are served in the small bar, with another adjacent room. It has a well-appointed (no-smoking) dining area with an extensive menu serving reasonably-priced food with generous portions. There is a large children's play area in the gardens. Infrequent bus services to Holt and Sheringham pass through Hempstead and Baconsthorpe villages, and the area has an extensive footpath network. ♨⇌◑◗▲

HETHERSETT

King's Head

36 Old Norwich Road
⏲ 11-2.30, 5.30-11; 12-3, 7-10.30 Sun
☎ (01603) 810206
Adnams Bitter; Greene King IPA, Abbot; Theakston Old Peculier, seasonal beers Ⓗ
This cosy pub on the outskirts of the village is a welcome sight from what was once the main arterial route connecting Norwich to London. The lounge bar, adjoining dining area and separate snug have a rustic charm enhanced by low ceilings, beams and large inglenooks, with warming fires on cold days. Quality food is available with a daily specials board. You may catch a glimpse of a fire engine emerging from the adjoining fire station. ♨Q❀◑◗P

HOCKWOLD-CUM-WILTON

Red Lion

114 Main Street
⏲ 11.30-2.30, 6-11; 11-11 Sat; 12-10.30 Sun
☎ (01842) 828875
Adnams Bitter; Greene King IPA; guest beer Ⓗ
Lively village local opposite a small green and a war memorial. It has been extended to include a no-smoking restaurant that has an excellent reputation. Try the carvery night (Wed), curry night (Mon), and steak night (Tue) – it is advisable to book. The pub holds a small beer festival in conjunction with the annual famous Hockwold Raft Race over the August bank holiday weekend. The middle bar counter has three fireplaces (non-functioning) embedded within. The popular music quiz (Sun eve) has turned into a good drinkers' night. Q❀◑◗P

HOLME-NEXT-THE-SEA

White Horse

40 Kirkgate Street
⏲ 11.30 (12 winter)-3, 6.30 (7 winter)-11; 12-3, 7-10.30 Sun
☎ (01485) 525512
Adnams Bitter (summer)**; Flowers Original; Marston's Pedigree; guest beer** (summer) Ⓗ
This 17th-century farmhouse was converted to a pub in 1840. The present landlord is the third generation of his family to run it since 1942. The bar has a traditional quarrystone floor and an unusual collection of police memorabilia from around the world. The 70-seat restaurant specialises in local fish. The pub is an excellent base for walking as it is located at the end of Peddars Way and at the start of the Norfolk Coastal Path. Q❀◑◗♣P

HORSEY

Nelson Head

Beach Road (300 yds off B1159, between Winterton and Sea Palling)
⏲ 11-2.30, 6 (7 winter)-11; 12-3, 7-10.30 Sun

INN BRIEF

KING'S LYNN

Fenman
Blackfriars Road
11-11; 12-3, 7-10.30 Sun
(01553) 761889
Greene King IPA, Abbot; guest beer Ⓗ
Large one-roomed locals' bar opposite the station, decorated with a railway theme.

Live & Let Live
18 Windsor Road
12.15-11; 12-10.30 Sun
(01553) 764990
Beer range varies Ⓗ
Traditional two-bar local, just off London Road opposite the Catholic church. Cask Marque accredited.

White Hart Stores
1 St James Street
11-11; 12-6.30 Sun
(01553) 760034
Greene King IPA; guest beers Ⓗ
Licensed since 1623, so the oldest bar in King's Lynn still open today. Always two guest beers.

MARTHAM

King's Arms
15 The Green
11 (12 Oct-Feb)-11; 12-10.30 Sun
(01493) 740204
Beer range varies Ⓗ
Large 17th-century pub overlooking the village green and pond. Has its own bowling green. A beer festival is held in Feb and occasional live music played.

MUNDESLEY

Ingleside Hotel
Cromer Road
11-11; 12-10.30 Sun
(01263) 720530
Adnams Bitter; Wolf Golden Jackal Ⓗ
Family-run hotel bar with bay windows and a lovely sea view. The house beer is brewed by Wolf.

NEW BUCKENHAM

King's Head
Market Place
12-3, 7-11; 12-3.30, 7-10.30 Sun
(01953) 860487
Adnams Bitter; guest beer Ⓗ
Two-bar village local with a carpeted lounge and a tiled and flagged back bar. Good menu (no food Mon eve).

☎ (01493) 393378

Woodforde's Wherry, Nelson's Revenge; guest beer [H]

Situated on Horsey marshes, this pub has survived at least two major floods, in 1937 and 1953. The location attracts walkers, naturalists and Norfolk Broads holidaymakers. It is 15 minutes' walk from the dunes, beach and Horsey Dyke, a popular mooring for boaters. The bar is warmed by a large log fire, and there are separate dining areas. All rooms display paintings (mainly local scenes and subjects) that are available for purchase. ⩇ቼ❀◑◗♣P

INGHAM

Swan Inn

Town Road (B1151)

⏲ 11-3, 7-11; 12-3, 7-10.30 Sun

☎ (01692) 581099

Woodforde's Mardler's, Kett's Rebellion, Wherry, Great Eastern, Nelson's Revenge, Norfolk Nog [H]

This large, flint building, typical in Norfolk, dominates Ingham corner. Heavily-beamed, with old photographs, farming memorabilia and a real fire, the pub has an appealing, olde-worlde atmosphere. It is split-level, the lower level is the drinking area and restaurant with a large food board, the bar is found on the upper level at the rear.
⩇Qቼ❀◑◗P

KENNINGHALL

Red Lion

East Church Street

⏲ 12-3, 6.30-11; 12-11 Fri & Sat; 12-10.30 Sun

☎ (01953) 887849

Greene King XX Mild, Triumph, Abbot; guest beers [H]

400-year-old pub that has been sympathetically refurbished, the quarry-tiled floor and wood panelling create a cosy atmosphere. There is one bar serving several drinking areas including a homely snug and a restaurant (no food Mon eve). It was awarded local CAMRA Pub of the Year 2000. The Red Lion provides accommodation and makes an excellent base to explore the locality. In a pleasant setting, overlooking the village church, the pub boasts its own bowling green. ⩇Q❀⇄◑◗♣P

KING'S LYNN ❊

Ouse Amateur Sailing Club

Ferry Lane (off King Street)

⏲ 12-4, 7-11; 12-11 Fri; 12.30-4, 8-10.30 Sun

☎ (01553) 772239

Bateman XB, XXXB; guest beers [G]

Located at the end of Ferry Lane, next to the West Lynn Ferry, this popular club offers a one-roomed bar with a wooden verandah overlooking the river. The building was taken over in the 1930s and has recently been extended to include a function room. There are normally seven beers and a cider stocked, generally including a strong beer and a dark beer. It was local CAMRA Club of the Year in 1998 and runner-up 2001. Lunch is served daily, except Sun. Show a CAMRA membership card or this Guide for entry. ⩇❀◑♣●

Stuart House Hotel

35 Goodwins Road

⏲ 7-11; 12-3, 7-10.30 Sun

☎ (01553) 774788

website: www.stuart-house-hotel.co.uk

Beer range varies [H]

Head up a gravel drive off Goodwins Road, near the Walks, to find this independent hotel with a public bar. The comfortable surrounds and friendly atmosphere prove popular with guests and a strong local trade is attracted by the regular events, including Sunday lunchtime jazz and blues evenings. There is an annual beer festival towards the end of July. ⩇❀⇄◗P

White Horse

9 Wootton Road

⏲ 11-3, 5.30-11; 11-11 Fri & Sat; 12-10.30 Sun

☎ (01553) 763258

Greene King IPA; guest beers [H]

Popular, lively local, with two separate bars, located near the Gaywood clock. Originally two houses, that were knocked through to make this bar in 1842, this is a traditional drinker's pub where games are played. Over the years an interesting variety of guest beers have been stocked, some rare to the district.
⊟♣P

LARLING

Angel

Norwich Road (A11, 1 mile S of Snetterton racetrack)

⏲ 10.30-11; 12-10.30 Sun

☎ (01953) 717963

Adnams Bitter; guest beers [H]

Outstanding free house that continues to thrive. The public bar is a gem and usually bustling with drinkers. Four guest beers are always available, usually lower strength and one pump is for mild only, by locals' request. Beers come from Cornwall to Orkney. The pub has strong farming connections and tends to be popular early evenings. Accommodation is superb but often full due to the proximity to Snetterton racetrack. Strong Norwich City FC support exists, both sides of the bar; away fans are very welcome. A beer festival is held in August. Quality food is served in the dining room and restaurant.
⩇❀⇄◑◗⊟⛺⇌(Harling Rd – limited service) ♣P⍞

LITTLE CRESSINGHAM

White Horse

A1108, W of Watton

⏲ 12-3.30, 7-11; 12-3, 7-10.30 Sun

☎ (01953) 883434

Flowers IPA; guest beer (summer) [H]

Friendly village local, run as a pub that serves good food, rather than a restaurant that sells beer. Two or three ales (including Mauldons) are always on handpump, looked after by the landlord who has a passion for beer. The pub has a reputation for home-cooked curries including the famous and fiery 'pili-pili' with successful eaters receiving a commemorative T-shirt. The pub houses a collection of old valve radios and has a games room with darts, bar billiards and shove-ha'penny. If you enjoy conversations about motorbikes you will be in the right place.
⩇Q❀⊟♣P

LYNG

Fox & Hounds

The Street
12-3, 5-11; 12-11 Sat; 12-4, 7-10.30 Sun
☎ (01603) 872316
website: www.foxandhoundslyng.co.uk
Buffy's Mild; Greene King IPA, Abbot; Woodforde's Wherry; [H] **guest beers** [H]/[G]

18th-century free house at the centre of the village featuring a low-beamed bar area with a large open fire and old pictures of the building. The separate (no-smoking) dining area offers a varied menu. The games room is suitable for under 14s. Jazz and folk sessions are regularly held, plus quizzes and food theme nights. Limited outdoor seating is available at the front, by the car park. The guest beers are usually from East Anglian breweries, with lined glasses provided on request. Mobile phones are discouraged.

MORSTON

Anchor

The Street
11-11; 12-10.30 Sun
☎ (01263) 741392 website: www.glavenvalley.co.uk
Woodforde's Wherry, Norfolk Nog; guest beer (summer) [H]

This 18th-century roadside inn consists of three main bars and a modern extension. Many old local photos, paintings, maps and sketches adorn the walls. With both an interesting local clientele and an eclectic mix of old wooden furniture this pub has a pleasant, traditional atmosphere. Offshore boat trips to view the seals can be booked at the pub. A daily bus service between Sheringham and King's Lynn passes the main road in front of the pub.

NORTH ELMHAM

Railway

40 Station Road (B1145) OS995202
11-11; 12-10.30 Sun
☎ (01362) 668300
Beer range varies [H]

Run by the same family for over 40 years, it's a comfortable pub with armchairs and cosy log fire. The brick and flint building is set back from the road and was once the Railway Hotel. Delicious home-made food is served in the small, intimate dining area. Local beers are featured and cider is sometimes available. There is a beer garden for summer drinking and camping is permitted in the pub grounds.

NORTH WALSHAM

Orchard Gardens

Mundesley Road
12-11; 12-10.30 Sun
☎ (01692) 405152
Courage Directors; guest beers [H]

Thriving local pub close to the town centre. Keen emphasis on real ale and up to four guest beers are offered at any one time, with a good mix of local beers and some from further afield. A beer festival is held over spring bank holiday weekend. Run by a musical family, there is live music every weekend and a wide range of social events are hosted throughout the year. The extensive beer garden is ideal on warm nights.

NORWICH

Alexandra

16 Stafford Street
10.30-11; 12-10.30 Sun
☎ (01603) 627772
Chalk Hill Tap, CHB, Flintknapper's Mild; guest beers [H]

INN BRIEF

NORWICH

Beehive
30 Leopold Road
(01603) 451628
Courage Best Bitter; Wolf Bitter; guest beers [H]
Genuine, unspoilt street-corner local. The three-bar layout offers one of the last snug bars in Norwich. Food served weekdays.

Coachmakers
9 St Stephen's Road
11-11; 12-10.30 Sun
(01603) 662080
Greene King IPA, Abbot; Wolf Golden Jackal, Wolf in Sheeps Clothing; Woodforde's Wherry [G]
Country pub in the city, mainly exposed brick and timber. Features a covered courtyard with heaters, and garden.

St Andrew's Tavern
4 St Andrew's Street
11-11; 12-10.30 Sun
(01603) 614858
Adnams Bitter, Broadside; Fuller's London Pride; guest beers [H]
City-centre pub with rear garden/patio and no-smoking conservatory (at lunchtime when food is served, no meals eves).

OLD HUNSTANTON

Neptune
85 Old Hunstanton Road
12-3, 5-11; 12-3, 7-10.30 Sun
(01485) 532122
Adnams Bitter; Greene King Abbot; guest beers (summer) [H]
Saved from redevelopment by new owners, excellent food and live music first Mon of the month.

STIBBARD

Ordnance Arms
Guist Bottom
5.30-11; 12-3, 5.30-11 Sat; 12-4, 7-10.30 Sun
(01328) 829471
Draught Bass; Greene King IPA, Abbot [H]
Old, unspoilt inn on the main Norwich-Fakenham road. Separate Thai restaurant at rear of pub, offers good quality service and food.

SWAFFHAM

George Hotel
Station Street (A1065)
11-2.30, 6.30-11; 11-2, 7-10.30 Sun
(01760) 721238
Greene King IPA, Abbot [H]
Oasis in a town not widely acclaimed for its real ale. Close to Europe's largest wind turbine and Ecotech.

TACOLNESTON

Pelican
136 Norwich Road
11.30-2.30 (not Tue), 5.30-11; 12-3, 7-10.30 Sun
(01508) 489521
Adnams Bitter, Broadside; Bateman XXXB; Greene King Abbot, Old Speckled Hen; Wells Bombardier; guest beers [G]
16th-century coaching inn with original beams. It has recently undergone sympathetic refurbishment.

Keep your copy of the Good Beer Guide up-to-date by contacting the CAMRA website, where you will find information about changes to pubs and breweries.
www.camra.org.uk/gbg

Victorian corner local that still retains two separate bars. The carpeted lounge provides a peaceful drinking atmosphere, while the public bar has bare boards, a pool table and a juke box for a livelier time. There is an interesting mix of artefacts from the old Reindeer Brewery and naval memorabilia. The outside drinking area is very popular in summer. ♨Q❀⊟♣●

Billy Bluelight

27 Hall Road

✪ 11-11; 12-10.30 Sun

☎ (01603) 623768

Woodforde's Mardler's, Kett's Rebellion, Wherry, Great Eastern, Nelson's Revenge, Norfolk Nog; Ⓗ guest beers Ⓖ

This Woodforde's flagship house is a traditional 1930s pub close to the city centre. The house beer is brewed by Woodforde's; Banham cider and a selection of bottle-conditioned beers are stocked. There is no fruit machine or juke box. The main section of the bar has a wooden floor while the small lounge area is carpeted. There is a midnight supper licence. Long alley skittles and pétanque are played. ♨❀◐♣●▯

Champion

101 Chapelfield Road

✪ 11-11; 12-10.30 Sun

☎ (01603) 765611

Greene King IPA, Abbot; guest beers Ⓗ

Former Whitbread pub, now a free house but still features Lacons windows. The Champion is a former winner of the Evening News Pub of the Year competition. Fine collections of water and toby jugs hang from the ceiling and the walls display boxing memorabilia. There is a small function room that is ideal for quizzes and meetings. The pub is within easy reach of bus routes. ◖♣✔

Coach & Horses

82 Thorpe Road (400 yds from rail station)

✪ 11-11; 11-10.30 (11-12 coffee/breakfast only) Sun

☎ (01603) 477077

Chalk Hill Tap, CHB, Dreadnought, Flinknapper's Mild, Old Tackle; guest beers Ⓗ

Situated two minutes' walk from Norwich rail station, it is the home of Chalk Hill Brewery (visible at the rear of the building). The large bar is divided into several drinking areas. The pub serves delicious food in huge portions so you need to be hungry. Barbecues are cooked on the patio in summer. Chess and dominoes are popular. Located close to the football ground so it can be crowded when home matches are played.

♨❀◐◗⇌(Norwich Thorpe) ♣●P

Fat Cat

49 West End Street

✪ 12 (11 Sat)-11; 12-10.30 Sun

☎ (01603) 624364

Adnams Bitter; Fuller's ESB; Greene King Abbot; Hopback Summer Lightning; Taylor Landlord; Woodforde's Wherry; Ⓗ guest beers Ⓖ/Ⓗ

Ale drinkers' paradise, a well-deserved 1998 national winner of CAMRA Pub of the Year. It offers regular ever-changing guest ales (up to 12) including milds, stouts and porter, Belgian lagers and beers, fruit wines and much more. A former Courage pub, it has just celebrated its tenth anniversary. Cask cider is always available. A Victorian, characterful pub that is famous far and wide, on busy nights it can be a struggle to reach the bar. It is a 15-minute walk from the city centre, or bus routes 19, 20, 21 and 22 stop nearby. ❀♣●✔

Iron Duke

Waterloo Road

✪ 11-11; 12-10.30 Sun

☎ (01603) 441182

Draught Bass; Greene King Abbot; Wolf Golden Jackal; guest beers Ⓗ

Undergoing gradual refurbishment as an ale house, the main bar, now open, features a tap room which will house up to 10 gravity-served ales. There are also six handpumps. The house beer Welly Boot, is brewed by Wolf. Most of the guest beers come from smaller micros up and down the country. There is also an unusual imported Bavarian lager on draught, plus a rotating selection of draught Belgian beers. The main bar features a recently discovered bomb shelter – view it through a glass panel in the floor. The new lounge will be the quiet area, complete with real fire. The owners are to be commended as the pub had not served real ale for many years. Bar billiards and bull ring are played and families are welcome in the garden area. ♨Q♿♣P▯

Ketts Tavern

Ketts Hill (50 yds from Gurney Rd/Barrack St roundabout on inner ring rd)

✪ 11-11; 12-10.30 Sun

☎ (01603) 628520

Buffy's Bitter; guest beers Ⓗ

Standing on the lower slopes of Mousehold Heath, the road and the pub commemorate the 1549 rebellion by Robert Kett of Wymondham and his followers against the landed classes' enclosure of the common land. The tavern is a more peaceful refuge. Children are welcome in the conservatory and pool room. Regular promotions are offered to CAMRA members. There is an extensive lunchtime menu and an arrangement with a local restaurant allows delivery of Indian takeaway meals that can be eaten in the pub. Discounts are available on carry-out beer and takeaway lunchtime food. ☕❀◐◗⇌(Norwich Thorpe) ♣P

King's Arms

22 Hall Road

✪ 11-11; 12-10.30 Sun

☎ (01603) 766361

Adnams Bitter; Greene King Abbot; Wolf Coyote; guest beers Ⓗ

One of the few pubs in the city to offer lined glasses, a former Greene King house serving an ever-changing range of ales from around East Anglia. Once every two months a themed range of beers is available. The pub is split into two sections, the lower half has sports on Sky TV and occasional film/video eves. Crib and dominoes are played. Bring your own food in from nearby takeaways. Overall a fantastic pub, a deserved winner of CAMRA East Anglian Pub of the Year 1999. ❀♣●▯

Ribs of Beef

24 Wensum Street

✪ 10.30-11; 12-10.30 Sun

☎ (01603) 619517
Adnams Bitter; Courage Best Bitter; Marston's Pedigree; Old Chimneys Military Mild; Woodforde's Wherry Ⓗ
This pleasant, riverside pub was voted Pub of the Year in 2001 by readers of the local newspaper. It serves six regular beers, including one mild, and a further six guest ales from breweries around the country. Banham cider is stocked. Home-cooked food is served daily at lunchtime, with booking advisable on Friday. Customers are encouraged to request their own favourite beers which leads to a varied and enjoyable selection. A riverside jetty is available for summer drinking. Q

Rosary Tavern
95 Rosary Road, Thorpe Hamlet
11.30-11; 12-10.30 Sun
☎ (01603) 666287 website: www.rosarytavern.co.uk
Adnams Bitter; Ⓗ **Draught Bass;** Ⓖ **Black Sheep Best Bitter;** Ⓗ **Fuller's London Pride;** Ⓖ **guest beers** Ⓗ
Very much a community local with football, crib, darts and quiz teams. The single-roomed pub has high-backed seating dividing the room in two. A conservatory and rear garden area are suitable for meetings and barbecues. Shut the box, shove-ha'penny and bar billiards are played. A wide variety of constantly-changing guest ales and Kingfisher cider are offered. The pub now features a Pasta Hour on Wednesday evening. P

Trafford Arms
61 Grove Road
11-11; 12-10.30 Sun
☎ (01603) 628466 website: www.traffordarms.co.uk
Adnams Bitter; Tetley Bitter; Woodforde's Mardler's; guest beers Ⓗ
Popular, open-plan pub serving a wide range of ales, normally including two milds (one is permanent). The house beers, Barley Boy and Picasso Palette, are brewed by Woodforde's. Kingfisher farm cider is available. A regular themed beer festival is held in a marquee during Valentine's week. Excellent roasts are served on Sunday; evening meals are by arrangement. The Terry Storer Memorial Cycle Rack is a fitting tribute to a popular CAMRA member. The pub is a short walk from the main shopping centre just behind Sainsbury's on bus route 17. The car park is limited to 10 cars. Shove-ha'penny, crib, skittles and dominoes are played. P

Whalebone
144 Magdalen Road (near Sewell Park)
11-11; 12-10.30 Sun
☎ (01603) 425482
Adnams Bitter; guest beers Ⓗ
This cream and maroon corner pub is both attractive from the outside and cosy on the inside. There are two separate bars, both have split-level floors and raised seating areas. The floors are wood with quarry tiles around the bar. The old Bullards sign in the rear bar is a notable feature, possibly indicating the former owners before it became a Courage pub. There are up to eight guest ales and a seasonal cider. A beer festival is hosted in May. P

Wig & Pen
6 St Martins at Palace Plain (100 yds from Cathedral, opp. Law Courts)
11.30-11; 12-5 Sun
☎ (01603) 625891
Adnams Bitter; Buffy's Bitter; guest beers Ⓗ
This cosmopolitan pub appeals to a wide range of drinkers and diners. A former 17th-century coaching inn, it is a short walk from the city centre so has a bustling local trade lunchtime and early evening. Recent developments include a combined no-smoking snug and dining area (available for meetings). Excellent food is served from an extensive, varied menu. The guest beers come from far and wide, usually from the smaller breweries. Chess, crib, dominoes and backgammon are played. The pub's nearest bus stop is Tombland, served by many routes.

OLD HUNSTANTON

Ancient Mariner
Golf Course Road
11-11; 12-10.30 Sun
☎ (01485) 534411 website: www:abacushotels.co.uk
Adnams Bitter, Broadside; Draught Bass; guest beers Ⓗ
Converted from barns attached to the Le Strange Arms Hotel, this busy pub has extensive gardens running down to the beach with views across the Wash to Lincolnshire. The bars are decked out with a nautical theme, and feature a boat attached to the ceiling. The old tiled floors, beams and church pews give the place a feeling of greater age than it actually has. The landlord is proud of his ales and organises trips to beer festivals (for customers). Accommodation is available at the adjoining hotel. Q P

ORMESBY ST MARGARET

Grange Hotel
Yarmouth Road
11-11; 12-10.30 Sun
☎ (01493) 731877
Beer range varies Ⓗ
The hotel stands in extensive grounds on the main coast road. There are two bars, both very comfortable. The pool table is well concealed in a separate room. The guest beers come from far and wide and are always interesting. Accommodation is available both in the hotel or in self-catering cottages. The garden has a children's corner. On the day of the survey, it was an excellent place to watch the Six Nations rugby. P

PORINGLAND

Royal Oak
44 The Street (B1332)
12-2 (2.30 Sat), 5-11; 12-3, 7-10.30 Sun
☎ (01508) 493734
Adnams Bitter; Mauldons Moletrap; Woodforde's Wherry; guest beers Ⓗ
Rare example of an ale house in rural Norfolk, featuring several guest ales and Cheddar Valley cider (polypins). Built in 1848, this locals' pub is much older than first thought, and has been extended over the years. A list of previous breweries and landlords appears on the website. A 'beer shrine' has been created in an alcove, which features, in turn, information on local

breweries. Mini-beer festivals are held in spring and autumn. Party nights include 'Burns' Night', 'Trafalgar Day' and 'Battle of Britain'. Only half-pint lined glasses are available. Q ☺ ❀ ♣ ⚈ P ⊓

PULHAM MARKET

Crown

The Green, Harleston Road

⌚ 12-3, 6.30-11; closed Mon; 12-3, 6.30-10.30 Sun

☎ (01379) 676652

Adnams Bitter (winter); **Buffy's Bitter** (winter); **guest beers** (summer) (G)

Large, thatched, listed building situated on the side of the green in the village centre. It has two distinctive rooms (one mainly for dining), both have heavily-beamed ceilings. A good-sized function room has been added, in keeping with the rest of the building. Four beers are served by gravity. The pub is particularly enjoyed by the local farming community. A monthly theme night is hosted with food and beer to match the occasion. ♨ ❀ ◑ ◗ ⊟ ♿ P ⊬ ⊓

PULHAM ST. MARY

King's Head

The Street

⌚ 11.15-3, 5.30-11; 11.15-11 Sat; 12-10.30 Sun

☎ (01379) 676318

Adnams Bitter; Buffy's Bitter; guest beer (H)

Late 17th-century, timber-framed pub with a friendly welcome. The cosy main bar has a large woodburner. A propeller from an early 20th-century airship is displayed over the fireplace. These were built on a local airfield and known as 'Pulham Pigs'. Good value meals (including specials and children's choices) are served in the bar, or no-smoking dining area. Food is available all day Sun. This family pub has something for all ages: a large garden with children's play area, bowling green and an adult games room in a converted stable. Champagne quiz nights are held fortnightly.
♨ ❀ ⇌ ◑ ◗ ♣ P

REEPHAM

King's Arms

Market Place

⌚ 11.30-3, 5.30-11; 12-11 Sat; 12-10.30 Sun

☎ (01603) 870345

Adnams Bitter; Draught Bass; Greene King Abbot; Woodforde's Wherry; guest beers (H)

Attractive listed building in the centre of the village overlooking the market place. The interior has lots of beams and exposed brickwork. There are three real fires ensuring the atmosphere is warm and inviting. There is a courtyard at the rear, complete with glass-topped well. In summer, regular jazz sessions are held on Sunday. ♨ ❀ ◑ ◗ ⊟ ♣ P

RINGSTEAD

Gin Trap Inn

High Street

⌚ 11.30-2.30, 6 (7 winter)-11; 12-2.30, 6 (7 winter)-10.30 Sun

☎ (01485) 525264

Adnams Bitter; Greene King Abbot; Woodforde's Nelson's Revenge; Norfolk Nog (H)

This village local is heavily into food. There is a split-level bar and a dining room where good value, interesting meals are served. Inside there is a small area for drinkers only, and outside a large garden which is very popular on summer days. In winter a welcoming fire competes for attention with the awesome array of traps and other agricultural implements. The five beers on offer are all from East Anglia, the house beer is Gin Trap Bitter, brewed by Woodforde's. A converted, self-catering barn is available for accommodation. ♨ ❀ ⇌ ◑ ◗ P

SAHAM TONEY

Old Bell

1 Bell Lane (from Watton take B1077 [Swaffham], 1 mile on right)

⌚ 11-3, 5-11; 11-11 Sat; 12-10.30 Sun

☎ (01953) 884934

Adnams Bitter; guest beers (H)

Traditional 200-year-old pub in a lovely setting overlooking the oldest mere (large pond) in the country. This family-run free house offers an ever-changing choice of guest ales. A wide range of home-made food, using local produce, is provided (including supplies by an award-winning butcher). A selection of chef's own desserts includes home-made ice creams. It is advisable to book at weekends. ♨ ☺ ❀ ◑ ◗ P ⊓

SMALLBURGH

Crown

North Walsham Road (A149)

⌚ 12-3, 5.30-11; 12-3, 7-11 Sat; 12-4 (closed eve) Sun

☎ (01692) 536314

Adnams Broadside; Greene King IPA, Abbot; Tetley Bitter; guest beer (H)

Comfortable, two-bar village local with a friendly atmosphere, this 15th-century coaching inn retains some of its original timbers. It is close to both the North Norfolk coast and the Broads. A cosy, welcoming log fire is in the bar where the tables and chairs are made from old beer casks. There is an attractive garden at the rear. A good selection of home-cooked food, including snacks, is available in the bar or dining room (eve meals until 9pm). Daily bus services pass the pub to and from North Walsham to Norwich and Great Yarmouth. No under-14s allowed in the pub.
♨ ❀ ⇌ ◑ ◗ P

SOUTH CREAKE

Ostrich Inn

1 Fakenham Road (B13555, Fakenham-Burnham Market)

⌚ 12-3 (not Tue), 7-11; 12-3, 7-10.30 Sun

☎ (01328) 823320

Adnams Broadside; Greene King IPA, Abbot; Woodforde's Nelson's Revenge; guest beer (H)

This true free house is centrally-located in a long, straggling village. A 17th-century, Grade II listed inn, its long, single bar is divided into different areas: cosy armchairs round a woodburner, a formal restaurant and comfortable bar area. An attached barn serves as a function and games room. Wheelchair WC and baby-changing facilities are available. A superb, comprehensive menu includes vegetarian and ostrich dishes. The accommodation, including one unit to disability standards, is handy for the North Norfolk coast. The ostrich is the crest of the Coke family of the huge Holkham estate. Limited bus services run between Fakenham and Burnham Market. ♨❀⇌◐◑♿⛺♣P

STALHAM

Swan
High Street
☼ 11-11, 12-10.30 Sun
☎ (01692) 581482
Adnams Bitter, Broadside ⊞
Comfortable two-bar pub that is popular with locals and tourists. Stalham is a small market town 15 miles north of Norwich, at the heart of the Norfolk Broads. There is a good network of footpaths locally, including part of the Weaver's Way. ♨Q❀◐◑⊟⛺♣P

STIFFKEY

Red Lion
44 Wells Road (A149)
☼ 11-3, 6 (7 winter)-11; 12-3, 6 (7 winter)-10.30 Sun
☎ (01328) 830522
Greene King IPA, Abbot; Woodforde's Wherry; guest beers ⊞
Situated on the main North Norfolk coastal road, this old flint and brick pub comprises three inter-connecting bars. There are pantiled floors and no less than four real fires, plus a conservatory, dining area and large garden patio. Having been closed for 20 years, this pub re-opened in 1990 after extensive refurbishment. Two guest beers are supplied exclusively by local Norfolk brewers. An extensive menu is available using fresh local produce (no frozen food). A daily bus service between Sheringham and King's Lynn passes along the main road at the front of the pub. ♨Q❀◐◑⛺♣P⊁

STRUMPSHAW

Shoulder of Mutton
Norwich Road
☼ 11-11; 12-10.30 Sun
☎ (01603) 712274
Adnams Bitter, Broadside; guest beers ⊞
Welcoming pub that is set back from the road. A recent extension has added a new lounge bar and games room (divided by a central fireplace). Booking is advisable at weekends for meals in the separate restaurant (no food on Sun eve). The bar boasts many sporting trophies. An extensive garden and pétanque courts add to the appeal of this pub. ❀◐◑♣P

THETFORD

Albion
93-95 Castle Street (opp. Castle Hill ancient monument)
☼ 11-2.30 (3 Fri & Sat), 6 (5 Fri)-11; 12-3, 7-10.30 Sun
☎ (01842) 752796
Greene King IPA, Abbot; guest beers ⊞
Two cottages knocked through to form a small, two-roomed local with plenty of chat and a genuinely warm welcome. Hide away in the enclosed rear patio or sit outside watching the world pass by. Set in the older part of town, this traditional flint-faced building has steadily built a reputation for good ale at reasonable prices. Guest ales are from Greene King. In winter it is a cosy retreat, in summer the view across the park towards the ancient fortification of Castle Hill is impressive. In a rapidly changing world, long may this establishment continue to maintain its traditional roots. ♨Q❀♣P✔

THORNHAM

Lifeboat
Ship Lane
☼ 11-11; 12-10.30 Sun
☎ (01485) 512236 website: www.lifeboatinn.co.uk
Adnams Bitter; Greene King IPA, Abbot; Woodforde's Wherry; guest beers ⊞
Situated on the edge of the coastal saltmarshes, this 16th-century smugglers' ale house has retained its character despite the addition of modern comforts. The interior of carved wood panels and old beams is lit by paraffin lamps, creating the perfect, cosy pub atmosphere. The conservatory has a 96-year-old vine which thrives on its daily dose of Abbot. There is a large garden and children's play area; children, dogs and muddy boots are all welcome. ♨Q❀⇌◐◑♿♣●P

TIBENHAM

Greyhound
The Street
☼ 6-11 (not Tue); 12-11 Fri & Sat; 12-10.30 Sun
☎ (01879) 677676
website: www.thetibenhamgreyhound.co.uk
Adnams Bitter Greene King IPA; guest beer ⊞
Cosy and atmospheric two-bar village pub with low beams and flagstones. With the exception of the fairy lights outside, little has changed over the years, although the pub dog is now a black and white one rather than grey, and the barn is now a pool room. The model B-24 Liberators hanging in the bar bear the markings of the 445th Bombardment Group which was based at Tibenham Airfield. Camping is available in the field at the rear. ♨Q❀⊟⛺♣P

TRUNCH

Crown
Front Street
☼ 12-2.30 (3 summer), 6-11; 12-10.30 Sun
☎ (01263) 722341
Greene King IPA; Shepherd Neame Spitfire; guest beers ⊞
This attractive free house was originally part of the former Trunch Brewery estate. It has a single bar, small, cosy restaurant and welcoming log fire. A selection of four real ales is offered with a larger choice in the summer months. An annual beer festival is held in August. The pub attracts locals and visitors. ♨Q❀◐◑♣P✔

UPPER SHERINGHAM

Red Lion
8 The Street (B1157, one mile out of Sheringham)
☼ 11.30-3, 6.30-11 (11.30-11 summer Sat); 12-3, 7-10.30 (12-10.30 summer) Sun
☎ (01263) 825408
Greene King IPA; Woodforde's Wherry; guest beers (summer) ⊞

Classic Norfolk village pub, formerly owned by Watneys who closed it in the early 1980s causing a local furore. Fortunately it was soon reopened. The main bar has a flagstone floor, wooden settles and a wood-burning fire. Tables and chairs in the centre of the room are handy for those who prefer to dine in the bar; a second no-smoking dining room is available. Six different fish and seasonal shellfish feature on the menu. The accommodation (in cottage-type rooms) offers superb sea views and is convenient for those visiting the North Norfolk Steam Railway and Mucklebergh Military Museum.
♨Q❀⇌◐▲≥P

UPTON

White Horse

17 Chapel Road
⏲ 11-11; 12-10.30 Sun
☎ (01493) 750696
Adnams Bitter, Broadside; St. Peter's Best Bitter; Ⓗ guest beers Ⓗ/Ⓖ
Popular village local that is handy for the Norfolk Broads. A traditional pub with a welcoming atmosphere and homely, large fireplace. Delicious, reasonably-priced, home-made food is served in a separate restaurant section. The take-away fish and chips on Friday are a local legend. Addlestones cider is available. The recently-added conservatory provides another drinking area and overlooks the garden. Camping facilities are provided at the rear of the pub.
♨❀◐▲♣●P

WALCOTT

Lighthouse

Coast Road (close to church)
⏲ 11-11; 12-10.30 Sun
☎ (01692) 650371
Adnams Bitter; Tetley Bitter; guest beers Ⓗ
This pub is very much part of village life, and organises many events: a carol service at Christmas, a firework display, barbecues in summer and a children's disco. It is not only popular with locals, many holidaymakers flock to the Lighthouse. The pub has a function room, unusually it features a marquee, and it has a separate no-smoking dining room. Pool and darts teams play regularly. Two guest beers are offered in summer and one in winter.
♨ठ❀◐▲P✔

WARHAM ALL SAINTS

Three Horseshoes ☆

Bridge Street
⏲ 11.30-2.30, 6-11; 12-2.30, 6-10.30 Sun
☎ (01328) 710547
Greene King IPA; Ⓗ Woodforde's Wherry; Ⓖ guest beer Ⓗ
Access is now only from the rear of the building. The main bar is genuine 1920s, complete with gaslights, wainscot panelling, scrubbed furniture, hatch bar and even a twister on the ceiling. The rest of the extended pub has been furnished in the same style, complete with early gaming machine. The modern toilets have full disabled access. The menu includes lunchtime snacks, and makes a feature of using local produce. Additional car parking is available in the field opposite the pub. Warham Hillfort is close at hand.
♨Q❀⇌◐♿♣P

WATTON

Breckland Wines (off licence)

80 High Street (opp. police station)
⏲ 9-9; 6-8 Sun
☎ (01953) 881592
Iceni Fine Soft Day Ⓗ
In this over-commercialised, sterile, impersonal world you can still get a bespoke service for the discerning ale drinker. Bottle-conditioned British beers are stocked as well as real ales from the cask from independent East Anglian brewers. Bring your own container for take-home beers from local micros. With its impressive range of wines, ciders, spirits and beers, this remains one of the true traditional off licences, rarely found these days.

WEST BECKHAM

Wheatsheaf Inn

Church Road (1 mile S of A148)
⏲ 12-3, 6.30-11; 12-3, 7-10.30 Sun
☎ (01263) 822110 website: wheatsheaf.org.uk
Woodforde's Wherry, Nelson's Revenge, Headcracker; guest beers Ⓗ
An extensive, regularly changing menu, offering good value and variety, ensures that this pub is very popular with both locals and visiting tourists looking to eat. No food is served on Sun eve. Bar snacks are sold and drinkers will find that the small bar has six cask ales on sale, including two guests. One beer is usually sold at a special low price. A games room along the corridor houses a pool table and dartboard. There is a large beer garden and self-catering accommodation is available on site. The X98 bus service between Cromer and King's Lynn runs daily through the village.
♨ठ❀⇌◐▲P

WEST SOMERTON

Lion

On B1152/B1159 jct
⏲ 11- 4 (3 winter), 6-11; 11-11 Sat; 12-5, 7-10.30 Sun
Greene King IPA, Abbot; guest beers Ⓗ
Run by the same licensees for the past 18 years, this traditional two-bar country local serves a good selection of real ales and food. Originally an old Lacons pub, it was closed by that brewery in 1955, thus rendering the village 'dry' until it was reopened as a free house almost 20 years later. Over 200 years old, the pub was originally thatched. It is a short walk from West Somerton Staithe providing refreshment for Broadland yachtsmen, along with regulars, ramblers and hikers. Guest beers invariably come from Mauldons and Woodforde's.
♨ठ❀◐⊟▲♣P

WEYBOURNE

Ship

The Street

✪ 12-3, 6 (7 winter)-11; 12-11 Sat; 12-4, 6 (7 winter)-10.30 Sun

☎ (01263) 588721

Greene King IPA, Abbot; guest beers 🄷

Characterful, 19th-century brick and flint building featuring Steward & Patteson windows. It was originally part of the Boldeng Monument estate (which included the former brewery). The pub comprises a comfortable lounge bar, dining room and games area with cosy real fires. It is popular with locals, birdwatchers and visitors to North Norfolk Railway (3/4 mile). Live music is occasionally featured.

₼❀◑ ⊟▲♣P⚡

WICKLEWOOD

Cherry Tree

116 High Street

✪ 12-2.30, 6 (7 winter)-11, 12-11 Sat; 12-10.30 Sun

☎ (01953) 606962

Buffy's Bitter, Mild; 🄶/🄷 **guest beers** 🄷

Leased by Buffy's Brewery, parts of this pub date back to the 17th century and the ceilings are very low. It has recently reopened after extensive sympathetic refurbishment. The L-shaped interior has a carpeted restaurant at one end, while the drinking area is divided into smoking and no-smoking areas, by a large central fireplace. All the beers are either served by handpump or gravity direct from the cellar. Banham cider is always available. Old and new customers will be warmly welcomed.

₼Q♉❀◑ ▲♣●P⚡

WINFARTHING

Fighting Cocks

The Street (B1077)

✪ 11-2.30 (not Mon), 5.30-11; 12-2.30, 5.30-10.30 Sun

☎ (01379) 643283

Adnams Bitter; guest beers 🄷

Imposing roadside inn offering a large, opened-up beamed main bar and a small, original games room. Guest ales are mainly from local breweries. Food is freshly prepared and home cooked. Live music is performed on certain weekends. A welcoming pub, it is popular with locals and visitors alike. Free camping is available to pub customers, rallies are catered for. There is an extensive footpath network locally, and Banham Zoo and Bressingham Gardens and Museum are nearby. Weekday bus services to Diss operate.

₼♉❀◑♿▲♣P

WINTERTON-ON-SEA

Fisherman's Return

The Lane (off B1159)

✪ 11-2.30, 6.30-11; 11-11 Sat; 12-10.30 Sun

☎ (01493) 393305

Woodforde's Wherry; guest beers 🄷

Attractive, 300-year-old flint and brick building, with wood panelling and inviting open fire. Run by a long-standing landlord and landlady who pioneered the introduction of guest ales while the pub was still tied to Grand Met. All meals are freshly prepared with an emphasis on local fish and game. The varying range of guest ales is unusually drawn from East Anglian brewers. The house beer is Woodforde's Fisherman's Ale and Westons Old Rosie cider is served. There is an interesting display of photos featuring former pubs of the area. The village actually stands on the site of the former Bulmer village, Winterton Ness having long since disappeared under the sea.

₼Q♉❀⇋◑ ⊟▲♣●P⚡

WOODBASTWICK

Fur & Feather

Slad Lane

✪ 11.30-3, 6-11; 11-11 summer; 12-10.30 Sun

☎ (01603) 720003

Woodforde's Mardler's, Kett's Rebellion, Wherry, Great Eastern, Nelson's Revenge, Norfolk Nog 🄷/🄶

The Woodforde's 'tap', the original building was three cottages before it was converted into a pub and restaurant. The floors are quarry tiles and the walls exposed brickwork which works well with the heavy oak furniture. A full range of Woodforde's ales is available on both gravity and handpump. The setting is idyllic, the building is surrounded by farmland and the garden a peaceful haven in which to enjoy a good pint. On Sundays customers can enjoy a jazz brunch from 10.30am.

♉❀◑♿♣●P⚡

WYMONDHAM

Green Dragon

6 Church Street

✪ 11.30-2.30, 6-11; 12-2, 7-10.30 Sun

☎ (01953) 607907

Adnams Bitter, Broadside; Greene King IPA 🄷

Dating back to the 15th century, this half-timbered building is one of the town's gems. Inside, the pub consists of an unspoilt, cosy, panelled snug featuring an imposing Tudor mantelpiece that sports a real fire. It is said that a tunnel once connected the bar to the nearby Benedictine abbey. A small, no-smoking restaurant specialises in freshly cooked food including Steak and Ale Dragon Pie as well as daily specials. No meals served on Sun eve.

₼Q❀⇋◑

Feathers

13 Town Green (400 yds W of town centre)

✪ 11-3, 7 (6 Fri)-11; 12-3, 7-10.30 Sun

☎ (01953) 605675

Adnams Bitter; Greene King Abbot; Marston's Pedigree, seasonal beers; guest beers 🄷

Situated a few minutes' walk from the market cross and the abbey, this friendly pub features the best selection of real ales in Wymondham. The decor is rustic with many old farm implements adorning the walls of the single-room bar, it is subdivided along one wall by wooden-posted booths. A small, sheltered courtyard offers a light alternative on a summer's day. Local groups use the upstairs function room for meetings. Mauldons brews the house beer. No food is served on Sun eve.

❀◑♣P

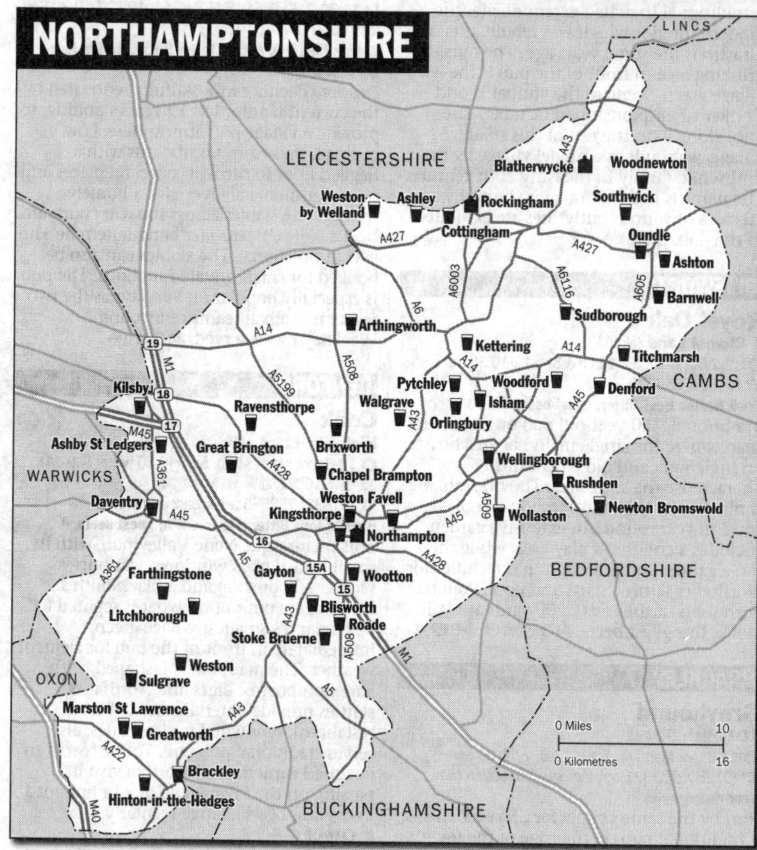

ARTHINGWORTH

Bull's Head

Kelmarsh Road (off A508)

12-3, 6.30-11; 12-11 Sat; 12-10.30 Sun

(01858) 525637

Adnams Bitter; Everards Tiger; Wells Eagle; guest beers Ⓗ

Threatened with closure two years ago, but now thriving, after a vigorous campaign by locals to save it, this large 1850s pub is essentially one bar on three levels, plus a dining area. The pub retains much of its original charm and character, including oak-beamed ceilings, olde-worlde memorabilia and open fires. Two changing guest beers supplement the regular range.

ASHBY ST LEDGERS

Olde Coach House

Main Street (off A361)

12-2.30, 6-11; 12-11 Sat; 12-10.30 Sun

(01788) 890349

Everards Old Original; Flowers Original; guest beers Ⓗ

This former 19th-century farmhouse is a popular village inn and a regular Guide entry. Built from local golden ironstone, like the rest of the picturesque village, it consists of a bar, with Sky TV, and a series of interconnected rooms leading to the award-winning restaurant. Beams, wood panelling and high-backed benches complement the walk-in fireplace. Children are welcome throughout. The guest ales come from local and small independent breweries; it hosts beer festivals spring and autumn and occasional barbecues in the large mature garden. Wheelchair WC.

ASHLEY

George

21 Main Street (off A427)

12-2, 6-11; 12-3, 7-10.30 Sun

(01858) 565642

Greene King IPA; guest beers Ⓗ

Welcome return to the Guide for this former Mansfield pub, now a free house, stocking three changing guest beers. Standing on a grassy bank in a pretty village, the pub features a traditional bar with a red quarry-tiled floor and wood-panelled seating. A dining area adjoins the bar, while to the rear is a small room that houses the Northamptonshire skittles table. One of the guest beers is always on special offer. A popular meeting place for local clubs; no food is served Sun eve or Mon.

ASHTON

Chequered Skipper

The Green (1 mile from A605, Oundle jct)

11.30-3, 6-11; 11.30-11 Sat; 12-10.30 Sun

(01832) 273494

Adnams Broadside; Oakham JHB; guest beers Ⓗ

A traditional thatched exterior belies the modern interior which was rebuilt after a disastrous fire some years ago. The outside drinking area in front of the pub is the village green, scene of the annual World Conker Championship in October. The pub, along with the rest of this small village, was built as a model village by the Rothschild family in the early 20th century. The name is taken from a rare butterfly and 10 cases of various butterflies are exhibited in the pub. Q❀◑♿♣P

BLISWORTH

Royal Oak

1 Chapel Lane (old A43)
12-2.30, 6-11; 12-11 Fri & Sat; 12-10.30 Sun
☎ (01604) 858372
Hook Norton Best Bitter; guest beers Ⓗ

Traditional, 300-year-old pub on the main road, where the single main bar area boasts an inglenook and old oak beams characterise the snug area. The no-smoking dining room specialises in home-cooked food all year round. An extensive garden includes a children's play area, while the large games/function room has facilities for Northants skittles, darts and pool. Popular with users of the canal, 200 yards away, it stocks five guest beers. ♔Q⛾❀◑♣P✔

BRACKLEY

Greyhound

101 High Street
11-3 (not Mon-Fri), 7-11; 12-3, 7-10.30 Sun
☎ (01280) 703331 website: www.pubsearch.com
Beer range varies Ⓗ

Run by the same couple for 25 years, this is a traditional pub on the edge of the town. Photos on the wall are testament to the good humour that this pub enjoys. It offers an ever-changing range of guest ales, plus a house beer named Skinny Mutt, brewed by Vale Brewery. The two bars lead into a restaurant specialising in Mexican food; reasonably-priced roasts are served on Sunday when it is advisable to book in advance. ♔❀◑♣

COTTINGHAM

Royal George

4 Blind Lane (off A427)
11-3, 5-11; 12-3, 7-10.30 Sun
☎ (01536) 771005
Marston's Pedigree; Museum Five Hides; guest beer Ⓗ

Stone pub, dating from 1766, in a commanding position overlooking the village rooftops and the Welland Valley. Inside are three distinct rooms, all on a tiered level, with the small bar serving beers brewed by the landlord at the Bass Museum; Hop Pit is brewed with the same malt as Five Hides, but using a different hop. To date, 30 different brews have been produced. An unusual selection of malt whiskies is also stocked. Five en-suite rooms cater for overnight guests, and a patio provides space for summer drinking. Q⛾❀🛏◑P

DAVENTRY

Coach & Horses

Warwick Street
11.30-2.30 (3 Fri), 5 (7 Sat)-11; 12-3, 7-10.30 Sun
☎ (01327) 876692
Greene King IPA, Abbot; Tetley Bitter, Burton Ale; guest beer Ⓗ

Former coaching inn, skilfully renovated by the current landlord of 19 years standing, to provide a village pub atmosphere. Low ceilings, well-worn floorboards with a flagged floor to the rear, open fireplaces and several intimate alcoves give a homely feeling. The stables across the rear courtyard host a New Orleans jazz band (alternate Thu eve) at no charge. The stables can also be booked for small private functions. The pub is especially popular on Sundays as the two resident football teams return home. Weekday meals served. ♔Q❀◐♣

DENFORD

Cock

High Street (off A45)
12-3 (not winter Mon), 5.30 (6.30 winter Sat)-11; 12-3, 7-10.30 Sun
☎ (01832) 732565 website: cock-inn.co.uk
Boddingtons Bitter; Flowers IPA; guest beers Ⓗ

This picturesque Nene Valley pub, with its small leaded glass windows, was once a saddler's/boot shop and a blacksmith's. Benches are put out on what is reputed to be England's smallest village green, immediately in front of the pub for clement weather. The main bar is L-shaped, with bare floorboards; darts and Northants skittles provide entertainment. A long restaurant, renowned for its curries, also serves traditional pub fare. To the rear is an enclosed garden. Well worth a visit if passing on the River Nene or A14 link road. Two guest beers change regularly. ♔Q❀◑⊟♣

FARTHINGSTONE

King's Arms

Main Street
12-3 (not Mon-Fri), 7-11 (not Mon or Wed); 12-3, 9-11 Sun
☎ (01327) 361604
Hook Norton Best Bitter; guest beers Ⓗ

Idyllic, 18th-century pub in an attractive location opposite the church. The L-shaped bar, which includes a comfortable armchair lounge area, is decorated with interesting ornaments. In a warm, friendly atmosphere, a range of up to three guest beers is complemented by home-cooked food at weekends (booking advised); traditional British cheeses are a speciality. Full of shrubs and herbs, the beautiful garden is a very restful place to enjoy a beer. A side room is used for Northamptonshire skittles. ♔❀◐Ⲗ♣P

GAYTON

Eykyn Arms

20 High Street
11.30-2 (3 Sat), 7-11; 12-3, 7-10.30 Sun
☎ (01604) 858361
Greene King IPA; Wells Eagle; guest beer Ⓗ

Run by the same landlord for 11 years and converted to a free house in 1994, the pub has a real community feel to it, with many old photographs in the bar evoking memories of the village. Named after Captain Eykyn, it has a lounge at the front

and a bar with skittles at the rear. The conservatory at the side is a no-smoking restaurant serving good value meals. The car park is located 75 yards from the pub.
Q ♣P

GREAT BRINGTON

Althorp Coaching Inn/Fox & Hounds

Main Street (2 miles from A428)
11-11; 12-10.30 Sun
☎ (01604) 770651
website: www.althorp-coaching-inn.co.uk
Fuller's London Pride; Greene King IPA, Abbot, Old Speckled Hen; guest beers Ⓗ
Despite being on the Diana Spencer memorial trail, this pub remains a friendly village local. The atmosphere is enhanced by stone-flagged floors, low beams and a real fire in an enormous inglenook. The boothed dining area serves as a live music venue on Tuesday evening. The courtyard makes a pleasant outdoor drinking area in the summer. The ladies' toilets are notable for the collection of china bedpans. Up to six guest beers are on tap, with a happy hour 5-7 weekdays. P

GREATWORTH

Inn

Chapel Road
12-2 (not Mon), 6.30-11; 12-3.30, 6.30-10.30 Sun
☎ (01295) 710976
Hook Norton Mild, Best Bitter, Double Stout, seasonal beers; guest beer Ⓗ
Possibly the shortest name in the county, but definitely one of the best welcomes; do not plan to stay for a short visit – it is not easy! This classic country pub, dating back to the 16th century, has a large bar with an inglenook and a no-smoking dining room, serving excellent quality food all week. A monthly fish and chip night is held (first Tue). Bric-à-brac is sold from one of the outbuildings and Aunt Sally is played in the garden at the rear. Not to be missed.
Q ♣P

HINTON-IN-THE-HEDGES

Crewe Arms

Off A43/A422
12-2.30 (not Mon or Tue), 6-11 (not Mon); 12-3, 7-10.30 Sun
☎ (01280) 703314
Fuller's London Pride; Hook Norton Best Bitter; Marston's Pedigree; guest beer Ⓗ
Classic country pub at the centre of a small hamlet. Choose from many rooms including an Italian restaurant in the former function room. The dining area within the pub is a no-smoking zone and serves good quality food. The bar has an open fire and the former games room is ideal for meetings. Folk sessions are held (alternate Sun eve) when everyone is welcome to perform. Overall, an excellent pub with quality food and beer, together with a welcoming atmosphere. Q ♣P

KETTERING

Piper

Windmill Avenue (off old A6, by Wicksteed Park)
11-3 (4 Sat), 6-11; 12-10.30 Sun
☎ (01536) 513870
Hook Norton Best Bitter; Theakston Old Peculier; guest beers Ⓗ
Popular, two-roomed 1950s estate pub, close to children's favourite, Wicksteed Park. It was voted local CAMRA Pub of the Year 2001, due to the enthusiastic landlord introducing a much more varied beer range, with five guests. The lively games room is frequented by younger drinkers. Note the pub sign features two different pipers.
♣P

KILSBY

George Hotel

Watling Street (A361/A5 jct)
11.30-3, 5.30 (6 Sat)-11; 12-10.30 Sun
☎ (01788) 822229
Adnams Bitter; Draught Bass; Greene King IPA, Abbot; guest beers Ⓗ
Detached pub, just off the A5, featuring a smart wood-panelled lounge, a dining room and a rear public bar. This former coaching inn was rebuilt after a fire in the 19th century with the same bricks that were used for Kilsby railway tunnel. It has a strong commitment to its real ales and fine home-cooked food. The George stages monthly live music (first Sat) and a Sunday evening quiz, when no meals are served.
Q ♣

LITCHBOROUGH

Old Red Lion

4 Banbury Road
11-3, 6.30-11; 12-3, 6.30-10.30 Sun
☎ (01327) 830250
Banks's Bitter; Marston's Pedigree; Morrells Varsity Ⓗ
Cosy, compact and homely, this stone village pub boasting flagstones, beams and a huge inglenook, is a very pleasant place to visit. One room offers pool, while another contains darts and Northants skittles. The pub fields a number of games teams. No food or bar snacks are served, however the pub is the only village amenity and is popular with locals, walkers and cyclists. Fruit wines are available. Q ♣P

NEWTON BROMSWOLD

Swan

6 Church Lane
11.30-2.30 (not Mon), 5-11; 11.30-3, 5.30-11 Sat; 12-3, 7-10.30 Sun
☎ (01933) 413506
Greene King IPA, Ⓗ **Abbot;** Ⓖ **guest beer** Ⓗ
Idyllic, quiet pub in a small hamlet on the rural Bedfordshire border. As such, it provides a welcome break for walkers and cyclists alike. With three inter-connecting rooms around a central bar, its traditional interior also incorporates a new conservatory where good value food is served (not Mon). To the rear is a games room where teams compete in the local skittles league. The pleasant garden is at the front. Q ♣P

INDEPENDENT BREWERIES

Frog Island Northampton
Rockingham Blatherwycke

NORTHAMPTON

Fish Inn

11 Fish Street (pedestrianised area)

⌚ 11-11; 7-10.30 Sun

☎ (01604) 234040

Courage Directors; Marston's Pedigree; Theakston Best Bitter; guest beers Ⓗ

Town-centre pub that has a traditional feel to it. There has been a pub on this site since 1750. The central serving area has secluded alcoves for those seeking privacy; look for the old photos and bottles on display. Very good food is on offer Mon-Sat, 11am-9.30pm. Very friendly bar staff attract a wide range of customers, mostly over-25s. A destination pub, not on the local circuit, it is handy for a rest from town-centre shopping. A T&J Bernard establishment, with the emphasis on quality, it always has three guest ales on tap. Bar billiards is played. ⇄◐◑⇌♣

King Billy

2 Commercial Street

⌚ 12-11; 12-10.30 Sun

☎ (01604) 621325 website: www.thekingbilly.com

Greene King Abbot, Old Speckled Hen; guest beers Ⓗ

The King Billy takes pride in being considered as an 'alternative' venue; a large town-centre pub, it enjoys a loyal following. Beer barrels are used as tables; look out for the Egyptian mummy case in the corner. Live music (free) pulls in the crowds (Thu-Sat eves); local groups vary from thrash metal to mainstream cover bands. Lunchtime food service is extended until 5pm Saturday and Sunday. It supports local charities, including the bikers' club that delivers Easter eggs to sick and needy children. ❀◐⇌

Malt Shovel Tavern

121 Bridge Street (facing Carlsberg Brewery)

⌚ 11.30-3, 5-11; 12-3, 7-10.30 Sun

☎ (01604) 234212

Banks's Bitter; Frog Island Natterjack; Fuller's London Pride, Tetley Bitter; guest beers Ⓗ

The East Midlands CAMRA Pub of the Year 2001 is full of breweriana, with many items from Phipps and NBC Breweries, which both brewed opposite (demolished in 1974 when the site was sold to Carlsberg). Up to nine guest beers, including a mild, are supplemented by regular beer festivals. A broad choice of Belgian bottled and draught beers, plus Belgian fruit gins, English country wines and over 50 single malt whiskies make this a discerning drinker's paradise, free from sparklers and gaming machines. Tasty home-cooked food is available, too (not Sun) and it is a top venue for live blues (Wed eve). Q❀◐♿⇌♣●

Racehorse

15 Abington Square

⌚ 11-11; 12-10.30 Sun

☎ (01604) 631997

Beer range varies Ⓗ

The pub's main, spacious single room is partly divided by a central bar, while a back room is used for functions and gigs, once or twice a week. The pub now has a free reign regarding cask beers and, although this is only a recent development, all seven lines dispense smaller breweries' beers. Free gigs are also staged in the front bar on Sunday; a quiz is held Mon eve. The pub benefits from a very large, partly paved garden, and fields a flourishing cricket team in summer. ❀♣P

Romany

Trinity Avenue

⌚ 11.30-11; 12-10.30 Sun

☎ (01604) 714647

Fuller's London Pride; Hop Back Summer Lightning; Tetley Bitter; guest beers Ⓗ

1930s V-shaped red brick roadhouse. The public bar houses pool tables and bar billiards as well as Northants skittles. The community-friendly management has a laid-back style, organising plenty of entertainment, including 'clash of the bands' (Tue), jam sessions (Thu) and karaoke/disco (Fri); live bands perform at weekends from 9pm. The pub enjoys a vibrant sports following, including rugby and soccer. Card-carrying CAMRA members can enjoy 10% off real ales (Tue and Wed). Meals are served 12-7. ❀◐⊟♣P

ORLINGBURY

Queen's Arms

11 Isham Road (off A509/A43)

⌚ 12-2, 6-11 Mon-Fri; 12-11 Sat; 12-10.30 Sun

INN BRIEF

BARNWELL

Montagu Arms

12-3, 6-11; 12-11 Sat; 12-10.30 Sun

(01832) 273726

Adnams Bitter, Broadside; guest beers Ⓗ

Atmospheric interior with exposed beams and flagstone floor. A large garden has a children's play area. Cask Marque accredited.

BRIXWORTH

Coach & Horses

Harborough Road

11.30-2.30; 5.30-11; 12-3, 5-10.30 Sun

(01604) 880329

Adnams Bitter; Black Sheep Best Bitter; Marston's Pedigree Ⓗ

Spacious, 17th-century, oak-beamed inn with two lounges and a restaurant serving a varied menu. A small patio has tables.

CHAPEL BRAMPTON

Brampton Halt

Pitsford Road

12-2.30, 5.30-11 (varies summer); 12-3, 7-10.30 Sun

(01604) 842676

Adnams Bitter; Everards Tiger, Original; Fuller's London Pride; guest beer Ⓗ

Next to Brampton Valley Way and Northampton & Lamport Railway, this former yardman's cottage is now a large, one-roomed pub.

ISHAM

Lilacs

39 Church Street

12-3, 5-11; 12-11 Sat; 12-4.30, 7-10.30 Sun

(01536) 723948

Greene King IPA, Ruddles Best Bitter, Triumph Ale; guest beer Ⓗ

Traditional, three-roomed pub with a bay-fronted lounge, snug, and large games bar. Community-focused, it hosts fundays.

KINGSTHORPE

Queen Adelaide

50 Manor Road

11.30-3, 5.30-11; 11.30-11 Fri & Sat; 12-3, 7-10.30 (12-10.30 summer) Sun

(01604) 714524

Adnams Bitter, Broadside; Banks's Bitter; Greene King IPA; Tetley Bitter; Webster's Yorkshire Bitter; guest beer Ⓗ

Popular old village local now part of Northampton. Two rooms, plus a popular skittles room. Large garden.

MARSTON ST LAWRENCE

Marston Inn

12-3 (not Mon); 7 (6 Sat)-11; 12-4, 7-10.30 Sun

(01295) 711906

Hook Norton Mild, Best Bitter, Old Hooky, Double Stout; guest beers Ⓗ

Everything a good country pub should have: a warm welcome, open fire and good conversation. An unspoilt gem.

☎ (01933) 678258
Courage Directors; Tetley Bitter; Taylor Landlord; guest beers Ⓗ
Well worth seeking out (drive around the village green looking for signs to Isham), this comfortable, carpeted village pub has a central lounge divided into three drinking areas around the bar. Additionally, there is a dining room and a snug, which acts as an unofficial no-smoking room, due to the lack of ashtrays. The sizeable garden has trestle tables and children's play equipment. A beer festival is hosted in a marquee in early summer. The pub is leased from Inn Partnership, but has negotiated a good range of up to five guest beers. Q❀◑P⊬

OUNDLE ❄

Ship Inn

18 West Street
11-11; 12-10.30 Sun
☎ (01832) 273918
website: www.theshipinn-oundle.co.uk
Draught Bass; Hop Back Summer Lightning; guest beers Ⓗ
Grade II listed building in the main street, 100 yards from the town centre, this Collyweston-slated pub is reputedly haunted by a previous landlord who flung himself from an upstairs window. A more regal pub ghost, Mary, Queen of Scots, can be found at the Talbot Hotel, just around the corner. The Ship is divided into several drinking areas which makes for a homely and cosy atmosphere. It hosts monthly live jazz nights (last Sun). ⋒Q❀⇌◑P⊬

RAVENSTHORPE

Chequers

Church Lane (off A428)
12-3, 6-11; 12-11 Sat; 12-3, 7-10.30 Sun
☎ (01604) 770379
Fuller's London Pride; Greene King IPA; Jennings Bitter; Thwaites Bitter; guest beer Ⓗ
In the shadow of the Church of Dionysius and its 13th-century tower, the Chequers was a farmhouse until 1900. Today, this Grade II listed establishment offers a warm welcome in an L-shaped bar which features a stone fireplace, bottles, jugs, tankards and loads of money! A small restaurant to the rear serves excellent home-cooked fresh food. A games room, housing Northants skittles and pool, can be found across the courtyard. Note that the northern beers are keenly priced. ⋒❀◑P

ROADE

Cock at Roade

1 High Street (A509, close to M1 jct 15)
12-11; 12-10.30 Sun
☎ (01604) 862544
Hook Norton Best Bitter; Greene King IPA; Shepherd Neame Spitfire; guest beer Ⓗ
Rejuvenated local at the village centre, with a lively atmosphere. Good, home-cooked meals are served in the no-smoking restaurant. Formerly a Mann's house, it has been refurbished with care and now offers a range of beers, always in good condition. The large garden has a children's play area and there is ample parking. It is worth making a detour from the M1 to visit this pub which caters for everyone. ⋒❀◑P

RUSHDEN

Rushden Historical Transport Society

The Station, Station Approach (N end of A6 one-way system)
12-3 (not Mon-Fri), 7.30-11; 12-3, 7.30-10.30 Sun
☎ (01933) 318988 website: www.rhts.co.uk.
Fuller's London Pride; guest beers Ⓗ
Joint winner of CAMRA Club of Britain 2000, recent refurbishment has not detracted from its gaslit charm, with walls adorned with railway pictures, loco name plates and old advertising signs. Five or six guest beers are stocked, totalling over 400 in the last year. There is a transport museum in the former waiting room. The society runs its working steam and diesel engines at steam-ups five times a year. It also owns three buses, two fire engines and other vehicles; an annual transport cavalcade is held every spring bank holiday. Not to be missed. ⋒Q❀P

SOUTHWICK

Shuckburgh Arms

Main Street

OUNDLE

Rose & Crown
11 Market Place
11-11; 11-10.30 Sun
(01832) 273284
Mansfield Cask Ale; Marston's Bitter, Pedigree Ⓗ
Town-centre lounge with dining area and a lively public bar. A rare local outlet for Marston's Bitter.

PYTCHLEY

Overstone Arms
The Stringers Hill
12-2.30, 7 (6.30 Sat)-11; 12-2.30, 7-10.30 Sun
(01536) 790215
Adnams Bitter; Marston's Pedigree; guest beers Ⓗ
Large, attractive, stone pub with a small bar and a restaurant, very popular for its excellent food (booking advised).

SULGRAVE

Star Inn
Manor Road
11-2.30 (12-3 summer), 6-11; 12-5, 7-10.30 (not winter eve) Sun
(01295) 760389
Hook Norton Best Bitter, Generation, Old Hooky Ⓗ
Ivy-clad pub opposite Sulgrave Manor, ancestral home of George Washington's family. An adult sanctuary; good food and B&B.

WELLINGBOROUGH

Rising Sun
1 Mill Road
12-11.30; 12-10.30 Sun
(01933) 272540
Courage Directors; John Smith's Bitter; guest beer Ⓗ
Pleasant, two-bar, private town pub, with access via an intercom. Games-oriented, it hosts Saturday night discos.

Check it out

Pubs in the Good Beer Guide may change ownership and the facilities listed could alter. If a visit to a pub involves a long journey, it's advisable to check before leaving that full meals, family facilities, accommodation or camping sites are still available.

⊙ 12-2 (not Mon or Tue), 6-11; 12-2.30 (3 summer), 7-10.30 Sun
☎ (01832) 274007
Fuller's London Pride; guest beers Ⓗ
Cosy village pub, dating from the 16th century under a thatched roof. Inside the single room is almost cut in two by the porch, with a low ceiling and a large inglenook at one end. A large, enclosed garden to the rear offers a variety of play equipment and wooden benches. The village cricket pitch stands next to it. There is another Shuckburgh Arms close by at Stoke Doyle, so navigate with care. Evening meals are served Wed-Sat. ⌂Q❀◐♣P

STOKE BRUERNE

Boat Inn
Bridge Road (off A508, opp. Canal Museum)
⊙ 9-3, 6-11; (9-11 summer); 12-10.30 Sun
☎ (01604) 862428 website: www.boatinn.co.uk
Adnams Bitter; Banks's Bitter; Frog Island Best Bitter; Marston's Bitter, Pedigree; guest beer Ⓗ
This popular canalside pub dates back to 1877 and has been run by the Woodward family for four generations. It formed part of the Duke of Grafton's estate until 1921. The thatched bars occupy the oldest part of the building and retain their original stone floors and open fires. The lounge offers bar snacks, and the bistro is busy with breakfasts and main meals. The restaurant, with its adjoining cocktail bar, overlooks the canal lock. Trips to the historic Blisworth tunnel are available on the Indian Chief narrowboat. ⌂❀◐♿♣P

SUDBOROUGH

Vane Arms
Main Street (off A6116)
⊙ 12-3 (not Mon-Wed), 5.30 (6 Sat)-11; 12-3, 7-11 Sun
☎ (01832) 733223 website: www./thevanearms.com
Beer range varies Ⓗ
Situated in a quiet, picturesque village, this stone and thatched pub sells six continually-changing guest beers, plus some country fruit wines. Although the lounge is spacious, several alcoves help create a warm, cosy atmosphere. The back bar is smaller and offers a number of games, including darts, Northants skittles and pool. Real cider is available occasionally. Three rooms with en-suite facilities are in a separate converted building. Well-prepared meals are served lunchtime (Sat and Sun) and Tue-Sat eves (booking advised). ⌂❀◐♣P

TITCHMARSH

Dog & Partridge
6 High Street (1/2 mile off A605)
⊙ 12-4 (not Mon-Fri), 6 (6.30 Sat)-11; 12-4.30, 7-10.30 Sun
☎ (01832) 732546
Wells Eagle, Bombardier, seasonal beers; guest beer Ⓗ
Centrally situated in the village, the pub offers a warm, friendly welcome from the long-serving landlord. The interior consists of one long room with a raised games area at one end. Northamptonshire (hood) skittles and table football are played. Outside there is a pleasant patio area. A regular Guide entry. ⌂Q❀♣P

WALGRAVE

Royal Oak
Zion Hill (off A43)
⊙ 12-3, 6-11; 12-10.30 Sun
☎ (01604) 781248
Adnams Bitter; guest beers Ⓗ
Comfortable, stone-built village local, popular for food as well as for the changing range of up to four guest beers. The front bar is partitioned into three areas, with dining at the side and a central smoking and drinking section. A small back bar serves a cosy lounge and a separate dining room. Northamptonshire skittles are played in a room on the other side of the car park. Barbecues are held in the garden on Sunday evenings in summer.
⌂Q❀◐♣P

WELLINGBOROUGH ❊

Old Grammarians Association
46 Oxford Street (off one-way system)
⊙ 12-2.30, 7-11; 12-11 Fri & Sat; 12-10.30 Sun
☎ (01933) 226188
Greene King IPA; Hook Norton Best Bitter, Old Hooky; guest beers Ⓗ
This sports and social club fields teams for most outdoor activities, including a successful rugby team. A friendly town-centre club, its small TV lounge, long bar and function/games room have recently been redecorated. Access is from the rear car park – press the voicecom button; a stair lift is provided for wheelchairs. Open to all, regular visitors will be asked to join. There are always three guest beers on tap at this former CAMRA East Midland Club of the Year, with one brewery having all its beer featured, once a month. A cider is occasionally stocked in summer. ◐♿P

WESTON

Crown
2 Helmdon Road
⊙ 12-2.30 (not Mon), 6-11; 12-10.30 Sun
☎ (01295) 760310
Greene King IPA; guest beers Ⓗ
Family-run local at the heart of the village, with a real community feel to it. It has a no-smoking family restaurant, serving good quality food, and a beamed function room which can be booked for special occasions. Live music is featured in the bar (Sunday eve). Locals talk of three ghosts which are friendly – very much like the rest of the clientele. It now opens all day Sunday throughout the year. Bed and breakfast is available. ⌂Q❀◐♣P

WESTON BY WELLAND

Wheel & Compass
Valley Road (off B664)
⊙ 12-3, 6-11; 12-4, 6-10.30 Sun
☎ (01858) 565864
Banks's Bitter; Greene King Abbot; Marston's Bitter, Pedigree; guest beer Ⓗ
Situated in the beautiful Welland Valley, this popular local has an L-shaped bar and a restaurant where the excellent food represents good value. Meals are available at all times. The Poachers Bar to the front is on a lower level and provides an intimate, relaxing place to drink. Low ceilings and

low-level wooden-backed seating add to the atmosphere. ⛫Q⛾❀◐◑P

WESTON FAVELL

Bold Dragoon

48 High Street (150 yds S of A4500)
✪ 11-3, 5.30-11; 11-11 Sat; 12-3, 7-10.30 Sun
☎ (01604) 401221
Boddingtons Bitter; Fuller's London Pride; Greene King IPA, Abbot; guest beers Ⓗ

Popular pub, just off the A4500. As well as four regular beers, it serves two constantly-changing guest ales. In the conservatory restaurant, excellent value meals are served (no food Sun). The spacious, traditional bar is lively with music and games, while the lounge is pleasant and compact, although it is frequently very busy. Outside, a small garden, plus a large patio area with benches and tables provides a convivial place to spend summer evenings. A pub for young and old alike, this was local CAMRA's Pub of the Year runner-up in 2000.
Q❀◐◑⊟♿♣P

WOLLASTON

Crispin Arms

14 Hinwick Road
✪ 12-11; 12-10.30 Sun
☎ (01933) 664303
Caledonian Deuchars IPA; Fuller's London Pride; Shepherd Neame Spitfire; Theakston Best Bitter; guest beers Ⓗ

Serving up to six real ales, this small, friendly pub is popular with locals, especially at teatime and early evening. Always warm and welcoming, the ambitious new management is enthusiastically developing social activities, including angling and golfing societies. A variety of prints and posters, plus relics of the boot and shoe industry, make this an interesting place to visit. A small paved area at the back is available for outside drinking.
⛫❀⊟♣P

WOODFORD

Duke's Arms

83 High Street (off A14)
✪ 12-2.30, 6.30-11; 12-11 Sat & summer; 12-10.30 Sun
☎ (01832) 732224
Greene King IPA; Hop Back Summer Lightning; guest beers Ⓗ

A welcome return to the Guide following a change of ownership for this stone pub that overlooks the village green. Originally called the Lord's Arms, it was renamed in the 19th century in honour of the Duke of Wellington, who was a frequent visitor to the village. Two rooms surround the bar, while a games room to the rear offers pool, Northants skittles and darts. Upstairs a restaurant is open at weekends; weekday meals are served in the lounge.
⛫❀◐◑⊟♿♣P

WOODNEWTON

White Swan

22 Main Street
✪ 12-2, 7 (6 Fri)-11; closed Mon; 12-2.30 (closed eve) Sun
☎ (01780) 470381
Adnams Bitter; Draught Bass; Otter Bright Ⓗ

Situated in the centre of the village, the pub lies at a right angle to Main Street. The interior consists of one long room with an eating area at the far end; the bar and drinking area are by the entrance. Coco the Clown used to frequent the pub, and he is buried in the local churchyard. The house bitter, Twelve Bore, is brewed by Bateman's; the cider is Addlestone's. The garden boasts a pétanque pitch. Q❀◐◑♿♣●P⊓

WOOTTON

Wootton Working Men's Club

23 High Street (near M1 jct 15)
✪ 12-2 (2.30 Sat; not Thu), 7-11; 12-5, 7-10.30 Sun
☎ (01604) 761863
Greene King IA; guest beers Ⓗ

A Guide regular, this club enjoys an excellent reputation for its ever-changing range of guest beers sourced from micro-breweries around the UK and Europe. The knowledgeable steward shows great enthusiasm for the ales and organises a beer festival in the car park in September. The club has a real pub atmosphere in the main bar area, which is now complemented by a quiet lounge area for adults only. Regional CAMRA Pub of the Year in 1997 and 1998, an example all clubs should emulate.
Q⛾♿♣P

The Discreet Barman

Over the mahogany, jar followed jorum, gargle, tincture and medium, tailor, scoop, snifter and ball of malt, in a breathless pint-to-pint. Discreet barman, Mr Sugrue thought, turning outside the door and walking in the direction of Stephen's Green. Never give anything away – part of the training. Is Mr so-and-so there, I'll go and see, strict instructions never to say yes in case it might be the wife. Curious now the way the tinge of wickedness hung around the pub, a relic of course of Victorianism, nothing to worry about as long as a man kept himself in hand.

Jack White,
The Devil You Know.

NORTHUMBERLAND

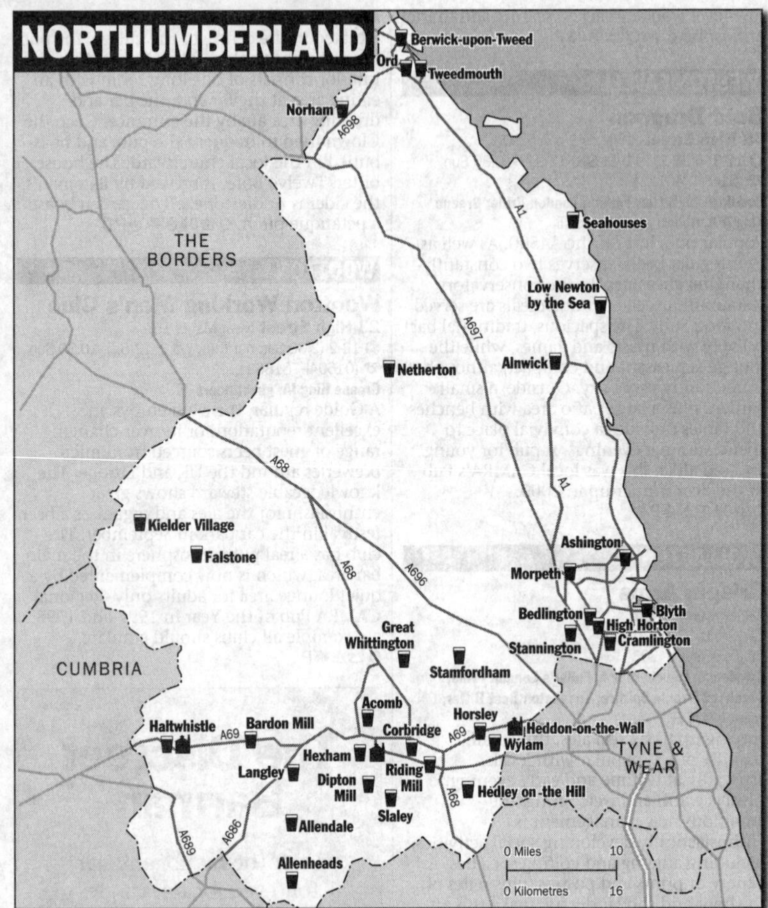

ACOMB

Miners Arms
Main Street

12 (5 winter)-11; 12-10.30 Sun

(01434) 603909

Black Sheep Best Bitter; Federation Buchanan's Best Bitter; Yates Bitter; guest beers

This unspoilt village pub has been a free house since 1750. A former Northumberland Pub of the Year, it is well worth a visit. Enjoy the friendly atmosphere and warm welcome. The house beer, Miners Lamp, is brewed by Big Lamp. The owner is a keen supporter of the local micros and their beers feature regularly as guests. Meals are served in the summer season, note the late opening times in winter.

ALLENDALE

King's Head
Market Place

11-11; 12-10.30 Sun

(01434) 683681

Jennings Mild, Bitter, Cumberland Ale, Cocker Hoop, Sneck Lifter, seasonal beers; guest beers

Built in the early 18th century, this public bar, a former coaching inn, is reputedly the oldest premises continuously used as a pub in the area. Proud of its lack of juke box and gaming machines, it offers a relaxing environment for locals, cyclists, ramblers and other tourists to gather. A number of visitors are attracted to the locality as it is known for its outstanding natural beauty. The pub hosts live music eves in the function room. Bus route No. 688 Hexham-Allenheads passes every two hours (approx.), less frequently on Sunday.

ALLENHEADS

Allenheads Inn

12-4, 7-11; 12-11 Fri & Sat; 12-10.30 Sun

(01434) 685200

website: www.theallenheadsinn.co.uk

Greene King IPA, Abbot; guest beers

Built as the family home of Sir Thomas Wentworth (in the 18th century), this pub is a fascinating find. It features a wealth of memorabilia, antiques and equipment throughout its many rooms: public bar, lounge, games and dining areas. Close to the Coast-to-Coast cycle route and a popular ski slope, the pub also attracts a number of hikers and ramblers. It is on the No. 688 Hexham-Allenheads bus route.

ALNWICK ❄

John Bull Inn
12 Howick Street
✪ 12-3 (not Wed), 7-11; 11-2, 7-11 Sat; 12-3, 7-10.30 Sun
☎ (01665) 602055 website: www.john_bull_inn.co.uk
Tetley Bitter; guest beers Ⓗ
Small, cosy local in a row of terraced houses. On entering the door you could be forgiven for thinking that you had walked into someone's house but carry on and find the bar, which offers regularly changing guest beers and one of the largest selections of malt whiskies in Northumberland. The bier shoppe offers every known Belgian bottle-conditioned beer including Trappist and Duvel. Triominoes (three-sided dominoes) is played. Have a relaxing drink in the sheltered beer garden. Q❀♣

ASHINGTON ❄

Bubbles Wine Bar
58A Station Road
✪ 11-11; 11-2am Fri & Sat; 12-10.30 Sun
☎ (01670) 850800 website: www.bubblesbar.co.uk
Beer range varies Ⓗ
Enter this unusual pub by a steep set of stairs or through the back yard, and find yourself in an excellent bar, which has a late licence at the weekend. The cask ales are usually from local breweries and the home-made lunchtime food will set you up for the rest of the day. There is a children's menu and discounted meals for senior citizens. Low-lit and restful during the day, evenings are more hectic with entertainment such as a disco, quiz and live music on various nights. ❀◐

BARDON MILL

Bowes Hotel
✪ 11 (4 winter Mon)-11; 12-10.30 Sun
☎ (01434) 344237
Beer range varies Ⓗ
Directly opposite the village green, this small hotel has a cosy public bar and a separate games room, with traditional beamed ceilings. The walls display photographs of village life in days gone by. Originally a coaching house, the adjacent building, owned by a pottery, once housed the stables. There is a separate restaurant serving excellent home-cooked fare. Close to the river, it is a popular stop-off point for walkers. Customers can enjoy quiz nights and live entertainment in the pub and can watch occasional quoits and conker competitions on the green. ⛰❀⛟◐◑⥃

BEDLINGTON ❄

Northumberland Arms
112 Front Street East
✪ 11-3 (not Mon or Tue), 7-11; 11-11 Thu-Sat; 12-10.30 Sun
☎ (01670) 822754
Beer range varies Ⓗ
This is very much a locals' pub where all are made to feel welcome. There is a comfortable atmosphere in the bar/lounge, with a pool room and a function room upstairs. A constantly-changing selection of real ales on three handpulls is offered with a good range of lunchtime meals (no food on Sun). A weekly quiz is held (Mon); the pub is busy when Bedlington Terriers FC have home matches, the football ground is nearby. ◐♣

BERWICK-UPON-TWEED

Barrels
Bridge Street
✪ 11-11; 12-10.30 Sun
☎ (01289) 308013
Boddingtons Bitter; Hadrian & Border Farne Island; guest beers Ⓗ
Situated at the Berwick end of the historic Elizabethan bridge over the Tweed, this pub is a splendid mix of traditional and modern, with an emphasis on both beer and food, as well as live music and entertainment. The pub has two rooms and a basement. It attracts a varied clientele and provides a major focal point for the people of Berwick. The mix of furniture in the ground-floor back room is as eclectic as the pub is diverse. ◐⥃

Foxtons
Hide Hill
✪ 11-11; closed Sun
☎ (01289) 303939
Caledonian Deuchars IPA; guest beers Ⓗ
Behind the guise of a wine bar/bistro, Foxtons serves fine beer in a busy, food-oriented environment. It is far superior to most of the pubs in the vicinity and demonstrates the potential to achieve success in a non-traditional outlet. Superb food, quality wine and above all excellent real ales make this pub well worth seeking out. ◐◑⥃

BLYTH

Oliver's Bar
60 Bridge Street
✪ 11 (1 Sat)-11; 12.30-10.30 Sun
☎ (01670) 540356
Greene King Old Speckled Hen; Thwaites Bitter; Wells Bombardier; guest beers Ⓗ
Comfortable town free house that was originally a newsagent's shop. The pub is small, only one room, but it is well decorated, cosy and friendly. It is an oasis in a town that is a real ale desert. What it lacks in size is more than compensated by comfortable surroundings with good ale and a pleasant atmosphere. Q

CORBRIDGE

Angel of Corbridge
Main Street
✪ 11-11; 12-10.30 Sun
☎ (01434) 632119
website: www.theangelofcorbridge.softnet.co.uk
Black Sheep Best Bitter or Special; guest beers Ⓗ
After 103 years of ownership by Scottish & Newcastle and its predecessors, this former Georgian coaching inn hotel became family-owned and run. Its large open-plan, bright and airy public bar is popular with more mature local drinkers. Note the artistic

INDEPENDENT BREWERIES

Black Bull Haltwhistle
Hexhamshire Hexham
Wylam Heddon-on-the-Wall

black and white photographs; subjects are members of the owners' families. The modern light wood style features in the restaurant, while the very plush lounge with easy chairs and piano is of darker panelled wood. The No. 685 Newcastle-Carlisle bus passes every hour. No food is served on Sunday evening. ⇔◑◗⊟▲⇌P

Dyvels
Station Road
3 (12 Sat)-11; (12-11 summer); 12-4, 7-10.30 Sun
☎ (01434) 633633
Draught Bass; Black Sheep Best Bitter; guest beers Ⓗ
Small but welcoming public bar of a family-owned country hotel. It features a heated garden and a pool room. Popular with tourists as a base for exploring Hadrian's Wall and the fine surrounding countryside, it is also well patronised by organised parties who use the train to travel to the Indian restaurant on the railway station, and the horse-racing fraternity visiting Hexham racecourse. Dogs are very welcome. The No. 602 Newcastle-Hexham bus passes every half-hour during the day.
⚘❀⇔◑◗⇌♣P

CRAMLINGTON

Plough
Middle Farm Buildings
11-11; 12-10.30 Sun
☎ (01670) 737633
Theakston XB; guest beers Ⓗ
In the former village centre of this expanding new town, this fine pub faces the parish church. Once a farm, the old buildings were sympathetically converted into the present establishment some years ago. The bar is small and busy with a door opening on to the outside seating area. The lounge is larger and comfortable with a round gingan acting as an extra sitting room. Guest beers are often from local micro-breweries. ❀◑◗⊟♿⇌P

DIPTON MILL

Dipton Mill Inn
Dipton Mill Road (2 miles from Hexham on Whitley Chapel road)
12-2.30, 6-11; 12-4, 7-10.30 Sun
☎ (01434) 606577
Hexhamshire Devil's Elbow, Shire Bitter, Devil's Water, Whapweasel, Old Humbug; guest beers Ⓗ
Well worth seeking out, this small, low-ceilinged inn is the tap for Hexhamshire Brewery. After exploring the local countryside, enjoy a drink in the pub's large garden which has a stream running through it. The keen landlord serves superb beers which are always available to accompany the great home-cooked meals. The pub has won several CAMRA awards in recent years.
⚘Q❀◑◗⊡

GREAT WHITTINGTON

Queen's Head Inn
12-2.30 (not Mon), 6-11; 12-3, 7-10.30 Sun
☎ (01434) 672267
Black Sheep Best Bitter; Hambleton Bitter; guest beers Ⓗ
This inn, dating from the 15th century, is reputedly the oldest in the county. Four handpumps serve a variety of guest ales. The house beer, Queen's Head Bitter, is brewed by Hambleton. Set in the heart of Hadrian's Wall country, the pub makes an ideal watering-hole. The food is excellent – all made with local produce whenever possible, the menu is extensive with dishes to suit all tastes. There is a small, friendly bar with a roaring fire in which to savour the quality ales on offer. ⚘Q◑◗P

HALTWHISTLE

Black Bull
Market Square

INN BRIEF

ALNWICK

Tanner's Arms
Hotspur Place
7 (12 Sat)-11; 12-10.30 Sun
(01665) 605553
Belhaven 80/-; Greene King Old Speckled Hen; Theakston Black Bull Ⓖ
Pleasant, welcoming atmosphere in this comfortable one-roomed local near historic Bondgate. Bar snacks are available.

ASHINGTON

Black Diamond Inn
29 Douth View
11-11; 12-10.30 Sun
(01670) 851500
Beer range varies Ⓗ
Former Co-op dairy; split-level bar with pool table and lounge/diner. An old red telephone box and pillar box grace the bar.

BEDLINGTON

Wharton Arms
Burdon Terrace
11-11; 12-10.30 Sun
(01670) 822214
Greene King Abbot; Tetley Bitter Ⓗ
Enjoy the lively atmosphere in this terraced town-centre pub. The bar and lounge feature wood panelling. Pool and darts are played.

EAST ORD

Salmon Inn
11-3, 6-11; 11-11 Fri & Sat; 12-10.30 Sun
(01289) 305277
Caledonian Deuchars IPA, 80/-; Greene King Old Speckled Hen Ⓗ
Welcoming ale house-style pub with real fire, garden, pool and TV. The menu boasts quality meals prepared with local produce.

FALSTONE

Black Cock Inn
12-3 (not winter), 6.30 (7 winter)-11; 12-2.30, 7-11 Sat; 12-3, 7-10.30 Sun
(01434) 240200
John Smith's Magnet; Theakston Cool Cask; guest beer Ⓗ
Lively village local near Kielder Dam on the reivers cycle route, provides accommodation, meals and pool. Black Cock Ale is John Smith's Bitter rebadged.

HORSLEY

Lion & Lamb
12-3, 6-11; 12-11 Fri & Sat; 12-10.30 Sun
(01661) 852952
Boddingtons Bitter; Castle Eden Ale; guest beers Ⓗ
Spacious pub with good food. Guest beers come from local micro-brewers, including Durham and Mordue.

KIELDER VILLAGE

Anglers Arms
12-3, 6-11; 12-11 Sat; hours may vary in winter; 12-10.30 Sun
(01434) 250072
Beer range varies Ⓗ
Beneath the castle, close to Kielder Water and the forest, this pub is the social heart of a small community.

Service

If you are unhappy with any aspect of service in a pub in the Guide, you should first complain to the manager or tenant of the pub, and then, if not satisfied, to the owner of the pub. Send a copy of your complaint, with any corrrespondence to GBG, CAMRA, 230 Hatfield Road, St Albans, Herts, AL1 4LW

⏲ 12-3 (not Mon-Wed; 12-4 Sat), 7-11; 12-3, 7-10.30 Sun
☎ (01434) 320463
Beer range varies Ⓗ
Superb pub boasting an open fire, wooden beams, horse brasses and a welcoming landlord. The small, low-ceilinged bar is already a showcase for many of the finest independent breweries, with guest ales from local micros. The owners are producing their own beers and try to have three different brews on handpump. ⌂Q⇌

HEDLEY ON THE HILL

Feathers

⏲ 12-3 (not Mon-Thu), 6-11; 12-3, 7-10.30 Sun
☎ (01661) 843607
Boddingtons Bitter; guest beers Ⓗ
Splendid country pub in a loft hilltop location. Real fires in both the bar and the lounge create a warm, friendly welcome. Quality food is offered evenings and weekend lunchtimes to accompany the range of three guest beers. The pub hosts a mini beer festival every Easter when there is a barrel race among local drinkers – the contestants have to roll a barrel uphill to the pub! The winners are well rewarded (with beer obviously). ⌂Q❀◖◗P

HEXHAM

Forum
Market Place
⏲ 11 (opens 10am for tea/coffee)-11; 12-10.30 Sun
☎ (01434) 609190
Courage Directors; Theakston Best Bitter; guest beers Ⓗ
Wetherspoon's split level conversion of a former picture house which retains some attractive Art Deco features and, unusually, an operating cinema upstairs. The old film screen has been replaced by a picture window affording superb views across the rooftops. At the heart of this historic town, the pub is close to the outdoor market, ancient abbey and Moot Hall. Children, ordering food, are admitted until 9pm (with restrictions). Forum opens at 10am (not Sun) for tea and coffee only; it offers a spacious no-smoking area. Q◖◗♿⇌⊁●

Tap & Spile
Battle Hill
⏲ 11-11; 12-3, 7-10.30 Sun
☎ (01434) 602039
Black Sheep Best Bitter; Theakston Best Bitter; guest beers Ⓗ
Offering the widest range of real ales in the area, this is still a flagship of the chain. With a typical ale house style, it has bare boards and a working service hatch. The comfortable environment is popular with local shoppers, tourists and live music fans; Northumbrian folk music is featured among other styles. The bus station is close at hand. Q◖⇌

HIGH HORTON

Three Horse Shoes
Hatherley Lane OS276794
⏲ 11-11; 12-10.30 Sun
☎ (01670) 822410
Greene King Abbot; Tetley Bitter, Burton Ale; guest beers Ⓗ
Well-established free house enjoying a good reputation for food and offering a wide selection of real ales from seven handpumps, including guests from local micro-breweries. Its mini beer festivals feature beers not usually found in the area. The pub, which overlooks the main road, has remained largely unchanged, however a glass conservatory, running the length of the building, has been added. Inside, beams and panels enhance the homely atmosphere. Children are welcome and there is an outdoor play area. ❀◖◗P

LANGLEY

Carts Bog Inn
3 miles off A69, on A686 to Alston
⏲ 12-3, 7-11; 12-3, 7-10.30 Sun
☎ (01434) 684338
Marston's Pedigree; Theakston Best Bitter; guest beers Ⓗ
Unspoilt country pub, owned and run by the same family for several generations. The current building dates from 1730 and is built on the site of an ancient brewery (circa 1521). An unusual open fire divides the two rooms and heats both. The pub name is derived from a steeply banked corner on the old road, where, on wet days, the horse-drawn carts were invariably bogged down. Excellent home-cooked food is available, making this a popular venue for Sunday lunch. ⌂Q☕❀◖◗♿P

LOW NEWTON BY THE SEA

Ship Inn
The Square
⏲ 11.30-3, 9 (7 Fri & Sat)-11 (11-11 summer); 12-4, 9-11 (12-10.30 summer) Sun
☎ (01665) 576262
Hadrian & Border Farne Island; guest beers Ⓗ
Less than 60 yards from an outstandingly beautiful sandy beach (car park at top of hill before you reach the village), this fine old National Trust-owned pub forms part of a square of terraced stone cottages once owned by fisherfolk. Recently transformed inside, it now features stripped pine floors and a wood-burning stove. An imaginative menu includes locally caught seafood and vegetarian options. It is popular with heritage coast walkers and birdwatchers. Occasionally, highly original live entertainment is laid on. ⌂Q❀🛏◖◗

MORPETH

Joiners Arms
3 Wansbeck Street
⏲ 12 (11 Wed, Fri & Sat)-11; 12-10.30 Sun
☎ (01670) 513540
Draught Bass; Tetley Bitter; guest beers Ⓗ
Old-style, traditional two-roomed pub, consisting of a basic but comfortable bar, that houses an unusual collection of stuffed birds and animals in glass cases. The small, cosy lounge has a pleasant view of the River Wansbeck. It has a good reputation for its beer and local micro-breweries' ales are often guests. A pub with no frills, it is just a friendly place to enjoy a good pint. Q⊟

Tap & Spile
23 Manchester Street
⏲ 11-11; 12-10.30 Sun

☎ (01670) 513894
Beer range varies Ⓗ
This is how a Tap & Spile should be! A small front bar which is often packed and a back lounge for more restful drinking and conversation. Three minutes' walk from Morpeth bus station, this pub is popular with a wide cross-section of visitors and is often the last port of call for ramblers enjoying the Northumberland countryside. A collection of board games is held behind the bar for customers to borrow. Weston's Old Rosie cider is stocked.
Q♣●

NETHERTON

Star Inn ☆

Off B634 from Rothbury
⌚ 12-1.30, 7-10.30 (11 Fri & Sat); winter hours may vary; 12-1.30, 7-10.30 Sun
☎ (01669) 630238
Castle Eden Ale Ⓖ
Unspoilt gem, unchanged for the last 80 years, it was originally built as an hotel for the new railway line. The line never reached the pub but fortunately the customers did. The pub is privately owned, and as you enter you feel as though you are in someone's living room. The beer is served direct from the cellar at a hatch in the panelled entrance hall. The bar area is basic, with benches around the wall. It is the only pub in Northumberland to appear in every edition of this Guide. Opening hours may vary, especially in winter, so please ring for details. Children are not allowed in the bar.
Q❀P

NORHAM

Masons Arms

16 West Street
⌚ 12-3, 7-11; 12-3, 7-10.30 Sun
☎ (01289) 382326
Castle Eden Bitter, seasonal beers; guest beers (summer) Ⓗ
Former Vaux-owned single-roomed pub in this village dominated by its castle. Attracting both Scots and English locals, at its heart is a welcoming fire within a decorative surround. Note the old Younger's mirror above. It also has some good leaded glass on the ceiling and walls, a fine collection of water jugs and a display of photographs of old Norham and the River Tweed in flood. The Tweed Cycle Way is nearby. Bus Route No. 23 Berwick-Kelso passes the pub every 90 minutes or so.
ጠQ⇋◐◑♿

RIDING MILL

Wellington

On A695
⌚ 11-11; 12-10.30 Sun
☎ (01434) 682531
Courage Directors; Theakston Best Bitter; guest beer Ⓗ
Originally a private residence for the postmaster of Newcastle, this large roadside inn dates back in part to 1660. After the well-publicised 'Northumberland witch trials' it became a notorious meeting place for a witches' coven. Licensed for over 175 years and named after the hero of Waterloo, it is now part of the food-oriented Chef & Brewer chain. However, its distinct drinkers' bar area, much frequented by locals, has the ambience of a good village pub.
ጠ❀◐◑♿⇌P

SEAHOUSES

Olde Ship Hotel

7-9 Main Street
⌚ 11-4, 6-11; 11-11 Fri & Sat; 12-10.30 Sun
☎ (01665) 720200 website: www.seahouses.co.uk
Beer range varies Ⓗ
The Olde Ship Hotel, owned by the same family since 1910, was originally built as a farmhouse about 1745 and first licensed in 1812. This nautically-themed two-star hotel boasts a main bar of tremendous character, lit by stained glass windows and warmed by a glowing open fire. Eight handpumps serve a good selection of real ales, with guest ales offered in summer. Friendly staff and regulars ensure a warm welcome.
ጠQ⇋◐⛺P

SLALEY

Travellers Rest

On B6306, 1 mile N of village
⌚ 12-11; 12-10.30 Sun
☎ (01661) 673231
Black Sheep Best Bitter; guest beers Ⓗ
Licensed for over 100 years, this welcoming inn started life in the 16th century as a farmhouse. Living up to its name, it offers the traveller an excellent choice of guest beers, wonderful food and accommodation. The bar has several distinct cosy areas and a large open fire. Stone walls, flag floors and comfortable furniture add to its appeal. There is a restaurant, but meals are also served in the bar; the menu is creative and extensive, using local produce. Children are welcome and there is a safe play area beside the pub.
ጠ❀⇋◐◑P

STAMFORDHAM

Bay Horse

On B6309
⌚ 11.30-3, 6.30-11; (open all day bank holidays); 12-3, 7-10.30 Sun
☎ (01661) 886244
Castle Eden Ale; Marston's Pedigree; guest beers Ⓗ
Overlooking the village green, next to an 11th-century church, this splendid pub dates back to around 1590. Originally a fortified farm, it then operated as a coaching inn. En-suite bedrooms have replaced the old hayloft, and a relaxing lounge/bar takes the place of the old farmhouse. Offering a warm ambience, the bar is very popular with locals and visitors; the area is steeped in the history of the Romans and the border reivers.
ጠ❀⇋◐◑P

STANNINGTON

Ridley Arms

⌚ 11.30-11; 12-10.30 Sun
☎ (01670) 789216 website: www.sjf.co.uk
Black Sheep Best Bitter; Taylor Landlord; guest beers Ⓗ
Well-designed pub belonging to the local chain, Sir John Fitzgerald's, the Ridley Arms is in a quiet village, now bypassed by the

A1. The main bar has a good-sized snug, a separate room known as the Ridley Room and a third area which leads to the restaurant. Wide doors and ramps ensure easy access for the disabled visitor. Two guest beers are always available, often from local micro-breweries. Excellent beers, good food and comfortable surroundings – what more could you want?
⛼Q❀◑◐♿P

TWEEDMOUTH

Angel
Brewery Bank
11-11; 12-10.30 Sun
☎ (01289) 303030
Hadrian & Border Rampart; guest beers H
Once the brewery tap for the Border Brewery, this pub is now in private ownership, and the brewery (as Hadrian & Border) has relocated to Newcastle. It has two rooms, one with a pool table. A former director of Border Brewery installed the wooden bar fittings, supplied by the nearby Crawford's joinery. The pub is ideally placed if you are going to the football or speedway at nearby Shieldfield Park. ⊟⇌P

WYLAM

Boathouse
Station Road
12-11; 12-10.30 Sun
☎ (01661) 853431
Beer range varies H
This pub, just next to Wylam Station, is the tap for the Wylam Brewery. The brewery is outside the village at Heddon-on-the-Wall, and the beers are loved by all who visit. The Boathouse has eight handpumps offering a variety of beers, which include the north-east micros. There are always at least two Wylam beers on offer. The house beer is also brewed by Wylam. Local CAMRA Pub of the Year 2001 – a warm, friendly welcome is assured.
⛼Q♨❀◑⇌

Omo Sapiens

If everything becomes subject to the dictates of accountants, marketing consultants, and so on, the profitability of the brewing industry may well increase. But we could find ourselves in a dreary world in ten years time – a world of consistent mediocrity, in which no one is much able to enjoy the extra money in his pocket.

I'm already worried by the way some of our competitors are changing their pubs out of all recognition, although we tend to do quite well out of it. But in a city like London, the friendly traditional pub provides a useful defence against loneliness, and a pleasant extension of people's often inadequate homes.

Fun pubs and trendy pubs may be all right for Leicester Square and the King's Road, but they aren't really what the majority of Londoners want. There was a lovely old Victorian pub in West London that's just been given the treatment. Waterfalls cascade on each floor through bars, restaurants and a discotheque. You have to cross a drawbridge to get in. I've often been tempted to go to the bar on the top floor there armed with a few packets of Tide.

John Young, *chairman of Young's of Wandsworth, in the early 1970s.*

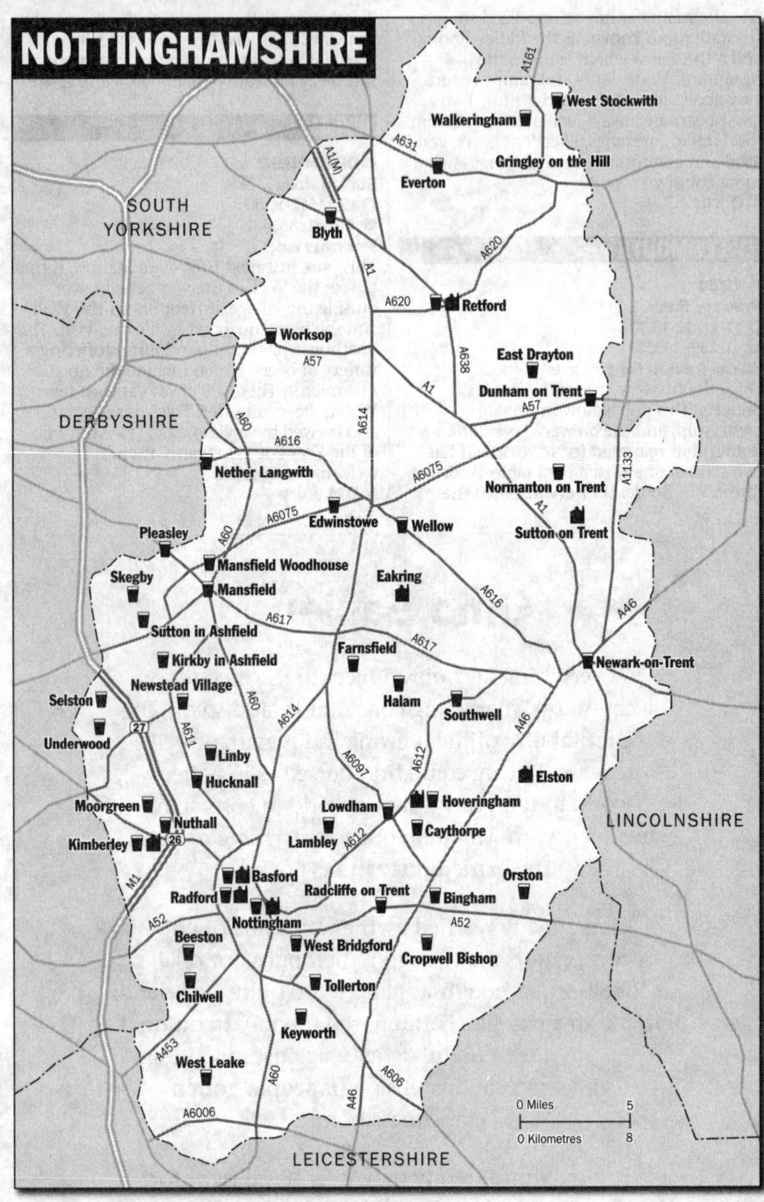

BASFORD

Fox & Crown
33 Church Street, Old Basford
12-11; 12-10.30 Sun
(0115) 942 2002
website: www.alcazarbrewing.co.com
Alcazar Ale, Nottingham Nog, New Dawn, Brush Bitter, Vixen's Vice, seasonal beers; guest beers H
Pleasant, popular pub, the tap for the Alcazar Brewery, which can be viewed through the window at the rear. A large mural of Robin Hood in Sherwood Forest has been painted on one outside wall, by a local artist. As well as the brewer's own beers, guest ales feature, along with regular beer festivals. A good range of food includes pizzas cooked on the premises – a house speciality. It hosts occasional live music.
P

Horse & Groom
462 Radford Road
11-11; 12-10.30 Sun
(0115) 970 3777
Belvoir Star Bitter; Courage Directors; Wells Bombardier; guest beers H
Genuine free house in the shadow of the former Shipstone's Brewery – the pub's original owner. The old Shipstone's sign remains on the façade, with various memorabilia around the pub. Eight beers are always on tap – five are ever-changing guest ales; the pub is keen to support local micro-breweries. A large function room at the rear is

available – they host an 'open mike' evening every Tuesday and occasional bands.
♨◖✔

BEESTON

Victoria Hotel

Dovecote Lane (by station)
⏲ 11-11; 12-10.30 Sun
☎ (0115) 925 4049 website: www.tynemill.co.uk
Bateman XB; Caledonian Deuchars IPA; Castle Rock Rylands Gold, Hemlock; Everards Tiger; guest beers Ⓗ
Buzzing Victorian architectural gem, a true free house. A traditional layout gives three, simply furnished rooms and a no-smoking restaurant. Mild is always available, alongside foreign beers, two ciders and 120 malts. The excellent varied menu, prepared by an award-winning chef, is complemented by carefully selected wines. Regular attractions include brewery evenings, free live music, wine tastings and a summer beer festival. ♨Q❀◖◗⊟♿⇌●P

BINGHAM

Horse & Plough

25 Longacre
⏲ 11-11, 12-10.30 Sun
☎ (01949) 839313
Belvoir Beaver Bitter; Courage Directors; Wells Bombardier; guest beers Ⓗ
Very popular pub, situated at the centre of the village, less than two minutes from the railway station. The pub has a large bar, with a low, beamed ceiling, and a restaurant upstairs. The three regular beers are complemented by three guest ales. The welcoming staff help foster a friendly atmosphere. ♨Q◖◗♿⇌P⊬✔

BLYTH

Angel Inn

Bawtry Road
⏲ 11-3, 6-11; 12-3, 6.30-10.30 Sun
☎ (01909) 591213
Hardys & Hansons Best Bitter, Classic, seasonal beers; guest beer Ⓗ
Situated just off the A1 on the South Yorks border, the pub is reputed to be the sixth oldest in the country, dating back to the 1300s. A former coaching inn, entry to the large car park is via an impressive archway. The pub is popular for its food. It is one of Hardys & Hansons most northern outposts. Until extra cellar space was created there was access to the 11th-century village church, via a passage under the road.
♨Q⚇❀⇄◖◗♿P⊬

CAYTHORPE

Black Horse

29 Main Street (take A612 from Lowdham island)
⏲ 11.45-2.30 (not Mon), 5.30-11; 7 (8 winter)-10.30 Sun
☎ (0115) 966 3520
Caythorpe Dover Beck Bitter; guest beers Ⓗ
Exactly what a village pub is about; dating back 300 years, it was reputedly a haunt of Dick Turpin. Magnificent home cooking is a speciality, using seasonal ingredients – try the fish. Your meal can be savoured with a pint of Caythorpe beer, brewed on the premises. Guest beers often include a second Caythorpe brew. Booking for eve meals (not served Sun) is essential. The pub maintains a friendship with a darts team from Bavaria. ♨Q❀◖◗♿P⊬⊡

CHILWELL

Cadland

342 High Road
⏲ 11.30-11; 12-10.30 Sun
☎ (0115) 951 8911
Draught Bass; M&B Mild; Tetley Bitter; guest beers Ⓗ
Since its refurbishment in 2001, the pub has enjoyed a new lease of life. Although now just a single bar, the layout provides discrete areas, separated by fireplaces, walls and glass shelved ornament displays. The relaxed, welcoming atmosphere is enhanced by the comfortable seating and friendly staff. A genuine pub atmosphere pervades, even though food is provided. It hosts weekly quiz nights and a beer festival in March.
♨❀◖◗♿P⊬

CROPWELL BISHOP

Wheatsheaf

11 Nottingham Road
⏲ 11-11; 12-10.30 Sun
☎ (0115) 989 2247
Mansfield Dark Mild, Riding Bitter, Cask Ale; Marston's Pedigree Ⓗ
This beamed former coaching inn is thought to be at least 400 years old and was a reputed haunt of Dick Turpin. The carpeted, split-level lounge has pictures and brasses on the walls; the public bar is tiled. A raised rear area contains a pool table and TV. Upholstered seats surround wooden tables throughout. Superb authentic Chinese banquets can be booked for parties of 10 or more in an upstairs room.
❀◖◗⊟♣P

DUNHAM ON TRENT

Bridge Inn

Main Street (A57)
⏲ 12-3, 5-11; 12-11 Sat; 12-10.30 Sun
☎ (01777) 228385
Broadstone Best Bitter; Greene King Ruddles County; guest beers Ⓗ
Warm, welcoming, village local, replete with interesting memorabilia, situated on the roadside near the Trent tollbridge. A centre for the local rural community, it also caters for travellers and diners with a good range of home-cooked food. Guest beers change regularly and always include one very keenly-priced ale.
♨Q❀⇄◖◗♿▲♣P

INDEPENDENT BREWERIES

Alcazar Basford
Broadstone Retford
Castle Rock Nottingham
Caythorpe Hoveringham
Hardys & Hansons Kimberley
Holland Kimberley
Mallard Nottingham
Maypole Eakring
Nathan's Elston
Nottingham Radford
Springhead Sutton on Trent

EDWINSTOWE

Forest Lodge
2-4 Church Street
⊙ 11-3, 5.30-11; 12-3, 6-10.30 Sun
☎ (01623) 824443
Beer range varies Ⓗ
17th-century coaching inn, restored to a high standard in traditional style. You may dine in the restaurant in the old barn, or the good quality food can be enjoyed in the adjacent bar area. The guest accommodation makes it an excellent base from which to explore the historic surrounding area. A cosy lounge bar, with open fire in winter, makes this a warm and welcoming inn. The house beer is from Kelham Island.
♨Q❀🛏◑◗♿P

EVERTON

Blacksmith's Arms
Church Street
⊙ 12-2, 5-11; 12-10.30 Sun
☎ (01777) 817281
Barnsley Bitter; John Smith's Bitter; Theakston Old Peculier; guest beers Ⓗ
Genuine, 18th-century free house at the heart of the village. Everton is a popular area for ramblers. Drinking areas include the locals' bar with its original tiled floor and settle. Duck under the old beam and you enter the games room (formerly the smithy). The restaurant puts an emphasis on home-cooked meals. The en-suite accommodation is in converted stables.
♨Q☕❀🛏◑◗⊟♿♣P⊽

FARNSFIELD

Red Lion
Main Street
⊙ 11-3, 6.30-11; 12-3, 6.30-10.30 Sun
☎ (01623) 882304
Mansfield Riding Bitter, Cask Ale, Banks's Bitter, seasonal beers; Marston's Pedigree Ⓗ
Family-run pub on the main road through the village in rural Nottinghamshire at the heart of Robin Hood country. A friendly atmosphere is complemented by the good food which can be enjoyed in the extended restaurant area. Popular with both locals and passing trade, for the last 10 years it has been a Mansfield tied house; since the sale to Wolverhampton & Dudley, beers from Marston's and Banks's have been introduced. ♨Q❀◑◗P⊽

GRINGLEY ON THE HILL

Blue Bell
High Street
⊙ 6 (12 Sat)-11; 12-10.30 Sun
☎ (01777) 817406 website: www.seatlestyle.com
Marston's Pedigree; John Smith's Bitter; guest beers Ⓗ
At the heart of the village, you will be welcomed by an open fire in winter. One small bar serves all the rooms, including a lounge with a large oak table and easy chairs. An unusual feature is the basement pool room. The pub prides itself on its food (no chips) which is served daily, except Monday. Attached to the premises a very fine restaurant serves mainly French food.
♨❀◑◗♣P

HALAM

Waggon & Horses
The Turnpike
⊙ 11-3, 5.30-11; 11-11 Sat; 12-10.30 Sun
☎ (01636) 813109
Fuller's London Pride; Wells Bombardier; guest beers Ⓗ
Popular pub at the centre of an unspoilt village near the historic town of Southwell, and convenient for visitors to the minster and the workhouse. In addition to the constantly changing range of real ales from breweries large and small, the food is of a consistently high standard. The restaurant is always popular (Sun eve meals finish at 6pm). The pub is an enthusiastic member of the Campaign for Real Food. Q❀◑◗♣P

HOVERINGHAM

Marquis of Granby
Main Street
⊙ 11.30-3 (not Mon), 5-11; 11-11 Thu-Sat; 12-10.30 Sun
☎ (0115) 966 3080
Beer range varies Ⓗ
Attractive village pub, comprising a narrow front bar, with pool table and darts, plus a lounge and dining areas. A popular starting and finishing point for country walks, the River Trent is five minutes on foot. The pub

INN BRIEF

EAST DRAYTON

Blue Bell Inn
Low Street
12-2.30, 6-11; 12-2.30, 6-10.30 Sun
(01777) 249509
Beer range varies Ⓗ
Traditional village pub of open-plan design with a no-smoking area. Food served Tue-Sun. Two ales change regularly.

MOORGREEN

Horse & Groom
11-11; 12-10.30 Sun
(01773) 713417
Hardys & Hansons Best Bitter, seasonal beers Ⓗ
Attractive, 17th-century country pub with large garden and children's play area. Food available 12-9 (8 Sun). Cask Marque accredited.

NEWSTEAD VILLAGE

Station Hotel
Station Road
11-3, 7-11; 12-3, 7-10.30 Sun
(01623) 753294
Oakwell Barnsley Bitter, Old Tom Ⓗ
At a station on the Robin Hood Line, this traditional local has a number of rooms, one with pool and darts.

NOTTINGHAM

Chestnut Tree
482 Mansfield Road, Sherwood
11-11; 12-10.30 Sun
(0115) 985 6388
Marston's Pedigree; guest beers Ⓗ
Large, modern single room, plus a dining area. Very popular at weekends; live music Thu and Sat eves. Good value food.

Coach & Horses
15 Upper Parliament Street
10.30-11; 12-10.30 Sun
(0115) 941 7107
Tetley Bitter; guest beers Ⓗ
Single-roomed, city-centre pub, five minutes' walk from the market square. Popular with the over-30s, especially at weekends.

Forest Tavern
257 Mansfield Road
12 (4 Mon & Tue)-11; 12-10.30 Sun
(0115) 947 5650
Caledonian Deuchars IPA; Castle Rock Forest Gold; Greene King Abbot; Woodforde's Wherry; guest beer Ⓗ
One-roomed, continental-style bar, stocking a good range of European draught and bottled beers. Food served all day.

has gained a reputation for its strong ales (mostly over 4% ABV). Morris dancers are a common sight and the pub hosts a steam tractor rally in June. Rocky, Max and Charlie are colourful local characters who have been known to use bad language – they are parrots! Lunches are served Tue and Wed, meals all day Thu-Sun.
P

HUCKNALL

Pilgrim Oak

44-46 High Street
10.30-11; 12-10.30 Sun
(0115) 963 2539
Courage Directors; Greene King Abbot; Shepherd Neame Spitfire; Theakston Best Bitter; guest beer H
Popular Wetherspoon's, converted from a Co-op store into a comfortable, large town-centre pub. Discrete drinking areas are provided by booths on either side of the room. The unusual name is a link to Byron – the pilgrim oak being found at Newstead Abbey. The history of Hucknall is celebrated by informative wall displays which include one dedicated to Eric Coates. Meals are served all day.
(Robin Hood Line) P

KEYWORTH

Fairway

Nottingham Road
11-11; 12-10.30 Sun
(0115) 937 5258
Beer range varies H
Friendly, 1960s estate pub converted to open plan, but plenty of large alcoves give distinct areas, including one with a pool table, another with a TV and a no-smoking area. The beers are constantly changing, often offering local and not-so-local micros' beers; Cannon Royall Fruiterer's Mild is usually stocked. Lunches are served every day except Monday; evening meals Wed-Sat. P

KIMBERLEY

Nelson & Railway

12 Station Road (opp. brewery)
11.30-3, 5-11; 11.30-11 Thu-Sat; 12-10.30 Sun
(0115) 938 2177
website: www.nelsonandrailway.fsnet.co.uk
Hardys & Hansons Best Bitter, Classic, seasonal beers H
Fine local, situated less than 150 yards from the brewery. The wood-panelled bar is complemented by the beamed lounge which has an adjoining dining area. The front garden is popular in the summer and the pub is renowned for its good value food and B&B accommodation. Sunday meals are served 12-6. The landlord has run this very impressive pub for over 30 years.
P

Stag Inn

67 Nottingham Road
5 (4.30 Fri; 1.30 Sat)-11; 12-10.30 Sun
(0115) 938 3151
Cains Mild; Greenalls Bitter; Marston's Pedigree; guest beers H
Characterful, two-roomed local, dating from 1537. A number of old-fashioned slot machines, in working order, are on display in both rooms. Above the bar an interesting collection of old photos depicts various aspects of Shipstone's – the former brewery that once owned the pub. A large rear garden and children's play area are added attractions. Look out for Tiffany, the large ginger pub cat.
Q

KIRKBY IN ASHFIELD

Countryman

Park Lane (B6018/B6019 jct)
11-11; 12-10.30 Sun
(01623) 752314
website: www.alibo.free-online.co.uk
Fuller's London Pride; Theakston Best Bitter, XB; guest beers H
Family-owned, two-roomed 18th-century pub, off the beaten track. The main bar area is cosy, with ample seating, a low, beamed ceiling, and a choice of up to six real ales; an occasional cider is stocked. The walls and ceiling are plastered with pump clips (mainly from micro-breweries) of past beers. The larger bar at the back hosts bikers night (Wed), live music (Fri) and may be booked for private parties. Home-cooked food is served Tue-Sun (not Sun eve). The new no-smoking restaurant has its own bar.
Q P

Globe
London Road
11-11; 12-10.30 Sun
(0115) 986 6881
Broadstone Best Bitter; Fuller's London Pride; Oakham JHB; guest beers H
Light, airy, popular pub near Trent Bridge; smart, but beer prices are very competitive.

Starting Gate
Candle Meadow
11-11; 12-4, 7-10.30 Sun
(0115) 987 8628
Courage Directors; Mansfield Cask Ale; Theakston XB H
Popular pub on edge of the city, next to the racecourse and scenic Colwick Country Park.

Turf Tavern
64 Upper Parliament Street
11-11; 12-10.30 Sun
(0115) 911 1719
Adnams Bitter; Draught Bass; Cains Mild; Tetley Bitter; guest beers H
Traditional, one-roomed, corner pub near the Theatre Royal. A house beer and food available.

PLEASLEY

Olde Plough
Chesterfield Road North
11.30-3, 5.30-11; 11-11 Sat; 12-3, 7-10.30 Sun
(01623) 810386
Marston's Bitter, Pedigree, seasonal beers H
Deservedly popular, open-plan pub which offers a wide choice of home-cooked food, including specials and a light menu.

RETFORD

Albert Hotel
Albert Road
11.30-11; 12-10.30 Sun
(01777) 708694
Hardys & Hansons Best Bitter; guest beers H
Cask Marque accredited, busy terraced pub. Food is served lunchtimes.

Clinton Arms
24 Albert Road
11-11; 12-10.30 Sun
(01777) 702703
Greene King IPA; John Smith's Bitter; Wells Bombardier; guest beers H
A Guide stalwart: a three-roomed pub near the canal basin. Popular, especially for live music and large-screen TV.

LAMBLEY

Robin Hood & Little John
82 Main Street
⏲ 12-3 (4 Fri & Sat), 6-11; 12-5, 7-10.30 Sun
☎ (0115) 931 2531
Mansfield Dark Mild, Cask Ale, Banks's Bitter; Marston's Pedigree Ⓗ
Popular pub, alleged to be the oldest in the village. It has a bar, lounge and a function room at the back, where the darts team play and there is a skittle alley. Meals are served lunchtime and evening. Background music is usually from the 1970s and '80s.
♨ ◑ ⊟ ♣ P ⊁

LINBY

Horse & Groom
Main Street
⏲ 12-11; 12-10.30 Sun
☎ (0115) 963 2219
Theakston Mild; guest beers Ⓗ
Multi-roomed gem of a village pub, north of Nottingham. The public bar, snug and 'Green' room all have open fires – the one in the public bar being an inglenook. Four cask ales are sold and the guests often come from small local breweries. The award-winning village is very picturesque. The pub enjoys a deserved reputation for good quality meals, served in all areas, including the restaurant. Regular music nights, hosted by a pianist, are staged (Tue) and quiz nights (Thu). ♨ Q ❀ ◑ ⊟ ♿ ♣ P

LOWDHAM

World's End Inn
Plough Lane (500 yds from A612/A6097 roundabout)
⏲ 12-3, 5.30-11; 12-4, 7-10.30 Sun
Mansfield Cask Ale; Marston's Bitter, Pedigree Ⓗ
Circa 1744, this pub has been separated from the main village by the bypass. Vibrant floral displays stand out against its white exterior; the interior features horse brasses, exposed beams, plates and jugs. The flag pole – easily seen from the main road – originated from Nottingham Forest FC, and apparently contains an ancient time capsule of old coins, recently added to with more coinage and business cards by the current landlord. The food menu is extensive; you can eat outside in summer. ♨ Q ❀ ◑ ♿ ⇌ P

MANSFIELD

Bold Forester
Botany Avenue (A38, 1/2 mile from bus station)
⏲ 11-11; 12-10.30 Sun
☎ (01623) 623970
Bateman XXXB; Boddingtons Bitter; Castle Eden Bitter; Flowers Original; Greene King Abbot; guest beers Ⓗ
Mansfield's leading ale house offers a constantly changing range of six guest beers, plus various ciders. This traditional, open-plan local has south-facing gardens and a terrace. Excellent, good value meals are served lunchtime and early evening (no-smoking area available). It hosts quiz nights (Tue and Thu) and live music (Sun eve). The tap room houses a pool table and a large-screen TV for sports. An established beer festival, with 30-plus beers is held annually around St George's Day.
❀ ◑ ♿ ⇌ (Robin Hood Line) ♣ ● P ⊁ ✓

Nell Gwynne
117 Sutton Road (A38, 1 mile W of centre)
⏲ 12-4 (not Mon-Thu), 7-11; 12-4, 7-10.30 Sun
☎ (01623) 659850
Beer range varies Ⓗ
Friendly local consisting of two rooms: a comfortable lounge with the atmosphere of a rural pub, and a games room for darts and television. It was a gentlemen-only private club (Bleak House) from 1927 to 2001, but now holds a full licence and offers a warm welcome to all visitors. The two real ales change regularly. It hosts a quiz night (Wed).
Q ♿ ♣

Railway Inn
9 Station Street
⏲ 11-11; 12-10.30 Sun
☎ (01623) 623086
Bateman XB Ⓗ
Rare Bateman's outlet in the Mansfield area. Although serving only one real ale it is one of the cheapest around. Convenient for the station and main shopping area, home-cooked food is available lunchtime and bar snacks in the evening. The pub serves a wide range of cocktails. It has featured regularly on TV and in the local press – once for a record attempt at being buried alive in the pub garden and once when a customer 'married' the pub!
Q ❀ ◑ ⊟ ⇌ (Robin Hood Line) ♣

MANSFIELD WOODHOUSE

Greyhound
82 High Street
⏲ 12-11; 12-3, 7-10.30 Sun
☎ (01623) 464403
Courage Directors; Mansfield Cask Ale; Theakston Cool Cask; guest beer Ⓗ
Friendly, two-roomed local: a comfortable, quiet lounge (which only gets noisy due to good conversation), and a lively tap room that houses a dartboard and pool table. On the main road through the village, it is about half a mile from the station on the Robin Hood Line. It is a frequent venue for CAMRA meetings, when everyone is made welcome and treated to excellent sausages, but otherwise food is not usually available.
❀ ⊟ ♿ ⇌ ♣ P

NETHER LANGWITH

Jug & Glass
Queens Walk (A632)
⏲ 11.30-11; 11.30-10.30 Sun
☎ (01623) 742283
Hardys & Hansons Best Bitter, Classic, seasonal beers Ⓗ
The inn (circa 1179) probably housed monks who farmed the nearby Welbeck Abbey. The first recorded licensee (in 1787), rented the buildings from the sixth Duke of Portland. It was an historic meeting place for coal miners and villagers. It has only had 16 licensees and has been refurbished to retain its charm and comfortable family atmosphere. Popular for outdoor drinking on the banks of the River Poulter, it serves an excellent range of home-cooked food. Accommodation is in three restored oak-beamed rooms. ♨ Q ❀ ◑ ♿ ⇌ (Robin Hood Line) ♣ P ⊁

NEWARK-ON-TRENT

Castle & Falcon
10 London Road
12-3 (not Tue or Thu; 4 Sat), 7-11; 12-4, 7-10.30 Sun
☎ (01636) 703513
website: www.castleandfalcon.co.uk
John Smith's Bitter; guest beers Ⓗ
Situated in the shadow of the former James Hole's Castle Brewery, this welcoming and friendly, no-nonsense local caters mainly for regulars. It offers three drinking areas: a bar, lounge and children's area, plus a function room. With around 20 different teams calling it home, it is often lively. The guest beers change on a regular basis and tasters are available. Outside is a long alley skittles pitch and a small patio.
❀ ≉ (Castle) ♣

Fox & Crown
4-6 Appletongate (near market square)
11-11; 12-10.30 Sun
☎ (01636) 605820 website: www.tynemill.co.uk
Castle Rock Hemlock, Vixen Gold; Everards Tiger; Hook Norton Best Bitter; Marston's Pedigree; guest beers Ⓗ
A Tynemill outlet opened in 1997, this is a superb town pub, consisting of a main drinking area with smaller areas leading off. The excellent range of beers varies weekly. Good value food is prepared using local produce, with daily specials. The pub hosts regular brewery nights and occasional live music. Close to the Palace Theatre, it is ideal to pop into before or after a performance.
Q ◑ ♿ ≉ (Castle/Northgate) ♣ ⚘ ⁄

Mailcoach
13 London Road
11.30-3, 5.30-11; 11-11 Sat; 12-3.30, 7-10.30 Sun
☎ (01636) 605164
Broadstone Best Bitter; Flowers IPA, Original; guest beers Ⓗ
Eleven consecutive entries in this Guide are testament to the quality of this former coaching inn, that dates back to 1778. There are three different, but comfortable drinking areas inside and a patio garden. The pub holds a beer festival at the end of May, in conjunction with the Newark beer festival and hosts regular live music (usually Thu). This popular free house lies close to the town centre. Cider is sold in summer.
❀ ◑ ≉ (Castle) P

NORMANTON ON TRENT

Square & Compass
(off A1, 10 miles N of Newark)
12-3, 5-11; 11-11 Fri & Sat; 12-10.30 Sun
☎ (01636) 821439
Beer range varies Ⓗ
Friendly, one-roomed village free house, parts of which are said to date back 500 years. A log fire is a feature of the beamed bar, with a no-smoking dining room at one end serving food daily (all day Sun). Wednesday is curry and quiz night. The varying range of three beers includes one from Maypole Brewery, owned by Kenny the landlord. Outside are a beer garden, play area and field for campers and caravans. One of the en-suite bedrooms has wheelchair access. ❀ ◑ ♿ ♣ P

NOTTINGHAM

Bell Inn
18 Angel Row, Old Market Square
10.30-11; 12-10.30 Sun
☎ (0115) 947 5241
Hardys & Hansons Best Mild, Best Bitter, Ye Olde Trip Ale, Classic; Marston's Pedigree; guest beer Ⓗ
Described as having a Tardis-like quality, small rooms at the front lead to a large main bar – a venue for jazz and other regular live music (Sun-Wed eves). It is one of three pubs jockeying for the 'oldest pub in Nottingham' title – its pub status dates back to at least 1437 – and it is on a local ghost tour. The food is excellent, served downstairs and in a smart upstairs restaurant. Pavement tables are set outside in summer. Q ❀ ◑ ✔

Fellows, Morton & Clayton
54 Canal Street
11-11 (midnight Fri & Sat); 12-10.30 Sun
☎ (0115) 950 6795
Castle Eden Ale; Fellows Bitter, Post Haste; Fuller's London Pride; Mallard Duck & Dive; guest beers Ⓗ
One-roomed pub with split-level areas, converted from a warehouse in the late 1970s, it is extremely popular with students and nearby office workers. It is the home of the city centre's first brew-pub (note that malt extract is used) and a regular outlet for local Mallard beers. An excellent, good value restaurant is situated at the rear of the pub, which is convenient for visitors to the nearby canalside development. ❀ ◑ ≉ ⁄

Frampton's Bar Bistro
11 St James Terrace
12 (1 Sat)-11; 1-10.30 Sun
☎ (0115) 941 1997
Beer range varies Ⓗ
Part of the redevelopment of the site of Nottingham's old general hospital, this bar offers accommodation and a comprehensive all-day menu, served in the upper level dining area. The bar and alcoves are decorated with photos of rock music celebrities, including Peter Frampton. Three changing guest beers are always on tap, usually from local brewers, Springhead and Nottingham. Q ◑ ≉

Lincolnshire Poacher
161 Mansfield Road
11-11; 12-10.30 Sun
☎ (0115) 941 1584
Bateman XB, XXXB; Castle Rock Poacher's Gold; Fuller's London Pride; guest beers Ⓗ
Two-roomed, traditional pub with wood floors (the smaller room is for non-smokers) with a garden and conservatory to the rear. The pub is popular with diners and the real ale fraternity doing the Mansfield Road crawl. Twinned with an Amsterdam bar, this was probably the first pub in Nottingham to sell an ever-changing range of real ales from micro-breweries on a regular basis. A varied and tasty menu is served. It hosts occasional live music and regular brewery nights. ❀ ◑ ♣ ⁄

Lloyds No. 1 Bar
1 Carlton Street, Hockley
11-midnight; 12-midnight Sun
☎ (0115) 988 1660
Beer range varies Ⓗ

Converted bank, located in a prominent spot at the top of Hockley. Described as a 'young at heart' pub, it features up-to-date music and plasma screens. The unusual high ceilings and polished wood floor provide excellent surroundings for a leisurely drink in the afternoon or for the faster-paced evenings (with late licence). Queues may form at weekends. ◑♿⚡●

Lord Nelson

11 Thurgaton Street, Sneinton

⚙ 11-3, 5-11; 11-4, 5.30-11 Sat; 12-4, 7-10.30 Sun

☎ (0115) 911 0069

Hardys & Hansons Best Mild, Best Bitter, Classic, seasonal beers Ⓗ

Originally two country cottages, this unusual pub has the appearance of a traditional country inn, albeit in the city. The 400-year-old former coaching inn now consists of four smallish rooms where generally the emphasis is on convivial conversation. Again, unusual for a town pub, it has a fine sheltered garden which helps make it a popular summer venue. Smoking restrictions only apply at lunchtime. No food is served Sat.

♔Q❀◑⊡♣⚡●

Olde Trip to Jerusalem ☆

1 Brewhouse Yard (below castle)

⚙ 11-11; 12-10.30 Sun

☎ (0115) 947 3171 website: www.triptojerusalem.com

Hardys & Hansons Best Mild, Best Bitter, Ye Olde Trip Ale, Classic, seasonal beers; Marston's Pedigree Ⓗ

Described as the 'world famous Ye Olde Trip to Jerusalem' with 1189 AD painted on the wall, it consists of a number of rooms downstairs, some cut out of the castle rock. Upstairs is the Rock Lounge which displays the haunted galleon and a modern tapestry depicting the history of Nottingham. Meals are served until 6pm. The top bar can be reserved for private functions. Not to be missed. Q❀◑⇌♣⚡

Red Lion

21 Alfreton Road (at Canning Circus)

⚙ 11-11; 12-10.30 Sun

☎ (0115) 952 0309

Boddingtons Bitter; Marston's Pedigree; guest beers Ⓗ

Up to eight different beers are available in this one-roomed split-level pub. Sporting events can be viewed on an unobtrusive TV at the back of the bar. An unusual outside drinking terrace is accessed up a flight of steps. Basic, good value food is served at lunchtimes (limited choice Sat); try the Tuesday evening special of bangers and mash for 75p with a pint. It opens at 11 on Sunday for brunch; house newspapers are produced. ❀◑

Salutation Inn

Maid Marian Way, Houndsgate

⚙ 11.30-11; 12-10.30 Sun

☎ (0115) 988 1948

Castle Eden Ale; Greene King Old Speckled Hen; Hook Norton Old Hooky; guest beers Ⓗ

Historic pub, one of three claiming to be the oldest in Nottingham. A staircase from the open-plan bar leads to an upper bar room. Stone flags, bare boards and beams prevail throughout this pub, close to Nottingham Castle. A plethora of haunted caves exists below, viewed by scheduled ghost tours in the summer. It is a regular outlet for Weston's Old Rosie cider. A comprehensive menu is served until 8pm. The upstairs function room can be booked. Q◑⇌●

Vat & Fiddle

12-14 Queens Bridge Road (near station)

⚙ 11-11; 12-10.30 Sun

☎ (0115) 985 0611

Caledonian Deuchars IPA; Castle Rock Meadows Gold, Hemlock; guest beers Ⓗ

Popular, down-to-earth single-roomed boozer at the edge of Nottingham's Meadows area. Photos on the walls show other long-since demolished Meadows pubs. Between the railway station and the football grounds, it is next door to Tynemill's Castle Rock Brewery. Ten handpulls serve up to five beers from Castle Rock and at least one mild. Belgian beers and up to 70 malt whiskies are also stocked. It stages occasional beer festivals and live entertainment. No meals are served Sun eve. Q❀◑⇌●

NUTHALL

Three Ponds

Nottingham Road (off M1 jct 26)

⚙ 11-11; 12-10.30 Sun

INN BRIEF

SKEGBY

Fox & Crown
116 Dalestorth Road
11-11; 12-10.30 Sun
(01623) 552436
Mansfield Cask Ale; Theakston Mild, XB; guest beer Ⓗ
Steak & Ale pub with no-smoking and restaurant sections, and a large-screen TV for sport.

SUTTON IN ASHFIELD

King & Miller
Kings Mill Road East
11-11; 12-10.30 Sun
(01623) 553312
Hardys & Hansons Best Bitter, Classic, seasonal beers Ⓗ
Open-plan pub; half is devoted to family dining with indoor children's play area. Public bar has no-smoking area. Cask Marque accredited.

WEST STOCKWITH

Waterfront Inn
Canal Lane
12-11; 12-10.30 Sun
(01427) 891233
John Smith's Bitter; guest beers Ⓗ
One-roomed pub with an eating area, overlooking the River Trent, Chesterfield Canal and the marina. Busy in summer.

WORKSOP

Liquorice Gardens
Newcastle Street
11-11; 11-10.30 Sun
(01909) 512220
Beer range varies Ⓗ
Busy, recently-opened, town-centre Wetherspoon's, with 10 cask ales and a no-smoking area. No music. Cask Marque accredited.

Missing?

If a pub is not listed in the Guide that you think is worthy of consideration, please let us know at GBG, CAMRA, 230 Hatfield Road, St Albans, Herts, AL1 4LW or camra@camra.org.uk. All recommendations are forwarded to CAMRA branches, which are responsible for choosing pubs.

☎ (0115) 938 3170
Hardys & Hansons Best Bitter, Classic, seasonal beers Ⓗ
Refurbished in 2000, it is now well established as one of the brewery's pubs that specialises in good food. The front bar area has the feel of a comfortable pub, while the rear is more attuned to diners. Food is served 11-9 (12-8 Sun). At the back of the pub is a patio and a spacious garden, complete with children's play area. See the old photographs of the area displayed inside.
❀◐◑♿P⚟✓

ORSTON

Durham Ox

Church Street OS769411
⏲ 12-3, 6-11; 11.30-11 Sat; 12-10.30 Sun
☎ (01949) 850059
Marston's Pedigree; guest beers Ⓗ
Delightful village pub for locals and visitors alike, it has a garden and pavement café tables in summer and a roaring fire in winter. There are hitching rails for horses and ferrets! The divided room features a whisky collection in one half, aviation pictures and memorabilia elsewhere. There is no hot food but filled rolls are made to order. Popular pub games are played. A third guest beer is stocked in summer.
♨Q❀♣P⚟▯

RADCLIFFE ON TRENT

Black Lion

Main Road
⏲ 12 (11 Sat)-11; 12-10.30 Sun
☎ (0115) 933 2135
Courage Directors; guest beers Ⓗ
Large, comfortable pub at the village centre, serving three ever-changing guest beers. Separate from the smart lounge is a refurbished and extended public bar, with a large-screen TV for sport. Regular live music is performed upstairs. Food is served 12-9, with an emphasis on home-cooked dishes and an extensive specials board. The enclosed garden, with children's play area, is popular with families. Cider is available in summer.
♨❀◐◑⊟♿⇌♣●P

RADFORD

Plough

17 St Peter's Street
⏲ 12-2.30, 5-11; 12-11 Thu-Sat; 12-10.30 Sun
☎ (0115) 942 2649
Nottingham Rock Mild, Rock Bitter, Legend, Extra Pale Ale, Bullion; guest beers Ⓗ
Friendly 1840s pub, rescued by its current owners from Whitbread, it is the tap for the Nottingham Brewery, housed in the buildings at the rear. Jazz is performed on Sunday lunchtime to accompany the popular lunches. Curry on Tue eve costs £1; chilli is free on Thursday. A real pub, designed for real people to enjoy Nottingham Ales – 'beers to be proud of' – it was Nottingham CAMRA's Pub of Excellence winner in January 2002.
♨Q❀◐◑⊟♣P

RETFORD ❄

Market Hotel

West Carr Road
⏲ 11-3, 6-11; 11-11 Sat; 12-4.30, 7-10.30 Sun
☎ (01777) 703278
Adnams Bitter; Bateman XXXB; Marston's Pedigree; Wadworth 6X; Young's Bitter; guest beers Ⓗ
Run by the same family for 40 years, this comfortable, deservedly popular, one-roomed pub serves up to 10 real ales – four of them as guests. Situated on the outskirts of town, in the suburb of Ordsall, it is just a few minutes' walk from the station. It is well known locally for its food, particularly the Sunday carvery, complemented by a small but varied wine list. Children are welcome early evening.
Q❀◐◑♿⇌P

Rum Runner

Wharf Road (opp. fire station)
⏲ 11.30-11; 12-10.30 Sun
☎ (01777) 860788
Taylor Landlord; guest beers Ⓗ
This very popular pub is presently north Nottinghamshire's only brew-pub. Broadstone beers are produced in the stables; the Two Water Grog is only available here (not even for beer festivals). It also serves a wide range of continental bottled beers. A small, quiet restaurant is open Thu-Sat eves and Sunday lunch; bar meals are available most of the time. The no-smoking lounge has large, comfortable sofas and can get very busy at weekends.
♨❀◐◑⇌♣⚟▯

SELSTON

Horse & Jockey

Church Lane (1/2 mile off B6018) OS464539
⏲ 12-2.30, 5-11; 12-3, 7.30-10.30 Sun
☎ (01773) 781012
Draught Bass; Ⓗ **Greene King Abbot; Taylor Landlord;** Ⓖ **guest beers** Ⓗ/Ⓖ
Family-run village local, dating back to 1664 and reputedly haunted. Allegedly only 12 pubs in England are older than this one, a local CAMRA Pub of the Year. Low, beamed ceilings and flagstoned floors feature in all its rooms: a main bar, snug, a lounge with working cast-iron range and a games room (pool and darts). Wednesday is folk night, when all are welcome – bring your own instrument. Good food is served weekdays; freshly carved roast meats feature most days.
♨Q⛴❀◐♿♣●P

SOUTHWELL

Bramley Apple

57 Church Street
⏲ 12-3, 5.30-11; 12-11 Sat; 12-10.30 Sun
☎ (01636) 813675
Springhead Bitter, Puritans Porter, Roaring Meg; guest beer Ⓗ
Taking its name from the home of the Bramley apple, this was the first pub owned by Springhead Brewery. It is run on the lines of a wine bar, serving home-cooked food (not served Sun eve). A minimum of four Springhead beers are on tap at any time, plus two continental lagers on draught, and a handpulled cider – the landlord will have no nitro on the premises.

The pub is a stone's throw from Southwell Minster which is well worth visiting. Limited parking. Q❀⇌◑◑♣P

Old Coach House

69 Easthorpe (A612, near racecourse)

11-5 (4 Fri; 12 Sat)-11; 12-10.30 Sun

☎ (01636) 813289

Draught Bass; guest beers H

This friendly, welcoming 17th-century free house offers an average of 20 different beers each week, six at any one time; shot glasses are used for sampling. On cold days three open fires make it easy to feel at home. For entertainment, many games are available, including a rare one for the area – cribbage. Southwell Racecourse and Minster are close by and the pub lies conveniently on the Newark-Nottingham bus route. Cider is stocked in summer. ⛪❀⊟♣♣

SUTTON IN ASHFIELD

Picture House

Fox Street (near bus station)

11-11; 12-10.30 Sun

☎ (01623) 554627

Greene King Abbot; Mansfield Dark Mild; Shepherd Neame Spitfire; Theakston Best Bitter; guest beers H

Open-plan Wetherspoon's pub, formerly a cinema. It tends to get very busy and noisy, due to the acoustics created by the very high ceiling. A large no-smoking section on an upper level doubles as a family area (children's certificate). The walls feature abstract paintings and pictures of old Sutton. Good value food is served all day. Usually two beer festivals are held annually. ◑◑♿⊬✔

TOLLERTON

Air Hostess

Stanstead Avenue (A606)

11.30 (12 Thu)-2.30 (not Mon), 5.30-11; 12-2.30, 7-10.30 Sun

☎ (0115) 937 2485

Mansfield Cask Ale; Nottingham Legend; guest beers H

Modern pub with an impressive sign, situated in the centre of the village, close to the Melton road. Its two rooms are decorated with aeronautical pictures and maps; the public bar has a pool table. A quiet and comfortable lounge benefits from views over the surrounding area. The pub has a thriving pétanque team which plays in the good-sized garden. The three guest beers vary regularly. Q❀◑◑♣P

UNDERWOOD

Red Lion

134 Church Lane (off B600)

12-3, 5.30-11; 12-11 Sat; 12-10.30 Sun

☎ (01773) 810482

Boddingtons Bitter; Marston's Pedigree; guest beers H

300-year-old, beamed village pub, run by a friendly landlord and staff. The bar area has a quarry-tiled floor with a step up to a raised carpeted dining area (children welcome in the latter). A good variety of excellent meals and snacks are served and barbecues are held in summer. The large garden has a paved patio, a lawn and a children's play area. On Monday evening a general knowledge quiz is held, and a raffle. Over the years it has won a number of local CAMRA awards. ❀◑◑P⊬

WALKERINGHAM

Three Horseshoes

High Street

11.30-3, 7-11; 12-4, 7-10.30 Sun

☎ (01427) 890959

Stones Bitter; Worthington Bitter; guest beers H

If you miss the pub sign as you drive down the High Street, just look out for the award-winning flower displays which include the most unusual use of an old butcher's bike. The pub consists of one large, lounge-style bar and a 54-seat restaurant at the rear. Home-cooked food is served daily from an extensive chalkboard menu, except Monday and Sunday evenings. The pub is popular with locals and visitors alike.

⛪Q◑◑♿⛺♣P⊽

WELLOW

Red Lion

Eakring Road (off A616)

11.30-3.30, 6-11; 11-11 Sat; 12-10.30 Sun

☎ (01623) 861000

Black Sheep Best Bitter; Castle Eden Ale; Wells Bombardier; guest beer H

400-year-old traditional pub with exposed beams, it stands opposite the maypole in a quiet village, close to Clumber and Ruffolk Parks. The Center Parcs resort, Shannon caravan park and Sherwood Castle Holiday Village are nearby. Facilities include a 20-seat restaurant, a bar for smokers and one for non-smokers, a snug and a garden.

Q❀◑◑⊟⛺♣P⊬

WEST BRIDGFORD

Meadow Covert

Alford Road, Edwalton

11-11; 12-10.30 Sun

☎ (0115) 923 2074

Hardys & Hansons Best Mild, Best Bitter, Ye Olde Trip Ale, Classic, seasonal beers H

Situated to the north of Edwalton, this fairly modern, two-roomed community pub has a games-oriented public bar, with two pool tables and a large-screen TV. The comfortable L-shaped lounge has plenty of room for drinkers and diners. Food is served until 7.30pm weekdays, 6pm at weekends; take-away fish and chips are available on Friday and Saturday until 11pm. The garden, with children's play area, hosts summer barbecues and beer festivals.

Q❀◑⊟♿♣P✔

Southbank Bar

1 Bridgford House, Trent Bridge

11.30-11; 9am-11pm Sat; 9am-10.30pm Sun

☎ (0115) 945 5541 website: www.southbank-bar.co.uk

Fuller's London Pride; Mallard Duck & Dive H

Very popular bar close to both Trent Bridge cricket ground and Nottingham Forest football ground. The pub has a number of large screens which show various sporting matches (cricket, rugby and football). Local office workers frequent the pub at lunchtime. The beer garden overlooks the River Trent and is well used in summer. Note the unusual weekend opening hours.

◑◑♿P

Stratford Haven

2 Stratford Road

10.30-11; 12-10.30 Sun

(0115) 982 5981

Bateman XB; Caledonian Deuchars IPA; Castle Rock Hemlock; Exmoor Gold; Hook Norton Old Hooky; guest beers H

Busy, no-gimmicks Tynemill pub, between the town centre and Trent Bridge cricket ground. Named as a result of a competition in the local press, the winning entry is on display. The range of beers includes at least one mild and a house beer, brewed by Castle Rock. The pub hosts monthly brewery nights featuring all the selected brewery's beers. A good menu includes a vegetarian choice and no chips. Plenty of parking space locally.

WEST LEAKE

Star Inn

Melton Lane

11-2.30 (3 Sat), 6-11; 12-3, 7-10.30 Sun

(01509) 852233

Draught Bass; guest beers H

White pub, on the outskirts of the village; its three rooms include a recently extended, no-smoking family room. The large garden and patio area afford views over the surrounding countryside. There are always two changing guest ales and mini-beer festivals are held twice a year. Evening meals are served. Two en-suite rooms, in the linked cottage, are recent additions.

WORKSOP

Greendale Oak

41 Norfolk Street

12-11; 12-4, 7-10.30 Sun

(01909) 489680

website: www.downourlocal.com/greendale-oak-worksop

Stones Bitter; guest beers H

Small, terraced pub built in 1790; its single bar still retains gas lights. A good range of home-made meals is prepared using all fresh produce. There is an ever-changing range of guest beers, one of which always is a mild. It fields active darts and dominoes teams. Well worth a visit.

Mallard Inn

Worksop Station, Carlton Road

11-11; closed Mon; 12-4 Sun

(01909) 530757

Beer range varies H

Formerly the Worksop Station buffet bar, this pub offers a warm, friendly welcome in one small, cosy and comfortable bar area. The building is within the old station, overlooking the railway line. Two guest beers are constantly changing and there is also a fine selection of Belgian beers and country wines. A further room is available downstairs for special occasions. A conker match is held here annually. Q P

Newcastle Arms

Carlton Road

11-11; 12-10.30 Sun

(01909) 485384

Beer range varies H

This small pub dates from 1910, but became a pool and snooker hall during the early 1980s; it reopened in the mid-1980s with a warm, friendly environment. A wide choice of home-cooked food is served (no meals Sun eve). Guest beers offer a wide variety and change regularly; also a selection of fruit wines is stocked. A popular quiz is held every Tuesday.

Children's certificates

When pubs are described as having 'children's certificates', this indicates that local licensing authorities are satisfied that the pubs in question have environments suitable for children under 14, and that meals and non-alcoholic drinks are available. Some authorities demand more wide-ranging facilities – such as no-smoking areas, an absence of gaming machines, nappy-changing provision, junior WCs and basins, and furniture suitable for small children – before granting certificates, which must be prominently displayed.

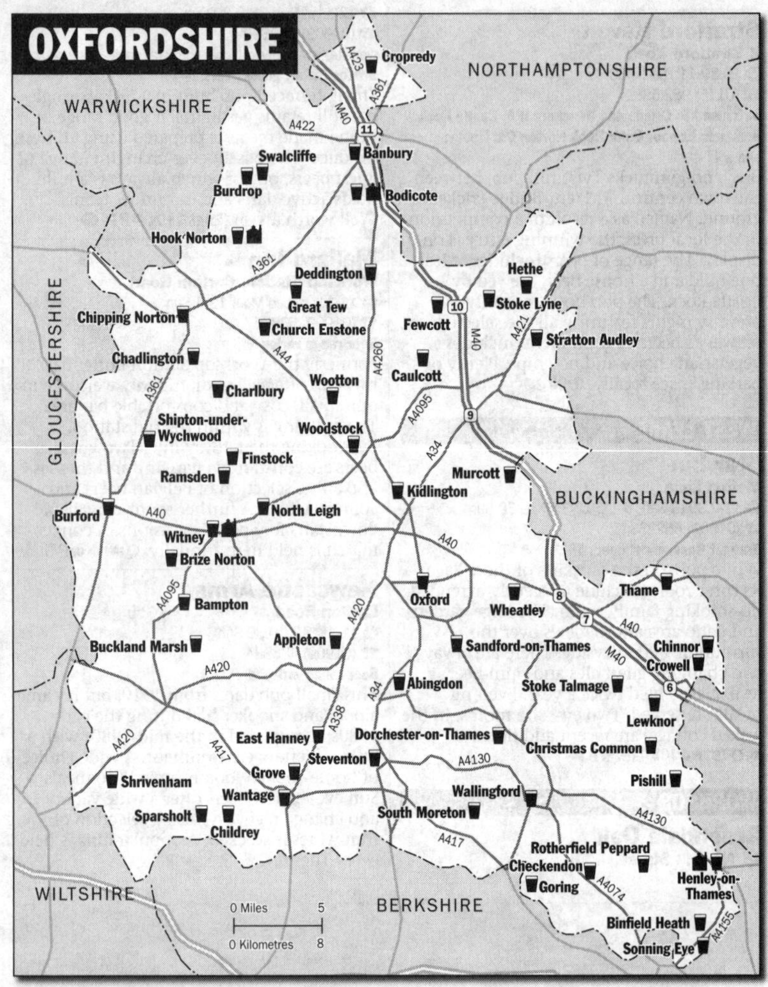

ABINGDON

Punch Bowl

Market Place

10.30-3, 7-11; 10.30-11 Mon, Fri & Sat; 12-3, 7-10.30 Sun

(01235) 520230

Greene King Morland Original H

A drinking house since 1587, the public bar is a traditional, lively venue for serious drinkers; in total contrast, the lounge bar is a wood-panelled room with an individual atmosphere. The drinker can unwind with a sense of bygone days when life moved at a much slower pace. At the centre of this historic market town, the Punch Bowl is overshadowed by the County Hall, built in 1682 by Christopher Kempster of Burford, the most trusted builder of Sir Christopher Wren. Q

BAMPTON

Elephant & Castle

Bridge Street

5 (12 Sat)-11; 12-5, 7-10.30 Sun

(01993) 850316

Adnams Bitter; Archers Village; H **Arkell's 3B;** G **Hook Norton Best Bitter; guest beers** H

This picturesque village local was reputedly built from stone salvaged from the nearby castle. A drinkers' pub, it offers an ever-changing range of guest beers, in addition to the regular brews. The interior is cosy, with beamed ceilings and stone walls; a collection of elephants adorns the lounge. The large garden at the rear is flanked by the old dairy buildings which have been converted into letting accommodation. Note that the pub is shut weekday lunchtimes.

Q P

Morris Clown

High Street

5 (12-Sat)-11; 12-10.30 Sun

(01993) 850217

Archers Village; Courage Best Bitter; guest beers H

Former Courage-owned local, with a single L-shaped bar, it was saved from closure many years ago by the present landlord and his father, and is now run as a free house. The bar is warmed by a huge log fire, and the walls are decorated with curious murals depicting local people. Aunt Sally, darts and bar billiards are all played in local leagues, though the village is most famous for its morris dancing connections, and an annual competition is held every spring bank holiday. ⛫Q❀♿♣🍎P

BANBURY ❊

Bell

12 Middleton Road (near station)
✪ 12.30-3, 7-11; 12-11 Sat; 12-5, 8-10.30 Sun
☎ (01295) 253169
Hancock's HB; Highgate Dark; guest beers Ⓗ

Dave and Shirley have been in charge of this friendly town pub for 18 years. The emphasis is on the community, with teams for most pub games, note the trophies. It has a bar and lounge, with a warming open fire, that are both in character. The Oxford Canal, railway and bus stations are all close by. Bar snacks are available Mon-Fri lunchtimes. ⛫❀⊟⇌♣P

Olde Reindeer

47 Parsons Street
✪ 11-11 (10 Mon); closed Sun
☎ (01295) 264031
Hook Norton Mild, Best Bitter, Generation, Old Hooky; seasonal or guest beer Ⓗ

This 15th-century inn, of great local historical importance, has been successfully restored by the current owners. The Globe Room panelling was held at the V&A Museum until 1946 and is now returned. It is riddled with underground passageways (now shut off), some leading to the old Banbury Castle. A warm, welcoming and relaxing pub, it also sells mulled and fruit wines. Evening meals (Mon-Sat) are now a feature in the Globe Room, in addition to the lunchtime bar menu. ⛫❀◐◑⇌P

BINFIELD HEATH

Bottle & Glass

Harpsden Road (N off A4155, 1/2 mile NE of village centre)
✪ 11-3.30, 6-11; 12-3.30, 7-10.30 Sun
☎ (01491) 575755
website: www.thebottleandglass.co.uk
Brakspear Bitter, Old, Special Ⓗ

Thatched, beamed, picturesque country pub with a flagstoned floor in its main bar; parts of the building date from the 14th century. The reasonably-priced, home-cooked food includes vegetarian options, traditional English roasts and salads (no meals Sun eve). The smaller right-hand bar is no-smoking. The large, well-tended garden features a well and a pond with a small waterfall. Q❀◐◑♣P⚟

BODICOTE

Plough Inn

9 High Street (off A4260, 1 mile S of Banbury)
✪ 11-2.30, 6-11; 12-3.30, 7-10.30 Sun
☎ (01295) 262327
website: www.banbury-cross.co.uk/bodicotebrewery
Bodicote Bitter, No. 9, Triple X, Porter Ⓗ

Doreen and Jim Blencowe have owned and run this old, beamed, pleasant village pub since 1957. Doreen cooks all meals to order with occasional help at busy holiday times. Well-behaved children are welcome up to 9pm. Son Jimmy, having learnt his craft at Ringwood, is responsible for brewing the four regular and occasional seasonal beers in the micro-brewery behind the pub. Well-attended beer festivals are held each February and August. The cider is Symons Scrumpy Jack.
⛫Q◐◑⊟🍎

BUCKLAND MARSH

Trout at Tadpole Bridge

Tadpole Bridge
(off A420, towards Bampton) OS335004
✪ 11.30-3, 6-11; 12-3 (7-10.30 May-Sept) Sun
☎ (01367) 870382 website: www.trout-inn.co.uk
Archers Village; Young's Bitter; guest beer Ⓗ

This Grade II listed building was built in the 17th century from local stone and has been a pub for over 100 years. The garden runs down to the River Thames and the pub is ideally situated for walks on the Thames path. It boasts a stone floor, original beams and some high-backed benches. Children are welcome throughout the pub which offers excellent cuisine and wines. Newly-built six-room accommodation matches the existing building well.
⛫Q❀🛏◐◑♿⛺♣P

BURDROP, SIBFORD GOWER

Bishop Blaize Inn

(1/2 mile off B4035, between Sibford Gower and Sibford Ferris)
✪ 12-2.30, 6-11; 12-3, 7-10.30 Sun
☎ (01295) 780323 website: www.bishopblaize.co.uk
Hook Norton Best Bitter; guest beers Ⓗ

Friendly, family-run pub where the large garden affords superb views towards the Stour Valley. This extended and refurbished 17th-century inn retains many original features in its three distinct areas: a small bar with inglenook and oak-beamed ceiling, a dining area, and a public bar with dartboard and fruit machine. The extensive menu (not served winter Tue eve) includes many home-cooked meals. Quiz nights, league darts, Aunt Sally and bar games are all on offer. ⛫❀◐◑♣P

BURFORD

Lamb Inn

Sheep Street
✪ 11-2.30, 6-11; 12-3, 7-10.30 Sun
☎ (01993) 823155
Badger Best; Hook Norton Best Bitter; Wadworth 6X Ⓗ

Stylish, characterful hotel with a cosy bar, comfortable lounge and smart accommodation (some of the guest rooms feature four-posters). The bar has a huge log fire, stone-flagged floor and a friendly, welcoming atmosphere. The Lamb exudes quality and good taste – the walk to the gents is like being on the set of the Antiques Roadshow – and drinkers are welcome to make use of the sumptuous lounges. The award-winning walled garden sometimes plays host to visiting morris dancers in summer.
⛫Q❀🛏◐◑⊟🥛

INDEPENDENT BREWERIES

Brakspear Henley-on-Thames (to close)
Hook Norton Hook Norton
Plough Inn Bodicote
Wychwood Witney

CAULCOTT

Horse & Groom

Lower Heyford Road

⌚ 11-3, 6-11; 12-3, 7-10.30 Sun

☎ (01869) 343257

Hook Norton Best Bitter; guest beers Ⓗ

From outside this stone and thatched pub looks a rural gem; step inside and you will not be disappointed. A warm, friendly welcome always awaits from behind the bar and from Harvey the Westie. One Hook Norton or another is always available, along with three constantly changing ales. The pump clips displayed near the open fire testify to nearly 200 ales annually. The food is as good as the beer, with à la carte meals, daily specials and a wide selection of speciality sausages. Local CAMRA Pub of the Year 2000 and 2001 – and rightly so! ⩚Q❀◐D

CHARLBURY

Rose & Crown

Market Street

⌚ 12 (11-Sat)-11; 12-10.30 Sun

☎ (01608) 810103 website: www.topbeerpub.co.uk

Beer range varies Ⓗ

Popular, traditional town-centre free house, 17 years in this Guide; a simply furnished split-level bar and pool room. The patio courtyard features a small pond. On the Oxfordshire Way long-distance path, it does not serve food, but walkers are welcome to eat their own. A pub for the discerning drinker who enjoys a good pint without cooking smells, it offers one of the best selections of real ale in the area. An excellent rotation of guest beers features many from micro-breweries.

⩚❀▲≉●

CHECKENDON

Black Horse

Burncote Lane (E off A4074; towards Stoke Row, left up narrow lane) OS667841

⌚ 12-2 (2.30 Sat), 7-11; 12-2.30, 7-10.30 Sun

☎ (01491) 680418

Brakspear Bitter; West Berkshire Good Old Boy; guest beer Ⓖ

Old coaching inn, which has been in the same family for 100 years, set in farm land on a road which appears to lead nowhere. The farm is run by the landlady's family. Local county types can be encountered in the three low-ceilinged rooms. Filled baguettes go down well with the fine gravity-dispensed ales (the guest comes from West Berkshire Brewery). Good cycling and walking country; you can even ride your horse here and tie it up outside.

⩚Q❀▲P

CHILDREY

Hatchet

⌚ 12-2.30 (3 Sat), 7-11; 12-4, 7-10.30 Sun

☎ (01235) 751213

Greene King Morland Original; guest beers Ⓗ

Very friendly local in a picturesque downland village setting. White-painted externally, it has changed little in over 100 years, its interior featuring beams adorned with horse brasses, beer taps and brass hatchets. The bar, stocking a good range of ever-changing guest beers, has an open-plan area for games and a quiet/dining area to one side. Nestling at the foot of the Ridgeway gives easy access to walkers and the landlord is sympathetic to passing campers.

❀◐♣P

INN BRIEF

APPLETON

Plough Inn

Eaton Road

12-3, 6-11; 12-3, 6-10.30 Sun

(01865) 862441

Greene King XX Mild, IPA, Morland Original; guest beers Ⓗ

This picturesque 17th-century stone building is one of the better Greene King pubs in the area.

BANBURY

Exchange

49-50 High Street

11-11; 12-10.30 Sun

(01295) 259035

Boddingtons Bitter; Courage Directors; Hop Back Summer Lightning; Shepherd Neame Spitfire; guest beer Ⓗ

Wetherspoon's conversion of the town post office. Meals are served all day. Cask Marque accredited.

BRIZE NORTON

Mason's Arms

Burford Road

12-2.30 (not Mon), 6.30-11; 12-3, 7-11 Sat; 12-4, 7-10.30 Sun

(01993) 842567

Courage Best Bitter; John Smith's Bitter; guest beers Ⓗ

Plain building of local stone – once a bakery. Popular with locals, it fields many pub games teams.

CHADLINGTON

Tite Inn

Mill End

12-2.30, 6.30-11; closed Mon; 12-3, 7-10.30 Sun

(01608) 676475

Beer range varies Ⓗ

Traditional free house, a focus for village activities – four ales include a house beer from Brakspear. Lovely garden; good food.

CHINNOR

Red Lion

3 High Street

11.30 (11 Sat)-11; 12-10.30 Sun

(01844) 351494

Brakspear Bitter; Fuller's London Pride; Greene King IPA; Hook Norton Best Bitter; Ⓗ **guest beers** (occasional) Ⓖ

Friendly village local, about 300 years old, originally three cottages. Food available lunchtimes and evenings (not Sun or Mon eve).

CHIPPING NORTON

Stones

1A Middle Row

10-11; 11-10.30 Sun

(01608) 644466

Beer range varies Ⓗ

Town-centre pub, recently refurbished. Two constantly changing beers come from small breweries. Heated terrace. Fresh food is cooked to order.

GROVE

Volunteer

Station Road

11-11; 12-10.30 Sun

(01235) 769557

Hook Norton Best Bitter, Generation, Old Hooky; guest beer Ⓗ

Hook Norton's southernmost pub. Has a relaxed, friendly atmosphere and a strong community focus. Large car park and children's play area.

HENLEY-ON-THAMES

Saracen's Head

129 Greys Road (off A4155)

12-2.30, 5.30-11; 12-11 Sat; 12-10.30 Sun

(01491) 575929

Brakspear Mild, Bitter Ⓗ

Popular, busy local which sells more mild than bitter or lager. An emphasis on pub games; the large garden is safe for children. No food. B&B – one double room.

MURCOTT

Nut Tree Inn

12-3.30, 5.30-11; 12-6 Sun

(01865) 331255

Hook Norton Best Bitter; Taylor Landlord; guest beers Ⓗ

Attractive 15th-century thatched inn where the main focus is food, but drinkers are very welcome.

CHIPPING NORTON ❊

Chequers

Goddards Lane (next to theatre)
⏲ 11-11, 12-10.30 Sun
☎ (01608) 644717 website: www.chequers-pub.co.uk
Fuller's Chiswick, London Pride Ⓗ
Town-centre pub consisting of four seating areas and a large restaurant in the covered courtyard and adjoining barn. Among its many awards from Fuller's and CAMRA are accolades for cellarmanship. An early recipient of Cask Marque status, the pub offers ample opportunity for conversation and company. Close to the theatre, it draws a varied clientele who gather around the log fire. ♨Q◐◑✔

CHRISTMAS COMMON

Fox & Hounds ☆

Off B480/B481 and B4009 OS715932
⏲ 11.30-3 (3.30 Sat), 6-11; 12-10.30 Sun
☎ (01491) 612599
Brakspear Mild, Bitter, Special, seasonal beers Ⓗ/Ⓖ
Lazy, peaceful walking country, with red kites above, is the location for this traditional Chilterns pub, which was recently refurbished and extended. Children are welcome in the new restaurant in the purpose-built Victorian-style barn, which has an open-plan kitchen. Organic food features on the menu (no meals Sun eve). Still a good drinking pub with three cosy rooms, your beer can be served straight from the barrel or by handpump, according to your preference. ♨Q❀◐◑⊟♿▲♣P

CHURCH ENSTONE

Crown Inn

Mill Lane
⏲ 12-2.30 (not Mon), 6-11; 12-2.30, 7-10.30 Sun
☎ (01608) 677262
Shepherd Neame Spitfire; guest beers Ⓗ
This family-run 17th-century Cotswold stone hostelry is situated in a small village between Woodstock and Chipping Norton. The beamed bar, together with the real fire and warm welcome from the landlord and landlady, immediately makes you feel at home. A range of at least three real ales is available and food is served to suit all tastes in a no-smoking restaurant. Peace and quiet is guaranteed, as there are no fruit machines or loud music. This really is worth a visit – you will not be disappointed!
♨Q❀⇌◐◑⊟♿P

CROPREDY

Red Lion

8 Red Lion Street (near Cropredy lock)
⏲ 12-3, 6 (5.30 summer)-11; 12-4, 7-10.30 Sun
☎ (01295) 750224
website: www.theredlioncropredy.tablesir.com
Hook Norton Best Bitter; Tetley Bitter; Wychwood Hobgoblin; guest beers Ⓗ
A warm welcome awaits at this cosy pub, close to the busy Cropredy lock. Built in 1545 of the local honey-coloured ironstone, under a thatched roof this three-roomed house is a classic for the area: a locals' bar with a traditional inglenook, family games room and a well-appointed restaurant whose emphasis is on traditional home-cooked food. Cropredy hosts the annual Fairport Convention concerts (Aug). Tricky to find, but worth seeking out.
♨☺❀◐◑♣P

CROWELL

Shepherd's Crook

The Green (off B4009 between Chinnor and M40 jct 6) OS744997
⏲ 11.30-3, 5-11; 11-11 Sat; 12-5, 7-10.30 (12-10.30 summer) Sun
☎ (01844) 351431
Batham Best Bitter; Hook Norton Best Bitter; Taylor Landlord; guest beers Ⓗ
In the foothills of the Chilterns, this comfortable inn was known as the Catherine Wheel until 1991. The current landlord, who took over in 1996, is a real ale fanatic and this is one of the few pubs to sell Batham's bitter locally. A former fish merchant, the landlord obtains supplies directly from the West Country and shellfish from the Norfolk coast, while excellent steak and kidney pies and steaks come from a local butcher. ♨Q❀◐◑♣P

DEDDINGTON

Crown & Tuns

New Street (A4260)
⏲ 11-3 (may vary afternoons), 6-11; 12-3, 7-10.30 Sun
☎ (01869) 337371
Hook Norton Mild, Best Bitter, seasonal beers Ⓗ
This traditional two-bar pub has appeared in every edition of this Guide. The building, on the main road through Deddington, dates from the 16th century when it served as a coaching inn and has two bay windows, with seats, overlooking the main road. B&B is offered in a homely atmosphere with full English breakfast. There is an Aunt Sally pitch, a game seemingly peculiar to this region, in the garden. ♨Q❀⇌◑⊟▲♣●

DORCHESTER-ON-THAMES

Chequers

20 Bridge End (off High St)
⏲ 12-2 (not Mon or Wed; 2.30 Fri; 3 Sat), 7-11; 12-3, 7-10.30 Sun
☎ (01865) 340015
Courage Best Bitter; Hook Norton Best Bitter; Wadworth IPA Ⓖ
Real ale is fetched from the cellar in this 300-year-old local that eschews electronic games and music. The no-smoking family room houses a bar billiards table (the pub team is one of the best in the country). Aunt Sally is played alternate Fri eves in summer while euchre and other games are also popular. This attractive village was once a Roman city, and boasts an abbey among its many fine, old buildings. Handy for walkers and the rivers Thames and Thame. Rolls and sandwiches are available.
♨Q☺❀⇌♣P⚡

EAST HANNEY

Black Horse

Main Street (off A338)
⏲ 12-2.30, 6-11; closed Mon; 12-3, 6-10.30 Sun
☎ (01235) 868212
Brakspear Bitter; Hook Norton Best Bitter; guest beers Ⓗ

This free house, on the main street of an attractive village, boasts a very pleasant garden and a spacious comfortable bar area with a relaxed atmosphere. Families are welcome and a small, but varied menu is served in the family dining area. There are always German specialities available and the German landlord keeps four of his native draught lagers, one of which is a wheat beer. An excellent bus service stops outside with connections to Wantage and Oxford.
Q❀(◗P⊬⊡

FEWCOTT

White Lion
Fritwell Road
✪ 7 (12 Sat)-11; 12-4, 7-10.30 Sun
☎ (01869) 346639
Beer range varies Ⓗ
Enterprising free house where the plush, comfortable bar boasts a range of four, ever-changing guest beers, often from smaller or less well-known breweries. This is very much a sportsman's pub, with opportunities for passive viewing on the bar TV and active participation in one of the pub's many teams. The garden has an Aunt Sally pitch. Being only five minutes' drive from the M40 (jct 10), it also draws a busy passing trade.
⌂❀♣P

FINSTOCK

Plough Inn
The Bottom (off B4022, N of Witney)
✪ 12-2.30 (3 Sat), 6-11; 12-3.30, 7-10.30 Sun
☎ (01993) 868333
Beer range varies Ⓗ
Thatched pub in an attractive setting: two comfortable beamed bars, plus a snug. Interesting features include an inglenook, old clocks, a lending library, old photos of village life and a piano. The two acres of well-kept gardens are popular in summer. Walkers, children and dogs are all welcome at this friendly pub that enjoys an enviable reputation for real ale, wine and food, much of which is free range and organically produced.
⌂❀⊭(◗⊟▲●P

GORING

Catherine Wheel
Station Road
✪ 11.30 (12 Sat)-3, 6-11; 12-3, 7-10.30 Sun
☎ (01491) 872379
Brakspear Mild, Bitter, Old, Special, seasonal beers Ⓗ
The oldest pub in an attractive riverside village on the Ridgeway and Thames long-distance footpaths, it is popular with walkers, cyclists and locals alike. The L-shaped bar on different levels extends into the often busy Forge bar dining area (children welcome). This bar used to be the blacksmith's shop and is complete with anvil. The large inglenook in 'the pit' is sought after by drinkers in the winter. Home-cooked meals includes vegetarian dishes and daily specials (no food Sun eve). Accommodation is in a nearby cottage.
⌂Q❀⊭(◗≢♣

GREAT TEW

Falkland Arms
Off A361 and B4022
✪ 11.30-2.30 (3 Sat), 6-11 (11.30-11 summer Sat); 12-3, 7-10.30 (12-10.30 summer) Sun
☎ (01608) 683653 website: www.falklandarms.org.uk
Wadworth IPA, 6X, seasonal beers; guest beers Ⓗ
In an idyllic thatched village, this award-winning pub is a haven for drinkers who enjoy an unspoilt, relaxed atmosphere without the intrusions of modern life. Simple wooden furniture, oak settles, flagstoned and bare-boarded floors, an inglenook and gentle lighting create a wonderful ambience, complemented by four guest beers, a range of malt whiskies, country wines, real cider, snuffs and clay pipes. This rural gem offers high quality food and accommodation (book).
⌂Q❀⊭(♣●⊘

HENLEY-ON-THAMES ✲

Bird in Hand
61 Greys Road
✪ 11.30-2.30, 5-11; 11.30-11 Sat; 12-10.30 Sun
☎ (01491) 575775
Brakspear Mild, Bitter; Fuller's London Pride; guest beers Ⓗ
Henley's only true free house, this friendly, one-bar, town pub attracts locals and visitors. It holds fortnightly fun quizzes (Wed or Thu eve). The surprisingly large garden, with aviary, pond and pets, is safe for children. The two guest beers are often from micros. The pub fields teams in both men's and ladies' local darts leagues. Reasonably-priced weekday lunches are served. Henley is famed for the Royal Regatta (July), its Festival (Sept) and the River and Rowing Museum. Q♉❀(▲≢♣

HETHE

Whitmore Arms
Main Street
✪ 12-2.30 (not Mon-Fri), 7 (6 Fri)-11; 12-2.30, 7-10.30 Sun
☎ (01869) 277654
Brakspear Bitter, Ⓗ **Special;** Ⓖ **Hook Norton Best Bitter,** Ⓗ **seasonal beer** Ⓖ
The Whitmore Arms retains all the attributes of a true community local and thus is the focal point for village life in Hethe. The bar is divided into two separate areas: a bare-boarded end, focusing on the pub's team sports such as darts and cricket, and a more comfortable end that offers a relaxed outlook on drinking and eating. Eve meals served Tue-Sat. The garden boasts an Aunt Sally pitch. ⌂Q❀(◗▲♣P

HOOK NORTON

Pear Tree Inn
Scotland End (near brewery)
✪ 11.30-2.30, 6-11; 11.30-11 Sat; 12-4, 7-10.30 Sun
☎ (01608) 737482
website: www.thepeartree.tablesir.com
Hook Norton Mild, Best Bitter, Old Hooky, Double Stout, seasonal beers; guest beer (occasional) Ⓗ
Rural gem: this traditional 18th-century village inn in an idyllic Cotswold setting has the privilege of being the Hook Norton brewery tap. The single bar, with exposed

oak beams decorated with dried hops, is warmed by a delightful log fire. Note the range of home-made walking sticks for sale. Home-cooked food (not served Sun eve), a large garden and three guest rooms make this an ideal place for a short or extended visit. Q P

KIDLINGTON

King's Arms

4 The Moors (off end of High St)
11-2.30, 6-11; 11-11 Sat; 12-10.30 Sun
(01865) 373004
Greene King IPA; Fuller's London Pride; guest beer [H]
Popular, attractive village pub, consisting of two small bars and a covered outdoor drinking area, where Aunt Sally is played – it is also used to host regular beer festivals. Reasonably-priced food is served Mon-Sat lunchtimes and evenings until 8pm. The guest beer changes regularly. P

LEWKNOR

Olde Leatherne Bottel

1 High Street (near M40 jct 6)
11-2.30, 6-11; 12-3, 7-10.30 Sun
(01844) 351482
Brakspear Bitter, Old, Special [H]
Classic, unspoilt, 400-year-old country inn, in a lovely Chilterns' edge village (complete with thatched school). Close to the M40, it is popular with travellers and locals who appreciate the low beams and three fireplaces (including an attractive inglenook). Two bars are separated by a central servery. Good value food, with daily specials and vegetarian options, is of high quality. The no-smoking family room and well-tended garden (with children's play area) are essential for the summer overspill. Guide regular. P

NORTH LEIGH

Woodman

New Yatt Road (off A4095, Witney-Woodstock road)
12-2.30, 6-11; 12-10.30 Sun
(01993) 881790
website: www.thewoodman.tablesir.com
Greene King IPA; Wadworth 6X; guest beers [H]
Popular, comfortable community pub, used by local societies and clubs. A well-kept garden with Aunt Sally is a bonus in summer. Long-established beer festivals are held at Easter and August bank holidays. A spacious bar, with simple wooden furniture, offers plenty of space for drinkers and diners; fresh flowers on the tables add a nice touch. There is an impressive illuminated 30ft deep well in the bar.
P

OXFORD

Angel & Greyhound

30 St Clements Street (across Magdalen Bridge from High St)
11-11; 12-10.30 Sun
(01865) 242660
Young's Bitter, Triple A, Special, seasonal beers [H]
Spacious one-bar pub, with patios to front and rear, and an adjacent public car park. Darts and bar billiards are played, and there is a selection of board games. It can get quite crowded of an evening during university term-time. Once called the Oranges and Lemons, the current name comes from the nearby meadows, which were used for grazing horses stabled at two coaching inns, the Angel (demolished in 1875) and the Greyhound (now part of Magdalen College). No food Sun eve.
Q

Bear Inn

6 Alfred Street (behind Town Hall)
12-11; 12-10.30 Sun
(01865) 728164
Bateman XXXB; Hancock's HB; Hook Norton Old Hooky; guest beers [H]
Ancient pub, one of the smallest in the city, renowned for its collection of ties. The pub comprises two small rooms, plus an entrance area, all served from its pewter-topped bar. Sympathetically refurbished two years ago, it was acquired by Fuller's in early 2002 and continues to thrive under its long-serving licensee. Five beers are usually available, including interesting guests.
Q

Butcher's Arms

5 Wilberforce Street, Headington
12-2.30, 5-11; 12-11 Fri & Sat; 12-10.30 Sun
(01865) 761252
Fuller's Chiswick, London Pride, ESB, seasonal beers [H]
Go past the Shark, first left, first right to find this busy, friendly, well-run Victorian local. (The Shark is in New High Street, Headington.) The single bar has been extended and there is a heated patio area, where barbecue parties can be booked. The pub has links to recently relocated Oxford United; it shows major sporting events on TV and hosts a quiz night (Sun). There is good wheelchair access. Food is available weekday lunchtimes.

Harcourt Arms

Cranham Terrace, Jericho
12-2.30 (3 Fri & Sat), 5.30-11; 12-3, 7-10.30 Sun
(01865) 310630
Fuller's Chiswick, London Pride, ESB [H]
This area of Jericho was built in 1871, and a pub has stood here ever since – the current building was put up by Ind Coope in 1935. Now owned by Fuller's, the two real fires and subdued lighting enhance its cosy atmosphere. It attracts a mix of locals and students, some of whom come to play the many board games available. Bar snacks are served until 10pm.
Q

Hobgoblin

108 St Aldates (opp. Town Hall)
11-11; 12-10.30 Sun
(01865) 250201
Wychwood Shires; guest beers [H]
Formerly the Bulldog, the Hobgoblin has been a real ale haven since it was refurbished in 1998. Six beers are usually available, normally two from owners Wychwood and four guests from all over the UK. Well in excess of 1,000 different beers have been dispensed since 1998, testified by the pump clips on the ceiling. A student-oriented pub, offering discounts, it is popular during term-time. Local CAMRA Pub of the Year 2000, it serves meals daily.

Lamb & Flag

12 St Giles
11-11; 12-10.30 Sun
(01865) 515787
Brakspear Bitter; Fuller's London Pride; Theakston Old Peculier; Wadworth 6X; guest beers Ⓗ
Low-beamed, 15th-century coaching inn, adjacent to St John's College, who reacquired the lease to the pub in 1998. Accessed from an historic passageway off St Giles, the pub has two bars and four distinct rooms. It boasts connections with Tolkien and CS Lewis, and inevitably, with Morse. Skinner's beers feature regularly as guests.
Q◐≢

Marlborough House

60 Western Road (near Folly Bridge)
11.30-2.30, 6-11; 11-11 Sat; 12-10.30 Sun
(01865) 243617
Bateman XB; Courage Directors; Greene King IPA Ⓗ
Small, friendly, back-street pub off the Abingdon road, popular with students and locals alike. It features three intimate downstairs rooms, including a table football room at the back, and a larger pool room upstairs. The vintage juke box still uses the old style, heavy 50p pieces, available from the bar. Darts is played and there is live music on Wednesdays. Reversing the trend, the Marlborough was built in 1888 as a private dwelling but converted into a pub in 1897. ♣

Old Bookbinder's Ale House

17-18 Victor Street, Jericho
12-11; 12-10.30 Sun
(01865) 553549
Morrells Oxford Blue; Ⓗ **guest beers** Ⓗ/Ⓖ
The first (and best) of Morrells' Ale House chain, this pub was refurbished and resurrected in 1999. Bric-à-brac and bare boards abound inside; devotees of Morse will recognise the exterior. Six beers are offered on handpump with up to eight on gravity from the stillage behind the bar. The landlord, Morrells' first Licensee of the Year, ensures this is a lively community pub featuring music and quiz nights – expect the unexpected here. A beer festival is held in June as part of the Jericho street festival.
♨◐♿♣●

Rose & Crown

14 North Parade Avenue
11-3, 5 (6 Sat)-11; 12-4, 7-10.30 Sun
(01865) 510551
Adnams Bitter; Marston's Pedigree Ⓗ
Classic Victorian north Oxford local, comprising two small rooms and a corridor served by a hatch. The garden is covered and heated in winter. This is a pub for conversation, free from intrusive music or machines, and attracts a mix of students, locals, academics, and chess-players. The licensee's love of ice hockey is reflected in the souvenirs that adorn the back room, and Formula One motor racing features strongly through customer connections. Oxford CAMRA Pub of the Year 2001.
♨Q❀◐♿♣

Turf Tavern

4 Bath Place
11-11; 12-10.30 Sun
(01865) 243235
Brakspear Special; Flowers Original; Greene King Abbot Ⓗ
Cosy, 18th-century tavern, tucked away down two alleyways – Bath Place in Holywell Street and St Helen's Passage in New College Lane. Two low, beamed bars offer up to eight varying guest beers and a small range of Belgian bottled beers. Three patios provide seating and some shelter – one is overlooked by New College bell tower and part of the city wall; braziers are used in winter. Ex-Hogshead, now a Laurel Pub Co house, food is served 12-7.30 daily. Q❀◐

Wharf House

14 Butterwyke Place
11-3, 5.30 (6 winter)-11; 11-11 Sat; 12-4, 7-10.30 Sun
(01865) 246752
Hook Norton Best Bitter; Ⓗ **guest beers** Ⓗ/Ⓖ
Built as offices for the adjacent wharf, it became a pub in 1851 and is one of only two original buildings in the ancient St Ebbes parish. Here are served real ales and cider from all over, plus authentic foreign kegs and a range of Belgian bottled beers. The plain and simple character of the pub, without fruit machines or bright lights, attracts a wide range of customers. A warm

INN BRIEF

RAMSDEN

Royal Oak
High Street
11.30-3, 6.30-11; 12-3, 7-10.30 Sun
(01993) 868213
Draught Bass; Hook Norton Best Bitter; guest beers Ⓗ
17th-century coaching inn of great character and comfort offering an imaginative menu, regular guest beers and well-appointed bedrooms.

SHIPTON-UNDER-WYCHWOOD

Shaven Crown
High Street
12-2.30, 5-11; 12-2.30, 5-10.30 Sun
(01993) 830330
Hook Norton Best Bitter; guest beers Ⓗ
14th-century inn with medieval courtyard garden. The attractive beamed bar is comfortably furnished. B&B; good food. A classic.

SPARSHOLT

Star
Watery Lane
12-3, 6-11; 12-11 Sat; 12-10.30 Sun
(01235) 751539
Butts Barbus Barbus; Greene King Morland Original; guest beers Ⓗ
Lively, friendly, 17th-century, oak-beamed village pub. Good food (not Sun eve). Children welcome. Bar billiards played. Accommodation.

WITNEY

Eagle Tavern
22 Corn Street
11-11; 12-10.30 Sun
(01993) 849564
Hook Norton Best Bitter, Generation, Old Hooky; guest beers Ⓗ
Recently refurbished as a Hook Norton one-roomed pub, it retains an old-fashioned feel. Vegetarian and vegan meals available.

House of Windsor
31 West End
12-3 (not Mon-Fri), 6-11 Sat; 12-4, 7-10.30 Sun
(01993) 704277
Fuller's London Pride; Hook Norton Best Bitter; Taylor Landlord; guest beer Ⓗ
17th-century coaching inn, a family-owned and run free house. Meals served Wed-Sat eves and Sun lunch.

❊ symbol next to a main entry place name indicates there are Inn Brief entries as well.

welcome awaits the stranger; be sure to make friends with the dog! Vinyl records played. Q❀⇌♣P

PISHILL

Crown

On B480, 5 miles N of Henley-on-Thames
🕘 11.30-2.30, 6-11; 12-3, 7-10.30 Sun
☎ (01491) 638364 website: www.crownpishill.co.uk
Brakspear Bitter; Fuller's London Pride Ⓗ

Attractive, 15th-century, brick and flint, former coaching inn, reputedly haunted. It is situated in excellent walking country towards the top of the Stonor Valley, about a mile from Stonor House and its magnificent parkland. Wisteria clads the frontage which features leaded-light windows. It is noted for its food in the splendid restaurant where children are welcome (no eve meals Sun). High quality accommodation is provided in a one-bedroomed cottage, complete with four-poster bed. The grounds also house a 400-year-old thatched barn which has been renovated to cater for functions.
ᗰQ❀⇋◐◑ ⊟P

ROTHERFIELD PEPPARD

Red Lion

Peppard Common (just off B481)
🕘 12-11; 12-10.30 Sun
☎ (01491) 628329
Brakspear Mild, Bitter, Special, seasonal beers Ⓗ

Traditional country local with 17th-century origins, it comprises two small bars and a small dining area. All the rooms have a warm, comfortable feel and are bedecked with sporting and military memorabilia. Reasonably-priced, good quality food is available most times (not Sun or Mon eve); children are welcome in the no-smoking dining room. The pub is noted for its very attractive enclosed garden, which caters well for children, and hosts barbecues and private functions. The pub also boasts a vibrant golf society, regular quiz nights (Mon eve), and a rather large, cumbersome, Old English Sheepdog. ᗰ❀◐◑♣P

SANDFORD-ON-THAMES

Fox

25 Henley Road
🕘 12-3, 6.30-11; 12-3, 7-10.30 Sun
☎ (01865) 777803
Morrells Oxford Blue; guest beer Ⓗ

This unrefurbished village pub has been run by the same family since 1919 and has been in the Guide since the 1980s. It serves the cheapest Morrells' beer for miles around. Very much a locals' meeting place, this classic two-roomed pub offers no food (unusual these days) and serves beer on gravity if required. ᗰQ❀⊟♣P

SHRIVENHAM

Prince of Wales

14 High Street
🕘 12-3, 6-11; 12-3, 7-10.30 Sun
☎ (01793) 782268 website: www.shrivenham.net
Wadworth IPA, 6X, seasonal beers; guest beers Ⓖ

Grade II listed, 17th-century pub: the main bar area has original beams and a real fire. The conversation of the mixed clientele overawes the quiet background music. A good range of home-cooked meals includes vegetarian options (no meals Sun eve). The pub provides daily newspapers, four-pint carry kegs and a regular quiz (Tue eve). Barbecues are held in the garden area. Look out for the 'on this day' history board, researched by the landlord. ᗰQ❀◐◑♣P

SONNING EYE

Flowing Spring

Henley Road (A4155)
🕘 11.30-11; 12-2.30, 7-10.30 Sun
☎ (0118) 969 3207
Fuller's Chiswick, London Pride, ESB, seasonal beers; guest beer (occasional) Ⓗ

Country local, with a sympathetic extension and balcony, overlooking the large garden (children's swings). The bar is now effectively an island almost surrounded by drinking areas. Pub food includes vegetarian options (eve meals Wed-Sat, also summer Tue) plus occasional barbecues. Walkers come from the footpaths in the surrounding countryside and the Thames long-distance footpath a mile away. A wheelchair WC is accessible from the car park, but pub access is up stairs. A tug-of-war team trains in the garden.
ᗰ≿❀⇋◐◑⅄♣P⊭

SOUTH MORETON

Crown

High Street (off A4130)
🕘 11-3, 5.30-11; 12-3, 7-10.30 Sun
☎ (01235) 812262
Adnams Bitter; Badger Tanglefoot; Wadworth IPA, 6X Ⓗ

Friendly, country, village local, which is simply furnished in rustic style. Children are welcome throughout the pub, which is near to Didcot's steam train centre. It is popular for good value meals (with vegetarian choices) and its quiz (Mon). It is advisable to book evening meals and Sun lunch. The Crown doubles as the local library; bring your unwanted books to be sold for charity. ≿❀◐◑♣P

STEVENTON

Cherry Tree

33 High Street
🕘 11.30-2.30, 5-11; 11-11 Fri & Sat; 12-10.30 Sun
☎ (01235) 831222
website: www.thecherrytreeinsteventon.com
Red Shoot Tom's Tipple; Wadworth IPA, 6X; Ⓗ **guest beers** Ⓗ/Ⓖ

Friendly village pub, on the main road through the village, the Cherry Tree was local CAMRA Pub of the Year 2002. The interior features exposed beams throughout its spacious bar areas. It is usual to find two guest beers alongside the regulars served, and mini-beer festivals are held occasionally through the year. It also offers an excellent range of home-cooked food. ᗰ❀◐◑P

STOKE LYNE

Peyton Arms ☆

🕘 12-3, 6-11; 12-11 Fri & Sat; 12-10.30 Sun
☎ (01869) 345285
Hook Norton Mild, Best Bitter, Old Hooky, seasonal beers Ⓖ

Traditional, multi-roomed, village beer house that has successfully missed out on 'improvements' and refurbishments over the years. The result is a cosy, unspoilt gem that retains the true qualities of a conversationalist's haven and has justifiably been recognised as part of CAMRA's national pub inventory. Beer is served directly from the cask and food is home cooked (no meals winter Mon-Thu). The garden offers views across open fields and has an Aunt Sally pitch.
♨Q♉❀◐▣⛺♣P⚡

STOKE TALMAGE

Red Lion ☆

(1¼ miles S of A40 at Tetsworth) OS681994
✪ Closed Mon; closed Tue-Thu lunchtimes; 12-2 (not Mon-Thu; 2.30 Sat), 6-11 (not Mon); 12-3.30, 7-10.30 Sun
☎ (01844) 281651
Beer range varies Ⓗ

Note the opening hours before you visit this unspoilt, basic, friendly pub, well supported by locals, and popular with walkers and cyclists. In the same family for 60 years, it is located in quiet countryside, part of a 20-acre livestock farm. Three beers are usually available – one generally from a local micro, plus one or two gravity-dispensed ciders. An Aunt Sally pitch and parts of the garden are floodlit; amusements are provided for children. Hook the fish and bar billiards are also played.
♨Q♉❀♿⛺♣●P

STRATTON AUDLEY

Red Lion

Church Street
✪ 12-3, 6-11; 12-11 Sat; 12-10.30 Sun
☎ (01869) 277225
Greene King Ruddles Best Bitter; Hook Norton Best Bitter; Wadworth 6X; guest beer (occasional) Ⓗ

Stone building in the village centre, the Red Lion consists of a single bar with wood floors and a real fire. An imaginative menu and interesting wine list ensure that the pub has a regular custom of diners, but a warm welcome is assured to drinkers as well. No eve meals Sun.
♨♉❀◐♿♣⚡

SWALCLIFFE

Stag's Head

The Green (B4035, 6 miles W of Banbury)
✪ 11.30-2.30 (3 Sat), 6.30-11; 12-3, 7-10.30 Sun
☎ (01295) 780232
website: www.stagsheadswalcliffe.co.uk
Brakspear Bitter; Hook Norton Best Bitter; guest beers Ⓗ

Small, 15th-century thatched inn on the edge of the Cotswolds, enjoying a reputation for good food. The main bar is cosy, with an open fire, old wooden pews, bookshelves and jugs hanging from the beams. A larger, no-smoking room lies off the main bar. The landlord's love of chillies is evidenced by bottles of sauce, posters and some fiery items on an extensive and imaginative menu. In summer the delightful landscaped garden is a treat. Opening hours may vary seasonally.
♨Q♉❀◐♣P⚡

THAME

Swan Hotel

9 Upper High Street
✪ 11-11; 12-10.30 Sun
☎ (01844) 261211
Brakspear Bitter; Hook Norton Best Bitter; guest beers Ⓗ

Market town hotel of 16th-century origin with a Tudor painted ceiling in the upstairs restaurant. Note the unusual furniture and fittings in the bar areas. Ideal for a quiet drink, doing business or meeting friends, the Swan offers two regularly changing guest beers from near and far. Good food is served in the bar and restaurant. Accommodation includes some four-poster beds. Outside seating is in a small shopping alley – formerly the yard when it was a coaching inn.
♨❀🛏◐

WALLINGFORD

Cross Keys

48 High Street
✪ 12-3, 5-11; 12-11 Fri & Sat; 12-10.30 Sun
☎ (01491) 826377
Brakspear Bitter, Old, Special, seasonal beers Ⓗ

Award-winning, unspoilt, 17th-century pub near Wallingford Museum and both town parks. Predominantly a beer drinkers' local, it fields teams in crib, darts and dominoes leagues. Low beams and polished wood floors feature. A small lounge bar leads through to a dining/function room. The public bar has steps up to the games room. Live music is staged twice a month. The large fenced garden, with a children's play area, stands on what are believed to be Saxon town ramparts.
❀◐⛺

WANTAGE

Royal Oak Inn

Newbury Street
✪ 5.30-11; 12-2.30, 7-11 Sat; 12-2, 7-10.30 Sun
☎ (01235) 763129
Wadworth 6X, JCB; West Berkshire Maggs Magnificent Mild, Dr Hexter's Wedding Ale, Dr Hexter's Healer; Ⓗ **guest beers** Ⓖ

Extremely popular with local real ale drinkers, the vast array of pump clips above the bar bears testament to the wide variety of guest and seasonal ales served here. The larger main bar proudly exhibits its many CAMRA Pub of the Year awards, and must be only one of a few in the Guide to have been given this award by two different county branches. The smaller public bar is of interest for its impressive display of naval memorabilia.
♨🛏▣♣●

Shoulder of Mutton ☆

Wallingford Street
✪ 12 (11 Fri & Sat)-11; 12-10.30 Sun
☎ (01235) 762835
website: www.shoulder-of-mutton.co.uk
Greene King Morland Original, Abbot; guest beers Ⓗ

Located just off the main square, this pub has recently undergone internal restoration although thankfully, due to the landlord's intervention, it has been done sympathetically ensuring that its character has been maintained. The pub comprises three areas: a small public bar, the main bar area and a cosy no-smoking snug. Cribbage and dominoes are among the traditional bar games played. ⛼❀⊟♣P⚟

WHEATLEY

Railway

24 Station Road

⏲ 12 (4 Mon)-11; 12-10.30 Sun

☎ (01865) 874810

website: www.railwaywheatley.co.uk/

Fuller's London Pride, ESB, seasonal beers Ⓗ

Do not go looking for the station! It is decorated with railway memorabilia, but the line from which this Victorian pub took its name was closed in the 1960s, as part of the Beeching cuts. A busy local with a smashing atmosphere, the pub attracts drinkers of all ages. The recently-added function room, Track 2, has a late licence and hosts live music events, in addition to being available for private hire. ◑P

WOODSTOCK

Black Prince

Manor Road

⏲ 12-2.30, 6-11; 12-11 Sat; 12-10.30 Sun

☎ (01993) 811530

Archers Village; Hop Back Summer Lightning; guest beers Ⓗ

Fine, stone, roadside pub in an historic village down the hill from Blenheim Palace. Good food is sold daily (not Sun eve) and four beers are usually available – Hop Back is rare for the area. A splendid suit of armour stands guard next to the huge fireplace in the beamed lounge, and some of this knight's weapons adorn the walls of the bar. The garden, on the banks of the River Glyme, is especially popular in summer.

⛼Q❀◑◗P⊟

WOOTTON

Killingworth Castle

Glympton Road (B4027)

⏲ 12-2.30, 6.30-11; 12-2.30, 7-10.30 Sun

☎ (01993) 811401

website: www.killingworthcastle.tablesir.com

Greene King IPA, Morland Original, Ruddles County Ⓗ

17th-century Cotswold coaching inn, comprising a long, beamed bar with log-burning stove and a small back bar with games, including bar billiards. Flagstone floors, simple pine furniture, bookcases and original country artefacts make this cheerful pub a popular gathering place for farmers, estate workers, villagers, walkers and tourists. An established venue for folk music – every Friday for the past 30 years; it also hosts modern jazz. The large garden offers barbecues in summer. Comfortable accommodation is in a modern barn conversion. Eve meals served Tue-Sat.

⛼Q❀⛟◑◗♣P✔

Future of Brakspear's Beers

W H Brakspear of Henley-on-Thames, whose beers are widely available in the Thames Valley area, will close its brewery by the end of 2002. The brands have been sold to Refresh UK, a company originally set up to market the Usher's beers from the former Trowbridge brewery, which now also owns the Wychwood Brewery in Witney. Brakspear will remain in business as a pub owner. In the short term, Refresh will have Brakspear's beers brewed mainly at Thomas Hardy in Burtonwood, with some brewed at Wychwood. Refresh plans to build a new brewery as close to Henley as possible. The problem will be finding a site that is not prohibitively expensive, and getting planning permission. Refresh is holding talks with local authorities anxious to provide employment in some areas of Oxfordshire. As Refresh's plans are to build a 'micro-brewery' it's clear that Brakspear's volumes are expected to be dramatically reduced, and low volume seasonal brands will probably disappear. Wychwood has a bottling facility and it's to be hoped that some of Brakspear's fine bottled beers, including the organic range, will survive.

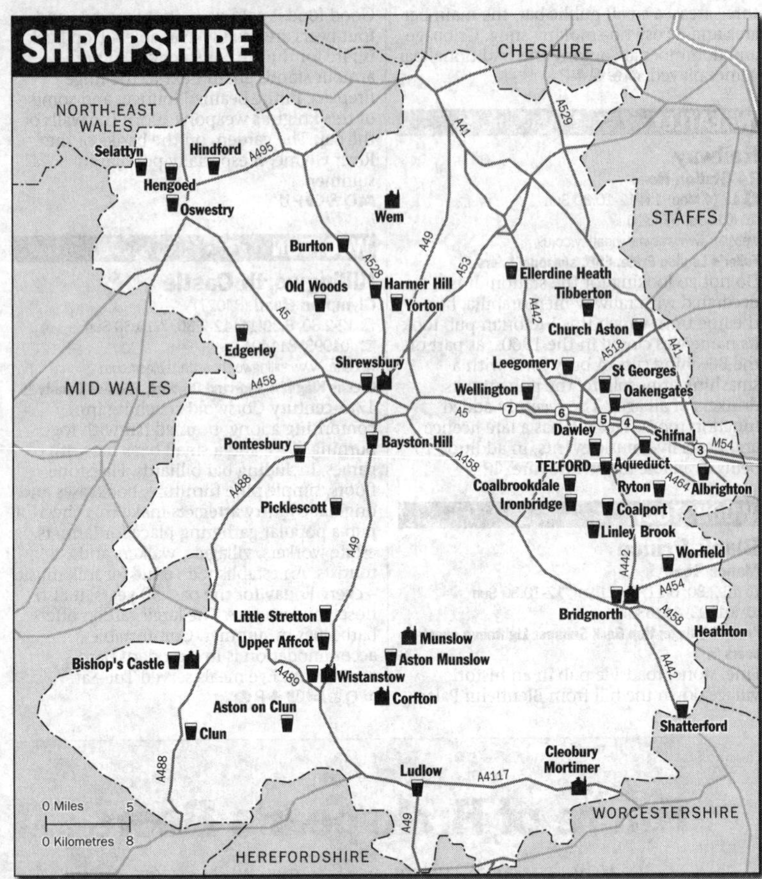

ALBRIGHTON

Harp Hotel

40 High Street

⊕ 12-11; 12-10.30 Sun

☎ (01902) 374381

Beer range varies Ⓗ

Basic two-roomed locals' pub on quieter nights, with a warm welcome from the landlord and a loud one from Max the dog. On music nights (four eves a week) the pub doubles as an internationally-known jazz venue, featuring artistes from around the world – many have their pictures on the lounge walls. The 'harp' in the pub's name is more likely to be the 'blues harp' rather than the Welsh or Irish variety.

❀⊞⚠⇌♣●P

ASTON MUNSLOW

Swan

On B4368, Bridgnorth-Craven Arms road

⊕ 11-2.30, 5-11; 11-11 Sat; 12-10.30 Sun

☎ (01584) 841415

Draught Bass; Worthington Bitter; guest beers Ⓗ

Warm and welcoming to all visitors, this multi-roomed timber-framed pub, built in 1350, is situated in the picturesque Corve Dale. The pub is being extended gradually, with a separate restaurant having opened in Easter 2002, and there are plans to add a brewery. It is run by the wife and family of the owner of Brooklyn Farm Cider. Cider takeaways are available to those who bring their own containers. ♨⛵❀◑⊞⚠♣●P

ASTON ON CLUN

Kangaroo

Clun Road (B4368, between Clun and Craven Arms) OS503981

⊕ 12-3 (not Mon & Tue), 7-11; 12-11 Fri & Sat; 12-10.30 Sun

☎ (01588) 660263

Wells Bombardier; guest beer Ⓗ

Cosy village pub with a warm, friendly atmosphere, near the station at Broome. No Aussie theme bar – the name dates from the 19th century. It has a games room and a large garden at the rear. Regular barbecues and an annual beer festival are held in summer. Home-cooked food features occasional international themed evenings. The house beer, Roo Brew, comes from the Six Bells Brewery at Bishop's Castle. Leave your name and address for a monthly newsletter listing forthcoming events.

♨❀◑⊞⚠⇌(Broome) ♣P

BAYSTON HILL

Compasses

Hereford Road (A49, 2 miles S of Shrewsbury)

⊕ 5 (12 Sat)-11; 12-10.30 Sun

☎ (01743) 872921

Draught Bass; Fuller's London Pride; guest beers Ⓗ

Unspoilt inn on the A49 southern approach

to Shrewsbury. A friendly welcome is guaranteed in this family-run pub which has been in the Guide for more than a decade. A traditional bar, with decor based on a maritime theme, and separate snug offer a beer range which includes a regularly changing guest. An attractive garden area to the rear is ideal for families. It overlooks a tranquil village green, hidden from the busy trunk road passing the front of the pub. An annual beer festival is held in spring.
Q❀⊟♿♣P⍻

BISHOP'S CASTLE

Castle Hotel
Market Square (at the top of the hill behind the Town Hall)
✪ 12-2.30, 6.30-11; 12-2.30, 7-10.30 Sun
☎ (01588) 638403
Draught Bass; Black Sheep Best Bitter; Hobsons Best Bitter; Six Bells Big Nev's Ⓗ
Fine period hotel lovingly cared for by its owners, comprising a public bar, lounge and a small snug bar, plus dining room. The latter two rooms and entrance hall in particular, boast much original woodwork. The furnishings and a host of local artefacts throughout help create a timeless ambience. A connoisseur collection of whiskies, and excellent home-cooked food provide the icing on the cake. Active participants in the town's annual July beer festival. The pub has a pleasant beer terrace.
♨Q❀⇔◑◗⊟♣P

Six Bells
Church Street
✪ 12-2.30 (not Mon, or winter Tue), 5-11; 12-11 Sat; 12-10.30 Sun
☎ (01588) 630144
Six Bells Big Nev's, Marathon Ale, Cloud Nine, Brew 101, seasonal beers Ⓗ
This 17th-century, two-roomed coaching inn is the tap for the Six Bells Brewery, situated behind the pub. Although quite small, both rooms are charming: the public bar has exposed stonework, beams and an inglenook, the lounge is carefully furnished and decorated to reflect its origins. Popular with locals it also offers generous portions of excellent, freshly prepared food. This multi-award-winning pub is integral to the town's annual real ale festival (July).
♨Q❀⊟♿♣

BRIDGNORTH

Black Horse
4 Bridge Street (50 yds from the bridge in Low Town)
✪ 6 (12 Sat)-11; 12-10.30 Sun
☎ (01746) 762415
Banks's Original, Bitter; Enville Ale; Hobsons Town Crier; guest beers Ⓗ
Classic old English ale house dating back to the mid-1700s. It has a small front bar with darts and dominoes. Note the antique back bar fitting. The main bar is typical of the period with a low ceiling and an abundance of wood panelling. The courtyard alongside the building provides a pleasant outdoor drinking area and is noted for its floral displays in summer. With its close proximity to the River Severn, it is a popular venue for fishermen to gather after a hard day on the river. Food is available during the summer months along with a traditional cider. ❀⇔♿⛺⇌(SVR) ♣P⊡

Railwayman's Arms
Platform One, Severn Valley Railway Station, Hollybush Road
✪ 12-3 (11-3.30 summer), 7-11; 11-11 Sat; 12-10.30 Sun
☎ (01746) 764361 website: www.svr.co.uk
Batham Mild, Best Bitter; Hobsons Best Bitter; guest beers Ⓗ
This characterful, charismatic drinking spot is of particular interest to steam enthusiasts, but appealing to all cask beer drinkers. You can drink in the bar, the old part of which is the original licensed refreshment room, boasting a superb Cheshire's Brewery (Smethwick) mirror, or sit out on the platform and soak up the atmosphere of the steam era, particularly pleasant in the evening when the trains are being put to bed. The three guest beers tend to be from smaller breweries, frequently local. Cider is stocked in summer. ♨Q❀⇌(SVR) ♣P

BURLTON

Burlton Inn
On A528, near B4397 jct
✪ 11-3, 6-11; 12-2, 7-10.30 Sun
☎ (01939) 270284
Banks's Bitter; guest beers Ⓗ
A true free house, this attractive and well-decorated country pub is near the north Shropshire lake (meres) district. It has one area laid out in an L-shape around the bar and, while occupied much of the time by satisfied diners, there is a warm welcome and space for drinkers who are able to enjoy local ales and brews from further afield. Behind the inn is a recently constructed two-storey building which provides six en-suite bedrooms. Lunchtime meals are served 12-2, and eve meals 6.30-9.45 (Sun 7-9.30).
♨Q❀⇔◑◗⛺♣P

CHURCH ASTON

Last Inn
Wellington Road (approx 1 mile from Newport)
✪ 12-11, 12-10.30 Sun
☎ (01952) 820469
Banks's Original, Bitter; Everards Tiger, Original; Hobsons Best Bitter; guest beers Ⓗ
Originally a two-roomed 19th-century pub now sympathetically refurbished by the present owners. It has been extended to provide a large, pleasant conservatory. Very popular for food, the pub is frequented by various age groups and is far enough out of town to keep it select and well worth a visit. The original quarry-tiled floor near the bar

INDEPENDENT BREWERIES

Corvedale Corfton
Crown Munslow
Dolphin Shrewsbury
Hanby Wem
Hobsons Cleobury Mortimer
Salopian Shrewsbury
Six Bells Bishop's Castle
Three Tuns Bishop's Castle (up for sale)
Wood Wistanstow
Worfield Bridgnorth

boasts a foot rail. Local CAMRA Pub of the Season, winter 2001-02. ❀◑P

CLUN

Sun

10 High Street

11-11, 12-3; 6-11 Sat; 12-3, 7-11 Sun

☎ (01588) 640559

Banks's Original; Hobsons Best Bitter; guest beer Ⓗ

Set, as Housman once said, in one of the quietest places under the sun, this 15th-century cruck-framed building has a wealth of exposed beams. The public bar with its huge stone flags and high-backed settles gives the impression that little has changed for years. The lounge is smart and comfortable and very much in keeping with the pub's ambience. Note the unusual set of 'Molly Martin' handpumps. Good value, home-cooked food is offered. To the rear, the patio is popular in fine weather. ♨Q❀⇔◑◑⊟⛺♣P

White Horse

The Square

12-3, 5.30-11; 12-11 Fri & Sat; 12-10.30 Sun

☎ (01588) 640305

Salopian Shropshire Gold; Worthington Bitter; Wye Valley Butty Bach Ⓗ

Comfortable, friendly local at the centre of a wonderfully timeless village. It has a single L-shaped bar with low beams and various rural implements hanging on the walls. A range of board games is provided for customers' entertainment. The reasonably-priced food is home made. Weston's cider is stocked. Enjoy a drink in the secluded garden at the rear. ♨❀◑◑♣●●✓

EDGERLEY

Royal Hill ☆

Between Melverley and Pentre OSSJ3517

12-2 (3 Sat, not winter), 6.30-11; 12-2, 7-10.30 Sun

☎ (01743) 741242

Salopian Royal Mild, Shropshire Gold Ⓗ

Set on a quiet road beside the River Severn, this pub offers spectacular views. The 18th-century building, recently added to CAMRA's National Inventory, has three cosy rooms, one of which is the tiny bar. Apart from the regular ale, additional beers are stocked from the Salopian Brewery. Canoeists, fishermen and locals are warmly welcomed. Camping is offered at the rear of the pub. The garden, across the road on the river bank, is somewhere to enjoy fish and chips on a summer evening, available from a visiting van 7pm Thu. ♨Q❀❀⊟⛺

ELLERDINE HEATH

Royal Oak

Midway between A53 and A442 OS603226

12 (11 Sat)-11; 12-10.30 Sun

☎ (01939) 250300

Draught Bass; Hobsons Best Bitter; Salopian Shropshire Gold; Shepherd Neame Master Brew Bitter; guest beer Ⓗ

Small and friendly rural pub, known locally as the Tiddlywink. It caters for children with a games room and play area in the garden. It is based around a central bar where the buzz of conversation is the only sound. The guest beer is normally from a local brewery, while the annual cider festival in July offers ciders from all over Great Britain. The beers, real cider and meals are reasonably priced, providing excellent value (no food is served on Tue). ♨Q❀◑◑♿⛺♣●●P

HEATHTON

Old Gate Inn

Between B4176 and A458 near Halfpenny Green

INN BRIEF

HARMER HILL

Red Castle

12-4, 6-11; 12-11 Fri & Sat; 12-10.30 Sun

(01935) 291071

Fuller's London Pride; Hobsons Best Bitter; Taylor Landlord, seasonal beers; guest beers Ⓗ

16th-century traditional local village pub with separate eating section and bar with games area. The pub is well known for fund-raising for local charities.

HINDFORD

Jack Mytton Inn

12-3, 6-11; (12-11 Easter-Sept; closed winter Mon); 12-3, 6-10.30 Sun

(01691) 679861

Beer range varies Ⓗ

Former farmhouse on the edge of Llangollen Canal with a large garden and well-appointed restaurant.

OSWESTRY

Oak Inn

47 Church Street

12-3 (4.30 Wed & Sat), 6-11; 12-4, 7-10.30 Sun

(01691) 652304

Draught Bass; M&B Brew XI; guest beer Ⓗ

Small local with a cosy simple bar and larger lounge, dating from 1720. Run by the same family for over 30 years. Good collection of brass and copper.

RYTON

Fox Inn

12-3 (4 Sat; not Mon), 7-11; 12-4, 7-10.30 Sun

(01743) 718499

Brains Rev James; Hobsons Best Bitter; Wood Shropshire Lad; guest beer Ⓗ

Two-roomed rural pub: public bar and no-smoking restaurant with superb views. Hosts an annual beer festival.

SELATTYN

Cross Keys ☆

Glyn Road

7-11; 12-4, 7-10.30 Sun (may vary)

(01691) 650247

Banks's Original, Bitter Ⓗ

A pub since 1840, in a 1770s building. Local photos are displayed in the small rooms. Convenient for Offa's Dyke. Phone ahead for extra opening hours.

SHREWSBURY

Armoury

Victoria Quay, Victoria Avenue

12-11; 12-10.30 Sun

(01743) 340525

Boddingtons Bitter; Wadworth 6X; Wood Shropshire Lad; guest beers Ⓗ

Large upmarket free house overlooking the River Severn. Interesting decor and excellent food complement five constantly changing guest beers.

Shrewsbury Hotel

Bridge Place

11-11; 12-10.30 Sun

(01743) 340382

Greene King Abbot; Hop Back Summer Lightning; Shepherd Neame Spitfire; Theakston Best Bitter; guest beers Ⓗ

Large L-shaped room, to include smoke-free dining area, divided into distinct areas for some privacy. Accommodation is offered. Cask Marque accredited.

Check it out

Pubs in the Good Beer Guide may change ownership and the facilities listed could alter. If a visit to a pub involves a long journey, it's advisable to check before leaving that full meals, family facilities, accommodation or camping sites are still available.

OS814923
✪ 12-2.30, 6.30-11; closed Mon; 12-3, 7-10.30 Sun
☎ (01746) 710431 website: www.oldgateinn.co.uk
Enville Ale; Greene King Abbot; Wells Bombardier Ⓗ
Busy pub in a rural part of the county serving food of restaurant quality (no meals Sun eve). The extensive menu is offered at reasonable prices and caters for all tastes. The two bars are decorated as you would expect a typical 16th-century inn to be, with welcoming log fires and a cosy atmosphere. Music is played at low volume so conversation is still possible. Addlestone's cider is sold. Children are welcome and the large garden has a safe play area. Well worth a visit. ♨❀◐◑●P⊁

HENGOED

Last Inn

Off B4579, 3 miles N of Oswestry OS680979
✪ 7-11; 12-3, 7-10.30 Sun
☎ (01691) 659747
Boddingtons Bitter; guest beers Ⓗ
A 1960s-style one-bar pub, embracing an older structure but with a traditional welcome, in the Welsh border area that is popular with tourists. Hengoed is Welsh for old wood; the pub name derives from its days as a cobbler's. In this Guide for over 20 years continuously, the guest beers are predominantly from regional and micro-breweries. A fine collection of vintage photographs (connected with the pub) and a large collection of brewery trays are displayed. It has featured in all editions of CAMRA's Good Pub Food. There is a large function room and the pool room has two tables. Evening meals are served (except Tue) and Sunday lunch.
♨Q♘◑♣P

LINLEY BROOK

Pheasant Inn

Britons Lane (off B4373, Bridgnorth-Broseley road)
OS680979
✪ 12-2, 7 (6.30 summer)-11; 12-3, 7 (6.30 summer)-10.30 Sun
☎ (01746) 762260
Beer range varies Ⓗ
Picturesque pub, set in idyllic rural countryside about halfway between Bridgnorth and Broseley, with a strong commitment to real ale and traditional pub values. It supports local breweries as well as stocking beers from further afield. Although a little hard to find on the first visit, it is well worth seeking out, as you will want to come back time and again. A room with a serving hatch contains a bar billiards table. The same licensee has run this pub for the past 19 years, and it has been a Guide entry every year.
♨Q❀◐◑♣P⊓

LITTLE STRETTON

Ragleth Inn

Ludlow Road (just off A49)
✪ 12-2.30, 6-11; 12-11 Sat; 12-10.30 Sun
☎ (01694) 722711 website: www.theraglethinn.co.uk
Brains Rev James; Hobsons Best Bitter, Old Henry; Theakston Old Peculier; guest beers Ⓗ
In good walking country, close to the Long Mynd, the Ragleth is named after a local hill. Dated 1650, this warm, quiet inn has an inglenook, oak beams, antiques and a brick and tiled floor. It is a true community pub used by many local social groups. The attractive garden has climbing frames, a children's trampoline and a rare tulip tree. There is always a Shropshire beer on tap and a selection of over 80 malt whiskies. Traditional games played in the bar include shove-ha'penny and skittles.
♨Q❀◐◑⊟⋀♣P⊁

LUDLOW

Charlton Arms

Ludford Bridge
✪ 12-11; 12-10.30 Sun
☎ (01584) 872813
Hobsons Best Bitter; guest beers Ⓗ
Overlooking the River Teme by Ludford Bridge, the Charlton Arms is a fine inn on the outskirts of the historic town. Enjoy a drink on the riverside patio. Five guest ales are supplied by breweries from the surrounding area, including Wood's and Wye Valley. Real perry and cider are sometimes available. An extensive menu offers good value, home-cooked food (vegetarian meals on request). This old coaching inn offers accommodation, with a full Shropshire breakfast. It hosts live folk music (third Fri) and provides a separate pool room. Look for the board outside which features some thoughtful sayings!
♨❀⊨◐◑⇹♣P⊓

Church Inn

Buttercross (in town centre, next to church)
✪ 11-11; 12-10.30 Sun
☎ (01584) 872174 website: www.thechurchinn.com
Brains Bitter; Hook Norton Old Hooky; Weetwood Eastgate Ale; Wye Valley Bitter; guest beers Ⓗ
This town-centre inn is the oldest in Ludlow, and the only free house within the town walls. The two bars are warm and welcoming with a real fire. Hook Norton beers are a firm favourite and the house beer, Falstaff, is locally brewed by Dunn Plowman. There is also a range of five ever-changing guest beers. A rare outlet for bottled Belgian beers and good food is served to complement them. The landlord is a former Mayor of Ludlow, and very keen on real ale. Situated close to the market square and castle, this is a must to visit or even stay.
♨Q♘⊨◐◑⋀⇹⊁⊓

Nelson Inn

Rocks Green (A4117, Kidderminster road)
✪ 12 (7 Tue)-11; 12-10.30 Sun
☎ (01584) 872908
website: www.thenelson.fsbusiness.co.uk
Banks's Original; Draught Bass; Worthington Bitter; guest beers Ⓗ
Wonderful, basic 300-year-old rural pub, on the outskirts of Ludlow, comprising two rooms. The lounge bar is decked out with musical instruments on the walls and a collection of mugs; the public bar houses a pool table and four-ring quoits. The pub reputedly has a ghost that plays dominoes. Regular beer festivals are held at Easter and the second weekend of Sept, and live music nights are staged. A new locally-produced cider is available. Next door is a guest house, convenient for longer stays.
♨Q❀◐◑⊟♣●P

OLD WOODS

Romping Cat

Near Bomere Heath
◷ 1-3 (not Wed or Fri; 12.30-3.30 Sat), 7-11; 12-2.30, 7-10.30 Sun
☎ (01939) 290273
Boddingtons Bitter; Fuller's London Pride; Holden's XB; Oakham JHB; Taylor Best Bitter; guest beer Ⓗ
This cosy one-roomed pub is situated a few miles north west of Shrewsbury along a quiet country road. It richly deserved the local CAMRA Pub of the Year award in 2001-02. Equally popular with town dwellers and country folk, many customers will have walked or cycled to enjoy the delights of the six handpumps. During the winter months an open coal fire affords a welcome, while in the summer the outside seating is very popular. Locals have always known it as the Cat even during its Southam's day when it was the Railway (visitors will spot the connection). No food is served but coffee is available at the bar.
♨Q❀♣P⊡●

PICKLESCOTT

Bottle & Glass

Off A49, at Dorrington
◷ 7-11 (12-2.30 Tue-Thu summer); 12-3.30, 7-10.30 Sun
☎ (01694) 751345
M&B Mild; Salopian Shropshire Gold; Wood Parish, Shropshire Lad; guest beer (summer) Ⓗ
Charming 17th-century stone-built, cottage-style inn, situated in a picturesque village on the slopes of the Long Mynd. The pub's interior is comfortable, with the ambience of a friendly country local. The public bar, with its low beams, exposed walls and large open fire is particularly attractive. There is a cosy lounge and a separate restaurant. You may encounter two landlords – one is a ghost. The pub has been declared a 'Euro-free zone'! ♨Q❀⇌◐◑P

PONTESBURY

Horseshoes

Minsterley Road OSSJ3906
◷ 12-3, 6-11; 12-4, 7-10.30 Sun
☎ (01743) 790278
Castle Eden Ale; Flowers Original; guest beers Ⓗ
Busy, friendly local in a large village, conveniently placed for walking in the South Shropshire hills. Very active in local games leagues, including pool, darts and dominoes, it hosts a quiz (Thu) and supports a cricket team in summer. Two regular guest beers from Cottage, Wye Valley or Hanby Brewery may be joined by a third. Two rooms are available for bed and breakfast; Sunday lunches are very popular.
❀⇌◐◑♣P

SHATTERFORD

Red Lion

Bridgnorth Road (A442)
◷ 11.30-2.30, 6.30-11; 12-3, 7-10.30 Sun
☎ (01299) 861221
website: www.redlionshatterford.co.uk
Banks's Original, Bitter; Ⓟ **Batham Best Bitter; guest beers** Ⓗ
Home of the hottest little coal fire in Shropshire, this pub was built in 1834 after the Duke of Wellington's beer house reform. The pub lies right on the Worcestershire border, a mile outside the village. The restaurant and one bar are no-smoking. Ramps and extra-wide doors have been fitted as well as a wheelchair WC and dedicated parking. Local seasonal produce is used (vegetables, game and meat) and the pub enjoys a good reputation for its fish dishes. Outside is a boules piste and the pub hosts the local league championship winners. ♨❀◐◑♿⛺P⊬⊡

SHIFNAL

White Hart

High Street
◷ 12-3, 5.30-11; 12-11 Fri & Sat; 12-10.30 Sun
☎ (01952) 461161
Enville Ale; Holden's Mild, Bitter, Special; guest beers Ⓗ
Three times winner of local CAMRA Pub of the Year (including 2002), this classic 400-year-old half-timbered inn attracts a friendly, mature and informative clientele. Seven ales are always on offer; four regular beers from local breweries and three guests – two premium ales plus a further session beer from around the UK. Excellent home-cooked food, including the famed range of real burgers, is available lunchtime (not Sun) in either of the two bars. Children are welcome until 7.30pm.
❀◐⇌♣P●

SHREWSBURY ❊

Belle Vue Tavern

115 Belle Vue Road
◷ 4 (12 Sat)-11; 12-10.30 Sun
☎ (01743) 362808
Draught Bass; Taylor Landlord; Worthington Bitter; guest beer Ⓗ
Previously known as Ye Olde Plough, it reverted to an early name, Belle Vue Tavern, 10 years ago. There is evidence of a pub called simply the Plough on or near this site, recorded in 1868. The present building, with its single room, is pleasantly out of character with the adjoining terraced properties, and is seen at its best during the summer months with its abundant display of tubs and baskets. For the pedestrian it is best approached via the Greyfriars footbridge, some 20 minutes' walk from the town centre. On the return journey the visitor is advised to visit the other pubs in the area. ♣

Coach & Horses

Swan Hill (to rear of Music Hall)
◷ 11-11; 12-10.30 Sun
☎ (01743) 365661
Draught Bass; guest beers Ⓗ
Set on a corner in a quiet side street just off the main shopping area, this busy pub can provide a quiet haven. In summer it has a magnificent window box/floral display. Victorian in style it has a compact wood-panelled bar and a larger restaurant with much magnificent reclaimed timber and exposed brickwork. This reverts to a lounge at night unless it is being used by booked parties. A full menu is available at lunch with lighter dishes offered up to 4pm. The house beer, Goodalls Gold, named after the landlord, is supplied by Salopian. Q◐⊟

Dolphin

48 St Michael's Street

⌚ 5-11; 12-3, 7-10.30 Sun

☎ (01743) 350419

Dolphin Best Bitter; guest beers Ⓗ

Popular ale house, within easy walking distance of Shrewsbury railway station. It is gaslit, and symmetrical in style, with one side being the bar, the other the lounge. The Dolphin Brewery has been brewing since December 2000 at the rear of the pub, and at least two house beers are usually on tap here. Up to five real ales are available altogether, plus an occasional cider (Weston's) in summer. Q⊟≹●

Loggerheads ☆

1 Church Street

⌚ 11-11; 12-3, 8-10.30 Sun

☎ (01743) 355457

Banks's Original, Bitter; Draught Bass; Marston's Pedigree; guest beers Ⓗ

One of the few pubs that Banks's has not been able to spoil 'by progress'! Situated in the heart of town, this classic Grade II listed boozer retains its original layout of four distinct, cosy bars. Three of these, including the lounge, are served from hatchways – two via a stone-flagged corridor. One is the former gentlemen-only bar, it has traditional settles and scrubbed-topped tables. The other, the poet's room, is wood-panelled. The guest beers change regularly and a policy of no music is pursued. Lunchtime food is served until 3pm (no food Sun). Q◐⊟≹▯

Three Fishes

Fish Street

⌚ 11.30-3, 5-11; 11.30-11 Fri & Sat; 12-3, 7-10.30 Sun

☎ (01743) 344793 website: www.threefishes.co.uk

Adnams Bitter; Fuller's London Pride; Taylor Landlord; guest beers Ⓗ

A first-time entry in last year's Guide, to this year's local CAMRA Pub of the Year shows the meteoric progress made by the current licensees. This family-run pub, which proudly defends a no-smoking policy throughout, has a range of up to five beers including one local brew. The 15th-century building stands in the shadow of two churches, St Alkmond's and St Julian's, within the maze of streets and passageways in the medieval quarter of the town. Food, freshly prepared, is available lunchtimes and early evenings. Sunday lunches are now served.

Q◐◗≹⊬●

TELFORD: AQUEDUCT

Britannia

Aqueduct Road

⌚ 10-3, 6-11; 11.30-11 Sat; 12-3, 7-10.30 Sun

☎ (01952) 591488

Banks's Original, Bitter; Marston's Pedigree Ⓗ

Built in 1860, this two-roomed pub is a strong focal point for the local community, it hosts meetings for the local historical society and has a number of regular charity events. While the pub does not have a separate no-smoking area, it does have a policy of no-smoking within two yards of both bars. Banks's range of special brews is stocked when available. ❀⊟P

COALBROOKDALE

Coalbrookdale Inn

12 Wellington Road

⌚ 12-3, 6-11; 12-3, 7-10.30 Sun

☎ (01952) 433953

website: www.coalbrookdale-inn.com

Adnams Broadside; Fuller's London Pride; guest beers Ⓗ

Lively pub, where the customer is almost overwhelmed with choice, from the well-kept beers to the marvellous meals, from the animated conversation and ghost stories to the 'characterful' choir. Enjoy looking at the fascinating collectables and memorabilia. The toilets are of note – not many landlords invite male customers to view the ladies! If one pub has to survive the onslaught of pub-chains and theme designers, this is it.

♛Q❀◐◗●⊬

COALPORT

Shakespeare Inn

Follow signs for China Museum

⌚ 6 (12 Sat)-11; closed Mon; 12-10.30 Sun

☎ (01952) 580675

Beer range varies Ⓗ

Opposite the tar tunnel and 100 yards from the Coalport China Museum, this lovingly restored inn fits wonderfully. Inside, the rustic brickwork and old photos of the area's industrial past blend together perfectly, making it a fine place to visit. The food is varied and of a very high standard (no eve meals served on Sun). The pub has three rooms, but is ostensibly open plan, a small patio and separate terraced garden (steep access and play area for children) are popular during the summer.

❀◐◗P▯

DAWLEY

Three Crowns

Hinkshay Road

⌚ 12-3 (4.30 Sat), 7-11; 12-4.30, 7-10.30 Sun

☎ (01952) 590868

Banks's Bitter; Marston's Pedigree Ⓗ

This pub is slightly off the beaten track, but well worth finding. The pub has been in the same family for the past 16 years. The large single room has a number of distinct areas, each with its own feel and atmosphere. This enables the pub to cater for a wide range of customers of all ages. It is well supported by locals, but everyone is made to feel welcome. ❀P

IRONBRIDGE

Golden Ball Inn

Newbridge Road (near jct of Madeley Rd and Wesley Rd)

⌚ 12-3, 5-11; 12-11 Sat; 12-10.30 Sun

☎ (01952) 432179 website: www.goldenballinn.com

Taylor Landlord; guest beers Ⓗ

Dating from the same era as the Gorge museums, this pub has had a licence since 1728. Enjoy the convivial atmosphere and fine ales and home-cooked fare in the wealth of nooks and crannies. The four guest beers always try to feature a local brewer and there is a large range of bottled Belgian beers.

♛❀⇌◐◗P⊬▯

Robin Hood

33 Waterloo Street (near Jackfield Free Bridge on B4373)
11-11; 12-10.30 Sun
☎ (01952) 433100
Banks's Original; Salopian Golden Thread; guest beers Ⓗ

Idyllically sited pub overlooking the River Severn in the Ironbridge Gorge, a World Heritage site. The customer has a choice of enjoying the warmth and cosiness of this free house (licensed since 1828), or enjoying the views from the patio area (wheelchair access). Children are catered for with an adventure playground and are allowed inside the pub until 9pm. Food is excellent and moderately priced (served from 12-2 and 7-9) with a carvery every Sunday lunch. Live music is hosted (Thu eve). ❀⇄◑♣P⊬

LEEGOMERY

Malt Shovel

Hadley Park Road
(off A442 Leegomery roundabout)
12-2.30 (3 Sat), 5-11; 12-3, 7-10.30 Sun
☎ (01952) 242963
Banks's Original; Marston's Pedigree; Tetley Burton Ale Ⓗ

Traditional two-roomed pub with open fires in the bar and lounge. The lounge is the lunchtime venue for business people and staff from the nearby business park. A wide range of reasonably-priced meals is served Mon-Fri, with a varied selection of rolls at other times. Home-made chips are a house speciality. At night the pub becomes a relaxing meeting place which resounds with laughter, conversation, the clink of glasses and pub games. A fine collection of brasses enhances the comfortable lounge.
⛫Q❀◑⊟♣P⊓

OAKENGATES

Crown Inn

Market Street (rear door adjacent to bus station)
12.30-3, 7-11; 12-11 Thu-Sat; 12.30-10.30 Sun
☎ (01952) 610888
website: www.crown.oakengates.com
Hobsons Best Bitter; Hook Norton Mild; guest beers Ⓗ

Highly noticeable with its distinctive yellow exterior, this characterful 1835 pub offers three separate drinking areas, adorned by pump clips. It hosts what may be the world's largest pub-based hand-pulled beer festival (first weekend in May and October) with 29 handpulls. Only 12 are used for the rest of the year. Music is played on Thursday (except August), at an acoustic club (Wed) and, in recorded form, at 'classics and crumpets' sessions on winter Saturday afternoons. Chess, draughts and Scrabble are available. ⛫❀⊟≠♣♣P⊬✔

Pear Tree Bridge Inn

Holyhead Road (B5061)
6 (12 Fri & Sat)-11; 12-10.30 Sun
☎ (01952) 272458
Courage Best Bitter; Wells Bombardier; guest beers Ⓗ

A friendly local on the old coaching route to and from Wales. The comfortable L-shaped room has a section for games and a carpeted lounge area for chatting and drinking. Live music features on Fri and Sat eves while Wed night is given over to acoustic music when everyone is free to participate. Quiz nights and various functions are held to raise money for chosen charities. A beer festival is hosted on the second weekend in July, with more than 25 ales on offer. ❀♿≠♣P✔

ST GEORGES

St Georges Sports & Social Club

Church Street
7 (12 Sat)-11; 12-3.30, 7-10.30 Sun
☎ (01952) 612911
Banks's Original, Bitter; guest beers Ⓗ

Situated next to one of Shropshire's cricket grounds, it is set in idyllic surroundings and is frequented by various sports teams and supporters. A recent winner of local CAMRA Club of the Year, this friendly venue is worth a visit because of the steward's enthusiasm and commitment to cask ales which change virtually on a daily basis. It is very busy at the weekends. A verandah is available for outdoor drinking. ❀P

WELLINGTON

Cock Hotel

148 Holyhead Road (B5061/ Mill Bank jct)
4 (12 Thu-Sat)-11; 12-4, 7-10.30 Sun
☎ (01952) 244954
Hobsons Best Bitter; Holden's Mild; Wye Valley Dorothy Goodbody's Wholesome Stout; guest beers Ⓗ

Regional CAMRA Pub of the Year 2001 is a fitting accolade for this consistently fine, independent ale house. Originally an 18th-century coaching inn, the stable courtyard is now an outside drinking area. The peaceful wood-panelled hotel reception area leads to a quiet no-smoking lounge on one side and to the Old Wrekin Tap bar on the other. This bar features breweriana from the defunct Wrekin Brewery and is a popular place to drink in Wellington.
Q❀⇄⊟♣♣P⊬⊓

Smithfield Inn

Bridge Road (opp. Morrisons supermarket)
11.30-3.30, 7-11; 11-11 Fri & Sat; 12-10.30 Sun
☎ (01952) 242795
Banks's Original; Tetley Bitter; guest beers Ⓗ

Former Wrekin Brewery house, built in the 1830s, situated just outside the town centre. Now a friendly and welcoming two-bar pub, very much at the heart of the local community and home to numerous local organisations as well as sports teams. A traditional bar with pool, darts and sport on TV, it is often lively, with occasional weekend music. The comfortable lounge with its old Wellington photos is altogether quieter and more staid. Guest beers come from around the country. Children are welcome in the lounge, the pub has a children's certificate. Lunchtime food is served (not Wed or Sun) and there is a barbecue area. ◑⊟≠♣

TIBBERTON

Sutherland Arms

High Street
12-2.30, 6 (5 Fri)-11; 12-11 Sat; 12-10.30 Sun
☎ (01952) 550533
Banks's Original; Marston's Bitter, Pedigree Ⓗ

Typical rural pub catering for all tastes, set in a picturesque village with a large garden partly shaded by an awning. Popular with the farming community, business people, students and staff from Harper Adams University College and passing visitors, the pub has a bar with a pool table, a lounge and a dining room. The wide range of food (served lunchtimes 12-2 and Tue-Sat eves 6.30-8.30), the beers, and a choice of over 100 whiskies, make this pub definitely worth a visit. It is on No. 519 Newport-Shrewsbury bus route. 🜂Q❀◐◑⊟♣P

UPPER AFFCOT (CHURCH STRETTON)

Travellers Rest Inn

On A49 between Church Stretton and Craven Arms
⌚ 11-11; 12-10.30 Sun
☎ (01694) 781275
website: www.travellersrestinn.co.uk
Draught Bass; Boddingtons Bitter; Coach House Gunpowder Mild; Hobsons Best Bitter; Wood Shropshire Lad; guest beers Ⓗ

Spacious roadside pub, a welcome stop for travellers as food is served all day. Accommodation consists of 12 en-suite bedrooms, two are suitable for wheelchair users. Camping is available in the pub's own grounds. Despite its name, the pub attracts locals and is the base for the Welsh League Pentre tug-of-war team (one-time Welsh champions). While the drinking area is one large extended room, there are many different sections including a quieter one and space for games, plus a no-smoking conservatory. Cider is available all year. The pub has a children's certificate.
Q❀🛏◐◑⊟♿⛺♣🍎P⚡

WISTANSTOW

Plough Inn

Take A489 off A49
⌚ 11.30-2.30, 6.30-11 (closed Mon eve); 12-2, 7-10.30 Sun
☎ (01588) 673251
Wood Parish, Special, Shropshire Lad, seasonal beers; guest beers Ⓗ

This pub is the Wood Brewery tap. The building dates from 1782. There are two main bars: the public bar a few steps down from the entrance is in two main sections. A games area is separated by a real fire from the drinking space. The lounge is large and serves as a restaurant. Evening meals are served Tue-Sat. Live music is occasionally played. Home-made pickles, chutneys and marmalades are for sale, also presentation packs of Wood's beer. Note the large collection of royal wedding beers.
🜂Q❀◐◑⊟♣🍎P

WORFIELD

Dog Inn (& Davenport Arms)

Main Street (off A454, 3 miles E of Bridgnorth)
⌚ 12-2.30, 7 (6 Sat)-11; 12-3, 7-10.30 Sun
☎ (01746) 716020
Courage Best Bitter, Directors; Highgate Dark; Wells Bombardier; guest beer (occasional) Ⓗ

A two-bar locals' pub attracting an ever-expanding clientele due to its well-kept beer and home-cooked food, using mainly local produce. Winner of Pub of the Year Good Eating award presented by Shropshire County Council, 2001. The pub was first licensed in 1790, but has since been sympathetically modernised and decorated, with interesting pictures. The pub is situated in a charming village, kept secret by its location at the end of a no-through road. Come early if you want to sit on the chesterfield. Monday is dominoes night. The pub has a children's certificate.
🜂Q❀◐◑⊟♣P

YORTON

Railway Inn

200 yds from Yorton railway station
⌚ 12-3.30, 6.30-11; 12-3.30, 7-10.30 Sun
☎ (01939) 220240
Salopian Golden Thread; Wadworth 6X; Wood Special, Shropshire Lad, guest beers Ⓗ

Near the picturesque village of Clive, this small friendly country pub has been run by the same family for 65 years. The simple bar with settle seating, quarry-tiled floor, dartboard and dominoes table is favoured by locals. The well-appointed lounge area, popular in summer, displays a fine collection of trophies, including 'Pinkie', a large carp caught at a local pool many years ago. This room is a regular venue for social events and meetings. Due to its close proximity to the station, the pub is very popular with rail travellers. The pub is a regional CAMRA Pub of the Year winner. There is a small area for outdoor drinking.
🜂Q❀⊟⇌♣P

Chemical Beer

I like lager beer, but the beer does not like me. Fifteen years ago I could drink fifty glasses of beer in one day and never got intoxicated and have no headache the next morning. But it seems the beer is changed. If I drink eight glasses of beer of an evening my head is ready to burst the next day. A friend of mine told me he drank beer freely at a picnic, and he was paralysed for three days. There is no beer I like better than lager beer, but the way they make it is a humbug. In former times they had a brewer to make beer, but now they have a chemist.

Letter to the New York Sun, 1882

SOMERSET

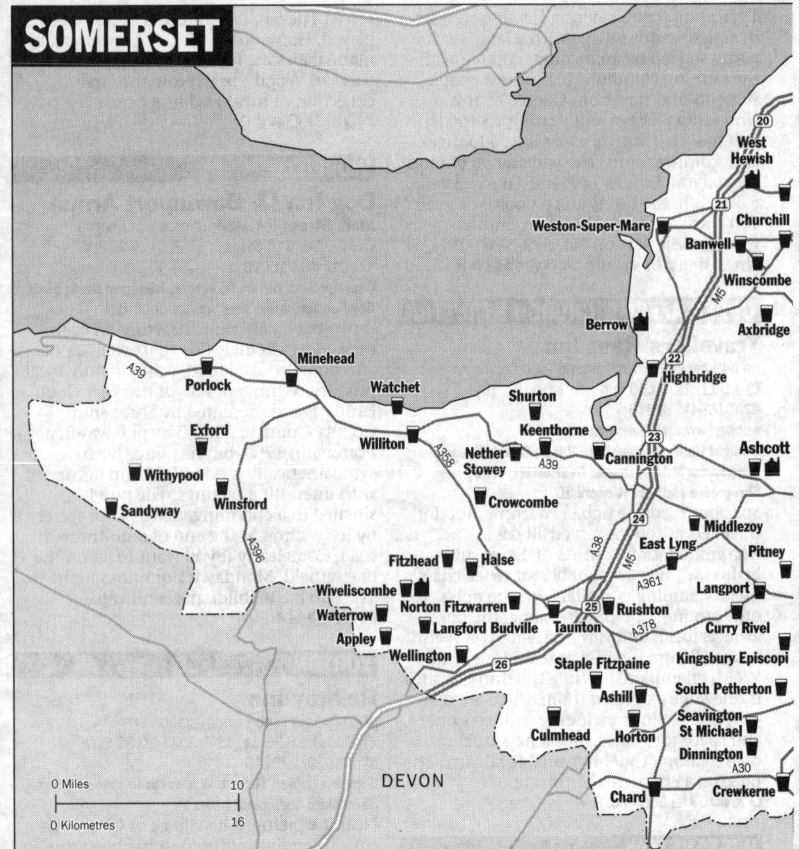

APPLEY

Globe Inn ☆

$2^1/_2$ miles N of A38 at White Ball Hill OS071215
11-3, 6.30-11 (closed Mon); 12-3, 7-10.30 Sun
(01823) 672327

Cotleigh Tawny; Palmer IPA; guest beer H

Wonderful rural gem, hidden away on the county border with Devon. The bar is basically a brick-floored corridor with a serving hatch and several cosy rooms leading off, full of collectables and curios. One room is for dining and one is a family room, although well-behaved children are allowed in all rooms but one. The pleasant garden has some children's play equipment. The food is outstanding (booking is essential at weekends).

ASHCOTT

Ring O'Bells

High Street (off A39)
12-2.30, 7-11; 12-2.30, 7-10.30 Sun
(01458) 210232 website: www.ringobells.com

Beer range varies H

Traditional multi-level inn near the village hall and church. It has cosy bar areas, a restaurant, a new function room with a skittle alley and an attractive garden. One beer from Ashcott's Moor Beer Company is usually featured, plus two guests from a varying and wide range. Wilkins cider is stocked. The pub has won several awards for its home-cooked food (same menu in the bars and restaurant). Families are welcome at this Somerset CAMRA Pub of the Year 1998.

ASHILL

Square & Compass

Windmill Hill (off A358) OS310166
12-2.30 (not Tue), 6.30-11; 12-3, 7-10.30 Sun
(01823) 480467

Exmoor Ale, Gold; guest beer H

Inviting, friendly, country pub, situated off the A358 near Ashill, towards Windmill Hill. The pub's extensive menu offers a wide choice of home-made food, prepared by their own chef. Superb views over the Blackdown Hills are a bonus; the pleasant large garden has a children's area. Exmoor ales are the beers of choice, with guests often available. Some good walks can be enjoyed nearby.

BABCARY

Red Lion

Main Street (off A37, 2 miles N of A303)
12-3, 6-11; 12-3, 7.30-10.30 Sun
(01458) 223230

Beer range varies H

Old-fashioned, thatched country pub in a pleasant village in rural Somerset. It pursues an ever-changing eclectic guest beer policy;

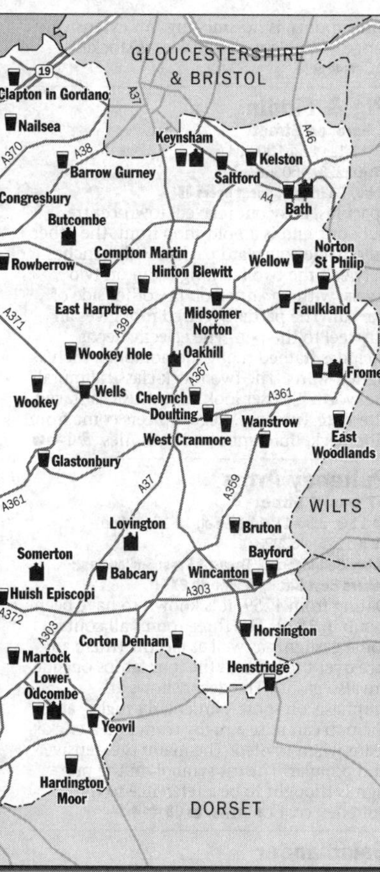

offering over 170 last year, mainly from south-west micros. The unspoilt locals' bar boasts huge flagstones, old settles, traditional bar games and a children's licence. It can be busy for food at weekends (booking recommended), prepared by an award-winning chef (no food Sun eve or Mon). Wilkins cider is stocked in summer.
Q❀◐▶⊟♣●P

BARROW GURNEY

Prince's Motto

Barrow Street (off A370)
✪ 10.30-11; 12-10.30 Sun
☎ (01275) 472282
Draught Bass; Butcombe Bitter; Wadworth IPA, 6X Ⓟ
Situated between Bristol and Weston-Super-Mare, this friendly, comfortable, three-roomed village inn is decorated in traditional fashion. At lunchtime many visit for the delicious home-cooked meals (served 12-2 weekdays), while in the evenings, a traditional pub atmosphere prevails; darts is particularly popular, and the pub fields a cricket team. The jovial landlord has long been associated with the pub and organises regular outings for the locals.
⚔❀◐♣P⁄

BATH ❀

Bell

103 Walcot Street
✪ 11.30-11; 12-10.30 Sun
☎ (01225) 460426 website: www.walcotstreet.com
Abbey Bellringer; Bath Gem; Smiles Best; RCH Pitchfork; Stonehenge Danish Dynamite; Ⓗ **guest beers** Ⓗ/Ⓖ
Popular city-centre pub, where live bands perform on the small central stage on Monday and Wednesday evenings and Sunday lunchtime. It comprises a long main bar and a collection of smaller rooms at the rear. At the back of the pub is an unexpectedly large terraced garden with plenty of seating. Much of the wall space inside is taken up with posters for local gigs and other forthcoming events in the Walcot area, which is known for its bohemian atmosphere and has some interesting shops. ❀⇌♣●

Coeur de Lion

17 Northumberland Passage
✪ 11-11; 12-8 Sun
Draught Bass; guest beers Ⓗ
Situated in a narrow passageway opposite the Guildhall in the city centre, this pub claims to be the smallest in Bath. As it contains only four tables in the single small bar, this may well be true. The intimate, bohemian atmosphere is enhanced by flowers and candles. In warm weather, the seating capacity is increased by tables and chairs outside the pub. Note the stained glass window at the front of the pub. No food is served Sunday; beware the early closing.
◐⇌♣

Hop Pole

Albion Buildings, Upper Bristol Road (opp. Victoria Park)
✪ 12-3, 5-11; 12-11 Fri & Sat; 12-10.30 Sun
☎ (01225) 446327
Bath SPA, Gem, Barnstormer; Butcombe Gold; guest beers Ⓗ
Baths Ales' first pub in Bath, this friendly place is situated between Victoria Park and the River Avon. Normally six real ales are available, including four from Bath Ales; a range of bottled foreign beers and an organic cider are also stocked. High quality food is available – Sunday lunches are particularly popular. An alleyway connects the pub to the river towpath, part of the Bath-Bristol cycle path; cycle racks are provided in the spacious garden. The Hop Pole was local CAMRA Pub of the Year 1999-2000.
❀◐▶♣⁄

INDEPENDENT BREWERIES

Abbey Ales Bath
Berrow Berrow
Butcombe Butcombe
Cotleigh Wiveliscombe
Cottage Lovington
Exmoor Wiveliscombe
Glastonbury Somerton
Milk Street Frome
Moor Ashcott
Nursery Keynsham
Oakhill Oakhill
Odcombe Lower Odcombe
RCH West Hewish

Lambretta's
8-10 North Parade

☼ 11-11; 12-10.30 Sun

☎ (01225) 463384 website: www.paradepark.co.uk

Abbey Bellringer; Banks's Bitter; guest beers 🄷

The large bar has been created by revitalising a previously derelict part of the Parade Park Hotel, which provides extensive accommodation. The bar retains the oak panelling which was originally in the room, together with the wooden shutters on the windows. There is a pervading sense of nostalgia for the eponymous scooter, with the bar displaying many posters and other memorabilia, together with a well-preserved example of the real thing.
❀⇆☽⇌♣

Old Farmhouse
25 Belvedere, 1 Landsdown Road

☼ 12-11; 12-10.30 Sun

☎ (01225) 316162

Abbey Bellringer; Draught Bass; Butcombe Bitter; Wadworth IPA, 6X 🄷

Rebuilt in 1892, on the site of a farmhouse dating from 1600, the pub is recognisable by its mock-Tudor style, which stands out from its Georgian surroundings. The large bar is divided into two areas; live jazz is performed in the rear bar most nights. The decor includes photographs and posters of jazz groups. The pub fields a football team and locals show a keen interest in shove-ha'penny. The pub sign is a caricature of the landlord. The small car park houses Abbey Ales Brewery. ❀♣P

Old Green Tree
12 Green Street

☼ 11-11; 12-10.30 Sun

Bath Barnstormer; RCH Pitchfork; Wickwar BOB; guest beers 🄷

Classic example of a traditional, unspoilt pub. Situated in a 300-year-old building in a narrow street near the centre of Bath, its atmosphere of dim cosiness pervades all three small, oak-panelled rooms. The comfortable lounge bar at the front is decorated with pictures of WWII aircraft; during Bath's annual Fringe Festival, these are replaced by the works of local artists. The back bar, which is the largest of the three rooms, is no-smoking. An extensive range of single malt whiskies is stocked.
Q☽⇌♣●⅟

Pig & Fiddle
2 Saracen Street

☼ 11-11; 12-10.30 Sun

☎ (01225) 460868

Abbey Bellringer; guest beers 🄷

Spacious, busy but relaxed, town-centre pub: one end is an old shop front, the other an outside courtyard packed with benches. Between the two is a long room on two levels, with an annex on the other side of the bar. The partially-glazed roof gives an airy feel to the pub. The eclectic decor includes framed rugby memorabilia, such as signed shirts. The two mock-classical murals are worth a closer look. Live music is staged alternate Tuesdays. Regular beers come from Hop Back, Butcombe and Bath Ales. ❀☽⇌●

Pulteney Arms
37 Daniel Street

☼ 11-3, 5.30-11; 11-11 Sat; 12-10.30 Sun

☎ (01225) 463923

Abbey Bellringer; 🄶 **Draught Bass; Smiles Best; Ushers Best Bitter; Wadworth 6X** 🄷

Dating from 1759, it is known to have been a pub in 1812. The three rooms all contain some gaslights as well as electric (there are five over the bar and the four lamps outside are also gaslit). The decor shows an emphasis on sport, particularly rugby, and the pub can raise a rugby team and a cricket team when invited. The menu is extensive and popular. The cat symbol on the pub sign is thought to be a reference to the Pulteney coat of arms. ☕☽◗⇌♣⅟

Salamander
3 John Street

☼ 12-11; 12-10.30 Sun

☎ (01225) 428889 website: www.bathales.com

Bath SPA, Gem, Barnstormer; guest beers 🄷

This former 18th-century coffee house has undergone many changes over the years, its most recent in 2001, from 'yoof' bar to Bath Ales pub is a definite improvement. Refurbished in the brewery's house style, with bare floorboards, wood panelling and hanging hops, the pub is subtly divided downstairs, with a restaurant upstairs. It

INN BRIEF

AXBRIDGE

Crown Inn
St Mary's Street
12-3, 7-11; 12-3, 7-10.30 Sun
(01934) 732518
Beer range varies 🄷
Free house: a quiet front and larger, busier back bar. Two beers (one from Cottage) plus Thatchers cider.

BANWELL

Bell
1 The Square
3 (12 Sat)-11; 12-10.30 Sun
(01934) 822330
Butcombe Bitter; Greene King Old Speckled Hen; guest beers 🄷
Live folk or blues is performed most Fridays; big on pub games and has a skittle alley.

BATH

Cross Keys
Midford Road, Combe Down
11-2.30, 6-11; 11-3, 7-11 Sat; 11-3, 7-10.30 Sun
(01225) 832002
Usher's Best Bitter, Founders Ale, Bishop's Tipple, seasonal beers; guest beers 🄷
Classic, wayside pub, in a largely residential area, with a strong local following and emphasis on food.

Hatchetts
6-7 Queen Street
11-11; 12-10.30 Sun
(01225) 425045
Abbey Bellringer; guest beers 🄷
Selling a rebadged local beer as a budget-priced house ale, this pub bears a motorbike theme.

CHELYNCH

Poacher's Pocket
12-3, 6-11; 12-3, 7-10.30 Sun
(01749) 880220
Oakhill Best Bitter; Wadworth 6X; guest beers 🄷
Comfortable, part 14th-century village pub, retaining a good local following despite the addition of a large function room and skittle alley.

CLAPTON IN GORDANO

Black Horse
Clevedon Lane
11-2.30, 5-11; 11-11 Fri & Sat; 12-3, 7-10.30 Sun
(01275) 842105
Draught Bass; 🄷 **Courage Best Bitter; Fuller's London Pride; Smiles Best;** 🄶 **Webster's Green Label** 🄷
14th-century free house, difficult to find. Child-friendly garden and good lunchtime food, Mon-Sat.

offers relaxed late Sunday lunches and a Sunday brunch; the restaurant menu includes beer-themed meals. The pub stocks a selection of bottled Belgian beers. ◑⊁

Star Inn

23 The Vineyards

⚙ 12-2.30, 5.30-11; 12-11 Sat; 12-10.30 Sun
☎ (01225) 425072 website: www.star-inn-bath.co.uk

Abbey Bellringer; Ⓗ **Draught Bass;** Ⓖ **guest beers** Ⓗ

This listed building, is one of the oldest pubs in Bath, first licensed in 1760. A recent refurbishment has done nothing to detract from the superb interior. The many small rooms feature oak panelling and 19th-century bar fittings. Barrels of Bass are brought up to the bar using a special lift which rises through a trap door behind the bar, to be served from jugs. The smallest bar, frequented by the older regulars, contains a long wooden bench known as 'death row'. ♔Q♉≷(Bath Spa)♣

BAYFORD

Unicorn Inn

On old A303

⚙ 12-2 (or later; not Mon), 7-11; 12-2, 7-10.30 Sun
☎ (01963) 32324

Draught Bass; Butcombe Bitter; Fuller's London Pride; guest beer Ⓗ

The Unicorn is restored to this Guide due to the consistent beer quality under new ownership, with improvement beyond recognition. Food is always fresh, with fish a speciality. There is a cosy new snug behind the fire at the end of the bar. This house is genuinely free of tie. Accommodation is in four en-suite rooms, one with a four-poster bed. ♔Q❀⇌◐◑P

BRUTON

Royal Oak

21-25 Coombe Street (B3081, Shepton Mallet road)

⚙ 12-2.30, 5 (6 Sat)-11; 12-2.30, 7-10.30 Sun
☎ (01749) 812215

Butcombe Bitter; guest beer Ⓗ

A warm welcome is guaranteed in this comfortable pub that offers an extensive range of reasonably-priced food, including a vegetarian menu and pensioners' lunches. The three real ales include a house beer (rebadged from various breweries) and a guest which changes weekly. The car park is fairly small but there is adequate parking in nearby streets. Q⇌◐◑≷♣P⊁

CANNINGTON

Malt Shovel Inn

Blackmoor Lane (off A39, E of Cannington)

⚙ 11.30-3, 6.30 (7 winter)-11; 12-3, 6.30-10.30 (not winter eve) Sun
☎ (01278) 653432 website: www.cannington.org.uk

Butcombe Bitter; Exmoor Fox; guest beers Ⓗ

This 300-year-old free house has been in this Guide since 1985. Situated north of the Quantock Hills near the coast, it attracts walkers and cyclists. Four real ales and Rich's cider are served. The bar area has an inglenook with a wood-burner. There is also a snug, dining room, family room (high chairs provided), function room and a large garden. Accommodation consists of one double and one twin room. Good value home-cooked food is served.
♔Q♉❀⇌◐◑♣●P

CHARD

Bell & Crown Inn

Coombe Street

⚙ 12-2.30 (not Mon; 3 Sat), 7-11; 12-3, 7-10.30 Sun
☎ (01460) 62470

Otter Bitter; guest beers Ⓗ

Converted from cottages, this pub retains gaslighting around the bar. The beer range comes mainly from West Country brewers, but some are from further afield. During the winter months (Sept-May), a monthly beer festival of local ales is held, usually on the first weekend. Good value food is available at lunchtimes. The cider is Weston's Scrumpy. ♔❀◐♣●P

CHURCHILL

Crown Inn

The Batch, Skinners Lane (small lane S of A38/A368 jct)

⚙ 12-3.30, 5.30-11; 12-11 Thu-Sat; 12-10.30 Sun
☎ (01934) 852995

Draught Bass; Palmer IPA; RCH Hewish IPA, PG Steam; guest beers Ⓖ

Local CAMRA Pub of the Year 1999, an unspoilt cottage-style pub of character

---

CURRY RIVEL

King William IV
High Street
12-3, 5.30-11; closed Mon; 12-3, 7-10.30 Sun
(01458) 251385
Teignworthy Reel Ale; guest beers Ⓖ
Four beers on gravity dispense in a traditionally refurbished single bar with flagstones. Food all sessions.

EXFORD

Crown Hotel
Park Street
11-2.30, 6-11; 11-11 Sat; 12-11 Sun
(01643) 831554
Exmoor Ale; guest beer Ⓗ
Cosy, half-timbered hotel bar, decorated with sporting prints, stuffed animals and hunting memorabilia.

White Horse Inn
11-11; 12-11 Sun
(01643) 831229
Exmoor Ale, Gold; Greene King Old Speckled Hen; Marston's Pedigree Ⓗ
Ivy-covered inn and hotel at the heart of Exmoor: log fires in winter and antlers on the wall.

FITZHEAD

Fitzhead Inn
12-2 (3 Sat; not Mon or Tue), 7-11; 12-3, 7-10.30 Sun
(01823) 400667
Cotleigh Tawny; guest beer Ⓗ
Cosy, 18th-century village pub serving excellent food. Accommodation includes one room adapted for the disabled.

GLASTONBURY

Rifleman's Arms
4 Chilkwell Street
12-11; 12-10.30 Sun
(01458) 831023
Butcombe Bitter, Gold; Greene King Abbot Ⓗ
Old beamed pub: two bars, plus pool and family rooms, close to the Tor. Car park.

HORTON

Five Dials
Goose Lane
12-3, 6-11; 12-2.30, 7-10.30 Sun
(01460) 55359
Sharp's Cornish Coaster; guest beer Ⓗ
Large, popular village local. A rare outlet for Sharp's beers in this area.

bordering the Mendip Hills. Two stone-floored bars, log fires, and pleasant outdoor seating areas are highlights. The high quality lunches are based on fresh local produce. Two to three guest beers are usually available. A true free house, it has been a Guide regular for many years, although the toilets are somewhat 'rustic'. In a popular area for walkers and near Dolebury Warren, it is always worth a visit. ♛Q❀◖▲P

COMPTON MARTIN

Ring O'Bells

Bath Road (A368)
⏲ 11.30-3, 6.30-11; 12-3, 7-10.30 Sun
☎ (01761) 221284
Butcombe Bitter, Gold; [H] Wadworth 6X; [G] guest beer [H]
Owned by Butcombe Brewery, this is very much a pub for all. Previously a local CAMRA Pub of the Year, it has an excellent family room, a lovely garden, ideal for balmy summer days, and sells good food at very reasonable prices. Various traditional games include the popular table skittles. A superb country inn, this is a Guide regular of many years' standing. ♛Q♨❀◖◗▲♣P

CONGRESBURY

Plough

High Street (off A370)
⏲ 11-2.30, 5-11; 11-11 Sat; 12-4, 7-10.30 Sun
☎ (01934) 832475 website: www.plough-inn.co.uk
Draught Bass; [P] Butcombe Bitter; [H] Wadworth 6X; Worthington Bitter; guest beers [P]
Friendly pub which, despite alterations over the years, retains its character, with flagstone flooring and several different drinking areas. It is well used by local clubs and organisations and hosts a quiz night (Sunday). No meals, except rolls and sandwiches at lunchtime, so the landlord can concentrate on providing quality cask ales for discerning customers. A beer festival is staged on August bank holiday. A boules court is in the garden. Regular buses run from Bristol and Weston-Super-Mare. ♛❀▲♣●P

White Hart

Wrington Road (off A370)
⏲ 11-2.30, 6-11; 12-3, 7-10.30 Sun
☎ (01934) 833303
Badger K&B Sussex, Best, Tanglefoot [H]
This 400-year-old half-timbered cottage-style hostelry is conveniently situated for the A370 and the M5 (four miles from junction 21). The main part is olde-worlde, with two inglenooks – one houses a wood-burning stove. Although the pub is food-oriented, its beer is always in fine fettle. At the back is a large conservatory, where food is served and children are allowed. The huge garden is also safe for children to play in. ♛Q❀◖◗♣P⊘

CORTON DENHAM

Queen's Arms

3 miles from A303, E of Sparkford
⏲ 12-2.30, 7-11; 12-3 Sun
☎ (01963) 220317
Arkells 3B; Cotleigh Tawny; guest beers [H]
Beers from all over the country are available at this pub that boasts one of the best selections of real ale in the area; the blackboard lists the forthcoming ales. There is also an excellent range of home-cooked meals to choose from (no food Mon). The pub is situated in ideal walking country and is a superb base for outings as bed and breakfast accommodation is available. The cider comes from Thatchers. ♛Q❀⇌◖◗⊟●P

CREWKERNE

Crown

34 South Street (A356)
⏲ 6.30-11; 7-10.30 Sun
☎ (01460) 72464
Ringwood Old Thumper; guest beers [H]
Former coaching inn, five minutes' walk from the town centre, the Crown, which dates back to the 17th century, has a small, quiet front bar, serving beers from Exmoor and Ringwood. The larger rear bar is popular with darts and skittles players. Both areas have been refurbished in traditional fashion. It is reputedly haunted by a woman who performs various domestic tasks. No food is available but reasonably-priced bed and breakfast is offered. The courtyard is pleasant for outdoor drinking in summer. ♛❀⇌⊟♣

CROWCOMBE

Carew Arms ☆

Signed from A358 between Taunton and Williton
⏲ 11.30-3, 6-11; 12-3, 7-10.30 (closed eve Jan & Feb) Sun
☎ (01984) 618631
Exmoor Ale; [G] guest beer [H]
Unspoilt village pub that time has forgotten, with well-preserved original features, notably a huge brick fireplace. The flagstone-floored public bar and comfortable back bar are separated by a large servery. Two or three beers from local breweries, and Lanes cider are served alongside wholesome traditional meals at reasonable prices. Situated at the foot of the hills, it makes an ideal base for exploring the Quantocks and the nearby West Somerset Railway. ♛Q❀⇌◖◗⊟▲♣●P

CULMHEAD

Holman Clavel

⏲ 12-3, 5 (6 Sat)-11; 12-3, 7-11 Sun
☎ (01823) 421432
Butcombe Bitter, Gold; guest beer [H]
Traditional country inn dating from the 14th century, featuring oak beams and real fires. In excellent walking country, this pub serves fine food (fish and local game are specialities) in a warm, friendly atmosphere. Guest beers often come from Hop Back and Church End. It is rumoured to be haunted by the ghost of a defrocked monk. Its unique name derives from 'Holman' which is holm oak, and 'Clavel' which is the beam above the fireplace. ♛Q❀◖◗▲♣P

DINNINGTON

Rose & Crown

OS404132
⏲ 11.30-3.30, 6-11; 12-4, 7-10.30 Sun
☎ (01460) 52397

Butcombe Bitter; Wadworth 6X; guest beers Ⓗ

Known locally as 'Dinnington Docks' this old pub is very popular with the friendly locals, who support regular charity functions. The bar area is decorated with old transport pictures and signs. The Docks Transport Society meets each month (first Wednesday) bringing a display of classic cars and motorcycles. The menu is varied and interesting, including a curry night (Tuesday) and roasts every lunchtime. Burrow Hill cider is sold.

♨Q☺❀◐♣●P

DOULTING

Abbey Barn Inn

⏲ 12-2.30, 6-11; 12-2.30, 7-10.30 Sun

☎ (01749) 880321

Draught Bass; Oakhill Best Bitter; guest beers Ⓗ

Separate public and lounge bars, together with a skittle alley allow the pub to cater for a wide variety of customers. Oakhill Best and Draught Bass, together with traditional cider are available along with regular guest beers. The pub is thought to have been rebuilt in 1725. The name and the medieval tithe barn opposite may point to a link with Glastonbury Abbey. Food is available when the bar is open. Individually decorated rooms are available for bed and breakfast.

♨❀⊏◐⊟♿♣●

EAST HARPTREE

Castle of Comfort

On B3134, Wells-Burrington road

⏲ 12-3, 6-11; 12-11 Sat; 12-10.30 Sun

☎ (01761) 221321

Draught Bass; Butcombe Bitter; guest beers Ⓗ

This 17th-century, stone cottage-style pub earned its name from providing refreshments to prisoners on their way to being hanged nearby. Situated on top of the Mendip Hills, it is only five minutes' drive from the famous Cheddar Gorge and Chew Valley lake. This hostelry welcomes children, having a big fenced-in field behind, with a play area. The beamed interior features a real tree trunk, holding up part of the ceiling. The licensee is the chef and hosts mini-beer festivals every Easter.

♨❀◐♣●P

EAST LYNG

Rose & Crown

On A361, 6 miles E of Taunton

⏲ 11-2.30, 6.30-11; 12-3, 7-10.30 Sun

☎ (01823) 698235

website: www.derek.mason.btinternet.co.uk

Butcombe Bitter, Gold; Palmer 200 Ⓗ

The timeless quality of this 13th-century coaching inn is enhanced by comfortable antique furniture and a large stone fireplace, housing a log fire. A varied menu of home-cooked food, including vegetarian dishes, is served in the main bar or in the no-smoking dining room which boasts an inglenook and old oak beams. The menu and directions can be found on the website; booking is advised (and can be done by e-mail), especially Friday and Saturday evenings.

♨Q❀⊏◐♿●P

EAST WOODLANDS

Horse & Groom

1 mile S of A361/B3092 jct

⏲ 11.30-2.30 (not Mon), 6.30-11; 12-3, 7-10.30 Sun

☎ (01373) 462802

Branscombe Vale Branoc; Greene King IPA; Wadworth 6X Ⓖ

Attractive pub, down a narrow country lane bordering the Longleat estate. An open fire, flagstoned floor and comfortable settles add to the atmosphere of the public bar where games are played. The ale range seldom varies, but proper cider and Czech Budvar on draught complement the beer. The lounge bar, conservatory and restaurant cater for diners (no food Sun eve). An imaginative menu uses fresh local ingredients; all bread is made on the premises. Sit in the pleasant garden bordered by unusual pollarded trees and you just might hear the lions.

♨Q❀⊏◐⊟⅄♣●P

FAULKLAND

Tucker's Grave ☆

On A366, 1 mile E of village

⏲ 11-3, 6-11; 12-3, 7-10.30 Sun

☎ (01373) 834230

Draught Bass; Butcombe Bitter Ⓖ

A real classic – a genuine country local that has not changed in many years (apart from new loos). The regulars are a friendly lot who enjoy the rough cider. The beers are kept in barrels in the bay window in the tiny middle room, from where the landlady will serve you. You can then drink in the comfortable parlour or the original settle-lined snug across the hall. Out the back is a pretty garden where you can admire the amazing roofline of this ancient pub. Tucker, by the way, hanged himself nearby.

♨Q❀●P

FROME

Griffin Inn

Milk Street

⏲ 5 (11 Sat)-11; 12-10.30 Sun

☎ (01373) 467766

website: www.milkstreetbrewery.co.uk

Milk Street Funky Monkey (spring), **Nick's, Zig Zag, Beer; guest beers** Ⓗ

Interesting pub in the older part of Frome, that has been sympathetically renovated by the present owners, Milk Street Brewery. A small brewhouse was constructed in the former function room, producing a wide range of good quality ales, which are sold alongside guest ales. The popular single bar has retained many of its original features – open fires, etched glass windows and wood floors. An African menu is featured Wednesday evening. There is a small garden. ♨Q❀◑≹♣P▯

HALSE

New Inn

Off B3227, signed from A358 OS142280

⏲ 12-2.30, 6-11; 12-2.30, 7-10.30 Sun

☎ (01823) 432352

Cotleigh Tawny; guest beers Ⓗ

A typical village inn, this free house dates from 17th century, with oak beams and a wood-burner in the cosy bar. Three real ales

are served from both local and other micro-breweries. There is a quiet bar with snug area, a no-smoking candlelit dining room (high-chairs provided), large skittle alley/function room and garden with tables. Excellent home-cooked food and en-suite accommodation are available. It is popular with visitors to the nearby West Somerset Railway.
♨Q❀⇌◐♣P

HARDINGTON MOOR

Royal Oak Inn (Sonny's)

Moor Lane (take Hardington Mandeville road from A30)
⏲ 12-2.30 (not Mon), 7 (6 Fri &Sat)-11; 12-2.30, 7-10.30 Sun
☎ (01935) 862354 website: www.sonnysroyaloak.co.uk
Butcombe Bitter; guest beers Ⓗ
Sonny was a long-serving previous landlord of this pub, situated some four miles west of Yeovil. A former farmhouse, it is adorned with hanging baskets in summer. Inside, the open-plan bar offers a friendly welcome and a good range of food (not served Mon). Ask to see the 'art gallery'. The landlord, a keen biker, welcomes motorcyclists. An annual beer festival is held in May. Parrots, Oscar and Dolly, preside over the pub.
♨Q❀◐♣●P

HENSTRIDGE

Bird in Hand

2 Ash Walk (100 yds S of A30/A357)
⏲ 11-2.30, 5.30-11; 11-11 Sat; 12-3, 7-10.30 Sun
☎ (01963) 362255
Draught Bass; guest beers Ⓗ
This cosy village pub, of thick stone walls and low ceilings, is a real gem. The bar is attractively set in a beamed room which has a fire at each end. Although main meals are not served, the bar snacks are superb and real value for money. Three real ales are usually on tap, as well as Taunton cider. Well worth a visit. ◐♿♣●P

HIGHBRIDGE

Cooper's Arms

Market Street (by station)
⏲ 11-3.30, 5-11; 11-11 Fri & Sat; 12-4, 7.30-10.30 Sun
☎ (01278) 783562
Fuller's London Pride; RCH East Street Cream, Double Header, seasonal beers; guest beers Ⓗ
This large pub is somewhat unusual in having a skittle alley incorporated into the bar area, making it popular for league games and fund-raising events. It has been Somerset CAMRA Pub of the Year runner-up on several occasions. Most guest beers are around 5% ABV (popular with the locals). There is a quiet lounge and another area with large-screen TV for major sporting events. A cosy atmosphere is enhanced by subtle lighting and exposed beams.
Q❀⊟⚠⇌♣P

HINTON BLEWITT

Ring O' Bells

Between A37 and A368 on hill above Bishop Sutton
OS594570
⏲ 11-3.30, 5 (6 Sat)-11; 12-3.30, 7-10.30 Sun
☎ (01761) 452239
Butcombe Bitter; Wadworth 6X; guest beers Ⓗ
Hilltop village inn on the edge of the Mendips, benefiting from views of Chew Valley, in a maze of minor roads between Bishop Sutton and Temple Cloud. The entrance is through a yard with outside tables. This small, friendly local is set back from the village green. Renowned for good quality food, it is popular in summer with ramblers and cyclists – children (and dogs) are also welcome

INN BRIEF

MIDSOMER NORTON

White Hart ☆
The Island
11-11; 12-10.30 Sun
(01761) 418270
Draught Bass; Butcombe Bitter Ⓖ
Victorian gem, its unchanged multi-roomed layout is well worth a visit, despite a somewhat neglected exterior.

MINEHEAD

Old Ship Aground
Quay Street
11-11; 12-11 Sun
(01643) 702087
Courage Best Bitter; Greene King Ruddles County; St Austell Dartmoor Best, Tribute Ⓗ
19th-century pub by a picturesque harbour, serving a varied menu. St Austell beers may change for seasonal brews.

ROWBERROW

Swan
Off A38, 3/4 mile S of A368
12-3, 6-11; 12-3, 7-10.30 Sun
(01943) 852371
Draught Bass; Butcombe Bitter, Gold; guest beer Ⓗ
Butcombe-owned scenic pub in a small village with a large garden, popular for food.

RUISHTON

Ruishton Inn
Church Road
12-2.30 (not Mon), 6-11; 12-2.30, 7-10.30 Sun
(01823) 442285
Wadworth IPA, 6X Ⓖ
Friendly village local where all food is prepared on the premises, using fresh ingredients.

SEAVINGTON ST MICHAEL

Volunteer Inn
6.30 (12 Sat)-11; 12-10.30 Sun
(01460) 240126
Beer range varies Ⓗ
Two-bar, roadside pub offering three guest beers, usually including Otter, plus a cider. Meals all sessions – good curries.

WATERROW

Rock Inn
11-3, 6-11; 12-3, 7-10.30 Sun
(01984) 623293
Cotleigh Tawny; Exmoor Gold Ⓗ
Traditional inn, set against a rock face in a beautiful valley. An interesting menu is served at all times.

WILLITON

Mason's Arms
2 North Road
11-3, 5.30-11; 11-3, 6.30-11 Sun
(01984) 639200
Fuller's London Pride; guest beers Ⓗ
16th-century thatched pub restored to a high specification, serving local guest beers. Food and accommodation available.

WINSFORD

Royal Oak Inn
11.30-2.30, 7-11; 12-2.30, 7-10.30 Sun
(01634) 851445
Cotleigh Barn Owl; Ⓗ **Exmoor Ale;** Ⓖ **guest beers** Ⓗ
Thatched inn in Exmoor's prettiest village: two bars, plus good food, with guest beers mainly in summer.

✻ symbol next to a main entry place name indicates there are Inn Brief entries as well.

here. The pub supports many sports teams.
⚱Q❀◑▲♣●P

HORSINGTON

Half Moon Inn

200 yds off A357 between Wincanton and Templecombe
12-2.30 (3 Sat), 6-11; 12-3, 7-10.30 Sun
☎ (01963) 370140

Gale's HSB; Wadworth 6X; guest beers Ⓗ

Alcohol has been made and sold on the site of the Half Moon Inn since the 17th century. The present owners have built up a successful and popular pub, specialising in local food (not served Sun eve) and real ales. The latter range from Hobden's Blackmore Ale (3.5% ABV) to Badger's Tanglefoot (5.1% ABV) with up to four others in between. Facilities include a function room where an annual beer festival is held.
⚱❀◑♿♣●P

HUISH EPISCOPI

Rose & Crown (Eli's)

On A372, 1 mile E of Langport
11.30-2.30, 5.30-11; 11.30-11 Fri & Sat; 12-10.30 Sun
☎ (01458) 250494

Teignworthy Reel Ale; guest beers Ⓗ

Known locally as Eli's, this 17th-century thatched inn has remained in the same family for well over a hundred years and has retained its original character. As there is no bar, the drinks are served from a flagstoned tap room, where locals and visitors mingle happily. Farmhouse cider is drawn from wooden barrels and the till consists of a simple drawer. Good home-made food is available, and the pub has its own campsite.
Q❀◑♿▲●P

KEENTHORNE

Cottage Inn

On A39
11-11; 12-10.30 Sun
☎ (01278) 732355

Draught Bass; Butcombe Bitter; Otter Bitter Ⓗ

On the main A39, this free house is an ideal place to break your journey, with plenty of parking, a large patio area (hosting occasional barbecues), and a children's play area. This is a 16th-century coaching inn and old traditional cider house, comprising two bar areas, with comfy armchairs and open fires in the winter, and a large function room. Coombes cider and well-priced pub food are served.
⚱❀◑♣●P

KELSTON

Old Crown

Bath Road (A431, 3 miles from Bath)
11.30-2.30, 5-11; 11.30-11 Sat; 12-10.30 Sun
☎ (01225) 423032

Draught Bass; Bath Gem; Butcombe Bitter, Gold; Wadworth 6X Ⓗ

Superb, low-ceilinged, 18th-century coaching inn. Owned by Butcombe Brewery, it features a flagstoned floor and church pew seats; note the old beer engine in the main bar. A friendly atmosphere and competitively-priced home-cooked food make this a busy, popular pub, with a small restaurant (eve meals Tue-Sat). No children under 14 are admitted. There is a large, attractive garden at the rear, and a roadside drinking area; the car park lies across a busy road. ⚱Q❀◑P

KEYNSHAM

Lock Keeper

On A4175, Willsbridge road
11-11; 12-10.30 Sun
☎ (0117) 986 2383

Smiles Best; Young's Bitter, Special, seasonal beers Ⓗ

On its own island, between the river and the Kennet and Avon Canal at the Keynsham locks and marina, this 16th-century building on four floors, has two rooms accessible via a spiral staircase – one is a splendid alcove-like area. Within five minutes of the Bristol-Bath cycle path, it caters for both locals and passing trade. Excellent food is served – specials change daily (no eve meals Sun). The extensive garden, with boules pitches, is superb for a lazy summer afternoon. ❀◑⇌♣P

Old Bank

20 High Street
11-11; 11-10.30 Sun
☎ (0117) 986 4766

Beer range varies Ⓗ

A most welcome addition to the Guide, this single bar local is the Nursery Brewery tap. Converted from a bank, it has a parquet floor and barrels for tables. The wide choice of beer includes three, ever-changing Nursery beers, plus three guest beers sourced from near and far. Continental draught beers from Belgium, Germany and Holland include Liefman's (bottled versions are also stocked). Comedy and live music nights feature regularly. Happy hour is 5.30-6.30 daily. ❀⇌●P

Ship Inn

93 Temple Street
12-3, 6.30 (5.30 Fri)-11; 12-11 Sat; 12-10.30 Sun
☎ (0117) 986 9841

Abbey Bellringer; Draught Bass; Courage Best Bitter; Worthington Bitter; guest beers Ⓗ

Unspoilt pub in a long, low building, its mullioned windows hinting at its age. With six or seven ales, including local guests, it has one of the widest ranges in the area. The bar, with mirrored back, in the large public bar, is Grade II listed. There is a cosy, busy lounge bar and a no-smoking converted stables bar, with mezzanine and an original horse trough. The sloping gardens and boules pitches overlook Keynsham Park and the River Chew. Evening meals are served Tue-Sat.
⚱❀◑⇌♣P⚡

KINGSBURY EPISCOPI

Wyndham Arms

12-3, 6.30-11; 12-3, 7-10.30 Sun
☎ (01935) 823239 website: www.wyndhamarms.com

Fuller's London Pride; Otter Bright; Worthington Bitter; guest beer Ⓗ

Atmospheric 17th-century hamstone inn, with open fire and flagstoned floor, frequented by locals, walkers and cyclists

visiting the Somerset Levels. Original beams and traditional decor enhance the relaxing ambience. A good range of food is available at all sessions. Skittles, darts and bar skittles are played. Local Burrow Hill cider is stocked. The Wyndham Blues & Roots Club operates monthly from the large function room. A spacious garden and outside seating complete the amenities here.
⩕❀⇌◑♣●P

LANGFORD BUDVILLE

Martlet Inn

½ mile off B3187, between Wellington and Milverton
✪ 12-2.30 (not Mon), 7-11; 12-3, 7-10.30 Sun
☎ (01823) 400262
Cotleigh Tawny, Barn Owl; Exmoor Ale Ⓗ
Old village inn that has seen some improvements over the years. The main bar area is flagstoned with exposed beams – very low in places – and a wood-burning stove, that effectively divides the no-smoking dining area from the bar. The comfortable lounge bar has a second wood-burner. A well-equipped skittle alley doubles as a function room, and the garden area has some children's play equipment. The pub has a good reputation for its menu, featuring home-cooked specials (booking advised).
⩕Q❀◑⊟♣P⚟

LANGPORT

Old Custom House

Bow Street
✪ 12-2.30 (not Mon), 4.30 (4 Mon)-11; 12-11 Fri & Sat; 12-3.30, 7-10.30 Sun
☎ (01458) 250332
Beer range varies Ⓗ
Two-bar town pub, offering three changing real ales, mostly from West Country breweries, including a standard and a higher gravity beer. The menu features a hot daily special for under £5, and other freshly-cooked local produce (evening meals Tue-Sat). A secluded garden, with barbecue area, leads to a free car park. Cycle hire, with access to the Parrett Trail, is available nearby. A customs office on this site handled victuals arriving on an adjacent waterway.
❀◑♣P

LOWER ODCOMBE

Mason's Arms

41 Lower Odcombe (off old Yeovil-Montacute road)
OS510158
✪ 12.30-3 (not Mon or Tue; 12-3 Sat), 7-11; 12-3, 7-10.30 Sun
☎ (01935) 862591
Butcombe Bitter; Odcombe Lower, Higher; Otter Bright; guest beer Ⓗ
Home of Odcombe Ales, and the only outlet for the one-barrel brewery, this 500-year-old hamstone and thatch inn, is a traditional country local. It has recently introduced bed and breakfast accommodation. Hearty pub meals are available most sessions, except Thursday evenings, when authentic curries are served; Sunday lunchtime is reserved for traditional roasts (no eve meals Mon or Tue). A beer and music festival is held in September. Taunton traditional cider is on handpump.
❀⇌◑⛺♣●P

MARTOCK

Nag's Head

East Street (off B3165)
✪ 12-2 (not Mon; 12-3 summer), 6-11; 12-3, 6-10.30 Sun
☎ (01935) 823432
Otter Bitter; guest beers Ⓗ
Two-bar hamstone pub, formerly a cider house, it is situated in a quiet position near the village centre. An extensive display of pump clips in the cosy, beamed lounge reflects the constantly changing guest beers. A weekday evening happy hour applies between 6 and 7pm. Meals and snacks are cooked to order. It hosts live music Saturday evening. Outside drinking areas include tables out the front and a garden behind. Accommodation is in a comfortable self-contained flat. The pub has a skittle alley.
❀⇌◑⊟⛺♣P⚟

MIDDLEZOY

George Inn

42 Main Road (1 mile from A372/A361 jct)
OS378327
✪ 12-2.30 (not Mon); 12-3 Sat, 7-11; 12-3, 7-10.30 Sun
☎ (01823) 698215
Butcombe Bitter; guest beers Ⓗ
17th-century traditional village pub of oak beams, stone flags and a log fire. Its location on the Somerset Levels, makes it popular with anglers, birdwatchers and walkers, as well as locals. Home-cooked food is served (not Sun or Mon eves), and there is always an excellent selection of cask ales, with regular appearances of favourites from the likes of Hop Back and Slaters (Eccleshall) Brewery. Somerset CAMRA Pub of the Year 2000. ⩕Q❀⇌◑♣P⚟

MINEHEAD ❄

Queen's Head Inn

Holloway Street (off the parade)
✪ 12-3, 6.30-11; 12-3, 6.30-11 Sun
☎ (01643) 706000
Draught Bass; Exmoor Gold, Hart; Greene King IPA; Oakhill XXX Mature; guest beer Ⓗ
Large, town-centre pub with one main bar, plus areas for dining and games. The interior makes much use of pine and has a very well-kept appearance. Popular with drinkers of all ages, it can sometimes be lively. Beers are kept in a traditional brick-floored cellar, to be served at the optimum temperature. An extensive range of food is available every day until one hour before closing. ◑⛺⇌(W Somerset Railway) ♣⚟

NAILSEA

Blue Flame

West End (1 mile SW of Nailsea) OS449690
✪ 12-3, 6-11; 12-11 Sat; 12-10.30 Sun
☎ (01275) 856910
Draught Bass; Fuller's London Pride; guest beer Ⓖ
Wonderfully unspoilt 19th-century pub on the outskirts of Nailsea. In addition to the real ales on offer, the pub also sells the

locally-produced Thatchers cider. Social events include barbecues in summer and occasional folk evenings. Crib, dominoes, darts and table skittles are also played. The very pleasant garden can get busy in summer. It is off the beaten track, but well worth seeking out. ⌂Q❀⅄♣●P

NETHER STOWEY

Rose & Crown

St Mary's Street

⚙ 12-11; 12-5, 7-10.30 Sun

☎ (01278) 732265

Beer range varies Ⓗ

Welcoming, 16th-century coaching inn at the centre of this lovely village, nestling at the foot of the Quantock Hills. An ideal base for walking, the pub enjoys a strong local following and ensures a good turnover of quality ales. The restaurant is open from Wednesday to Saturday, serving home-grown and home-cooked meals. Coleridge Cottage can be found nearby, together with places of local historical interest. Three handpumps serve real ales from many local breweries. Q❀⇌◐◑◫♣●

NORTON FITZWARREN

Cross Keys

At A361/B3227 jct W of Taunton

⚙ 11-11; 12-10.30 Sun

Courage Best Bitter, Directors; guest beer Ⓗ

Large Chef & Brewer pub where the guest beer is changed regularly. The extensive menu features fresh fish as a speciality; a good wine list is also available. The pub dates back to 1860 and an extensive garden at the side and rear offers a very pleasant drinking area. A good local bus service runs from Taunton seven days a week – six services stop outside the pub. ⌂❀◐◑P

NORTON ST PHILIP

Fleur de Lys

⚙ 11-3, 5-11; 11-11 Sat; 12-3, 7-10.30 Sun

☎ (01373) 834333

Butcombe Bitter; Wadworth IPA, 6X Ⓗ

This ancient stone building has been extensively but sympathetically refurbished. The repositioned bar is on the site of the old passageway through which the pub ghost reputedly passed on his way to gallows in the rear garden. Very good value, tasty food is served. Opposite is the medieval George Inn, an ale house since 1323.
⌂Q◐◑♣P

PITNEY

Halfway House

Pitney Hill (B3153, between Langport and Somerton)

⚙ 11.30-3, 5.30-11; 12-3.30, 7-10.30 Sun

☎ (01458) 252513

Butcombe Bitter; Cotleigh Tawny; Hop Back Crop Circle, Summer Lightning; Teignworthy Reel Ale; guest beers Ⓖ

Excellent example of a traditional village pub serving a wide variety of local ales, plus Hecks cider in winter, Wilkins in summer. No juke box, music or machines detract from the buzz of friendly conversation. Flagstoned floors make it ideal for walkers' boots. An excellent selection of home-cooked curries is offered in the evening (no food Sun). National CAMRA Pub of the Year 1996 and Somerset Pub of the Year '95, '97 and 2001; a real gem. The regular bus 54 between Yeovil and Taunton stops outside. ⌂Q❀◐◑⅄♣●P

PORLOCK

Ship Inn

High Street (A39, foot of hill)

⚙ 11-11; 12-11 Sun

☎ (01643) 862507 website: www.shipinnporlock.com

Draught Bass; Cotleigh Barn Owl; Courage Best Bitter; guest beers Ⓗ

This picturesque thatched inn, dating from the middle ages, is a great base for exploring Lorna Doone country. The cosy bar area boasts a Victorian beer engine, while the oldest part of the building bears a notable ancient window. Renowned visitors in the past have included poets Robert Southey and Samuel Taylor Coleridge. Guest beers come from the likes of Oakhill, Cotleigh, Cottage, Clearwater and Barum. The last Friday of the month usually sees a spontaneous folk session.
⌂Q♨❀⇌◐◑◫⅄♣●P

SALTFORD

Bird in Hand

58 High Street (200 yds from Saltford Hall)

⚙ 11-3, 6.30-11; 11-3.30, 6-11 Fri & Sat; 12-4, 6.30-10.30 Sun

☎ (01225) 873335

Abbey Bellringer; Draught Bass; Courage Best Bitter; Moles Tap Bitter Ⓗ

The pub nestles quietly in the older part of Saltford village, a short distance from the meandering River Avon and even closer to the Bristol-Bath cycle path (originally a railway line). Good home-cooked food is served in the no-smoking conservatory dining area of this smart cottage hostelry, that affords wonderful views over the Avon Valley. There is a small family area where children are welcome. Pétanque is played. Thatchers cider is on tap. Wheelchair WC.
❀◐◑♿♣●P

SANDYWAY

Sportsman's Inn

Road between Withypool and North Molton OS793332

⚙ 12-3 (not Mon), 6.30-11; 12-3, 7-10.30 Sun

☎ (01643) 831109 website: www.sportsmans.co.uk

Exmoor Ale, Fox; Ⓗ **guest beers** Ⓗ/Ⓖ

Situated in a small hamlet high up on Exmoor, near the Devon border, this inn is popular with locals and tourists. It was converted from two cottages in the 1840s, retaining the original inglenooks, now at each end of the roomy bar and restaurant area, also an old well. Food is sourced from local producers, while the beers are mainly from Exmoor Brewery, with their seasonal specials often appearing as guests. The cider is Hancock's. ⌂Q❀⇌◐◑●P

SHURTON

Shurton Inn

About 1 mile from Hinkley Point power station

⚙ 12-2.30, 6-11; 12-3, 7-10.30 Sun

☎ (01278) 732695

Butcombe Bitter; Exmoor Ale; guest beer Ⓗ

Welcoming village inn with a wood-panelled bar area and another set aside for meals, although you can eat anywhere in the pub. Set close to the north Somerset coast, it is ideally situated for birdwatching at nearby Steart Point. Also convenient for the Quantock Hills, it makes a good base for walkers; the overnight accommodation includes one room adapted for disabled customers. Lanes cider is stocked. An annual summer beer festival is held.

Q❀◐◑♿⛺♣●P

SOUTH PETHERTON

Brewer's Arms

18 St James Street (1/2 mile off A303)

11.30-2.30, 6-11; 12-10.30 Sun

☎ (01460) 241887

Otter Bitter; Worthington Bitter; guest beers [H]

Near the A303, this 17th-century former coaching inn is at the centre of a hamstone village. Guest beers come from all around the country. A beer festival is held over the late May bank holiday and a festival of Somerset beers and ciders on August bank holiday weekend. The new restaurant which serves excellent home-cooked meals, boasts an 18th-century bread oven. The enclosed courtyard is delightful in summer. Somerset CAMRA Pub of the Year 1999.

❀◐◑⛺♣●✔

STAPLE FITZPAINE

Greyhound Inn

Signed from A358

12-2.30 (3 Sat), 6 (4.30 Fri)-11; 12-3, 7-10.30 Sun

☎ (01823) 480227

Exmoor Ale; Otter Ale; guest beer [H]

16th-century, Grade II listed, former hunting lodge with four en-suite bedrooms, in a lovely rural setting between Taunton and the Blackdown Hills. The extensive menu features seasonal dishes, freshly prepared to order. The flagstoned bar area has barrel stools and serves a series of rambling, connected rooms with old timbers and natural stone walls. Lanes farmhouse cider and daily newspapers are available. A mini-beer festival is held in August. The pub opens earlier on summer weekdays.

❀◐◑⛺♣●P⚡

TAUNTON

Hankridge Arms

Hankridge Way, Riverside (retail park, off M5 jct 25)

11-11; 12-10.30 Sun

☎ (01823) 444405

Badger Best, Tanglefoot; guest beers [H]

Dating back to the 16th century, this former farmhouse is now a Grade I listed building, carefully renovated to retain original features such as inglenooks, flagstones, exposed timbers and a priest's hole. The single bar provides ample seating for both drinking and dining. Guest beers are from Hall & Woodhouse's King & Barnes range, or the Gribble Brewery. The Tapestry Restaurant (mainly no-smoking), offers a varied menu with all meals home-cooked using fresh ingredients.

❀◐◑♿⛺P✔

Harpoon Louie's

75 Station Road

6-11 (11.30 diners); 7-10.30 Sun

☎ (01823) 324404

Otter Ale; guest beers [H]

Friendly welcoming bar/restaurant where up to four real ales are sourced from micro-breweries both local and from further afield. The subtly-lit restaurant is on split levels, with wooden floors and stone walls; a good range of bar meals is also served at reasonable prices. Close to the cricket ground, it is a favourite haunt of fans. There is always lively conversation in the bar, where a variety of games are played. The pub only opens at lunchtime in December.

◐◑⇌●

Mason's Arms

Magdelene Street (by St Mary's Church)

10.30-3, 5-11; 10.30-11 Sat; 12-4, (closed eve) Sun

☎ (01823) 288916

website: www.masonsarms.freeuk.com

Draught Bass; Exe Valley Bitter; Otter Bitter; guest beer [H]

Town-centre, traditional English free house with a convivial atmosphere. This pub dates back to 1809 and boasts an interesting history, which Taunton's longest serving licensee will be happy to relate. The four handpumps include one for a rotating guest beer, drawn up from the stonewalled cellar directly below the bar. An interesting menu includes grillstone steaks and unusual soups. This Somerset CAMRA Pub of the Year 2002 offers a good wine list.

Q❀◐◑♣P

Wyvern Club

Mountfields Road (turn off B3170 to Corfe)

7-11; 12-2.30, 7-10.30 Sun

☎ (01823) 284591

Exmoor Ale; guest beers [H]

Large, busy, sports and social club serving evening meals until 10pm (9pm Sun), also hot and cold bar snacks and Sunday lunches. Guest beers are often from West Country micro-breweries as well as more well-known brands. The comfortable surroundings and friendly bar staff ensure a warm welcome. The bar is also open when home cricket, football and rugby matches are played. The club's large function room and skittle alley are both for hire. Show this Guide or CAMRA membership card for entry.

❀◑♿♣P

WANSTROW

The Pub

Station Road

12-3 (not Mon), 6.30-11; 12-3, 7-10.30 Sun

☎ (01749) 850455

Beer range varies [H]/[G]

A gem – friendly, well-kept village local where a cosy lounge bar with flagstoned floors leads to a small restaurant. The public bar keeps three barrels on gravity, while another two or three guest beers are on handpump, along with farmhouse cider. The beers change on a regular basis. A skittle alley leads off the public bar. A small but very imaginative menu is offered; all food is home made and served when the pub is open. Well worth a visit. ♨Q❀◐◑⊟♣●P

WATCHET

Star Inn

Mill Lane (left after museum on road to Blue Anchor)
⊙ 12-3, 6.30-11; 12-3, 7-11 Sun
☎ (01984) 631367
Draught Bass; Otter Bitter; guest beers Ⓗ
Built in 1680, the Star was once three cottages. Close to the sea, and with a large public car park nearby, this is an ideal pub to visit at lunchtime or evening. Guest ales are changed regularly and there is an emphasis on locally-brewed beers. A warm atmosphere, a friendly welcome and some excellent food (including huge portions of cod and chips) make this pub well worth a visit. An extensive garden lies behind the pub. ♨Q⊠❀◐◑⇌(W Somerset Railway)♣

WELLINGTON

Cottage Inn

31 Champford Lane
⊙ 11-3, 6-11; 12-4, 7-10.30 Sun
☎ (01823) 664650
Fuller's London Pride; Otter Bitter, Ale; Juwards Bitter Ⓗ
Friendly, back-street local, just off the main street, near the Wellesley theatre and cinema. The chimney breast divides the bar area into public and lounge, which is characterised by black beams, lots of brass knick-knacks, pictures and old maps. Home to local darts and skittles teams, and a carnival club, there is usually someone to chat to here. The pub offers good value, basic bar lunches (no food Sun).
❀◐⊟♿A♣P

WELLOW

Fox & Badger

Railway Lane
⊙ 11.30-3.30, 6-11; 11.30-11 Fri & Sat; 12-10.30 Sun
☎ (01225) 832293 website: www.foxandbadger.co.uk
Badger Best; Draught Bass; Butcombe Bitter; Wadworth 6X Ⓗ
Cosy, two-bar pub in the village centre. Unusually, the public bar is carpeted while it is the lounge that has flagstones. There is a skittle alley at the rear. The same long-term guest beer is usually on tap for some months. It offers an extensive and good value menu of traditional and more unusual dishes (eve meals Fri and Sat). It can be difficult to park. ♨⊠❀◐◑⊟♣●

WELLS

City Arms

69 High Street
⊙ 10-11; 12-10.30 Sun
☎ (01749) 673916
Butcombe Bitter; Oakhill Mendip Gold; Palmer IPA; guest beers Ⓗ
The splendid, cobbled courtyard is a notable feature of this old city-centre pub, part of which used to be the jail. One of the few bastions of real ale left in Wells, the landlord maintains a traditional, old-style hostelry, with the emphasis on good beer and food. The regular beers, plus a dark offering in winter, are supported by a wide range of guest beers and British bottled beers. Food, freshly cooked, uses local ingredients where possible. ⊠❀◐◑♣●

WEST CRANMORE

Strode Arms

Due S of A361, E of Shepton Mallet
⊙ 11.30-2.30, 6.30-11; 12-3, 7-10.30 Sun
☎ (01749) 880450
Oakhill Best Bitter; Wadworth IPA, 6X; guest beer Ⓗ
In an idyllic setting, in a pretty village overlooking the duckpond, the pub stands next to the local steam railway. Originally a 15th-century farmhouse, a roaring log fire, complete with railway line fender, greets you in winter. A guest ale is stocked between Easter and Christmas; Wilkins cider, straight from the barrel, is also served. No-smoking bar and restaurant areas are available. A varied menu is based on fresh ingredients, with all meals prepared on the premises.
♨Q❀◐◑●P⍉

WESTON-SUPER-MARE

Dragon

15 Meadow Street (High St/Regent St jct)
⊙ 10-11; 12-10.30 Sun
☎ (01934) 621304
Courage Directors; Shepherd Neame Spitfire; Theakston Best Bitter; guest beers Ⓗ
Town-centre pub, handy for shops and the seafront, offering the usual Wetherspoon's competitive prices with deals on beers and food. Meals are available all day until 10pm. It hosts twice-yearly beer festivals – normally at Easter and Hallowe'en. It shows good support for local breweries, with beers from Butcombe, Exmoor and RCH on tap regularly, but be prepared for rather slow service at busy times. Interesting facts about the town are displayed on the walls.
Q❀◐◑♿A⇌●⍉⊘

Off the Rails

Station Approach, Station Road
⊙ 10-11; 12-10.30 Sun
☎ (01934) 415109
Beer range varies Ⓗ
Cosy, small, single-roomed pub serving two or three real ales, which are often from local breweries such as RCH. With two TVs, a free juke box and three fruit machines, it enjoys a strong local following. Note the 19th-century photos of Weston Station. Staff are friendly and show interest in customers' requests for other beers. Adjoining the bar is the station buffet where children are welcome. A⇌

Regency

22-24 Lower Church Road (opp. technical college near seafront)
⊙ 11-11; 12-10.30 Sun
☎ (01934) 633406
Draught Bass; Bath Gem; Boddingtons Bitter; Wadworth 6X; guest beer (occasional) Ⓗ
Popular single bar, with a pool room, run by friendly staff. It is situated opposite Weston College, with the seafront, High Street and Playhouse Theatre all nearby. It gets busy at lunchtime when good value, varied food is served. It has a small patio at the rear. The pub attracts a good variety of customers, locals and tourists alike. ❀◐♣

WILLITON ❄

Forester's Arms

55 Long Street

⏲ 11-11; 12-10.30 Sun

☎ (01984) 632508

Cotleigh Tawny, seasonal beers; Worthington Bitter Ⓗ

In an ideal position for exploring the nearby coastline or the surrounding Quantock and Brendon Hills, this 17th-century former coaching inn is situated on the edge of Williton near the West Somerset Railway. Beers from the Cotleigh Brewery feature strongly, as they have done almost since they were first brewed, while guest beers are often (but not always) from other local breweries. Popular with locals, the pub has a friendly atmosphere.

(W Somerset Railway) P

WINCANTON

Bear Inn

12 Market Place (opp. Town Hall)

⏲ 11-11; 12-10.30 Sun

☎ (01963) 32581

Draught Bass; Greene King Abbot; Ringwood Best Bitter; guest beers Ⓗ

This former 18th-century coaching inn has a comfortable, large, single bar with blackened beams and a log fire, where four real ales are normally on tap. This busy pub, popular with locals and visitors alike, serves excellent home-cooked food and provides extensive accommodation. Darts, pool and skittles are all played, away from the main bar area. Q P

WINSCOMBE

Winscombe Club

Sandford Road

⏲ 11-2.30 (3 Sat), 7-11; 12-3, 7-10.30 Sun

☎ (01934) 842624

Courage Directors; Wickwar BOB; guest beer Ⓗ

Friendly village social club, where a variety of activities, including skittles, pool and fortnightly live music take place. The guest beer is often rare and regularly showcases Somerset breweries such as Moor and Berrow; prices are very attractive. The cider is from Thatchers. CAMRA members are welcome on production of a membership card. A small patio has tables for outdoor drinking.

WITHYPOOL

Royal Oak Inn

A few yards uphill from Barle River bridge

⏲ 11-11; 12-11 Sun

☎ (01643) 831506/7

Exmoor Ale, Stag Ⓗ

Cosy, homely two-bar Exmoor inn in the heart of good riding and walking country. Both bars sport plenty of rural paraphernalia, such as stags' heads, plus, more unusually, a letter from Eisenhower, who stayed there in WWII. The outside wall still bears the old Usher's logo. Popular with both visitors and locals, it is recommended for its excellent food, which often includes game from local shoots. Lanes cider is stocked in summer.

Q P

WIVELISCOMBE

Bear Inn

10 North Street

⏲ 11-11; 12-10.30 Sun

☎ (01984) 623537

Cotleigh Tawny, seasonal beers; Hop Back GFB; guest beers Ⓗ

Friendly, town-centre pub, usually serving two guest beers. The 17th-century buildings contain a bar area and a restaurant area where families are welcome; home-made food is served. There is a large garden and patio at the rear, with a boules pitch. Beer-lovers' weekends are organised in conjunction with two local breweries.

P

WOOKEY

Burcott Inn

Wookey Road (B3139, 2 miles W of Wells)

⏲ 11.30-2.30, 6-11; 12-3, 7-10.30 Sun

☎ (01749) 673874

Beer range varies Ⓗ

Deservedly popular country pub where at least two different ales are served across the copper-topped L-shaped bar. Old pine tables, settles and a real fire help create a welcoming atmosphere. There is something for everyone here – a games room for darts and shove-ha'penny, cribbage competitions every Thursday and an excellent menu that includes daily specials (no eve meals Sun or Mon in winter). The extensive garden boasts the remains of a cider press and splendid views of the Mendips. Q P

WOOKEY HOLE

Wookey Hole Inn

Wookey Road (opp. Wookey Hole caves, near Wells)

⏲ 12-2.30, 6-11 (may vary in summer); 12-3.30, 7-10.30 Sun

☎ (01749) 676677 website: www.wookeyholeinn.com

Beer range varies Ⓗ

Unusual conversion of an old village pub where the emphasis is on high quality 'fusion' food. The single bar divides into a split-level dining area and two drinking areas, complete with sofas and low tables. The style is more continental café-bar than traditional country pub, but it works well. The beer range consists of at least four constantly changing guests and several Belgian beers on draught. Live jazz is performed most Sunday lunchtimes.

Q P

YEOVIL

Armoury

1 The Park

⏲ 11.30-2.30, 6-11; 11-11 Thu-Sat; 12-10.30 Sun

☎ (01935) 471047

Butcombe Bitter; Wadworth IPA, 6X, JCB, seasonal beers; guest beers Ⓗ

Lively, typical, town pub, formerly an armoury, where bar meals and snacks are available lunchtime and evenings. Traditional pub games are played by several home teams; the newly-refurbished skittle alley can be viewed on closed circuit TV in the adjoining bar. The pub has limited parking but there is a free public car park opposite where waiting is limited to one hour. P

Leave the car at home

Public transport to pubs

BUSES

Bus Traveline
Most bus timetable enquiries are now dealt with through the National Traveline which is operated under a standard call number by local authorities across the UK for countrywide information:

Telephone: (0870) 608 2608
Textphone: (0870) 241 2216

Information & Journey Planner Websites – some may cover other transport modes.
www.pti.org.uk; www.traveline.org.uk

Other sources of information can be found through your local County, District or Unitary Council or Passenger Transport Executive to ascertain correct contact details. Details of these together with train operating company telephone numbers appear in full in the National Rail Timetable (from main stations and W H Smith shops), or others in the **www.ukbus.co.uk website.**

COACHES

National Express
Scottish City Link

For longer distance coach service timetables & planners contact National Express – their line number is:

National Express (08705) 808080
Website: www.gobycoach.com

Scottish Citylink (08705) 505050
Website: www.citylink.co.uk

TRAINS

National Train Information Line
The national hotline for all train information is:

Telephone: 08457 484950
Minicom: 0845 60 50 600

Other Rail Timetable & Fare Information and Journey Planning Websites:

Enquiries
www.nationaltrainenquiries.co.uk; www.railtrack.co.uk

Planning
www.travelinfosystems.com

Current state of rail services
www.nationalrail.co.uk

Booking services
www.thetrainline.com

London
www.londontransport.co.uk
(This covers Buses, Trams, Underground, River, Docklands Rail and Victoria Coach Station)

Europe & Foreign
www.raileurope.co.uk
www.railchoice.co.uk

Many of the above websites often refer to a further local site for additional detailed information.

OTHER WEBSITES

Other important bus websites often give information – the main ones are as follows:

www.ukbus.co.uk
Station Master Bus & Train Information & Journey Planners with telephone numbers

www.arriva.co.uk
Arriva Buses, Trams & Trains
www.firstgroup.com First Group Buses, Trams & Trains

www.stagecoachplc.com
Stagecoach Buses, Trams & Trains

www.londontransport.co.uk
for all London.

Many local authorities are setting up their own websites and call centres – information available by local contact. Some other main and smaller bus and coach operators also have these facilities.

Important: Don't rely on information from websites being 100% accurate and up-to-date – contact the appropriate telephone service to check before travelling.

For other information about contacts, but not timetable or service enquiries, please contact the CAMRA Public Transport Task Group by email MikePCAMRA@aol.com or by post via CAMRA, 230 Hatfield Road, St Albans, Herts, AL1 4LW.

STAFFORDSHIRE

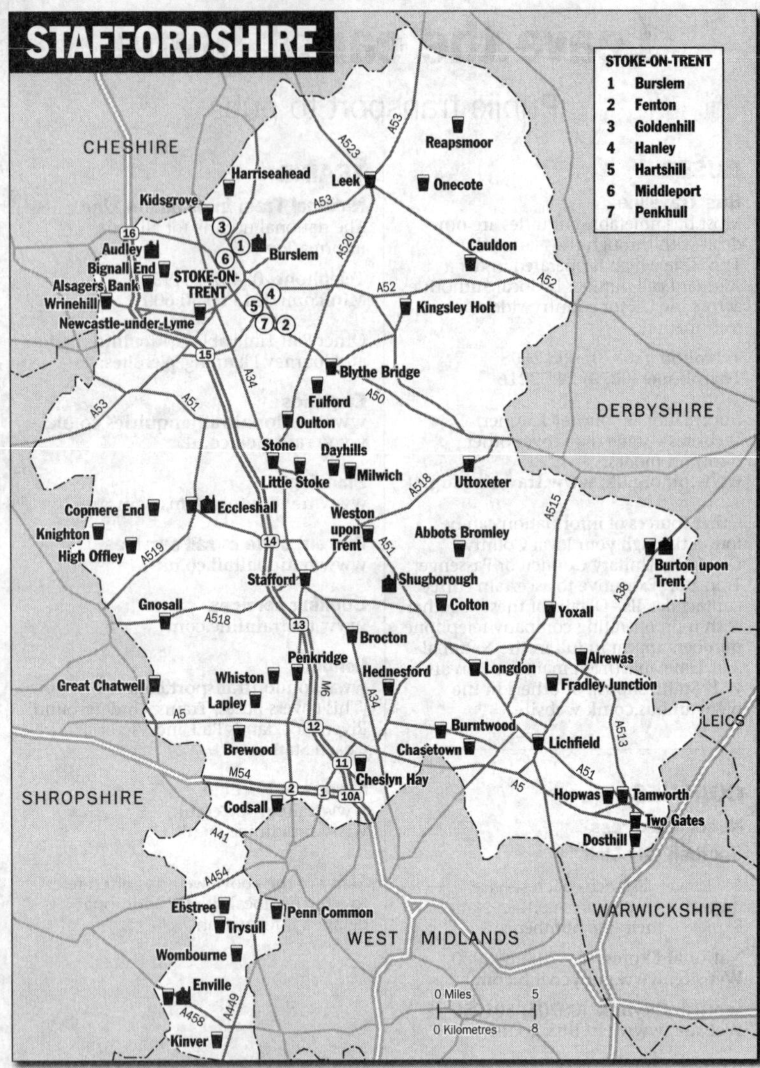

ABBOTS BROMLEY

Coach & Horses

High Street (B5014)
11.30-3, 5.30-11; 12-10.30 Sun
(01283) 840256
Marston's Pedigree; Tetley Bitter H

Very comfortable country pub situated at the east end of the village in a rural setting, close to Blithfield Reservoir. The single L-shaped room features a small raised area where the bar billiards table used to be. There is also a small side room. P

ALREWAS

George & Dragon

120 Main Street
11-2.30, 5-11; 11-11 Fri & Sat; 12-10.30 Sun
(01283) 791476
Banks's Bitter; Marston's Pedigree H

Village focal point, and very popular with visitors, the main bar is divided into three very distinct areas, with a lounge through a door to the right. This doubles as a dining room when meals are served (Mon-Sat). It is well worth the short walk from Bridge 48 on the Trent & Mersey Canal and is right by a bus stop on the Burton-Lichfield route.
P

ALSAGERS BANK

Gresley Arms

High Street (B5367)
12-3, 6-11; 12-11 Sat; 12-10.30 Sun
(01782) 720297
Beer range varies H

Family-run village local that benefits from commanding views over Cheshire and beyond to Wales. The pub has a traditional bar, lounge, dining room and a games-cum-children's room. The garden and play area are popular in summer with families and walkers, and there is a telescope. The beer range features up to five ever-changing beers, mainly from micros and smaller independent breweries.
P

BIGNALL END

Plough Inn

2 Ravens Lane (B5500, 1/2 mile E of Audley)
12-3, 7-11; 12-11 Fri & Sat; 12-10.30 Sun
(01782) 720469
Banks's Bitter; guest beers H

Popular pub where the constantly changing guest beers come mainly from small independent and micro-breweries. The Plough comprises a traditional bar and split-level lounge, plus a dining area serving excellent value meals (no food Sunday evening). This is a former local CAMRA Pub of the Year.

BREWOOD

Swan Hotel

Market Place
12-2.30 (3 Fri; 4 Sat), 7-11; 12-10.30 Sun
(01902) 850330
Mansfield Riding Bitter; Marston's Pedigree; Theakston XB; guest beers H

Comfortable, former coaching inn, with low, beamed ceilings: two cosy snugs and a skittle alley upstairs. It stands in the centre of Staffordshire's Best-Kept Village (seven times running). Normally two guest beers are available, chosen with flair. A regular CAMRA award-winner at branch and county level, the Swan was once regional Pub of the Year. It is not far from the Shropshire Union Canal and a bus from Wolverhampton stops right outside. No food is served Sun. P

BROCTON

Chetwynd Arms

Cannock Road (A34)
11-11; 12-10.30 Sun
(01785) 661089
Banks's Original, Bitter; Marston's Pedigree; guest beer H

Extended over the years, but the 'Chet' retains its charm. The bustling public bar, where traditional games are played, is a haven for drinkers. The comfortable lounge accommodates both drinkers and diners, with meals served all day until 9.30pm. The garden has a children's play area. Brocton is an ideal base for exploring Cannock Chase, an area of natural beauty. The pub is involved in local charities, the highlight event being the annual harvest festival. P

BURNTWOOD

White Swan

2 Cannock Road
5-11; 12-11 Sat; 12-3.30, 7-10.30 Sun
(01543) 675937
Ansells Best Bitter; Greene King Abbot; Tetley Burton Ale; guest beer H

Dating from the 1860s, when it was built as a private residence, the White Swan is a justifiably popular community local. The single, long, narrow room with its collection of china plates is, unusually, entered via a sliding door. The pub is reputedly haunted by the ghost of a man who hanged himself over the cellar trap last century and the landlord attests to having had eerie experiences. P

BURTON UPON TRENT

Bass Museum (Burton Bar)

Horninglow Street (A511)
11-7 (5 Sat); 12-5 Sun
(01283) 511000 (ext. 3513)
website: www.bass-museum.com
Draught Bass; Worthington White Shield; guest beers H

Large, comfortable, single-roomed bar inside the Bass Museum, now owned by Coors Brewers. A conservatory and picnic tables in the large garden cater for overspill. Constantly changing cask beers are mostly brewed on site by the Museum Brewing Company, with at least four on tap. Local CAMRA Pub of the Year 2001, it is the home of the famous Worthington White Shield. Museum admission is free for current card-carrying CAMRA members; see the shire horses and steam engines. Q P

Burton Bridge Inn

24 Bridge Street (A511)
11.30-2.15, 5.30-11; 12-2, 7-10.30 Sun
(01283) 536596
Burton Bridge Golden Delicious, Bridge Bitter, Porter, Festival, seasonal beers; guest beer H

Formerly the Fox & Goose (note the inn sign), this sensitively refurbished mid 17th-century pub is the Burton Bridge Brewery tap and fronts the brewery itself. The smaller front room, with wooden pews, displays awards and brewery memorabilia. The oak-beamed, panelled back room is no-smoking, with oak tables and chairs. Both rooms are served from a central bar. A good range of malt whiskies, and fruit wines are stocked. A function room and skittle alley are upstairs. Q

Cooper's Tavern

43 Cross Street
12-3, 5.15-11; 12-3, 7-10.30 Sun
(01283) 532551
Draught Bass; H **Hardys & Hansons Best Bitter, Classic** G

Classic, unspoilt 19th-century ale house, once regarded as the Bass Brewery tap. The intimate inner tap room has barrel tables and bench seats; the beer is served from a small counter, next to the cask stillage, using a mixture of gravity and handpumps. The comfortable lounge, often hosts impromptu folk music (Tuesday evening). The small no-smoking family room is sometimes used for functions. Lunches are good value. Q

Derby Inn

17 Derby Road (A5121)
11-3, 5.30-11; 11-11 Fri & Sat; 12-3, 7-10.30 Sun
(01283) 543674

INDEPENDENT BREWERIES

Burton Bridge Burton upon Trent
Eccleshall Eccleshall
Enville Enville
Marston's Burton upon Trent
Old Cottage Burton upon Trent
Shugborough Shugborough
Titanic Burslem
Tower Burton upon Trent
Townhouse Audley

website: www.tv13.freeserve.co.uk/derbyinn/
Marston's Pedigree Ⓗ
Friendly, traditional brick-built local situated towards the edge of the town. The lively bar bears railway pictures and related memorabilia, while the small, wood-panelled lounge displays a full set of CAMRA Burton beer festival glasses. It is very much a community pub where locally-produced fruit, vegetables, eggs and cheese are sold in the bar, mainly at weekends.
Q⊟♣

Devonshire Arms
86 Station Street
⊙ 11-2.30, 5.30-11; 11-11 Fri & Sat; 12-3, 7-10.30 Sun
☎ (01283) 562392
Burton Bridge Golden Delicious, Bridge Bitter, Porter, Stairway to Heaven, seasonal beer; guest beer Ⓗ
Popular old pub, Grade II listed, and one of three Burton Bridge hostelries in the town. It comprises a small public bar (with table football) and a larger, comfortable lounge with a no-smoking area. Note the 1853 map of Burton and unusual arched wooden ceilings. A dark beer (porter or stout) is always on tap. Belgian and German bottled beers and English fruit wines are also stocked. The rear patio boasts a fountain. Derby and Uttoxeter bus services stop outside; limited parking. ❀◐⊟≈♣P⊭

Thomas Sykes
Anglesey Road
⊙ 11.30-2.30, 5 (7 Sat)-11; 11.30-11 Fri; 12-2.30, 7-10.30 Sun
☎ (01283) 510246
Draught Bass; Marston's Pedigree; guest beers Ⓗ
Classic ale house, created in the former stables and wagon sheds of the old Thomas Sykes Brewery, and now a listed building. The high ceiling, cobblestoned floor and breweriana of the main bar provide an unspoilt, traditional atmosphere. A small lounge is served through a hatch, and skittles may be played in the large function room. Note the unusual anvil table. Two guest beers are normally available. Children are admitted until 8.30pm. Q♉❀⊟≈♣P

CAULDON

Yew Tree Inn
Off A52/A523 OS077493
⊙ 11-3, 6-11; 12-3, 7-10.30 Sun
☎ (01538) 308348
Draught Bass; Burton Bridge Bridge Bitter; Titanic Mild Ⓗ
Near Cauldon quarries, this stone pub has been in the same family for over 40 years. The antiques and collectables have to be seen to be believed – grandfather clocks, working polyphons and pianola, a penny farthing, and bottled King ale, all make this a must to visit. The pub features regularly on TV and other media, and was recently voted Collectors Pub of the Year on Channel Four. Try the pork pies and pickled eggs. Q♉❀♣P

CHASETOWN ❊

Uxbridge Arms
2 Church Street
⊙ 12-3, 5.30-11; 12-11 Fri & Sat; 12-10.30 Sun
☎ (01543) 674853
Draught Bass; Stones Bitter; guest beers Ⓗ
This popular, comfortable local was Lichfield CAMRA Pub of the Year in 2002. The split-level lounge has a collection of china plates and there is also a busy extended bar and a pool room. Outdoor drinking is on the forecourt. Three regularly changing guest beers, often from smaller breweries, are always on tap, and an extensive selection of malt whiskies and country wines are stocked. No meals are served Sun eve.
❀◐◑⊟♣P

INN BRIEF

ALREWAS
Crown Inn
Post Office Road
12-2.30, 5-11; 12-2.30, 7-10.30 Sun
(01283) 790328
Draught Bass; Greene King Abbot; Marston's Pedigree Ⓗ
Traditional village inn, near the post office, with a cosy public bar and a snug.

BLYTHE BRIDGE
Duke of Wellington
305 Uttoxeter Road
12-3, 6-11; 12-3, 7-10.30 Sun
(01782) 395129
Fuller's London Pride; Greene King Abbot; guest beers Ⓗ
Popular village pub serving lunchtime food, near the station, opposite a bus stop. Good choice of beers and draught cider.

BURNTWOOD
Drill Inn
Springle Styche Lane
12-11; 12-10.30 Sun
(01543) 674092
Tetley Bitter; guest beers Ⓗ
In a rural setting with a spacious lounge, the pub stages live entertainment Friday evening.

BURTON UPON TRENT
Lord Burton
154 High Street
11-11; 12-10.30 Sun
(01283) 517587
Draught Bass; Marston's Pedigree; Shepherd Neame Spitfire; Theakston Old Peculier; guest beers Ⓗ
Typical, busy Wetherspoon's pub close to the town centre with a good selection of low-priced beers.

CHASETOWN
Junction
High Street
12-4 (not Mon-Fri), 7 (4.30 Fri)-11; 12-10.30 Sun
(01543) 686240
M&B Brew XI; guest beers Ⓗ
Traditional, popular local dating from the 1850s at the bottom of the High Street, with a single L-shaped room.

DAYHILLS
Red Lion
6.30-11; 12-3, 6.30-10.30 Sun
(01889) 505474
Draught Bass; Worthington Bitter; guest beer Ⓗ
Rural gem, situated on a farm. Primarily a one-bar pub, but when busy a second room is commissioned.

EBSTREE
Hollybush
Ebstree Road
12-3, 5.30-11 (12-11 summer Sat); 12-4, 7-10.30 (12-10.30 summer) Sun
(01902) 895587
Greene King Abbot; Tetley Burton Ale; guest beer Ⓗ
Two-roomed country pub with open fires and garden with children's play area. No food Sun eve.

FULFORD
Shoulder of Mutton
Meadow Lane
12-3, 7-11; 12-11 Sat; 12-10.30 Sun
(01782) 388960
Flowers Original; Greene King IPA, Abbot Ⓗ
17th-century pub with a natural cellar, carved from solid rock. It hosts occasional beer festivals. Food available.

KINGSLEY HOLT
Blacksmith's Arms
39 Shawe Park Road
12-11; 12-10.30 Sun
(01538) 752336
Burtonwood Bitter, Top Hat; guest beer Ⓗ
Friendly, welcoming, traditional village pub with a large garden.

CHESLYN HAY

Woodman Inn

Brook Road (off B4156, via Littlewood Lane)

12-3, 7-11; 12-11 Fri & Sat; 12-10.30 Sun

(01922) 413686

Theakston Best Bitter, XB; guest beer H

Welcoming, two-roomed pub on a housing estate off the Walsall to Cannock road. Very much the pub of its community; pool is played here. This former brewhouse used its own spring, which runs through the cellar. Two guest beers are rotated regularly. The conservatory is a no-smoking family area. Evening meals are served Tue-Sun. It is difficult to locate for first-time visitors, but is worth the effort. P

CODSALL

Codsall Station

Chapel Lane

11.30-2.30, 5-11; 11-11 Sat; 12-10.30 Sun

(01902) 847061

Holden's Bitter, Special, seasonal beers; guest beer H

Local CAMRA Pub of the Year 2001, this sensitively restored building is a working main line station. The comfortable interior, displaying worldwide railway memorabilia, comprises a snug, conservatory, bar and lounge. Holden's brew the occasional Railway Bitter house beer, and a chalkboard announces forthcoming guest ales and food specials (no food Sun eve). Outside is a floodlit boules pitch and raised terrace, where you can watch the trains go by.

Q P

COLTON

Greyhound

Bellamour Lane (off B5013)

5.30 (12 Sat)-11; 12-10.30 Sun

(01889) 586769

Banks's Original; Greene King Abbot; Wadworth 6X; guest beer H

Unspoilt, village pub, refurbished by Banks's Brewery in the mid-1980s. The splendid bar features a stone floor, brick-lined fireplace and authentic exposed beams. Meals are served Thu-Sat, plus Sunday lunchtime. A mile from Rugeley Trent Valley Station to the south, it lies two miles from Blithfield Reservoir to the north.

P

COPMERE END

Star

($1^1/_2$ miles W of Eccleshall) OS803294

12-3, 6-11; 12-11 Sat; 12-3, 7-10.30 Sun

(01785) 850279

Draught Bass; Mansfield Cask Ale; guest beer (occasional) H

Off the beaten track, this cosy, traditional establishment is popular with walkers, cyclists and anglers. Parts of the building are thought to be around 200 years old. The Star angling club makes good use of Cop Mere, a 42-acre lake situated opposite. The garden is set out with tables and has a large lawned area with trees and children's swings. Delicious home-cooked meals, but no food is served Sun eve. Guest beers are sold in summer, and at Christmas and Easter.

Q P

DOSTHILL

Fox Inn

105 High Street (A51, midway between Tamworth and Kingsbury)

12-3 (not Mon), 6-11; 12-3, 6-10.30 Sun

(01827) 280847

Ansells Mild; Draught Bass; Tetley Bitter; guest beers H

Welcoming roadside local, guaranteed to offer an excellent range of cask ales, with three guests normally available, which regularly feature the products of Church End. There is a comfortable lounge and bar; the former leads to a restaurant which should be booked at busy times (no eve meals Sun). Outside, is a garden drinking area. A good range of country wines, and single malt whiskies are stocked. The pub can be reached via the 115/116 bus route.

Q P

ECCLESHALL

George Inn

Castle Street

11-11; 12-10.30 Sun

(01785) 850300

website: www.thegeorgeinn.freeserve.co.uk

Eccleshall Slaters Bitter, Original, Top Totty, Premium, Supreme, seasonal beer H

As the home of the Eccleshall Brewery, the George is best known for stocking the full range of Slaters award-winning, well-hopped ales. Since being bought by the Slater family, 10 years ago, the neglected 17th-century coaching inn has been thoughtfully renovated. It now offers bar and lounge areas, excellent meals, which can be taken in the pub's own café bar, and 10 en-suite bedrooms. Deservedly popular, the George is situated at Eccleshall's main crossroads. P

ENVILLE

Cat Inn

Bridgnorth Road (A458)

12-2.30 (3 Sat), 7-11; closed Sun

(01384) 872209

Enville Ale; Everards Beacon; guest beers H

The nearest outlet to Enville Brewery, this 16th-century inn boasts four rooms, many with original features, one being used for games. Bar snacks are served, but more elaborate fare is available in the highly recommended restaurant. The outdoor drinking area occasionally doubles as a boules pitch. Unusually, the pub does not open on Sunday but this may change. Fruit wines are sold in the bar. Q P

FRADLEY JUNCTION

Swan Inn

OS140140

11-3, 6-11; 11-11 Sat & summer; 12-3.30, 7-10.30 (12-10.30 summer) Sun

(01283) 790330

Ansells Mild, Best Bitter; Marston's Pedigree; Tetley Burton Ale H

As the centrepiece of a terrace of buildings devoted to the canal industry, the Swan has retained most of its original character. The public bar boasts a beamed ceiling and high-backed settles. The apparently modest lounge is complemented by a larger area created from a former cellar, accessed down a small flight of steps. Situated at the picturesque junction of the Coventry and Trent & Mersey Canals, it gets exceptionally busy at weekends during the holiday season.

GNOSALL

Horns

21 High Street (off A518)
12-3, 5-11; 12-11 Fri & Sat; 12-10.30 Sun
(01785) 822441
website: www.thehorns.rout56.co.uk
Draught Bass; Fuller's London Pride; Tetley Bitter; guest beer H

One of the oldest buildings in the village, parts of the pub date back to the 17th century. This lively community local has a sports-mad bar and quieter, recently refurbished lounge. Fortnightly folk nights and regular quizzes are held. The pub also helps with local fund-raising. The vegetarian restaurant opens Thu-Sat evenings and Sunday lunch; it doubles as a tea shop during the day (Mon-Sat).

GREAT CHATWELL

Red Lion

2 miles E of A41, near Newport OS792143
5 (12 Sat)-11; 12-10.30 Sun
(01952) 691366
Everards Beacon, Tiger; Flowers IPA; guest beers H

Family-run country pub in a small village, the Red Lion comprises two bars, a restaurant and a large games room. Part of the building dates from the 18th century, and it was sensitively refurbished and extended in 1991, when a children's play area and an aviary were created in the garden. A popular local venue in summer, it enjoys a reputation for good value food, and for being family-friendly.

HARRISEAHEAD

Royal Oak

42 High Street
12-3 (not Mon-Fri), 7-11; 12-3, 7-10.30 Sun
(01782) 513362
Courage Directors; John Smith's Bitter; guest beers H

This 19th-century free house was an ale house before becoming fully licensed in 1889. A central bar serves the lively public bar on one side, and the equally popular lounge on the other. It is very much a local, drawing many customers from the neighbourhood, but it also welcomes visitors. Around 15 Belgian and German bottled beers are available. There is a darts team and a golf society. The car park exit is through the door marked 'Ladies'.

HEDNESFORD

Queen's Arms

37 Hill Street (A460)
12-3, 7-11; 12-3, 7-10.30 Sun
(01543) 878437
Draught Bass; Highgate Dark; Worthington Bitter P

Popular, two-roomed pub, south of the town centre on the Cannock to Rugeley road. The first landlord here was recorded in 1866. The lounge hosts quizzes on a Monday evening. The bar is decorated with many brasses, copper kettles and miners' lamps. Meals are very good value.

HIGH OFFLEY

Anchor

Peggs Lane, Old Lea (by Bridge 42 of Shropshire Union Canal) OS775256
11-3, 6-11 (winter: 7-11 Fri & Sat, not Mon-Thu eves); 12-3, 7-10.30 (not winter eve) Sun
(01785) 284569
Marston's Pedigree (summer)**; Wadworth 6X** H/G

On the Shropshire Union Canal, this Victorian two-bar inn is a rare example of an unspoilt, country pub. Cask ales are dispensed by jug from the cellar. This free house has been run by the same family since 1870, when it was called the Sebastopol. Busy in the summer with canal traffic, it has a canalware gift shop at the rear. This local CAMRA Pub of the Year 2000 is not easily found by road, but is well worth the trip.

HOAR CROSS

Meynell Ingram Arms

OS133234
12-11; 12-10.30 Sun
(01283) 575202

INN BRIEF

LICHFIELD

Fountain Inn
169 Beacon Street
11.30-11; 12-3, 7-10.30 Sun
(01543) 300527
Ansells Mild; Marston's Pedigree; guest beers H
Convivial single-roomed pub with a conservatory restaurant overlooking Beacon Park. No food Sun eve.

STAFFORD

Picture House
Bridge Street
11-11; 12-10.30 Sun
(01785) 222941
Banks's Original; Boddingtons Bitter; Courage Directors; Greene King Abbot; Shepherd Neame Spitfire; guest beers H
Wetherspoon's pub in a lavishly refurbished ex-cinema, on Stafford's main shopping street, by the river. Cask Marque accredited.

Stafford Arms
43 Railway Street
12-11; 12-4, 7-10.30 Sun
(01785) 253313
Titanic Best Bitter, White Star; guest beers H
Town-centre pub opposite the station, with a wide choice of beers; food and accommodation available.

STOKE-ON-TRENT: *GOLDENHILL*

Red Lion
899 High Street
7 (4 Wed & Thu; 3 Fri; 12 Sat)-11; 12-10.30 Sun
(01782) 782288
Tetley Bitter, Burton Ale; Wells Bombardier; guest beer H
Comfortable main road pub near the city boundary, with a garden and play area behind.

HANLEY

Unicorn
40 Piccadilly
11-11; 12-2, 7-10.30 Sun
(01782) 281809
Draught Bass; Fuller's London Pride; guest beer H
Friendly, city-centre pub at the heart of the cultural quarter; one long room and cosy areas. Snacks served.

PENKHULL

Marquis of Granby
51 St Thomas's Place
12-11; 12-10.30 Sun
(01782) 847025
Banks's Original; Marston's Bitter, Pedigree H
Imposing, two-roomed pub in the village centre serving good value lunches daily. Garden at the rear.

Marston's Pedigree; Taylor Landlord; guest beer H
Originally part of the Earl of Shrewsbury's estate, this unspoilt 16th-century pub takes its name from the family who purchased nearby Hoar Cross Hall – now a fashionable health spa. The pub boasts exposed beams, quarry-tiled floors and open fires. The bar offers different drinking areas and there is a small lounge. The restaurant/function room was converted from outbuildings. A paved courtyard, with fishpool, provides outdoor drinking space. ⌂Q❀⇋◐♣P

HOPWAS

Red Lion
Lichfield Road (A51)
11.30-2.30, 5-11; 11.30-11 Sat; 12-10.30 Sun
☎ (01827) 62514
Ansells Mild, Best Bitter; Marston's Pedigree; guest beer H
Canalside village pub, with a safe garden and large car park, on the Tamworth to Lichfield road. The three guest beers are usually changed fortnightly. Part of the lounge has been designated as a dining area. The pub has a friendly atmosphere.
Q❀◐⊟♣P

KIDSGROVE

Blue Bell
25 Hardingswood (canalside, near Tesco)
7.30-11; 1-4, 7-11 Sat; closed Mon; 12-4, 7-10.30 Sun
☎ (01782) 774052
Beer range varies H
Celebrated, genuine free house of four small rooms. Most beers are from micros and small breweries nationwide – more than 1,100 in four years. On a busy weekend evening four of the six handpumps may change clips. Real cider or perry, German and Czech draught lager, wheat beer, plus over 30 Belgian and German bottled beers provide real choice. No TV, juke box, or bandits disturb the atmosphere. On Sunday evening folk musicians play ad hoc at this local CAMRA Pub of the Year 1999-2002.
Q❀⇌●P⊬

KINVER

Olde White Harte Hotel
111 High Street
11.30-11; 12-10.30 Sun
☎ (01384) 872305
Banks's Original, Bitter, P **seasonal beers** H
Old village-centre pub dating back to the early 17th century, when it was a coaching inn on the old route from Chester to the West Country. The interior of this lively pub has been fully modernised, and is now largely open plan, but it does have a separate, no-smoking verandah. The enclosed patio at the rear has a children's play area. Meals are served all day.
❀◐P⊬⊟

Plough & Harrow
82 High Street
5.30 (5 Fri)-11; 12-11 Sat; 12-10.30 Sun
☎ (01384) 872659
Batham Mild, Best Bitter, XXX (winter) H
Lively, two-roomed pub, known as the Steps, as its various areas are on ascending levels the further back you go. At the front and bottom is the no-frills public bar, behind and above that is a split-level lounge which hosts live music at weekends. The pub is only 500 yards from the Staffs & Worcs Canal. Food is served all day at weekends, not at all on weekdays. Traditional cider is sometimes available in summer. ❀◐⊟♣●P

Vine Inn
1 Dunsley Road (off High St)
11-11; 12-10.30 Sun
☎ (01384) 877291
Enville Ale; Wood Shropshire Lad; guest beers H
One-roomed canalside pub, founded in competition with the Lock Inn that once stood opposite. The Vine subsequently extended into adjacent cottages over the years, and most of the interior walls were removed in1980. Nowadays it has extensive canalside gardens incorporating a children's play area. Food is served all day at weekends and in summer. ❀◐P⊟

KNIGHTON

Haberdasher's Arms
Between Adbaston and Knighton OS753276
12.30 (5 Wed)-11; 12-10.30 Sun
☎ (01785) 280650
Banks's Original, Bitter; guest beers H
Sadly, country pub closures have been a common occurrence over the last decade. This pub is an example of a closure threat with a happy ending. In 1997 over 200 villagers signed a petition to save the Haberdasher's Arms. Built in the 1840s, this traditional community pub has four rooms and one small bar. The large garden is used for local events including an annual potato club show. It was voted local CAMRA Pub of the Year in 1999. ⌂Q❀⊟▲♣P

LAPLEY

Vaughan Arms
Bickford Road ($1^1/_2$ miles N of A5, near Penkridge) OS874130
12.30-2.30 (not Mon), 7-11; 12-3, 6.30-11 Sat; 12-3, 7-10.30 Sun
☎ (01785) 840325
Banks's Original; Marston's Bitter, Pedigree; guest beers H
Friendly village pub named after the Vaughan family who resided at Lapley Hall. The pub was originally located 200 yards from its current site, but moved in the 1890s due to complaints by Hall residents of rowdiness at closing times. Food is a prominent feature, and the Vaughan Arms enjoys an excellent local reputation. Regular quizzes are held and it is a convivial meeting place for local clubs, establishing it firmly as a community pub. ⌂❀◐♿▲♣P

LEEK

Blue Mugge
17 Osborne Street (between A53 and A523)
11-2.30 (3 Fri), 6-11; 11-4, 7-11 Sat; 12-10.30 Sun
☎ (01538) 384450
Draught Bass; guest beer H
Originally the Queen's Arms, the pub was renamed in 1976. Do not be fooled by the exterior – it is bigger than you might expect inside, with rooms radiating from an island bar. One room is dedicated to Queen

Victoria, another to Winston Churchill. The beer is competitively-priced and guest beers change regularly. Note that the handpumps are unusually positioned in the centre, rather than on the bar top. This friendly, back-street local caters for all ages. ❀◖⊟♣

Bull's Head

35 St Edward Street

11-11 (midnight Fri & Sat); 12-10.30 Sun

☎ (01538) 370269

Beartown Kodiak Gold; guest beers Ⓗ

Located on one of the best streets for a pub crawl and catering for a mainly younger clientele, the quality of the beer is one of the main reasons for the popularity of this friendly pub. A narrow, long drinking area, rises up several levels, and has a serving area in the middle. The juke box will not be to everybody's taste, but has an excellent selection. A late licence applies Friday and Saturday evenings.

Den Engel

23-25 St Edward Street

5 (12 Fri & Sat)-11; 12-3, 7-10.30 Sun

☎ (01538) 373751

Beer range varies Ⓗ

Outstanding, even in an exceptional drinking town, this prominent brick building houses a superb Belgian-style bar. Up to four ever-changing cask ales are supplemented by a selection of over 130 Belgian bottled beers, all served in the correct glass by waiters. Of the 40-plus Belgian genevers, one is always being promoted. A small, but cosy, Flemish restaurant on the first floor offers beer-based cuisine including Stoverij (beef in Belgian beer); lunches are served Fri and Sat, eve meals Wed-Sat. Q◖◗♣

Wilkes' Head

16 St Edward Street

11-11; 12-10.30 Sun

☎ (01538) 383616

Whim Arbor Light, Magic Mushroom Mild, Hartington Bitter, Hartington IPA; guest beers Ⓗ

The town's second oldest pub, a coaching inn circa 1800, it always keeps a fine selection of Whim beers and ever-changing guests. Entered through narrow, awkward swing doors, on the left is the music/family room; on the right is the bar, beyond which is a comfortable window seat. At the back is the third room, a snug rather than a lounge. On Monday evening acoustic instrumentalists are welcome – any music, and three music festivals are staged in summer. ❀

LICHFIELD

Acorn Inn

12 Tamworth Street

11-11; 12-10.30 Sun

☎ (01543) 263400

Banks's Bitter; Courage Directors; Theakston Best Bitter; guest beers Ⓗ

This large Wetherspoon's is flanked by pubs on both sides and is deservedly popular with all ages. This is not only due to the choice of real ales, but also the excellent service and competitive pricing policy. Note the purpose-built bridge over the drinking area to enable the delivery of cask to the stillage. Acorn was the name of the neighbouring pub and was adopted at the request of a local drinker.

Q◖◗♿⇌(City)⊬●

Earl of Lichfield

10 Conduit Street

11-11; 12-10.30 Sun

☎ (01543) 251020

Marston's Bitter, Pedigree, seasonal beers; guest beer (occasional) Ⓗ

Popular, market pub, known locally as the Drum, apparently since the days during the 1800s when army recruiting officers used to stand outside to the sound of a drum. Around 30 years ago the small, single-roomed pub took over an adjacent barber's shop which became the bar. A more recent change resulted in an open-plan design on two levels with bare floorboards. An extensive coffee menu is featured. Lunches are served Mon-Sat. ❀◖⇌(City)

George & Dragon

28 Beacon Street

12-11; 12-3.30, 8-10.30 Sun

☎ (01543) 263554

Banks's Original, Bitter; Ⓟ **Marston's Pedigree** Ⓗ

Small, traditional, two-roomed local, situated close to the cathedral. From the front, the basic public bar is to the right and the exceptionally cosy lounge to the left. The adjacent building on the city side is a former tollhouse which years ago provided

INN BRIEF

STONE

Star

21 Stafford Street

11-11; 12-10.30 Sun

(01785) 813096

Banks's Original, Bitter; Marston's Pedigree, seasonal beers Ⓗ

16th-century pub and restaurant, serving food all day. On the Trent & Mersey Canal, particularly popular in summer.

TRYSULL

Bell Inn

Bell Road

11.30-3, 5.30-11; 12-4, 7-10.30 Sun

(01902) 892871

Batham Best Bitter; Holden's Bitter, Golden Glow, Special; guest beer Ⓗ

Welcoming village pub and restaurant, that hosts seasonal cabaret evenings. No food Sun eve.

TWO GATES

Bull's Head

Watling Street

12-2.30 (3 Sat), 6.30-11; 12-2.30, 7-10.30 Sun

(01827) 287820

Banks's Original; Marston's Pedigree Ⓗ

Comfortable, sporting pub in a farmhouse-style building, with appropriately decorated lounge, a bar and an outdoor area.

WRINEHILL

Crown Inn

Den Lane

12-3 (not Mon), 6-11; 12-4, 6-10.30 Sun

(01270) 820472

Adnams Bitter; Banks's Original; Marston's Bitter, Pedigree; guest beer Ⓗ

Renowned for its location, appearance, atmosphere and good quality home-made food. Same licensee for 26 years.

Check it out

Pubs in the Good Beer Guide may change ownership and the facilities listed could alter. If a visit to a pub involves a long journey, it's advisable to check before leaving that full meals, family facilities, accommodation or camping sites are still available.

a good reason for travellers to terminate their journey at the pub. The flag of St George hangs permanently over the front door. ❀⊟⇌(City) ♣P⊓

Queen's Head

Queen Street (near centre)
✪ 12-11; 12-3, 7-10.30 Sun
☎ (01543) 410932
Adnams Bitter; Marston's Pedigree; Taylor Landlord; guest beers Ⓗ

Welcoming, popular local, a rare example of a Marston's Ale House. It was named to commemorate the accession of Queen Victoria in 1837. This elongated, one-roomed establishment is a mecca for lovers of real ale and real cheese as the house speciality is the large cheese counter offering a superb selection. It is home to many sports fans, including two local cricket teams. Well worth the short walk from the city centre. Q◖⇌(City) ♣

LITTLE STOKE

Little Stoke Cricket Club

The Sid Jenkins Cricket Ground, Uttoxeter Road (B5027)
✪ 4 (12 Thu-Sat)-11; 12-10.30 Sun
☎ (01785) 812558 website: www.littlestoke.com
Tetley Bitter; Wells Bombardier; guest beer Ⓗ

Formed in 1946, from the amalgamation of Aston-By-Stone and Christ's Church cricket clubs, the ground was purchased in 1952 from the proceeds of the tea ladies! It now boasts a superb clubhouse, where four handpulls dispense good ale with guest beers from the Carlsberg-Tetley range. Pride is taken in the facilities and the public are made very welcome by the members. This family-friendly club competes in the North Staffs/South Cheshire league – good cricket and fine ale make a great combination. ❀♿♣P

LONGDON

Swan with Two Necks

40 Brook End (off A51)
✪ 12-2.30 (3 Sat), 7-11; 12-3, 7-10.30 Sun
☎ (01543) 490251
Ansells Best Bitter; Tetley Burton Ale; guest beers Ⓗ

Superb village local that has featured in the Guide for nearly a quarter of a century. Although run by a French landlord, alongside his English wife, as much devotion is shown to the constantly changing guest ales as the excellent food. A friendly atmosphere prevails in the bar, but children under 14 (and dogs) are only permitted in the pleasant garden, which is very popular in summer. A gem – not to be missed. ⛰Q❀◖◗P

MILWICH

Green Man

On B5027
✪ 12-2 (not Mon-Wed), 5-11; 12-11 Sat; 12-10.30 Sun
☎ (01889) 505310
Draught Bass; Marston's Pedigree; Worthington Bitter; guest beer Ⓗ

This superb village local dates from the late 15th century; a list of landlords since 1792 is displayed in the bar. It is popular with both tourists and the locals. Guest beers turn over quickly; old favourites mingle with ales from obscure micros, so you never can predict what will be on. Marston's Pedigree has been added to its regular portfolio since last year. The pub has a large grass plot with benches. Lunches are available Thu-Sun. ⛰❀◖⛺♣P

NEWCASTLE-UNDER-LYME

Albert Inn

1 Brindley Street (off A34/A53 ring road)
✪ 11-3 (not Tue-Thu), 5-11; 12-11 Fri; 11-4, 7-11 Sat; 12-4, 7-10.30 Sun
☎ (01782) 615525
Burtonwood Bitter, Top Hat Ⓗ

Victorian street-corner local, popular with all ages, it was named after Queen Victoria's consort. Licensees have been traced back as far as 1861, the year of Albert's death. The single drinking area is comfortably furnished – bench seats run down both sides – the walls are adorned with photographs of old Newcastle and a collection of clay pipes hangs over the entrance. The tiled mural on the exterior is a modern replacement. ♣

Hogshead

21 Ironmarket (near library)
✪ 10.30-11; 12-10.30 Sun
☎ (01782) 619430
Boddingtons Bitter; Caledonian Deuchars IPA; Greene King Abbot, Old Speckled Hen; Hook Norton Old Hooky, guest beers Ⓗ

In the pedestrianised zone of a town centre noted for floral displays, this three-storey pub was converted from a shop and is a blend of old and new – look out for the old pulpit. Although quiet enough at lunchtimes, it can be crowded and noisy late evenings, particularly at weekends. It hosts regular theme nights. Smoking restrictions apply in a designated area during food service 10.30am-8.30pm (8pm Fri and Sat; 12-3pm Sun). Use side entrance for wheelchair access. ◖◗♿

Museum Inn

29 George Street (on A52, 1/4 mile E of centre)
✪ 12-11; 12-4, 7-10.30 Sun
☎ (01782) 623866
Draught Bass; Flowers Original; Worthington Bitter Ⓗ

Beginning life in 1841 as the Farmer's Arms, the pub acquired its present name in 1867 when a 'Museum of Curiosities', now long gone, appeared on the premises. This characterful pub contains an unspoilt, long public bar, where traditional pub games and conversation dominate. The comfortable lounge is suitable for a quieter drink, and is also available for parties and meetings. Two changing guest beers are normally available. ❀⊟♣

New Smithy

Church Lane (A527, midway between Wolstanton Marsh and church)
✪ 11 (12 Sat)-11; 12-10.30 Sun
☎ (01782) 740467
Draught Bass; Everards Beacon, Tiger; guest beers Ⓗ

Destined to be a church car park, the former Archer was saved from demolition by a vigorous local campaign and reopened as a free house in 2001. Well renovated by its new owner, this beer haven offers three guest beers at extremely competitive prices.

The split-level interior has a narrow standing area fronting the bar, with seating either side. Inspect the 'beer bible' on the lectern. It hosts charity nights and summer barbecues, and imposes a strict no-swearing policy. ❀♣P

ONECOTE

Jervis Arms

On B5053, by River Hamps
12-3, 7-11; 12-10.30 Sun
☎ (01538) 304206
Draught Bass; guest beers H

Popular country pub on the southern edge of the Peak District, famous for its excellent food, which is available all day (12-9.30) on Sunday. Family-friendly, it has a large riverside garden with well-maintained play equipment for young children. Guest beers usually include one from Titanic, plus rarities. Frequented by walkers, the pub is also a good stop on the way to or from Alton Towers. Admiral Jervis was an aide to Lord Nelson.

OULTON

Brushmaker's Arms

8 Kibblestone Road
12-3, 6.30-11; 12-3, 7-10.30 Sun
☎ (01785) 812062
Draught Bass; Worthington Bitter; guest beer H

One mile north-east of Stone, this gem of a village pub has a basic, unspoilt bar. Pictures and postcards of Oulton and Stone adorn the walls, reflecting a bygone era. The lounge is small, as is the patio. Guest ales often come from Robinson's and Black Sheep. It mainly attracts locals, but visitors are always made welcome. The darts team is based in the bar where conversation is learned and lively. Q❀♣P

PENKRIDGE

Railway

Clay Street (A449)
12-2.30, 5-11; 12-11 Fri & Sat; 12-10.30 Sun
☎ (01785) 712685
Banks's Original, Bitter; P **guest beer** H

Converted in the 1830s from cottages to a pub for railway construction workers who were barred from the village's other pubs, the Railway is much quieter and more welcoming now. The extended original building houses the lounge and small restaurant. The bar has been a garage, mortuary and auctioneers' in its time. The licensee sells far more Banks's beer than any other Pubmaster house in the area. The quality meals are excellent value (no food Sun eve). ❀♣P

PENN COMMON

Barley Mow

Pennwood Lane (follow signs for Penn golf club from A449) OS949902
12-2.30, 6-11; 12-11 Sat; 12-10.30 Sun
☎ (01902) 333510
Banks's Original; Greene King Abbot; Tetley Burton Ale; guest beers H

Small, low-beamed pub on the fringes of Wolverhampton, dating from the 1630s, with a small extension added in 1999. Next to Penn Common and the golf club, it is well known for its excellent home-made food – the meat is supplied from the landlord's own butcher's shop. The garden and children's play area are very popular in good weather. It stands at the end of the Seven Cornfields path, which is well trod by Wolverhampton drinkers heading for the Barley Mow. ❀P

REAPSMOOR

Butcher's Arms

Off B5053 Thorncliff-Warslow road OS082014
2-4.30, 7-11; 2-4.30, 7-10.30 Sun
☎ (01298) 84477
Beer range varies H/G

This isolated, rural gem is difficult to find, but worth the effort. A stone-built former farm-pub set in open moorland, it comprises several small rooms, some of which used to house cattle. Each room has a cosy fire in winter. The layout is partly open plan, but it is traditionally decorated and furnished. Excellent walking can be enjoyed in the Peak District National Park; free camping is available to customers behind the pub. Q♣P

STAFFORD

Lamb

Broad Eye (inner ring road, opp. Sainsbury's)
11-11; 12-10.30 Sun
☎ (01785) 243992
Banks's Original; Draught Bass; Everards Tiger; guest beers (occasional) H

The Lamb is a corner local which, thanks to the redevelopment of Stafford town centre, now finds itself on the inner ring road, surrounded by major retail outlets and Stafford College. Acquired by Punch Taverns in 1999 and extensively refurbished in 2000, the outcome is a bright, airy, welcoming hostelry, offering good value food and a friendly atmosphere. The pub stands opposite Stafford's famous windmill which is undergoing an exceedingly slow restoration. Evening meals are served Mon-Thu, until 8pm. ♣

Railway

23 Castle Street
12-3 (not Mon-Fri), 6-11 Sat; 12-3, 7-10.30 Sun
☎ (01785) 605085
Draught Bass; Greene King Abbot; Tetley Bitter; guest beer H

Like the surrounding terraced housing of Castletown, the inn was built soon after the Grand Junction Railway reached Stafford in 1837. It remains Stafford's best example of a Victorian street-corner local, despite slight alterations recently which relieved pressure on the often crowded bar by opening up two other rooms. Parking is difficult, but it is just a five-minute walk northwards from the station. ❀♣

Tap & Spile

59 Peel Terrace (off B5066)
4.30 (2 Fri; 12 Sat)-11; 12-10.30 Sun
☎ (01785) 223563
Beer range varies H

Thriving beer house, selling an incredible volume and variety of cask ales, its local CAMRA Pub of the Year award for 2002 was well deserved. Built early last century, the name change from Cottage by the Brook nine years ago coincided with a sensitive refurbishment, four distinct drinking areas being retained. The first pub locally with a proper no-smoking area, the Tap & Spile also has a free bar billiards table, several sports teams and Saturday evening music. ♣

Vine Hotel

Salter Street

10.30-11; 12-10.30 Sun

(01785) 244112

Banks's Original, Bitter, Ⓟ seasonal beers Ⓗ

One of Stafford's oldest inns, the Vine's customers have included a man who regularly slept in a coffin and, in 1758, the first forger of Bank of England notes. Now a comfortable hotel with 27 en-suite rooms, the Vine retains some of its olde-worlde character, unlike the many circuit venues nearby. It is situated in the pedestrianised town centre near the Market Square. Starting with early morning breakfast, meals are served all day until 9pm. P

STOKE-ON-TRENT: *BURSLEM*

Bull's Head

St John's Square

12-2 (not Mon-Wed), 5-11; 12-11 Fri & Sat; 12-10.30 Sun

(01782) 834153

Titanic Mild, Best Bitter, Lifeboat, Premium, White Star; guest beers Ⓗ

Titanic's only tied house, situated half a mile from the brewery. Comprising a traditional bar and comfortable lounge, both bear a Titanic naval theme plus brewery memorabilia; the bar has an imaginative juke box. It always keeps an extensive range of Titanic beers, plus guest ales from small independent and micro-brewers and stages regular beer festivals. This former local CAMRA Pub of the Year has a bar billiards table. Q♣

Old Smithy

52-54 Moorland Road

12-11; 12-10.30 Sun

(01782) 827039

Draught Bass; Everards Beacon, Tiger; guest beer Ⓗ

Previously known as the Bowler Hat, this pub was closed for several years, but has now been reopened by a sympathetic management. Well furnished throughout, the original single, large lounge bar, has expanded into an adjoining property, to provide a darts room and a small walled patio. The Smithy is a rare Potteries outlet for Everards' beers, backed up by a regularly changing guest. Well-priced lunchtime snacks are served. It is used by Port Vale FC home supporters. ♣

Vine Inn

Hamil Road

12-11; 12-10.30 Sun

(01782) 827468

Courage Best Bitter, Directors; guest beers Ⓗ

1930s pub, refurbished in recent years, but retaining the atmosphere of a local. One main room, with a pool table, is to the left of the bar, and a small side room to the right. Beers are always competitively priced. The regulars provide teams for the pool league, 'Derby 9' card league and ladies' darts league. TV is always available for sporting events. The pub is used by Port Vale FC visiting supporters, without problems. This solid, reliable local is at the centre of Burslem. ♣

FENTON

Malt 'n' Hops

295 King Street

12-3.30, 7-11; 12-3.30, 7-10.30 Sun

(01782) 313406

Courage Directors; guest beers Ⓗ

Busy, genuine free house, extended over the years to cope with its popularity. Its split-level layout gives the impression of two rooms: a traditional bar by the main entrance leads to a comfortable lounge area. At least four ever-changing guest beers, including a mild, usually come from small breweries; Bursley Bitter is a house beer. Draught and bottled Belgian beer are stocked. Very much a beer-oriented pub, it enjoys a strong local following. (Longton)

Potter

432 King Street (A50, 1/2 mile from Longton Station)

12 (11 Sat)-11; 12-10.30 Sun

(01782) 311968

Draught Bass; Coach House Dick Turpin; guest beers Ⓗ

Genuine, traditional free house, where real ale aficionados from far and wide can rely upon a choice of no less than six beers on handpump, with one a traditional mild, all from independent and micro-breweries. This 100-year-old pub comprises a main bar, games room and a back snug, that doubles as a meeting room. This friendly pub is an excellent place to visit. (Longton) ♣

HARTSHILL

Jolly Potters

296 Hartshill Road (on A52, Newcastle Road)

3 (12 Fri & Sat)-11; 12-10.30 Sun

(01782) 845254

Draught Bass; Greene King IPA; Museum Joules Bitter; Taylor Landlord; guest beers Ⓗ

Situated within the Hartshill conservation area, close to hospital complex, this is a rare example of a typical Potteries pub. First licensed as a beer house in 1834, you can still enjoy a quality pint in traditional surroundings. The small public bar acts as a servery to three other small rooms, accessible from a central corridor, often full of standing drinkers during busy periods. The absence of juke box, pool table or gaming machines allows for friendly conversation. ♣

MIDDLEPORT

White Swan

Newport Lane

11-11; 11-4.30, 7-11 Sat; 12-3, 7-10.30 Sun

(01782) 813639

Draught Bass; Boddingtons Bitter; Castle Eden Ale; Coach House Gunpowder Strong Mild; Flowers IPA; Greene King Old Speckled Hen Ⓗ

A real community local, set among the 'pot banks' in the back streets. It attracts local drinkers, pottery workers and football fans for the friendly atmosphere and lively conversation – usually about golf. The open-plan layout gives the impression of two rooms. A genuine free house, it offers a good range of beers, including (rare for the Potteries) a cask mild. ⚒⊟≠(Longport) ♣

STONE ❄

Pheasant

Old Road (off A520, turn at Langtry's)
⚙ 11.30-11; 12-10.30 Sun
☎ (01785) 814603
website: www.downourlocal.com/pheasantinn
Banks's Original; Marston's Pedigree; John Smith's Bitter; guest beer Ⓗ

This superb street-corner local, dating from the 18th century, is tucked away in the north of the town. In wet weather a small stream flows through the cellar! It has a basic bar which is lively and games oriented, boasting darts and crib teams. The lounge is divided into three distinct areas, and is very comfortable. Lunchtime food represents great value. The pleasant patio is popular in summer. ❀◐⊟≠♣

Swan

18 Stafford Street (A520 by Trent & Mersey Canal)
⚙ 11-11; 12-10.30 Sun
☎ (01785) 815570 website: www.into-stone.co.uk
Beer range varies Ⓗ

This 18th-century, Grade II listed building was converted to a pub in the mid-19th century, and superbly renovated in 1999 into the comfortable hostelry it is today. Guest beers bring a diversity of ale to a town bereft of choice during the 1980s and '90s. A beer festival every July coincides with the Stone town festival. It hosts weekly live entertainment with a quiz on Tuesday. Basic food is available Mon-Sat, the Staffordshire oatcake dishes are superb. Traditional cider, Apples or Saxon is always stocked. ⚒❀◐♿●

TAMWORTH

Albert

32 Albert Road (near station)
⚙ 5-11; 12-3, 7-11 Sat; 12-3, 7-10.30 Sun
☎ (01827) 64694
Banks's Original, Bitter; guest beer (occasional) Ⓗ

Popular local where a warm welcome is guaranteed, handy for the station. This previous local CAMRA Pub of the Year has roadside seating for outdoor drinking in summer. The occasional guest beer is usually from the W&D portfolio. Bar snacks in the form of toasties are available weekend lunchtimes. ❀⇌⊟♿≠♣P▯

Globe Hotel

Lower Gungate
⚙ 11-11; 12-10.30 Sun
☎ (01827) 60455
Draught Bass; M&B Mild; guest beer Ⓗ

Comfortable town-centre pub popular with all ages. The large bar is flanked by a drinking section, a lounge area, complete with settees and high-backed chairs, and a raised dining area. It is home to the Tamworth Jazz Club, who meet on Wednesday evenings. Guest beers are often unusual for the area. It is handy for the Exotikka balti house. ⇌◐◑≠

Jailhouse Rock Café

97a Lichfield Street
⚙ 12-11; 12-10.30 Sun
☎ (01827) 61280
Marston's Pedigree; guest beer Ⓗ

Lively pub on the edge of the town centre. Recently refurbished, it attracts a varied clientele including bikers. Loud rock music is played in the back room by the pub's own DJ. Pool, table football and quiz machines are all available, plus a large-screen TV for sport. The guest beer changes regularly. Topless barmaids are employed on Sunday lunchtime. The patio may provide a welcome retreat. ❀◐◑♿⚟

UTTOXETER

Roebuck

Dove Bank
⚙ 11-2, 5-11; 11-11 Fri & Sat; 12-3, 7-10.30 Sun
☎ (01889) 565563
Theakston Best Bitter, XB; guest beers Ⓗ

Serving three guest beers, this pub offers the best choice of real ales in town and is well patronised by discerning drinkers. Dating from the 17th century, this former beer retailing premises became a pub about 100 years ago. There are five distinct bar areas which support several games teams and a football team. The outside drinking area is not suitable for children. It is handy for Uttoxeter National Hunt racecourse which also hosts antique fairs. Local CAMRA Pub of the Year 2001. ❀⇌⅄≠♣P

Vaults

Market Place
⚙ 11-3 (4 Wed, Fri & Sat), 5.30 (5 Fri; 7 Sat)-11; 12-3, 7-10.30 Sun
☎ (01889) 562997
Draught Bass; Marston's Pedigree; Worthington Bitter Ⓗ

One of the town's oldest pubs where wine used to be made on the premises, the Vaults is a sound ale house which has remained virtually unchanged for decades. Lined up behind the narrow, terraced frontage are three rooms, each having an emphasis on traditional pub games; darts is keenly played in the front and back rooms while table skittles can be enjoyed in the middle. Acoustic instrumental jam sessions take place on the last Sunday of each month. ⊟⅄≠♣

WESTON UPON TRENT

Woolpack

The Green
⚙ 11-11; 12-10.30 Sun
☎ (01889) 270238
Banks's Original, Bitter; Marston's Pedigree Ⓗ

Often referred to as the Inn on the Green, the Woolpack is an excellent village pub that caters well for locals and diners. Four bays inside the pub are evidence that the building was originally a row of cottages, and it is recorded as being owned by the Bagot family in the 1730s. Over the years the pub has been thoughtfully extended, maintaining separate areas for drinkers and diners. ⚒❀◐◑⊟♣P

WHISTON

Swan

Two miles W of Penkridge OS895144
⚙ 12-2 (not Mon or Tue; 12-3 Sat), 6-11; 12-10.30 Sun

☎ (01785) 716200

Banks's Original; Holden's Bitter; guest beers Ⓗ

With an emphasis on excellent beer and superb food, new owners have transformed an unviable pub into a thriving one. Midlands micro-brewers supply most of the guest beers, while as much local produce as possible is used for the à la carte and lunchtime bar meals (no food Sun eve). Built in 1593, the oldest part is the small bar that caters well for the local farming community. The six acres of grounds include a children's obstacle course.

WOMBOURNE

New Inn

1 Station Road (1/2 mile from A459/A463 jct)

11-11; 12-10.30 Sun

☎ (01902) 892037

Banks's Original, Bitter; Ⓟ **seasonal beers** Ⓗ

Large roadhouse-style pub, close to the village centre, served by buses from Wolverhampton, Stourbridge and Kinver. The basic bar is popular with locals for pub games, including pool, and there is a large, multi-area lounge. Outside is a grassed, well-equipped children's play area. Lunches are served Mon-Sat – the pies and burgers are home made. Weekend barbecues are held (weather permitting) plus quizzes (Tue) and entertainment (Thu).

YOXALL

Golden Cup

Main Street (A515)

12-2.30, 5-11; 12-11 Sat; 12-10.30 Sun

☎ (01543) 472295

Marston's Pedigree; guest beers Ⓗ

Impressive 300-year-old inn opposite St Peter's Church. A smart lounge caters for diners, attracted by the extensive menu, while pool, crib, darts and dominoes are played in the public bar. The award-winning garden extends to the River Swarbourn and the grounds include a caravan and camping area. The inn displays a large number of hanging baskets throughout the spring and summer.

Q

London beer in the 18th century

Would you believe it, although water is to be had in abundance in London and of fairly good quality, absolutely none is drunk? The lower classes, even the paupers, do not know what it is to quench their thirst with water. In this country nothing but beer is drunk and it is made in several qualities. Small beer is what everyone drinks when thirsty; it is even used in the best houses and costs only a penny a pot. Another kind of beer is called porter...because the greater quantity of this beer is consumed by the working classes. It is a thick and stong beverage, and the effect it produces if drunk in excess is the same as that of wine; this porter costs threepence the pot. In London there are a number of houses where nothing but this sort of beer is sold. There are again other clear beers called ales, some of these being transparent as fine old wine. The prices of ale differ, some costing one shilling the bottle and others as much as one shilling and sixpence. It is said more grain is consumed in England for making beer than making bread.

– **Cesar de Sassure**, London, 1726.

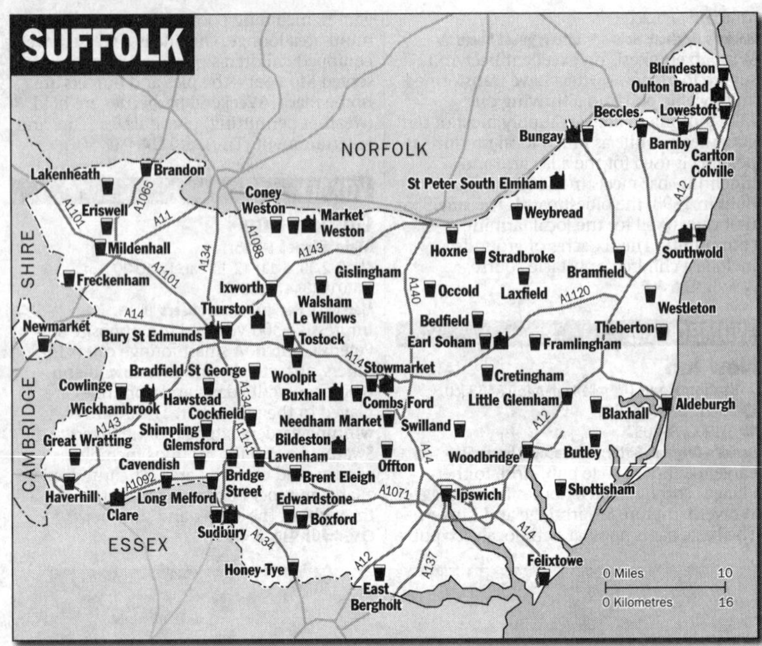

ALDEBURGH

Mill Inn

Market Cross Place

11-3, 6-11; 11-11 Fri & Sat; 12-10.30 Sun

☎ (01728) 452563 www.themillinn.com

Adnams Bitter, Broadside, seasonal beers Ⓗ

Street-corner inn opposite the old Moot Hall, once the centre of the town but now almost on the beach due to coastal erosion. Food is served in all bar areas and there is a rear dining room which doubles as a meeting room for local clubs. The pub has strong ties with the RNLI. On the beach nearby, you can buy fresh fish from the fishermen's huts. Walk up the hill to visit the church with Crabbe and Britten memorials, the latter's is a fine window designed by John Piper. In the churchyard there is another memorial, close to the graves of the brave men who perished in the 1899 lifeboat disaster.

White Hart

222 High Street

11-11; 12-10.30 Sun

☎ (01728) 453205

Adnams Bitter, Broadside, seasonal beers Ⓗ

Small, cosy, one-roomed wood-panelled bar with a welcoming fire in winter. The multi-coloured leaded glass windows may be a relic from its days as the public reading room. There is a patio area to the rear and benches on the front pavement to watch the world go by. It is popular with locals and tourists, both landlubbers and seafarers. There is occasional live music. The short bracing walk, along the shingle sea defence to the Martello tower, will certainly work up a thirst.

⛼❀⛿♣✔

BECCLES

Bear & Bells

Old Market (next to bus station)

11.30-3, 5.30-11; 12-3, 7-10.30 Sun

☎ (01502) 712291

Adnams Bitter; Greene King IPA; guest beers Ⓗ

Close to the town centre and within walking distance of the River Waveney, this pub is handy for visitors to the Broads. This fine Victorian pub is located on a site which has supported licensed premises since the 16th century. There is a central bar with an eating area to one side providing home-cooked meals (no meals on Mon). A private function room is available and there is a garden to the rear. Three guest ales are sold, often including beers from local micros.

Q❀◑⇌P

BEDFIELD

Crown

Church Lane (head N from Earl Soham)

11.30-3 (may vary), 6-11; 12-4, 7-10.30 Sun

☎ (01728) 628431

Greene King IPA; guest beer Ⓗ

Small, cosy pub off the beaten track, which is well worth seeking out. The pub has been a regular entry in this Guide. It features a separate no-smoking area. A fine illustration on the wall details the method of construction of this timber-framed building. Food is not served on Tuesday. This is one of the few pubs locally to have a bar billiards table. ⛼❀◑⛺♣P⚟

BLAXHALL

Ship

On road to Tunstall at W end of village

12-2.30, 7-11; 12-3, 7-10.30 Sun

☎ (01728) 688316

Adnams Bitter; Woodforde's Wherry; guest beers Ⓗ

An 18th-century inn with low beamed

ceilings, situated in a small village set on coastal heathlands. This pub has long been a venue for traditional local songs and music. A terrace to the front is pleasant for summer drinking. Accommodation is offered in a separate building close to the pub, all guest rooms have en-suite facilities. ⛼Q❀⇌◐♣P⚟

BOXFORD

White Hart

Broad Street

✪ 12-3, 6-11; 12-3, 7-10.30 Sun

☎ (01787) 211071 website: www.white-hart.co.uk

Adnams Broadside; guest beers Ⓗ

Timber-framed free house beside the little River Box in the centre of this attractive village, with many timber-framed buildings. The church is worth a visit and has an unusual 17th-century font cover. A widely varied menu offers good value for money. In the 19th century the pub was home to the Boxford Brewery and during the 20th century to the legendary Tornado Smith, the wall-of-death rider whose pet lion rode in the sidecar – see their photographs in the bar and ask the landlord where the lion is buried. The pub is now the meeting place of the Hadleigh and District Classic Motorcycle Club. Usually at least two guest beers are stocked. ⛼❀◐♣P

BRADFIELD ST GEORGE

Fox & Hounds

Felsham Road

✪ 11.30-3, 5.30-11; closed Mon; 12-3, 7-10.30 Sun

☎ (01284) 386379

website: www.maypolegreenbarns.co.uk

Buffy's IPA; Nethergate Suffolk County; guest beer Ⓗ

On the village outskirts close to the historic coppiced woodland of the Suffolk Wildlife Trust, this free house and country restaurant is a beautifully restored Victorian inn. Refurbished to provide a combination of a real ale pub with an à la carte restaurant and B&B accommodation, it offers excellent service and a warm welcome. The comfortable, attractive interior has two wood-fronted bar areas, one of which has a woodblock floor, pine seating and a wood-burning stove. Fast gaining a reputation for superb meals. ⛼Q❀⇌◐⊟P

BRAMFIELD

Queen's Head

The Street

✪ 11-3, 6-11; 12-2.30, 7-10.30 Sun

☎ (01986) 784214

Adnams Bitter, Broadside, seasonal beers Ⓗ

Charming 16th-century pub, the main bar has an impressive high, beamed ceiling and large brick fireplace, old farm tools hang from the walls. Steps lead down to the lower bar where children are welcome, while the small no-smoking dining room is through a passage from the main bar. This passage has an exposed section of wattle-and-daub wall. The food served is certified organic, mostly from local suppliers. Close to the pub, the thatched church of St Andrew has the only detached round tower in Suffolk; inside is a fine medieval screen. Across the road from the church, look out for a crinkle crankle wall. ⛼Q❀◐P

BRANDON

Five Bells

Market Hill

✪ 11-11; 12-10.30 Sun

☎ (01842) 813472

Greene King IPA, Abbot Ⓗ

Pleasantly situated at the corner of the market square (market days Thu and Sat), it is ideal for a relaxing pint after the rigours of shopping! The building is quite ancient, based on a 17th-century timber-framed structure with some later extensions. The exterior is now flint faced in local style as are many houses in the locality. Nearby is Brandon Heritage Centre with much to interest visitors including exhibits of local history and information on attractions of which Thetford Forest, with its fine walks, is the most famous. ❀⊟⇶♣P

BRENT ELEIGH

Cock ☆

Lavenham Road OS941478

✪ 12-3, 6-11; 12-3, 7-10.30 Sun

☎ (01787) 247371

Adnams Bitter; Greene King IPA, Abbot Ⓗ

Absolute gem! Always spotless and well cared for, this pub manages to transport you back to a time most pubs have long forgotten. In the winter both tiny bars are snug and warm, in summer with the door open the bar is at one with its surroundings. Good conversation is guaranteed – sit and listen and you will be involved. Close to Lavenham and the beautiful Brett Valley, the comfortable accommodation is recommended. This pub is CAMROT (Campaign for Real Outside Toilets) approved. Do not miss it! ⛼Q❀⇌⊟♣●P

BUNGAY ❊

Fleece

St Mary's Street

✪ 11-11; 12-10.30 Sun

☎ (01986) 892192

Adnams Bitter; Fuller's London Pride; guest beer Ⓗ

Formerly called the Cross Keys (of 16th-century origin), the pub name was changed to the Fleece in 1711. The façade was redesigned in the present mock-Tudor style in 1910. It is situated close to the castle and facing Buttercross Market. The bar area creates an olde-worlde impression,

INDEPENDENT BREWERIES

Adnams Southwold
Bartrams Thurston
Bury Street Stowmarket
Cox & Holbrook Buxhall
Earl Soham Earl Soham
Green Dragon Bungay
Greene King Bury St Edmunds
Kings Head Bildeston
Lidstones Wickhambrook
Mauldons Sudbury
Nethergate Clare
Old Cannon Bury St Edmunds
Old Chimneys Market Weston
Oulton Oulton Broad
St Peter's St Peter South Elmham

families are welcome in the no-smoking area. There is a patio garden and car park at the rear with a recent extension created by the purchase of the property next door.
♛❀◖▲P⊬

Green Dragon
29 Broad Street
✪ 11-3, 4.30-11; 11-11 Fri & Sat; 12-3, 7-10.30 Sun
☎ (01986) 892681
Green Dragon Chaucer Ale, Bridge Street Bitter, H seasonal beers G/H
Bungay's only brew-pub. The brewery is situated in outbuildings adjacent to the car park to the rear (tours by arrangement). This lively town pub has a separate public bar and lounge. The dining room, which doubles as a family room, leads to the garden, surrounded by hops. Lunchtime meals are served weekdays and speciality food nights are held (Wed – curry, Fri – fish and chips). Flexible hours depend on demand and during the summer months the pub is open all day Sunday if it is busy. Bottle-conditioned seasonal ales are available.
♛❀◖▲♣P

BURY ST EDMUNDS

King's Arms
23 Brentgovel Street
✪ 11-11; closed Sun
☎ (01284) 761874
Greene King IPA, Abbot, Old Speckled Hen; guest beers H
Just outside the main town square, this one-bar pub is popular with customers of all ages. A fascinating photo collection and interesting artefacts are displayed. The 'happy hour' ales are served in large pint-and-a-half beer glasses. It is one of very few pubs in the town centre offering an outside drinking area, which not surprisingly is well used in summer. The unusually named meals are excellent value and served promptly. ♛❀◖

Old Cannon
86 Cannon Street
✪ 12-3 (not Mon), 5-11; 12-3, 7-10.30 Sun
☎ (01284) 768769 website: www.oldcannon.co.uk
Old Cannon Best Bitter, Gunner's Daughter, seasonal beer; guest beers H
Formerly the St Edmund's Head, this pub/brewery is on the same site as the original Cannon Brewery (established in 1847). It reopened in December 1999 and has rapidly become known as the place in town for the real ale fan. The full range of Old Cannon beers is brewed on site, with the brewing vessels situated in the bar. At least two guest beers from around the country are sold. A high quality menu and accommodation are available at this excellent new venture. Play lie dice and traditional pub games here.
♛Q❀◖◗♿♣P

Queen's Head
39 Churchgate Street
✪ 11-11; 12-10.30 Sun
☎ (01284) 761554 website: www.queens-head.org.uk
Adnams Broadside; Nethergate IPA; guest beers H
This lively town-centre pub, a former 18th-century coaching inn, has survived the tests of time. It has been extended and modernised in recent years but still retains its original charm. A true free house, it is dedicated to providing good quality beer at competitive prices. The staff at this family-run pub are welcoming and there is a comprehensive menu offered all day until 9pm. There is a large conservatory, a games room with pool table and the sizeable patio is gas heated to allow year-round use.
❀◖◗♣⊬●

Rose & Crown
48 Whiting Street

INN BRIEF

BARNBY

Swan Inn
Swan Lane
11-3, 7-11; 12-3, 7-10.30 Sun
(01502) 476646
Adnams Bitter, seasonal beers; Draught Bass; Greene King IPA, Abbot H
Comfortable pub with large restaurant specialising in fish (booking advisable). Cask Marque accredited.

BLUNDESTON

Plough
Market Lane
12-2.30, 7-11; 12-3, 7-10.30 Sun
(01502) 730261
Adnams Bitter, Broadside; Greene King IPA H
Village inn with Dickensian connections. The timbered, large main bar houses bar skittles. The lounge serves quality food.

BRIDGE STREET

Rose & Crown
11-3, 6.30-11; 12-3, 7-10.30 Sun
(01787) 247022
Greene King IPA, Abbot G
Good roadside pub which backs on to the main A134, with a pretty frontage on to Bridge Street village.

BUNGAY

Chequers Inn
23 Bridge Street
12 (11 Sat)-11; 12-10.30 Sun
(01986) 893579
Adnams Bitter; Fuller's London Pride; guest beers H
17th-century inn, locally known as Bungay's permanent real ale festival, regularly serving up to nine ales.

CARLTON COLVILLE

Bell Inn
The Street
11-3, 7-11; 11-11 Fri & Sat; 12-10.30 Sun
(01502) 582873
Oulton Wet & Windy, Excelsior; guest beers H
Open-plan inn, with flagstone floor and central fireplace, owned by Oulton Brewery. Restaurant facilities and pleasant garden.

CONEY WESTON

Swan
Thetford Road
12-3, 5 (6 Sat)-11; 12-3, 7-10.30 Sun
(01359) 221295
Greene King IPA, Abbot; guest beers H
Typical village pub serving the community. Good evening meals; traditional games are played. Cask Marque accredited.

EAST BERGHOLT

Royal Oak (Dickey)
East End Lane
11.30-2.30, 5.30-11; 11.30-3, 6-11 Sat; 12-3, 7-10.30 Sun
(01206) 298221
Greene King IPA, Abbot; seasonal beers H
Excellent rural pub, may be difficult to find (follow signs to Grange campsite). Cask Marque accredited.

ERISWELL

Chequers
The Street
11-2, 5.30-11; 12-3, 7-10.30 Sun
(01638) 532478
Greene King IPA, Abbot H
19th-century pub in country estate village. Food is available at all times with Tex-Mex a speciality. Enjoy Breckland walks nearby.

GLEMSFORD

Angel
Egremont Street
5-11; 7-10.30 Sun
(01787) 281671
Greene King IPA, Abbot; guest beers G
Traditional pub, reputedly the oldest in the village. Said to be haunted by Cardinal Wolsey's secretary, John Cavendish.

⏲ 11.30-11; 11-3, 7-11 Sat; 12-2.30, 7-10.30 Sun
☎ (01284) 755934
Greene King XX Mild, IPA, Abbot; guest beer Ⓗ
Highly recommended and still very much a town local. This listed red-brick and tile-faced street-corner pub has been run by the same family for 27 years. Retaining two bars plus a rare off-sales counter, the interior is traditional and immaculate; both bars have a subtle pig theme. It is within sight of Greene King's Westgate Brewery and frequented by all ranks of its staff. It is well-known for the mild which nearly outsells the IPA. Good value lunches are on offer Mon-Sat. Pub games are played and help with the crossword is always welcome.
⛟◐⊟♣

BUTLEY

Oyster
Orford Road
⏲ 11.30-3, 6-11 (opening hours may be extended); 12-3, 7-10.30 Sun
☎ (01394) 450790
Adnams Bitter, Broadside Ⓗ
Low ceilings, traditional furnishings and rustic decor make this a fine country pub for those seeking a tranquil spot. Caravans are welcome and there is a menagerie for children. The ancient woodland of Staverton Thicks is nearby, while Orford, with its interesting church, castle (English Heritage) and river, is only three miles to the east.
⛫Q❀◐◑⛺♣P

CAVENDISH

Bull
High Street
⏲ 11-3, 6-11; 12-3, 7-10.30 Sun
☎ (01787) 280245
Adnams Bitter, Broadside Ⓗ
This old pub is in one of the most picturesque villages in Suffolk. It has a heavily timbered single bar with several dining and drinking areas. It is a rare Adnams tied house for the west of the county. A wide selection of home-cooked food is available. Owing to its superb local reputation, booking is advisable for weekend evenings and Sunday lunch. On warm days a pint can be enjoyed on the rear terrace.
⛫Q❀◐◑♿P

COCKFIELD

Three Horseshoes
Stows Hill (A1141 Lavenham to Bury St Edmunds road)
⏲ 11-3 (not Tue), 6-11; 12-3.30, 7-10.30 Sun
☎ (01284) 828177
website: www.threehorseshoespub.co.uk
Greene King IPA; guest beer Ⓗ
Pink-washed, 14th-century thatched inn with fine gardens and splendid rural views. The restaurant has one of the oldest king post roofs in Suffolk. The comfortable bar is heavily beamed and offers three handpulled ales. Delicious home-made food is sold (no meals on Tue). Camping facilities are available for five caravans plus tents. Traditional pub games, such as ring the bull, are played.
⛫♨❀◐◑⊟♿⛺♣P

COMBS FORD

Gladstone Arms
2 Combs Ford (1 mile from Stowmarket town centre on Needham road)
⏲ 11-3, 5 (6 Sat)-11; 12-3, 7-10.30 Sun
☎ (01449) 612339
Adnams Bitter, Broadside Ⓗ
Adnams tied house situated in a hamlet on the southern outskirts of the market town of Stowmarket. The pub has a large bar with several distinct drinking areas. Beyond the car park, the beer garden is pleasantly located beside a small stream. Lunches are served 12-2 daily and evening meals from 7-9 (not Sun). The pub is only a mile away from the Museum of East Anglian Life, which is well worth a visit. ❀◐◑♣P

COWLINGE

Three Tuns
Queen's Street (1½ miles N of A143 Haverhill-Bury St Edmunds)
⏲ 12-2 (not Mon), 5 (12 Sat)-11; 12-10.30 Sun
☎ (01440) 821847
Adnams Bitter, Broadside; guest beer Ⓗ
This gem of a village local has recently come alive after many doldrum years with periods of inactivity and closure. Vigorous local and CAMRA protests were heard when permanent closure loomed, but these dastardly plans were thwarted! The superb beamed bar is estimated to be 16th century, and of course 'Three Tuns' indicates a very ancient pub. A new dining area has been opened up from former living accommodation. Cowlinge (pronounced coolinge) is a dispersed village with a long street and no real centre, so do not despair if the pub is not apparent immediately. Note no meals are prepared on Mon. ❀◐◑P

CRETINGHAM

Bell
The Street
⏲ 11-2.30, 6-11; 12-10.30 Sun
☎ (01728) 685419
Adnams Bitter; Earl Soham Victoria; guest beer Ⓗ
This building once housed four cottages dating from the 17th century. The pub is situated in a pretty village in the upper reaches of the Deben Valley. In 1887 a macabre event occurred locally – the parish curate murdered the vicar by cutting his throat with a razor as he lay in bed! This charming inn has an oak-beamed interior, the small snug bar is a special delight. An interesting menu is available and a beer from Mauldons is on offer.
⛫Q❀⛟◐◑♣P⍻

EARL SOHAM

Victoria
On A1120
⏲ 11.30-3, 5.30-11; 12-3, 7-10.30 Sun
☎ (01728) 685758
Earl Soham Gannet Mild, Victoria, Sir Roger's Porter, Albert Ale Ⓗ
No-frills village pub that offers something for everyone. Beers are from the local brewery, located across the road, they are keenly priced and complemented by wholesome home-cooked meals, using local produce where possible. The pub's football

team has had great success in the recent past and has even appeared at Wembley. Benches and tables to the front of the pub are well used in summer. ♨Q❀◐◑♣●P

EAST BERGHOLT ❄

Hare & Hounds

Heath Road

◎ 12-2.30, 5-11; 12-2.30, 6-10.30 Sun

☎ (01206) 298438

Adnams Bitter, Broadside; Ⓗ guest beers Ⓖ

Friendly, traditional village pub with a relaxed, cosy atmosphere and long-standing landlord and landlady celebrating more than 26 years' service here. Built in the 15th century it retains a pargetted ceiling (deep plaster relief), circa 1590, in the lounge. Guest beers are mainly from local breweries. No food is served on Tuesday. This fine pub caters for everyone, it offers a family room, pleasant garden and a separate public bar. ♨Q♉❀◐◑⊟♿▲♣P

EDWARDSTONE

White Horse

Mill Green OS951429

◎ 12-2 (not Mon, Tue & Thu), 6.30-11; 12-3, 7-10.30 Sun

☎ (01787) 211211

Greene King IPA; guest beers Ⓗ

Off the beaten track so an OS map is needed to find this two-bar rural free house. It boasts an interesting collection of enamel signs in both bars and a wide choice of pub games, including ring the bull in the public bar. The pub wall, facing the road has Olivers lettering, a brewery taken over by Greene King in 1919. One of the guests is usually a dark beer. Caravans are welcome at the camp site. Accommodation is available in newly built holiday homes in the pub grounds. On early summer evenings you can often hear nightingales calling from nearby woods. ♨Q❀⇌◐◑⊟▲♣P

FELIXSTOWE (WALTON)

Half Moon

303 Walton High Street

◎ 12-2.30, 5-11; 12-11 Sat; 12-3, 7-10.30 Sun

☎ (01394) 216009

website: www.halfmoonfelixstowe.com

Adnams Bitter, Broadside; guest beer Ⓗ

Splendid, traditional drinkers' pub with a friendly welcome. No fruit machines, electronic music or food, but darts, dominoes and cribbage can be played in the public bar, as can a piano should you wish to entertain (or annoy!) your fellow customers. The lounge is larger, with a small section partitioned off for non-smokers. Note the stained glass screens above the bar. Both bars display old photographs of the area. Ask about 'the word of the week'. Euros accepted. ♨Q❀⊟▲♣P⊬

FRAMLINGHAM

Station

Station Road

◎ 12-3, 5-11; 12-3, 7-10.30 Sun

☎ (01728) 723455

Earl Soham Gannet Mild, Victoria, Sir Roger's Porter, Albert Ale, Jolabrugg (Christmas) Ⓗ

Much in this pub reflects the railway era. An intimate, cosy drinking area lies beyond the main bar, and there is a fine bank of handpumps arrayed. There is plenty of interest locally – walk from the pub to the town centre passing the tomb house of Thomas Mills. Visit the castle where Mary Tudor was proclaimed queen, and the church of St Michael with its fine tombs and outstanding organ. Can you find Framlingham's two early Victorian pillar boxes with their vertical slits? ♨Q❀◐◑♣P

FRECKENHAM

Golden Boar

The Street

◎ 11.30-11; 12-6 (12-10.30 summer) Sun

☎ (01638) 723000

Adnams Bitter; Courage Directors; Fuller's London Pride; guest beers Ⓗ

A former coaching inn with 16th-century origins. The village is said to have been the most inland port in the country in the past. Recent extensive restoration has exposed many original features, the most magnificent of these is a huge fireplace surround created from stones believed to have come from an old church after it was razed to the ground in the 15th century. Excellent home-cooked food is provided with a specials board; booking is advised, especially for lunches (sometimes food not available eves). Newly completed chalet accommodation is available. ❀⇌◐◑♿♣P

GISLINGHAM

Six Bells

High Street

◎ 12-3, 7 (6 Fri)-11; 12-3, 7-10.30 Sun

☎ (01379) 783349

Beer range varies Ⓗ

Spacious pub in the centre of the village. It supports micro-breweries and has a fine display of pump clips decorating the walls. A large function room at the back welcomes all parties or meetings. Fine home-made food is served in the bar or in the no-smoking Columbine restaurant, where an interesting menu is served (no food Mon). Note the well, illuminated to display the drop to the water. The Columbine has connections with the local church: it is believed that the 15th-century stained glass window features one of the earliest pictorial records of these flowers in the country. Q♉❀◐◑♿▲♣P

GREAT WRATTING

Red Lion

School Road

◎ 11-2.30, 5-11; 11-11 Sat; 12-3, 7-10.30 Sun

☎ (01440) 783237

Adnams Bitter, Broadside; guest beer (summer) Ⓗ

One of the prettiest and most instantly recognisable pub exteriors in the county, with its distinctive whalebone arch over the doorway. This family-run Adnams tied house has a separate restaurant and cosy public bar. Functions are catered for in the summer months with a permanent marquee erected to the rear of the pub overlooking the gardens and meadows. ♨Q❀◐◑⊟P

HAVERHILL

Queen's Head

Queen Street

⏲ 11-11; 12-10.30 Sun

☎ (01440) 702026

Courage Best Bitter; Greene King Old Speckled Hen; Nethergate Suffolk County, Augustinian Ale; guest beers [H]

Handsome Grade II listed building dating from 1470, quite possibly the oldest property in town. Traditional etched glass in the ground-floor windows gives character to a popular pub in the main shopping area (pedestrianised during the day). Inside, a cosy atmosphere is created by three bars; one largish with games, such as pool, but two other small rooms are gems and just invite settling down for a pint. Straightforward pub food at reasonable prices is available lunchtimes Mon-Sat.

◐⊟♣P

HONEY-TYE

Lion

On A134

⏲ 11-3, 5.45-11; 12-10.30 Sun

☎ (01206) 263434

website: www.thelionleavenheath.co.uk

Adnams Bitter; Greene King IPA; guest beers [H]

Large free house on the main Sudbury to Colchester road near Leavenheath. The single bar leads to an informal dining area, then on to a separate restaurant. The pub strikes a good balance between food and drink, and keeps its community focus. The food offered is varied and freshly prepared. Two guest beers are usually available. Wheelchair access is via the restaurant.

ᗑQ❀◐◑♿♣P✔

HOXNE

Swan

Low Street

⏲ 11-3, 6-11; 12-10.30 Sun

☎ (01379) 668275

Adnams Bitter, Broadside; [G] **guest beers** [H]

Spectacular timber-framed building which was formerly a bishop's residence in a tranquil spot at the centre of this historic village, with secluded lawns for summer use. Log fires roar in all three main rooms to provide a cosy refuge in winter. Regional and micro-breweries feature among the three guest beers which are complemented by imaginative food. ᗑQ❀◐◑♣P

IPSWICH ❄

Fat Cat

288 Spring Road

⏲ 12 (11 Sat)-11; 12-10.30 Sun

☎ (01473) 726524

Adnams Bitter; [H] **Crouch Vale Brewers Gold; Fuller's London Pride; Hop Back Summer Lightning;** [G] **Woodforde's Wherry,** [H]/[G] **Norfolk Nog; guest beers** [G]

Old-fashioned Victorian-style ale house about 15 minutes' walk from the town centre. Furnished in traditional yet comfortable style, with wooden and tiled floors and bench seating, the walls are adorned with tin advertising signs. Up to 20 ales are on offer, many from local breweries and are dispensed from the tap room, which is visible from the bar. It was Suffolk CAMRA Pub of the Year 1998. The hops from the garden have been used by Old Chimneys to create special ales. Banham cider and Belgian bottled and draught beers are sold. A selection of home-made snacks is provided, but customers are welcome to

INN BRIEF

HAWSTEAD

Metcalfe Arms

Lawshall Road

12-2.30, 5.45-11; 12-11 Sat; 12-10.30 Sun

(01284) 386321

Greene King IPA, [H] **Abbot;** [G] **guest beers** [H]

Taking its name from the 19th-century MP, this pub has a tiled public bar and hosts live folk music in summer.

IPSWICH

Dales

Dales Road

11-2.30, 4.30-11; 6.30-11 Sat; 12.30-3.30, 7-10.30 Sun

(01473) 250024

Adnams Bitter; Woodforde's Wherry; guest beers [H]

Modern two-bar free house with home-cooked lunches and themed evening meals. Outside drinking on the patio and lawn in summer.

MARKET WESTON

Mill

Bury Road (B1111)

12-3, 7-11; closed Mon; 12-3, 7-10.30 Sun

(01359) 221018

Adnams Bitter; Greene King IPA; Old Chimneys Military Mild, Great Raft Bitter [H]

Free house serving superb fresh food and keeping two ales from the local Old Chimneys Brewery.

MILDENHALL

Queen's Arms

42 Queensway

12-2.30, 6-11; 12-4, 7.30-11 Sat; 12-3.30, 7.30-10.30 Sun

(01638) 713657

Greene King IPA, Abbot; guest beer [H]

Excellent, comfortable communal pub offering food, games, camping and accommodation.

SOUTHWOLD

Harbour Inn

Blackshore

11-11; 12-10.30 Sun

(01502) 722381

Adnams Bitter, Broadside, seasonal beers [H]

Riverside pub, in fine setting to the south of the main town. It has an interesting split-level interior.

STRADBROKE

White Hart

Church Street

11.30-3, 6.30-11; 12-3.30, 7-10.30 Sun

(01379) 384310

Adnams Bitter; Greene King IPA; guest beer [H]

Historic pub with a brisk trade most evenings; a community resource for 200 years, despite efforts to build on its bowling green.

WOODBRIDGE

Cherry Tree

75 Cumberland Street

11.30-3, 6.30-11; 12-3.30, 7-10.30 Sun

(01394) 382513

Adnams Bitter, Regatta, Fisherman, Tally Ho; guest beer [H]

17th-century one-bar pub with a wide selection of reasonably-priced home-cooked food. Cask Marque accredited.

Missing?

If a pub is not listed in the Guide that you think is worthy of consideration, please let us know at GBG, CAMRA, 230 Hatfield Road, St Albans, Herts, AL1 4LW or camra@camra.org.uk. All recommendations are forwarded to CAMRA branches, which are responsible for choosing pubs.

bring their own food or order a takeaway (ask at the bar). Camping is possible on the pub lawn by arrangement. Q ❀ ⛺ ⇌ (Derby Rd) ♣ ●

Greyhound

9 Henley Road

☼ 11-2.30, 5-11; 11-11 Sat; 12-10.30 Sun

☎ (01473) 252105

Adnams Bitter, Regatta, Fisherman, Broadside, Tally Ho; Fuller's London Pride; guest beers [H]

Busy community pub just a short walk from the town centre. A traditional-style public bar is complemented by a larger lounge and outdoor patio drinking area. Pub games are available, such as darts (including the local variation known as 'fives'), dominoes, cards and chess. The menu offers some unusual home-cooked dishes and changes with great regularity. Q ❀ ◐ ◑ ⊟ ♣ P

Milestone Beer House

5 Woodbridge Road (opp. Odeon)

☼ 12-3, 5-11; 12-11 Fri & Sat; 12-10.30 Sun

☎ (01473) 252425

website: www.milestonebeerhouse.co.uk

Adnams Bitter; Greene King IPA; guest beers [H]/[G]

Tolly mock-Tudor pub with a large patio drinking area at the front, where you can spot the milestone which gives the pub its name. Regular music nights and the wide range of real ales make this a popular local which attracts visitors from further afield, including members of the audience and stars from the nearby Regent Theatre. Real ciders may be available and the choice of whiskies is worthy. Home-cooked meals include vegan and vegetarian options at value-for-money prices (no food Thu-Sun eves). An added attraction is the skittle alley at the rear of the pub. ❀ ◐ ◑ ♿ ♣ P ⊓

IXWORTH

Greyhound

49 High Street

☼ 11-3, 6-11; 12-3, 7-10.30 Sun

☎ (01359) 230887

Greene King XX Mild, IPA, Abbot, seasonal beers [H]

This welcoming, traditional three-bar pub retains a marvellously intimate snug. An inn has stood on this site since Tudor times. Pub games are keenly promoted here: dominoes, crib, darts and pool are played. Games evenings are held to raise funds for local charities. Bar meals are served daily, 11-2 and 6-8. The pub takes party bookings with a choice of catering, roast dinners or buffet menus for 8-20 people. ❀ ◐ ◑ ⊟ ⛺ ♣ P

LAKENHEATH

Brewer's Tap

54 High Street

☼ 12-11; 12-4.30, 7-10.30 Sun

☎ (01842) 862328

Beer range varies [H]

Probably originating as a workman's cottage in the village centre, this small pub of character is a find for real ale enthusiasts, being truly 'free' in an area dominated by one brewer (Greene King). Always a good atmosphere, this is a village local without doubt. Do not be put off by the small frontage – an extension and patio at the rear make the pub more spacious than it appears. Good value food is available at lunchtimes. Evening meals must be booked. ❀ ◐ ◑ ♣

LAVENHAM

Angel Hotel

Market Place

☼ 11-11; 12-10.30 Sun

☎ (01787) 247388

Adnams Bitter; Greene King IPA; Nethergate Suffolk County; guest beer [H]

Lavenham is reputedly England's finest medieval village and this is its oldest inn, first licensed in 1420. It sits opposite the Guildhall in the market place. The choice of eating and drinking areas includes some that are no-smoking, with ample space in the garden or on the front terrace in summer. A busy place for food, the menu changes twice daily and all meals are prepared from fresh ingredients on the premises. All the beers on handpump are brewed in Suffolk. There are eight comfortable, well-equipped, en-suite guest rooms with good value midweek breaks. ♨ Q ❀ ⊨ ◐ ◑ ♿ ♣ P

LAXFIELD

King's Head (Low House) ☆

Gorams Mill Lane (off B1117, below churchyard)

☼ 12-3, 6-11; 11-11 Tue; 12-4, 7-10.30 Sun

☎ (01986) 798395

Adnams Bitter, Regatta, Fisherman, Broadside, Tally Ho; Fuller's London Pride; guest beers [G]

A pub without a bar; in the finest tradition of the beer house, ales are dispensed by gravity from the tap room at the back. Multiple rooms (including a separate dining section) and outdoor drinking areas provide convivial space for all. No fruit machines, electronic music or TV, but plenty of real atmosphere! Tuesday afternoons feature informal traditional music sessions. Pub games are available, such as shove-ha'penny, cribbage and dominoes. Awarded CAMRA East Anglian Pub of the Year 2001 and featuring on the National Inventory listing, this pub should not be missed! ♨ Q ❀ ◐ ◑ ⛺ ♣ P

LITTLE GLEMHAM

Lion Inn

OS341584

☼ 12-3, 6-11; 12-11 Sat; 12-10.30 Sun

☎ (01728) 746505

Adnams Bitter, Regatta, Fisherman; guest beers [H]

As you travel along the busy A12 north from Ipswich, this pub is a convenient and pleasant watering-hole. It offers a friendly atmosphere with an attractive garden to enjoy a pint. To complement the ales, a wide range of reasonably-priced food is prepared and cooked on the premises. ♨ Q ☋ ❀ ◐ ◑ ♣ P ⚟

LONG MELFORD

Swan

Hall Street

☼ 11.30-2.30, 5-11; 12-3, 7-10.30 Sun

☎ (01787) 378740

Greene King IPA, Abbot, guest beer (summer) [H]

The Swan opened in 1767 as a brew-pub, part of the two-storey brewhouse remains as a garage and store. Greene King bought the pub from Olivers of Sudbury in 1919. Very much a village pub, teams are fielded for many games and sports, including a bobsleigh team which meets to raise money for local charities. A display of local history has been collected by the landlord and is displayed in the lounge. Part of the rear bar is designated 'Tudor corner' and is devoted to and used by the participants in Kentwell Hall's Tudor recreations which are just one of Melford's attractions. An extensive, enclosed garden is available. No food is served Mon eve. Q❀◐⊟♣✓

LOWESTOFT

Oak Tavern

Crown Street West (B1074)

✪ 10.30-11; 12-10.30 Sun

☎ (01502) 537246

Adnams Bitter; Greene King Abbot; guest beers Ⓗ

Good, lively drinkers' bar situated on the north side of town with an open-plan design. The walls are adorned with Belgian beer memorabilia at one end. Four real ales are always on tap, one of which is a house beer brewed by Woodforde's. An extensive range of Belgian bottled beers is served in the appropriate glass. Very popular with sports fans, it has a large-screen TV for sports events, and fields its own football, pool and darts teams. ❀⇌♣P

Triangle

29 St. Peter's Street

✪ 11-11; 12-10.30 Sun

☎ (01502) 582711

Oulton Bitter, Gone Fishing, seasonal beers; guest beers Ⓗ

Popular, town-centre, two-bar pub situated on the Triangle Market Place. The cosy front bar has a wooden floor and real fire. The open-plan back bar offers a pool table. Customers are welcome to bring their own food. Live music is staged twice weekly. Guest ales from all over the UK and Eire are enjoyed throughout the year. A guest cider is often available. Quarterly beer festivals are held. ⛼⊟⇌●

NEEDHAM MARKET

Limes Hotel

99 High Street

✪ 11-11; 12-10.30 Sun

☎ (01449) 720305 website: www.elizabethhotels.co.uk

Adnams Bitter; Greene King IPA; guest beer Ⓗ

Dating from the 15th century, this imposing town-centre inn is deservedly popular with real ale drinkers. It features exposed brickwork, low beams and an unusual walk-round inglenook. Bugs bar is the livelier of the two drinking areas while His Lordship's Lounge is more relaxed and has wood-panelled walls and well-upholstered chairs. There are plenty of tempting special meal promotions. Weekend breaks are available and the inn reputedly has a ghost. This hostelry is well worth a visit.

❀⇔◐⇌P

NEWMARKET

New Wellington

81 Cheveley Road (follow signs to Clare from clock tower in High Street)

✪ 11.30-2.30, 6-11; 12-3, 7-10.30 Sun

☎ (01638) 662137

Greene King XX Mild, IPA, Abbot Ⓗ

Situated on the south-east edge of town, this locals' pub is a find for cask mild enthusiasts. Newly refurbished and reshaped to provide one largish bar with bare wood floor and separate dining area, decorations are on a horsy theme as you would expect in Newmarket. The pub is community-based and proudly displays evidence of local charity fund-raising. Good value home-cooked food is sold, but no Sunday lunches. Limited parking.

❀◐♣P

OCCOLD

Beaconsfield Arms

Mill Road

✪ 12-3, 6-11; 12-4, 6.30-10.30 Sun

☎ (01379) 678033

Adnams Bitter; Greene King IPA, Ⓗ **Abbot** Ⓖ

350-year-old, village-centre local close to the pleasant and interesting small town of Eye. The main bar area has a low beamed ceiling, a flagstone floor and a large, old fireplace, giving a traditional country pub ambience. Separate sections for pool and for dining adjoin the main drinking area. Food served is freshly prepared, value-for-money fare. Popular with all age groups, it offers a rare opportunity to try Greene King Abbot served straight from the cask. The pub has a pool team and dominoes and cribbage are also played. Children's play facilities are provided.

⛼❀◐♣P

OFFTON

Limeburners

Willisham Road

✪ 12-2 (not Mon), 5-11; 11-11 Sat; 12-4, 7-10.30 Sun

☎ (01473) 658318

Adnams Bitter; guest beer Ⓗ

A two-bar roadside local which offers a large garden with barbecue facilities. The pub takes its name from a disused lime kiln in the old quarry opposite. Known as Offton Limeburners and situated right on the boundary of Offton, the pub is actually in the parish of Willisham. Enjoy the music on Sunday when it is buskers' night. Pub games are played and food is served daily. ❀◐♣P

SHIMPLING

Bush

The Street

✪ 12-3, 5.30-11; 12-3, 7-10.30 Sun

☎ (01284) 828257

Greene King IPA, Abbot; guest beer Ⓗ

The Bush is reputed to be one of the oldest inn symbols, dating from Roman times when a bush would be displayed outside a hostelry offering lodging or refreshment. The Bush in Shimpling (circa 1750), was a farriers' yard before becoming a pub. It is a cosy, low-ceilinged, two-bar village local offering good-value home-cooked specials from a varied menu (no food on Sun eve). The beer garden and children's play area offer the attraction of a veritable menagerie including a goat, rabbits, chickens and ducks. ⛼❀◐⊟P

SHOTTISHAM

Sorrel Horse Inn

OS321446
12-2.30, 7-11; 12-2.30, 7-10.30 Sun
(01394) 411617
Adnams Bitter; Tolly Cobbold Original G

Two-bar, thatched, 15th-century beamed village pub, reputed to have been the haunt of smugglers and the notorious local character, Margaret Catchpole (twice sentenced to death, she was transported to New South Wales in 1801). The coast at Bawdsey nearby bears many remains of conflict, such as Martello towers and World War I pill boxes. Also close by is the site of the Sutton Hoo ship burial from early Anglo-Saxon times – now a new and much-vaunted National Trust attraction. The grassed area in front of the pub is used for summer drinking. Bar billiards and twister are played. Q P

SOUTHWOLD

Lord Nelson

East Street
10.30-11; 12-10.30 Sun
(01502) 722079
Adnams Bitter, Broadside, seasonal beers H

Always a busy and lively pub full of locals and holidaymakers. Children are welcome in the small side room and the partly covered patio at the back. Well-behaved dogs are welcome everywhere. Expect plenty of memorabilia relating to England's greatest naval hero. The roaring log fire in winter is always inviting after a walk on the nearby beach. The pub is known for its reasonably-priced food and beer; a well-deserved frequent entry in this Guide.

STOWMARKET

Royal William

53 Union Street
11-3, 6 (5 Fri)-11; 12-3.30, 7-10.30 Sun
(01449) 674553
Greene King IPA, Old Speckled Hen H

The premises only had a full licence granted in 1966, having previously held only an ale licence. In truth not much else about this small back-street local has changed during the intervening years. Darts, dominoes and crib are played regularly. The beer is kept in a back room. Just round the corner from the fine Victorian railway station, there are some characterful, timber-framed buildings to be seen in Stowupland Street.

Stag Tavern

44-46 Bury Street
11-11; 12-10.30 Sun
(01449) 613980
Greene King IPA H

Formerly part of a butcher's shop, the exterior of the building is partly tiled. Inside there is a large bar area with plenty of seating and a pool table. The pub's own micro-brewery, Bury Street, has been in production since November 2001. A variety of its beers are sold here including Pat Murphy's Porter, Mr Murphy's Mild and the best bitter, BBB. You can see the brewery through a glass panel behind the pool table. Lunchtime food is offered Mon-Sat.

STRADBROKE

Queen's Head

Queens Street
11.30-3, 6.30-11; 12-10.30 Sun
(01379) 384384
Adnams Bitter; Greene King IPA, H **Abbot;** G **Woodforde's Mardler's, Wherry; guest beer** H

Good deals on both beer and the weekday special lunch are features of this pub. The Greene King IPA is offered at £1 a pint in the hour from 6.30pm on weekdays. An annual jazz and beer festival is held in May. The building is a timber-framed structure with castellated front. It once doubled up as a courtroom and corn exchange, the part used now hosts a collection of naval memorabilia which commemorates old tars from the village who served in the Royal Navy. A gravelled area with a pergola is used for outdoor drinking. P

SUDBURY

Waggon & Horses

Acton Square
11-3, 6.30 (5 Fri)-11; 12-3, 7.30-10.30 Sun
(01787) 312147
Greene King IPA; guest beer H

Back-street local that offers a warm welcome. It has several drinking areas and a small restaurant (where booking is advised). Guest beers tend to be from the Greene King list. The landlord is a local councillor and former mayor of Sudbury and, as can be seen from the beer garden in summer, is active within the Sudbury in Bloom organisation.
Q

SWILLAND

Moon & Mushroom

High Road
12-3, 6-11; closed Mon; 12-3, 7-10.30 Sun
(01473) 785320
Buffy's Norwich Terrier, Hopleaf; Nethergate Umbel Ale; Wolf Coyote; Woodforde's Wherry, Norfolk Nog G

Popular, out-of-the-way pub with a welcoming landlord and landlady, the latter cooks the excellent meals. Oak beams, low ceilings and an open fire make this a cosy pub in winter. All real ales are served by gravity dispense from cooled casks. While here why not have a game of shove-ha'penny? In warmer weather relax with a pint on the patio.
Q P

THEBERTON

Lion

The Street
11-3, 5.45-11; 12-3, 6.45-10.30
(01728) 830185 website: www.thelioninn.co.uk
Adnams Bitter; Woodforde's Wherry; guest beers H

Brick-built, roadside village local opposite the thatched, round-towered church. The list of guest beers changes regularly and many come from East Anglian breweries. Many old local photographs are displayed and these include some of the Zeppelin shot down here in 1917. Quiz nights are held on Wednesday to help raise funds for local charities. There is a meadow available for camping and caravans behind the pub.
P

TOSTOCK

Gardeners Arms

Church Road

11.30-2.30, 7-11; 12-3, 7-10.30 Sun

(01359) 270460

Greene King IPA, Abbot, seasonal beers H

Standing close to the village green, this splendid old building retains many original low beams. The lively public bar has a stone floor and offers darts, pool and crib. The lounge bar has a large open fireplace and carver chairs; there is a no-smoking dining area. Reasonably-priced, home-made food and tasty snacks are served (no meals all day Sun, or Mon or Tue eves). This popular pub has an extensive garden and patio area that are wonderful in summer. P

WALSHAM LE WILLOWS

Six Bells

Sumner Road

11.30-2.30, 5.30 (6.30 Sat)-11; 12-2, 7-10.30 Sun

(01359) 259726

Greene King XX Mild, IPA, Ruddles Best Bitter, Abbot H

Former wool merchant's house in the centre of this pretty village. This substantial thatched building partly dates from the 16th century. High quality, heavily carved timbers are exposed in the main bar. The six individual rooms and two bars offer a great variety. The use of open studs allows some rooms to be light and airy, while the huge fireplaces and dark timbers create a cosy atmosphere. This traditional pub is run by a local couple, who were regulars before taking it on. They concentrate on beer sales so only sandwiches and rolls are served at lunchtime (no food Sun). Dog friendly!

Q P

WESTLETON

White Horse

Darsham Road

12-3 (4 Sat), 7-11; 12-4, 7-10.30 Sun

(01728) 648222

Adnams Bitter, Broadside, seasonal beers H

Attractive setting by the village green and duckpond, this brick-built local has Dutch-style gables. Inside, the main bar is split into two distinct areas, while down a few stairs is a separate dining room. A popular pub with walkers on the heritage coast, it makes an ideal place to retreat after a day's birdwatching at the nearby RSPB reserve at Minsmere. P

WEYBREAD

Crown

The Street

11-11; 12-10.30 Sun

(01379) 586710

Greene King IPA, Abbot; guest beers H

Open all legally permitted hours, this Victorian pub offers hospitality in the form of fine ales, food and accommodation – a range few hostelries in the area can match. Speed through the village and you could miss a chance to enjoy this fine pub – the sandwich boards advertising the monthly curry night should guide you safely in. Interesting local photographs are displayed on the bar walls.

P

WOODBRIDGE

Anchor

16-19 Quay Street

12-11; 12-10.30 Sun

(01394) 382649

Greene King IPA, Abbot, seasonal beers H

The original 17th-century building was given a Victorian extension when the railway came to Woodbridge. The older part of the property is at a lower level to the rear of the intimate, panelled front bar with its array of seating. The station, theatre and cinema are just across the road and the pub is a few minutes' walk from the river and the Tide Mill. The station car park opposite is free after 6pm.

WOOLPIT

Bull Inn

The Street

11 (11.30 Sat)-3, 6-11; 12-3.30, 7-10.30 Sun

(01359) 240393 website: www.bullinnwoolpit.co.uk

Adnams Bitter; Young's Bitter, seasonal beers; guest beers H

A true community pub supporting numerous local charities and sports teams. This very welcoming, family-run business offers good home-cooked food throughout the week (no meals on Sun eve). There is a separate restaurant area. A large car park with garden leads off the former main Cambridge-Ipswich road. This small but ancient village, which once had 10 pubs and two annual fairs, is interesting to walk around. St Mary's church is a must to visit.

P

Cloudy Beer

The job of filling tankards was not one that could be done in a hurry, for he liked them full, with just the right amount of head on them. I was not allowed to pour beer for the old man as one day I had joggled the barrel and had made the contents cloudy. This was, I think, the only sin which he had not forgiven me. Anything else was pardonable, but to make beer undrinkable was a very high blasphemy.

Ruthven Todd, *Bodies In A Bookshop*, 1946

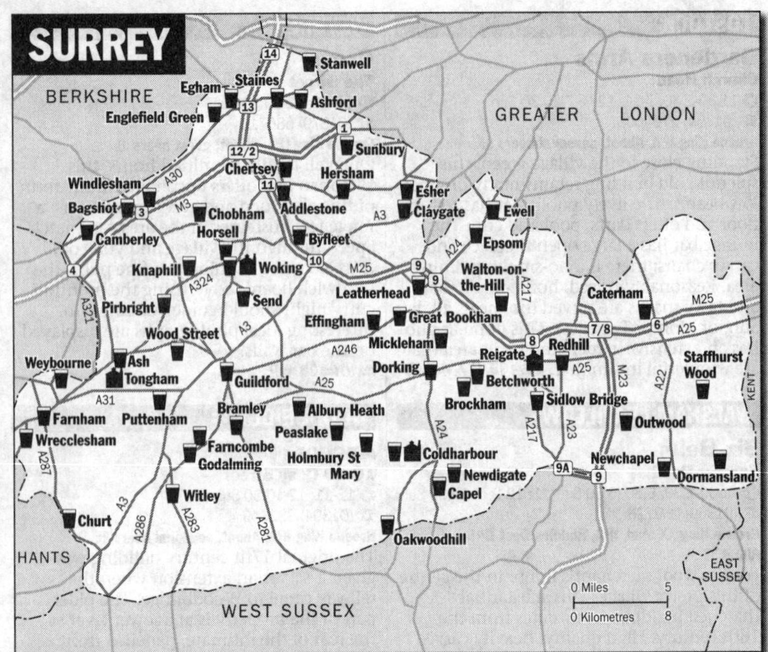

ADDLESTONE

Queen's Arms

107 Church Road (B3121)

11-3, 5.30-11; 11-11 Sat; 12-3, 7-10.30 Sun

(01932) 847845

Courage Best Bitter; Young's Special, guest beer H

Down-to-earth local, with a friendly atmosphere and welcoming Irish landlady. Courage Best is on special offer at lunchtime. A monthly quiz is held (last Thu eve). It is situated on the western side of the town, to get there, take No. 436 bus. ❀◐♣P

ALBURY HEATH

William IV

Little London (S of Shere) OS066467

11-3, 5.30-11; 12-3, 7-10.30 Sun

(01483) 202685

Flowers IPA; Hogs Back TEA, Hop Garden Gold; guest beers H

Traditional, 16th-century country pub, popular with walkers. The lower part of the bar is divided into two areas and boasts flagstones, beams and a large inglenook. A third, carpeted, area at the back, up a few steps, is mainly used by diners (eve meals Tue–Sat). The two guest beers change regularly.
⌂Q❀◐▶♣P

ASHFORD

King's Head

4 Feltham Road (B377)

11-11; 12-10.30 Sun

(01784) 244631

Adnams Broadside; Boddingtons Bitter; Courage Best Bitter H

Local pub with a bright refurbished frontage and additions. It has a large, relaxed bar area and a dedicated restaurant where an elaborate menu is supplemented by a smaller snack menu of jacket potatoes and baguettes. Pub golf society meetings are held here. ⌂Q❀P

BAGSHOT

Foresters Arms

173 London Road (A30, Camberley road)

12-2.30, 6-11; 12-3, 7-10.30 Sun

(01276) 472038

Courage Best Bitter; Fuller's London Pride; Greene King Ruddles Best Bitter; Hogs Back TEA; guest beers H

Comfortable little pub lying just outside Bagshot village centre. A reputation for good beer ensures a high turnover, allowing the landlord to maintain four regular ales plus three guests. Good pub grub, ranging from sandwiches to roasts, attracts a busy lunchtime trade. This is very much a community pub, where all generations can feel at home. An adjoining skittle alley, with its own bar, can be hired for private functions.
❀◐♣P

BETCHWORTH

Dolphin Inn

The Street (off A25)

11-3, 5.30-11; 11-11 Sat; 12-10.30 Sun

(01737) 842288

Young's Bitter, Triple A, Special, Waggledance (summer), **Winter Warmer** H

This busy local is also very popular with visitors. The building dates from the 16th century and features a flagstone floor with two inglenooks. A good selection of food is served in the three bars, with specials always available. This managed house is noted for serving some of the best pints of Young's around; a good range of wines is also kept.
⌂Q❀◐▶♣P

BRAMLEY

Jolly Farmer

High Street (A281)

⏲ 11-3, 6-11; 12-3, 7-10.30 Sun

☎ (01483) 893355 website: www.jollyfarmer.co.uk

Badger K&B Sussex, Best; Hogs Back TEA; Hop Back Summer Lightning; Taylor Landlord; guest beers Ⓗ

Historic building whose origins date back to the 18th century, this was once a coaching inn on the route from Oxford to Littlehampton. One L-shaped bar has two drinking areas either side of the entrance porch. An amazing collection of esoteric artefacts includes stuffed animals, horns, old advertisements and beer mats – many of which are from defunct breweries. Q❀⛟◐◑♿♣●P

BYFLEET

Plough

104 High Road (off A245)

⏲ 11-3, 5-11; 12-3, 7-10.30 Sun

☎ (01932) 353257

Courage Best Bitter; Fuller's London Pride; guest beers Ⓗ

Enduring and popular free house where seven handpumps dispense an ever-changing range of interesting guest beers. An L-shaped central bar serves three drinking areas, one of which is a no-smoking conservatory where children are welcome. Elsewhere, wooden beams, no-nonsense tables and chairs, and a roaring fire are complemented by agricultural implements, corn dollies and tankards. Do not disturb the gentle conversation with a mobile phone – they are banned. Limited parking. ⩕Q♨❀◑♣P✔

CAMBERLEY

Cambridge

121 London Road (A30, High St jct)

⏲ 12-11; 12-10.30 Sun

☎ (01276) 26488

Flowers Original; Fuller's London Pride; Hook Norton Old Hooky; Taylor Landlord; Wadworth 6X; guest beer Ⓗ

The Cambridge Hotel was built in 1862, so-called because Camberley was known as Cambridge Town at that time. The somewhat startling blue and yellow exterior belies a spacious, comfortable interior, offering a warm welcome. Six real ales should satisfy any thirst, while good food at sensible prices is available for much of the day (no food Sun). It stages live blues Wednesday (no charge). ⛟◐◑⇌P

CAPEL

Crown

98 The Street (off A24)

⏲ 11-2.30, 5-11; 11-11 Sat; 12-10.30 Sun

☎ (01306) 711130

Fuller's London Pride; guest beers Ⓗ

This large, two-bar village local dates from the 17th century. The lively front bar screens televised sport, and pub games are played in a raised area. The rear lounge leads to a restaurant – this part of the pub is quieter. The guest beers change frequently; their names are written in chalk on the clips, and often come from the Cottage Brewery. The pub makes a good stop for travellers between London and the south coast. ❀◐◑⊟♣P⚡

CATERHAM

King & Queen

34 High Street (B2030)

⏲ 11-11; 12-10.30 Sun

☎ (01883) 345438

Fuller's Chiswick, London Pride, ESB Ⓗ

Three distinct drinking areas are served from a single bar in this 400-year-old building, which has been a pub for about 160 years. The small front bar is for drinking; one of the two rear rooms houses a dartboard, while the other has an inglenook and a small dining area. The menu features authentic oriental dishes (no food Sun). ⩕❀◐◑♣P✔

CHERTSEY

Coach & Horses

14 St Anns Road (B375)

⏲ 12-11; 12-3, 7-10.30 Sun

☎ (01932) 563085

Fuller's Chiswick, London Pride, ESB, seasonal beers Ⓗ

Well-run pub on the edge of town, serving the full range of Fuller's regular beers. Prices vary a lot, depending on the strength of the beer. Food is not served Mon eve or weekends, but at other times includes vegetarian options. In summer the outside is decorated with flowers, floodlit after dark. ❀⛟◐◑♣P✔

CHURT

Crossways Inn

Churt Road (A287)

⏲ 11-3.30, 5-11; 11-11 Fri & Sat; 12-4, 7-10.30 Sun

☎ (01428) 714323

Cheriton Best Bitter; Courage Best Bitter; Ⓗ **Ringwood Fortyniner; guest beers** Ⓖ

Situated on a corner in a small village, this is the epitome of a good English pub where conversation reigns in both the public and saloon bars. Four or five guest beers and four real ciders are always available. The frequently-changing guests now number some 400 a year. Lunchtime sees the addition of excellent well-priced home-made food. The popular summer beer festival offers about 40 ales from across the UK. Q❀◐♿⛺♣●P

CLAYGATE ❄

Foley Arms

Foley Road

⏲ 11-11; 12-10.30 Sun

☎ (01372) 463431

Young's Bitter, Special, seasonal beers Ⓗ

Situated prominently on a bend, close to the heart of the village, this imposing Victorian local attracts a varied clientele. The lounge bar is quite sedate; the public somewhat livelier. The pub is home to

INDEPENDENT BREWERIES

Boston Experience Woking
Hogs Back Tongham
Leith Hill Coldharbour
Pilgrim Reigate

morris dancers who practise in the attached hall that also hosts a folk club (Fri eve). Barbecues are held in the large garden on summer weekends; a well-equipped children's play area makes it popular with families. ₼Q❀ᗡ⊟♿⇌♣P

Griffin
58 Common Road
✪ 11-11; 12-10.30 Sun
☎ (01372) 463799
Archers Village; Fuller's London Pride; guest beer Ⓗ
Tucked away in residential Claygate, this pleasant, relaxing pub can be hard to find but is only a short walk from the village (and on the K3 bus route). Well worth seeking out for its enterprising beer range, both the saloon and the lively public bars are served from the horseshoe-shaped bar. The public features a large-screen TV, and the saloon boasts fine Mann, Crossman and Paulin windows. A good selection of home-cooked meals includes fish and chips on Friday night (eve meals served Fri and Sat). ₼Q❀ᗡ◗⊟♿♣P

COLDHARBOUR

Plough Inn
Coldharbour Lane (Leith Hill-Dorking road)
OS152441
✪ 11.30-3, 6-11; 11.30-11 Sat; 12-10.30 Sun
☎ (01306) 711793
Hogs Back TEA; Leith Hill Crooked Furrow, Tallywhacker; Ringwood Old Thumper; Taylor Landlord; guest beers Ⓗ
Nestling in the Surrey hills, with the St George's cross flying outside, this is a gem of a rural brew-pub. The cosy bar features eight handpumps, one being devoted to Biddenden cider. Excellent home-made meals are served at all sessions, both in the dining room and, in summer, in the large back garden. The two-barrel capacity Leith Hill Brewery is located at the rear. Guest accommodation has been recently created. ₼Q⛆❀⛟ᗡ◗●P

DORKING ❊

Cricketers
81 South Street (A25, one-way system, westbound)
✪ 12-11; 12-10.30 Sun
☎ (01306) 889938
Fuller's Chiswick, London Pride, ESB, seasonal beers Ⓗ
This Fuller's pub, on the edge of the town centre, is dominated by the single bar with standing room and seats on all sides. The pub has been established a long time and its brick-lined sandstone cellars keep a constant temperature, maintaining the beers in prime condition; they allegedly once concealed smuggled liquor. The pub features bare brick walls, decorated with old photographs; the TV shows major sporting events. Outside is a Georgian walled garden. ₼❀ᗡ⊘

Old House at Home
24 West Street (A25, one-way system, eastbound)
✪ 12-3, 5.30-11; 12-3, 7-10.30 Sun
☎ (01306) 889664
Young's Bitter, Special, Winter Warmer Ⓗ
15th-century, one-bar town local in a street crowded with antique shops. The bar billiards table has been beautifully rebuilt. Television only disturbs during the occasional football match. A quiz night (Thu) and monthly folk music (third Sun eve) complete the entertainment on offer. A small dining area at the rear serves traditional English food (not Sun eve). ₼❀ᗡ◗⇌♣

Pilgrim
Station Road (by Dorking West Station)
✪ 11-3, 5-11; 11-11 Fri & Sat; 12-3, 7-10.30 Sun
☎ (01306) 889951
Adnams Bitter; Fuller's London Pride; Ringwood Old Thumper; guest beer (occasional) Ⓗ
Locals' pub not far from the town centre, and handy for the few trains which stop at Dorking West Station. The single bar has a pool table and darts down a couple of steps at one end and a restaurant area off to the side at the other end. There is also a large garden. The guest beer will probably be from one of the larger independent breweries. No food Sun eve. ❀⛟ᗡ◗⇌(West)♣P

DORMANSLAND

Old House at Home
63 West Street
✪ 11-3, 6-11; 12-3, 7-10.30 Sun
☎ (01342) 832117
Shepherd Neame Master Brew Bitter, Best Bitter, Ⓖ **Spitfire, Bishops Finger** Ⓗ
This 16th-century inn is to be found away from the village centre. Hops surround the bar and brasses decorate the walls of this very friendly pub. The menu features good home-made food, with a larger choice available Wed-Sat (no meals Sun eve). A small room houses a dartboard. Ask about the pink elephant! ₼Q❀ᗡ◗♣P

EFFINGHAM

Plough
Orestan Lane OS118538
✪ 11-3, 5.30-11; 12-3, 7-10.30 Sun
☎ (01372) 458121
Young's Bitter, Special Ⓗ
Wonderful rural retreat; drink Young's beers in a relaxed atmosphere free of all background music and fruit machines. Its attractive exterior, approached via a narrow wooden porch, opens up to one bar and two drinking areas. It can be very busy, especially with diners in the early evening and at weekends. However, the beer is never secondary and when the diners disappear the discerning drinkers emerge. A good enclosed garden at the rear has children's play equipment. Q❀ᗡ◗P

EGHAM ❊

Crown
38 High Street (B388)
✪ 11 (12 Sat)-11; 12-10.30 Sun
☎ (01784) 432608
Adnams Bitter, Broadside; Fuller's London Pride; Greene King Abbot; guest beers Ⓗ
Cosy, old-style pub: a large beamed room surrounds the bar, decorated with casks and barrels. A huge collection of beer mats is pinned to the ceiling, while old wooden floors add to the authenticity. Pool and TV are kept to one side of the bar, with a quiet area on the other. The garden and

conservatory are used by families. Popular with students and locals, its full food menu includes home-made specials. It hosts a beer and cider festival in September. P

ENGLEFIELD GREEN

Beehive

34 Middle Hill (off A30 at Egham Hill)
11-3, 5-11; 11-11 Fri & Sat; 12-10.30 Sun
(01784) 431621 website: www.beehiveinn.co.uk
Fuller's London Pride; Gale's HSB; McMullen Country; guest beers H

Small, refurbished one-bar village pub serving the local community and nearby university. It is usually busy throughout the week, with food served, except for Sat and Sun eves. Tea and coffee are always available and country wines. There are quiz nights, karaoke and live music; games include shut the box. The guest beer changes regularly and there are well-attended beer festivals staged in the garden at summer bank holiday weekends. P

EPSOM

Amato

18 Chalk Lane (off the Epsom Downs end of Worple Rd)
11-3, 5-11; 11-11 Sat; 12-4, 7-10.30 Sun
(01372) 721642
Adnams Bitter, Broadside; Fuller's London Pride; Young's Bitter H

Friendly, welcoming one-bar hostelry on the outskirts of Epsom. Two real fires, along with a nice garden, make it a pub for all seasons. Named after the 1838 Derby winner, it is full of equine artefacts. A story arose among gypsies that the name of the Derby winner would appear chalked on the well outside at dawn on Derby Day. The food range is interesting and well-priced, hence, both drinkers and diners are equally welcome. Evening meals served Tue-Sat. Small car park. P

Barley Mow

12 Pikes Hill (off A2022)
11-11; 12-10.30 Sun
(01372) 721044
Fuller's Chiswick, London Pride, ESB H

This large Fuller's pub changed management in 2001, but remains committed to good quality real ale. There are several distinct seating areas around the central bar, along with a big garden, which can get very busy in the summer. The best place to park your car is at the top left-hand corner of the Upper High Street public car park – a short alleyway leads to the pub. Food is available at all sessions, except Fri and Sun eves.

ESHER

Albert Arms

82 High Street (A307)
11-11; 12-10.30 Sun
(01372) 465290
Draught Bass; Boddingtons Bitter; Brakspear Special; Hogs Back TEA; Marston's Pedigree; Young's Bitter H

Two bars have been combined to create a horseshoe bar counter and a long restaurant area to one side, where stuffed fish are displayed. Food, under the direction of an Italian chef, has become an increasingly important element here and weekend booking is recommended for the restaurant when a jazz pianist performs (Sat eve and Sun lunch). The pub, however, remains a genuine family-owned free house and is convenient for Claremont Gardens and Sandown Park races. No food Sun eve.

EWELL

Eight Bells

78 Kingston Road (off A240/B2200)

INN BRIEF

ADDLESTONE

Waggon & Horses
43 Simplemarsh Road
11-11; 12-10.30 Sun
(01932) 828488
Usher's Best Bitter, seasonal beers H
Picturesque family local with an impressive garden, real fire, quiz and music nights. Evening meals served Wed-Sat.

ASH

Dover Arms
Dover Corner, Guildford Road
11-3.30, 6-11; 11-4, 7-11 Sat; 12-4, 7-10.30 Sun
(01252) 326025
Beer range varies H
Distinctive roadhouse with two contrasting bars to suit all tastes. On '20 Group' of bus routes from Aldershot to Guildford.

BROCKHAM

Royal Oak
Brockham Green
11-3, 5.30-11; 11-11 Fri & Sat; 12-10.30 Sun
(01737) 843241
Fuller's London Pride; Harveys BB; Wadworth 6X; guest beer (occasional) H
Two-roomed pub in a lovely position opposite the village green. Good food is available (not Sun eve).

CHOBHAM

Castle Grove
Scotts Grove Road
11-2.30 (3 Fri), 5.30-11; 11-3.30, 6-11 Sat; 12-3, 7-10.30 Sun
(01276) 858196
Greene King IPA; Young's Bitter; guest beer H
Originally planned as a railway station for a line that was never built; a large, lively public bar contrasts with a smaller saloon.

CLAYGATE

Swan
2 Hare Lane
11-11; 12-10.30 Sun
(01372) 462582
Fuller's London Pride; guest beers H
Main bar with stripped tables and pews leads to a restaurant area. Pub menu at lunchtime, Thai food eves (not Sun).

DORKING

Queen's Head
Horsham Road
11-11; 12-10.30 Sun
(01306) 883041
Fuller's Chiswick, London Pride, ESB H
Lively, family-run pub with an attractive exterior, featuring pool, darts, sport on TV and a garden for children.

EGHAM

Compasses
158 Thorpe Lea Road
11-11; 12-10.30 Sun
(01784) 454354
Badger Best, Tanglefoot; guest beers H
Refurbished 1930s pub with a comfortable lounge, in a residential area. No meals but snacks available. Garden where children are welcome.

ESHER

Bear
71 High Street
11-11; 12-10.30 Sun
(01372) 469786
Young's Bitter, Triple A, Special, seasonal beers H
Handsome, 18th-century coaching inn, where a long single bar links several drinking areas (one no-smoking). Food all sessions.

EWELL

Horton Park Country Club
Hook Road, West Ewell
(020) 8393 8400
Young's Bitter, Special H
Modern lounge bar in a golf complex, open to all. A patio gives view of greens. Sandwiches available, plus adjoining restaurant

⏲ 12-11; 12-10.30 Sun
☎ (020) 8393 9973
Greene King IPA, Abbot; guest beers Ⓗ
Cheery, welcoming pub with a strong local following. A semi-circular bar encompasses supping areas to the left and right. There is a sizeable food area at the rear. The landlord – a Burton Guild of Master Cellarman – has worked hard to supplement the Greene King range with guest beers. The pub is a considerable charity fund-raiser (charity night is Fri). Live music, folk-oriented, is performed Sat eve (and occasionally Thu); quiz night is Sun (when no meals are served). Live TV sport is shown. The garden includes a children's area.
❀◑◗⇌(West) P

FARNCOMBE

Cricketers
37 Nightingale Road
⏲ 12-3, 5.30-11; 12-11 Sat; 12-10.30 Sun
☎ (01483) 420273
Fuller's Chiswick, London Pride, ESB, seasonal beers Ⓗ
A rare example of a back-street local dominated by ale sales – the landlord boasts that more London Pride is sold here than anywhere else. Proud to be 14 consecutive years in this Guide, he has a special display of all previous stickers. A series of separate drinking areas includes a no-smoking dining section (no food Sun eve). A quality establishment in all respects, it rightly wins awards from Fuller's (Country/Local Pub of the Year 2000 and 2001). Q❀◑◗⇌♣✔

FARNHAM

Lamb
43 Abbey Street (off A287)
⏲ 11-2.30, 5-11; 11-11 Fri & Sat; 12-10.30 Sun
☎ (01252) 714133
Shepherd Neame Best Bitter, Spitfire, seasonal beers Ⓗ
A very friendly atmosphere is engendered by a good mix of customers of all ages and from all walks of life in this back-street local between the station and town centre. Past the pool table, the back door leads to a highly-regarded roof terrace garden, glorious in the summer. Real ales are poured directly into your glass from casks immediately behind the bar in the ground-level cellar. Added attractions include live music (Fri eve), popular Sunday roasts, a pool team and two quiz teams. No food Sun eve or Tue. ♨❀◑◗⇌

Queen's Head
9 The Borough (A287/A325 one-way system)
⏲ 11-11; 12-10.30 Sun
☎ (01252) 726524
Gale's Butser, GB, HSB, seasonal beers; guest beers Ⓗ
A Gale's pub since 1888 and a Guide regular, this town-centre pub is a must for visitors to one of the finest Georgian towns in the country. The pub itself may in fact pre-date the rest of the buildings in the street by 150 years. Things to look out for include the tiny suntrap of a garden to the rear of the pub and a suitably-placed old Watney's plaque. A real ale treasure. Lunches served Mon-Sat.
♨Q❀◑⊟⇌✔

Shepherd & Flock
22 Moor Park Lane (A31/A325)
⏲ 11-3, 5.30-11; 11-11 Fri & Sat; 12-10.30 Sun
☎ (01252) 716675
Courage Best Bitter; Hogs Back TEA; Ringwood Old Thumper; guest beers Ⓗ
This genuine free house stands on Europe's largest inhabited roundabout. The front door opens to reveal eight handpumps, five of them constantly changing; check out the 'coming soon' board. The car park entrance leads to a room used mainly for dining, though plain drinking is always welcome if tables are not booked for the Sunday carvery and high quality menu through the week. There is a cash machine on the way to the back door, leading to the large, gated back garden. More seating is outside at the front. ♨❀◑◗P

GODALMING

Red Lion
1 Mill Lane (High St jct)
⏲ 11-11; 12-10.30 Sun
☎ (01483) 415207
Harveys BB; guest beers Ⓗ
Free house, offering five ever-changing guest beers and an escape from more recent licensed developments in the town centre. With the buildings dating from 1696, high ceilings and even a balcony, grace the public bar, which was once the Oddfellows Hall and later a grammar school, attended by Jack Phillips (the Titanic's radio operator). An enterprising landlord holds regular beer festivals and special events, including egg rolling on Easter Sunday. Local CAMRA Pub of the Year 2002. Eve meals served Tue-Sat. Q❀◑◗⊟♿⇌♣

GREAT BOOKHAM

Anchor
161 Lower Road (off A246, via Eastwick Rd)
⏲ 11-3 (3.30 Sat), 5.30-11; 12-3, 7-10.30 Sun
☎ (01372) 452429
Courage Best Bitter, Directors; guest beers Ⓗ
A wonderful welcome awaits you at this 500-year-old, Grade II listed hostelry. The single bar has lovely wood flooring, posts and beams – but mind your head. A large inglenook and exposed brick walls add to its unspoilt character. Very popular for the good lunchtime food (served Mon-Sat). Outside an award-winning garden has plenty of wooden seating, some stocks and a pond. The pub has been in this Guide for 10 years. ♨❀◑♿♣P

GUILDFORD ✻

Robin Hood
Sydenham Road
⏲ 11-3, 5-11; 11-11 Fri & Sat; 12-4.30 Sun
☎ (01483) 888307
Draught Bass; Young's Bitter Ⓗ
Just up the road from Guildford Castle, this family-run pub extends a friendly welcome to all. One of only a few locals left around the town centre. A single bar turns round towards a quieter raised area past the coffin-shaped phone booth. The filling home-cooked lunches offer a rewarding escape from the town shops close by. Live music most Friday evenings, means it is frequently

packed out – try the side door if you can't get in through the front. Parking is limited. ◑P

Varsity Bar

Egerton Road (off A3 at university exit, past Tesco, near hospital)

✪ 12-11 (8.30 Sat); 12-10.30 Sun

☎ (01483) 306224

website: www.unisport.co.uk/varsity-bar.htm

Beer range varies Ⓗ

University sports bar outside the town centre, open to all. An enterprising choice of three beers is always available with at least one strong ale. Future offerings are displayed on boards. It hosts two beer festivals – in the spring for bottled beers and in the autumn for cask. It can be boisterous on match days (Wed and Sat), but there are quieter moments. The entrance is via the shop. Buses from the town centre to the hospital stop nearby. ◑P

HERSHAM

Royal George

Hersham Road (off A244)

✪ 11-11; 12-10.30 Sun

☎ (01932) 220910

Young's Bitter, Special, seasonal beer Ⓗ

1960s local, with two spacious bars, named after a ship from the Napoleonic Wars. The comfortable surroundings make it popular with all, and the provision of newspapers in the lounge is a nice touch. A wide range of home-cooked lunches is available, from sandwiches to full meals; Sunday roasts are very popular and there are summer barbecues. Quizzes are held Sun and Tue eve, with free food. ♨❀◑⊟♿♣P

HOLMBURY ST MARY

King's Head

Pitland Street (50 yds off B2126)

✪ 11-3, 6-11; 11-11 Sat; 12-10.30 Sun

☎ (01306) 730282

Beer range varies Ⓗ

Just off, but hidden from, the main road and away from the village centre, this free house offers a warm welcome to motorists, cyclists and walkers. Featuring bare boards and basic furniture, a six-pump beer engine and two open log fires complete the picture of a lively rural local. The ever-changing beer range often draws on local micro-breweries. Good food is served all sessions, except Sun eve. A great place for ramblers to take a midday break. ♨❀◑◗♣P

HORSELL

Plough

Cheapside (off South Rd) OS996599

✪ 11-3, 5-11; 11-11 Sat; 12-10.30 Sun

☎ (01483) 714105

Fuller's London Pride; Greene King Abbot; Marston's Pedigree; Young's Bitter; guest beers Ⓗ

Delightful retreat on the edge of the village, bordering on Horsell Common. Set back from the road, it is easily missed; the entrance is through a small porch. Small, compact and friendly, it can be very busy with diners enjoying the excellent food (not served Sun eve) and on quiz nights (Wed). An imaginative guest beer policy is likely to include Beckett's and Itchen Valley, or beers from further afield, such as Sharp's from Cornwall. Well worth leaving Woking town centre to find. ❀◑◗P

LEATHERHEAD

Running Horse

Bridge Street (off B2122)

✪ 11-11; 12-10.30 Sun

☎ (01372) 372081

Badger K&B Sussex; Greene King Old Speckled Hen; Marston's Pedigree; Tetley Burton Ale; Young's Bitter; guest beer Ⓗ

This charming Grade II* listed pub serves an excellent range of ales including the increasingly rare Burton Ale. Although its own car park is very small, there is an adjacent public car park. The pub has a large main bar with various seating areas and a smaller public bar. There is a courtyard garden for summer drinking. A pub not to be missed. No food Sun eve. Q❀◑◗⊟⇌♣P

MICKLEHAM

King William IV

Byttom Hill (off A24, southbound)

✪ 11-3, 6-11; 12-3, 7-10.30 Sun

☎ (01372) 372590 website: www.king-williamiv.com

Adnams Bitter; Badger Best; Hogs Back TEA; guest beer Ⓗ

A notable feature of this 18th-century pub is its terraced garden, affording wide views across Mole Valley. An ideal refreshment stop after a walk on Mickleham Downs, it is a quiet pub with an open fire in the main bar, and a small adjacent bar. An extensive range of quality food is the pub's speciality. Parking can be a problem but the pub shares spaces with Frascati's Restaurant at the bottom of the hill, from where it is a short but steep walk.

♨Q❀◑◗

Running Horses

Old London Road

✪ 11.30-3, 5-11; 11.30-11 Sat; 12-3.30, 6-10.30 Sun

☎ (01372) 372279

Adnams Bitter; Fuller's London Pride; Greene King Abbot; Young's Bitter Ⓗ

Former coaching inn, dating back to the 16th century, in the heart of good walking country, it lies close to Box Hill (NT) and Mickleham Downs. This comfortable pub is warmed by a large fire in the bar. The restaurant serves a wide range of food, including Sunday lunches. The pub's name derives from the 1828 Derby run-off after a tie. Nearby is Surrey's popular Denbies Vineyard and visitor centre.

♨Q☕❀⇋◑◗

NEWCHAPEL

Blacksmith's Head

Newchapel Road (B2028, just E of A22)

✪ 11-3, 5.30-11; 12-3, 6-11 Sat; 12-3 (closed eve) Sun

☎ (01342) 833697

Brakspear Bitter; Fuller's London Pride; guest beers Ⓗ

Situated near the Mormon Temple, the pub's L-shaped bar has a restaurant area off to the side. The plant-lover's garden, with a pond, is a testament to the owners' previous occupation as landscape gardeners. One of the guest beers changes regularly and is usually from a small independent brewery, the other is likely to be from Harveys. ₼❀⛟◑◗⛺♣P✔

NEWDIGATE

Surrey Oaks

Parkgate Road, Parkgate (between Newdigate and Leigh) OS205436
✪ 11.30-2.30, 5.30-11; 11.30-3, 6-11 Sat; 12-3, 7-10.30 Sun
☎ (01306) 631200 website www.surreyoaks.co.uk
Adnams Bitter; guest beers Ⓗ

The 'Soaks' is well known for the quality of its beer (three guests are always available). Dark beers are popular in winter, wheat beers in summer. The very attractive tile-hung pub dates from the 16th century and boasts stone-flagged floors and an inglenook, along with three distinct drinking areas. The no-smoking restaurant serves good quality home-cooked food, with daily specials (eve meals Tue-Sat). CAMRA regional Pub of the Year 2001, it hosts a beer festival over the August bank holiday weekend. ₼Q❀◑◗♣🍎P

OAKWOODHILL

Punchbowl

Oakwoodhill Lane (off A29)
✪ 11-11; 12-10.30 Sun
☎ (01306) 627249
Badger Best, Tanglefoot; Gribble Fursty Ferret Ⓗ

Delightful pub, opposite the village cricket green. Originally two cottages dating from the 15th century, it became a tavern in the 1800s and remains popular with walkers, anglers and the local hunt. Its proximity to Stane Street, the London-Chichester Roman road, adds to the air of antiquity. The building is tile-hung and incorporates a large inglenook and huge local flagstones. Even the pigsty (in the car park) is a listed building. Excellent home-cooked food is supplemented by a magnificent barbecue area outside in summer.
₼Q⛟❀◑◗⊟♣P⚟✔

OUTWOOD

Castle

Millers Lane
✪ 12-3, 5.30-11; 11-11 Sat; 12-10 Sun
☎ (01342) 842754
Adnams Bitter; Brakspear Bitter; Fuller's London Pride; Greene King Old Speckled Hen; guest beer (occasional) Ⓗ

Warm, comfortable single-roomed free house where three distinct drinking areas include one for non-smokers. Recently refurbished, it features wood panelling, an open fire and old photos of the village. A varied menu, with food cooked to order, is available every day. No TV or music (except for a very occasional live band) makes it a good place for a quiet drink or meal. Children welcome afternoons and early evening. Ramblers also welcome. It is very quiet Sunday evenings. ₼Q❀◑◗P⚟

PIRBRIGHT

Royal Oak

Aldershot Road (A324)
✪ 11-11; 12-10.30 Sun
☎ (01483) 232466
Boddingtons Bitter; Flowers IPA, Original; Hogs Back TEA; guest beers Ⓗ

In a rural location and yet so close to urban areas, the picturesque Royal Oak is set back from the road, with a large garden to satisfy even the most energetic of children. Go past the floral displays and through the porch to at least four drinking areas (but no children inside). Its support of local independent breweries is reflected in the ever-changing range of beers. This local CAMRA Pub of the Year 2001 is just off bus route 28 (Woking-Guildford). ₼❀◑◗♿P⚟✔

PUTTENHAM

Good Intent

62 The Street (off B3000)
✪ 11-2.30, 6-11; 11-11 Sat; 12-10.30 Sun
☎ (01483) 810387
Courage Best Bitter; Theakston Old Peculier; Young's Bitter; guest beers Ⓗ

Wonderful, relaxing retreat in a quiet, attractive village, yet close to the busy A31. A series of different drinking areas includes one dominated by a magnificent fireplace. Diners are well catered for – try fish and chips in newspaper on Wed eve, and children are welcome in the designated dining area (eve meals Tue-Sat). Expect to see walkers and their dogs, given the proximity of the North Downs Way.
₼Q❀◑◗⛺♣P

REDHILL

Garland

5 Brighton Road (A23, S of centre)
✪ 11-11; 12-3, 7-10.30 Sun
☎ (01737) 760377
Harveys XX Mild, Pale Ale, BB, Armada, seasonal beer Ⓗ

This excellent town pub was built in 1865 as the Anchor. It is Harveys' only Surrey pub and sells their entire range of beer (including bottles, for which there is a menu). It is not immediately apparent, but the bar is decorated with over 2,000 clowns. Darts is played enthusiastically, but does not intrude. This comfortable pub is a contrast to Redhill's themed bars, and is one of a dying breed in Surrey – a really good town-centre local. Good value food is available weekdays. ❀◑⇌♣P✔

Home Cottage

Redstone Hill (behind the station)
✪ 10.30-11; 12-10.30 Sun
☎ (01737) 762771
Young's Bitter, Special, Winter Warmer Ⓗ

This large, busy community pub offers three distinct drinking areas in one room. The front section tends to be fairly sedate and houses the real fire. Round the side and to the back of the bar is the somewhat noisier public bar area; big-screen football matches are shown at the back. The final drinking area is a large conservatory, where children are admitted at lunchtime. Note the fine bank of handpumps in the front bar. Sunday meals are served 12-6. ₼◑⇌P

SEND

New Inn

Send Road (A247)
✪ 11-2.30, 5.30-11; 12-3.30, 7-10.30 Sun

☎ (01483) 724940
Adnams Bitter; Fuller's London Pride; Marston's Pedigree; guest beers Ⓗ
The original inn stood on the other side of the road, but moved into an old mortuary on its present site, adjoining the Wey Navigation (built in the 1660s to move grain from Farnham to the Thames and London). Modern-day boaters make the pub immensely popular in summer, with its three drinking areas (watch the step into the far bar). Pleasant walks can be enjoyed in the summer, across the fields to Old Woking. Good food served. Q❀◐◑P

SIDLOW BRIDGE

Three Horseshoes
Ironsbottom (off A217, by the Peugeot garage) OS252461
⏲ 12-2.30, 5.30-11; 12-3, 7-10.30 Sun
☎ (01293) 862315 website: www.sidlow.com
Fuller's London Pride, ESB; Harveys BB; Young's Bitter; guest beer Ⓗ
Good country local that has recently been extended without any loss of character, and is now able to offer accommodation and a meeting room. The clientele tends to be mature, but all are welcome. The beer is lovingly cared for and the London Pride is regarded as a local legend. Very good, affordable home-made food is available at lunchtime. The pub is a convenient stop en-route for Gatwick Airport. ♨Q❀⛟◐P⊘

STAINES

Beehive
35 Edgell Road (S of centre, off B376)
⏲ 11-11; 12-10.30 Sun
☎ (01784) 452663
Courage Best Bitter; Fuller's London Pride Ⓗ
Three-roomed pub, tucked away from the hustle and bustle of central Staines. The public bar has a bank of four handpumps. A real fire warms the lounge, where an extensive collection of stone bottles is displayed, and wood panelling features. Look out for the ceramic beehives at the back of the lounge bar. Nostalgic (!) gents' loos are outside. ♨❀⛟◐⊟≉♣

Bells
124 Church Street (off B376)
⏲ 11-11; 12-10.30 Sun
☎ (01784) 454240
Young's Bitter, Triple A, Special, seasonal beers Ⓗ
Friendly, comfortable pub at the quieter end of town with excellent wheelchair access and helpful staff. The seasonal ales from Young's and Smiles change throughout the year and a good selection of Young's bottled beers is always available. Serving the local community and businesses, within easy reach of the town centre and river, the Bells was voted local CAMRA Pub of the Year 2001. No food Sun eve. Q❀◐◑♿

George
2-8 High Street (A308)
⏲ 11-11; 12-10.30 Sun
☎ (01784) 462181
Courage Best Bitter; Shepherd Neame Spitfire; Greene King Abbot; guest beers Ⓗ
Town-centre Wetherspoon's on two floors: downstairs is most popular; upstairs is used as overspill, and it is quieter. Local history is depicted on various plaques around the rooms. Beer festivals are held throughout the year, when up to 30 ales are served over a week; normally up to six ales are on tap. Wheelchair access and WC. Parking nearby. Q◐◑♿≉⚟⊘

STANWELL

Rising Sun
110 Oaks Road
⏲ 11.30-11; 12-10.30 Sun
☎ (01784) 244080
Draught Bass; Greene King Abbot; Tetley Burton Ale Ⓗ
Comfortable, one-bar pub, adjacent to Heathrow Airport cargo area. Although off the beaten track, it is well worth seeking out. Aircraft models and football scarves adorn the bar; note too the models made by a local engineer. Two TVs are often tuned to sporting events, however they are not intrusive and there are areas for a quiet drink. One of the best bets for a good pint locally. ❀◐◑P

SUNBURY

Flower Pot
Thames Street, Lower Sunbury
⏲ 11-11; 12-10.30 Sun
☎ (01932) 780741
Adnams Bitter; Brakspear Bitter; Fuller's London Pride; Greene King Abbot; Hogs Back TEA Ⓗ
Large village hotel close to the river Thames in the old Sunbury area described by Dickens in Oliver Twist. A selection of beers is always available in a 'clean air' atmosphere; there is usually background music or TV playing in the bar. Recently redecorated without being modernised, meals are served in the restaurant that leads off the bar. Tiny car park. ♨⛟◐◑P⊘

WALTON-ON-THE-HILL

Chequers
Chequers Lane (B2220)
⏲ 11-11; 12-10.30 Sun
☎ (01737) 812364
Young's Bitter, Special, seasonal beers Ⓗ
This large 19th-century pub has been owned by Young's for nearly 50 years. A number of rooms surround a single bar. The back bar is the largest, with several others towards the front, leading to a high class restaurant, although food is also sold in the bar. Fresh fish is a speciality. Meals are served all day Sat and until 8pm Sun. The village is in horse training country. ❀◐◑P

WINDLESHAM

Bee
School Road (40 yds from A30)
⏲ 11-11; 12-10.30 Sun
☎ (01276) 479244
Brakspear Bitter; Courage Best Bitter; Hop Back Summer Lightning; Young's Special; guest beer Ⓗ
An inn since around 1865, this unpretentious rural pub serves five cask ales, and food ranging from ploughmans to curry (no food Mon). Monthly live jazz is staged (third Thu) and in summer there is live jazz in the garden (alternate Sundays). The garden includes a children's play area, and on fine summer afternoons the barbecue is brought into use. The Bee has

an active golf society and two clay pigeon-shooting teams. ❀◑◗♣P

WITLEY

White Hart

Petworth Road (A283)

11.30-3.30, 5-11 (11.30-11 summer); 12-4, 7-10.30 Sun

(01483) 683695

Shepherd Neame Master Brew Bitter, Best Bitter, Spitfire, seasonal beers Ⓗ

Deceptively large roadside pub with two contrasting bars. The public is small, cosy and friendly. The saloon is much larger and more airy with a big fireplace and restaurant extension. The large 'sunken' garden offers scope to calm even the most energetic of children. The original pub sign is in the Victoria & Albert Museum. A strong local following includes a rugby and golf society. Evening meals served Tue-Sat.

WOKING

Wetherspoon's

51-59 Chertsey Road

11-11; 12-10.30 Sun

(01483) 722818

Courage Directors; Hogs Back TEA; Shepherd Neame Spitfire; Theakston Best Bitter; guest beers Ⓗ

An established part of town-centre life and as far as real ale drinkers are concerned the highlight. Often three or four ever-changing guest beers, are tapped and get replaced in the course of an evening. Dominated by an HG Wells theme, it boasts an invisible metal man and a push button-operated ceiling clock that goes in reverse as a time machine. Deservedly popular, it gets crowded

WOOD STREET

Royal Oak

89 Oak Hill OS958510

11-3 (3.30 Sat), 5-11; 12-2.30, 7-10.30 Sun

(01483) 235137

Courage Best Bitter; Hogs Back TEA; guest beers Ⓗ

Outstanding free house having notched up over 1,500. Four interesting guests are of the 'impossible-to-guess' kind with one always being a mild. One of the best pubs in the county, it is a must for any discerning drinker in the Guildford area. The excellent menu is health-conscious – expect a choice of vegetables and potatoes, but definitely not chips (no food Sun). Served by bus from Guildford, but beware evening return times. A real cider is sometimes stocked.

WRECCLESHAM

Bat & Ball

15 Bat & Ball Lane, Boundstone (off Upper Bourne Lane) OS834444

12-3, 5.30-11; 12-11 Fri & Sat; 12-10.30 Sun

(01252) 794564

Archers Village; Brakspear Bitter; Fuller's London Pride; guest beers Ⓗ

Excellent free house, sporting seven handpumps, relatively isolated, despite being close to housing, pedestrian access is via the Bourne stream or by steps at the rear of the pub which are challenging in the dark. You have to be 'in the know' to gain road access and be prepared for a bumpy ride. Even so, it is popular with both drinkers and diners. Children are catered for in the conservatory/extension and a superb garden.

Sandrock

Sandrock Hill, Upper Bourne (off B3384, towards Rowledge) OS830444

11-11; 12-10.30 Sun

(01252) 715865 website: www.sandrockpub.co.uk

Batham Best Bitter; Enville Ale; Cheriton Pots Ale; guest beers Ⓗ

Fantastic real ale mecca, offering a flavour of the Black Country. It holds (in early March) one of the longest continuous pub beer festivals in the country. Bus services run close to the pub, or take a taxi from Farnham Station. 25 years ago local CAMRA wrote of this place, 'worth a visit if only for the pleasure of leaving again'. Things have certainly changed – proof that an excellent landlord, good beer and dedicated drinkers can make a change for the better. No food Sun.

INN BRIEF

GUILDFORD

Plough
16 Park Street
11-11; 12-10.30 Sun
(01483) 570167
Draught Bass; Fuller's London Pride; Young's Special Ⓗ
Friendly, one-bar traditional pub in an area dominated by trendy bars, close to the station. Lunches served (not Sun).

KNAPHILL

Knap
134 High Street
12-2.30, 5-11; 12-11 Fri & Sat; 12-10.30 Sun
(01483) 473374
Young's Bitter; guest beers Ⓗ
Relatively new addition to the real ale scene, and now approaching 100 beers. Summer beer festival with blues staged in the garden.

PEASLAKE

Hurtwood Inn Hotel
Walking Bottom
11-3, 5.30-11; 11-11 Sat; 11-11 Sun
(01306) 730851
Hogs Back Hair of the Hog, TEA, seasonal beer Ⓗ
Comfortable hotel bar that serves as a village local, in a good area for walking. Food served every lunchtime and evening.

STAFFHURST WOOD

Royal Oak
Caterfield Lane
11-3.30, 5.30-11; 12-3.30, 7-10.30 Sun
(01883) 722207
Adnams Bitter; Draught Bass; Larkins Best; Swale Whitstable Oyster Stout; guest beer (summer) Ⓗ
Rural pub, which enjoys a very good reputation for food (especially fish), in good walking country. No food Sun, or Mon eve.

WEYBOURNE

Running Stream
66 Weybourne Road
11-3, 5-11; 11-11 Fri & Sat; 12-3, 7-10.30 Sun
(01252) 323750
Greene King IPA, Ruddles Best Bitter, Morland Original, Abbot; guest beer Ⓗ
Named after the stream that used to control the cellar temperature; the single bar displays novelty clocks. Cask Marque accredited.

WITLEY

Star
Petworth Road
12-2.30, 4.30-11; 12-11 Fri & Sat; 12-3, 7-10.30 Sun
(01428) 684656
Adnams Broadside; Courage Best Bitter; Triple fff Alton's Pride Ⓗ
Grade II listed building which has been a pub since the 19th century; two bars. Food served (not Sun eve or Mon lunch). Enclosed garden.

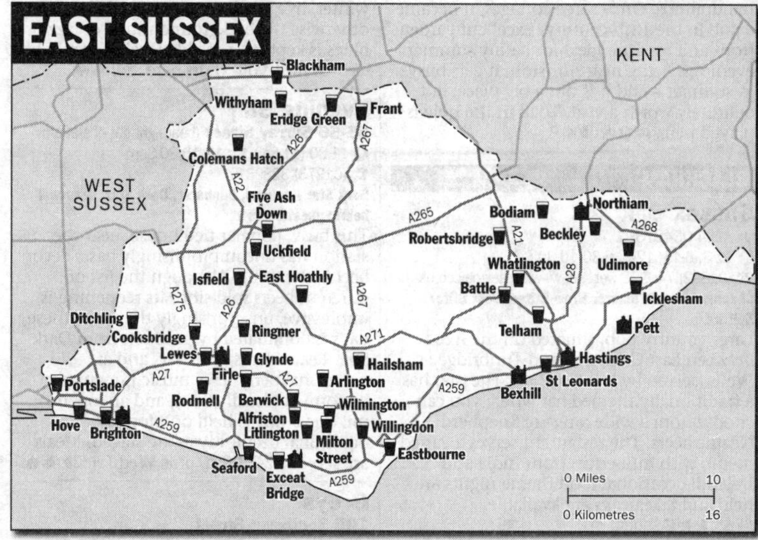

ALFRISTON

Smugglers Inn

Waterloo Square

11-3, 6.30-11; 12-3, 7-10.30 Sun

(01323) 870241

Harveys BB, seasonal beers; Sussex Pett Progress H

The Smugglers is a very old building at the village centre, by the market cross. The hop-strewn main bar boasts a large fireplace and the walls display kitchen utensils and butterflies in cases; the seating is rather low. Several small rooms lead off the main bar. The pub gets very busy with diners in good weather – it is a popular stop for walkers on the South Downs Way. Q

ARLINGTON

Old Oak Inn

From A22 follow signs for speedway, fork left after 1½ miles OS558078

11-2.30, 6-11; 12-2.30, 7-10.30 Sun

(01323) 482072

Badger Best; Harveys BB; guest beers G

Large old pub just outside the village near the speedway stadium, but quiet nonetheless. It comprises a large comfy bar area and an adjacent barn-style restaurant. All beers are served by gravity straight from barrels set at the rear of the bar area – see the list on the wall for what is available. The pub is an ideal start/finish point for walking – ask if you want to leave your car, as there are public car parks nearby.

Q P

BATTLE

Chequers Inn

Lower Lake (A2100/Marley Lane jct)

11-11; 12-10.30 Sun

(01424) 772088

Fuller's London Pride; Harveys BB; guest beers H

This busy 15th-century inn is once more a haven for real ale drinkers and lovers of fine food. The pub, situated to the south of the High Street, has a long rectangular bar, exposed beams, two open fires and a no-smoking dining room. The garden overlooks the site of the Battle of Hastings. A large inglenook and an original outside wall, now internal, are features of the dining room. Very much part of the community, it fields a darts and football team. P

BECKLEY

Rose & Crown

Northiam Road (B2188/B2165 jct)

11-3, 5.30-11; 11-11 Fri & Sat; 12-11 Sun

(01791) 252161

Fuller's ESB; Harveys BB; Hook Norton Best Bitter; guest beers H

First-class free house serving a great range of beers at their very best, many of which come from distant breweries. This spacious family pub offers separate areas for drinkers and diners. The long bar has a wood floor and decorative hops. Locals and visitors are made most welcome in this country pub which offers an excellent menu and fine views from the garden. Q P

BERWICK

Cricketers Arms

S of A27 just W of Drusilla's roundabout

11-3, 6-11; (11-11 summer); 12-10 (10.30 summer) Sun

(01323) 870469

website: www.cricketersberwick.co.uk

Harveys BB, seasonal beers G

Notwithstanding sympathetic updating, this pub remains a gem, with a quarry tiled floor in the main bar and dining area. All beers are served straight from barrels kept in a room behind the bar – so don't look for

INDEPENDENT BREWERIES

Cuckmere Haven Exceat Bridge
First Inn Last Out Hastings
Harveys Lewes
Kemptown Brighton
Rother Valley Northiam
Sussex Pett
White Bexhill

handpumps. Once three cottages, it became a pub in the 18th century. Excellent gardens front and rear, are ideal for balmy summer evenings. Being near Alfriston, it gets busy in summer – and it is not a big place, but definitely worth a visit. Toad in the hole is played here. ⛰Q❀◐◑♣P

BLACKHAM

Sussex Oak

On A264 OS487392
⏲ 11-3, 6-11; 12-3, 6.30-10.30 Sun
☎ (01892) 740273 website: www.sussex-oak.co.uk
Shepherd Neame Master Brew Bitter, Best Bitter, Spitfire Ⓗ

Large country pub, situated on the A264 between East Grinstead and Tunbridge Wells (served by bus No. 238). The pub has a traditionally themed bar where you can choose from a wide range of Shepherd Neame beers. The restaurant serves a varied menu, with influences from India and Ireland; occasional food theme nights are held and takeaways are available.
⛰❀◐◑≢(Ashurst) ♣P

BODIAM

Castle

Opp. entrance to castle
⏲ 11-3, 6-11 (11-11 summer Sat); 12-10.30 Sun
☎ (01580) 830330
Shepherd Neame Master Brew Bitter, Spitifre, seasonal beer Ⓗ

Rural Shepherd Neame pub in the scenic Rother Valley on the Kent border. Bodiam Castle, the impressive National Trust property, stands opposite, and it is well worth making a visit to both Castles. An extensive menu featuring local produce, is displayed in the main bar above the imposing fireplace. This pleasant, quiet pub is ideal for a peaceful pint.
⛰Q❀◐◑≢(Kent & E Sussex Rlwy) P

BRIGHTON ✲

Basketmakers Arms

12 Gloucester Road (N of Prince Regent pool)
⏲ 11-11; 12-10.30 Sun
☎ (01273) 689006
Gale's Butser, GB, HSB, Festival Mild; guest beers Ⓗ

Traditional street-corner pub, attracting a diverse clientele. This single bar Gale's tied house can be very busy evenings and at weekends. The walls are decorated with antique adverts and storage tins. Situated in the North Lane area of unusual shops, and close to the theatres, it stocks a good range of malt whiskies. Featured in CAMRA's Good Pub Food, meals are served daily at lunchtime, and weekday evenings. ◐◑≢✔

Battle of Trafalgar

34 Guildford Road
⏲ 11-11; 12-10.30 Sun
☎ (01273) 327997
Fuller's London Pride; Harveys BB; Young's Bitter, Special Ⓗ

Popular pub, a short walk up a steep hill from the station. The small frontage is deceptive as the interior is spacious, with a separate dining area. As the name suggests, the decor features pictures of old sea battles and other nautical memorabilia; note the collection of bottles above the bar. In winter, live jazz is usually staged (Sun eve), otherwise the background music of jazz or blues is kept at a sensible level. It would be easy to miss your train here. ❀◐≢♣

Evening Star

55-56 Surrey Street (bear right out of station)
⏲ 11.30 (11 Sat)-11; 12-10.30 Sun
☎ (01273) 328931
Dark Star Hophead, Sunburst, Dark Star, seasonal beers; guest beers Ⓗ

This busy, popular tied house, near the station has uncompromisingly basic decor; beer is the thing. Although the list of different beers sold since its reopening is impressive, unsurprisingly the range these days is dominated by products from Dark Star. Real cider is available, and an occasional perry. Live music is regularly performed (usually Sun), and an 'open-mike' evening is held on Monday; occasional beer festivals are staged. Meals are served 12-7 Mon, plus Wed-Fri. ◐◑≢●

Greys

105 Southover Street
⏲ 11-3 (not Mon), 5.30-11; 11-11 Sat; 12-3.30, 7-10.30 Sun
☎ (01273) 680734 website: www.greyspub.com
Taylor Landlord; guest beer Ⓗ

As well as real ale, a variety of other attractions are to be found here. An extensive range of Belgian bottled beer is always available and can make a very good accompaniment to the innovative, high quality food that is presented by the award-winning chef (eve meals Tue-Thu, plus Sat). The pub hosts live music on Sunday and Monday evenings and a number of well-known entertainers have played at this somewhat unusual venue. ◐◑

Hand in Hand

33 Upper St James's Street (off A259)
⏲ 12-11; 12-10.30 Sun
☎ (01273) 699595
Kemptown Brighton Bitter, Kemptown, Ye Olde Trout Ale, SID; guest beers Ⓗ

Reputed to be the smallest pub in Britain with its own brewery and, possibly, the lowest prices in Brighton. Resembling a large front room with a bar and wallpapered with old newspapers, the collection of ties, fairy lights and earthenware pots decorating the ceiling provide a comfortable atmosphere. Kemptown ales, brewed on the premises, are supplemented by a range of imported German beers. ●

Lord Nelson

36 Trafalgar Street (off A23)
⏲ 11-11; 12-10.30 Sun
☎ (01273) 695872
Harveys XX Mild, Pale Ale, BB, Armada, seasonal beers Ⓗ

Offering the full Harveys' range, this gem near the station attracts both commuters and regulars. Its two bars are separated by an unusual screen that acts as an information board for the many in-house sporting organisations. The patio acts as an outside gallery for exhibitions by local artists. The excellent menu (Mon-Sat), including daily specials, is popular with local workers. It may be busy on Brighton & Hove Albion home match days.
⛰❀◐≢✔

Prestonville

64 Hamilton Road

5 (4 Fri; 12 Sat)-11; 12-10.30 Sun

☎ (01273) 701007

Gale's Butser, GB, HSB, seasonal beers; guest beer (occasional) [H]

Hard to find, but well worth the effort, a friendly street-corner pub, where the single bar is decorated with breweriana and old photos of Brighton. Free from electronic games or pool, instead it hosts regular quizzes and live music. It keeps a good choice of single malt whiskies (look out for special offers) and a range of country wines. The menu (served evenings and weekend lunchtimes) includes good, home-made food such as burgers and chilli. ❀◐◑✔

Sir Charles Napier

50 Southover Street

5 (12 Fri & Sat)-11; 12-10.30 Sun

☎ (01273) 601413

Gale's Butser, GB, HSB, seasonal beers; guest beer [H]

Ultra-traditional corner local on one of the city's steepest hills. The single bar splits naturally into three areas, all adorned with photos of old Brighton pubs, maps and memorabilia of Sir Charles Napier. The low level piped music is often overwhelmed by the buzz of conversation, the full range of Gale's country wines is stocked and a good quality wine of the month is featured. Lunches are served Fri-Sun and an occasional themed meal is offered Fri eve. ❀◐♣

COLEMANS HATCH

Hatch Inn

400 yds S of A2110 OS452335

11.30-3, 5.30-11 (11-11 summer Sat); 12-10.30 Sun

☎ (01342) 822363 website: www.hatchinn.co.uk

Harveys BB; Larkins Traditional; guest beers [H]

This single-bar village pub features exposed beams that are particularly low in places. Popular with cyclists, it is also accessible by bus from East Grinstead, Tunbridge Wells and Crawley, but parking can be difficult. This is a genuine free house where local ales are supported. Daily newspapers are provided for customers. A very good menu (changed daily) is served most sessions (eve meals Tue-Sat); a no-smoking dining area is available. ♨❀◐◑P⊔

COOKSBRIDGE

Pump House

Main Road

11-3, 6-11; 11-11 Sat; 12-10.30 Sun

☎ (01273) 400528

Harveys BB; guest beer [H]

U-shaped local next to the station, the pub ensures that micro-breweries' products are regularly on offer, as evidenced by the large number of their pump clips. Noted for friendly conversation at the bar, there are comfortable, quiet areas to sit in as well. A pool table is set away from the main area. Live music is often staged on Friday evening. The food here is excellent. ❀◐◑⇌P

DITCHLING

White Horse

16 West Street (B2116, just W of crossroads)

11-11; 12-10.30 Sun

☎ (01273) 842006

Harveys BB; guest beers [H]

Large, popular free house, run by a CAMRA member, voted local CAMRA Pub of the Year in 1998, and runner-up each year since. The village church stands opposite, and Anne of Cleves' house is nearby. The pub is near the foot of Ditchling Beacon, the highest point on the South Downs. There is a games area with darts and bar billiards, and a restaurant, serving an extensive food menu with vegetarian options. The cellar is said to be haunted. ♨❀◐◑♣P✔

EASTBOURNE

Arlington Arms

Seaside

11-11; 12-4 Sun

☎ (01323) 724365

Harveys Pale Ale, BB, seasonal beers [H]

This two-bar pub has just been refurbished. The bars are mainly used by drinkers, and a room off the saloon bar is used for meals and meetings. Darts and pool are available in the extended public bar; it gets very busy with locals on games nights (toad in the hole is also played here). The pub has a large garden. ❀◐◑⊟♣P✔

Buccaneer

10 Compton Street (near theatres)

11-11; 12-10.30 Sun

☎ (01323) 732829

Marston's Pedigree; Tetley Bitter, Burton Ale; guest beers [H]

Busy pub at the heart of Eastbourne's theatreland, popular with theatre-goers and actors. This large one-bar pub has a partitioned seating area and a raised no-smoking section at the rear, overlooking the tennis courts of Devonshire Park. The walls are adorned with curios, ranging from taps and spiles to autographed theatre posters and old pictures of Eastbourne. Guest beers change quickly. ❀◐♿⇌

Lamb

High Street, Old Town (A259, 1 mile W of centre)

10.30-3, 5.30-11; 10.30-11 Fri & Sat; 12-4, 7-10.30 Sun

☎ (01323) 720545

Harveys Pale Ale, BB, seasonal beers [H]

Popular pub, in part dating back to 1290; a passage leading from the cellar to the nearby parish church of Eastbourne is now closed, but was reputedly used by worshippers after the service. The attractive beamed building comprises three rooms with two bars; make sure you look at the pictures on the wall. A good food selection means it is often busy with diners. It has a very small car park and a pavement area for outdoor drinking. Q◐◑⊟⇌P✔

EAST HOATHLY

King's Head

1-3 High Street (off A22)

11-4, 6-11; 12-4, 7-10.30 Sun

☎ (01825) 840238

Fuller's London Pride; Harveys BB Ⓗ
Spacious village-centre pub, with many interesting features, much used by locals. It has a restaurant that serves food of the highest quality every day, while the bar menu includes fresh fish cooked in beer batter to eat in or take away. Tables and chairs are set out on the forecourt for outdoor drinking. The village is a turning off the bypass, which makes it quiet. The pub runs competitions for charities throughout the year. The car park is small.
❀◑◐P

ERIDGE GREEN

Huntsman

Eridge Road (off A26, next to station)
✪ 12-2.30 (3 Sat), 6-11; 12-3, 6-11 Sun
Badger K&B Sussex, Tanglefoot; guest beers Ⓗ
Homely, two-bar pub in a hamlet near Tunbridge Wells. You can easily miss the turning, as this pub is just off the A26 at the bottom of the hill. Now run by Badger, a hearty menu of international cuisine is served alongside more traditional pub food. Next to the River Medway, and close to the Uckfield branch line, this popular pub draws a varied clientele. The car park is small.
Q❀⊟≷ (Eridge) P

EXCEAT BRIDGE

Golden Galleon

On A259, E of Seaford
✪ 11-11; 12-4 (10.30 summer) Sun
☎ (01323) 892247 website: www.goldengalleon.co.uk
Cuckmere Haven Downland Bitter; Best Bitter, Guvnor, Golden Peace; guest beers Ⓗ/Ⓖ
As you walk into the pub you will see the brewery on the right at the top of the steps. The single bar, with two rooms off it, started out as a tea bar. As it is just off the South Downs Way it is very popular with walkers (daytime), attracting locals and diners in the evenings. It is particularly busy if the weather is good. The garden affords views across the valley to the English Channel. Q❀◑◐♿▲●P

FIRLE

Ram Inn ☆

The Street (1/2 mile off A27)
✪ 11.30-11; 12-10.30 Sun
☎ (01273) 858222
Harveys BB; guest beers Ⓗ
Village local with three bars: a main bar, family room and a no-smoking bar. The village of Firle nestles below the South Downs in good walking country. An excellent selection of high quality food includes a children's menu. There is also a play area and, unusually, baby-changing facilities in both gents' and ladies' toilets. Local societies regularly use the bars to perform traditional Sussex music.
ᨖQ❀◑◐♣●P⁄◻

FIVE ASH DOWN

Fireman's Arms

400 yds off Uckfield bypass (old A26)
✪ 11-3; 11-11 Sat; 12-3, 6.30-11 Sun
☎ (01825) 732191
Badger IPA; Harveys BB; guest beers Ⓗ
Busy local, run by a steam railway enthusiast who has connections with the Bluebell Railway a few miles away. On New Year's Day there is a vintage steam engine rally. A range of games is available in the public bar, while the saloon area is mainly used for eating (no meals Tue eve). It can be difficult to find as the old A26 is now bypassed.
ᨖQ◑◐♣●◻

INN BRIEF

BRIGHTON

Bedford Tavern
30 Western Street
10.30-11; 12-10.30 Sun
(01273) 739495
Harveys BB; Marston's Pedigree; guest beers Ⓗ
Advertised as 'a country pub in the heart of town', it is situated between the seafront and Western Road.

Dover Castle
43 Southover Street
12-11; 12-10.30 Sun
(01273) 688276
Shepherd Neame Master Brew Bitter, Spitfire, seasonal beers Ⓗ
Pub in a conservation area, serving a wide choice of vegetarian food and ethnic cuisine. A DJ plays music until late most eves.

Pump House
46 Market Street
11-11; 12-10.30 Sun
(01273) 827421
Draught Bass; Fuller's London Pride; Harveys BB Ⓗ
Set in the heart of the historic Lanes, and built over medieval cellars, the wood-panelled interior is multi-roomed.

Regency Tavern
32-34 Russell Square
11-3, 6-11; 12-3, 7-10.30 Sun
(01273) 325652
Draught Bass; Fuller's London Pride; Greene King Abbot; Harveys BB; Tetley Bitter; guest beers Ⓗ
Large, open-plan pub in a narrow alleyway linking Regency and Russell Squares. Reputedly haunted by three ghosts.

FRANT

Abergavenny Arms
Frant Road
12-3, 6-11; 12-3, 7-10.30 Sun
(01892) 750233
Fuller's London Pride; Harveys BB; Rother Valley Level Best; Taylor Landlord; guest beer Ⓗ
Spacious roadhouse on the busy A267 with two large bar areas; home-cooked food.

LEWES

Brewer's Arms
91 High Street
10.30-11; 12-10.0 Sun
(01273) 479475
Harveys BB; guest beers Ⓗ
Comfortable lounge and boisterous games bar; note the Page & Overton ceramic plaques. Biddenden cider on hand pump.

Snowdrop
119 South Street
11-11; 12-10.30 Sun
(01273) 471018
Harveys BB; Hop Back Summer Lightning; Ringwood Old Thumper; guest beers Ⓗ
Eccentrically-designed pub on outskirts of town, with decor based on Ancient Rome.

Check it out

Pubs in the Good Beer Guide may change ownership and the facilities listed could alter. If a visit to a pub involves a long journey, it's advisable to check before leaving that full meals, family facilities, accommodation or camping sites are still available.

GLYNDE

Trevor Arms

The Street (1/2 mile off A27, near station)
11-11; 12-10.30 Sun
(01273) 858208
Harveys Pale Ale, BB, seasonal beers H
Friendly local, tucked away in a picturesque South Downs setting. The pub is very near the station and close to the world-famous Glyndebourne Opera House. Two bars cater for a wide range of customers. The large main bar displays pictures of village life. It has a secluded snug, plus a restaurant area, although food can also be eaten in the public bar. The large garden is popular with families in summer.

HAILSHAM

Grenadier Hotel

67 High Street
10.30-11; 12-10.30 Sun
(01323) 842152 website: www.grenadier2000.com
Harveys XX Mild, BB, Armada; guest beers H
Large, bustling, town-centre pub, one of Harvey's oldest. Two distinct bars, plus a little hatch, indicate this once had a public saloon and jug and bottle bar. Noted for its charity-giving, its Milk and Ale Club has given over £100,000 to Guide Dogs for the Blind. When licensing hours were relaxed there was no change here, as the pub had a market licence. The garden has a play area and the pub has a children's certificate. The guest beers are supplied by Harveys.
P

HOVE

Cliftonville Inn

98-101 George Street
10.30-11; 12-10.30 Sun
(01273) 726969
Courage Directors; Hop Back Summer Lightning; Shepherd Neame Spitfire; Theakston Best Bitter; Greene King Abbot; guest beers H
This busy Wetherspoon's pub, offering five guest beers, is quite a mecca for real ale drinkers. A converted store in Hove's pedestrianised shopping area, it serves reasonably-priced meals all day. While retaining the no-smoking area, there has a been a successful division of the original open-plan seating into smaller, more amenable areas. Hosting its own beer festivals twice yearly (April and Oct), it is also close to the town hall, home of Sussex CAMRA's beer festival. Q

Eclipse

33 Montgomery Street (S of railway, between Hove and Aldrington)
11-3, 5-11; 11-11 Sat; 12-10.30 Sun
(01273) 272212
Harveys Pale Ale, BB, Armada, seasonal beers H
Traditional pub in Poet's Corner, a quiet part of town. Fire gutted the premises in 1992, but after total refurbishment by Harveys, it reopened in 1995, and was rapidly re-established as a haunt for Brighton & Hove Albion fans, who played a role in saving the club from closure. Bearing a horse-racing theme, the pub sign shows Eclipse and Diamond, two horses galloping past the winning post. Evening meals are available Tue-Sat in this highly successful Harvey's venture.
Q (Aldrington/Hove)

ICKLESHAM

Queen's Head

Parsonage Lane (off A259)
11-11; 12-10.30 Sun
(01424) 814552
Beer range varies H
Welcoming country inn, slightly off the beaten track, but still popular. It stocks five or six varied ales of increasing strength, which combined with excellent, affordable meals, make this a must to visit. Built in 1632, this cosy, timber-framed building, with two log fires, benefits from superb views over the Brede Valley. Live music is performed every Tuesday evening.
Q P

ISFIELD

Laughing Fish

Station Road (W off A26, 2 miles S of Uckfield)
11.30-3, 5.30-11; 11-11 Sat; 12-4, 7-10.30 (12-10.30 summer) Sun
(01825) 750349
Greene King IPA, Ruddles County, Old Speckled Hen; guest beers H
Victorian village local, situated near a level crossing of a disused railway which is now the Lavender Line restaurant. The wildfowl reserve at Bentley is nearby. An underground stream helps to maintain a consistent temperature in the cellar. The bars are approached by steps up to a porch which was reputedly blown up by Canadian troops in WWII and rebuilt by them, while billeted in the pub. P

LEWES

Black Horse

55 Western Road
11-2.30, 5.30 (6 Sat)-11; 12-2.30, 7-10.30 Sun
(01273) 473653
Greene King IPA, Triumph, Abbot; Harveys BB, seasonal beers; guest beers H
This former coaching hotel, circa 1800, is now a family-run town local. It features two contrasting bars; the larger, popular, public bar displays a collection of bottled beers and fascinating old photographs. Pub games include the Sussex game of toad in the hole. The smaller lounge bar is a quiet oasis of calm, even though it contains a piano.
Q

Gardener's Arms

46 Cliffe High Street
11-11; 12-10.30 Sun
(01273) 474808
Archers Golden; Harveys BB; guest beers H
Sympathetically restored after the serious floods of October 2000, this one-bar pub is a favourite for shoppers and offers a warm welcome to visitors. An imaginative guest beer range, which often includes Arkells or Archers, gives a clue as to the landlord's footballing loyalties. The pub also displays a notice board dedicated to Lewes FC and memorabilia from Berwick Rangers. The landlord proudly displays his CAMRA Silver Selection Visitors Certificate. The cider is from Biddenden.

Lewes Arms
Mount Place
⌚ 11-11; 12-10.30 Sun
☎ (01273) 473152
Greene King Abbot; Harveys BB, Old (winter) Ⓗ
Historic, 17th-century curved-fronted pub, built into the castle ramparts. A tiny front bar, a terrace on the upper level (accessible via the stairs) and a small stage in the function room are just some of its features. The pub organises many charity fund-raising events including the pea throwing world championships! The games room houses toad in the hole as well as darts. Well-behaved children are welcome to use this room until 8pm. No mobile phones!
♨Q◐⇌♣

LITLINGTON

Plough & Harrow
Between Alfriston and Exceat OS523018
⌚ 11-3, 6.30-11; 12-3, 6.30-10.30 Sun
☎ (01323) 870632
Badger IPA, Best; Harveys BB; guest beer Ⓗ
Spacious country pub nestling in a quiet village in the South Downs; it is very popular with walkers and locals. The attractive interior has seating made from old barrels. A wide range of meals is served daily, there is a designated dining area.
♨Q❀◐◑P

MILTON STREET

Sussex Ox
Off A27 OS534041
⌚ 11-3, 6-11; 12-3, 6-10.30 Sun
☎ (01323) 870840
Harveys BB; Hop Back Summer Lightning; guest beers Ⓗ
Interesting, spacious, country pub situated in the Cuckmere Valley, comprising a traditional bar area, a family room and a restaurant (booking essential). Four beers are always available, with a range of strengths and styles to suit everyone Excellent food is served in all areas. A small campsite (with access by prior permission) is well placed for the South Downs, and set in idyllic countryside.
Q❀◐◑ΔP⚡

PORTSLADE

Stanley Arms
47 Wolseley Road (400 yds N of station)
⌚ 11 (12 Fri & Sat)-11; 12-10.30 Sun
☎ (01273) 701590
Beer range varies Ⓗ
A Victorian street-corner local, the Stanley has been at the forefront of real ale promotion for five years. Stocking three ever-changing beers from independent breweries, it attracts a discerning clientele. A good place to meet and socialise, the pub won local CAMRA Pub of the Year 1999, 2000 and 2001. It stages frequent live music, fields crib, football and cricket teams, and runs trips to beer festivals and breweries. Their own beer festival (Sept) is a very popular event.
♨Q❀⊟⇌(Fishergate) ♣●⊡

RINGMER

Cock Inn
Uckfield Road (off A26)
⌚ 11-3, 6-11; 12-3, 7-10.30 Sun
☎ (01273) 812040
Fuller's London Pride; Harveys XX Mild (summer), **BB, Old; guest beers** Ⓗ
Dating from the 16th century, this cosy beamed pub is situated on a slip road off the A26, near the turning to Ringmer. There is an emphasis on food here, so the bar area can be crowded at peak times. Most tables are in rooms off the bar. Children are welcome in the dining area. Approached up stone steps, there is an adjoining garden. The bar of this award-winning pub is dominated by an inglenook. ♨❀◐◑P

RODMELL

Abergavenny Arms
⌚ 11-3.30, 5.30-11; 11-11 Sat & summer; 12-10.30 Sun
☎ (01273) 474796
Harveys BB; guest beer Ⓗ
The pub is situated in a country village, about four miles south of Lewes. This two-bar local, which runs regular beer festivals, is popular for food (served Tue-Sat and Sun lunch). Happy hour is 5.30-6.30. This smartly decorated pub boasts a well inside and two ghosts. It is close to Virginia Woolf's former home. The garden is popular in summer. Live music is staged on Friday. ♨❀◐◑P

ROBERTSBRIDGE

Ostrich
Station Road
⌚ 11-11; 12-10.30 Sun
☎ (01580) 881737
Adnams Bitter or Larkins Chiddingstone; Harveys BB; guest beer (occasional) Ⓗ
Spacious, open-plan pub that was once the station hotel. Many interesting pictures adorn the interior and its superb Italian-style garden, with many tropical plants, should not be missed. Basic bar snacks are available at lunchtime. The pub has a games room. ♨❀⊟⇌P

ST LEONARDS

Bull
530 Bexhill Road (A259)
⌚ 12-3, 6-11; 12-4, 7-10.30 Sun
☎ (01424) 424984
Shepherd Neame Master Brew Bitter, Best Bitter, Spitfire or seasonal beer Ⓗ
Roadside pub, noted for its range of Shepherd Neame beers, served at their very best. This friendly local has a dining rom, serving an excellent menu (book at weekends; no food Sun eve). A large car park at the rear offers much more space than appears at first sight. The pub is at the western end of St Leonards so it is handy for Glynde Gap shops. Bar billiards is played here. ♨Q◐◑♿♣P

Dripping Spring
34 Tower Road (off A2100)
⌚ 12-3, 5-11; 11-11 Fri & Sat; 12-3, 7-10.30 Sun
☎ (01424) 434055
website: www.thedrippingspring.fsnet.co.uk

Goacher's Light; Taylor Best Bitter; guest beers Ⓗ
Superb, family-run local situated in the 'bohemian' quarter of town. An ever-changing selection of guest beers makes this a beer lover's dream. A winner of many CAMRA accolades, including Sussex Pub of the Year three years running, the walls display an impressive collection of pump clips – to date 2,000 different ales have been sampled. An annual beer festival is held in late September and theme weekends (for example dark beers) add to this pub's great appeal.
❀⇌(Warrior Sq.) ♣●▯

Duke
48 Duke Road, Silverhill
⏲ 11-11; 12-10.30 Sun
☎ (01424) 436241
Greene King IPA; Old Speckled Hen; guest beers Ⓗ
Traditional, busy, street-corner pub tucked away, but well worth seeking out. Six beers are usually on tap, with stronger beers predominating. The pub hosts an excellent beer festival on the first May bank holiday each year. Q❀⊟♣

Horse & Groom
Mercatoria (off London Rd)
⏲ 11-3.30, 5-11; 12-4, 7-10.30 Sun
☎ (01424) 420612
Adnams Broadside; Greene King IPA; Harveys BB; guest beer Ⓗ
First-class free house in the heart of old St Leonards, it serves a good range of beers at their very best. The circa 1829 listed building has an unusual horseshoe-shaped bar, which has, in effect, created two separate bars; one leads to a further quiet room at the rear of the pub. No food is served on Sunday. ⛰Q❀◖◗⇌(Warrior Sq.)

SEAFORD

Wellington
Steyne Road (near seafront)
⏲ 11-11; 12-10.30 Sun
☎ (01323) 890032
Greene King IPA, Ruddles County, Abbot, Old Speckled Hen; Harveys BB; guest beers Ⓗ
Recently refurbished former Beards pub, the Wellington is comfortable and friendly, with two contrasting bars: a large lounge and a smaller public bar, boasting nine handpumps. The 'Welly' is popular with all age groups. Its function room doubles as a family room and no-smoking drinking area during the day (children welcome until 7pm). The pub fields pool and darts teams and hosts regular folk music (Fri eve, except school holidays). ⛰Q🐴❀◖⊟⇌♣⚟

TELHAM

Black Horse
Hastings Road (A2100)
⏲ 11-3, 6-11; 12-3, 7-10.30 Sun
☎ (01424) 773109
Shepherd Neame Master Brew Bitter, Spitfire, Bishops Finger, seasonal beers Ⓗ
A splendid Shep's pub on the outskirts of Battle, it is an interesting weatherboarded building with a pleasant interior. It has a skittle alley in the attic and two boules pistes outside. An annual music festival is held in a marquee every spring bank holiday, now known as the Biggest Little Festival in Britain. Monthly jazz is performed in the bar every fourth Wednesday. Occasional folk music sessions are held as well. Good food is served from an extensive menu. ⛰Q❀◖◗♣P

UCKFIELD

Alma
Framfield Road (B2102, E of centre)
⏲ 11-2.30, 6-11; 12-2, 7-10.30 Sun
☎ (01825) 762232
Harveys XX Mild, Pale Ale, BB, Old, Armada, seasonal beers Ⓗ
In a largely residential area to the east of the town, this is the only pub for miles around selling the full range of Harvey's ales. The saloon and no-smoking family rooms are airy and comfortable. Despite renovation a few years ago, the public bar retains its traditional atmosphere. Run by the same family for generations, it has won several awards and is a true local. The garden is very small and adjoins the car park. No food Sun. Q🐴❀◖⊟♿⇌♣P⚟▯✔

UDIMORE

King's Head
Rye Road (B2089, W of village)
⏲ 11-4 (not winter Mon), 5.30-11; 12-4, 7-10.30 (not winter eve) Sun
☎ (01424) 882349
Harveys BB; guest beers Ⓗ
Built in 1535 and extended in the 17th century, this traditional village ale house boasts beams, two open fires, wood floors, and a very long oak bar which was installed in the 1930s. The pub serves excellent home-cooked food and has a no-smoking dining room. Situated in an area of outstanding natural beauty, many scenic walks can be enjoyed in the vicinity.
⛰Q🐴❀◖◗♿♣P

WHATLINGTON

Royal Oak
Woodmans Green (A21)
⏲ 11-3, 5.30-11; 12-4, 7-10.30 Sun
☎ (01424) 870492
Harveys BB; Sussex Pett Progress; guest beers Ⓗ
A good stopping-off point on the way into Hastings on the A21, this family-run pub is situated in the small hamlet of Whatlington. With a split-level layout, one of the two upper levels is a no-smoking area. There is a deep well inside the pub, near the bar and a wonderful large inglenook that holds a roaring log fire in winter. An extensive menu is available.
⛰❀◖◗♿P⚟

WILLINGDON

Red Lion
99 Wish Hill
⏲ 11-11; 12-3, 7-10.30 Sun
☎ (01323) 502062
Badger K&B Sussex, Best, Tanglefoot; Gribble K&B Mild Ale, Fursty Ferret Ⓗ
This two-storey, half-timbered building was originally a small cottage ale house which once had a mangle room where the local washerwoman would wring out clothes for a penny a bundle. It boasts a famous literary reference: George Orwell in Animal Farm

described Mr Jones the farmer as sitting in the tap room of the Red Lion at Willingdon. This quiet village pub has one large bar, with a games area at one end, a new no-smoking lounge, and a nice garden. ❀◐♣●P⊬

WILMINGTON

Giant's Rest

The Street (A27)
⏲ 11-3, 6-11; 12-3, 6-10.30 Sun
☎ (01323) 870207
Harveys BB, Old; Taylor Landlord Ⓗ
Lovely quiet free house nestling on the South Downs, alongside the Long Man landmark. Popular with walkers and locals, an appealing feature of the pub is the puzzles and games on all the tables. In fine weather you can sit in the garden at the front of the pub. The food is highly recommended. ❀◐♿♣P⊬

WITHYHAM

Dorset Arms

On B2110, between Hartfield and Groombridge
OS493357
⏲ 11-3, 5.30-11; 12-3, 7-10.30 Sun
☎ (01892) 770278 website: www.dorsetarms.co.uk
Harveys Pale Ale, BB, seasonal beers Ⓗ
Picturesque old pub, built in 1556, set in what was once the industrial heartland of England. Its unspoilt low-ceilinged bar has a floor of unvarnished local oak. The restaurant serves good food. There is a large grassed area in front of the pub which is busy on warm days. Ashdown Forest is not far away and worth visiting. No. 291 buses run regularly from East Grinstead and Tunbridge Wells, Mon-Sat daytime. ⩕❀◐♣P✔

Government Drops Its 'Full Pint' Pledge

In March 2002, CAMRA attacked the government for ditching its election pledge to protect consumers from short beer measures and ensuring drinkers get a full pint. CAMRA hit out at a Department of Trade and Industry consultation document that proposes to make it legal for pubs to serve pints with only 95 per cent liquid. Mike Benner, CAMRA's Head of Campaigns and Communications said, 'The Labour Party has been promising a full pint since 1997 and now appears to be bowing down to big business and sticking two fingers up at Britain's 15 million beer drinkers by proposing to make it legal to serve pints of beer up to 5 per cent short. This is despite the fact that realistic proposals already exist for a 100 per cent average liquid pint law.' The policy statement in the Consumer section of the official Labour Party web site hasd been changed since January 2002, removing the commitment to ensure consumers 'get a full pint'.

Mike Benner said, 'Ministers who have already given their backing to an honest pint law and the 154 Labour backbenchers who have signed a parliamentary motion calling for full pints will be up in arms over plans to legalise short measure.'

The Government's decision to ditch existing proposals for 100 per cent average pints, has been announced despite the following:

- Current industry self-regulation has failed – nine out of 10 pints are still less than 100 per cent liquid and one out of four pints are less than the industry guidelines of 95 per cent minimum.
- The DTI has received complaints and support for a full pint law from over 9,000 consumers
- Joan Walley MP's Early Day Motion calling for a full liquid pint has over 220 signatures from MPs
- Research shows that over 80 per cent of adults think a pint should be 100 per cent liquid
- Wolverhampton & Dudley, the biggest regional brewer and pub operator, offers 100 per cent pints in all its Banks's pubs.
- Debates in the trade press show a split in the industry, with many licensees and pub staff supporting full pints
- Several ministers have made full pint promises since 1997. Robin Cook; "Any short measure is a clear public scandal…", 24 January.
- Research suggests that pubs which already serve 100 per cent liquid pints are cheaper on average than pubs that do not, despite unsubstantiated industry claims that full pints will lead to higher prices.

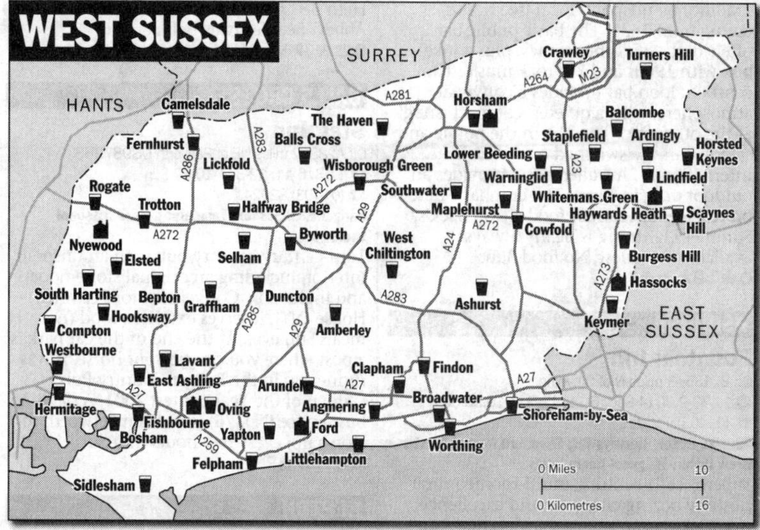

AMBERLEY

Sportsman

Rackham Road

11-2.30 (3 Sat), 6-11; 12-3, 7-10.30 Sun

(01798) 831787

website: http://freespace. virgin.net/mob.club

Fuller's London Pride; Young's Bitter; guest beers H

This 17th-century free house, affording excellent views of Amberley wild brooks, is popular with walkers and diners, as well as real ale lovers. Home of the Miserable Old Buggers Club, there are three bars, each with its own character; one contains a hexagonal pool table. The restaurant is in the conservatory. The house beer, Welton's Miserable Old Buggers Brew (3.5% ABV) is a highly quaffable ale. Accommodation is now available. Q P

ANGMERING

Spotted Cow

High Street (100 yds off B2225)

10.30-3, 5-11; 10.30-11 Sat; 12-10.30 Sun

(01903) 783919

Fuller's London Pride; Greene King Old Speckled Hen; Harveys BB; guest beer H

Despite its High Street address, this 18th-century ex-smugglers' haunt is actually located down a semi-rural lane on the village edge. It features a quiet public bar, popular with locals and walkers, and a very popular restaurant where children are allowed. Spacious outdoor facilities include a children's play area and a boules pitch, used every Sunday by a local club. It hosts occasional hog roasts, charity events and live music. Q P

Woodman Arms

Hammerpot (A27, 1 mile N of Angmering, eastbound access only)

11-3, 6-11; 12-3, 7-10.30 Sun

(01903) 871240

website: www.thewoodmanarms.co.uk

Gale's Butser (summer), **GB, HB; seasonal or guest beer** H

16th-century, low beamed Gale's house, popular for its home-made food, including themed nights (book Sun lunch, no food Sun eve). It hosts live music, including folk nights (alternate Sun), charity quiz nights and barbecues in the award-winning gardens. Walkers are actively welcomed – leaflets detailing local walks are provided and are guided in bluebell season. A wide range of Gale's country wines is stocked. The pub has won awards for cellarmanship and its toilets. Q P

ARDINGLY

Oak Inn

Street Lane 200 yds from B2028

11-3, 5-11; 11.30-11 Fri & Sat; 12-10.30 Sun

(01444) 892244 website: www.theoakardingly.co.uk

Harveys BB; guest beers H

Originally three labourers' cottages dating from the 14th century, this friendly pub features an inglenook and oak beams – crash helmets may be required in some places! The ghost of the 'grey lady' sometimes sits in the bar. The restaurant serves excellent food, plus take-away fish and chips (Friday eve; no food Sun eve). Guest beers change monthly and usually come from local independent breweries. Walkers are welcome; buses 81, 82 and 88 run between Haywards Heath and Crawley (not eves). Q P

ARUNDEL

King's Arms

36 Tarrant Street

11-3, 5.30-11; 11-11 Sat; 12-10.30 Sun

(01903) 882312

Fuller's London Pride; Young's Special; guest beers H

INDEPENDENT BREWERIES

Arundel Ford
Ballard's Nyewood
Dark Star Haywards Heath
Gribble Inn Oving
Hepworth Horsham
King Horsham
Rectory Hassocks

Traditional, unspoilt, local free house, dating from 1625. The basic public bar offers darts and other games, plus a juke box with 1960s and 70s rock music. The central saloon bar provides a convivial atmosphere, with a quieter, compact 'snug' at the other end. The TVs in the public and saloon bars are switched on for rugby internationals. A walled patio provides an outdoor drinking area. The emphasis here is on real ale rather than food – Hop Back's Summer Lightning is nearly always available as a guest. No food Sun.
Q❀◖⊟⛺⇌♣

ASHURST

Fountain Inn

On B2135, 3 miles N of Steyning
⏲ 11.30-2.30 (4 Sat), 6-11; 12-3, 7-10.30 Sun
☎ (01403) 710219
Adnams Bitter; Harveys BB; Shepherd Neame Master Brew Bitter; Ⓗ **guest beers** Ⓖ/Ⓗ
Superb, 16th-century, multi-roomed rural hostelry oozing character and excellence, overlooking the village duck pond. Local CAMRA Pub of the Year 2001, it comprises two cosy bars, with flagstones, open fires and low beams, plus a dining room offering a tantalising menu of freshly prepared food (not served Sun or Mon eves). The pleasant gardens house a restored working cider press and a converted barn that doubles as a function room and skittles alley.
♛Q❀◖◗P

BALCOMBE

Cowdray Arms

London Road (B2036/B2110 jct, 1½ miles N of village)
⏲ 11-3, 5.30-11; 12-3, 7-10.30 Sun
☎ (01444) 811280
Greene King IPA, Abbot; Harveys BB; guest beers Ⓗ
Popular roadside, one-bar Greene King pub, a regular Guide entry and local CAMRA Pub of the Year 1998. Two- and four-pint carryouts are available. It has a children's certificate and a small, safe garden. A good selection of reasonably-priced, home-cooked food is offered on the bar and restaurant menu, plus a specials board. A large airy conservatory is for non-smokers. The pub is close to High Beeches Gardens, and Worth Abbey. Beer festivals held.
Q♉❀◖◗♿♣P⅟

BALLS CROSS

Stag Inn

Off A283, 2 miles NE of Petworth OS987263
⏲ 11-3, 6-11; 12-3, 7-10.30 Sun
☎ (01403) 820241
Badger K&B Sussex, Tanglefoot, K&B seasonal beers Ⓗ
16th-century country pub with an unspoilt interior, including an original stone floor and inglenook. Convenient for Petworth House (NT), it serves excellent food (no meals Sun eve). At the end of the car park is a post where you can tie your horse. It was runner-up in the Badger Country Pub Garden of the Year contest 2001. A daytime bus service (No. 76) runs from Petworth to Horsham, every two hours (not Sun).
♛Q❀◖◗♣P

BEPTON

Country Inn

Severals Road (1 mile SW of Midhurst) OS870206
⏲ 11-3, 5-11; 11-11 Fri, Sat & summer; 12-10.30 Sun
☎ (01730) 813466
Draught Bass; Ballard's Midhurst Mild; Taylor Landlord; Young's Bitter; guest beer Ⓗ
Situated a mile from the A286, this single-bar village local has a developing food trade. No food is available on winter Sunday evenings, but book for Sunday lunch and monthly special food nights. It also hosts occasional live entertainment. At the rear is a large garden. A guest beer from an independent brewer is always on tap. Games include shove-ha'penny and table skittles. ♛Q❀◖◗♣P

BOSHAM

White Swan

Station Road (Bosham roundabout on A259)
⏲ 12-3, 5-11; 12-4.30, 6-11 Sat; 12-4.30, 6.30-10.30 Sun
☎ (01243) 576086
Hop Back Crop Circle, Summer Lightning; Young's Bitter; guest beers Ⓗ
An inn for 300 years, this roadside local is spacious, but cosy with beams, bare

INN BRIEF

BROADWATER

Old House at Home
77 Broadwater Street East
11-2.30, 6-11; 11-3, 6-10.30 Sun
(01903) 232661
Draught Bass; Harveys BB; Wells Bombardier Ⓗ
Popular, two-bar wood-panelled pub, with a large conservatory. Snacks and meals served.

CAMELSDALE

Mill Tavern
Liphook Road, Shottermill
11-3, 6-11; 12-4, 7-10.30 (12-10.30 summer) Sun
(01428) 643183
Fuller's London Pride; Wells Bombardier; guest beers Ⓗ
Reputedly haunted, 15th-century pub with a garden. Two independent guest beers change regularly.

DUNCTON

Cricketers
On A285, Chichester road, 2½ miles S of Petworth
11-2.30, 6-11; 12-3 (closed eve) Sun
(01978) 342473
Fuller's London Pride; Young's Bitter Ⓗ
Restaurant-cum-pub, rather than a pub with meals (book).

FELPHAM

Old Barn
42 Felpham Road
11-11; 12-10.30 Sun
(01243) 821564
Hop Back Summer Lightning; Ringwood Best Bitter; Shepherd Neame Master Brew Bitter; guest beers Ⓗ
Busy free house, near Butlins, with a cosy front bar and rear games area. TV is on for big matches. Food available.

FINDON

John Henry's Bar
The Forge, Nepcote Lane
11-11; 12-10.30 Sun
(01903) 877277
Hop Back Summer Lightning; Ringwood Best Bitter; guest beer Ⓗ
Friendly bistro bar drawing a cosmopolitan clientele, with lots going on.

FISHBOURNE

Woolpack Inn
71 Fishbourne Road (A259)
11-11; 12-10.30 Sun
(01243) 785707
Adnams Bitter; Greene King Abbot; Young's Bitter; guest beer Ⓗ
Large, 1930s pub serving traditional lunchtime meals and Thai food eves. Boules and bar billiards played.

bricks and a log fire. With easy access by road and rail, it now has a larger car park, and improvements to the patio garden make it more family-friendly without detracting from its traditional pub atmosphere. The skittle alley doubles as a family room. The excellent restaurant offers locally caught fish as a speciality (no meals Sun eve). Highly recommended.
⌂Q❀◑◐♿⛺⇌♣●P▽

BURGESS HILL

Watermill Inn

1 Leylands Road, Worlds End (near Wivelsfield station)
⏲ 11-11; 12-10.30 Sun
☎ (01444) 235517
Fuller's London Pride; Young's Bitter; guest beers [H]
Single-bar community pub on the outskirts of Burgess Hill. A different guest ale is available every weekend from the SIBA range. Traditional food is served every lunchtime and most evenings. Sky TV is switched on for major sporting events. The enclosed garden hosts barbecues and occasional live music is performed. Background music kept at a sensible level encourages conversation. This is a regular venue on the local CAMRA trail.
⌂❀◑⇌♣P

BYWORTH

Black Horse

100 yds from A283
⏲ 11-2.30 (3 Sat), 6-11; 12-3, 7-10.30 Sun
☎ (01798) 342424
Cheriton Pots Ale; Fuller's London Pride; guest beer [H]
Dating from the 1790s, this popular village free house has rustic charm and two distinct assets: quality food and good real ale. The bar is for drinkers, mainly local residents, and is very welcoming, with a warm, friendly atmosphere. The remainder of the pub is given over to diners and is often very busy (booking is advisable, especially at weekends). The large, sloping garden at the rear affords good views of the Sussex Downs.
⌂Q❀♣P

CLAPHAM

Coach & Horses

Arundel Road (A27)
⏲ 11-3, 5.15-11; 12-4, 7-10.30 Sun
☎ (01903) 264665
Adnams Bitter; Fuller's London Pride; Greene King Abbot; Young's Special; guest beers [H]
Former coaching inn, still providing food and drink for both travellers and locals. Punch Taverns' Finest Cask Scheme means there is usually a guest beer from an independent brewery. A large clock, presented to former boxer and licensee, Terry Spinks, dominates the main bar, which has limited seating; additional seating is available in the rear bar, where children (and dogs) are welcome. The dining area offers a wide selection of dishes. It hosts monthly music nights and a weekly quiz (Tue). ⌂Q❀◑◐♣P

COMPTON

Coach & Horses

The Square (B2146)
⏲ 10.30-2.30 (3 Sat), 6-11; 12-3, 7-10.30 Sun
☎ (023) 9263 1228
Fuller's ESB; guest beers [H]
16th-century pub in a charming downland village, surrounded by excellent walking country. The large front bar has two open fires and a bar billiards table. There is also a smaller rear bar, a fine beamed restaurant and a skittle alley. Guest beers always offer an interesting selection. The pub is on the square of a lively village; the annual square dance is worth watching if you can get tickets. Local CAMRA Pub of the Year 2001.
⌂Q❀◑◐♣

COWFOLD

Hare & Hounds

Henfield Road (A281, 400 yds from A272 jct)
⏲ 11-2.30 (11.30-3 Sat), 6-11; 12-3, 7-10.30 Sun
☎ (01403) 865354
Harveys BB; Shepherd Neame Master Brew Bitter; guest beer [H]
Popular, Victorian village local refurbished in 1995. The brick front bar has a solid timber top made from wood recovered locally after the 1987 hurricane. The main area has a slab

---

HORSHAM

Beer Essentials
30A East Street
10-7; closed Mon & Sun
(01403) 218890
Beer range varies [G]
Small off-licence selling draught ale and cider in refillable containers; around 80 bottled beers in stock.

Boar's Head
Worthing Road
11-11; 12-10.30 Sun
(01403) 254353
Badger K&B Sussex, Best, Tanglefoot; Gribble Inn Fursty Ferret [H]
Dated 1761, with open fireplace and flagstone floor, overlooking the town, it has a restaurant and garden.

Coot
Cootes Avenue
11-2.30, 5.30-11 (11-11 summer); 12-3, 5.30-10.30 Sun
(01403) 254404
Draught Bass; Fuller's London Pride; Hancock's HB; Wells Bombardier [H]
Estate pub, recently renovated, with repro furniture, but still has two bars. Music and theme evenings staged.

HORSTED KEYNES

Green Man
11.30-3, 5.30 (6 Sat)-11; 12-3, 7-10.30 Sun
(01825) 790656
Harveys BB; Greene King IPA, Abbot; guest beers [H]
1700s pub, near Bluebell Railway, with impressive inglenook and a no-smoking bar. Food served. Cask Marque accredited.

LICKFOLD

Lickfold Inn
11-3, 6-11; 12-3, 7-10.30 Sun
(01798) 861285
Beer range varies [H]
15th-century oak-beamed free house with a nice garden and restaurant serving imaginative cuisine.

SHOREHAM-BY-SEA

Green Jacket
225 Upper Shoreham Road
11.30-3, 6-11; 11.30-11 Sat; 12-10.30 Sun
(01273) 452556
Draught Bass; Harveys BB; Wadworth 6X; guest beers [H]
Spacious, 1930s three-bar local near Buckingham Park, offering six real ales and restaurant food.

floor, with a carpeted saloon at one end; a family no-smoking area has recently been added at the other end. A large display of pewter tankards hangs from the main beams. Buses between Horsham and Brighton run Mon-Sat (Nos 107 and 89).
ᨓ⛱❀◐◑P⊁

CRAWLEY

Shades
85 High Street
⊛ 10-11; 12-10.30 Sun
☎ (01293) 514105
Boddingtons Bitter; Caledonian Deuchars IPA; Greene King Abbot; Hook Norton Old Hooky; guest beers Ⓗ
The 14th-century building was Chandlers Brewery until bought by Whitbread in the 18th century. The pub, which recently abbreviated its name from Brewery Shades, has a sinister past – it used to have holding cells for the local police. A passage linked the pub with the George Hotel opposite; condemned prisoners would be led through and hanged in the High Street in front of the George. Both the Shades and the George are reputedly haunted. Meals are served 10-7 daily.
◐≠

EAST ASHLING

Horse & Groom
On B2178, 2½ miles NW of Chichester
⊛ 12-3, 6-11; 12-6 (closed eve) Sun
☎ (01243) 575339
website: www.horseandgroom.sageweb.co.uk
Draught Bass; Harveys BB; Hop Back Summer Lightning; Young's Bitter Ⓗ
Originally a forge, this 17th-century inn retains much character, with its flagstone floor, old settles and half-panelled walls in the bar, heated by a fine old commercial range. Sympathetically extended, with much use of knapped Sussex flints, the comfortable dining area offers a good quality, diverse menu of home-made dishes (no food Sun eve). An integral 17th-century flint barn has been converted to provide accommodation in oak-beamed, en-suite rooms.
ᨓQ❀⊏◐◑▲♣●P

ELSTED

Three Horseshoes
Between Midhurst and Harting
⊛ 11-2.30, 6-11; 12-3, 7-10.30 Sun
☎ (01730) 825746
Ballard's Best Bitter; Cheriton Pots Ale; Fuller's London Pride; Tayor Landlord; guest beers Ⓖ
Traditional village pub, originally a drovers' inn, the lower bar is believed to have once been a butcher's shop. Low beams and small rooms create a very cosy, friendly atmosphere. The huge garden affords lovely views and now has an outdoor privy! The pub marks the start of some wonderful walks. Its open fires and excellent home-cooked food could also be a great way to finish; it is one of the stops on the Ballard's charity walk. ᨓQ❀◐◑P

FERNHURST

King's Arms
Midhurst Road (A286, ¾ mile S of village)
⊛ 11.30-3, 5.30 (6.30 Sat)-11; 12-3, (closed eve) Sun
☎ (01428) 652005
Hogs Back TEA; Ringwood Best Bitter; Ventnor Golden; guest beers Ⓗ
Sussex sandstone pub set below Henley Hill escarpment. This true free house has been a pub since the 17th century. The wood-panelled interior has a drinking area at one end, and a restaurant and private dining room at the other. The wide-ranging, seasonal menu specialises in fish. It boasts a large, enclosed garden and a Sussex barn hosts the late summer beer festival. Interesting guest beers are always stocked. 24 hours' notice is needed for camping behind the pub. ᨓQ❀◐◑▲♣P

FINDON ✻

Findon Manor Hotel
High Street
⊛ 12-2.30, 6-11; 12-10.30 Sun
☎ (01903) 872733
Adnams Bitter; Badger Tanglefoot; Fuller's London Pride; Harveys BB Ⓗ
This is a classy country house hotel. The building was originally the village rectory, dating back to 1584, and it was Monty's billet during the last war. Surprisingly in such an establishment, the bar (known as the Snooty Fox) offers four well-kept beers,

INN BRIEF

Royal Sovereign
6 Middle Street
11-11; 12-10.30 Sun
(01273) 453158
Badger K&B Sussex; Brakspear Special; Castle Eden Ale; Flowers Original; Fuller's London Pride; Young's Special Ⓗ
Lively back-street local, off the High Street, identifiable by its United Brewery's exterior.

SOUTH HARTING

Ship
12-3, 6-11; 11-11 Sat & summer; 12-10.30 Sun
(01730) 825302
Cheriton Pots Ale; Palmer IPA; guest beer Ⓗ
17th-century inn at the village centre, with a genuine public bar (rare for these parts).

SOUTHWATER

Hen & Chicken
Worthing Road
11-3, 5.30-11; 12-3, 7-10.30 Sun
(01403) 730349
King Horsham Best Bitter; guest beer Ⓗ
First outlet for King's ale, also serving an ambitious range of food. Several buses stop outside.

WARNINGLID

Half Moon
The Street
11.30-3, 5-11; 11.30-11 Sat; 12-10.30 Sun
(01444) 461227
Wells Bombardier; guest beers Ⓗ
Traditional rural village pub serving food home-cooked food; well worth a visit. On No. 273, Crawley-Brighton bus route.

Poor beer

If you consider beer quality in a pub is not up to standard please let us know immediately. Write to GBG, CAMRA, 230 Hatfield Road, St Albans, Herts, AL1 4LW or camra@camra.org.uk. If the pub has a Cask Marque symbol, write to Cask Marque at the address in its editorial feature at the front of the Guide.

and a steady stream of locals rub shoulders with unwinding diners. The garden houses a boules pitch. ⌂Q❀⛟◑♿P

Gun Inn

The Square

⏲ 11-11; 12-10.30 Sun

☎ (01903) 873206

Adnams Bitter; Fuller's London Pride; Gale's HSB; Harveys BB Ⓗ

Timber-framed building, much altered over the years, the Gun dates back to about 1450. No trace now remains of the brewhouse, buttery, gunsmith's shop or cockpit that featured in a 1722 inventory, but at least the pub is still standing, despite Whitbread's demolition plans of the late 1990s. Now carefully refurbished as a free house, it offers a comfortable lounge bar, two dining rooms and a pleasant garden. ⌂Q❀◑

GRAFFHAM

Forester's Arms

3 miles W of A285, just N of the South Downs OS931177

⏲ 11.30-2.30, 6-11; 12-3, 6.30-10.30 Sun

☎ (01798) 867202

Hop Back Summer Lightning; Taylor Landlord; guest beers Ⓗ

Fine, traditional country pub, built in 1609 and extended in Victorian times. Formerly run by Chichester brewers, Henty and Constable, its name derives from its use as a meeting place for the Free Foresters. An impressive inglenook with blazing logs in winter, and an attractive garden in summer, make this a popular venue, as does its proximity to the South Downs Way and other fine walking country. No evening meals winter Sun. ⌂Q❀◑⛺P

HALFWAY BRIDGE

Halfway Bridge Inn

On A272, midway between Midhurst and Petworth

⏲ 11-3, 6-11; 12-3, 7-10.30 Sun

☎ (01798) 861281

Cheriton Pots Ale; Fuller's London Pride; Gale's HSB; guest beer Ⓗ

Smart, 18th-century coaching inn with a rural atmosphere. The many inter-connecting rooms, each with an open fire, are often filled with diners, but drinkers are catered for in the rear bar which leads through to a patio area. Guest beers are normally from local independent brewers, and there is an unusual selection of table games to play. Eight double bedrooms are in a converted Sussex barn at the rear. ⌂Q❀⛟◑♣●P

THE HAVEN

Blue Ship ☆

1½ miles S of Bucks Green OS084306

⏲ 11-3, 6-11; 12-3.30, 7-10.30 Sun

☎ (01403) 822709

Badger K&B Sussex, Best, seasonal beers Ⓖ

Unspoilt rural pub with flagstone floors, scrubbed tables and a large inglenook – a real gem. Beer is served through two small serving hatches, and an extensive range of wholesome meals is served lunchtimes and Tue-Sat eves. Of the several rooms in the pub, one is dedicated to Newfoundland dogs which are bred nearby; occasional dog shows are held in summer. The NSU Owners Club meets here and holds an annual rally in the adjacent field. ⌂Q☺❀◑⊟♿♣P⊁

HERMITAGE

Sussex Brewery

36 Main Road (A259, ½ mile E of Emsworth)

⏲ 11-11; 12-10.30 Sun

☎ (01243) 371533

Smiles Best; Young's Bitter, Special, seasonal beers Ⓗ

Cosy, bare-boarded local with open fires. Young's supply a full range of beers, including Hermitage Best. A Grade II listed building, this pub is traditional with a capital T. On the edge of the fishing village of Emsworth, local fish is a speciality in the restaurant, but there is also an extensive special sausage menu in both the bar and restaurant. The lovely walled garden is an added attraction. ⌂Q❀◑⛺⇌(Emsworth) P

HOOKSWAY

Royal Oak

¼ mile off B2141, between North Marden and Chilgrove OS815162

⏲ 11.30-2.30, 6-11; closed Mon; 12-3, 6-10.30 (not winter eve) Sun

☎ (01243) 535257

Gale's HSB; guest beers Ⓗ

Tucked away in a valley close to the South Downs Way, this rural gem was built as a lunch stop for the 'guns' on West Dean estate shoots. King Edward VII was a frequent patron, but now walkers and cyclists enjoy its peaceful setting. Reasonably-priced, home-cooked food complements the four ales which include Hooksway Bitter from Hampshire Brewery, and often a strong dark beer. A brass shell case is struck to call 'time'. ⌂Q☺❀◑⛺♣P⊁

HORSHAM ❊

Stout House

29 Carfax

⏲ 10-3, 5-11; 10-4, 6-11 Sat; 12-4, 7-10.30 Sun

☎ (01403) 267777

Badger K&B Sussex, Tanglefoot, K&B seasonal beers Ⓗ

Very popular, friendly, town-centre pub which concentrates on beer (food is limited to snacks). Traditionally refurbished with wood beams and panels, the cellar is at the same level as the bar and is visible through a window in the door. Bare boards feature in the front part of the pub, carpet at the rear. Cribbage is played here. ♿⇌♣✔

Malt Shovel

15 Springfield Road

⏲ 11-11; 12-10.30 Sun

☎ (01403) 254543 website: www.maltshovel.com

Adnams Bitter; Draught Bass; Ⓗ **Black Sheep Best Bitter;** Ⓗ/Ⓖ **Brakspear Bitter;** Ⓗ **guest beers** Ⓗ/Ⓖ

Spacious, ex-Hogshead pub stocking a wide range of beers, together with draught cider, usually Biddenden. Between 200 and 300 beers are sold each year; helpful staff will normally let you try a taster. Belgian bottled beers are also kept. A beer festival is held (usually Feb/March) at this local CAMRA

Pub of the Year 1998 and '99. The outside drinking area overlooks the site of the old King & Barnes Brewery. The hanging baskets were commended by Horsham in Bloom. Meals are served 12-5.
⌂❀◐◑≠♣●P

KEYMER

Greyhound

Keymer Road
✪ 11-11; 12-10.30 Sun
☎ (01273) 842645
Courage Best Bitter; Harveys BB; guest beers Ⓗ
Friendly, comfortable village pub opposite Keymer church. The main features of interest are the old beams, which carry a large collection of mugs and jugs, and an inglenook. The pub's age is not known, but it is reckoned to be at least 250 years old. Some years ago an extension was added to make a dining area, and this blends in well (no food Sun eve or Mon). The public bar has bar billiards, rather than the ubiquitous pool table. Q❀◐◑⊟♣P

LAVANT

Earl of March

On A286, 2 miles N of Chichester
✪ 10.30-3, 6 (5.30 summer)-11; 10.30-11 Sat; 12-3, 7-10.30 Sun
☎ (01243) 774751
Ballard's Best Bitter; Cottage Golden Arrow; Itchen Valley Fagin's; Ringwood Old Thumper; guest beers Ⓗ
Friendly village pub, popular with visitors and locals alike. The large wood-panelled single bar exhibits a fine display of ships' badges and other artefacts. A vista of the South Downs is afforded from the compact garden. Historic Goodwood motor racing circuit and the annual Festival of Speed hillclimb are nearby. Good value food features local game and fish in generous home-cooked portions. The pub has a children's certificate and hosts live music (Thu eve). ❀◐◑♣●P

LINDFIELD

Linden Tree

47 High Street
✪ 11-3, 6-11; 12-3, 7-10.30 Sun
☎ (01444) 482995
Arundel Castle; Harveys BB; Marston's Pedigree; Ringwood Old Thumper; guest beers Ⓗ
Popular free house with a shop-like frontage, near the pond in a picturesque village. The long-awaited extension into former bank premises next door will provide more room for diners. For the drinker, normally six real ales are available, all from independent brewers. From the small outdoor drinking area at the rear, the remains of a long-defunct brewery may be glimpsed. ⌂Q❀◐

LITTLEHAMPTON

Dewdrop

96 Wick Street
✪ 10.30-3, 5.30-11; 10.30-11 Sat; 12-10.30 Sun
☎ (01903) 716459
Gales's GB, HSB; Ringwood XXXX Porter Ⓗ
Built in 1860 as part of a row of terraced houses, this unassuming and welcoming free house is one of an increasingly rare breed of down-to-earth locals. The compact saloon bar was originally the house next door, dating from a distant time before the spacious public bar was converted from three bars. Weekday lunches are served. Q◐⊟♣

LOWER BEEDING

Plough

Leech Pond, Hill Road (B2110, 500yds from A281 jct)
✪ 11-3, 5.30-11; 11-11 Fri & Sat; 12-10.30 Sun
☎ (01403) 891277
Badger K&B Sussex, Best, Tanglefoot, seasonal beers Ⓗ
Basic no-frills, two-bar pub offering comparatively cheap beer for the area. Convenient for Leonardslee Gardens, it is situated on the outside of a sweeping bend, which has caused a few lorries to 'drop in' over the years. The current licensees have been at the pub for nearly 20 years, originally with King & Barnes. Snacks and sandwiches are available at lunchtime. An hourly bus service (No. 89) runs along the A281 from Haywards Heath to Horsham (Mon-Sat).
⌂Q❀⊟♣P

MAPLEHURST

White Horse

Park Lane (midway between A281 and A272)
OS190246
✪ 12 -2.30 (11.30-3 Sat), 6-11; 12-3, 7-10.30 Sun
☎ (01403) 891208
Harveys BB; Weltons Pride & Joy; guest beers Ⓗ
Country pub, benefitting from stunning views over the Sussex Weald. The selection of guest beers increases from three (weekdays) to up to five at weekends. The landlord of 20 years standing, won local CAMRA's Pub of the Year in 2000 and 2001. The local gardening club meets here (Sat morning). Reputedly the widest bar in Sussex (12'6" x 3') and a spacious no-smoking conservatory add interest. A post bus from Horsham runs twice a day, Mon-Fri. Games include shut the box and bagatelle.
⌂Q☋❀◐◑♣●P⅍

OVING

Gribble Inn

Gribble Lane
✪ 11-3, 5.30-11 (11-11 summer); 12-3, 7-10.30 (12-10.30 summer) Sun
☎ (01243) 786893
Gribble Fursty Ferret, Gribble Ale, Reg's Tipple, Plucking Pheasant, Pig's Ear, seasonal beers Ⓗ
Originally two agricultural worker's cottages, this 16th-century thatched pub is home to Gribble Brewery's award-winning beers (the brewhouse adjoins the skittle alley). A mobile ph.one-free zone, drinkers happily mingle with diners in all areas. Traditional good quality food is always available, but once a month (Tue) special trad jazz themed food evenings (Thai, Chinese, Cajun, curry, etc.) are staged. A delightful cottage garden, and a good family room complete the facilities.
⌂Q☋❀◐◑♿♣P⅍

ROGATE

White Horse Inn

East Street (A272, E of Petersfield)
12-3, 6-11; 12-10.30 Sat; 12-10.30 Sun
☎ (01730) 821333
Ballard's Wassail; Cheriton Pots Ale; Hop Back Summer Lightning; Ringwood Fortyniner; guest beers Ⓗ

A coaching inn since 1598, now a traditional country pub, with oak beams, flagstone floor and hug log fire in its large bar. It usually stocks six real ales, plus an occasional cider. The car park at the rear backs on to the village sports field. The pub has its own cricket, rugby and darts teams. This popular village pub has an excellent restaurant serving home-made food but bar snacks are also available. This is a gem. Q❀◑◐♿♣●P

SCAYNES HILL

Sloop

Freshfield Lock, Sloop Lane OS385244
12-3, 6 (5.30 Fri)-11; 12-10.30 Sun
☎ (01444) 831219
Greene King XX Mild, IPA, Ruddles County, Abbot; seasonal beers; guest beers Ⓗ

Situated next to the River Ouse, and close to the Bluebell Railway, the oldest part of this pub has been a watering-hole from 1815, and was originally a pair of lock-keeper's cottages. The public bar, where real ale is cheaper than in the lounge, is decorated with railwayania. Bar billiards is housed in the Shoot Room. Smoking is discouraged in the lounge, where well-regarded food is served. It hosts occasional live music and the Sloop Festival (July). Q❀◑◐♣P

SELHAM

Three Moles

1 mile S of A272, midway between Midhurst and Petworth OS935206
12-2, 5.30-11; 11.30-11 Sat; 12-10.30 Sun
☎ (01798) 861303 website: www.thethreemoles.co.uk
Ballard's Midhurst Mild; King Horsham Best Bitter; Skinner's Betty Stogs Bitter; guest beers Ⓗ

Traditional, small country pub, set well off the beaten track in the Rother Valley, the Moles was opened in 1872 to serve Selham Station but has long outlived the railway line. It remains a welcoming free house of great character where no food is sold, but whose guest beers are often from far-flung small breweries. The unusual name comes from the coat of arms of the owners, the Mitford family. Local CAMRA Pub of the Year 2002. Q❀♣P

SHOREHAM BY SEA ❄

Buckingham Arms

35-37 Brunswick Road
11-11; 12-10.30 Sun
☎ (01273) 453660
Badger K&B Sussex; Greene King Abbot; Harveys BB; Hop Back Summer Lightning Ⓗ

Situated close to Shoreham railway station, this independent free house offers up to ten real ales, including at least three guest beers from around the country. Deservedly popular with regulars, commuters and visitors, background music is kept to a level to encourage conversation. Monthly live acts are advertised in advance. In summer, the patio garden is a veritable suntrap. No food is available on Sunday. Small car park. ❀◑⇌♣P

Red Lion Inn

Old Shoreham Road (by old tollbridge)
11-3, 5.30-11; 11.30-11 Sat; 12-10.30 Sun
☎ (01273) 453171
Courage Directors; Harveys BB; guest beers Ⓗ

An ever-changing range of guest beers is a highlight of this 16th-century former coaching inn. Its location on the Downslink Way makes the pub popular with walkers and cyclists; a no-smoking restaurant serves good food. Watch out for the low ceiling in the lower bar area. The patio offers views over the Downs and Lancing College. The Adur beer festival is held here at Easter. Q❀◑◐P

SIDLESHAM

Crab & Lobster

Mill Lane (750 yards off B2145) OS862973
11-3, 6-11; 12-3, 7-10.30 (not winter eve) Sun
☎ (01243) 641233
Cheriton Pots Ale; Itchen Valley Fagin's; guest beers Ⓗ

Pleasant, two-bar, 15th-century village inn by Pagham Harbour, popular with walkers, cyclists and ornithologists. The pub is a tranquil haven of real character, with oak beams and log fires. An excellent, varied menu of reasonably-priced meals includes crab and lobster dishes, plus vegetarian options. The long-standing landlord makes everyone welcome. Q❀◑◐P

STAPLEFIELD

Jolly Tanners

Handcross Road
11-3, 5.30-11; 11-11 Sat; 12-10.30 Sun
☎ (01444) 400335
Fuller's Chiswick, London Pride; Harveys BB; guest beer Ⓗ

Cosy free house opposite the village green, the pub dates back to 1600. A former coaching inn and hotel, photographs of the locality are displayed. A good selection of home-cooked food attracts custom in large numbers. This local CAMRA Pub of the Year 2002 is a regular Guide entry, where mild is sold all year round. Q❀◑◐♣P

TROTTON

Keeper's Arms

250 yds E of Trotton Bridge traffic lights on A272
12-2.30; 5.30-11; 12-11 Fri & Sat; closed Mon; 12-10.30 Sun
☎ (01730) 813724
Ballard's Best Bitter; Cheriton Pots Ale; Hop Back Summer Lightning; guest beers Ⓗ

Delightful country pub close to the church. An oak-panelled bar, wood floor, beams and homely soft furnishings around a log fire provide total relaxation. Note the private collection of intriguing ornaments and furniture. Reservations are recommended for the excellent restaurant (closed Sun eve and Mon); bar food is available 12-2. The patio is a very popular drinking area in summer. The beer range includes seasonal brews.
Q❀◑◐●P

TURNERS HILL

Red Lion

Lion Lane OS342357
11-3, 5.30-11; 12-10.30 Sun
(01342) 715416
Harveys Pale Ale, BB, seasonal beers H
The local branch of CAMRA was formed here. Recent improvements to this traditional village pub include a new upstairs restaurant (also available for functions). The Sunday lunchtime roast is highly recommended (evening meals served Fri and Sat). However, the Red Lion has retained its village pub atmosphere and is well worth a visit. Buses 82, 84 and 85 from East Grinstead or Crawley will take you there (not Sun). Pub games include marbles.
Q P

WESTBOURNE

Cricketers Inn

Commonside
12-3, 5-11; 12-11 Fri & Sat; 12-10.30 Sun
(01243) 372647
Ballard's Best Bitter; Triple fff Alton's Pride; Ringwood Fortyniner, Old Thumper; guest beer H
This 300-year-old pub was rescued from closure a few years ago by villagers' protest. Now a free house, and a supporter of local small breweries, its name comes from the cricket pitch that used to exist on the common opposite. The story of a former landlord who shot his wife here in 1854 can be read in the bar. Set amid housing, this mainly serves locals, hosting a weekly quiz (Thu) and occasional live music. P

WEST CHILTINGTON

Five Bells

Smock Alley (signed on Storrington road)
OS091172
12-3, 6-11; 12-3, 7-10.30 Sun
(01798) 812143
Badger K&B Sussex; guest beers H
Run by a fifth generation landlord and deservedly in the Guide for many years, this welcoming hostelry is a beer drinker's haven, where one of the guest beers is always a mild. Collections of lamps, brasses and bottled beers feature in the bar area while diners are catered for in a conservatory-style restaurant (evening meals served Tue-sat). Biddenden cider is served straight from the barrel. Devil among the tailors is played here.
Q P

WHITEMANS GREEN

Ship

On B2114/B2115 jct
12-3, 5.30-11; 12-11 Sat; 12-3, 7-10.30 Sun
(01444) 413219
Fuller's London Pride; Harveys BB; Taylor Landlord; guest beers G
Compact, busy village local where the experienced landlord is fiercely proud of his gravity-served real ales. There is plenty of room for diners and the bar is surprisingly spacious, with a large open fire. Panelled and exposed brick walls are adorned with local and thematic memorabilia. Pub games are housed in a designated area.
P

WISBOROUGH GREEN

Cricketers Arms

Loxwood Road (off A272)
11-2.30, 5.30-11; 11-11 Sat; 12-10.30 Sun
(01403) 700369
Cheriton Pots Ale; Fuller's London Pride; Wadworth 6X; guest beer H
Attractive old country pub with woodblock floors and low beamed ceilings, setting off the central wood-burning stove. It is the home of English motor mower racing, hosting regular meetings. Overlooking the village green, a daytime bus service (No. 76) runs from Petworth and Horsham (not Sun). Good food is served (no meals Sun eve). P

WORTHING

Castle Tavern

1 Newland Road
11-3, 5.30-11; 11-11 Fri & Sat; 12-3, 7-10.30 Sun
(01903) 601000 website: www.castletavern.com
Harveys BB; Hop Back Summer Lightning; Shepherd Neame Bishops Finger; guest beers H
Cheery free house, offering six real ales and a quality menu that includes regular themed evenings. The pub boasts original stripped wood flooring in the main bar, a dining area and comfortable patio. An eclectic mix of live music is performed (Sat), as well as weekly folk sessions. An expanding collection of breweriana sits alongside musical memorabilia. An annual beer festival is held in April – an ideal time to try out the rare game of shuffleboard. No meals served Sun eve or Mon.
(Central) P

Charles Dickens

56 Heene Road
11-11; 12-10.30 Sun
(01903) 603791
Harveys BB; Taylor Landlord; Woodforde's Wherry; guest beers H
Traditional free house just back from the seafront on three floors, it has been much improved in recent years. An interesting selection of ales is always available as are full restaurant facilities, seven days a week. A no-smoking area is on the first floor, while in the basement is the Copperfield Suite, used for functions. Occasional beer festivals, music and quiz nights happen regularly.

George & Dragon

1 High Street, Tarring
11-3, 5.30-11; 11-11 Fri & Sat; 12-10.30 Sun
(01903) 202497
Courage Directors; Hop Back Summer Lightning; John Smith's Bitter; Wells Bombardier; Young's Bitter; guest beer H
Once a medieval village, Tarring retains much of its village character, despite having been swallowed by Worthing. The early 17th-century pub thrives as a place where locals gather to enjoy the simple pleasures of good company, conversation and fine beers. The single bar, with low, exposed oak beams and dark wood panelling incorporates a cosy snug and a no-smoking eating area (no food Sun). The pub supports several darts, football and cricket teams. It has a pleasant, tranquil garden.
Q (West) P

Selden Arms

41 Lyndhurst Road (near hospital)
11 (12 Sat)-11; 12-10.30 Sun
☎ (01903) 234854
Ringwood Best Bitter, Fortyniner; Wolf Bitter H

The Selden Arms, a genuine free house, sets the standard for quality and range of cask conditioned ales. Six busy handpumps serve an average of 100 different ales each year, almost always including a dark beer. It also keeps a selection of Belgian bottle conditioned beers. A short walk from the main station, it is handy for the town centre and bus routes. Some interesting photographs of past and present Worthing pubs adorn the walls. No evening meals are served Sun. Local CAMRA Pub of the Year 2002. ⇌ (Central) ♣

Swan

79 High Street (opp. Safeway)
11-2.30, 6 (5.30 Fri)-11; 11-11 Sat; 12-10.30 Sun
☎ (01903) 232923
Greene King Abbot; Harveys BB; Shepherd Neame Spitfire; guest beer H

Festooned with hops, this one-bar pub has a dining area, two real fires and a comfortable patio. Collections of brass, bottles and glasses are displayed alongside agricultural implements. Bar billiards is played in the main bar area where dogs are welcome at quiet times. It hosts weekly food theme evenings, where value for money is the key. Folk music sessions are held monthly and weekly discos complete the music scene. Bus routes 5, 5A and 7 run from the town centre. ⇌ (Central) ♣

YAPTON

Lamb Inn

Bilsham Road (B2132, S of village)
11-3, 5.30 (5 Sat)-11; 12-4.30, 6.30-10.30 Sun
☎ (01243) 551232
Greene King Abbot; Harveys BB; guest beer H

This friendly roadside pub on the southern edge of the village was originally a cottage. Surprisingly spacious, it features a large open fireplace with a 17th-century backplate, a brick floor and beamed ceiling. The no-smoking dining room caters for all tastes with first-class, home-made food. The family garden is equipped with play facilities, an animal corner and pétanque pistes. This excellent community pub is kept as traditional as possible.
Q ♣P

Maypole Inn

Maypole Lane (off B2132, 1/2 mile N of village)
OS978041
11-3, 5.30-11; 12-3, 7-10.30 Sun
☎ (01243) 551417
Ringwood Best Bitter; guest beers H

Small, flint-faced free house, tucked down a lane, away from the village centre. The lane was cut off by the railway in 1846 and the pub has enjoyed quiet isolation ever since. The cosy lounge boasts an impressive log fire and an imposing row of seven handpumps, dispensing an ever-changing range of independent beers. The large public bar has darts, pool, TV and a juke box. A skittle alley is also available (booking necessary).
Q ♣ P

Fizz warning

Some national breweries produce both cask-conditioned and 'nitro-keg' versions of their beers. Boddingtons Bitter, John Smith's Bitter, Tetley's Bitter and Worthington fall into this category. Nitro-keg beers, often promoted as 'smooth' or 'cream-flow' products, are filtered and pasteurised in the brewery, and served in pubs by a mix of applied carbon dioxide and nitrogen gases. They are bland, served extremely cold, and any hop character is lost by the use of applied gas. To add insult to injury, the keg founts that serve such beers are often topped by small dummy handpumps. As a result of lobbying by CAMRA, some producers of cask and nitro versions of the same beer now include the word 'cask' on pump clips for the genuine article. For example, both John Smith's Bitter and Tetley's Bitter now carry the word 'cask' on pump clips for the real thing. For the sake of brevity, and as the Good Beer Guide lists only cask-conditioned beers, we refer simply to John Smith's Bitter and Tetley Bitter. The Coors Brewing brand, Worthington, is labelled Worthington Bitter in cask form, and – bizarrely – Worthington Best Bitter in the nitro-keg version. Always choose the living rather than the dead.

TYNE & WEAR

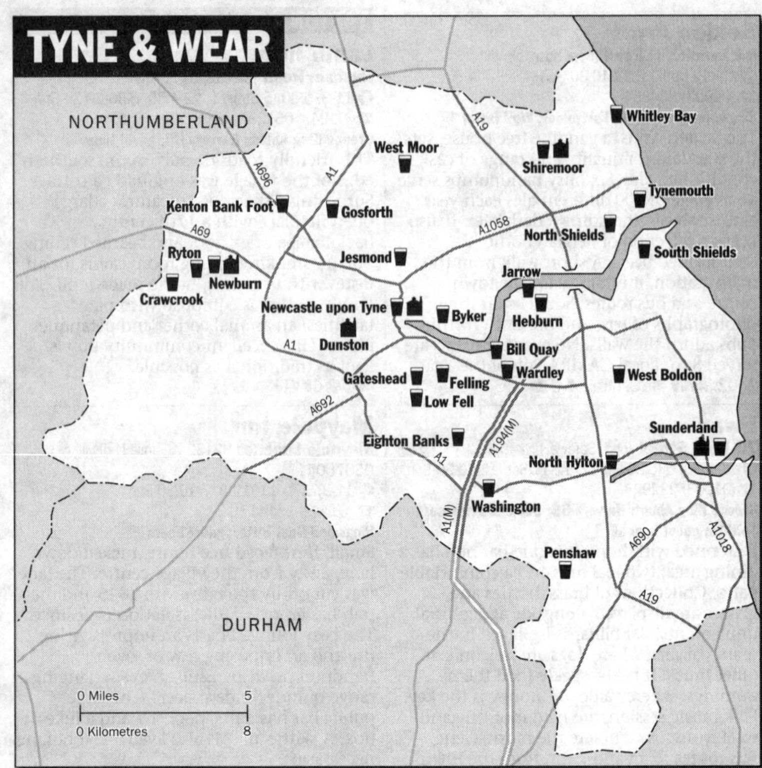

BILL QUAY

Albion

Reay Street (foot of hill on river bank)
4 (12 Sat)-11; 12-10.30 Sun
☎ (0191) 469 2418
Black Sheep Best Bitter; Fuller's London Pride; guest beers H

Overlooking a wide bend in the River Tyne, this square-shaped comfortable lounge bar has a conservatory (with pool table). Excellent views are afforded across heavily industrialised Tyneside. Its committed owners are particularly keen to support real ales produced by north-east micro-breweries and, unusually for the area, also sell a real cider, Weston's Old Rosie. Not surprisingly the pub attracts many regular customers from outside the immediate catchment area. Regular quiz nights and live music sessions are hosted. (Pelaw) P

BYKER

Cluny

36 Lime Street
11-11; 12.30-3.30, 5.30-11 Mon; 12-10.30 Sun
☎ (0191) 230 4474
Banks's Bitter, Big Lamp Prince Bishop Ale; Mordue Five Bridge Bitter; Workie Ticket, seasonal beers; guest beers H

Excellent pub conversion; the building (dating back to the 1840s) started life as a mill and then became warehouses (a bond for Cluny Whisky – hence the name). It now comprises a bar/café, art gallery and performance area. Guest beers are from local micros, seasonal beers from Durham are stocked and there is a rotating range of continental beers and a good rum selection. There is no sign over the pub door; the entrance is down the cobbled bank leading to the Ouseburn next to Byker City Farm. Good quality food is served all day.

Free Trade

St Lawrence Road
11-11; 12-10.30 Sun
☎ (0191) 265 5764
Hadrian & Border Gladiator; Marston's Pedigree; Mordue Five Bridges Bitter, Workie Ticket, seasonal beers H

One of the very few pubs named after a political movement, this is a straightforward, plain and simple drinking house. Stunning views extend over the River Tyne and its bridges. The single bar serves the main room and smaller seating area that is set down a few steps. Friendly regular customers, smiling service and consistently good quality beer all adds up to create a great atmosphere. The weekly quiz is held on Wednesday evening. The free juke box offers classic 60s rock while music of a gentler, drifting nature characterises Sunday afternoons.

Tyne

1 Maling Street
12-11; 12-10.30 Sun
☎ (0191) 265 2550 website: www.thetyne.com
Black Sheep Best Bitter; Durham Magus, seasonal beers; Mordue Five Bridges Bitter, Workie Ticket, seasonal beers H

This very popular, single-roomed pub rests below Glasshouse Bridge, which acts as an unusual roof to the beer garden, so it can be used whatever the weather. Live music on

Wednesday and Sunday attracts a larger number of visitors; Bank holiday Monday sessions are legendary. However the pub is worth visiting at any time to sample the good beer and interesting sandwiches. ❀

FELLING

Old Fox

Carlisle Street

12-11; 12-10.30 Sun

☎ (0191) 420 0357

Banks's Bitter; guest beers H

Friendly local with a good range of beers, in an area with a deserved, growing reputation for quality cask ale pubs. The Fox has three distinct drinking areas and a paved section serves as a garden. The pool table and juke box do not dominate and an inviting open fire provides a focal point in winter.

Wheatsheaf

26 Carlisle Street

12-11 (may vary); 12-10.30 Sun

☎ (0191) 420 0659

Big Lamp Bitter, Prince Bishop Ale H

This welcoming inn, rebuilt in 1907, has an impressive faience exterior and a number of the original cut and etched windows survive. Owned by the local Big Lamp Brewery, the entire wooden-floor area of the former pub is now one room, retaining the original bar and impressive back fitting. Darts and dominoes are played, and there are impromptu music sessions some evenings.

GATESHEAD

Borough Arms

80-82 Bensham Road

11-3, 6-11; 11-11 Fri & Sat; 12-10.30 Sun

☎ (0191) 478 1323

Draught Bass; Black Sheep Best Bitter; Wells Bombardier; guest beers H

Lively, no-frills community local with the only real ale in or near the town centre. The pub has no pool table or juke box, but has had bare boards since long before they became trendy. Note the pub's sign, it depicts Gateshead's ancient coat of arms and the origin of the town's name. It is adjacent to the renovated Windmill Hills Park that offers commanding views over Newcastle and the Tyne Valley. Weekly folk/acoustic music and pop quiz eves are hosted. The Borough Arms is handy for public transport interchange. Children are not admitted. Lunchtime meals are served on weekdays 12-2.

P

GOSFORTH

County

70 High Street

12 (11 Fri & Sat)-11; 12-10.30 Sun

☎ (0191) 285 6919

Courage Directors; Greene King Old Speckled Hen; Marston's Pedigree; Theakston Best Bitter; Wells Bombardier; guest beers H

One of the most well-known pubs in the area, the County is an imposing listed building, guarding the southern end of the High Street. Notorious for links with the criminal underworld during the 19th century: read the full history on plaques outside the entrance. Many original Victorian features have been retained in this unspoilt, popular pub that tends to be busy at weekends. The L-shaped bar offers six regular beers and two ever-changing guest ales. A separate function room is available for hire. No eve meals are served Fri or Sat.

Q (Regent Centre)

HEBBURN

Dougie's Tavern

Blackett Street (on riverside road 5 mins from Jarrow metro station)

11.30am-2.30am; 11.30am-2.30am Sun

☎ (0191) 428 4800 website: www.dougiestavern.co.uk

Theakston Cool Cask; guest beers H

Located near the banks of the River Tyne, this friendly pub is named after the grandfather of the family, Douglas Hedley. Various 'happy hours' take place: Mon-Fri 2-9pm, Sat 11.30am-2.30pm and 6-7pm, Sun 6-9pm. Food is served afternoons and entrtainment includes evenings with live music on Thursday, occasional 'sportsman's evenings' and weekly quizzes. The pub holds a children's certificate; it is child-friendly with a secure outdoor play area and garden. Usually two or three guest beers are available on handpull.

(Jarrow) P

JARROW

Ben Lomond

Grange Road West

11-11; 12-10.30 Sun

☎ (0191) 483 3839

Courage Directors; Shepherd Neame Spitfire; Theakston Best Bitter; Wadworth 6X; guest beers H

Typical town-centre Wetherspoon's pub offering good value beer and food. The large partitioned ground-floor bar has stories of old Jarrow and pictures depicting local engineering history. Although there is no music or TV, the bar area is always lively. There is additional seating in a quieter section on the first floor.

Q

KENTON BANK FOOT

Twin Farms

22 Main Road

11-11; 12-10.30 Sun

☎ (0191) 286 1263 website: www.sjf.co.uk

Mordue Workie Ticket; Taylor Landlord; guest beers H

New building, in traditional style, on the site of two old farms. The pub has a spacious, open-plan main room but, by the clever use of alcoves, it has the feel of several small rooms. Two real log fires and a huge black kitchen range add character. The two guest beers change weekly and food is available all day.

Q (Bank Foot) P

INDEPENDENT BREWERIES

Big Lamp Newburn
Darwin Sunderland
Federation Dunston
Hadrian & Border Newcastle upon Tyne
Mordue Shiremoor

LOW FELL

Aletaster

706 Durham Road (jct of Durham Road and Chowdene Bank)
12 (11 Sat)-11; 12-10.30 Sun
(0191) 487 0770
Everards Tiger; Jennings Cumberland Ale; Mordue Workie Ticket; Taylor Landlord; guest beers H

Now tenanted by a pub company, although this suburban, main road ale house-style pub is still instantly recognisable as a former T&J Bernard house. George IV, the pub's original name, is depicted in a window. The Aletaster can be very busy, customers attracted by the good range of ales and guests (11 handpulls) and, unusually for the area, a real cider (Weston's Old Rosie). A courtyard serves as a garden and occasional beer festival, weekly live music and quizzes, are hosted. P

NEWBURN

Keelman

Grange Road
12-11; 12-10.30 Sun
(0191) 267 0772
Big Lamp Bitter, Summerhill Stout, Prince Bishop Ale, Premium, seasonal beers H

A Grade II listed building now houses the Big Lamp Brewery and its brewery tap. The pub opened in the former water pumping station in 1996 and the brewery – the region's oldest micro-brewery – soon followed. The sympathetically converted building offers the full range of Big Lamp beers, which have built up a strong following since the brewery moved from a district in Newcastle, still known as the Big Lamp. Good value food is available. The adjoining lodge offers quality accommodation along with an outdoor drinking area in an attractive setting by Tyne Riverside Country Park. The keelmen, boatmen who plied the Tyne shipping coal, are commemorated in old photographs. P

NEWCASTLE UPON TYNE

Bodega

125 Westgate Road
11-11; 12-10.30 Sun
(0191) 221 1552 website: www.sjf.co.uk
Big Lamp Prince Bishop Ale; Durham Magus; Mordue Workie Ticket; guest beers H

The highlight of every visit to this pub, apart from the excellent beer selection, is a study of the two original glass ceiling domes. The Bodega is very popular with football fans and attracts music-lovers too as it is next to the Tyne Theatre and Opera House. Customers mix together creating a friendly atmosphere. The single bar room offers a number of standing and seating spots, including snug cubicles. The house beer, Number 9, is brewed by the local Mordue Brewery and reflects footballing interests (it is the shirt number worn by generations of famous Magpies' centre forwards). (Central)

Bridge Hotel

Castle Square
11.30-11; 12-10.30 Sun
(0191) 232 6400
Black Sheep Best Bitter; Boddingtons Bitter; Mordue Workie Ticket; guest beers H

This large pub looks towards the keep of the old 'new' castle and rests at the side of Stephenson's massive high level bridge, immortalised in Get Carter. One large room is divided by partitions with a raised area at one end. Prints of old Newcastle and railway memorabilia adorn the walls. At the back of the pub is a patio garden encircled by the old town wall, offering excellent views over the River Tyne. The upstairs function room hosts what is reputed to be the oldest folk music club in the country. (Central)

Crown Posada ☆

33 The Side
11 (12 Sat)-11; 7-10.30 (closed lunch) Sun
(0191) 232 1269
Draught Bass; Jennings Bitter; guest beers H

Tiny, but always welcoming, this pub is possibly, architecturally, the finest in Newcastle. Beautiful stained glass windows, unusual ceilings and wood-clad walls all add to the appeal. The pub is long and narrow, known locally as the Coffin. It has comfortable seating at one end and a tiny snug at the other. It can get busy, as it is now on the circuit following the regeneration of the quayside. If, while in

INN BRIEF

CRAWCROOK

Rising Sun
Bank Top (1/2 mile S of main crossroads)
12-11; 12-10.30 Sun
(0191) 413 3316
Boddingtons Bitter; Castle Eden Ale; Mordue Workie Ticket; guest beers H
LIvely, thriving local well situated, on most of the Tyne Valley routes between Blaydon and Hexham. Spacious interior affords selection of drinking areas.

EIGHTON BANKS

Lambton Arms
Rockcliffe Way
11-11; 12-10.30 Sun
(0191) 487 8137
Beer range varies H
Pleasant roadside pub with excellent views of the countryside. Food available all day and choice of four regularly changing ales.

JARROW

Greyhound
Hedworth Lane
11-11; 12-10.30 Sun
(0191) 489 7539
Draught Bass; Greene King Old Speckled Hen; guest beer H
Large pub with bar, lounge and extensive garden for summer barbecues. Popular for Sunday lunch.

JESMOND

Punch Bowl
125 Jesmond Road
11-11; 12-10.30 Sun
(0191) 281 2552
Courage Directors; Marston's Pedigree; Theakston Cool Cask, XB; guest beers H
Long-standing pub of 130 years, retains separate public bar and lounge. Regularly features TV sport.

NEWCASTLE UPON TYNE

Head of Steam
Neville Street
12-11; 12-10.30 Sun
(0191) 232 4379
Black Sheep Best Bitter; Caledonian Deuchars IPA; guest beers H
Two-roomed pub with upstairs and basement bars, very popular with younger crowd. The owner runs a chain of pubs.

NORTH SHIELDS

Prince of Wales
2 Liddell Street
12-3 (not Tue), 7-11; 11-11 Sat; 12-10.30 Sun
(0191) 296 2816
Samuel Smith OBB H
Restored in traditional style, featuring green glazed bricks and French embossed windows; sitting room, bar and pool room.

Newcastle, you only have time to visit one pub, make it this one.
Q ⇌ (Central) ⊖ (Monument)

Duke of Wellington
High Bridge
11-11; 12-10.30 Sun
☎ (0191) 261 8852
Marston's Pedigree; Tetley Bitter, Burton Ale; guest beers H
Single-roomed pub stocking a rapidly changing range of guest beers from all over the country. The pub history boasts that a former licensee was one of the world's largest men, weighing in at about 50 stone! It can get very busy especially at weekends as the pub is just off the infamous Bigg Market. However, if it is quiet, take time to study the collection of prints relating to the Iron Duke.
⇌ (Central) ⊖ (Monument)

Hotspur
103 Percy Street
11-11; 12-10.30 Sun
☎ (0191) 232 4352
Courage Directors; McEwan 80/-; Theakston Best Bitter, Old Peculier; guest beers H
Mirror-clad walls make this single-roomed, city-centre pub appear more spacious. A full frontage of windows enhances this and allows light to flood in. The landlord is keen to offer his customers the widest choice of guest beers, and the selection is one of the best in the city. The pub can be very busy on match days. ⊖ (Haymarket)

New Bridge
2 Argyle Street
11-11; 12-10.30 Sun
☎ (0191) 232 1020
Beer range varies H
Recently refurbished, and very comfortable pub featuring some fascinating old photographs of the building of Tyne Bridge and some decorative old mirrors. The Millennium Bridge, the latest to span the Tyne, can be viewed from the side door. Two constantly changing guest beers generally come from local independent micro-brewers. Good home-made food is served at lunchtime. A weekly quiz is held on Wednesday.
⊖ (Manors) ♣

Newcastle Arms
57 St Andrews Street
11-11; 7-10.30 Sun
☎ (0191) 232 3567
Black Sheep Best Bitter; Fuller's London Pride; guest beers H
Close to St James' Park football ground, this one-roomed pub can be very busy on match days. A large-screen TV shows sporting events. There is a seating area, tables at which to stand, and stools in the bay window. Food is available at lunchtime 11.30-2. Friendly atmosphere in which to enjoy good beer. ⊖ (St James)

NORTH HYLTON

Shipwright's Hotel
Ferryboat Lane
11-4, 7-11.30; 12-3, 7-11 Sun
☎ (0191) 549 5139
Greene King Abbot; Jennings Cumberland Ale; Marston's Pedigree; guest beer H
On the banks of the River Wear, this 350-year-old coaching inn is under the A19 Hylton Bridge. The bar area features exposed beams, brasses and an impressive collection of chamber pots. The pub has been under the same management for 23 years and has been in every edition of the Guide since 1978. Exotic food such as ostrich, alligator, crocodile and kangaroo features. The pub offers good value accommodation. Bikers are very welcome as the landlord is a keen motorcyclist.
P

NORTH SHIELDS

Magnesia Bank
Camden Street
11-11 (12 Thu-Sat); 12-10.30 Sun
☎ (0191) 257 4831
Black Sheep Best Bitter, Special; Durham Magus; Mordue Workie Ticket; guest beers H
Splendid town-centre pub, winner of many awards for food and music as well as beer. Local CAMRA Pub of the Year on numerous occasions, this is a friendly, family-run inn with a reputation for excellence. The bar has three seating areas; two are raised sections. It is the official Mordue Brewery tap and also stocks Durham and other local

SUNDERLAND

Harbour View
Benedict Road, Roker
11-11; 12-10.30 Sun
(0191) 567 1402
Draught Bass; guest beers H
Single-roomed lounge bar that overlooks Roker Marina. Up to three guest beers stocked, often from local Darwin Brewery.

TYNEMOUTH

Fitzpatrick's
29-30 Front Street
11-11; 12-10.30 Sun
(0191) 257 8956
Beer range varies H
Part of the Sir John Fitzgerald chain, this spacious pub has a raised seating area and snug. Popular with TV sports fans.

WASHINGTON

Three Horseshoes
North Hylton Road
11-11; 12-10.30 Sun
(0191) 536 4183
Draught Bass; Caledonian Deuchars IPA; Greene King Old Speckled Hen; Jennings Cumberland Ale; guest beers H
Friendly, two-roomed inn, adjacent to Nissan car plant. Popular with families. Strong emphasis on food. Games area.

Washington Arts Centre
Biddick Lane, Fatfield
11-11; 12-10.30 Sun
(0191) 219 3455
Marston's Pedigree; Taylor Landlord H
Attractive open-plan bar in council-run arts centre. Check out the local arts and crafts on sale nearby.

WEST BOLDON

Black Horse
Rectory Bank
11-11; 12-10.30 Sun
(0191) 536 1814
Greene King Old Speckled Hen; guest beers H
Traditional-style pub with small bar and separate restaurant. Two guest beers are usually offered.

WHITLEY BAY

Fat Ox
278 Whitley Road
12 (11 Sat)-11; 12-10.30 Sun
(0191) 251 3852
John Smith's Bitter; guest beers H
Situated on a corner site, this pub has one large room offering various areas for drinking, chat and pool.

beers. Good quality food using local produce is served (12-3, 5-9 Mon-Wed; 12-10 Thu-Sat; 12-9 Sun). A weekly quiz is hosted on Sun and live music on Wed, Fri and Sat eves. ◑⊖♣

Porthole

11 New Quay
11-11; 12-10.30 Sun
☎ (0191) 257 6645
Courage Directors; guest beers H
Another popular watering-hole on the riverside, this 1834 free house is close to the North-South Shields ferry landing. The pub has a nautical theme. One regular and two guest ales are available from a management team keen to restore this pub's position on the real ale trail. Jazz is played on Wed lunchtime and a range of live music is performed on Tue, Fri and Sun eves. ❀◐

Tap & Spile

184 Tynemouth Road
12 (11.30 Sat)-11; 12-10.30 Sun
☎ (0191) 257 2523
Caledonian Deuchars IPA; Greene King Ruddles County; Jennings Cumberland Ale; John Smith's Magnet; guest beers H
Still run as a Tap & Spile with a manager keen to uphold the tradition of real ale. It was awarded Tyneside & Northumberland CAMRA Pub of the Year 2001. Regular themed beer festivals are held in this two-roomed (part no-smoking) pub. Good food is served (12-2, 5.30-9 Mon-Fri; 11.30-9 Sat; 12-3 Sun) and Weston's Old Rosie cider is stocked. ◐◑⊖♣

PENSHAW

Monument

Old Penshaw Village (signed from A183)
11-3, 6-11; 11-11 Sat; 12-4, 7-10.30 Sun
☎ (0191) 584 1027
Beer range varies H
Welcoming country inn that is hidden away in Penshaw old village, close to the popular local landmark Penshaw Monument. This friendly local consists of a bar (more or less) divided into two areas which are comfortably snug, an open fire at each end should the weather be cool. A smaller room at the rear is dedicated to pool and darts. Quiet during the afternoon, but a plethora of evening entertainment is offered, ranging from quizzes to local amateur music. Barbecues are held in summer. ⅏Q❀P

RYTON

Old Cross

Old Ryton Village (signed from B6317)
11 (4 winter)-11; 12-11 Sat; 12-10.30 Sun
☎ (0191) 413 4689
John Smith's Magnet; Wells Bombardier; guest beers H
Originally a coaching house which served the Gateshead to Hexham route, the present building dates from 1909 and is situated close to the village cross, hence the name. It has a large one-roomed bar with a raised area to the rear. Doors open on to a patio area when the weather permits. The clientele are mainly local and very friendly. The upper floor houses an authentic Italian restaurant serving excellent food, with interesting decor and unusual dining furniture. ❀◐◑

SHIREMOOR

Shiremoor Farm

Middle Engine Lane
11-11; 12-10.30 Sun
☎ (0191) 257 6302
Mordue Workie Ticket; Taylor Landlord; guest beers H
A Fitzgerald-owned, award-winning conversion of derelict stone farm buildings by designer Alan Simpson. Recently extended, it retains the original conical raftered former 'gin gang' which now serves as the highly recommended restaurant. A thriving lunchtime trade means it can get busy but never overcrowded. The pub is, happily, free of distractions – no juke box, gaming machines or pool table. Designated smoke-free areas coupled with an efficient, but unobtrusive, air extraction system guarantee comfort. This is a superb setting in which to enjoy excellent beers.
Q❀◐◑P⅟

SOUTH SHIELDS

Alum House

River Drive (next to ferry landing)
11-11; 12-10.30 Sun
☎ (0191) 427 7245
Banks's Bitter; Marston's Pedigree; guest beers H
Old pub on the banks of the Tyne, with a fine view across the river. It has a sparsely furnished bar and a smaller room with high-backed settles. It is reputedly haunted by three ghosts, and is the meeting place of the Twilight World's Paranormal Society every Wednesday in the cellar bar. Sunday is quiz evening and Thursday is buskers' night. Three guest ales are available and the house beer, Alum Ale, comes from Durham Brewery. This is a good place to wait for the North Shields ferry. ⊖

Bamburgh

Bamburgh Avenue
11-11; 12-10.30 Sun
☎ (0191) 427 5523
Flowers Original; Greene King Abbot; Tetley Bitter; guest beers H
Situated on the main Sunderland to South Shields coast road and overlooking the sea, the pub is also within sight of the finishing line of the Great North Run. The spacious, open-plan interior has a raised seating area and family room separate from the bar. Good value meals are served during the day and the pub is very popular with visitors during the summer months. ◐◑▲P

Beacon

Greens Place
11-11; 12-10.30 Sun
☎ (0191) 456 2876
Adnams Broadside; Cameron's Strongarm; Marston's Pedigree H
The Beacon was named after the guiding lights at the mouth of the River Tyne which were built in the 18th century. A local business man, John Turnbull, had the originals replaced at a cost of £60 in 1832. This open-plan pub is an excellent venue to enjoy a pint of real ale, and the spectacular outlook over the river is popular with visitors and locals. The walls of the pub are

decorated with photographs on a nautical theme and views of old South Shields. Good value bar meals, served by friendly staff, can be enjoyed in a quiet atmosphere.
⊄⊖

Chichester Arms

Chichester Road (A194/B1298 jct, outside metro station)
✪ 11-11; 12-10.30 Sun
☎ (0191) 420 0127
Federation Buchanan's Best Bitter; Tetley Bitter, Burton Ale Ⓗ
Large, street-corner local that is easily accessible by bus and metro. There is no variation in the beer range but the Buchanan's is often sold at a cheaper rate. The staff are friendly and helpful – a prominently displayed notice advises drinkers that the staff will willingly top up a glass if the head on the beer is too large. The pub appeals to a more mature clientele.
Q⊄⊖ (Chichester)

Dolly Peel

Commercial Road
✪ 11-11; 12-10.30 Sun
☎ (0191) 427 1441
Courage Directors; Taylor Landlord; guest beers Ⓗ
Dolly Peel was a local fishwife, famous for smuggling and following her husband after he was press-ganged into the Navy during the Napoleonic Wars. It is a peaceful two-roomed pub with no fruit machine or pool table to distract anyone from the main pleasure of trying any of the six handpull ales always available. The pub has previously been voted local CAMRA Pub of the Year and still maintains its traditional feel of an English public house. It attracts a mostly mature clientele.
Q❀⊖ (Chichester) P

Riverside

3 Commercial Road
✪ 12-11; 12-3, 7-10.30 Sun
☎ (0191) 455 2328
Black Sheep Special; Courage Directors; Taylor Landlord; Theakston Cool Cask; guest beers Ⓗ
This genuine free house is a single-roomed bar. There is seating around the bar and on a raised area at the rear. Although busy at weekends, service is always friendly and efficient. It was CAMRA North-East Pub of the Year in 2000 and local Pub of the Year for the past three years. The regular beers are complemented by two frequently changing guests beers and a cider or perry. A quiz night is held on Tuesday.
⊖

Stag's Head

45 Fowler Street (400 yds N of Town Hall)
✪ 11-11; 12-10.30 Sun
☎ (0191) 456 9174
Draught Bass; Stones Bitter; Worthington Bitter Ⓗ
Thriving town-centre pub located close to South Shields metro and bus stations. Dating back to the 19th century, the small bar is decorated with photographs of old South Shields. It offers a welcome relief to shoppers during the day and holds popular 1960s, '70s and '80s theme nights. At weekends the bar gets very busy, but there is an upstairs room which is normally quieter.
⊖

Steamboat

51 Mill Dam
✪ 12-11; 12-10.30 Sun
☎ (0191) 454 0134
Wells Bombardier; guest beers Ⓗ
Situated on the Mill Dam close to the River Tyne, the pub is one of the oldest in South Shields and has a heavily nautical theme. It is decorated with seafaring photographs and other artefacts on the wood-panelled walls. The main bar is busy, particularly at weekends, but this is offset by the lounge which is usually quieter. The pub regularly features four guest ales. ⊖

SUNDERLAND

Fitzgerald's

10-12 Green Terrace
✪ 11-11; 12-10.30 Sun
☎ (0191) 567 0852
Beer range varies Ⓗ
Large open-plan pub on the edge of the city centre. The main bar is in Art Deco-style with lots of woodwork and stained glass. The smaller chart room is decked with maritime artefacts and has a large TV for sports. Up to 10 beers are on sale, the largest range in the area: beers from Darwin/Brewlab regularly appear. A quiz is held in the chart room on Monday and Tuesday. It is part of the Sir John Fitzgerald chain. ⊄≋⊖ (Park Lane/University)

Ivy House

Worcester Terrace (off Stockton Road)
✪ 11-11; 12-10.30 Sun
☎ (0191) 567 3399
Beer range varies Ⓗ
A charismatic landlord runs this single-roomed pub with a long central bar behind Park Lane Interchange. Close to the University and although popular with students it attracts a wide ranging clientele. The many TV screens are a magnet for sports fans and the Ivy is very busy on home match days. Wednesday is quiz night and there is live music on Thursday. Up to six beers are available, guests from Caledonian appear regularly. No food is served on Sunday. ⊄≋⊖ (Park Lane) P ✔

King's Arms

Beach Street
✪ 4.30 (12 Sat)-11; 12-10.30 Sun
☎ (0191) 567 9804
Taylor Landlord; guest beers Ⓗ
This pub, one of the oldest in Sunderland, is situated away from the main road but is one of three in a chain; the other two are the Ropery and Saltgrass. The management provide a free shuttle bus at weekends between the three pubs. Live music is well supported at weekends. In traditional style, it has an exposed timber floor and an inviting coal fire in the bar area. The small sitting areas which are carpeted and adjacent to the bar area are wood-panelled to dado height. Well worth a visit.
❀⊖ (University/Millfield)

New Derby

Roker Baths Road
✪ 11-11; 12-10.30 Sun
☎ (0191) 548 6263
Draught Bass; guest beers Ⓗ

Large open-plan pub – designed with the wishes of the regulars in mind. Adjacent to the site of the former Roker Park, it is still popular on match days for those who make the trek to the Stadium of Light. An ever-changing range of guest ales, all well kept, make this pub a must for the discerning beer-hunter. Food is served 12-2.30 and 5-7.
◐ ⊖ (Stadium of Light) ♣

Ropery
Websters Bank, Deptford
12-3; 5-11 (12 Fri & Sat); 12-10.30 Sun
☎ (0191) 514 7171
Castle Eden Ale; guest beers Ⓗ
Multi-roomed inn on the banks of the River Wear. An early 19th-century building, once a ropeworks, it was converted to a pub in 1985. It comprises a restaurant, function room and bars with live music (Fri, Sat and Sun) with other mid-week entertainment. This friendly pub offers good value food. As part of a triangle of pubs, there is free transport provided at weekends between the King's Arms and Saltgrass.
❀◐ ♿ ⊖ (Pallion) P

Saltgrass
36 Ayres Quay, Deptford
11.30-2.30, 4-11; 11.30-11 Fri & Sat; 12-3, 7-10.30 Sun
☎ (0191) 565 7229
Draught Bass; Marston's Pedigree; guest beers Ⓗ
This former Vaux pub sits in the shadow of the former shipyards. The pub has a small public bar adorned with ship's artefacts and dominated by a roaring open fire. A quiz night is held on Tuesday. The pub is under the same ownership as the King's Arms and the Ropery, and there is free transport between all three at weekends. Up to four beers from the Pubmaster's list are usually available.
◐ ⊖ (University/Millfield)

TYNEMOUTH

Copperfields
Hotspur Street
12-11; 12-10.30 Sun
☎ (0191) 293 6666 website: www.grand-hotel-uk.com
Durham Magus; Mordue Geordie Pride; guest beers Ⓗ
Cosy, relaxing public bar of the aptly-named Grand Hotel that is located on the clifftops. It is a short distance from the noisy, often crowded circuit pubs on Front Street, but a world away in terms of atmosphere. It was built as a seaside home for a 19th-century Duchess of Northumberland. The internal etched glasswork, based on the characters from the novels of Charles Dickens, is worth a look. Evening meals are served until 7pm.
◐ ♿ ⊖ P

Dolphin
King Edward Road
11-11; 12-10.30 Sun
☎ (0191) 257 4342
Flowers Original; Taylor Landlord; Tetley Bitter; guest beers Ⓗ
A much-improved local that offers rotating guest beers along with the regular fine ales. The front bar is for drinking and a large room at the rear serves good value food lunchtime and evenings. This popular pub has a friendly atmosphere. ◐ ♿ ⊖

Tynemouth Lodge Hotel
Tynemouth Road
11-11; 12-10.30 Sun
☎ (0191) 257 7565
website: www.tynemouthlodgehotel.co.uk
Draught Bass; Belhaven 80/-; Caledonian Deuchars IPA; guest beer Ⓗ
Built in 1799, this free house has been a Guide entry since 1984, following its purchase by the current owner; a very welcoming CAMRA member and activist. The pub is noted in the area for reputedly having the highest Draught Bass sales on Tyneside, and, unusually, for featuring Scottish real ales. This comfortable single-roomed lounge bar is next to Northumberland Park and near the Coast-to-Coast cycle route.
Q ❀ ⊖ P

WARDLEY

Green
White Mare Pool (A184/B1288 jct)
11.30-11; 12-10.30 Sun
☎ (0191) 495 0171 website: www.sjf.co.uk
Courage Directors; Fuller's London Pride; Taylor Landlord; guest beers Ⓗ
Easily accessible by road, most of the customers of this upmarket pub arrive by car. Part of the Sir John Fitzgerald's chain, it is based on the design of South African golfer Gary Player's home and overlooks an 18th green. Its comfortable Victorian-style public bar is popular with large-screen TV sports fans. This contrasts markedly with its restaurant specialising in English cuisine, and the whitewashed walls of its glazed lounge. There is a travel lodge nearby. Sports and general quizzes are held weekly and occasional beer festivals feature.
❀◐ ♿ P

WASHINGTON

Sandpiper
Easby Road, Biddick
11-11; 12-10.30 Sun
☎ (0191) 415 1733
Boddingtons Bitter; Castle Eden Ale; Flowers Original; guest beers Ⓗ
Modern single-storey estate pub with a small public bar that features large-screen TV and a pool table. This contrasts with a larger, stone-floored lounge serving good value meals and snacks. Up to three guest beers are available. A quiz night is held on Tuesday. The pub is popular with local football teams at weekends. It is one of only a handful of pubs in Washington serving cask ales.
❀◐ ♿ ♣ P

Steps
47-49 Spout Lane
11-11; 12-10.30 Sun
☎ (0191) 415 0733
Beer range varies Ⓗ
Located in Washington old village, it is close to the tourist attraction, Washington Old Hall. This one-roomed divided bar/lounge is comfortable, warm and friendly. Once no larger than an average front room, it has been

extended over the years and has increased in character. Popular with all ages, the pub retains its value for cask ales, maintaining three guest ales at all times. Background music, a large-screen TV for sporting events, and quizzes contribute to the entertainment. Good lunchtime meals are available, snacks only eves.
◐

WEST MOOR

George Stephenson
Great Lime Road
✪ 12-11; 12-10.30 Sun
☎ (0191) 268 1073
website: www.georgestephensoninn.com
John Smith's Magnet; McEwan 80/-; guest beers Ⓗ
Winning its class in North Tyneside in Bloom, for superb external displays, was a fitting celebration for this pub's centenary in 2001. Much altered over its 100 years, it is now split into two areas that, when required, can become a single room by opening the dividing doors. An established music venue, it hosts live bands Wed, Thu and Sat, plus a weekly quiz (Mon) and other occasional events. Frequently changing guest beers often feature smaller breweries, including those from the local area. The main rail line passes right by the pub patio.
❀P

WHITLEY BAY ❄

Briar Dene
71 The Links
✪ 11-11 (public bar may close afternoons); 12-10.30 Sun
☎ (0191) 252 0926 website: www.sjf.co.uk
Black Sheep Best Bitter; Greene King Old Speckled Hen; Mordue Workie Ticket; guest beers Ⓗ
A former tollhouse with a well-earned reputation for good quality beer and food. The well-lit lounge has coloured leaded glass above the bar and overlooks the links, St Mary's lighthouse and the sea. An indoor children's play area leads off this large lounge. The smaller rear bar features TV, pool and darts. Three new beers each week and up to six guest ales have meant over 1,700 different beers have been served. Regular beer festivals are held.
❀◐◑♿▲♣P⊬

Rockcliffe Arms
Algernon Place
✪ 11-11; 12-10.30 Sun
☎ (0191) 253 1299 website: www.sjf.co.uk
Beer range varies Ⓗ
Compact Sir John Fitzgerald's one-roomed community pub, offering old-style drinking in pleasant surroundings. Enter by the snug or the lounge doors, attractively decorated with stained glass. The single bar is partitioned to serve the two distinct drinking areas. Regular darts and dominoes nights are hosted, plus a quiz evening.
❀⊖♣

Healthy Drinking

For most people, alcohol in moderation is more likely to improve rather than damage their health. Because alcohol is dangerous in excess, its advantages are often overlooked.

Set yourself a limit before you start an evening's drinking. Try to keep track of when and what you drink. Avoid drinking on an empty stomach.

It is better to drink at meal times, or at any rate with some food. Snacks should be served when drinks are offered. Be aware of the difficulties of measuring a drink when pouring one at home. Most home-poured gins and whiskies are at least double the tot provided by the local publican.

Drink slowly, and dilute spirits with at least as much water. This might shock the Scots but it would help their health.

Dr Thomas Stuttaford,
To *Your Good Health,* Faber, 1997.

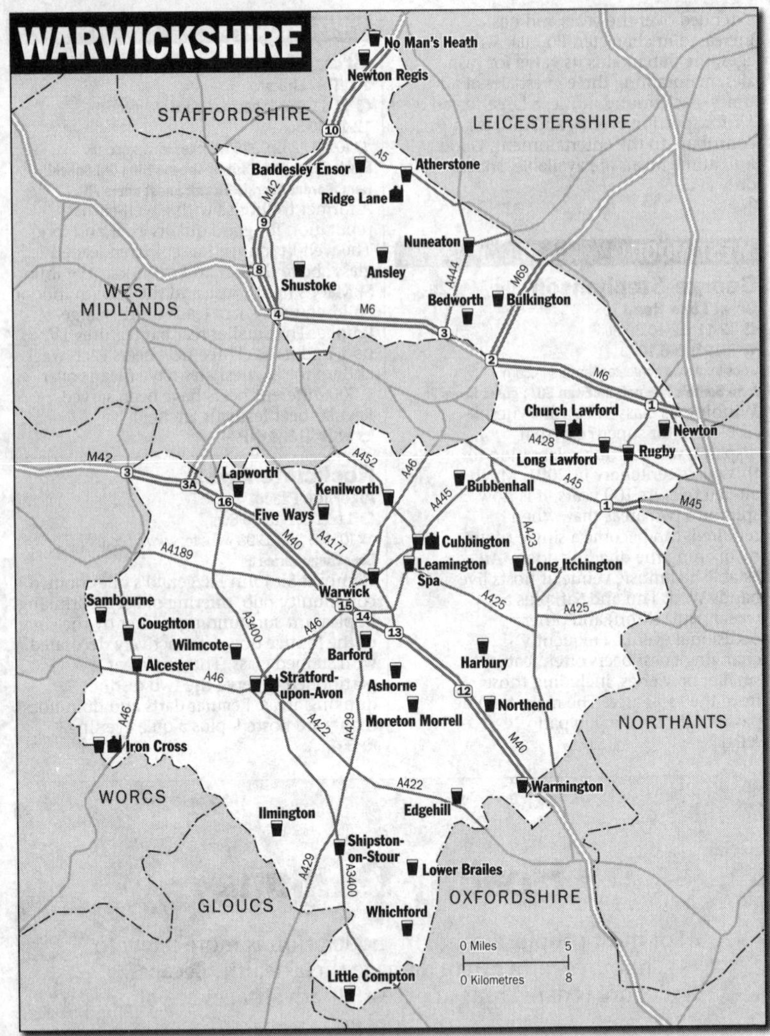

ALCESTER

Holly Bush

37 Henley Street

12-11; 12-10.30 Sun

☎ (01789) 762482

Banks's Bitter; Brakspear Bitter; Cannon Royall Fruiterer's Mild; Uley Bitter; guest beers Ⓗ

Former market town hotel, tucked away behind the town hall and church. Recent refurbishment has increased the number of rooms from two to five. There is a function room and extensive garden, with barbecue, at the rear. Oak and pine wall panelling abound and bare wood or flagstone floors. Normally seven or eight real ales are available and two beer festivals are held a year, one during June's Alcester and Arden Folk Festival. The regular folk sessions and 'singarounds' are popular. **Q ♣ P**

Three Tuns

High Street

12-11; 12-10.30 Sun

☎ (01789) 762626

Goff's Jouster; Hobsons Best Bitter; guest beers Ⓗ

Single-bar pub on the High Street, where small-paned bull's-eye windows make it look more like an antique shop. Inside, among the low beams and flagstone floor, the antiquity of the building is revealed by a glass panel in one wall, exposing the wattle and daub construction. No piped music, no pool table, no food – just how pubs used to be. It serves an ever-changing range of eight beers from micros and independents, and fruit wines. **Q ♣**

ANSLEY

Lord Nelson Inn

Birmingham Road

12-2.30, 5.30-11; 12-11 Sat; 12-10.30 Sun

☎ (024) 7639 2305

Draught Bass; M&B Brew XI; guest beers Ⓗ

Food-oriented, family-run free house renowned for its excellent cuisine. The 90-seater Victory restaurant offers both an English and French menu. A chauffeur-driven Rolls Royce can be hired to celebrate a special occasion. In the smaller Mary Rose restaurant, tasty bar meals include home-made dishes and a good choice on the specials board. The recently refurbished bar has an excellent range of guest beers verified by the collection of pump clips. The No. 17 bus stop is adjacent.

ASHORNE

Cottage Tavern

Off B4001 OS303577

12-2.30 (not Mon or Tue), 5.30-11; 12-4, 7-10.30 Sun

(01926) 651410

website: www.cottagetavern@ashorne.com

Adnams Bitter; guest beers

Traditional country village pub with open-plan lounge and dining area, a warm and welcoming atmosphere and an open fire during the colder spells. Evening meals are served Thu-Sat – however, bookings can be accepted for other times. Yet another instance of a pub that had been closed but has reopened under new ownership and is now well supported by the local community and passing ramblers. Darts, dominoes and crib are played. A genuine free house.

ATHERSTONE

Market Tavern

Market Street

11-11; 12-10.30 Sun

Warwickshire Best Bitter, Lady Godiva, St Patricks, Golden Bear, seasonal beers; guest beers

The first pub owned by the Warwickshire Brewing Company. As such, the brewery's beers dominate the array of handpumps. There are usually six cask ales available and a mild is normally included. Kingston Press cider is sold. The pub is set in the Market Square area of Atherstone, so watch out for the cobbles and the activities on Shrove Tuesday. Inside, there is a basic lounge and quiet rear room. Shove-ha'penny is played. Food is currently limited to rolls, and there are no chips, children or juke boxes to disturb the drinking. An oasis in a town where micro-brewed beer is rare.

BADDESLEY ENSOR

Red Lion Inn

The Common

12-3 (not Mon-Thu), 7-11; 12-3, 7-10.30 Sun

(01827) 713009

Banks's Original; Marston's Pedigree; guest beers

Candlelit tables and a roaring fire enhance the relaxed atmosphere in this traditional, one-roomed village local. Up to three guest beers are on tap, the choice changes frequently. Peaceful, yet friendly, the Red Lion is well worth a visit. Note the restricted weekday opening hours.

BARFORD

Granville Arms

52 Wellesborne Road

12-3, 6-11; 12-11 Fri & Sat; 12-10.30 Sun

(01926) 624236

Hook Norton Best Bitter; Warwickshire Lady Godiva; guest beer

An extended Georgian pub, the main part retains its essential three-bay symmetry. Inside, the two bars are decorated in warm shades of brick and timber. Plenty of old photographs of the village adorn the walls, and tucked away is an old mangle. A wood-panelled corridor with a manorial feel leads to the separate no-smoking dining area. Excellent quality and choice of dishes, prepared by an award-winning chef; evening meals are served until 9.30pm (9pm Sun). The Granville family once owned nearby Wellesbourne Hall. Easy to reach from M40 junction 15.

BEDWORTH

White Swan

All Saints Square

11-11; 12-10.30 Sun

(024) 7631 2164

Wells Eagle, Bombardier

Large corner pub in the town centre. The small bar has a games area to one side, and there is a spacious lounge. Folk club meetings are held regularly (second Wed each month), with the highlight of the folk year, the National Folk Festival hosted in Bedworth at the end of November. This friendly, well-run pub is busy at weekends, when the discos attract many customers. Lunchtime food is served Mon-Sat.

BUBBENHALL

Malt Shovel

Lower End

12-2.30 (3 Sat), 6-11; 12-3, 7-10.30 Sun

(024) 7630 1141

Ansells Bitter; Draught Bass; M&B Brew XI; Tetley Bitter; guest beer

Busy, pleasant village local with a large L-shaped lounge bar to the front, and a smaller public bar to the rear. Meals are available all sessions (except Sun eve in winter), with separate lunch and evening menus. Behind the spacious car park is the pub's delightful, enclosed beer garden with adjoining bowling green. The pub boasts football and bowls teams. There is also a small front patio. Popular with walkers and convenient for visitors to nearby Ryton Pools Country Park and the National Agricultural Centre at Stoneleigh.

BULKINGTON

Olde Chequers Inn

Chequers Street

12-3, 7 (6 Thu)-11; 11-11 Fri & Sat; (hours may vary in summer); 12-10.30 Sun

(024) 7631 2182

website: www.oldechequersinn.co.uk

Draught Bass; M&B Mild, Brew X1; guest beers

Excellent example of a village free house, sympathetically extended without spoiling the original, local feel. The separate restaurant can be busy at times (booking advised for Sunday lunch). A new, well-appointed games area is home to the two

INDEPENDENT BREWERIES

Church End Ridge Lane
Cox's Yard Stratford-upon-Avon
Frankton Bagby Church Lawford
Queen's Head Iron Cross
Warwickshire Cubbington

darts teams, football has a good following as this pub has two teams in local leagues. The Olde Chequers looks picturesque in summer, with colourful hanging baskets and a very pleasant beer garden. ⌂❀♣P

Weavers Arms

12 Long Street, Ryton (off Wolvey Rd)
⊙ 12-3, 5-11; 12-11 Sat; (hours may vary in summer); 12-10.30 Sun
☎ (024) 7631 4415
Draught Bass; M&B Brew XI; guest beers Ⓗ
Small, friendly free house, well supported by locals, who enjoy participating in the village carnival, the pub's fête, and golf matches, all in aid of charities. The regulars run teams in the local games leagues. Darts, dominoes and crib are played. Lunchtime food is available Tue-Sun. The now famous Pork Pie Club is held every Thursday night. It is always amusing to take part in, or just listen to, the impromptu lunchtime quiz. ⌂❀◑♣

CHURCH LAWFORD

Old Smithy

1 Green Lane (off A428, 4 miles from Rugby)
⊙ 11-3, 5.30-11; 11-11 Sat; 12-10.30 Sun
☎ (024) 7654 2333 website: www.theold-smithy.com
Ansells Mild; Greene King IPA, Abbot; Tetley Bitter; guest beers Ⓗ
This large, friendly, picturesque village pub caters for just about everybody. A traditional drinking area is complemented by a no-smoking restaurant at one end, and an unobtrusive hidden games room at the other. It also has a large car park next to the children's play area. Upwards of seven real ales are usually available, featuring at least one from the Frankton Bagby Brewery, which is situated behind the pub. The thriving food trade does mean that securing a table can be difficult at busy times, but the meals are top quality. ⌂Q❀◑♿♣P

COUGHTON

Throckmorton Arms

On A435, 100 yds from Coughton Court
⊙ 11-11; 12-10.30 Sun
☎ (01789) 766366
Draught Bass; Fuller's London Pride; Hancock HB; Taylor Landlord Ⓗ
Ignore the garish exterior, the large open-plan interior is divided into raised seating areas, and cosy corners with settees and open fires. Good food, lunchtime snacks and meals along with four real ales is what the pub aims to provide. Nearby is the National Trust's Coughton Court with its Gunpowder Plot connections. ⌂Q❀⛺◑◐◑♿P⚟

CUBBINGTON

Queen's Head

20 Queen Street
⊙ 12-11; 12-10.30 Sun
☎ (01926) 429949
Ansells Mild, Bitter; Draught Bass; guest beer Ⓗ
Cosy Victorian pub with a public bar, pool room and comfortable lounge. This is a real community local where young and old meet and where often the loudest noise is the conversation. The vast display of pump clips testifies to the range and popularity of the guest beers, a blackboard lists upcoming guest ales already in the cellar. A fishing club, golf society and darts team all use the pub, and major sports events are shown on a large-screen TV. ⌂Q◑♣P

FIVE WAYS

Case is Altered ☆

Case Lane (off Claverdon road at A4141/A4177 jct)
OS225701
⊙ 12 (11.30 Sat)-2.30, 6-11; 12-2, 7-10.30 Sun
☎ (01926) 484206
Greene King IPA; Hook Norton Old Hooky; Ⓖ **Jennings Mild; guest beer** Ⓗ
Lovely, unspoilt, rural pub some 350 years old. The traditional bar is decorated with an old price list and poster of the defunct Leamington Spa brewery – Lucas, Blackwell & Arkwright. A separate room houses the bar billiards table, that takes old 6d coins (available from the bar, for a donation to charity). The lounge bar with comfortable, old-fashioned armchairs opens Friday and Saturday evenings and Sunday lunchtime. No children, dogs, music, games machines or mobile phones are permitted – just fine

INN BRIEF

BEDWORTH

Travellers Rest
Bulkington Road
12-5, 7-11; 12-11 Fri & Sat; 12-5, 7-10.30 Sun
(024) 7631 3687
Worthington Bitter; guest beers (occasional) Ⓗ
Near the station, a small free house that is very much a traditional locals' bar with a cosy lounge.

EDGEHILL

Castle
11.15-2.30, 6.15-11; 12-3, 6.15-10.30 Sun
(01295) 670255
Hook Norton Best Bitter, Old Hooky, seasonal beers; guest beer Ⓗ
70ft high round tower overlooking the Civil War battlefield. A pleasant garden affords panoramic views over several counties. B&B available.

ILMINGTON

Howard Arms
Lower Green
11-2.30, 6.30-11; 12-3, 6-10.30 Sun
(01608) 682226
Everards Tiger; North Cotswold Genesis; guest beers Ⓗ
Stone-built inn on the village green with award-winning food in a cosy atmosphere; flagstone floors, oak beams and an inglenook.

KENILWORTH

Clarendon House Hotel
6 High Street
11-11; 12-10.30 Sun
(01926) 857668
Greene King IPA, Abbot; Hook Norton Best Bitter; guest beers Ⓗ
Comfortable continental-style hotel bar. Food is available all day, and two guest beers are usually on offer.

LEAMINGTON SPA

Benjamin Satchwell
112-114 The Parade
10.30-11; 12-10.30 Sun
(01926) 883733
Courage Directors; Greene King Abbot; Hop Back Summer Lightning; Shepherd Neame Spitfire; Theakston Best Bitter; guest beers Ⓗ
Popular, large, split-level town-centre Wetherspoon's, converted from two shops. Busy at weekends and most evenings. Cask Marque accredited.

LONG LAWFORD

Sheaf & Sickle
Coventry Road (A428)
12-2.30, 6-11; 12-11 Sat; 12-10.30 Sun
(01788) 544622
Ansells Best Bitter; Tetley Bitter; guest beers Ⓗ
Friendly local with a quiet snug and a busier bar. Excellent food; the only pub locally with its own cricket pitch.

ales and friendly company. Warwickshire CAMRA Pub of the Year 1996 and 2001.
⛼Q❀♣P

HARBURY

Shakespeare Inn

9 Mill Street (near shops)
12-3 (4 Sat), 6 (7 Sat)-11; 12-3, 7-10.30 Sun
☎ (01926) 612357
Flowers IPA; Taylor Landlord; guest beer Ⓗ
Converted 16th-century, black and white, half-timbered farmhouse, the pub has been opened up inside, although separate drinking areas remain. A huge inglenook dominates and a new conservatory at the rear doubles as the restaurant. Lunchtime food is served daily and evening meals on Tue-Sat. Situated at the heart of the village, the pub plays an active role in the community. It hosts meetings, games and enters a float in the carnival. Watch out for the ghost, Edward, who has not been seen for years. ⛼❀◐◑▭♣P

IRON CROSS

Queen's Head & Fat God's Brewery

11 (12 winter)-11; 12-10.30 Sun
☎ (01386) 871012 website: www.fatgodsbrewery.co.uk
Fat God's Bitter, Morris Dancer, Mild, Thunder & Lightning, Gods Wallop; guest beers Ⓗ
Home of the Fat God's Brewery, which can be seen at the rear of the pub, producing five real ales. It holds a 10-day beer festival in late June, with over 25 beers from micros as well as the Fat God's range. It features special food offers on weekday evenings, and a restaurant extension has recently been added. Take-away service is also available for both beer and food. Local CAMRA Pub of the Year 1999 and 2000.
⛼❀◐◑♿♣P

KENILWORTH ❊

Albion Tavern

81 Albion Street (on road to Stoneleigh)
12-11; 11-11 Sat; 12-10.30 Sun
☎ (01926) 852793
Adnams Bitter; M&B Brew XI Ⓗ
Traditional Victorian local, probably the most unspoilt pub in town. A pleasant and popular bar hosts darts, crib, dominoes, a regular quiz, and monthly music nights. Beware when entering, the dart throw is across the front door. Enjoy a peaceful drink in the small, tidy lounge, which is often brightened up with fresh flowers. The courtyard, complete with water feature, provides a useful alternative during better weather. Filled rolls are available at lunchtime. Q❀▭♣P

Earl Clarendon

127 Warwick Road (A452)
12-2, 5-11; 12-11 Sat; 12-10.30 Sun
☎ (01926) 854643
Marston's Bitter, Pedigree Ⓗ
Traditional local on the High Street, known as Bottom Clad by the regulars. This friendly pub has two drinking areas served by a central bar – a comfortable public bar to the front and a quieter lounge to the rear. Fund-raising quizzes are held (alternate Wed eves). In summer, the garden provides a haven from the busy road. The doorstep sandwiches at lunchtime are renowned (no food Mon or Sun). ❀◐

Old Bakery Hotel

12 High Street (near A429/A452 jct)
12-2 (not Mon-Fri), 5-11; 12-2, 6.30-10.30 Sun
☎ (01926) 864111
Black Sheep Best Bitter; Hook Norton Best Bitter; Taylor Landlord Ⓗ
In the old, and most picturesque part of this small town, close to the Abbey Fields recreation grounds and the castle ruins, this is a sympathetically restored and extended, family-run hotel, parts of which date from the 17th century. A peaceful bar, free from music, TV or games machines, welcomes residents and visitors alike. Outside, a small patio area has a few seats around the covered 17th-century well. Local CAMRA award-winner in 2001, this pub is well worth a visit. Wheelchair access is at the rear. Q❀⇌♿P

LAPWORTH

Navigation

Old Warwick Road (B4439)
11-3, 5.30-11; 11-11 Sat; 12-10.30 Sun
☎ (01564) 783337
Draught Bass; M&B Brew XI; guest beer Ⓗ
Over 300 years old, the Navigation pre-dates the Grand Union Canal which it stands beside. The traditional bar has a flagstone floor, log fire and stuffed fish on the walls. A sympathetic extension at the rear has allowed expansion of the kitchen and additional space for diners, who are guaranteed tasty home-cooked meals of Herculean proportions. On long summer evenings the canalside gardens entice drinkers, including those who moor their boats alongside. ⛼Q❀◐◑▭Å⇌●P

LEAMINGTON SPA ❊

Somerville Arms

4 Campion Terrace (take Leicester St from centre)
11-3 (not winter Mon-Wed), 5.30-11; 11-11 Sat; 12-10.30 Sun
☎ (01926) 426746
Adnams Broadside; Ansells Mild, Best Bitter; Greene King IPA, Abbot; Tetley Burton Ale Ⓗ
This popular, unchanging drinkers' pub enjoys a friendly atmosphere and is well worth seeking out. It has a large, busy bar at the front and a smaller cosy lounge at the rear. Each room has its own drinking motto displayed: 'Real ale for your health' and 'Abound in hops all who enter here'. The pub is named after Captain Somerville, a local magistrate in Victorian times. Q▭♣

LITTLE COMPTON

Red Lion

Off A44
12-2.30, 6-11; 12-3, 7-10.30 Sun
☎ (01608) 674397 website: www.red-lion-inn.com
Donnington BB, SBA Ⓗ
This Cotswold-stone local, in Warwickshire's most southerly village, boasts a strong community involvement, an Aunt Sally pitch and, unusually, a real public bar. It serves good food and is renowned for the quality of its steaks and fresh fish. Set in beautiful countryside, it is

ideal as a touring base (always fully booked during Cheltenham National Hunt Festival) and is only a couple of miles from the megalithic Rollright Stones. A portable ramp allows disabled access to the restaurant. ♨Q❀⛟◑◐⊟♿⛺♣P

LONG ITCHINGTON

Harvester Inn

6 Church Road

⊙ 11-3, 6-11; 12-10.30 Sun
☎ (01926) 812698

Hook Norton Best Bitter, Old Hooky; guest beer Ⓗ

This pub is a conversion from two houses (circa 1800) and was a Hunt-Edmunds outlet before becoming a free house in 1976. The character and prices are down-to-earth. It has its own restaurant but is in no way connected to the restaurant chain of the same name. Camping facilities are available a short stroll away. The Harvester has a long record of appearances in this Guide. Q◑◐⛺♣P

LOWER BRAILES

George Hotel

High Street

⊙ 12-11; 12-10.30 Sun
☎ (01608) 685223

Hook Norton Mild, Best Bitter, Generation, Old Hooky, seasonal beers Ⓗ

This sympathetically restored, Grade II coaching inn incorporates elements from the 16th to 18th centuries. An extensive garden and loggia includes an Aunt Sally pitch. It hosts frequent live jazz and blues events, and has a coin-operated Internet terminal on the upstairs landing. The restaurant often stages themed evenings and costume dinners, while a take-away service is available for curries (Mon) and fish and chips (Wed). Morris men and mummers gather here to celebrate St George's Day (23 April). ♨❀⛟◑◐⊟♣P

MORETON MORRELL

Black Horse

⊙ 11.30-3, 6-11; 12-3, 7-10.30 Sun
☎ (01926) 651231

Hook Norton Best Bitter; guest beer Ⓗ

Situated in the heart of the village, this pub is definitely worth a visit. It has a compact bar with wooden settles around the walls. A pub full of characters, it is popular with students from the local agricultural college and with walkers. A relaxing atmosphere prevails. The tasty baps are good value. The guest beer is usually from a small independent brewery. Relax and enjoy a drink in the peaceful garden. ❀♿⛺

NEWTON REGIS

Queen's Head

Main Road

⊙ 11-2.30, 6-11; 12-2.30, 7-10.30 Sun
☎ (01827) 830271

Draught Bass; M&B Brew XI; guest beer Ⓗ

Two-roomed village pub with a friendly atmosphere. It is popular with customers of all ages – young and old. Excellent food at reasonable prices is served daily. Please note, no bookings taken. The guest beer changes regularly. Large car park available. ♨Q❀◑◐⊟♣P

NO MAN'S HEATH

Four Counties

Ashby Road (B5493)

⊙ 11.30-3, 6.30-11; 12-3, 7-10.30 Sun
☎ (01827) 60455

Banks's Original; Everards Original; Marston's Pedigree; guest beer Ⓗ

This former coaching inn on the border of four counties was once a refuge for highwaymen. The guest beer is usually from small breweries, it changes weekly and is never below 4% strength. Darts, crib, cards and dominoes are played, and a quiz night is held weekly. Children are welcome before 9pm, and the charming landlady provides a friendly greeting. It is used most by regulars, some from as far as Birmingham, for good value pub food and quality ale.
♨Q❀◑◐♿♣P⚟

NORTHEND

Red Lion

Bottom Street (signed on B4100, opposite army camp)

⊙ 11.30-2.30, 6-11 (closed winter Mon); 12-3, 6-11 Sat; 12-3, 7-10.30 Sun
☎ (01295) 770308

Taylor Landlord; guest beer Ⓗ

Idyllic, one-bar country pub at the foot of the Burton Dassett Hills. This genuine free house keeps a constantly changing guest ale. It has a very friendly atmosphere, and is popular with locals, ramblers, cyclists and

INN BRIEF

NEWTON

Stag & Pheasant

27 Main Street

12-3, 6-11; 12-3.30, 7-10.30 Sun
(01788) 860326

Banks's Original, Bitter, guest beers Ⓗ

Former farmhouse with thatched roof; the oldest A-frame building in Warwickshire. Good value meals (no food Sun eve).

STRATFORD-UPON-AVON

Pen & Parchment

Bridgefoot

11-11; 12-11 Sun
(01789) 297697

Taylor Landlord; guest beers Ⓗ

Seven real ales – try before you buy or order a discounted four-pint jug. Belgian bottled beers available.

WARMINGTON

Plough Inn

Church Hill

12-3, 5.30-11; 12-3, 7-10.30 Sun
(01295) 690666

Greene King IPA; Hook Norton Best Bitter; Marston's Pedigree; guest beers Ⓗ

Stone-built village pub dating from the Civil War. Warm, welcoming atmosphere, low beamed ceiling and open fire; good food.

WILMCOTE

Mason's Arms

6 Aston Cantlow Road

11-3, 5.30-11 (11-11 summer); 12-4, 7-10.30 (12-10.30 summer) Sun
(01789) 297416

Black Sheep Best Bitter; Hook Norton Best Bitter; guest beers Ⓗ

Welcoming pub within 1/4 mile of Mary Arden's house, station and canal. Conservatory, restaurant and reasonably priced beer offered.

people drawn to it by its reputation for good beer and fine food. There is a wide ranging menu and the food is freshly prepared by the resident chef. The garden and patio afford panoramic views. Traditional pub games are played in the evening. ⌂❀◐◑♣P

NUNEATON

Fox Inn

The Square, Attleborough

11-11; 12-10.30 Sun

(024) 7638 3290

Mansfield Dark Mild, Cask Ale; Marston's Pedigree H

Attractive, deceptively spacious, two-roomed traditional local. The well-used bar has a carpeted games area and the lounge has a relaxed atmosphere. Both rooms are well furnished, making a visit pleasant at anytime. Tuesday evening is very popular with the locals, it is quiz night, so both rooms can be busy. You can eat and drink in the patio garden, surrounded by hanging baskets for that al fresco feel. No food is served on Sunday. ❀◐◑♣

RUGBY

Alexandra Arms

James Street (next to multi-storey car park)

12.3.30, 5-11; 12-11 Fri & Sat; 12-3, 5-10.30 Sun

(01788) 578660

website: www.rugbycamra.org.uk/alexandraarms

Ansells Best Bitter; Greene King Abbot; Marston's Pedigree; guest beers H

Rugby CAMRA Pub of the Year for an unprecedented four years running. The L-shaped lounge is comfortable, and lively debate among the locals is almost guaranteed. The games room at the rear is popular with rock fans attracted by the well-stocked juke box. The ex-bowling green serves a more useful purpose as a venue for beer festivals. There are two rotating guest beers featuring Wye Valley and Beowulf. These are augmented by bottled Belgian beers. Q❀◐◑♣

Merchant

6-7 Little Church Street

11-3, 6-11; closed Mon; 11-3, 6-10.30 Sun

(01788) 570070

B&T Shefford Bitter; Everards Tiger; guest beers H

Fine old building, formerly belonging to a local wine merchants. It has only been a pub for a few years but has already had four different identities. A traditional house with flagstone floors and plenty of wooden seating, it currently stocks at least six guest ales, complemented by draught and bottled Belgian beers. It hosts occasional beer festivals. ◑

Raglan Arms

50 Dunchurch Road

12-2.30 (not Mon-Wed), 5-11; 11.30-11 Sat; 12-3.30, 7-10.30 Sun

(01788) 544441

Ansells Mild, Best Bitter; Fuller's London Pride; Marston's Bitter, Pedigree; guest beers H

Small, traditional, friendly pub, close to the town centre. Of interest locally are the Rugby School and the Rugby Football Museum. There is as traditional bar to the rear, and comfortable lounge to the front, and the new landlord has gone out of his way to improve the decor. The landlord is an ex-professional rugby player and the pub has strong sporting associations with no less than two football teams. There is a darts team with plans to form dominoes and crib teams. With two guest beers alongside the four regular beers, this is still one of the best pubs in town for both range and quality of real ale. Q❀♣P

Seven Stars

40 Albert Square

12-4, 7-11; 11-11 Sat; 12-10.30 Sun

(01788) 544589

Wells Eagle, Bombardier; guest beers H

Tucked away, the Seven Stars is easily missed, which would be a shame. The front room is reminiscent of a working men's club, functional but comfortable. When a darts or skittles match is being played it can be very crowded and lively. The rear room is more like a traditional lounge and houses a pool table. There is also a conservatory. Now stocking two guest beers, the range is interesting and covers the less obvious choices. A well-deserving recipient of Cask Marque accreditation.

❀♣

Three Horseshoes Hotel

22 Sheep Street

11-2.30, 7-11; 7-10.30 Sun

(01788) 544585

Greene King IPA, Abbot; guest beer H

Just off one of Rugby's main pedestrian areas, the 'Three Shoes' is an oasis of calm, hemmed in by theme bars. An 18th-century coaching inn, there are three distinct drinking areas. The front room has a real fire for the cold winter nights. The quiet room at the back, with no TV or music, makes an ideal venue for informal get-togethers. The small side bar has a TV for those who can not go without. There is an extensive food menu, with up to five specials, advertised as GM free. Limited parking available.

⌂Q◐◑P

Victoria

1 Lower Hillmorton Road

12-2.30, 6-11; 12-11 Sat; 12-2.30, 7-10.30 Sun

(01788) 544374

Beer range varies H

Triangular-shaped local on the edge of town, it is well worth a visit. Pool and darts are played in the public bar. The lounge, decorated in a Victorian style, provides a good environment to enjoy the guest beers – which are often drawn from the local breweries: Church End, Frankton Bagby and Warwickshire. Lunches are served Mon-Sat.

◐

SAMBOURNE

Green Dragon

The Village Green (between A435 and A441)

11-2.30, 6-11; 12-2.30, 7-10.30 Sun

(01527) 892465

Draught Bass; Hobsons Best Bitter; M&B Brew XI H

This 17th-century inn overlooks the attractive village green. Oak beams, brasses and pewter add to the character of the two bars and restaurant. It enjoys a reputation for good food and boasts connections with the comedian, Tony Hancock. Modern en-suite accommodation is available, in chalet-style double rooms. ♨Q❀⇔◐◑P

SHIPSTONE-ON-STOUR

Black Horse

Station Road (off A3400, by Watery Lane)
OS258409
✪ 12-3, 7-11; 12-3, 7-10.30 Sun
☎ (01608) 661617
website: www.shipston.ukf.net/business/blackhorse/blackhorse.htm
Greene King IPA, Abbot; guest beer Ⓗ

Ancient stone and thatched pub with an oddball character. It has an old-fashioned feel where drink, conversation and amusement hold sway. Teetering on the edge of the Cotswolds, tucked away just off the main road, it was originally a row of sheep farmers' cottages, dating back to the 12th century. It was granted a licence in 1540. Guest beers often feature local (and more far-flung) micros. Aunt Sally is played. ♨❀◐◑⊟♣P

SHUSTOKE

Griffin Inn

Church Road (B4116)
✪ 12-2.30, 7-11; 12-3, 7-10.30 Sun
☎ (01675) 481205
website: www.midlandspubs.co.uk/warwickshire/griffininn
Bateman Mild; Marston's Pedigree; RCH Pitchfork; Theakston Old Peculier; Wells Bombardier; guest beers Ⓗ

Local CAMRA Pub of the Year 1998, 2000 and 2001. Ever-changing guest beers of uncompromising quality ensure a regular clientele from far and near. Choose from nine beers, and among the throng of customers, enjoy the atmosphere of a real English pub with real fires and excellent food, all set in an unspoilt, 360-year-old village inn. A conservatory provides an ideal area for children if the garden is weather-bound. A large car park and rural setting ensure a friendly atmosphere rarely encountered in today's hectic life. Real cider is served in summer. ♨Q☋❀◐♿♠P

WARWICK

Globe Hotel

8-10 Theatre Street
✪ 11-11; 12-10.30 Sun
☎ (01926) 492044
M&B Brew XI; Taylor Landlord; guest beers Ⓗ

> The train was over half an hour behind its time and the Traveller complained to the Guard of the train; and the Guard spoke to him very bitterly. He said: 'You must have a very narrow heart that you wouldn't go down to the town and stand your friends a few drinks instead of bothering me to get away'.
>
> Jack B Yeats (1871-1957).

Do not be put off by the elephants guarding the entrance to this 18th-century Grade II listed building. The hotel's restaurant is now the Warwick Thai Elephant, serving excellent Thai cuisine. The plush lounge bar serves a choice of three quality ales, sometimes including a guest beer from a local independent brewery. Two first floor function rooms are available for hire and there are 11 guest rooms. The Globe Hotel is ideally situated for visiting Warwick Castle and other tourist attractions.
❀⇔◐◑⩓P

Old Fourpenny Shop Hotel

27 Crompton Street
✪ 12-2.30 (3 Sat), 5.30 (6 Sat)-11; 12-11 Fri; 12-3, 6-10.30 Sun
☎ (01926) 491360
website: www.a1tourism.com/uk/oldfourpenny.html
Greene King Ruddles, Best Bitter; RCH Pitchfork; guest beers Ⓗ

Popular town local near the racecourse featuring a constantly changing range of six real ales. Warwickshire's CAMRA Pub of the Year 2000 and regular entry in this Guide, a pub has existed on this site since around 1780, with the current Georgian building dating from circa 1800. Officially the Warwick Tavern then, its nickname 'Fourpenny Shop' was coined by navvies building the canals, who could get a coffee and a tot of rum for 4d. The relaxed and cosy single bar features upmarket pub meals. ⇔◐◑⩓P

Simple Simon

105 Emscote Road (near canal bridge on Warwick to Leamington road)
✪ 11-3, 6-11; 12-3, 6-10.30 Sun
☎ (01926) 774078
Flowers IPA, Original; Wadworth 6X; guest beers Ⓗ

Dating back to at least 1830, this large corner pub was originally called the Elephant and Castle. It was renamed in 1970, possibly because at the time a pie factory was situated opposite. The public bar has a sports theme, with autographed shirts and other items on the walls. The main bar is decorated with prints and old pictures of Warwick, while the small dining area has railway paintings and model trains. Ask about the unusual pub game, shut the box. The patio faces the main road.
❀◐◑⊟♣

WHICHFORD

Norman Knight

✪ 12-2.30, 7-11; 12-2.30, 7-10.30 Sun
☎ (01608) 684621
website: www.thenormanknight.co.uk
Hook Norton Best Bitter; guest beers Ⓗ

Traditional village pub, with a stone-flagged floor and exposed timbers, in an idyllic setting facing the extensive village green. Its name commemorates Sir John de Mohun, a garter knight who is buried in the nearby parish church. Popular with visitors and locals, the pub has its own caravan site and two holiday cottages. Evening meals are served Friday and Saturday only, lunches available Wed-Mon. Aunt Sally and shove-ha'penny are played enthusiastically. The two or three guest beers show an adventurous variety – they are almost always from micros. ◐◑

Taxing Credulity

Chancellor's duty cut aided the micros but ignored hard-pressed regionals

IN HIS 2002 BUDGET, Chancellor Gordon Brown said he was cutting beer duty immediately and the result would mean pints cheaper by 14 pence in time for the World Cup in June in many brew-pubs and country pubs.

The cheap beer did not materialise. When the fine print of the duty decrease was analysed, only Britain's micro-breweries had gained. Regional brewers had missed out – and, as a result, some of them may be driven out of business.

Whitehall's gloss on the announcement said that the majority of Britain's brewers would benefit from the duty cut. What the statement failed to point out was that the majority – around 400 micro-brewers – account for no more than one per cent of total beer sales.

It was great news for the micros. Through their trade organisation, the Society of Independent Brewers (SIBA), they have argued for years in favour of a sliding scale of duty in Britain, with the bigger brewers paying proportionately more than the middling and small ones.

In the event, Chancellor Brown cut the middle rank of brewers out of the equation. His duty cut means that:

- Brewers who produce less than 3,000 barrels a year will have their duty cut in half – a saving of around £40 a barrel.

- Brewers producing up to 18,000 barrels will get a graded discount that could save them £120,000 a year each.

The reductions were greeted with understandable delight by the micros. SIBA spokesman Nick Stafford of Hambleton Brewery in Yorkshire, said: 'We are finally going to reap the rewards of years and years of campaigning, and it will make a significant difference to the chances of growth for hundreds of small breweries.' He predicted that many micro-brewery owners would use the savings on duty to buy their own pubs, and that publicans would also start to brew on their premises.

But most micros said there was no possibility of cutting the price of beer. Even if they reduced their wholesale prices, there was no guarantee the pub companies would pass on the saving to drinkers. From the pubcos track record, it was far more likely they would pocket any cuts.

A number of small brewers told the Guide they would invest in better equipment. Several said the duty cut would help keep them in business. One leading micro-brewery owner in London said he was seriously contemplating selling his brewery but the Budget decrease had proved a lifeline. He said his margins were so small there was no question of his being able to cut the price of his beer.

Regional brewers reacted to the Budget with alarm and anger. Jim Burrows of Brakspear (see main editorial) accused Gordon Brown of discriminating against the middle rank of brewers. 'He could have set the upper limit at 200,000 hectolitres, but he has left out a whole raft of regional brewers in the 30,000-200,000 hectolitre band.'

Simon Loftus of Adnams said Britain's brewing heritage was at stake. In a letter to all MPs, he said: 'To set the ceiling any lower than 200,000 hectolitres would be to make an entirely artificial distinction between regional brewers and their smaller competitors. The smallest brewers have a price advantage of approximately 30 pence a pint.'

Chancellor Gordon Brown: ignored plight of regional brewers

WEST MIDLANDS

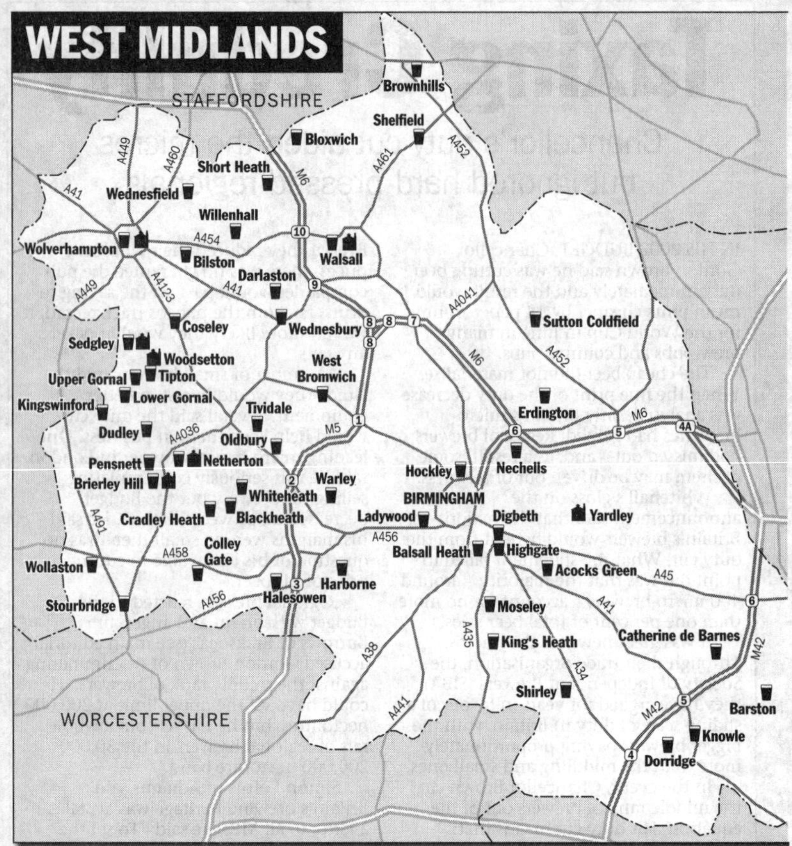

ALLESLEY

Rainbow Inn

73 Birmingham Road (off A4114)

11-11; 12-10.30 Sun

☎ (024) 7640 2888

Courage Best Bitter, Directors; Greene King IPA; Rainbow Piddlebrook Ⓗ

Located in a village to the west of Coventry, this pub is very much a focal point of the community, enjoyed by drinkers of all ages. The Rainbow's own popular session beer, Piddlebrook is brewed in Coventry's only brewery, housed in a rear stable block. Car park access is tricky but the pub is conveniently located on the main Coventry-Birmingham bus route (service 900). Evening meals (not Sat or Sun) are served in the lounge. ❀◑ P

BARSTON

Bull's Head

Barston Lane

11-2.30, 5.30-11; 11-11 Sat; 12-10.30 Sun

☎ (01675) 442830

Adnams Bitter; Draught Bass; guest beers Ⓗ

Beamed country pub, partly dating back to 1490; a genuine village local, it also offers a warm welcome to passers-by. This loyal supporter of independent breweries won the local CAMRA Pub of the Year 1998 and 2000 and boasts 10 consecutive entries in this Guide. Split into three rooms, including a restaurant in the original part of the building, it serves excellent home-cooked food Mon-Sat. Log fires and horse-racing memorabilia feature strongly. Q❀◑P

BERKSWELL ✻

Railway

547 Station Road

12-2.30, 5-11; 12-11 Sat; 12-3, 7-10.30 Sun

☎ (01676) 533284

Adnams Broadside; Draught Bass; Greene King Ruddles Best Bitter; M&B Brew XI; guest beer Ⓗ

Formerly railway workers' cottages dating from 1846, this welcoming one-roomed pub resembles a station buffet bar. Divided into two ends – one has comfortable seating and a real fire, the other houses the pool table and dartboard – it is used by locals of all ages. Five real ales, including a regularly changing guest beer, are stocked. The landlord hosts weekly themed food evenings and the occasional quiz. Limited lunchtime bar food is available. Car parking space is limited. ❀⇌♣P

BILSTON ✻

Olde White Rose

20 Lichfield Street

12-11; 12-4, 7-10.30 Sun

☎ (01902) 498339

Beer range varies Ⓗ

A Grade II listed frontage leads to a long, narrow interior with an eating area to the side. Recent improvements include a

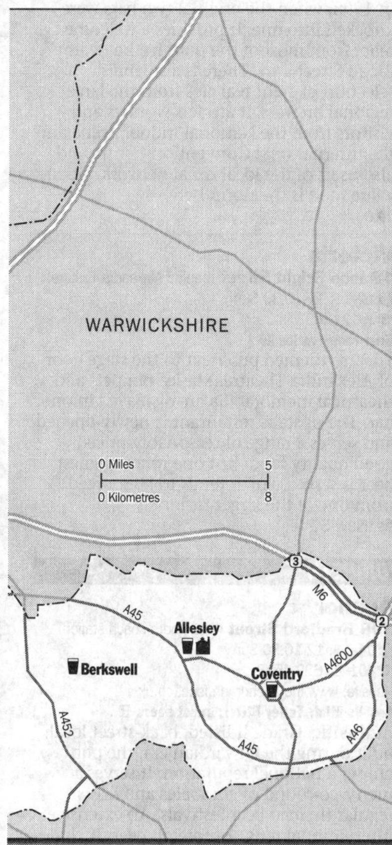

bierkeller, conservatory and a garden. Twelve beers are normally available, many unusual for the area. Good value, home-cooked food is served 12-9 Mon-Sat; Sunday lunch is popular and food is now also available Sun eve. Convenient for Bilston bus station, this local CAMRA Town Pub of the Year 1999 gives discount on beer to card-carrying CAMRA members.
❀◑ ⊖ (Bilston Central)

Trumpet

58 High Street

11.30-3, 7.30-11; 12-3, 7-10.30 Sun

☎ (01902) 493723

Holden's Mild, Bitter, Golden Glow, Special; guest beer H

The original name of this small, one-roomed pub, the Royal Exchange, was changed to reflect its fame as a superb jazz venue. Staged each evening and Sunday lunch, different jazz styles are showcased. Entry is free, but a collection plate is passed around. Trumpets hang from the ceiling, and the walls are covered with photographs. Handy for the metro and bus station.
⊖ (Bilston Central)

BIRMINGHAM: *ACOCKS GREEN*

Spread Eagle

1146 Warwick Road

11-11; 12-10.30 Sun

☎ (0121) 708 0194

Banks's Original; Greene King Abbot; Hop Back Summer Lightning; Shepherd Neame Spitfire; Theakston Best Bitter; guest beers H

Popular Wetherspoon's pub in part of a former supermarket. The L-shaped bar is split into two rooms, with different atmospheres. The regular ales are supplemented by two guest beers from small brewers, bringing choice to an area previously devoid of real ale. The pub walls feature prints of famous Warwickshire figures, including the Kingmaker and JRR Tolkein, who lived a few miles away.
Q◑ ♿ ≠ (Acocks Green) P ⚡ ✔

BALSALL HEATH

Old Moseley Arms

Tindal Street

12-11; 12-10.30 Sun

☎ (0121) 440 1954

Ansells Best Bitter; Enville Ale; Greene King Abbot; guest beer H

Pub comprising two ground-floor rooms and an upstairs pool room. The public bar is decorated with various framed cuttings of stories concerning locals. The pub cricket team and, for some obscure reason, a massive Titanic print also feature. Fifteen minutes from Edgbaston Cricket Ground, it is popular with students and Moseley's more cosmopolitan element. It can be crowded when major sports events are shown on the large-screen TV. ❀

CITY CENTRE ❄

Figure of Eight

236 Broad Street

11-11; 12-10.30 Sun

☎ (0121) 633 0917

Boddingtons Bitter; Courage Directors; Hop Back Summer Lightning; Shepherd Neame Spitfire; Theakston XB; guest beers H

Recently refurbished Wetherspoon's pub at the heart of the bustling Broad Street area. It provides a rare oasis of reasonably-priced beer in an otherwise expensive locality. The pub has a substantial collection of books, while pictures of old Birmingham and miscellaneous prints adorn the walls. A dining area has recently been created. The pub has space for outdoor drinking at the back and is extremely popular with local office workers.
❀◑ ♿ ≠ (Five Ways) ⊖ (Snow Hill) ⚡ ✔

Old Fox

54 Hurst Street (opp. Birmingham Hippodrome)

11.30-midnight (2am Fri & Sat); 12-11 Sun

☎ (0121) 622 5080

Greene King Old Speckled Hen; Marston's Pedigree; Tetley Bitter; guest beers H

The pub stands opposite the Birmingham

INDEPENDENT BREWERIES

Banks's Wolverhampton
Batham Brierley Hill
Beowulf Yardley
Goldthorn Wolverhampton
Highgate Walsall
Holden's Woodsetton
Sarah Hughes Sedgley
Olde Swan Netherton
Rainbow Allesley

Hippodrome and is also convenient for the Chinese Quarter. It is reported that Charlie Chaplin and other stars used the pub when they were appearing at the theatre. The links to the theatre are illustrated by memorabilia that adorn the walls. There is usually a choice of at least six real ales served in the two rooms from an island bar, but the range is limited to three guests during the week. Tables and chairs are available on the pavement (weather permitting).

(New St)

Old Joint Stock

4 Temple Row West (opp. cathedral)

11-11; closed Sun

(0121) 200 1892

Beowulf seasonal beer; Fuller's Chiswick, London Pride, ESB; guest beer H

This sumptuous Grade II listed building was previously a bank. The resplendent interior cleverly mixes neo-classical and Victorian gothic styles with Roman statuettes, a cupola and colonnades adding to the palatial feel. The central bar is surrounded by an open-plan drinking area that still permits some privacy. The decor is plush and smart. A multi-award winner, the pub is popular with office workers and shoppers, becoming especially busy Friday evenings. Meals served 12-7 Mon-Sat.

(New St/Snow Hill)

Prince of Wales

84 Cambridge Street (next to National Indoor Arena)

12-11; 12-10.30 Sun

(0121) 643 9460

Ansells Mild, Best Bitter; Marston's Pedigree; Tetley Mild; guest beers H

The 150-year-old building was refurbished in 1998, when the original two bars were knocked into one. It provides a welcome relief from most of the pubs in the nearby Broad Street area. There is a splendid selection of eight real ales from the large regional brewers. It attracts workers and visitors from the National Indoor Arena and the International Convention Centre and also users of the local canal network. Good value food is the norm here.

Victoria

48 John Bright Street (behind Alexandra Theatre)

12-11; 12-10.30 Sun

(0121) 633 9439

Beer range varies H

Theatre-themed pub next to the stage door of Alexandra Theatre. Masks, puppets and theatrical memorabilia are displayed in one bar. The upstairs restaurant is newly-opened and serves a range of reasonably-priced, good quality food. Just one rotating guest beer is served which tends to be sourced from one of the larger regionals.

(New St)

DIGBETH

Anchor ☆

308 Bradford Street (by Digbeth coach station)

11-11; 12-10.30 Sun

(0121) 622 4516

website: www.the-anchor-inn.fsnet.co.uk

Ansells Mild; Tetley Bitter; guest beers H

Authentic, Grade II listed, back-street local, built during the Edwardian era, the pub enjoys a national reputation. It serves a merry-go-round of guest ales and hosts regular themed beer festivals. An extensive international range of foreign beers includes draught Belgian brews. Pictures illustrating

INN BRIEF

BERKSWELL

Bear Inn

Spencer Lane

11-11; 12-10.30 Sun

(01676) 533202

Courage Directors; Theakston Best Bitter; guest beers H

Attractive, 16th-century inn in a pleasant village location with real fires, quality food and ales to match. A drinkers' bar is upstairs.

BILSTON

Sir Henry Newbolt

45-47 High Street

10.30-11; 12-10.30 Sun

(01902) 404636

Greene King Abbot; Shepherd Neame Spitfire; Theakston Best Bitter; guest beers H

Recent conversion by Wetherspoon's, offering the usual range of beers and food. Named after a local figure. Cask Marque accredited.

BIRMINGHAM: *CITY CENTRE*

Bull

1 Price Street

11-11; 12-10.30 Sun

(0121) 333 6757

Adnams Broadside; Marston's Pedigree; guest beers H

Friendly, cosy, two-roomed 18th-century pub with a relaxing atmosphere. Note the extensive jug collection and etched Ansells window.

Hogshead

29a Newhall Street

12-11; closed Sun

(0121) 200 2423

Boddingtons Bitter; Flowers Original H

Lively, brightly decorated, two-roomed pub, dispensing beers from larger regionals. Gets busy Friday and Saturday evenings. Cask Marque accredited.

HIGHGATE

City Tavern

Bishopsgate Street

11.30-11; 12-10.30 Sun

(0121) 643 8467

Highgate Dark, Saddlers, Old Ale H

Comfortable Highgate pub with 1930s decor in its two bars; note the windows. A peaceful retreat off the Broad Street run.

HOCKLEY

White House

99 New John Street West

11-11; 12-10.30 Sun

(0121) 523 0782

Holden's Mild, Bitter, Golden Glow H

Basic, no-frills estate pub, recently acquired by Holden's and frequented by a mixed clientele.

KING'S HEATH

Station

7 High Street

11-11; 12-10.30 Sun

(0121) 444 1257

Tetley Bitter, Burton Ale H

Friendly, cosy pub on the edge of a busy shopping area. Comedy nights are held.

BLACKHEATH

Bell & Bear Inn

71 Gorsty Hill Road, Rowley Regis

11-11; 11-3, 6-11 Sat; 12-3, 7-10.30 Sun

(0121) 561 2196

Greene King Old Speckled Hen; Highgate Dark; Taylor Landlord; Tetley Burton Ale; Wood Special H

400-year-old listed building: one large room with various areas for drinking and eating. The rear terrace affords views for miles.

BLOXWICH

Royal Exchange

24 Stafford Road

12 (4.30 Mon-Thu winter)-11; 12-3, 7-10.30 Sun

(01922) 494256

Highgate Dark, seasonal beers H

18th-century pub where the traditional public bar has an emphasis on sport, plus a lounge and snug. Live entertainment Wed eves.

the pub's history adorn the walls. Twice winner of local CAMRA Pub of the Year competition. ❀◑ ≈(New St/Moor St) ●⅟

White Swan ☆

276 Bradford Street

⊙ 11-3, 4.15-11; 12-3, 7-10.30 Sun

☎ (0121) 622 2586

Banks's Original, Bitter Ⓗ

Definitely unspoilt by progress, and listed in CAMRA's inventory of historic interiors, this pub is situated in the Irish Quarter. Divided into a bar and a small lounge with tiled ceiling and walls, it retains the original bar featuring Ansells Brewery's etched glass. A small collection of books is provided to help while away the time in this regular Guide entry. Expect a good atmosphere when the Irish are playing on TV.
≈(Moor St)

Woodman ☆

106 Albert Street

⊙ 11-11; 12-10.30 Sun

☎ (0121) 643 1959

Ansells Mild; Tetley Bitter; guest beers Ⓗ

This CAMRA national-inventory-listed, turn-of-the-century pub dispenses probably the best-kept mild in Birmingham. Another increasingly rare example of being 'unspoilt by progress', its etched windows and tiling are of especial note. A friendly and serene haven, the Woodman is situated off the beaten track, away from the bustle of the city centre. A gem. Evening meals are served 5-8 (not Sun). ◑ ⊟ ≈(Moor St)

ERDINGTON

Charlie Hall

49 Barnabas Road (opp. Little Market)

⊙ 10-11; 12-10.30 Sun

☎ (0121) 384 2716

Boddingtons Bitter; Hop Back Summer Lightning; Marston's Pedigree; Shepherd Neame Spitfire; Theakston Best Bitter; guest beers Ⓗ

This large Wetherspoon's house, which is named after a locally-born actor who appeared in some 30 Laurel and Hardy films, was formerly a bingo hall. Many photographs of the comic duo are displayed on the walls. The pub has been well refurbished and consists of one long room with two ceiling heights. Wood panelling has been used throughout and there are a number of alcoves for privacy. The rear patio is a bonus when the weather is clement. Q ❀◑ ♿ ≈⅟ ✔

Lad in the Lane

28 Bromford Lane (400 yds N of A38)

⊙ 11-11; 12-10.30 Sun

☎ (0121) 377 7471

Ansells Mild; Marston's Pedigree; Tetley Bitter Ⓗ

The oldest pub in Birmingham, it was originally constructed in 1306 and has been magnificently renovated. The view from the outside is of a timber-framed building with leaded windows. Inside, the immediate impact is the sight of the black exposed joints and rafters. The lounge is in three different sections on two levels. Decorative touches include a Welsh dresser and a wooden bicycle. The large garden is popular with regulars and visitors in summer. No meals are served Sunday.
❀ ◑ ♣ P

HARBORNE

Bell Inn

11 Old Church Road

⊙ 12-11; 12-10.30 Sun

☎ (0121) 427 0934

Beer range varies Ⓗ

Set in the back streets, this smart, 18th-century hostelry stands in a peaceful, quasi-rural location away from the hustle and bustle of Harborne. The small bar, serving extremely expensive ales from the larger regionals, is surrounded by a snug and a drinking/dining area. Evening meals are served Mon-Sat. The drinking area outside has a bowling green attached. This characterful, homely pub serves an affluent local community. Note the quaint outside toilets. Q ◑ ♿ P

White Horse

2 York Street

⊙ 11-11; 12-10.30 Sun

☎ (0121) 427 2063

Marston's Pedigree; Tetley Bitter, Burton Ale; guest beers Ⓗ

Busy Tetley Festival Ale House at the heart of the local community. An island bar dispenses up to eight real ales, but choice is restricted to larger regionals and national brands. Pictures of old Harborne and breweriana decorate the walls in this thriving side-street pub. Sky TV, impromptu music sessions, and unobtrusive background music combine to create a pleasant drinking environment. Meals are served 12-7 Mon-Sat.
◑ ⊟ ♣ ●

HIGHGATE ❊

Lamp Tavern

257 Barford Street

⊙ 12-11; 7-10.30 Sun

☎ (0121) 622 2599

Church End Gravediggers; Everards Tiger; Stanway Stanney Bitter; Wadworth 6X; guest beer Ⓗ

Small, friendly, back-street local near the wholesale market area, the Lamp is the only regular outlet for Stanway beers in Birmingham. The cosy front bar is popular both at lunchtime and evenings. The well-appointed back room hosts regular live music sessions, and is also booked by various local societies for midweek meetings.
≈(New St/Moor St)

HOCKLEY ❊

Black Eagle

16 Factory Road (near Soho House Museum)

⊙ 11.30 (12 Sat)-3, 5.30 (7 Sat)-11; 11.30-11 Fri; 12-3, (closed eve) Sun

☎ (0121) 523 4008

Ansells Mild, Best Bitter; Marston's Pedigree; Taylor Landlord; guest beers Ⓗ

Very friendly pub, three times winner of Birmingham CAMRA Pub of the Year. Rebuilt in 1895, it retains most of the original features, including Minton tiles. One of the few pubs selling Beowulf beers from Birmingham's only brewery. It is the city's only entry in CAMRA's Good Pub Food (no meals Sun eve). Close to the Soho House Museum, the famous Jewellery Quarter and its

museum, it is an ideal destination for both the ale connoisseur and sightseer. Beer festivals are staged here.
(Benson/Soho Rd)

Church Inn

22 Great Hampton Street (A41)
11.45-11; 12-3, 6-11 Sat; closed Sun
(0121) 515 1851
Batham Best Bitter; Greene King Abbot, Old Speckled Hen; guest beer H
This excellent, old-fashioned pub is the current Birmingham CAMRA Pub of the Year. Over 160 years old, it has a justified reputation for the quality of its food – there is an extensive menu specialising in steaks, grills and roasts, and the portions are huge. Choose from over 80 whiskies, mostly single malts. The bar is divided into two and shares one serving bar; many old photographs adorn the walls. Another small bar, with its collection of film star photographs, is opened on request.
(Jewellery Qtr/Snow Hill) (St Pauls)

KING'S HEATH

Pavilions

229 Alcester Road South
12-11; 12-10.30 Sun
(0121) 441 3286
Banks's Original, Bitter; Marston's Pedigree H
An 1860s building has been transformed into a modern, welcoming local. This two-roomed pub has a very stylish interior displaying old photos of King's Heath. A good food menu is on offer to complement the three beers. A quiz night is held twice-weekly (Mon and Wed). P

LADYWOOD

Fiddle & Bone

4 Sheepcote Street
11-11; 12-10.30 Sun
(0121) 200 2223 website: www.fiddle-bone.co.uk
Adnams Bitter; Everards Tiger; Marston's Pedigree; guest beer H
Canalside pub, renovated by two ex-City of Birmingham Symphony Orchestra members, it lies close to an extensively redeveloped area of Brum. Unsurprisingly, the pub has a musical theme, with live music performed every day of the year and bars adorned with musical instruments. The upper bar has wooden flooring while the lower bar is flagstoned. The pub has been nominated as Birmingham's Best Live Entertainment Venue for 2002. The house beer is Courage Best rebadged.
(New St/Five Ways) P

MOSELEY

Prince of Wales

118 Alcester Road
12-11; 12-10.30 Sun
(0121) 449 4198
Ansells Mild; Greene King Abbot; Tetley Burton Ale; guest beer H
This cosy, unspoilt, three-roomed pub is popular with both students and locals. It can become very busy on Friday and Saturday evenings, standing as it does in a cosmopolitan district of Birmingham. Largely unchanged since the turn of the last century, it is one of the few pubs still serving Ansells Mild on draught. Q

NECHELLS

Villa Tavern ☆

307 Nechells Park Road
11.30-2.30, 5-11; 11.30-11 Fri & Sat; 12-4, 7-10.30 Sun
(0121) 326 7466
Ansells Mild, Best Bitter; Marston's Pedigree; guest beer H
A sign on the outside of this Victorian style building indicates that it was built in 1897, whereas it was actually built in 1925. Nonetheless, it has a splendid interior – note the stained glass bow window in the lounge. The three rooms (bar, lounge and function room) are served by a single bar. This is very much a community pub which supports two dominoes teams and a pool team. Lunches are served on weekdays and on Sunday. Q (Aston) ♣P

BLACKHEATH

Lighthouse

153 Coombs Road (A4099, 1/2 mile from A459 jct)
12-11; 12-10.30 Sun
(0121) 602 1620

INN BRIEF

COSELEY

White House
1 Daisy Street
11-3, 6-11; 12-3, 7-10.30 Sun
(01902) 402703
Ansells Mild, Greene King Abbot; Tetley Bitter; guest beers H
Imposing, two-roomed local dominating the crossroads. Food available lunchtime and early eve except Sun. Pop quiz Sun eve.

COVENTRY

Alexander Wines (off-licence)
112 Berkeley Road South, Earlsdon
10-2, 5.30-10.30; 11.30-2.30, 7-10.30 Sun
(024) 7667 3474
Independent off-licence which stocks around 200 British and continental beers, about 50 of which are bottle-conditioned.

Caludon Inn
St Austell Road, Wyken
12-3, 6-11; 12-3, 7-10.30 Sun
(024) 7645 3669
Ansells Mild, Best Bitter; guest beers H
Friendly estate pub with two rooms, fielding darts and dominoes teams. No food Sat lunch or Sun eve.

DARLASTON

Prince of Wales
74 Walsall Road
2 (12 Fri & Sat)-11; 12-10.30 Sun
(0121) 526 6244
Holden's Mild, Bitter, Golden Glow, Special H
Traditional, two-roomed roadside pub with a large garden and children's play area. Occasional entertainment Fri eves.

DORRIDGE

Railway
Grange Road
11-3, 4.30-11; 11-11 Sat; 11-10.30 Sun
(01564) 773531
Draught Bass; M&B Brew XI; guest beers H
Family-run pub serving good value food lunchtimes and eves. The public bar has a real fire.

DUDLEY

Full Moon
58-60 High Street
10-11; 12-10.30 Sun
(01384) 212294
Banks's Original; Enville Ale; Greene King Abbot; Shepherd Neame Spitfire; Theakston Best Bitter; guest beers H
Wetherspoon's pub in the centre of town, five minutes' walk from the bus station (via market place), popular with all. Cask Marque accredited.

Enville Ale; Greene King IPA; guest beers Ⓗ
This pub (now owned by Brains) has a long history as the Anchor, including serving thirsty bargees who 'legged' through the canal tunnel nearby. Nautical artefacts festoon the walls and ceiling of the bar; leading off is a lower level with a row of alcoves along one side used by diners (eve meals served Tue-Sat). Live music is usually played in the bar Wed eve, and a monthly blues night is staged (first Sun); a folk club operates on alternate Thu. Other amenities include a portable skittle alley for hire and a wheelchair WC. ❀◑◐♿≈ (Old Hill) ♣🍎P⊘

Waterfall

132 Waterfall Lane
✪ 12-3, 5-11; 12-11 Fri & Sat; 12-10.30 Sun
☎ (0121) 561 3499 website: www.midlandspubs.co.uk
Batham Best Bitter; Enville Ale; Holden's Special; Hook Norton Old Hooky; Marston's Pedigree; guest beers Ⓗ
Halfway up the very steep Waterfall Lane, this pub is now a favourite with local real ale fans. The present management has been here since spring 2000, serving five regular ales and six guests. Food is served in the lounge, while darts players and a quiet crowd can be found in the rear bar. Look up the pub on the website where it is listed under the town of Old Hill.
❀◑◐⊟≈ (Old Hill) ♣P⅟⊘

BLOXWICH ❄

Lamp Tavern

34 High Street (B4210)
✪ 12-11; 12-10.30 Sun
☎ (01922) 479681
Holden's Mild, Bitter, seasonal beers Ⓗ
Cosy Holden's one-roomed roadside pub, just south of Bloxwich town centre. Originally farm buildings and stables, it retains much 'olde-worlde' character. A community pub, it fields thriving darts, dominoes and crib teams, and holds barbecues in the garden on fine summer evenings. The pub serves bar snacks, lunchtimes and evenings and is attached to the popular Lamp Tavern Restaurant, which serves evening meals Tue-Sat and Sunday lunches. ❀♣P

Stag

Field Road (off B4210)
✪ 12-11; 12-10.30 Sun
☎ (01922) 405775
Adnams Bitter; Banks's Original; guest beers Ⓗ
Fine example of an Art Deco-style pub dating from the 1930s, this splendid building boasts some fine features. Three distinct areas are served by one main bar where the landlord offers ever-changing guest beers (up to eight). The pub has recently been saved from demolition and redevelopment by local CAMRA and community action, and is now a successful, popular establishment. No evening meals served Sun. ⩩Q❀⛟◑◐⊟♣P

Turf Tavern ☆

13 Wolverhampton Road (off A34, opp. park)
✪ 12-3 (3.30 Sat), 7-11; 12-3, 7-10.30 Sun
☎ (01922) 407745
RCH Pitchfork; guest beers Ⓗ
Walsall CAMRA Pub of the Year 2000 and 2001, this Grade II listed building, in a conservation area of Bloxwich, is an unspoilt gem. In the same family for 130 years, the pub is known locally as 'Tinky's'. It provides a haven from regular hustle and bustle. A tiled floor in the bar adds to its character, while two other rooms are full of nostalgia. Four handpulled beers are regularly on offer, one of which is normally a mild. Q❀⊟≈

BRIERLEY HILL

Bell

172 Delph Road (off A4100)
✪ 12-11; 12-3, 7-10.30 Sun
☎ (01384) 572376
Greene King IPA, Abbot; Marston's Pedigree; Olde Swan Entire; Tetley Bitter; guest beers Ⓗ
This two-roomed pub stands at the bottom of the eight locks on the Dudley Canal known as the Delph Nine. It has a roomy main bar on the right as you go in and a cosier lounge on the left. A small garden at the rear is used for barbecues in summer. Food is served 12-2.30 and 5.30-8.30.
⩩❀◑◐♣P

Vine (Bull & Bladder)

10 Delph Road (A459)
✪ 12-11; 12-10.30 Sun
☎ (01384) 78293
Batham Mild, Best Bitter, XXX Ⓗ
Famous Black Country brewery tap, at the top of Delph Road, whose imposing frontage proclaims the Shakespearian quotation: 'Blessing of your heart, you brew good ale'. An unspoilt bar and extension into the former butcher's shop (winner of CAMRA's Joe Goodwin Refurbishment Award 1996) lie either side of a central passageway. This leads to a long lounge and small family room, which is also used as a food service area for the excellent bar snacks and meals (weekday lunchtime).
⩩Q♉❀◑⊟♣P

Waterfront

6-7 Waterfront
✪ 11-11; 12-10.30 Sun
☎ (01384) 262096
Banks's Original, Bitter; Courage Directors; Shepherd Neame Spitfire; Theakston Best Bitter; guest beers Ⓗ
Welcoming Wetherspoon's pub on the Dudley No. 1 Canal (moorings nearby) situated in the Waterfront office complex, and close to the 'Merry Hell' shopping centre. Frequented by office staff weekday lunchtimes, its proximity to other bars and clubs makes this pub a popular evening choice at weekends. The famous Delph Locks can be reached by a canalside stroll. The standard Wetherspoon's menu and specials are served all day until 10pm.
Q◑◐♿⅟⊘

BROWNHILLS

Royal Oak

68 Chester Road (A452)
✪ 12-3, 6-11; 12-3, 7-10.30 Sun
☎ (01543) 452089
Ansells Mild, Best Bitter; Greene King Abbot; Tetley Bitter, Burton Ale; guest beers Ⓗ
This large, friendly pub, which was built in 1937 has been refurbished in the Art Deco style of the period. It is renowned for its good quality, but reasonably-priced food

which can be enjoyed in the lounge or no-smoking dining room (booking is recommended for Sunday lunch). The two guest beers normally come from local breweries. Traditional games include shut the box. ⛫❀◐⊟♣P

CATHERINE DE BARNES

Boat Inn

222 Hampton Lane

✪ 11.30-11; 12-10.30 Sun

☎ (0121) 705 0474

Courage Directors; Tetley Bitter; guest beers Ⓗ

This Miller's Kitchen pub is an enthusiastic supporter of real ale and often features unusual guest beers. Although basically one-roomed, with an emphasis on meals, there is a separate dining area for families and non-smokers. The pub often holds special celebratory events for Christmas and other seasonal occasions. Watch out for special promotions, including reduced price meals for boat-users, the Grand Union Canal runs alongside. Local CAMRA Pub of the Year 2001. ❀◐♿♣P

COLLEY GATE

Why Not

Why Not Street (1/2 mile from A458, Windmill Hill)

✪ 12-3, 6-11; 12-11 Sat; 12-3, 7-10.30 Sun

☎ (01384) 561019

Banks's Original; Batham Best Bitter; guest beers Ⓗ

Pleasant, rambling local tucked away in a side street on the edge of the Black Country. The Why Not comprises a front lounge favoured by drinkers plus several smaller areas popular with diners. The front lounge boasts a real fire and two large glass cabinets, containing collections of bottles and miniatures. Copperware, bric-à-brac, pot plants and green ceilings combine to make the dining areas a pleasant environment in which to enjoy the excellent menu. ⛫❀◐◗♣●

COVENTRY ❄

City Arms

Earlsdon Street, Earlsdon

✪ 11-11; 12-10.30 Sun

☎ (024) 7671 8170

Courage Directors; Greene King Abbot; Shepherd Neame Spitfire; Theakston Best Bitter; guest beers Ⓗ

Large 1930s pub, subject to many refurbishments, the latest being a recent Wetherspoon's revamp. This present incarnation includes all the usual Wetherspoons' features such as a no-smoking area, all-day food service, and the welcome addition of an outside drinking area. It is very popular with younger drinkers on Friday and Saturday evenings when doormen are employed. No children admitted at any time. Q❀◐♿P⊘

Craven Arms

58 Craven Street, Chapelfields (1 mile from centre, off B4106)

✪ 11 (4 Tue)-11; 12-4, 7-10.30 Sun

☎ (024) 7671 5308

Flowers Original; Hook Norton Old Hooky; John Smith's Bitter; guest beer Ⓗ

Popular community pub, run by friendly bar staff, in the old watch-making district of the city, where some of the buildings retain their original 'top shops'. The area was featured in a Time Team TV programme. Live entertainment is provided Sunday evening. There is a welcoming fire in winter and barbecues are held on the patio in summer. Pool and darts are played in a games area.

⛫❀◐♣

Gatehouse Tavern

46 Hill Street (behind Leigh Mills car park)

✪ 11-3, 5-11; 11-11 Thu-Sat; 12-10.30 Sun

☎ (024) 7625 6769

website: www.gatehousetavern.com

Draught Bass; Fuller's London Pride; guest beers Ⓗ

This free house was originally the gatehouse to a Victorian worsted and woollen factory (now demolished and replaced by a multi-storey car park). At present it is a small one-roomed bar, but plans are in hand for an extension. At least one Church End beer is usually available. A mecca for rugby union fans, the landlord is so rugby-mad that he has fitted stained glass windows celebrating the home unions. Evening meals are served weekdays.

❀◐◗

INN BRIEF

KNOWLE

Vaults

St John's Close

12-2.30, 5.30-11; 12-11 Sat; 12-10.30 Sun

(01564) 773656

Ansells Mild; Greene King IPA; Tetley Bitter, Burton Ale; guest beers Ⓗ

Recently relocated into adjoining premises, serving interesting guest beers and real cider. Food available at lunchtime.

LOWER GORNAL

Miners Arms (Chapel House)

Ruiton Street

4 (12 Fri & Sat)-11; 12-10.30 Sun

(01902) 882238

Holden's Mild, Bitter, Ⓟ **Golden Glow; guest beers** Ⓗ

One-roomed local near Five Ways. On the 257 bus route.

PENSNETT

Fox & Grapes

176 High Street

11 (12 Fri & Sat)-11; 12-10.30 Sun

(01384) 261907

Batham Mild, Best Bitter, XXX Ⓗ

Acquired by Batham's to replace the now-demolished Holly Bush, this open-plan local is near Russells Hall Hospital.

STOURBRIDGE

Red Lion

Lion Street

12-3.30, 7-11; 12-11 Sat; 12-3, 7-10.30 Sun

(01384) 397563

Enville White; guest beers Ⓗ

Welcoming, two-roomed pub with a separate dining area, close to the town centre. Good value food, especially Sunday lunches.

SUTTON COLDFIELD

Bishop Vesey

63 Boldmere Road

11-11; 12-10.30 Sun

(0121) 355 5077

Boddingtons Bitter; Courage Directors; Hop Back Summer Lightning; Greene King Abbot; Shepherd Neame Spitfire; guest beers Ⓗ

Typical Wetherspoon's interior with a no-smoking area. On a bus route. Good choice of food; pleasant service. Cask Marque accredited.

TIVIDALE

Barleymow

City Road

4 (12 Fri & Sat)-11; 12-4, 7-10.30 Sun

(01384) 254623

Banks's Original, Tetley Bitter, Burton Ale; guest beers Ⓗ

Pub games and sports-oriented bar; comfortable lounge. Real fires in both. On 120 Birmingham-Dudley bus route. Food includes Sun lunch.

Malt Shovel

93-95 Spon End (B4101, off inner ring road, jct 7)
12 (4 Mon & Tue)-11; 12-10.30 Sun
☎ (024) 7622 0204
Donnington SBA; Tetley Bitter; guest beers Ⓗ
Traditional wood-panelled pub where a central bar serves three drinking areas. An upstairs bar selling continental beers opens weekend evenings. The pub is traditionally decorated, with a large inglenook in one room and paintings by the landlord. Guest beers usually include at least one from Church End, but also feature other micro-breweries. Cosy and welcoming, the pub serves large Sunday lunches, but no other meals. ♨❀P

Nursery Tavern

38-39 Lord Street, Chapelfields (1 mile W of centre, off Allesley Old Road))
11-11; 12-10.30 Sun
☎ (024) 7667 4530
Banks's Original; Courage Best Bitter; John Smith's Bitter; guest beers Ⓗ
Family-run community pub in a terraced street in the historic watch-making area. Two front rooms are served by a central bar; the third room at the rear is quieter, welcomes families, and is regularly used for traditional pub games and quiz nights. The pub runs vibrant Formula One and Rugby Union supporters' clubs and displays memorabilia relating to both sports. It organises an annual summer beer festival at Coventry Rugby Football Union Stadium and hosts regular social events. Q❀☾♣

Old Windmill

22-23 Spon Street (near city centre shopping area)
11-11; 12-3, 7-10.30 Sun
☎ (024) 7625 2183
Banks's Bitter; Courage Directors; Greene King Old Speckled Hen; Marston's Pedigree; Wells Bombardier; guest beers Ⓗ
Situated in medieval Spon Street is one of Coventry's oldest pubs; with low beams and flagstoned floor, customers are greeted by a snug, welcoming atmosphere. The back room contains a brewing vessel, which formed part of the old brewery equipment. Popular with the local folk scene, it stages regular music nights. Quality home-cooked food caters for vegetarian, vegan and coeliac diets as well as offering generous Sunday roasts. ♨☾♿⇌♣⊁

Rose & Woodbine

40 North Street (near football ground)
12-4 (11 Fri & Sat); 12-5, 7-11 Sun
☎ (024) 7645 1480
Ansells Mild; Draught Bass; M&B Brew XI; Tetley Bitter Ⓗ
This friendly local lies about one and a half miles north-east of the city centre. It is one of the few outlets in Coventry for real mild, yet it is reasonably priced and worth seeking out. Situated just half a mile from Coventry City's football ground, it is very popular when the team are playing at home. It is essentially a one-roomed pub, since the bar is given over to pool. ❀☾

Royal Oak

28 Earlsdon Street, Earlsdon
5-11; 12-3, 7-10.30 Sun
☎ (024) 7667 4140
Ansells Mild; Draught Bass; Tetley Bitter; guest beers Ⓗ
Busy, 19th-century drinkers' pub that draws a mixed clientele. The main bar serves two distinct drinking areas where table service is also available. The floor and furniture are stripped wood, including a number of large communal tables. A third drinking area, with its own bar (open at peak times), is accessed through the rear patio area which features hanging baskets in the summer. This rear bar boasts a large mural of Victorian Earlsdon. It is one of a small number of Coventry pubs still selling a real mild. ♨Q❀

Town Wall Tavern

Bond Street (behind Belgrade Theatre)
11-11; 12-10.30 Sun
☎ (024) 7622 0963
Draught Bass; M&B Brew XI; guest beers Ⓗ
Friendly, city-centre pub, it comprises a public bar, a lounge, which has recently been sympathetically extended, and the 'Donkey Box' which must be the smallest snug in Coventry. The owner, an enthusiastic supporter of traditional ales,

---

WALSALL

Hogshead
9-19 Leicester Street
11-11 (1am Sat); 12-10.30 Sun
(01922) 616963
Boddingtons Bitter; Brakspear Bitter Ⓗ
New building constructed behind a preserved red sandstone façade. Discount for card-carrying CAMRA members.

Red Lion
69 Park Street
10.30-11; 12-5 Sun
(01922) 622380
Banks's Bitter Ⓗ
Friendly, town-centre pub with a good choice of lunchtime food. Note the fine late Victorian frontage.

WEST BROMWICH

Churchfield Tavern
18 Little Lane
11-11; 11-10.30 Sun
(0121) 588 5468
Banks's Original, Bitter, Ⓟ **seasonal beers** Ⓗ
Four-roomed community pub: bar, lounge, dining room and family room, plus a garden with children's play area and bowling green.

WOLLASTON

Princess
115 Bridgnorth Road (A458)
11-11; 12-3.30, 7-10.30 Sun
Banks's Original; Wadworth 6X; Wells Bombardier; guest beers Ⓗ
Former M&B pub, now owned by Enterprise Inns and refurbished in traditional manner to appeal to all. Good value food.

WOLVERHAMPTON

Horse & Jockey
Robert Wynd, Woodcross
12-3, 5.30-11; 12-4, 7-10.30 Sun
(01902) 659666
Banks's Original, Bitter; Greene King Abbot; Marston's Pedigree; Tetley Bitter; guest beer Ⓗ
Popular local with real fires. A bar, lounge, garden and restaurant serving excellent, freshly-cooked food (not Sun eve).

Moon under Water
53-55 Lichfield Street
11-11; 12-10.30 Sun
(01902) 422447
Banks's Original, Bitter; Hop Back Summer Lightning; Greene King Abbot; Shepherd Neame Spitfire; guest beers Ⓗ
Large Wetherspoon's with a central servery and dining area. Can be a problem getting served. Cask Marque accredited.

also owns a bakery which supplies fresh rolls to the pub daily. A rare outlet for gravity-dispensed traditional cider in the city centre, it is very handy for Belgrade Theatre.
⌂Q♉◐⊟♣●

Whitefriars Olde Ale House
114-115 Gosford Street
11-11; 12-10.30 Sun
☎ (024) 7625 1655
Tetley Bitter; guest beers Ⓗ
One of Coventry's oldest buildings (circa 1335), it has been renovated as a gem of a pub, and nominated for a joint CAMRA/English Heritage award. With two rooms downstairs and a labyrinth of smaller rooms upstairs, this subtly-lit pub is atmospheric. Exposed brickwork, beams festooned with hops, murals and open fires add character. It offers up to four guest beers and occasional beer festivals. Three-course Sunday lunches are served from 1pm. It hosts live music (Sun eve) and impromptu sessions during the week.
⌂Q❀◐♿

CRADLEY HEATH

Moon under Water
164-166 High Street
10-11; 12-10.30 Sun
☎ (01384) 565419
Banks's Original; Greene King Abbot; Hop Back Summer Lightning; Shepherd Neame Spitfire; Theakston Best Bitter; guest beers Ⓗ
This traditional-style Wetherspoon's shop conversion has been a hit with locals of all ages in an area hitherto lacking in beer choice. It is handy for High Street shoppers and only a five-minute walk from the railway station/bus interchange. Should this prove too strenuous, several local bus services stop right outside the door.
Q❀◐◑♿⚌⚟✔

DARLASTON ❊

Boat
Bentley Road South
12-2.30 (3 Sat), 6 (5 Fri; 7 Sat)-11; 12-3, 7-10.30 Sun
☎ (0121) 526 5104
Banks's Original, Bitter; Greene King IPA; guest beers Ⓗ
Friendly, 1930s pub next to Bentley Bridge and the Walsall Canal. The pub has won the Avebury Taverns national award for Cask Excellence two years running. Three guest beers and Weston's Old Rosie cider are stocked. The cosy, two-roomed pub fields thriving dominoes and crib teams. Barbecues are held in the garden on fine summer evenings and lunches are served Mon-Sat. Fishing permits are available here.
⌂❀◐♣●P

Fallings Heath Tavern
248 Walsall Road
12-3, 7.15-11; 12-2.30, 7.30-10.30 Sun
☎ (0121) 526 3403
Ansells Mild, Best Bitter; guest beers Ⓗ
This three-roomed roadside pub was built in 1937 between Walsall and Darlaston. The bar is noted for its porcine memorabilia. A family room adjoins the garden; the lounge is quiet and comfortable. There is also an off-licence at the front of the pub.
Q♉❀⊟♣P⊓

DUDLEY ❊

Lamp Tavern
116 High Street
12-11; 12-10.30 Sun
☎ (01384) 254129
Batham Mild, Best Bitter Ⓗ
A short walk from Dudley town centre takes you to the Lamp. It boasts a lively public bar, which has been sympathetically refurbished, and a cosy lounge. The former Queen's Cross Brewery at the rear now houses a function room with its own bar, which is available for meetings and social events. Across the car park the Lamp Cottage offers accommodation on a bed and breakfast basis. Q❀⇌⊟♿♣P

HALESOWEN

Hawne Tavern
76 Attwood Street
4.30-11; 12-11 Sat; 12-10.30 Sun
☎ (0121) 602 2601
Banks's Original, Bitter; Batham Best Bitter; guest beers Ⓗ
This 130-year-old tavern in the Short Cross area was once a tiny pub serving local miners and button-makers. It has long since absorbed neighbouring cottages, and now has a sizeable bar with pool table and alcoves, a small lounge, and a rear garden. The current owner has greatly increased the real ale trade by offering four guests, and runs at least three beer festivals a year. No meals on Sunday, just sandwiches.
⌂❀◐♿♣⊓

Somer's Sports & Social Club
The Grange, Grange Hill (B4551/A456 jct)
12-2.30, 6-11; 12-2, 7-10.30 Sun
☎ (0121) 550 1645
Banks's Original, Bitter; Batham Mild, Best Bitter; Olde Swan Original; Taylor Landlord; guest beers Ⓗ
Standing in 12 acres, this Georgian house was the home of a local forge-master, before becoming a club in 1950. The drinking area is served from a long bar, and is notable for the many sports trophies displayed in the comfortable lounge area. To gain admission, visitors should produce a copy of this Guide or CAMRA membership card. Groups of five or more should phone ahead to check if they can be admitted. Snacks available and up to six guest beers. ♉❀P

Waggon & Horses
21 Stourbridge Road (1/4 mile from bus station)
12-11; 12-10.30 Sun
☎ (0121) 550 4989
Batham Best Bitter; Enville Ale; guest beers Ⓗ
On the main Birmingham to Stourbridge bus route, just outside Halesowen town centre, this pub is a popular watering-hole, generally stocking 15 real ales, that change regularly, with plenty of unusual brews for the adventurous drinker. The staff at this free house really know their beer, so just ask and they will find something for you to try. Sandwiches and hot snacks are available.
⊟♣●

KINGSWINFORD

Park Tavern

182 Cot Lane (1/2 mile from Kingswinford Cross)
✪ 12-11; 12-3, 7-10.30 Sun
☎ (01384) 287178
Ansells Best Bitter; Batham Best Bitter; guest beers Ⓗ
Situated approximately half a mile from the centre of Kingswinford, this pub is very popular with all drinkers. The bar caters for sports enthusiasts – the pub has its own golf society – and there is a separate lounge; both rooms are comfortably furnished. Nearby, the fascinating Broadfield House Glass Museum is worth a visit. Kingswinford is served by buses from Dudley, Stourbridge and Wolverhampton. ❀⊟♣P

LOWER GORNAL ❄

Black Bear

86 Deepdale Lane
✪ 5-11; 12-5, 7-11 Sat; 12-4, 7-10.30 Sun
☎ (01384) 253333
Shepherd Neame Master Brew Bitter, Spitfire; guest beers Ⓗ
This community pub has been untouched by brewery or pub company for over 20 years. It has evolved, through private ownership, into a characterful drinking establishment. Originally an 18th-century farmhouse it is now integrated into the built-up area behind the Milking Bank estate. The pub keeps up to four guest beers on tap, depending on demand, plus an interesting whisky selection. Ten minutes' uphill walk from Gornal Wood bus station, services from Dudley, Woverhampton and Stourbridge stop here.
⌂❀♣

Fountain

8 Temple Street (A4175)
✪ 12-3, 6-11; 12-11 Fri & Sat; 12-4, 7-10.30 Sun
☎ (01384) 242777
Enville Ale; Holden's Golden Glow, Special; Hook Norton Old Hooky; guest beers Ⓗ
Vibrant free house just 'up the bonk' from Gornal Wood bus station. Up to half a dozen guest beers, two real ciders and, for Europhiles, Czech Budweiser Budvar and Hoegaarden wheat beer complete a formidable draught range. In the bottle you will find a small, mainly Trappist selection of Belgian ales. The completion of a new dining room and kitchen has led to a growing culinary reputation (no food Sun eve). ❀◐◑♣●

NETHERTON

Olde Swan

89 Halesowen Road (A459)
✪ 11-11; 12-4, 7-10.30 sun
☎ (01384) 253075
Olde Swan Original, Dark Swan, Entire, Bumble Ale, seasonal beers Ⓗ
Characterful brewery tap on the main Dudley-Cradley Heath road. In addition to the wonderfully unspoilt bar and cosy back snug, there is a plush lounge/dining room and upstairs function room. Diners should note the lower age limit (14 years), which is strictly adhered to, and book early, particularly at weekends. The excellent fare has proved as popular as the expanding range of home-brewed ales. Canesta and chess played. ⌂Q◐◑⊟♿♣P⚟

OLDBURY

Waggon & Horses ☆

Church Street (off A4034, 3/4 mile from M5 jct 2)
✪ 12-3, 5-11; 12-11 Fri & Sat; 12-3 (closed eve) Sun
☎ (0121) 552 5467
Brains Bitter; Enville White; Holden's Special; Marston's Pedigree, Olde Swan Entire; guest beers Ⓗ
Situated on the edge of what remains of Oldbury town centre, this Grade II listed Victorian corner pub is opposite the sprawling 'pagoda palace' that is Sandwell Council's HQ. To the right of the entrance is a magnificent bar with high, copper-panelled ceiling, original tiles and imposing back-bar. To the left is a smaller room for non-smokers. A first-floor function room is also available. Food is served Mon-Fri (Wed-Fri eves). ⌂◐◑⊟⇌⚟

SEDGLEY

Beacon Hotel ☆

129 Bilston Street (A463)
✪ 12-2.30, 5.30-10.45; 12-3, 6-11 Sat; 12-3, 7-10.30 Sun
☎ (01902) 883380
Sarah Hughes Pale Amber, Sedgley Surprise, Dark Ruby, Snow Flake; guest beer Ⓗ
Well-restored, multi-roomed Victorian brewery tap, a short walk from the town centre 'Bull Ring', and the 558 bus stop. Its four rooms each have their own character, one being used for families (straight ahead, at rear of pub). The other rooms and short corridor surround a snob-screened island bar. There is also a conservatory. Q♨❀♣P

SHELFIELD

Four Crosses

1 Green Lane (off A461)
✪ 12-11; 12-3, 7-10.30 Sun
☎ (01922) 682518
Banks's Original, Bitter; Ⓟ **guest beers** Ⓗ
Imposing, detached pub over 200 years old; part of the building was once a blacksmith's. On entering, the visitor will find mosaic flooring and stained glass, remnants of a bygone age. The traditional saloon bar is warmed by a coal fire; the guest beers are dispensed in the quieter, comfortable lounge. It is the nearest thing to a good old basic boozer in the area. Children, accompanied by adults, may use the passageway. ⌂Q❀⊟♣P

SHIRLEY

Bernie's Real Ale Off-Licence

266 Cranmore Boulevard (off A3400)
✪ 12-2 (not Mon), 6 (5.30 Fri)-10; 11-3, 5-10 Sat; 12-2, 7-9.30 Sun
☎ (0121) 744 2827
Beer range varies Ⓗ/Ⓟ
Coming up to 20 consecutive years in this Guide and deservedly so, Bernie's is an oasis in a relative beer desert. It is also renowned among local real ale drinkers as the place to go for beers from micros never normally seen in the Solihull area. A warm welcome is assured and the owners offer the opportunity to try before you buy.

Red Lion
171 Stratford Road
11-3, 5.30-11; 11-11 Sat; 12-3, 7-10.30 Sun
☎ (0121) 744 1030
Ansells Mild; Boddingtons Bitter; Marston's Pedigree; Tetley Bitter; guest beer Ⓗ
Do not let the exterior of this boxy 1960s pub, which replaced an old coaching inn, put you off as the interior was refurbished some time ago. The front room is divided into three distinct areas, one no-smoking, with greyhound-racing memorabilia above the bar. The back room has a pool table, juke box and a large-screen TV. Food is served Mon-Sat lunchtimes until 2pm.

SHORT HEATH

Duke of Cambridge
82 Coltham Road
12-3.30, 7-11; 12-3.30, 7-10.30 Sun
☎ (01922) 408895
Draught Bass; Greene King Old Speckled Hen; Ⓗ **Highgate Dark; Worthington Bitter;** Ⓟ **guest beers** Ⓗ
Highly commended in Walsall CAMRA's Pub of the Year 2001, this family-run free house, originally a farm cottage, has been a pub since the 1820s. The public bar has a wood-burning stove and displays of model commercial vehicles. The lounge is split into two, with an aquarium in the dividing wall and original beams exposed in the front half. Both bar and lounge have electronic air cleaners. The large family room has a pool table. Filled rolls are sold at lunchtime. Q P

STOURBRIDGE

Hogshead
21-26 Foster Street (off ring road, near bus and rail stations)
12-11; 12-10.30 Sun
☎ (01384) 370140
Boddingtons Bitter; Enville White; Hook Norton Old Hooky; Wadworth 6X; guest beers Ⓗ
Formerly a newspaper office, this large, single-roomed pub has a long bar, where various seating areas on two levels add character. Low background music is played. Regular quizzes carry a cash prize. Card-carrying CAMRA members can claim a reduction on the cost of their pint. The cider range varies – two choices are usually available. A well-priced menu includes adventurous specials as well as standard Hogshead fare. (Town)

New Inn
2 Cherry Street (off B4186, via Glebe Lane)
2 (12 Sat)-11; 12-10.30 Sun
☎ (01384) 393323
Adnams Bitter; Ansells Mild; Draught Bass; Enville Ale; Greene King Abbot Ⓗ
Classic two-roomed local in a residential area, well worth the effort to find. The traditional bar includes a wide-screen TV for Sky Sports, the smart, L-shaped lounge has three themed areas: poppies, circus clowns and the landlord's corner dedicated to golf. Unobtrusive music is played in both rooms. The pub stocks an excellent range of 'top shelf' drinks, particularly single malt whiskies. Snacks are available at all times, evening meals can be booked.
P

Plough & Harrow
107 Worcester Street (B4186, Heath Lane jct)
12-2.30, 6-11; 12-11 Sat; 12-3.30, 7-10.30 Sun
☎ (01384) 397218
Enville White; Greene King IPA; Marston's Pedigree; guest beer Ⓗ
One-roomed pub with a U-shaped bar leading to various small drinking areas. This is a smart, friendly pub where the decor includes old photographs of local scenes. The garden is open in summer; access is via the bar area. Apart from the well-kept ales the pub is also recommended for its excellent bar food (no evening meals served Sun or Tue). Customers can use the public car park in the Heath Lane entrance to the local park, opposite the pub.
Q

Royal Exchange
75 Enville Street (A458)
1 (12 Sat & summer)-11; 12-10.30 Sun
☎ (01384) 396726
Batham Mild, Best Bitter, seasonal beers Ⓗ
Terraced pub on a busy road, opposite a public car park. One of the inns in the Batham's estate, this pub has two public rooms, a lively bar, where the decor is on an Irish theme, and a small lounge. An additional upstairs room is not normally open to the public but is available for private hire. At the rear, the large paved patio is popular in summer. All areas are accessed through a narrow passageway. Snacks are usually available.
Q

Shrubbery Cottage
28 Heath Lane, Oldswinford (B4186, 1/4 mile W of A491 jct)
12-11; 12-3, 7-10.30 (12-10.30 summer) Sun
☎ (01384) 377598
Holden's Mild, Bitter, Special, seasonal beers Ⓗ
A regular in this Guide, dedicated to good ale and conversation. Low-key background music replaced a juke box and there is no dartboard to detract from the friendly atmosphere, although Sky TV is switched on for major sporting events, particularly golf, as the landlord is a fanatic (note the memorabilia). Quizzes are held regularly. The pub is situated near Stourbridge College and is frequented by students at lunchtime.
Q (Junction) P

SUTTON COLDFIELD

Duke Inn
Duke Street, Maney (off Birmingham road)
11-11; 12-10.30 Sun
☎ (0121) 355 1767
Ansells Mild, Best Bitter; Draught Bass; Greene King Abbot; Tetley Bitter, Burton Ale Ⓗ
The pub is close to several modern and refurbished pubs and is regarded by many customers as the only real pub left in the area. Its own refurbishment in 2000 left the pub virtually unchanged in structure and character, as requested by the regulars. Sky TV (not always on) and two gaming machines detract slightly from the atmosphere, but conversation is not affected. The garden, originally a bowling green, is well used in the summer.
Q P

Laurel Wines

63 Westwood Road (opp. Sutton Park)
12-2, 5.30-10.30; 12-10.30 Sat; 12-2, 7-10 Sun
(0121) 353 0399
Batham Best Bitter; guest beers G
Highly recommended real ale off-licence, offering a constantly changing selection of beers, including the unusual as well as old favourites from near and far. Sample tasting is encouraged. It also stocks a wide range of British and continental bottled beers. P

TIPTON

Rising Sun

116 Horseley Road (1/4 mile from Gt Bridge bus station)
12-2.30 (3 Fri & Sat), 5-11; 12-3, 7-10.30 Sun
(0121) 530 2308
Banks's Original, Bitter; guest beers H
This former CAMRA award-winning free house is endeavouring to reassert itself under new tenants. An airy high-ceilinged public bar contrasts with a cosy lounge, boasting two real fires. Out the back a secluded courtyard is ideal for summer drinking. Three guest ales are usually available plus Thatcher's cider. Take the 74 bus from Birmingham or Dudley and alight at Gt Bridge; Dudley Port railway station is one mile away.

Waggon & Horses

131 Toll End Road, Ocker Hill (A461)
5 (12 Fri & Sat)-11; 12-3.30, 7-10.30 Sun
(0121) 502 6453
Banks's Hanson's Mild; Olde Swan Entire; Worthington Bitter; guest beers H
This recently refurbished and reopened free house features a mock-Tudor frontage whose central doorway leads to a spacious bar to the left and a comfortable lounge to the right, where the mock-Tudor theme continues. The regular beers are complemented by up to five guest ales. Take bus 311, 312 or 313 from Dudley or Wednesbury and alight at Ocker Hill. Wednesbury Parkway metro stop is three-quarters of a mile away.

UPPER GORNAL

Britannia Inn

109 Kent Street (A459)
12-3 (4 Fri), 7-11; 12-11 Sat; 12-4, 7-10.30 Sun
(01902) 883253
Batham Mild, Best Bitter, XXX H
Peaceful, friendly drinkers' local dating from 1780. Its 19th-century tap room has handpumps set against the wall and is now used as a no-smoking room. The more recent, but equally comfortable front bar has just been refitted. The garden out the back is lovely in summer. The excellent 558 bus service passes this must-see pub.
Q P

Jolly Crispin

Clarence Street (A459)
11-11; 12-10.30 Sun
(01902) 672220
Banks's Bitter; Courage Directors; Wells Bombardier; guest beers H
Genuine free house at the Sedgley end of Upper Gornal. Despite the different address it is just up the street from the Britannia (see above). Four or five guest ales compete for bar space with the regular beers. The new owners plan to build up the food trade, which is currently limited to bar snacks (Mon-Sat lunch, and Mon-Wed eves). Note that the opening hours have been extended. The 558 bus from Wolverhampton stops right outside.
Q P

WALSALL

Tap & Spile

John Street (near magistrate's court, off B4210)
12-3, 5.30-11; 12-11 Fri & Sat; 12-3, 7-10.30 Sun
(01922) 627660
Wells Eagle; guest beers H
Friendly, Victorian, two-roomed pub where the tiled frontage has given rise to its local name of the 'Pretty Bricks'. Good value food is served (except Sun and Mon eve). A regular curry club is featured. Seven guest beers is the norm here. A function room is available; Wednesday evening is quiz night.
Q

Victoria

23 Lower Rushall Street
12-11; 12-3, 7.30-10.30 Sun
(01922) 725848
Everards Tiger; Greene King IPA, Abbot, Old Speckled Hen; Taylor Dark Mild; guest beers H
This two-roomed, traditional ale house dates from the 1800s but was largely rebuilt in 1901. Situated just off the town centre, the 10 cask beers on offer always include a mild and five guests, mainly from micro-breweries, attracting discerning drinkers from far and wide. A small function room is available on the first floor. The former Tower Brewery at the rear is now a private residence.

Walsall Arms

17 Bank Street (behind Royal Hotel)
12-3, 6-11; 12-5, 7-10.30 Sun
Mansfield Dark Mild, Cask Ale; Marston's Bitter, Pedigree H
Traditional, terraced back-street gem. An interesting interior includes a saloon bar with a quarry-tiled floor and smart red and gold bench seats. A smaller intimate snug allows the art of conversation to be practised. An unusual back bar drinking area and a traditional skittle alley complete the facilities here. Photographs of old Walsall abound in all rooms.

Walsall Cricket Club

Gorway Road
7.30 (12 Sat)-11; 12-11 (varies winter) Sun
(01922) 622094
website: www.walsallcricketclub.co.uk
Adnams Bitter; Banks's Original; Marston's Bitter H
Established in 1830, Walsall Cricket Club has occupied this site since 1907. It is affiliated with Walsall hockey, bowls and bridge clubs. The comfortable lounge has a friendly, sporting atmosphere. Most of the week the bar is manned by members themselves. Four cricket teams, plus juniors, are supported and for matches in good weather the lounge is opened on to a patio area, affording a view right across the green. Emphasis is placed on family socials. Admission is by CAMRA membership card.
P

White Horse

Green Lane, Birchills (A34, 1 mile N of centre)
12-3, 5-11; 12-11 Fri; 11.30-11 Sat; 12-4, 7-10.30 Sun
☎ (01922) 631272
Banks's Original, Bitter P
The pub's regulars are heavily into social activities, such as darts, crib, dominoes and weekly karaoke nights. At least 100 years old, it boasts a comfortable bar with a surprisingly low ceiling. A tiny, intimate snug can be found at the rear. The pub has developed a reputation for no-nonsense, traditional food (served weekdays) – the home-made steak and kidney pies are particularly popular. ❀◐◑♣P

White Lion

150 Sandwell Street
12-3, 6 (5.30 Fri)-11; 12-11 Sat; 12-5, 7-10.30 Sun
☎ (01922) 628542
Adnams Bitter; Ansells Mild, Best Bitter; Fuller's London Pride; Tetley Burton Ale; guest beers H
Imposing Victorian street-corner pub, where the classic bar, with its sloping floor, is by far the most popular room. A splendid, comfortable lounge caters for the drinker who likes to languish, while the pool room has two tables. It hosts monthly quizzes, occasional live music and barbecues in the garden in summer. ❀◐♣

WARLEY

Plough

George Road (off A4123)
12-4, 5.30-11; 12-11 Sat; 12-10.30 Sun
☎ (0121) 552 3822
Adnams Bitter; Banks's Original; Draught Bass; M&B Mild; guest beers H
This 18th-century building, originally a farmhouse, is now a community pub. The lounge comprises four distinct cosy drinking areas on different levels. The bar focuses on pub games and sport. The 128 Birmingham to Blackheath bus stops outside, and the 126 Birmingham to Wolverhampton bus stops nearby on the Wolverhampton road. ❀♣P

WEDNESBURY

Old Blue Ball

19 Hall End Road
12-3, 5-11; 12-11 Fri; 11.15-5, 7-11 Sat; 12-3, 7-10.30 Sun
☎ (0121) 556 0197
Draught Bass; Everards Original; H **Highgate Dark; Stones Bitter;** P **guest beer** H
Three-roomed, back-street pub. The bar has a small collection of drinks and cigarette mirrors. There is a cosy snug and a large family room. The central corridor that joins the three rooms features a display of beer mats and a short history of Everards Brewery. Behind the building is a beer garden with a bench area that is popular in summer. Q❀♣

WEDNESFIELD

Pyle Cock

Rookery Street
10.30-11; 12-10.30 Sun
☎ (01902) 732125
Banks's Original, Bitter, P **seasonal beers** H
Built in 1867 this splendid pub retains its three rooms. Off the entrance corridor is the traditional bar with wooden settle backs and etched windows depicting a Pyle Cock. The small smoke room and rear lounge are served from a hatchway in the corridor. This rare survivor has recently been listed locally, and can be easily visited by public transport as it is on a major bus route with frequent services. ❀P

Vine

35 Lichfield Road (A4124, over canal bridge at end of High St)
11-3, 7-11; 12-3, 7-10.30 Sun
☎ (01902) 733529
Burton Bridge Stairway to Heaven; Flowers IPA; guest beers H
Recently awarded local heritage status, the Vine comprises three newly painted rooms, each with a coal fire. This friendly local is convenient for the Wyrley and Essington Canals and stands on the bus route between Wolverhampton and Bloxwich. A classic 1930s pub it has a function room upstairs. Weston's cider is sold. Q❀P

WEST BROMWICH

Billiard Hall

St Michael's Ringway (off High St opp. new bus station)
10-11; 12-10.30 Sun
☎ (0121) 580 2892
Banks's Original, Bitter; Greene King Abbot; Hop Back Summer Lightning; Shepherd Neame Spitfire; Theakston Best Bitter; guest beers H
This single-storey building with its striking stone relief pediment originally stood on St Michael's Street before it made way for the modern ring road. Since it won a CAMRA/English Heritage Conversion to Pub Use award the interior decor has been softened somewhat by a 2001 refurbishment. The prices are competitive, even by Wetherspoon's standards.
Q◐◑⊖(Central)

Old Crown

56 Sandwell Road (near A41/A4031 jct)
12-3.30, 5-11; 12-11 Sat; 12-3.30, 7-10.30 Sun
☎ (0121) 525 4600
website: www.midlandspubs.co.uk
Beer range varies H
Superb back-street free house, about 10 minutes' walk from the town centre. It stocks three ever-changing guest beers, mostly from independent brewers, but is renowned locally for its flavoursome and reasonably-priced food (no meals Sun; evening meals available Sat). Its popularity with all manner of working folk means it can get busy at lunchtime.
◐⊖(Dartmouth St)

Vine

Roebuck Street (near M5 jct 1)
11-2.30, 5-11; 11.30-11 Fri; 12-11 Sat; 12-10.30 Sun
☎ (0121) 553 2866
Beer range varies H
Cleverly extended street-corner local on the outskirts of town. It is handy for the M5 motorway and West Bromwich Albion FC, on whose match days it can get busy. It has one rotating guest ale, but the main attraction is the spectacular barbecue at the

very back of the pub. Food is available 12-2 and 6-10 (9.30 Mon and Tue).
❀ ◐ ⇌ (Galton Bridge) ⊖ (Kenrick Pk) ⊡

Wheatsheaf
379 High Street
⏲ 11-11; 12-3, 7-10.30 Sun
☎ (0121) 553 4221
website: www.midlandspubs.co.uk/westbromwichwheatsheaf.htm
Holden's Mild, Ⓟ Bitter, Ⓟ/Ⓗ Golden Glow, Special, seasonal beers; guest beers Ⓗ
Classic Black Country local at the Carter's Green end of the High Street. It has an extended lounge, popular with lunchtime diners and a characterful front bar, favoured by horse-racing devotees. The licensee's enterprise and enthusiasm has led to articles in both local and national newspapers. Inexpensive wholesome food is available 11-2.45, plus Sunday roasts (12-2.30).
❀ ◐ ⊟ ⊖ ♣ ⊡

WHITEHEATH

Whiteheath Tavern
400 Birchfield Lane (near M5 jct 2)
⏲ 12-3.30 (not Mon-Fri), 8-11; 12-3.30, 8-10.30 Sun
Ansells Mild; Banks's Original; Ⓟ Boddingtons Bitter Ⓗ
This pub is a true community local, run by the same licensee for 20 years. At the front is a bright, spacious, traditional games-oriented bar. To the rear is a comfortable lounge. The head of the Titford Branch Canal is nearby. The 404 West Bromwich to Blackheath bus passes the pub, while the 126 stops on the A4123 nearby. ⊟ ♣

WILLENHALL

Falcon Inn
77 Gomer Street West (off B4464, behind flats)
⏲ 12-11; 12-10.30 Sun
☎ (01902) 633378
RCH PG Steam, Pitchfork; Greene King Abbot; Olde Swan Dark Swan; guest beers Ⓗ
Large,1930s pub, handy for the town centre and the Lock Museum, it stands to the west of town, near a high-rise block. The bustling bar boasts 10 handpumps, serving a selection of up to eight good value beers. In the quieter lounge the beers are listed on a blackboard. Also available is a good range of malt whiskies. The pub fields its own darts and cricket teams. Q ❀ ⊟ ♣ ⚟ ⊡

Malthouse
The Dale, New Road
⏲ 11-11; 12-10.30 Sun
☎ (01902) 635273
Banks's Bitter; Enville Ale; Greene King Abbot; Hop Back Summer Lightning; Shepherd Neame Spitfire; guest beers Ⓗ
Wetherspoon's outlet, on the site of an 18th-century malthouse which was converted to a cinema, the Coliseum, in the early 20th century. The cinema was rebuilt and enlarged in 1932, becoming a bingo hall in 1967. Although on several levels, wheelchair access to most areas is possible. From the smallish entrance, the pub expands Tardis-like into a large drinking area. Beer festivals are held every year to commemorate St George's Day and Hallowe'en.
Q ❀ ◐ ♿ ⚟ ✓

Robin Hood
54 The Crescent (off B4464, 200 yds from McDonald's)
⏲ 12-3, 5 (7 Sat)-11; 12-3, 7-10.30 Sun
☎ (01902) 608006
Tetley Bitter, Burton Ale; guest beers Ⓗ
Small, cosy, single-roomed pub, next to the railway line. One or two guest beers are normally available, together with a good selection of country wines. Regular quiz nights are held on alternate Mondays. Local archers practise on the adjacent field at weekends before opening time, and on weekdays in summer. Outside drinking is possible in a paved area by the car park. ❀P

WOLLASTON ❄

Unicorn
145 Bridgnorth Road (A458)
⏲ 12-11; 12-4, 7-10.30 Sun
☎ (01384) 394823
Batham Mild, Best Bitter, seasonal beers Ⓗ
This former brewhouse was purchased by Batham's some seven years ago and has earned a reputation of serving one of the best pints in the estate. The old brewhouse remains at the side of the pub, but sadly will never brew again as the costs are prohibitive. The house itself is very much a basic, two-roomed traditional drinkers' pub, popular with all ages. A sandwich may be ordered at most times. This is a pub which is genuinely 'unspoilt by progress'. Q ❀ ⊟

WOLVERHAMPTON ❄

Chindit
113 Merridale Road
⏲ 11-11; 12-10.30 Sun
☎ (01902) 425582
Beer range varies Ⓗ
Deservedly popular, two-roomed local serving three guest beers, usually from SIBA members. Acoustic music nights are held every Friday and an annual beer festival is staged over the early May bank holiday weekend. Buses 513 and 543 from the city stop outside. The pub was built in the late 1940s and named in honour of the men of the Staffordshire Regiment who served in Burma during World War II. The history of the Chindits is displayed in the lounge.
⊟ ♣ ✓

Clarendon Hotel
38 Chapel Ash
⏲ 11-11; 12-10.30 Sun
☎ (01902) 420587
Banks's Original, Bitter; Ⓟ guest beer Ⓗ
The imposing façade of this turn-of-the-century Banks's Brewery tap, opens to a much renovated interior. The large L-shaped lounge has been created from three rooms. The snug retains its original features. It gets very busy on match days, due to the wide-screen TV – upstairs is a substantial meeting room. Breakfast is served from 8am, and it is very popular at lunchtimes. ☕ ◐ ⚟ ⊡

Combermere Arms
90 Chapel Ash (A41)
⏲ 11-3, 5.30-11; 12-11 Fri & Sat; 12-10.30 Sun
☎ (01902) 421880
Banks's Hanson's Mild, Mansfield Riding Bitter,

Bank's Bitter; guest beer Ⓗ
This lovely terraced pub is named after Viscount Combermere, second-in-command to Wellington during the Peninsular War of 1810. It consists of three rooms, and a passageway that leads to a covered patio and garden. There is only one bar but it also opens on to the passageway. Cobs and hot drinks are available at lunchtime in one room. Note the tree growing in the gents.

Great Western

Sun Street (opp. disused low level station)
11-11; 12-3, 7-10.30 Sun
☎ (01902) 351090
Batham Best Bitter; Holden's Mild, Bitter, Golden Glow, Special; guest beer Ⓗ
Built in 1869 on the corner of two terraced streets opposite the now disused low level station, it is the only building from those streets to survive. The original pub has been extended, but in accordance with its listed status. With its speedy service of excellent home-cooked food and quality beers, it attracts a wide range of customers and gets very busy on Wolves match days. Note the railway memorabilia. (High Level) P

Hogshead

186 Stafford Street
11-11; 12-10.30 Sun
☎ (01902) 717955
Adnams Bitter; Brakspear Bitter; Enville Ale; Hook Norton Old Hooky; Ⓗ **guest beers** Ⓗ/Ⓖ
City-centre pub serving up to eight cask ales, plus a choice of Belgian beers. With three no-smoking areas, it is popular with all ages, but 18-25 year olds dominate on Friday and Saturday evenings. Originally called the Vine, it was built to serve the soldiers of the South Staffs Regiment whose drill hall stood behind the pub. After a period of use as offices it was reborn as the Hogshead in the mid-1900s.
(St George's)

Homestead

Lodge Road, Oxley (off A449 at Goodyear Island)
12-2.30 (3 Sat), 6-11; 12-3, 7-10.30 Sun
☎ (01902) 787357
John Smith's Bitter; Tetley Bitter; guest beer Ⓗ
Converted from an old farmhouse after the war, this large estate pub has been a consistent Guide entry for the last two decades. Throughout this period it has been run by the same family. The pub consists of a sizeable bar, popular with darts players, and a spacious, comfortable lounge. Buses 503, 504 and 506 stop on the main Stafford road (ask for the stop after Goodyear Island). Cars can reach the pub via estate roads from the same island. P

Newhampton

Riches Street, Whitmore Reans (off A41, 1½ miles from centre)
11-11; 12-10.30 Sun
☎ (01902) 745773
Courage Best Bitter, Directors; Marston's Pedigree; Wells Bombardier; guest beers Ⓗ
Outwardly a street-corner local, the pub is Tardis-like inside, with four bars and a function room. Outside, the garden includes a large bowling green and children's play area. Quality home-made food is available; the smoke room becomes no-smoking when food is served. It stocks ever-changing guest beers and ciders, and at busy times they can get through three or four guests a session. The three main bars cater for all sections of the community.

Queen's Arms

13 Graiseley Row (off A449, behind metal castings factory)
12-3, 5-11; 11-11 Fri; 11-4, 7-11 Sat; 12-3.30, 7-10.30 Sun
☎ (01902) 428999
Burtonwood Top Hat; guest beers Ⓗ
Small, back-street local in an industrial area. Previously a home-brew house, it is a rare outlet for Burtonwood beers in the city, and normally has two guest beers on tap. The food is good value. The Queen's has an active dominoes team and hosts occasional karaoke sessions. Within easy reach of the 256 bus route to the south-west of the city, it maintains a cosy atmosphere even though it has been knocked into a one-bar pub. P

Swan (at Compton)

Bridgnorth Road, Compton
11-11; 12-10.30 Sun
☎ (01902) 754736
Banks's Original, Bitter Ⓟ
The Swan is a welcoming, Grade II listed inn, dating from 1777. The traditional bar has wooden settles and beams, and a faded legend over the fireplace proving its coaching history. There is a also a central servery, a lounge, games room and an upstairs function room where various clubs meet. This is a basic, unspoilt and friendly pub, with a patio area for summer drinking. Buses stop nearby. Q P

Tap & Spile

35 Princess Street
11-11; 12-10.30 Sun
☎ (01902) 713319
Banks's Original, Bitter; guest beers Ⓗ
Three-roomed, city-centre pub, comprising a narrow open bar area with large-screen TV for sports events, and two snugs (the rear one exhibiting a collection of old bottles and prints). Popular for Wolves home games, it is also handy for weekend clubbers. Good home-cooked food is available weekdays (and sometimes Sat lunchtime). An enterprising range of ever-changing guest beers is offered at inviting prices at this local CAMRA Best City Pub 2001. (St George's)

> Poor John Scott lies buried here;
> Although he was both hale and stout
> Death stretched him on the bitter bier;
> In another world he hops about.
>
> *from the tomb of a Liverpool brewer.*

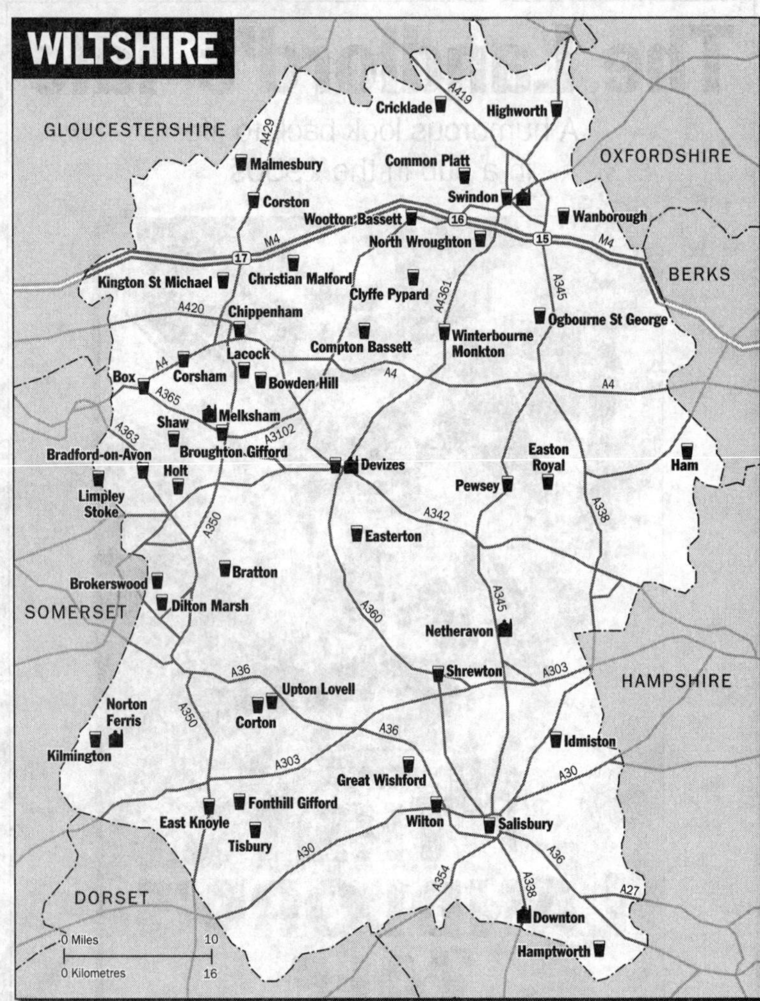

BOWDEN HILL, LACOCK

Bell Inn

The Wharf

11.30-2.30, 7 (6 Fri, 11.30-11 Sat)-11 (not Mon eve); 12-10.30 Sun

☎ (01249) 730308

Wadworth 6X; Wickwar Coopers WPA; guest beers Ⓗ

Free house in converted 140-year-old canal cottages, on the former Wilts and Berks Canal. The line of the long-closed canal is difficult to trace, but a new Sustrans cycleway (following the route) is shortly to open. The pub is in the attractive hamlet of Bowden Hill, between the National Trust village of Lacock and a highly thatched village, Sandy Lane. The Bell is renowned for its meals but is just as welcoming to those who only want a drink. Be careful before you take a seat as the pub cat likes to go to sleep in the bar. ❀◐♿⛺P⊬

Rising Sun

32 Bowden Hill (1 mile E of Lacock)

11.30-3, 6-11; 12-10.30 Sun

☎ (01249) 730363

Moles Tap Bitter; Best Bitter; Landlord's Choice (occasional), **Molennium, Molecatcher, seasonal beers; guest beers** Ⓗ

Traditional 17th-century single-bar roadside local offering wide views over the Avon vale. There is a large garden with children's play area. The ancient building on the common opposite is the conduit house; the water supply is gathered from hilltop springs and piped to Lacock Abbey. Situated on old Bath road, a highwayman would hold up mail coaches nearby as the horses laboured up the hill, before escaping to his hide-out (said to be monks' chapel) in the next village. The pub is, in effect, the brewery tap for Moles in nearby Melksham. ♨❀◑🍎P

BOX

Quarryman's Arms

Box Hill (in a maze of lanes, ring for directions)

11-3, 6-11; 11-11 Fri-Sat; 12-10.30 Sun

☎ (01225) 743569

Butcombe Bitter; Moles Best Bitter; Wadworth 6X; Ⓗ **guest beer** Ⓖ

Many people have lost their way trying to find this pub, as it is hidden away in a maze of little lanes, but the effort is well worthwhile. Inside, the main bar is

decorated with maps of the old stone mines that riddle the hill underneath the village. The views overlooking the Box Valley are superb from the windows of the dining area, while you tuck into the excellent food served.
⛫Q ✿⇌◑ ▲♣P

BRADFORD-ON-AVON ❄

Beehive

263 Trowbridge Road (next to the canal)
⏲ 12-2.30, 7-11; 12-3, 7-10.30 Sun
☎ (01225) 863620
Butcombe Bitter; Ⓗ guest beers Ⓗ/Ⓖ
Situated close to the Kennet and Avon Canal, this former brothel(!) stocks an ever-changing range of five guest beers. The pub was built in the early 19th century to provide refreshment for the canal trade. The large garden to the rear has chickens as well as the more usual children's play area. Beers are served on gravity or from two genuine Victorian handpumps. The walls boast a range of genuine old playbills from all over the country. CAMRA stalwarts will feel a rush of nostalgia when they see the old Watney's Red Barrel pump on the bar! No lunches served on Tuesday or evening meals on Sunday.
⛫Q✿◑♣P

Bunch of Grapes

14 Silver Street
⏲ 12-11; 12-10.30 Sun
☎ (01225) 863877
Smiles Best, Bristol IPA; Young's Bitter, Triple A, Special Ⓗ
Town-centre pub near the antique shops, easily recognised by the grapevine growing over the front (it fruits in summer). A welcoming pub with wooden floors, its panelled walls are painted a soft peach colour. There are three levels, each creating a separate drinking area, plus a separate restaurant upstairs (advisable to book). The whole pub has an air of good taste, from the decor to the wall prints. It can get very busy at times and, as it is not large, it can appear crowded. A rare Young's pub in this area. The garden can only be used in summer.
✿◑⇌

BRATTON

Duke

⏲ 11.30-3, 7-11; 11.30-11.30 Sat; 12-3, 7-10.30 Sun
☎ (01380) 830242
Moles Best Bitter; guest beers Ⓗ
Situated in an interesting village at the base of Westbury White Horse, it has won many accolades, including Sunday Roast Pub of the Year and Best Pub Loos. During the present landlord's era it began as an Usher's house but is now affiliated to Moles. Guest beers have been introduced to support the Moles' ales. A cosy lounge bar/restaurant (will possibly become no-smoking) and a friendly public bar, catering for the local trade, create an establishment to suit two very different types of clientele. The landlord is an excellent chef, producing an interesting and varied menu. The camping facilities nearby are only available in summer.
✿⇌◑ ⊟♿▲♣P⚡

BROKERSWOOD

Kicking Donkey

Between A36 and A350, near Westbury
⏲ 11.30-2.30 (3 Sat), 6 (6.30 Sat)-11 (11.30-11 summer); 12-10.30 Sun
☎ (01373) 823250
Moles Tap Bitter; Stonehenge Danish Dynamite; Wadworth 6X; guest beers Ⓗ
17th-century inn, formerly known as the Yew Tree, with exposed beams, brasses and flagstoned floors. The interior is divided into three drinking areas and a restaurant with exceptionally good food. The popular garden caters well, with seating for 200, a children's play area and, in the summer, a bouncy castle. It is an easy walk to Brokerswood Country Park, a family-oriented nature reserve, with camping and caravan sites. ⛫Q ✿◑▲♣P

BROUGHTON GIFFORD

Bell on the Common

2 miles W of Melksham, off B3107
⏲ 11-11; 12-10.30 Sun
☎ (01225) 782309
Wadworth IPA, 6X, seasonal beers Ⓗ
This handsome, old pub stands on the edge of the extensive village green. It has two contrasting bars, a smart bar (with a copper top) attached to the restaurant, and the public bar, which is very much a true locals' hangout, complete with wooden settles and old tables. However, you will receive a warm welcome in either. A games room is next to the public bar. The garden is large and safe for children and in summer barbecues are held here. The food in the restaurant is highly rated and the 'Waddies' is some of the best you will find.
⛫ ✿◑⊟♣P●

CHIPPENHAM

Old Road Tavern

Old Road (N of station footbridge)
⏲ 11-4, 5.45-11; 11-11 Fri & Sat; 12-10.30 Sun
☎ (01249) 652094
Courage Best Bitter; Fuller's London Pride; guest beers Ⓗ
In a quiet street near the railway, this traditional drinkers' pub is housed in a 130-year-old Grade II listed building. The pub has separate bar and lounge areas, a pool room and a function room. It is known as the Garage and is the headquarters of the Chippenham Town morris men. Indeed, music (folk and blues) is central to the life of this pub. Regular folk music sessions are held on Sunday nights and there are often performers on Saturday evening. In addition, practices or jam sessions can break out almost any time. It offers the best choice of ale in the town. A true community pub. ✿◑⊟⇌♣

INDEPENDENT BREWERIES

Archers Swindon
Arkells Swindon
Hobden's Norton Ferris
Hop Back Downton
Moles Melksham
Stonehenge Netheravon
Wadworth Devizes

CHRISTIAN MALFORD

Rising Sun

Station Road (1/2 mile from B4069)
12-2.30, 6.30-11 (closed Mon); 12-2.30, 7-10.30 Sun
(01249) 721571
Hook Norton Best Bitter; guest beers H
Delightful village inn that was once a blacksmith's. The original building dates from the turn of the 20th century. A number of real ales are kept and Black Rat cider. The separate bar and dining room have a real country feel. The cosy bar is decorated with fascinating memorabilia. A varied menu with fresh produce, usually local, is served in the airy dining room. The back garden includes a boules pitch. Limited daytime bus service runs (not Sun). A triumph for planning control, this pub was bought as a private residence and closed, but the council held firm and it was resold to open once more as a pub.

CLYFFE PYPARD

Goddard Arms

Wood Street OS074769
12-2.30, 7-11; 11-11 Sat; 12-10.30 Sun
(01793) 731386
Wadworth 6X; guest beers H
Clyffe Pypard is a small village which is worth seeking out for a visit to the Goddard Arms. The pub acts as a focus for many activities including hosting a dog show in September. Exhibitions by local artists are ongoing and provide a constantly changing backdrop. The pub is on many levels and has a traditional skittle alley. Wadworth 6X is a regular beer but two other beers are genuine guests, normally from the smaller breweries. The pub now offers accommodation.

COMPTON BASSETT

White Horse

Off A4 E of Calne, or take A3102 from Lyneham
11-3, 5-11; 12-3, 7-11 Sun
(01249) 813118
Badger Tanglefoot; Wadworth 6X; guest beers H
This is the village where, a few years ago, a disgruntled resident hacked down the church belfry door and cut the bell ropes as she objected to the noise. Do not let that put you off! Despite the pub name, the chalk white horse is in the next village. This pub has been greatly improved in recent years and now serves superb food and a wide range of beers. It has pointed gables, characteristic of the older buildings here; the village was once part of a landed estate. Sunday lunch is particularly good value – eat in the bar by the log fire in winter (do not feed Bruno the dog), or opt for the no-smoking restaurant. Cider is served in summer. There is a popular skittle alley.

CORSHAM

Two Pigs

38 Pickwick
7-11; 12-2.30, 7-10.30 Sun
(01249) 712515
website: www.twopigs.freeserve.co.uk
Stonehenge Pigswill; guest beers H
Lively free house with an ever-changing range of at least three guest beers, plus Pigswill, the house beer which is brewed by Stonehenge Brewery. A splendid pub catering for over-21s only; the long, rustic bar, flagstoned floor and wood-panelled walls add to the character and cosy atmosphere. Outside seating is provided under cover in an area called the Sty. Live blues music is staged on Monday evening. Regular local CAMRA Pub of the Year, it is closed at lunchtime (except Sun). The

INN BRIEF

BRADFORD-ON-AVON

Rising Sun
231 Winsley Road
12-11; 12-10.30 Sun
(01225) 862354
Archers Village; Draught Bass; Moles Tap Bitter H
Welcome outlet for Moles in a popular local on the outskirts of the town centre. Live music performed at weekends.

COMMON PLATT

Foresters Arms
11-3, 6-11; 12-3, 7-10.30 Sun
(01793) 770615
Courage Best Bitter; Greene King Ruddles Best Bitter; Wadworth 6X H
Very popular two-bar pub with pleasant staff. Large children's play area and garden; booking for meals advisable.

CORSHAM

Great Western
21 Pound Pill
11-3 (not Mon), 5-11; 12-11 Sat; 12-4, 7-10.30 Sun
(01249) 713838
Abbey Bellringer; Wadworth 6X; Young's Bitter; guest beer (occasional) H
Friendly, traditional community pub near the railway, south of the town. No lunchtime food on Sun.

EAST KNOYLE

Fox & Hounds
The Green OS871313
11.30-2.30, 6-11; 12-3, 7-10.30 Sun
(01747) 830573
Smiles Best; Young's Bitter, Special; guest beer H
This once well-known free house was acquired by Smiles, then by Young's. Glorious views, but hard to find.

HAM

Crown & Anchor
11.30-2.30 (not Mon), 6-11; 11.30-11 Sat; 12-10.30 Sun
(01488) 668242
Archers Village, Best Bitter H
Typical village pub with a cosy bar warmed by a real fire in winter. Just off the Wayfarers Walk footpath.

HAMPTWORTH

Cuckoo
11.30-2.30 (3 Sat), 6-11; 12-3, 7-10.30 Sun
(01794) 390302
Cheriton Pots Ale; Hop Back GFB, Summer Lightning; Ringwood Best Bitter; Wadworth 6X G
Picturesque village pub on the edge of the New Forest. Huge garden with children's play area and pétanque terrains.

KINGTON ST MICHAEL

Jolly Huntsman Inn
11-2.30, 6 (5.30 Fri)-11; 12-3, 7-10.30 Sun
(01249) 750305
Badger IPA, Tanglefoot; Draught Bass; Wadworth 6X; Wickwar BOB; guest beer H
Friendly village local offering good food. The pub has a separate dining area, and stages live music (Wed).

LIMPLEY STOKE

Hop Pole
Woods Hill
11-3, 6-11; 12-3, 7-10.30 Sun
(01225) 723134
Draught Bass; Butcombe Bitter; Courage Best Bitter H
In beautiful countryside, charming pub with cosy, wood-panelled bar and larger lounge. It featured in The Titfield Thunderbolt.

MALMESBURY

Three Cups
The Triangle
11-2.30, 6-11; 11-11 Sat; 12-10.30 Sun
(01666) 823278
Beer range varies H
Friendly local close to the abbey with a lively public bar and quiet lounge. Hobbes, the 17th-century philosopher lived nearby.

faintly eccentric decorations have been lovingly collected by the landlord, some with a porcine theme. ⛼❀

CORSTON

Radnor Arms

✪ 12-3 (not Tue), 5.30-11; 12-11 Sat; 12-10.30 Sun
☎ (01666) 823389
Hook Norton Best Bitter; RCH Pitchfork; guest beers Ⓗ
Welcoming, 19th-century village pub located between Malmesbury and M4 junction 17, serving both local and passing trade. The guest beers change regularly and during the summer months Black Rat cider is available. There is an extensive menu from baguettes to steaks, with a hog roast on bank holiday Mondays. The Radnor has its own darts team, a quiz (Sun eve), TV for rugby and other sports, and a pool table in the rear barn in summer. ⛼❀◐◑♣●P

CORTON

Dove

✪ 12-3 (3.30 Sat), 6.30-11; 12-4, 7-10.30 Sun
☎ (01985) 850109 website: www.thedove.co.uk
Oakhill Best Bitter; guest beers Ⓗ
Welcoming village pub in the heart of the Wylye Valley. There is a candlelit conservatory and a separate restaurant (where children are served). The food is excellent, with a varied lunchtime menu and a more sophisticated evening choice using, where possible, local ingredients including game and fish. Recent improvements allow drinkers much more space in the bar area which has a polished wood floor and an open fire. Three ales are usually on handpump. There is a large, pleasant garden. Corton is situated on the Wiltshire cycleway. ⛼Q❀⇌◐◑♿P

CRICKLADE

Red Lion

74 High Street
✪ 12-11; 12-10.30 Sun
☎ (01793) 750776
Moles Best Bitter; guest beers Ⓗ
This friendly, traditional local dates back to the 16th century (in parts). The eight handpulls supply a regularly changing selection with over 600 different beers served since the pub became a free house 18 months ago. The walled garden and patio are ideal in the summer. The licensees concentrate on the ales and provide no food, other than nibbles. However, if you check in advance you may be able to purchase local award-winning pasties. Weston's and Thatcher's cider are sold in summer. ⛼Q❀♿♣●P

DEVIZES

British Lion

9 Estcourt Street
✪ 11-11; 12-10.30 Sun
☎ (01380) 720665
Beer range varies Ⓗ
This very popular, basic, down-to-earth pub is full of character. The landlord has a strong commitment to real ale, with a range of five to eight different beers offered each week. Real cider is always available; Weston's First Quality and Thatcher's Cheddar Valley. Traditional pub games, including pool, are played, along with a regular Saturday morning 'open quiz'. Ideal for good conversation and a relaxing drink with friendly staff; it is well worth a visit. A big supporter of the annual real ale festival held at the wharf in July. ❀♣●P⊡

Cavalier

Eastleigh Road
✪ 11-11; 12-10.30 Sun
☎ (01380) 723285
Wadworth IPA, 6X, seasonal beers Ⓗ
The licensees here have a decent amount of experience in the trade and it shows. In tandem with Wadworth, they have created a village-style pub from a modern building in the middle of a residential area. Although it comprises a single bar, the effect is of a sweep from public bar to eating area, via the saloon bar. The pub has built a good reputation for its meals. The 'try before you buy' idea, that could win converts to real ale, has been enthusiastically embraced. Q❀◐◑♣P✔

Fox & Hounds

Nursteed
✪ 11-3, 6-11; 12-10.30 Sun
☎ (01380) 723789
Wadworth IPA, 6X Ⓗ
Very traditional Wadworth's country pub, though actually situated on the edge of Devizes. It modestly retains its rural character and picturesque appearance, including thatched roof, much admired from the roadside – even if the locals do not wear smocks while supping their ales outside, watching the horses and carts on the Andover road! There is also a large beer garden at the rear. Inside, there is a comfortable bar area which serves excellent food. The pub has a popular skittle alley and function room for community use. This is still very much a real pub for locals and visitors alike. Q❀◐◑▲♣P

Hare & Hounds

Hare & Hounds Street
✪ 11-3, 7-11; 12-3, 7-10.30 Sun
☎ (01380) 723231
Wadworth IPA, 6X; seasonal beers Ⓗ
Many people have an idea of what 6X should taste like. If you want the definitive answer then come to this pub. At first sight, it is none too spectacular but if you take time to look, you will find that this traditional back-street local has more than a few listed features. The fact that it has the street named after it gives a clue as to its true age. The Hare & Hounds is warm and welcoming with friendly staff; it won't feature in any adverts for alcopops – and you can't say fairer than that. Lunchtime food is served on Sat. ⛼Q❀♣P✔

DILTON MARSH

Prince of Wales

94 High Street
✪ 12-3 (not Mon or Tue), 7-11; 12-3, 7-10.30 Sun
☎ (01373) 865487
Fuller's London Pride; Thwaites Bitter; Wadworth 6X; guest beers Ⓗ
Friendly, welcoming village local. A single bar serves two drinking areas plus a small

pool table annexe and a large skittle alley. The pub participates in local skittles, crib and pool leagues. In addition, there is a quiz every Sunday evening. The factually incorrect pub sign has featured in a Japanese pub-sign guide! Can you spot the error? ❀◑ ⇌♣P

EASTERTON

Royal Oak

11 High Street (B3098)
11-3, 5.30-11; 12-3, 7-10.30 Sun
☎ (01380) 812343
Wadworth IPA, 6X, seasonal beers; guest beers Ⓗ

There are plenty of interesting features in this thatched, 16th-century village pub, ask to see the lute. An excellent varying menu of delicious home-cooked food makes it very popular, the midweek lunches are particularly good value. The Wadworth range and occasional guest beers are very well kept by the landlord. He has created a relaxed atmosphere and organises pub-related outings. Welcoming conversation around the bar makes it a pleasant local to visit. ♨Q♉❀◑♿P⅟

EASTON ROYAL

Bruce Arms ☆

Easton Road (B3087)
11-2.30 (3 Sat), 6-11; 12-3, 7-10.30 Sun
☎ (01672) 810216 website: www.brucearms.co.uk
Fuller's London Pride; Wadworth 6X; guest beer Ⓗ

Listed on the CAMRA national inventory, this traditional pub dates back to the 1840s and little has changed since the bar was fitted in 1934. The tables and benches are believed to be more than 150 years old. The pub is quite isolated with no buildings around so the locals travel some distance. It boasts its own cricket pitch (on the opposite side of the road) and a large back room features a skittle alley and pool table. ♨Q♉❀⊟⋀♣P

FONTHILL GIFFORD

Beckford Arms

Halfway between Tisbury and Hindon OS931312
12-11; 12-10.30 Sun
☎ (01747) 870385
Greene King Abbot; Hop Back GFB; Taylor Landlord; guest beer Ⓗ

This remote inn lies in superb Wiltshire countryside at a crossroads between Tisbury and Hindon, close to Fonthill Lake. It is a fine 17th-century stone building. The high-ceilinged public and lounge bars are spacious, yet intimate, with the lounge leading to cosy dining areas, and, beyond, to the garden room with peaceful views to the lawn and trees. Three regular beers are accompanied by one changing guest. Meals are high quality, and should usually be booked. Solitaire, chess and dominoes are played. ♨Q♉❀⇔◑ ⊟♣P

GREAT WISHFORD

Royal Oak

Langford Road
12-2.30, 6-11; 11-11 Sat; 12-10.30 Sun
☎ (01722) 790079 website: www.stayinapub.com
Hop Back GFB; guest beers Ⓗ

Frenchman Nick Deschamps runs this traditional village pub with his family. Handy for walking, cycling and fishing, the pub is also a centre of village life. There are six guest beers normally on offer in the oak-panelled bar. A beer festival with over 20 ales is held every year on the weekend nearest the village oak apple festival on May 29th. ♨♉❀⇔◑⋀♣P

HIGHWORTH

Wine Cellar

10 High Street
7 (5.30 Wed & Thu; 1 Fri; 12 Sat)-11; 12-5, 7-11 Sun
☎ (01793) 763828
Archers Village, Best Bitter; guest beer Ⓖ

This little gem is hard to find. Take the steps behind the door next to the Indian takeaway on the south side of the market square, and you find yourself in a cellar that was once the kitchen for one of the houses above. As the name implies, there is an extensive range of wine as well as the beer. There are also 55 malt whiskies stocked and Black Rat cider. It is said that there was a tunnel leading to the church on the other side of the square, dating from the English Civil War. A discount is available to CAMRA members on production of a valid membership card. ●⅟

HOLT

Tollgate Inn

Ham Green (B3105, between Bradford-on-Avon and Melksham)
11.30-2.30, 6.30-11; closed Mon; 12-2.30 (closed eve) Sun
☎ (01225) 782326
Beer range varies Ⓗ

This, recently refurbished, old village pub is superb. The range of four to five ales, which changes every week, is very imaginative with a good selection of local beers and many from smaller brewers further away. Excellent, wholesome food is served in the upstairs restaurant and the bar, while the garden at the rear overlooks a pretty valley (though rather spoilt by the Nestlé factory!). The pub as a whole has a very upmarket atmosphere, with comfortable sofas in the bar, but drinkers are very welcome. Try your hand at boules in the summer. ♨Q❀◑P

IDMISTON

Earl of Normanton

Tidworth Road (4 miles N of Salisbury on A338)
11-3, 6-11; 12-3, 7-10 Sun
☎ (01980) 610251
Cheriton Pots Ale, Best Bitter; Hop Back Summer Lightning; guest beers Ⓗ

Popular, roadside local in an idyllic setting. The elevated garden affords superb views of the Bourne Valley. The pub is renowned for its excellent food and warm, welcoming atmosphere. A perfect stop for a friendly drink, snack or meal. ♨❀⇔◑P

KILMINGTON

Red Lion Inn

On B3092, 2½ miles N of A303 at Mere
11.30-3, 6.30-11; 12-3.30, 7-10.30 Sun
☎ (01985) 844263
Butcombe Bitter; Butts Jester; guest beers Ⓗ

The Red Lion lies between two popular tourist attractions, the Wiltshire Downs and Stourhead Gardens (NT). Originally a farmworker's cottage, it boasts a single, cosy bar with flagstoned floors, two large fires, and beyond, a small no-smoking area. The three beers always include an interesting guest. The pub is popular with darts players and shove-ha'penny enthusiasts, who should think twice before challenging the expert landlord! Walkers are always welcome, and their dogs (except when lunches are served).
⛫Q❀⇔◑♣●P⊬

LACOCK

Red Lion

1 High Street
⊛ 11.30-2.30, 6-11; 11-11 Sat & summer; 12-3, 7-10.30, (11.30-10.30 summer) Sun
☎ (01249) 730456
Wadworth IPA, 6X, JCB; guest beers Ⓗ
Imposing 18th-century inn situated in the attractive setting of a National Trust village with greystone houses and half-timbered cottages. It stands close to the abbey, the home of photographic pioneer, Fox Talbot, with a museum of his work. The street outside the pub often alters its character for film and television period costume drama productions. Many of the film crew and actors often reside in the pub during the time of filming. The open-plan bar has peaceful areas with subdued lighting.
⛫❀⇔◑P⊬

MALMESBURY ❄

Red Bull Inn

Bristol Road (follow Sherston road out of Malmesbury about 1 mile)
⊛ 12.30-2.30 (not Mon-Thu; 11.30-3.30 Sat), 6.30-11; 12-3.30, 7-10.30 Sun
☎ (01666) 822108
Flowers IPA; Fuller's London Pride; Wadworth 6X; guest beer Ⓗ
Large rural pub frequented by locals during the winter months. The extensive garden with play area makes it a good choice in fine weather. A skittle alley adjoins the main bar and there is a small lounge. Snacks are served at lunchtime. It is situated beyond the boundaries of the town which was the home of Dyson vacuum cleaners, until production was moved to Malaysia. The area has many attractive stone buildings and the remains of a medieval abbey. ⛫ర❀⊟♣P

Whole Hog

8 Market Cross
⊛ 11-11; 12-10.30 Sun
☎ (01666) 825845
Archers Best Bitter; Wadworth 6X; Young's Bitter; guest beers Ⓗ
Close to the market cross and abbey in the centre of Malmesbury, a bustling small town, this friendly pub offers a good and ever-changing selection of real ale. It opens throughout the day with reduced beer prices during 'happy hour' (5-7). Reasonably-priced dishes can be chosen from the extensive menu. This popular pub attracts locals and visitors and has a wine bar feel, well worth a visit.
Qర◑♣

NORTH WROUGHTON

Check Inn

Woodland View (from Swindon follow signs for Wroughton, once over M4 first right)
⊛ 11.30-3.30, 6.30-11; 11.30-11 Fri & Sat; 12-10.30 Sun
☎ (01793) 845584
Beer range varies Ⓗ
Genuine free house serving six real ales, imported lagers and bottled beers. This ex-roadside stop has been cut off by the M4 and isolated in a cul-de-sac. The pub has recently benefited from a large extension and now provides accommodation. The guest beers change frequently. Good home-cooked food is available at a reasonable price, hot pot night (Tue) offers a bargain at 95p. 2001 Swindon and North Wilts CAMRA Pub of the Year; pub games, including pétanque, are played.
⛫Q❀⇔◑⊟▲♣●P⊬⊍

OGBOURNE ST GEORGE

Old Crown

Marlborough Road (signed off A346)
⊛ 12-3 (not Mon), 6-11; 12-3, (closed eve) Sun
☎ (01672) 841445
website: www.theinnwiththewell.com
Wadworth 6X; guest beer Ⓖ
Cosy pub in the Og Valley, just off the busy A346. The main feature of this 300-year-old pub is the 90ft well in the dining area. The bar is small and comfy and despite the handpumps every pint is drawn from the barrel in the cellar. A changing guest beer and a comprehensive menu means there is something of interest for diners and drinkers. A separate accommodation block makes this pub a good base for the Ridgeway path. ⛫Q❀⇔◑▲♣P⊬

PEWSEY

Coopers Arms

37-39 Ball Road (off B3087) OS170595
⊛ 12-2 (4 Sat), 6 (7 Sat)-11; 12-4, 7-10.30 Sun
☎ (01672) 562495
Butts Barbus Barbus; Wadworth 6X; guest beer Ⓗ
Well-hidden, but worth discovering, this back-street pub in a splendid, thatched building, is full of character. A wealth of entertainment is provided, live music, comedy and quiz nights are hosted regularly. A pool table is housed in a separate room. Real cider is stocked in summer. ⛫ర❀▲⇌(Pewsey Vale) ●P

SALISBURY ❄

Deacon's Alms

118 Fisherton Street
⊛ 5 (12 Fri & Sat)-11; 12-10.30 Sun
☎ (01722) 504723
Cheriton Village Elder, Best Bitter; Hop Back GFB, Summer Lightning; guest beers (occasional) Ⓗ
Popular split-level pub, five minutes' walk from the city centre. The small front bar has bare floorboards, the back bar has table football and a TV for sporting events. There are occasional guest beers and oversized glasses are always used. ⇔⇌♣⊍

Royal George

17 Bedwin Street
⊛ 11-11; 12-10.30 Sun

☎ (01722) 327782 website: www.royalgeorge.com
Adnams Bitter; Ringwood Best Bitter, Fortyniner Ⓗ
Named after the sister ship of HMS Victory, this Grade II listed pub was an inn in the 15th century. The low, beamed bar gives this city pub a country feel. Popular with locals, the Royal George is well known for its involvement in the crib, darts, football and pool leagues. The Fortyniner is sometimes replaced by a guest beer. Lunches are served on weekdays. ❀◐♣P

Tom Brown's
225 Wilton Road
✪ 12-3 (not Mon-Fri), 6-11; 12-3, 7-10.30 Sun
☎ (01722) 335918
Goldfinch Tom Brown, Flashman's Clout, Midnight Blinder Ⓗ
This Goldfinch Brewery house has a strong community spirit, it is popular with locals and enters teams in pool and darts leagues. A TV shows sports such as rugby and the Grand Prix races, otherwise there is background music and the buzz of conversation. The pub is midway between London and Exeter and was originally called the Halfway House. ♣

Village Free House
33 Wilton Road (A36, near St Paul's roundabout)
✪ 12 (4 Mon)-11; 12-10.30 Sun
☎ (01722) 329707
Abbey Bellringer; Taylor Landlord; guest beers Ⓗ
Friendly city local that attracts visitors arriving by rail, especially on steam trips. There are numerous railway items including signs and locomotive horns. The pub specialises in beers unusual in the area – the three ever-changing guests usually include a mild or a stout. There is a separate cellar bar available for functions. Local CAMRA Pub of the Year 2001. ⇌♣

Wig & Quill
1 New Street
✪ 11-11; 12-3, 7-10.30 Sun
☎ (01722) 335665
Wadworth IPA, 6X, JCB; guest beers Ⓗ
This 16th-century building has only been a pub since 1977 when it opened as Burke's Bar. It was Wadworth's first outlet in the city and has one long bar which serves three distinct drinking areas. The regular beers are served from wood casks which can be viewed through a window between the bar and the ground floor cellar. The guest beers include Wadworth's seasonal beers. Quiz nights and live music feature. ❀◐♣⚟●

Winchester Gate
113 Rampart Road
✪ 3 (12 Thu-Sat)-11; 12-10.30 Sun
☎ (01722) 322834
website: www.milkstreetbrewery.co.uk
Crouch Vale Brewers Gold; Milk Street Gulp, Beer; guest beer Ⓗ
Former coaching inn on the site of the city's east tollgate. It has been taken over by Milk Street Brewery and extensively refurbished. A hop festival is staged in October and live music and barbecues are held in the large garden during the summer. There is no juke box but background music is played in the public bar. Folk and jam sessions are hosted monthly in this welcoming pub. ♨❀◰♣P

Wyndham Arms
27 Estcourt Road (off ring road, near swimming pool)
✪ 4.30 (3 Fri; 12 Sat)-11; 12-10.30 Sun
☎ (01722) 331026
Hop Back GFB, Best Bitter, Crop Circle, Summer Lightning, seasonal beers Ⓗ
Home of the Hop Back Brewery and although brewing has moved to Downton, it is still regarded as the brewery tap. The head of Bacchus greets customers as they enter this haven of real ale. A single, long, narrow bar has two small rooms adjacent, one of which is no-smoking and welcomes families. The Wyndham Arms attracts customers from all walks of life, young and old. ♉⚟

SHAW

Golden Fleece
Folly Lane
✪ 11-2.30 (3 Sat), 6-11; 12-3, 7-10.30 Sun
☎ (01225) 702050
Butcombe Bitter, Gold; Marston's Pedigree; Wickwar BOB Ⓗ
This old coaching inn is on the main road from Bath. There is a comfortable bar and a restaurant in the new, attractive extension. The large, pretty garden overlooks the village cricket pitch. At the front of the pub

INN BRIEF

SALISBURY

Queen's Arms
9 Ivy Street
11-3.30, 5.30-11; 11-11 Mon, Fri & Sat; 12-10.30 Sun
(01722) 341053
Banks's Bitter; Greene King IPA; Usher's Best Bitter Ⓗ
This reputedly haunted, 14th-century pub claims the longest continuous licence in the city. It has a single split-level bar.

Red Lion Hotel
Milford Street
11-2.30, 6-11; 11-11 Sat; 12-2.30, 6-10.30 Sun
(01722) 323334
Draught Bass; Ringwood Best Bitter; guest beer Ⓗ
13th-century former coaching inn, one of Salisbury's oldest buildings. The guest beer is often unusual for the area.

SWINDON

Savoy
38-40 Regent Street
11-11; 12-10.30 Sun
(01793) 533970
Archers Best Bitter; Greene King Abbot; Hop Back Summer Lightning; Shepherd Neame Spitfire; Wadworth 6X; guest beers Ⓗ
Converted ex-cinema, it features cinema stills and old books. The four guest beers change often. Cask Marque accredited.

UPTON LOVELL

Prince Leopold
12-3 (not Mon), 7-11; 12-3 (closed eve) Sun
Ringwood Best Bitter, XXXX Porter; guest beers (summer) Ⓗ
Welcoming pub with riverside garden. Built in 1887, it was named after Queen Victoria's youngest son, a regular visitor.

Poor beer

If you consider beer quality in a pub is not up to standard please let us know immediately. Write to GBG, CAMRA, 230 Hatfield Road, St Albans, Herts, AL1 4LW or camra@camra.org.uk. If the pub has a Cask Marque symbol, write to Cask Marque at the address in its editorial feature at the front of the Guide.

is a skittle alley. Beers include Wickwar Brand Oak Bitter, more popularly known as BOB and quite rare in this area. The bar food is simple and filling, while the restaurant offers normal pub fare.
❀◐◑♣P

SHREWTON

George Inn

London Road (1/2 mile E of A360, follow High St)
✪ 11.30-3 (not Tue), 6-11; 12-3, 7-11 Sun
☎ (01980) 620341
Courage Best Bitter; Flowers Original; John Smith's Bitter; Wadworth 6X; guest beers H
Friendly local pub with good passing trade. The spacious, unspoilt bar offers a good atmosphere. A beer festival is held on August bank holiday weekend. Traditional music is played outside most summer weekends, and there is a popular skittle alley.
♨❀◐◑♣P

SWINDON ❋

Beehive

55 Prospect Hill
✪ 12-11; 12-10.30 Sun
☎ (01793) 523187 website: www.bee-hive.co.uk
Morrells Varsity, seasonal beers; guest beers H
The Beehive is a long-established pub known for its quirky yet welcoming atmosphere. The multi-level layout features an old blue police box (as part of the entrance) and displays some unusual artwork. Tucked away behind Swindon College, close to the town centre, this hostelry is popular with students and locals. The three guest ales change regularly, and live music events are staged frequently.
♨⇌♣

Duke of Wellington

27 Eastcott Hill
✪ 12-2, 6.30-11; 12-11 Sat; 12-3, 7-10.30 Sun
☎ (01793) 534180
Arkells 3B, seasonal beer G
The only pub in Swindon where Arkells is served on gravity. This is a typical back-street local, consisting of a bar and a very cosy snug. It was named after the famous duke, not for his exploits at Waterloo, but as a tribute to his 1830 Beer House Act. This allowed private houses to sell beer, it was about to be repealed but Arkells bought two houses and converted them into this unspoilt pub. It opened in March 1869 just before the law changed in October of that year. Crib is played (Wed eve).
♨❀⇌♣

King's Arms Hotel

20 Wood Street
✪ 11-11; 12-3, 7-10.30 Sun
☎ (01793) 522156
Arkells 2B, 3B, Kingsdown, seasonal beers H
This fine Victorian building, simply known locally as King's, has a wonderful façade dating from 1870. The hotel has 16 rooms and a bustling bar. It was fully refurbished in 2002 and now stocks the full range of Arkells beers including seasonals. The central location makes the bar very busy at weekends. Live music is performed (Thu-Sun eves).
⇔◐◑♿P

Plough

26 Devizes Road (at jct of Devizes and Croft Road)
✪ 12-2.30, 6-11; 12-11 Fri & Sat; 12-3, 7.30-10.30 Sun
☎ (01793) 535603
Arkells 2B, 3B H
Originally opened some time prior to 1855, it was bought by local brewers, Arkells, in 1867. In 1881 part of the garden was sold to the Swindon and Marlborough railway. The pub has outlasted the railway and is now perched above the cutting which marks the divide between Croft Road and Devizes Road. The cutting now contains a footpath and cycleway. This is a friendly local and is ideal for a quiet drink, a contrast to the larger, noisier bars around the corner in Newport Street. ♣

Steam Railway

14 Newport Street
✪ 12 (11 Sat)-11; 12-10.30 Sun
☎ (01793) 538048
Wadworth 6X; guest beers H
Traditional, friendly bar on the right-hand side of a much larger bar. There are nine handpumps available, offering a regularly changing variety of guest beers. It tends to be very busy at weekends, especially when major sporting events are broadcast, so arrive early for a good view. Lunchtime food is served until 6pm. ♨Q☕❀◐♣●✓

TISBURY

Boot Inn

High Street
✪ 11-2.30, 7-11; 12-3, 7-10.30 Sun
☎ (01747) 870363
Courage Best Bitter; guest beers G
17th-century in origin, this fine village pub built of Chilmark stone has been licensed since 1768. Ron Turner has been landlord here since 1976 and maintains a friendly, relaxed atmosphere which appeals to both locals and visitors. Although an Eldridge Pope house, the beers stillaged behind the bar no longer include Dorchester ales, but do feature a changing selection from the company list. Tasty food is served Wed-Mon. The spacious garden is an added attraction. ♨❀◐◑⛺⇌♣P

South Western Hotel

Station Road
✪ 12-3.30, 6-11; 12 (11.30 Sat)-11 Fri; 12-3.30, 7-10.30 Sun
☎ (01747) 870160
Fuller's London Pride; Young's Bitter; guest beer (occasional) H
Opposite the station, this welcoming, Victorian inn has several separate drinking areas. The walls are decorated with railway memorabilia and local items of interest collected over the years. Although handpumps feature on the bar, beer is often served direct from the cask in the ground-floor cellar. Meals are served Fri-Wed.
❀⇔◐◑⛺⇌♣P

WANBOROUGH

Harrow

High Street
✪ 12-2.30 (3 Sat), 6-11; 12-3, 7-10.30 Sun
☎ (01793) 790622

Adnams Bitter; Shepherd Neame Master Brew Bitter; Wadworth 6X; guest beer Ⓗ
By far the oldest pub in Wanborough, the Harrow & King's Head (as it was then known) was old in 1747, when the earliest dated deed changed hands. For part of the 19th century it was a brew-pub, until the equipment was removed when the Wanborough Brewery opened next door. It is now a popular two-bar pub with a wide range of food. The open fire features some of the largest logs you will have ever seen.
⛼Q❀◐◑⊟P

Plough
High Street
✪ 12-2.30, 5-11; 12-11 Fri & Sat; 12-3, 7-10.30 Sun
☎ (01793) 790523
Draught Bass; Fuller's London Pride; Moles Tap Bitter; Wadworth 6X; guest beer Ⓗ
Attractive thatched Grade II listed building. It was opened as a beer house after 1830. In 1854 the local constable commented that it was the most disorderly house in the village. Despite this, it remained open and is the only Wanborough pub to have always sold real ale. The present licensee's father gutted the bland 1950s interior with his own hands, exposing the beams, bare walls and open fireplaces. It is now a cosy, warm pub with much character. Look out for the skull behind the bar. Weekday lunches are served, evening meals Mon-Sat.
⛼Q❀◐◑⊟♣P

WILTON

Bear Inn
12 West Street (close to market square on A30)
✪ 11-2.30 (3 Sat), 4.30 (5.30 Sat)-11; 12-3, 6-10.30 Sun
☎ (01722) 742398
Badger Best Ⓗ
Charming, beamed pub with a cosy single bar. It dates from the 16th century and stands in the centre of this historic small town. The landlord has been at the pub for more than 25 years and offers a friendly welcome to regulars and visitors alike. Pub games are played and there is a pleasant beer garden. The main town car park is close by. ⛼❀♣

WINTERBOURNE MONKTON

New Inn
Follow signs off A4361 N of Avebury
✪ 12-2.30 (3 Sat), 6-11; 12-3, 7-10.30 Sun
☎ (01672) 539240
Greene King IPA; Wadworth 6X; guest beers Ⓗ
Friendly local, clearly signed off the Avebury to Swindon road. The cosy bar area has a real fire and pub memorabilia on display. There is a separate restaurant and huge children's play area in the garden. A worthwhile diversion if visiting the famous Avebury prehistoric site – it can be busy in the summer months. Weston's and Black Rat cider are available. Try your hand at table skittles. No food is served on Sun eve or Mon. ⛼❀⇌◐◑⛺♣●P

WOOTTON BASSETT

Five Bells
Wood Street (off High St near the church)
✪ 12-2.30, 5-11; 12-11 Sat; 12-10.30 Sun
☎ (01793) 849422
Fuller's London Pride; Hancock's HB; Young's Bitter; guest beers Ⓗ
Cosy, little thatched local with a black and white façade. It has a low ceiling with beams and an open fire. On entering, one's gaze is drawn towards the bar with six handpumps and the blackboards with a good selection of home-made dishes. There is a front bar and a back room; wood panelling, bric-à-brac and local pictures together with ample seats and tables create a pleasant, homely environment. Addlestone's cider is served.
⛼Q❀◑♣●P

Choosing Pubs

CAMRA members and branches choose the pubs listed in the Good Beer Guide. There is no payment for entry, and pubs are inspected on a regular basis by personal visits; publicans are not sent a questionnaire once a year, as is the case with some pub guides. CAMRA branches monitor all the pubs in their areas, and the choice of pubs for the guide is often the result of democratic vote at branch meetings. However, recommendations from readers are welcomed and will be passed on to the relevant branch: write to Good Beer Guide, CAMRA, 230 Hatfield Road, St Albans, AL1 4LW; or send an e-mail to camra@camra.org.uk.

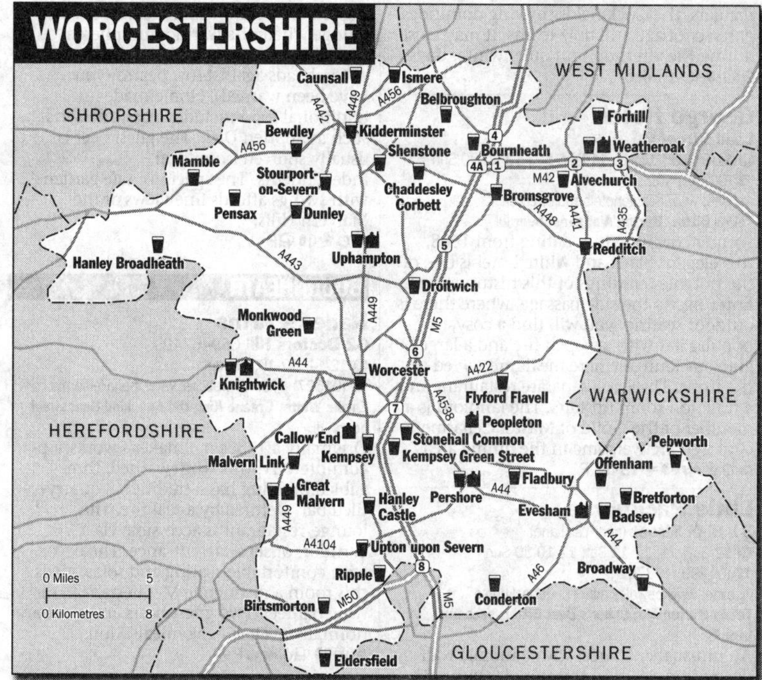

BADSEY

Round of Gras

Bretforton Road

11-3, 5-11; 11-11 Fri & Sat; 12-10.30 Sun

☎ (01386) 830206

Flowers IPA; Uley Pig's Ear; guest beers H

This large roadside inn, the former Royal Oak was renamed many years ago by a former landlord, the legendary 'Buster' Mustoe, in honour of the asparagus that is the speciality in this part of the Vale of Evesham. Naturally 'gras features on the menu in its brief season (around May), but fresh local produce is prominent all year round. The pub boasts a collection of old implements used in asparagus growing and other memorabilia. Wheelchair WC.

♨❀◑◗♿♣●P⊁

BELBROUGHTON

Talbot

Hartle Lane (B4188)

11.30-11; 12-10.30 Sun

☎ (01562) 730249

Banks's Original, Bitter; Enville Ale; guest beer H

Large pub with a small, old bar connected to a larger room with a fire and Sky TV where stripped wood panelling gives a light, modern feel. The garden has barbecue facilities for summer and the restaurant serves a wide range of food. A convenient cash machine sits next to the video games. Like other pubs in this smart commuter village, this is an expensive place to drink.

♨Q❀◑◗●P

BEWDLEY ❊

Black Boy

50 Wyre Hill (follow Sandy Bank from B4194 at Welch Gate)

12-3, 7-11; 12-3, 7-10.30 Sun

☎ (01299) 403523

Banks's Original, Bitter; Marston's Pedigree, seasonal beers H

Not to be confused with the much larger Black Boy Hotel in the Wribbenhall part of Bewdley, this is a comfortable local dating back several hundred years. Situated a short, but steep, walk from the town (and worth the effort) the Black Boy was carefully refurbished some years ago, yet retains separate rooms and all its charm as a friendly local. The licensee proudly displays a number of cellar awards. Well-behaved children may be allowed in the games room when not in use, but check first. ♨Q❀⊟♣

Cock & Magpie

1 Severnside North (riverfront, upstream of Bewdley Bridge)

11-11; 12-10.30 Sun

☎ (01299) 403748

Banks's Original, Bitter P

Only rarely defeated by the River Severn in flood, it is hoped that the determined drinker will no longer need a pair of wellies, with the advent of a flood barrier in Bewdley. This small, traditional two-roomed pub displays photographs depicting floods over many years in the bar. Offering a friendly welcome to visitors as well as

INDEPENDENT BREWERIES

Brandy Cask Pershore
Cannon Royall Uphampton
Evesham Evesham
Malvern Hills Great Malvern
St George's Callow End
Teme Valley Knightwick
Weatheroak Weatheroak
Wyre Piddle Peopleton

regulars, the Cock fields thriving dominoes, darts, cribbage and quiz teams. It may close during the afternoon on quiet winter days.
Q ⊟ ≠(SVR) ♣ ⊽

George Hotel

Load Street
11-3, 5.30-11; 11-11 Fri & Sat; 12-10.30 Sun
☎ (01299) 402117
website: www.georgehotelbewdley.co.uk
Tetley Bitter, Burton Ale; guest beer Ⓗ
Former coaching inn, dating from 1608, this elegant black and white hotel is one of the notable buildings of this historic town. Entering via the side passage, where there is outdoor seating, you will find a cosy, popular bar with an open fire and a large, gracious lounge where meals are served at the front. There is a separate restaurant and a function room upstairs. The landlord is a member of the Guild of Master Cellarmen. Children are welcome in the dining areas.
Q ≠(SVR) P

Little Packhorse

31 High Street (near Lax Lane)
12-3, 6-11; 12-11 Sat; 12-10.30 Sun
☎ (01299) 403762
website: www.bewdley.actinet.net/packhorse
Tetley Burton Ale; Usher's Best Bitter, seasonal beer Ⓗ
An unusual entrance, with a mosaic wall decoration, leads to this popular pub with cosy inter-connecting rooms. An array of unusual memorabilia and hop garlands adorn the walls and beams and there are humorous touches dotted around (look for the horse's hoof prints leading up to the bar). The food is good; reservations are recommended. A variety of seating styles, assorted table sizes and a real fire contribute to the good atmosphere.
Q

BIRTSMORTON

Farmer's Arms

Birts Street (off B4208) OS790363
11-3, 6-11 (11 -11 summer Sat); 12-3, 7-10.30 Sun (12-10.30 summer) Sun
☎ (01684) 833308
Hook Norton Best Bitter, Old Hooky; guest beer Ⓗ
Classic black and white village pub, tucked away down a country lane. The large bar area with a real old-fashioned inglenook is complemented by a smaller lounge where the warm atmosphere is typically interrupted only by the crack of foreheads against low beams (you have been warned). Home-made traditional food includes classic desserts such as Spotted Dick. The guest beer is usually sourced from local independents. The spacious, safe garden with swings affords fine views of the Malvern Hills.
Q P

BOURNHEATH

Nailer's Arms

62 Doctors Hill OS946740
12-11; 12-10.30 Sun
☎ (01527) 873045 website: www.thenailersarms.com
Enville White; Greene King Old Speckled Hen; guest beers Ⓗ
Originally a 1780s nailmaker's workshop-cum-brewery, this whitewashed, three-gabled building has a traditional quarry-tiled bar, warmed by a real fire. The lounge/restaurant is accessible via a corridor, or separate entrance. The decor, with comfortable seating and sofas, gives this room a distinctive Mediterranean or wine bar feel. Two guest beers and cider are normally available. No meals Mon.
♣ P

BRETFORTON

Fleece ☆

The Cross
11-3, 6-11; 11-11 Sat; 12-10.30 Sun
☎ (01386) 831173
Ansells Best Bitter; Hook Norton Best Bitter; Uley Pig's Ear; guest beers Ⓗ
Famous old National Trust property, where the interior is untouched by the passage of time: several small rooms, inglenooks, open fires, antique furniture and a world famous collection of 17th-century pewterware are its hallmarks. One of the stars of CAMRA's national inventory of historic pub interiors, it was willed to the NT by former landlady, Lola Tamplin. There is a large garden, orchard, children's play area and an historic tithe barn. Weston's Old Rosie cider is usually supplemented by a guest. Q ♣

INN BRIEF

ALVECHURCH

Weatheroak Ales
25 Withybed Lane, Withybed Green
5.30-8.30; 5-9 Fri & Sat; closed Mon & Sun
(0121) 445 4411
Weatheroak Ale; guest beers Ⓗ
Real ale off-licence run by Weatheroak Brewery's owner, stocking draught ales, ciders and a good range of bottle-conditioned beers.

BEWDLEY

Black Boy Hotel
Kidderminster Road
11-11; 12-10.30 Sun
(01299) 402119
Enville Ale; guest beers Ⓗ
Friendly, 14-roomed hotel, a two-minute walk from the Severn Valley Railway station. The menu specialises in fish.

BROMSGROVE

Red Lion
73 High Street
11-11; 12-3, 7-10.30 Sun
(01527) 835387
Banks's Hanson's Mild, Original, Bitter; guest beer Ⓗ
Small, single bar, locals' town pub, with a patio/garden. Bar snacks available.

CAUNSALL

Anchor
12-4, 7-11; 12-3, 7-10.30 Sun
(01562) 850254
Draught Bass; Stones Bitter; SP Sporting Ales Joust Bootiful Ⓗ
Pleasant, two-roomed pub, popular with village locals; a short walk from the Staffs & Worcs Canal.

FLYFORD FLAVELL

Boot Inn
Radford Road
12-2.30 (11-3 Sat), 6-11; 12-3, 7-10.30 Sun
(01905) 820462
Draught Bass; Everards Tiger; Fuller's London Pride; Greene King Old Speckled Hen; Worthington Bitter Ⓗ
Busy local, with a pool table, inglenook and restaurant area.

KIDDERMINSTER

Railway Train
81 Offmore Road
11-11; 12-10.30 Sun
(01562) 740465
Banks's Original, Bitter Ⓟ
Basic locals' boozer, near the station with smoke room, pool room and L-shaped bar.

BROADWAY

Crown & Trumpet

Church Street

☉ 11-2.30 (3 summer Mon-Thu), 5-11 (11-11 summer Fri & Sat); 12-4, 6-10.30 (12-10.30 summer) Sun

☎ (01386) 853202

website: www.cotswoldholidays.co.uk

Flowers Original; Greene King Old Speckled Hen; Hook Norton Old Hooky; Stanway Stanney Bitter; guest beers Ⓗ

This 17th-century Cotswold inn, just behind the green in picturesque Broadway, boasts many period features: beams, a settle and open fire. It hosts live music and a wide selection of games including ring the bull. In winter the Stanney Bitter is replaced by Lords-a-Leaping, and in summer by Cotteswold Gold, brewed exclusively for the pub. All food is freshly prepared using local produce – even the ice cream. A perfect watering-hole while walking the Cotswold Way. Overnight guests may choose the room with the Breton wedding bed.

♨❀⇌◑◗♣P

BROMSGROVE ✲

Ladybird

2 Finstall Road, Aston Fields (A448 by station)

☉ 11-11; 12-10.30 Sun

☎ (01527) 878014

Batham Best Bitter; Hobsons Best Bitter; guest beer (occasional) Ⓗ

Formerly the Dragoon, this pub has been redecorated since being saved from closure in 1997. The use of pine gives a light, airy feel to the bar and lounge. The dining area remains no-smoking even when the good value food is not being served. There are three function rooms, the largest is on the ground floor, the other two upstairs, catering for up to 120 people. Located on the outskirts of town, within a residential community, the pub is well served by public transport. ❀◑◗⊟♿⇌P

CHADDESLEY CORBETT

Swan

High Street

☉ 11-3, 6-11; 11-11 Sat; 12-3, 7-10.30 Sun

☎ (01562) 777302 website: www.midlandspubs.co.uk

Batham Mild, Best Bitter, XXX (winter) Ⓗ

Circa 1606, this comfortable village pub is set in a picturesque black and white timbered village. The traditional bar enjoys a friendly atmosphere; a large high-ceilinged lounge, a small drinking area to the rear and a restaurant on the other side complete the accommodation. No meals are served Sunday evening or Monday; jazz bands play Thursday evening and occasionally Irish bands perform. A large garden at the rear offers summer barbecues. The cider is Weston's Old Rosie.

♨Q❀◑◗⊟♣●P

CONDERTON

Yew Tree Inn

☉ 12-3, 5.30-11; 12-4, 5.30-10.30 Sun

☎ (01386) 725364

Wadworth 6X, seasonal beers; guest beer Ⓗ

Cotswold stone building, next to the road in the middle of the village on the southern edge of Bredon Hill. Composed of several rooms with traditional wooden seating and beams, it has a large garden to the rear. Food is served lunchtime and evenings from a changing menu. Q❀◑◗⊟

DROITWICH

Gardener's Arms

47 Vines Lane (400 yds from Worcester road N of town)

☉ 12-11; 12-10.30 Sun

☎ (01905) 772936

Banks's Hanson's Mild, Bitter; Ⓟ **guest beer** Ⓗ

Welcoming two-roomed pub, with a cosy lounge, situated in a quiet road beneath Dodderhill church, it is close to Vines Park, the Droitwich Canal and this historic town's centre. There is a pleasant, terraced garden with a children's play area and the car park is to the right of the pub. A comprehensive bar menu includes traditional Sunday lunches (no food Wed). The draught cider is Weston's Traditional.

❀◑◗⊟⇌●P⊓

Old Cock

Friar Street (opp. Norbury Theatre)

☉ 11.30-3, 5.30-11; 12-3, 7-10.30 Sun

☎ (01905) 774233

Banks's Mild; Marston's Bitter, Pedigree, seasonal beers Ⓗ

Droitwich's oldest licensed premises where a central bar serves four open-plan rooms; it is popular for its food and with theatregoers. Dating back to the 17th century, it is situated in the old part of the town, directly opposite the main entrance to the Norbury Theatre, it features a restaurant, function room and a patio garden. Guest beers are from W&D's range.

❀◑◗⇌

Railway Inn

Kidderminster Road (from A38, Westlands island next to canal) OS896636

☉ 12-3, 5.30-11 (12-11 summer); 12-3, 5.30-10.30 (12-10.30 summer) Sun

☎ (01905) 770056

Banks's Hanson's Mild; Marston's Bitter, Pedigree; guest beers Ⓗ

This is a very friendly, basic, two-roomed pub by the Droitwich Canal, near the centre of this old market town. It displays a wealth of railway memorabilia, a high level model railway and many interesting pictures. The freshly prepared bar food is excellent quality and good value (not served Mon eve). A rooftop patio overlooks the canal. The pub holds regular beer festivals, with a variety of traditional musical entertainment. The guest beers are from Banks's/W&D. ❀◑◗⊟⇌♣P

DUNLEY

Dog Inn

Stourport Road (A451 Stourport-Great Witley road)

☉ 12-3, 5-11; 11-11 Fri & Sat; 12-10.30 Sun

☎ (01299) 822833

Banks's Original; Enville Ale; Hobsons Best Bitter; guest beers Ⓗ

Two-bar village pub: the main bar houses a pool table and there is a small snug that can be used by families. The comfortable L-shaped lounge has a dining area at one end and a large fireplace at the other. Outside, the garden has a bowling green and a small play area for children, overlooking open countryside. ♨Q❀⇄◑◐⊟⛺♣P

ELDERSFIELD

Greyhound

Lime Street (N of B4211/B4213 jct) OS814305
⏲ 11.30-2.30 (3 Sat), 6 (7 Mon)-11; 12-3, 7-10.30 Sun
☎ (01452) 840381 website: www.greyhoundinn.co.uk
Draught Bass; Butcombe Bitter; guest beer Ⓖ
A good map and a compass will help to find this rural watering-hole, hidden away in a labyrinth of winding lanes. However, the effort is well worthwhile to find a friendly country pub with benchwood seating, pub games (including quoits and skittles), a wood-burning stove and a cosy, no-smoking lounge where more serious food is served (including Sunday roast). The tranquil garden houses a dovecot. Two beer festivals are held each year, in June and October. No food Mon. ♨Q❀◑◐♣P⊬

FLADBURY

Chequers Inn

Chequers Lane
⏲ 11-2.30, 6-11; 12-3, 7-10.30 Sun
☎ (01386) 860276
website: www.chequers-inn-fladbury@hotmail.com
Fuller's London Pride; Wyre Piddle Piddle in the Wind; guest beer Ⓗ
Large inn dating from 1372, set back from the village green. The spacious open bar, once three separate rooms, boasts exposed beams and a range fire at one end. The restaurant, at the rear of the pub, serves a wide range of food, making best use of locally produced ingredients. Eight bedrooms are provided for overnight guests with a residents' lounge. ♨Q❀⇄◑◐♣

FORHILL

Peacock

Icknield Street (about halfway between A435 and A441 near Wythall) OS54755
⏲ 12 (11 Thu-Sat)-11; 12-3, 7-10.30 Sun
☎ (01564) 823232
Courage Directors; Enville Ale; Hobsons Best Bitter; Moorhouses Black Cat; Theakston Old Peculier; guest beers Ⓗ
Situated on Icknield Street, the old Roman Road, this is a very popular country pub with a friendly atmosphere; oak beams, flagstone floors and real fires abound. It comprises a public bar and a large lounge, split into four areas, one of which is no-smoking. Very popular with diners, it offers a varied menu. Three interesting, changing guest beers are stocked in addition to five regulars. Local CAMRA Pub of the Year 1998. ♨Q♉❀◑◐⊟♣P⊬

GREAT MALVERN

Great Malvern Hotel

Graham Road
⏲ 10-11; 11-10.30 Sun
☎ (01684) 563411
website: www.great-malvern-hotel.co.uk
Fuller's London Pride; Hobsons Best Bitter; Wood Shropshire Lad; guest beer Ⓗ
Victorian hotel in the town centre near the theatre complex, making it an excellent choice for pre- and post-performance refreshment. Built during Malvern's heyday as a spa, the hotel has a friendly public bar and offers a comprehensive menu featuring local produce, such as the award-winning local sausages. Meals can be enjoyed in the bar or adjoining no-smoking brasserie (no food Sun). Limited parking. ♉⇄◑◐≢♣P⊬

Malvern Hills Hotel

Wynds Point (A449/B4232 jct, British Camp)
⏲ 11-11; 12-10.30 Sun
☎ (01684) 540690
Black Sheep Best Bitter; Greene King Abbot; Hobsons Best Bitter; Malvern Hills Black Pear; guest beer Ⓗ
Oak-panelled bar in an upmarket retreat on the Malvern Hills, directly opposite the British Camp hill fort and the Red Earl's dyke. The Worcestershire Way – which passes within a few yards – further increases the popularity of the hotel with walkers. Fine views from the heated patio extend across Herefordshire to the Black Mountains. Wholesome bar food is complemented by a full restaurant menu. ♨❀⇄◑◐♣P⊬

HANLEY BROADHEATH

Tally Ho

On Martley road, B4204, 5 miles from Tenbury Wells
⏲ 11.30-2.30, 7-11; 11.30-11 Sat; 12-10.30 Sun
☎ (01886) 853241
Beer range varies Ⓗ
Lively roadside country inn, with a popular (and good value) conservatory restaurant. Oak beams and log fires give winter appeal, with the views from the garden and conservatory providing the perfect backdrop for a summer pint. A house bitter and mild are provided by the Cannon Royall Brewery. Two guest ales split typically as one from a national brewer and one from a local micro. ♨♉❀◑◐⊟♣P

HANLEY CASTLE

Three Kings ☆

Church End (off B4211)
⏲ 12-3 (may vary), 7-11; 12-3, 7-10.30 Sun
☎ (01684) 592686
Butcombe Bitter; Thwaites Bitter; guest beers Ⓗ
15th-century country inn, reigning local CAMRA Pub of the Year and twice winner of the CAMRA National award, it celebrated 90 years with the same family in 2001 and the 2,000th different beer served in 2002. The small snug is dominated by its inglenook. The larger Nell's bar features another real fire, hops and beams. It stages an annual beer festival (Nov), organised music sessions every Sunday and occasional Saturday, but informal jam sessions can happen at any time. A real gem. ♨Q♉❀⇄◑◐♣●

ISMERE

Old Waggon & Horses

Stourbridge Road (A451)
⏲ 11.30-3, 6-11; 12-3, 7-11 Sun
☎ (01562) 700298
Banks's Original, Bitter; Ⓟ **Marston's Pedigree; guest beer** Ⓗ
Good, honest pub, unusual for having a separate bar, of the old-fashioned variety with a quarry-tiled floor and panelled bar front. The more cosy lounge has ample

seating, two fireplaces, exposed beams and displays a wealth of pump clips and whisky containers over the bar. A dining area, which admits children, is at one end of the L-shaped lounge. The menu offers a wide choice, with Thai food served on Sunday. Guest beers come from the Banks's range.
⁂Q❀◐◑⊟♣P⊓

KEMPSEY

Walter de Cantelupe

34 Main Road

12-2, 6-11 (closed Mon); 12-2, 7-10.30 Sun

☎ (01905) 820572

Malvern Hills Black Pear; Taylor Landlord; guest beers Ⓗ

Attractive free house, three miles south of Worcester and 10 minutes' walk from the River Severn. The bar has an inglenook and, for the summer, there is an attractive walled garden (dogs welcome). A wide selection of beers and wine is complemented by an ever-changing, high quality food menu; the ploughmans and doorstep sandwiches, made with local bread, are specialities. Look out for the annual outdoor paella party and the biennial beer elections. Two large bed and breakfast rooms are available.
⁂Q❀⇌◐◑⊟P

KEMPSEY GREEN STREET

Hunstman Inn

Green Street (from A38 at Kempsey, via Post Office Lane, 2 miles)

12-3 (not Mon), 6-11; 12-4, 7-10.30 Sun

☎ (01905) 820336

Batham Best Bitter; Everards Beacon, Tiger Ⓗ

Comfortable free house of several rooms whose homely atmosphere makes it popular with locals. The owner's undertake a 100-mile round trip to collect the Batham Best Bitter. The bar and restaurant areas have exposed beams and open fires throughout – all of which contributes to a strong food trade. The impressive separate skittle alley has its own bar. ⁂Q♉❀◐◑⊟P

KIDDERMINSTER ❊

Boar's Head

39 Worcester Street (opp. Safeway)

12-11; 12-3, 7-10.30 Sun

☎ (01562) 68776

Banks's Original, Bitter; Camerons Bitter, Strongarm; Marston's Pedigree; guest beer Ⓗ

Victorian, town-centre, two-bar pub: the small, but comfy lounge, partly oak-panelled, has settles and subdued lighting; the bar has a more basic feel with bar stools and tables. A passageway leads to a covered courtyard furnished with wooden tables and chairs. A working red telephone box is built into the wall between the bar and courtyard. The guest beer is usually from the Banks's range; the cider is Weston's Old Rosie. No food Sun. ⁂Q❀◐⇌●⊓

King & Castle

SVR Station, Comberton Hill (next to main line station)

11-3, 5-11; 11-11 Sat; 12-10.30 Sun

☎ (01562) 747505

Batham Best Bitter; Highgate Dark; Wyre Piddle Royal Piddle; guest beers Ⓗ

Unusually, this smart, comfortable pub is a 1980s recreation of a GWR refreshment room of the 1930s. At the Kidderminster terminus of the Severn Valley Railway, plenty of railway memorabilia can be admired in the single long room which is divided into distinct seating areas. Children are welcome (away from the bar) until 9pm. A wheelchair WC, on the station concourse, is open when the railway is running. The Royal Piddle is brewed especially for the pub.
⁂Q❀◐◑♿⇌●

Red Man

Blackwell Street (near ring road by Stourbridge island)

10-11; 12-10.30 Sun

☎ (01562) 67555

Adnams Broadside; Fuller's London Pride; Greene King IPA, Abbot, Old Speckled Hen; guest beer Ⓗ

This pub styles itself as 'the country pub in the town'. The front lounge/dining room lends itself to this concept, with wood-panelled walls, an exposed beam, partition and inglenook. Around the walls are memorabilia and prints, while hops adorn the bar. It is almost two pubs in one, having a quiet front lounge but a livelier rear bar/games room with TV sports and pool tables. For drivers, tea, coffee and hot chocolate are available; meals are served 12-7.
Q♉❀◐⊟♣P

KNIGHTWICK

Talbot

On B4197, 400 yds from A44 jct OS572560

11-11; 12-10.30 Sun

☎ (01886) 821235

Hobsons Best Bitter; Teme Valley T'Other, This, That, seasonal beer Ⓗ

Family-owned hotel, partly 14th-century, in an idyllic setting next to the old coach bridge over the Teme. The Teme Valley Brewery, also owned by the family, is to the rear. Imaginative, good quality food, made wherever possible from local (even home-grown) organic produce can be enjoyed in the bar or the oak-panelled dining room; a take-away menu is also available. A monthly farmers' market is held outside the hotel at lunchtime (second Sun).
⁂Q❀⇌◐◑⊟●P

MALVERN LINK ❊

Nag's Head

1 Bank Street (off Graham Rd by Link Common)

11-11; 12-10.30 Sun

☎ (01684) 574373

Greene King IPA; Marston's Pedigree; Wood Shropshire Lad; guest beers Ⓗ

Thriving, roomy, yet intimate pub. A selection of newspapers and other reading material together with pot plants, pictures and knick-knacks contribute to a home-from-home atmosphere. An extended bar area, with separate lounge, offers refuge for those seeking a quieter drink. The garden areas have patio heaters so that the view across Malvern Link Common towards the Severn Valley can be enjoyed late into the evening. Limited parking.
⁂❀⇌◐◑⇌♣●P

MAMBLE

Sun & Slipper

Signed from A456, approx 1/4 mile
12-3 (not Mon), 6.30-11; 12-3, 7-10.30 Sun
(01299) 832018
Banks's Original, Bitter; Hobsons Best Bitter, Town Crier H
In a classic village setting on a small green, but with a large car park to the rear, the pub has a small, attractive outdoor drinking area to the side, while indoors are two rooms: one a cosy bar area with a pool table, the other is a restaurant. The nearby craft centre is highly recommended when visiting Mamble. No meals Sun eve.

MONKWOOD GREEN

Fox

Follow signs to Wichenford, off A443 at Hallow
OS803601
12.30-2.30, 6.30-11; 12-5, 7-11 Sat; 12-5, 7-10.30 Sun
(01886) 889123 website: www.4avisit.com/sw3
Cannon Royall Arrowhead, Muzzle Loader; guest beer H
Single-bar country pub bordering common land, comprising two distinct drinking areas, one with an inglenook and beamed ceiling. A rare outlet for Barker's farmhouse cider and perry, it is popular with walkers and cyclists, due to its proximity to Monkwood Nature Reserve. Bar snacks made from local produce are served at lunchtime, evening cooked meals can be prepared for parties by arrangement. A plethora of traditional (darts, skittles) and unusual (devil-among-the-tailors, pétanque) games are on offer. Informal folk music sessions are staged monthly.

OFFENHAM

Bridge Inn

Boat Lane (follow signs to the ferry; there is no ferry!)
11-11; 12-10.30 Sun
(01386) 446565
Caledonian Deuchars IPA; guest beers H
Ancient riverside inn, with its own moorings and a garden leading down to the Avon. The eponymous bridge was washed away in the 17th century and replaced by a ferry, so it is often locally called the Boat. Devastated by the 1998 floods, it has been completely refurbished and retains a vibrant public bar, which serves as HQ to several local clubs and sports teams. No intrusive music invades the lounge (usually!). A courtesy minibus is available to collect and return groups.

PEBWORTH

Mason's Arms

Broad Marston Road
12-2 (3 Sat), 6 (7 Sat)-11; 12-3, 7-10.30 Sun
(01789) 720083
Hook Norton Best Bitter; Wyre Piddle Piddle in the Hole; guest beers H
Friendly local in a village well off the beaten track of Shakespeare and Cotswold tourism, it boasts the largest skittle alley in the area, which until recently, doubled as a small-bore rifle range. There are steps down into the pub, but a portable ramp is available. Hook Norton alternates with Wyre Piddle as the regular beer, and there are usually three guests from micros or independents, each changing approximately twice weekly. A take-away menu is available, no food is served on Tue.

PENSAX

Bell

On B4202, Clows Top-Great Witley road
12-2.30 (not Mon), 5-11; 12-10.30 Sun
(01299) 896677
Enville Bitter; Hobsons Best Bitter; guest beers H
Comfortable, country pub with an L-shaped bar, featuring pew-style cushioned seating, wood panelling and a wood-burning stove. Note the collection of old beer mats above the bar. Off the quarry-tiled entrance is a quiet snug where children are welcome, and a passage leading to a no-smoking dining room. The guest beers often come from local independents, and two beers are normally under 4% ABV; the cider is supplied by Weston's.

PERSHORE

Brandy Cask

25 Bridge Street
11.30-2.30 (3 Sat), 7-11; 12-3, 7-10.30 Sun
(01386) 552602
Brandy Cask Whistling Joe, Brandy Snapper, John Baker's Original; Courage Directors; Greene King Ruddles Best Bitter; guest beers H
Busy, town-centre free house, home of the Brandy Cask Brewery. The large, landscaped garden running down to the River Avon is popular in the summer, particularly during the annual beer festival (August bank holiday weekend). Ale Mary occasionally joins the regular Brandy Cask brews, but there are usually two further guests. Enjoyable bar food and a good restaurant complete the package.

REDDITCH

Gate Hangs Well

98 Evesham Road, Headless Cross
11-2.30, 6 (5.30 Thu & Fri)-11; 12-3, 7-10.30 Sun
(01527) 401293 website: www.gatehangswell.co.uk
Ansells Mild, Best Bitter; Greene King Abbot, Old Speckled Hen; Tetley Bitter H
Popular, one-roomed pub where interesting corners give some privacy. A small garden at the side of the pub opens in summer. There is no car park, but a free public car park is not far away (beware: licensees of the pub opposite are enthusiastic clampers). The warm, friendly atmosphere makes this a very pleasant environment in which to enjoy the excellent beer; the Sky TV and juke box are not overpowering.

Woodland Cottage

102 Mount Pleasant (Evesham Rd)
12-3, 5.30-11; 12-11 Fri & Sat; 12-10.30 Sun
(01527) 402299
Batham Best Bitter; Taylor Landlord; guest beer H
Situated at one of the highest points in Redditch, benefiting from spectacular views over the town from the car park, parts of the building are believed to date back to Elizabethan times. A large, open-plan lounge with a single long bar is divided into smaller areas. Frequent events such as quiz

nights, karaoke, live bands (Thu eve) and occasional folk bands (Fri and Sat eves) all contribute to the pub's lively, convivial atmosphere. Two guest beers often showcase local breweries. ❀P

SHENSTONE

Plough

Off A450/A448 OS865735
12-3, 6-11; 12-3, 7-10.30 Sun
☎ (01562) 777340
Batham Mild, Best Bitter, XXX (winter) H

Off the beaten track, the Plough is well worth seeking out. It houses a bar and a divided lounge. A homely, cosy pub, with a real fire, one section of the lounge displays a collection of pictures of the Falklands War. Outside is a covered enclosed courtyard where children are allowed. The front of the pub has tables and benches on a small grassed area. The ales are reasonably priced. ⌂Q❀♣P

STONEHALL COMMON

Fruiterer's Arms

From Norton, first left after garden centre OS882489
12-2, 6-11; 12-10.30 Sun
☎ (01905) 820462
Beer range varies H

Sizeable country inn, with a restaurant and conservatory, its extensive menu attracts a strong food trade. The comfortable, homely bar area has wood panelling and an open fire. Three guest beers are the norm, offering strong support for local micros. The large garden affords extensive views to the Malverns and Bredon. Children can play in the impressive adventure area. Council-approved disabled access and wheelchair WC are a plus. ⌂Q❀◐♿P

STOURPORT-ON-SEVERN

Old Crown

9 Bridge Street
11-11; 12-10.30 Sun
☎ (01299) 825693
Banks's Original; Courage Directors; Shepherd Neame Spitfire; Theakston Best Bitter; guest beers H

Wetherspoon's pub, close to the riverside and amusement park. One large room, the bar is down one side and there is plenty of seating; photos of old Stourport hang on the walls. The outside patio area overlooks one of James Brindley's historic river basins. Meals are served until 10pm daily.
Q❀◐♿▲♣P⊬

UPHAMPTON

Fruiterer's Arms

Uphampton Lane (off A449 at Reindeer Pub)
OS839649
12.30-3, 7-11; 12-3, 7-10.30 Sun
☎ (01905) 620305
Cannon Royall Fruiterer's Mild, Arrowhead, Muzzle Loader, seasonal beers; John Smith's Bitter H

Although off the beaten track, this is a much sought-out public house. The brewery at the rear provides most of the beer, but it is by no means the only attraction. Two rooms of very different character are served by a central bar where swan necks are unknown. Local produce is sometimes sold from behind the bar. A hidden gem to be savoured. ⌂Q❀◐♣P

UPTON UPON SEVERN

White Lion Hotel

High Street
11-11; 12-10.30 Sun
☎ (01684) 592552
website: www.whitelionhotel.demon.co.uk
Greene King Abbot; guest beers H

16th-century hostelry in a riverside town with strong Civil War connections, it comprises two distinct drinking areas: tables, chairs and upholstered bench seating around the bar, comfy sofas in the lounge. Upmarket bar meals (not Sat eve or Sun lunch) are served alongside a full restaurant menu. Generally three guest ales cover a wide range of strengths, and at least one is from a local micro. Spear dispense from the cask ensures that the beers can survive regular flooding of the cellar.
Q❀◐▲P

WEATHEROAK

Coach & Horses

Weatheroak Hill (Alvechurch-Wythall road)
OS56741
11.30-2.30, 5.30-11; 11.30-11 Sat; 12-10.30 Sun
☎ (01564) 823386

INN BRIEF

MALVERN LINK

New Inn
105 Lower Howsell Road
11-11; 12-10.30 Sun
(01886) 832359
Banks's Original, Bitter; P **Mansfield Cask Ale** H
Friendly local, with a strong community and fund-raising spirit. Basic public bar, plush lounge and a large garden. Children welcome.

RIPPLE

Railway Inn
Station Road
11.30-3 (not Mon-Fri); 12-3, 6.30-10.30 Sun
(01684) 592225
Beer range varies H
Close to the Severn, ideal for walkers and anglers, it has a large games area. Two beers usually – mostly from local micros.

WORCESTER

Berkeley Arms
School Road, St Johns
11.30-3, 5-11; 11.30-11 Sat; 12-3, 7-10.30 Sun
(01905) 421427
Banks's Hanson's Mild, Original, Bitter, P **seasonal beers** H
Traditional local with a distinct bar and lounge. A family room is available except Tue eve (darts fixture).

Swan with Two Nicks
28 New Street
11-11; 7-10.30 Sun
(01905) 28190
Boddingtons Bitter; guest beers H
Multi-level free house with extensive oak fittings and beams. Guests normally include a local offering. Restaurant upstairs.

Missing?

If a pub is not listed in the Guide that you think is worthy of consideration, please let us know at GBG, CAMRA, 230 Hatfield Road, St Albans, Herts, AL1 4LW or camra@camra.org.uk. All recommendations are forwarded to CAMRA branches, which are responsible for choosing pubs.

Black Sheep Best Bitter; Weatheroak Light Oak, Weatheroak, Redwood; Wood Shropshire Lad; H guest beers H/G
Attractive rural pub, with its own brewery. A quarry-tiled bar with a real fire and functional seating is complemented by a two-level lounge and modern restaurant (with wheelchair access) to the side. The surrounding gardens make it ideal for summer outings. As well as the Weatheroak ales, a good selection of guest beers is available and frequent beer festivals are held. Local CAMRA Pub of the Year 1999, 2000 and 2001. ♨Q❀⊟♣P

WORCESTER ✻

Bell

35 St Johns (W side of the Severn)
11-3, 5.30-11; 11-4, 7-11 Sat; 12-2.30, 7-10.30 Sun
☎ (01905) 424570
Fuller's London Pride; M&B Brew XI; guest beers H
Pub for beer drinkers, drawing a friendly regular clientele. The Bell has one main bar, two side rooms (one of which can be used by families), a skittle alley, function room and a patio. Darts, dominoes and cribbage are all played. The two guest beers frequently come from local breweries and change about twice a month. ❀♣

Bush

4 The Bull Ring, St Johns (W side of the Severn)
11-3, 5.30-11; 11-11 Sat; 12-3, 7-10.30 Sun
☎ (01905) 421086
Banks's Bitter; guest beers H
The public bar is the main drinking area of this Victorian pub, with a splendid wooden bar frontage and etched and stained glass windows. The small lounge is served by a hatch at the back of the bar. The restaurant upstairs opens Mon-Sat evenings and Sun lunchtime, with a full vegetarian menu. Bar snacks are served lunchtime and a limited bar menu early eve (not Sun). Live music is staged Sun eve. Four guest beers range from the commonplace to rare. ◑

Dragon Inn

51 The Tything (by Magistrate's Court)
12-3, 4.30-11; 11-11 Sat; 12-3, 7.30-10.30 Sun
☎ (01905) 25845
Beer range varies H
Recently refurbished Grade II listed Georgian town ale house, offering an ever-changing selection of seven ales, always including a mild and one cider. Stouts and porters are available in winter. The owner/landlord collects many of the ales personally from around the country in his little red van. Good quality meals, coffee and snacks are available, and can be served alfresco in summer. No food at weekends. Q❀◐♿⇌(Foregate St)♣●

Plough

23 Fish Street (next to fire station)
12-2.30, 5-11; closed Mon; 8-10.30 Sun
☎ (01905) 21381
Shepherd Neame Spitfire; guest beers H
Listed, two-roomed pub with hidden priest's holes and alleged smuggling tunnels to the Severn. The landlord is proud of his Basque origins and his nickname of 'Tony Never Opens' – the result of slightly idiosyncratic opening hours. Another quirk to watch out for is the fines for mobile phone usage (although they are donated to the air ambulance). Local micros are supported enthusiastically. Good value, simple bar snacks are served at lunchtime, when an area is set aside for non-smokers. Q❀⇌(Foregate St)

Salmon's Leap

42 Severn Street (opp. Worcester porcelain factory)
11.30-2.30 (not Mon), 6-11; 11-11 Sat & summer; 11-10.30 Sun
☎ (01905) 726260
website: www.thesalmonsleap.co.uk
Taylor Landlord; guest beers H
The pub is convenient for the cathedral, River Severn and Diglis Canal Basin. A large collection of pump clips bears testament to the rapid turnaround of guest ales. Buffets can be provided for parties by arrangement. Barbecues are held on fine Saturday evenings in summer. Sky TV is switched on for live sport, when the normal peaceful atmosphere can be disturbed. Q❀◐◑♿⇌(Foregate St)♣P⊬

Cool Beer

Ah! My beloved brother of the rod, do you know the taste of beer – of bitter beer – cooled in the flowing river? Take your bottle of beer, sink it deep, deep in the shady water, where the cooling springs and fishes are. Then, the day being very hot and bright, and the sun blazing on your devoted head, consider it a matter of duty to have to fish that long, wide stream. An hour or so of good hard hammering will bring you to the end of it, and then – let me ask you avec impressement – how about that beer? Is it cool? Is it refreshing? Does it gurgle, gurgle, and 'go down glug' as they say in Devonshire? Is it heavenly? Is it Paradise and the Peris to boot? Ah! If you have never tasted beer under these or similar circumstances, you have, believe me, never tasted it at all.

Francis Francis, By Lake *and River,* 16th century.

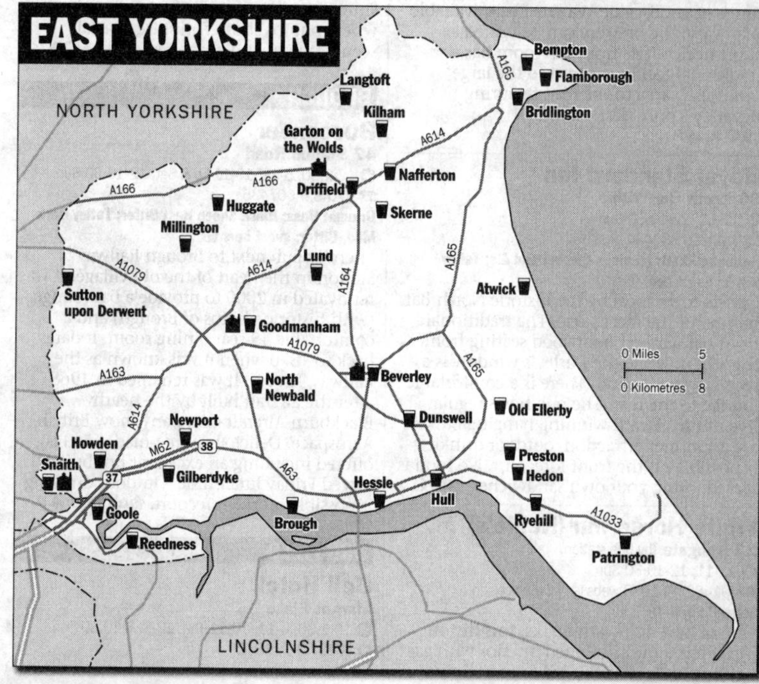

Yorkshire (East)

ATWICK

Black Horse

Church Street

11.30-3, 6-11; 11.30-11 Sat; 12-10.30 Sun

(01964) 532691

John Smith's Bitter; guest beer Ⓗ

Two miles north of Hornsea, overlooking the village green, this building dates from the mid-18th century and has a central hallway separating the extended bar and dining area. The cottage-style decor is enhanced by old pictures, prints and low, beamed ceilings. Food comes in generous portions with a specials board, and curry nights as added attractions. The pub fields darts, dominoes and cricket teams. Listen carefully for the footsteps of the previous landlord. ❀◐◑▲♣P

BEMPTON

White Horse Inn

30 High Street

11-4 (4.30 Fri & Sat), 7-11; 12-4.30, 7-10.30 Sun

(01262) 850266

Draught Bass; John Smith's Bitter; Taylor Landlord Ⓗ

Former Moors & Robsons house, situated a mile from the RSPB centre and cliffs. Built in 1938, the pub retains its original blue tiled roof. The comfortable, open-plan lounge has period wood panelling and solid wood bar. Old photographs of Bempton and village life are displayed. Originally an hotel, the old bell pushes are still in place above the bench seating. The current spacious layout dates back 40 years when the old rooms were opened out. The former tap room now houses a pool table. Sympathetic renovation was carried out in 2001. ♨❀◐▲⇌♣P

BEVERLEY ❄

Cornerhouse

2 Norwood

12-2.30, 5-11; 12-11 Fri; 11-11 Sat; 12-10.30 Sun

(01482) 882652

Black Sheep Best Bitter; Greene King Abbot; Rooster's Yankee; Taylor Landlord; Tetley Bitter; guest beers Ⓗ

Former Tetley pub, known as the Valiant Soldier, this historic building was gutted by the previous owners as a Firkin indentikit pub for youngsters. Fortunately this gimmick did not last and the Cornerhouse has quickly become a well-respected pub/café bar serving quality fare in colourful surroundings. Guest beers, Weston's Old Rosie cider, 50 single malts, vodkas, gins and cocktails are available. Food is a speciality, mostly home made, served until 8pm. Curry night is Tuesday and English breakfast is served weekends 10-1. ❀◐◑●P

Hodgson's

Flemingate (opp. Army Transport Museum)

12-11; 12-10.30 Sun

(01482) 880484 website: www.hodgsonspub.com

Tetley Bitter; Wawne Monks Mild, Waghen, Melsa; guest beers Ⓗ

Surrounded by playing fields, this imposing Georgian residence was converted last century into a sports and social club. It became a pub in 1996 and Wawne Brewery moved here in 2001, from nearby Tickton, to establish their first public house. The

INDEPENDENT BREWERIES

Garton Garton on the Wolds
Goodmanham Goodmanham
Old Mill Snaith
Wawne Beverley

range of good-value Wawne beers available may vary; the brewery can be visited at short notice. The front tap room has a traditional feel in contrast to the large food/disco area to the rear, featuring Beverley's only skittle alley.
◑⊟≠♣P

Royal Standard Inn
30 North Bar Within
✪ 12-11; 12-10.30 Sun
☎ (01482) 882434
Bateman XXXB; Jennings Cumberland Ale; Tetley Bitter; guest beer Ⓗ
Classic town local by the historic North Bar, handy for the racecourse. The traditional front bar features bentwood seating from the 1920s, while the Darley's window is a recent reproduction. There is a comfortable lounge to the rear. The pub hosts regular live music. Award-winning hanging baskets are a summer attraction, outdoor drinking is possible on the front forecourt. No food is served; bring your own sandwiches. Q❀⊟

White Horse Inn (Nellie's) ☆
22 Hengate (by bus station)
✪ 11-11; 12-10.30 Sun
☎ (01482) 861973 website: www.nellies.co.uk
Samuel Smith OBB Ⓗ
One of Beverley's landmarks, this historic inn offers a multi-roomed interior with gas lighting and stone-flagged floors; all five rooms often have coal fires. The building was owned by the Collinson family from the 1920s until the death of Miss Nellie Collinson in 1976, when it was acquired by Sam Smith's who, thankfully, made minimal changes. Good value, home-cooked lunches (not served Mon) include Sunday roasts. Folk and jazz eves are held in the upstairs function room. The rear courtyard is available for summer drinking.
♨Q❀◐⊟♣P⅟

Woolpack Inn
37 Westwood Road (near Westwood Hospital)
✪ 12-3, 5-11; 12-11 Fri & Sat; 12-10.30 Sun
☎ (01482) 867095
Burtonwood Bitter, Top Hat; guest beer Ⓗ
Superbly located in a Victorian residential street, this inn started life as a pair of cottages, built around 1830. The Woolpack was sensitively restored in late 2001, retaining its cosy snug and a small extension into the beer garden. Enjoy tasty home-made meals (not served Sat or Sun eves) including specials, Friday steak nights and a Sunday carvery. The guest beer changes monthly. A weekly quiz is hosted (Thu). Q❀◐◑

BRIDLINGTON ❄

Old Ship Inn
90 St John Street (1 mile NW of centre)
✪ 11.30-11; 12-10.30 Sun
☎ (01262) 670466
Tetley Bitter; Webster's Yorkshire Bitter; Worthington Bitter; guest beers Ⓗ
Thriving former Vaux local, originally two dwellings, with two rooms off a central corridor to the left, and three to the right. Alterations in the 1980s resulted in the present front lounge, front snug and a large rear bar. The lounge walls are adorned with prints of famous sailing ships; the front snug resembles a small Victorian parlour where photos show Yorkshire coastal scenes, towns and characters. Q❀◐◑⊟♣⅟

BROUGH

Buccaneer
47 Station Road
✪ 12-2.30, 5-11; 12-11 Fri & Sat; 12-10.30 Sun
☎ (01482) 667435
Draught Bass; Black Sheep Best Bitter; Tetley Dark Mild, Bitter; guest beer Ⓗ
Friendly pub next to Brough Railway Station in the heart of the old village. It was renovated in 2000 to provide a bar lounge (with historic photos of Brough) and a comfortable 45-seat dining room. It dates back to 1870 when it was known as the Railway Tavern. It was renamed in 1968 after the aircraft built by the nearby Blackburn Aircraft Company, now British Aerospace. Delicious home-made food is offered including an excellent hot buffet served Friday lunchtime. Outdoor drinking is possible on the forecourt. ❀⇐◐◑≠♣P

DRIFFIELD

Bell Hotel
Market Place
✪ 10-2.30, 6-11; 10-11 Thu; 12-3, 7-10.30 Sun
☎ (01377) 256661
website: www.thebellindriffield.co.uk
Beer range varies Ⓗ
Historic coaching inn situated in the town centre. The entrance hall opens on to a long, wood-panelled bar to the right featuring red leather seating, substantial fireplaces, antiques and paintings which lend a quality feel. Four guest beers, some from Yorkshire micros, are usually available, plus a choice of some 250 malt whiskies. A covered courtyard has bistro seating and old photographs of Driffield. The restaurant opens 7-9.30. Q⇐◐◑⊟♿P

Mariner's Arms
47 Eastgate South (near cattle market)
✪ 3 (12 Sat)-11; 12-4.30, 7-10.30 Sun
☎ (01377) 253708
Burtonwood Bitter, seasonal beers; guest beers Ⓗ
This traditional, street-corner local is well worth seeking out as an alternative to the John Smith's outlets that dominate the 'Capital of the Wolds'. Formerly part of the original Hull Brewery estate, the pub has retained two rooms. It is situated in a residential, terraced side street and has a basic bar and a more comfortable lounge. The long-standing licensees create a very friendly atmosphere. ❀⊟≠♣P

DUNSWELL

Ship Inn
Beverley Road
✪ 11-11; 12-10.30 Sun
☎ (01482) 859160
John Smith's Bitter; Tetley Bitter, Burton Ale; guest beer (occasional) Ⓗ
This white-painted inn, fronting the old Hull-Beverley road, once served traffic on the nearby River Hull. Two log fires warm the welcoming interior which is partly divided to form a dining area with church pew seating. It is a rare local outlet for Tetley Burton Ale; beers from the local

Wawne Brewery are occasionally available. Special events and barbecues are held in the adjoining paddock. The pub's name is reflected in the internal decor with nautical memorabilia. Evening meals are served until 7pm. ⋒❀◑♣P

FLAMBOROUGH

Seabirds

Tower Street

11.30-2-30, 7 (6.30 Sat)-11; 12-3, 8-10.30 Sun

☎ (01262) 850242

John Smith's Bitter; guest beer ⊞

Just inside this pleasant seaside village pub stands a cabinet full of stuffed seabirds. The bar to the right bears a fishing theme, plus a collection of pump clips detailing the many guest beers previously offered. There is an emphasis on seafood and the specials board changes daily. All food is home cooked (meals not served Sun eve). The Seabirds is popular with walkers and bird enthusiasts: spectacular cliffs and Bempton RSPB Sanctuary are close by. The pub is closed Mon eve between mid-Sept and mid-June. ⋒❀◑⊟▲P

GILBERDYKE

Cross Keys Inn

Main Road (B1230, W edge of village)

12-11; 12-10.30 Sun

☎ (01430) 440310

Black Sheep Best Bitter; John Smith's Bitter; Tetley Bitter; guest beers ⊞

Village pub with strong local support, situated on the old A63 (now bypassed by the M62). A listed building, dated 1750, it was originally known as Mook's Inn after its Dutch owners. There is a bar/lounge with a split-level snug displaying traditional brewery mirrors. A long-established beer house, it serves premium guest beers, draught Hoegaarden and up to two real ciders. ⋒❀♣●P

GOODMANHAM

Goodmanham Arms

Main Street

8 (7 Fri)-11; 12-5, 7-11 Sat; 12-10.30 Sun

☎ (01430) 873849

Black Sheep Best Bitter; Goodmanham Wolds Delight, Goodman Hammer ⊞

Close to the Wolds Way footpath, this pleasant inn is popular with walkers. The two bars have attractive red and black chequered tiled floors. The main bar has a coal fire, the other room has a seating area warmed by a log burner. At the front is a small garden. A brewery opened in outbuildings in early 2002; it offers two beers. The gents' WC is located in the small car park. Additional parking is available nearby. ⋒Q❀P

GOOLE

City & County

Market Square

11-11; 12-10.30 Sun

☎ (01405) 722600

Greene King Abbot; Shepherd Neame Spitfire; Taylor Landlord; Theakston Best Bitter; guest beers ⊞

This imposing building in the old market square was once a Midland Bank. Wetherspoon's have retained much of the original architecture, in particular the banking hall with its high vaulted and patterned glass windows. Beer engines on the long bar are in the hands of attentive staff. Visit the toilets and marvel at the balustrade upon which many customers must have hauled themselves to the manager's office. The pub has a children's certificate.

Q❀◑♿⇌⊁

Macintosh Arms

13 Aire Street

11-11; 12-10.30 Sun

☎ (01405) 763850

Greene King Old Speckled Hen; Tetley Dark Mild, Bitter; guest beer ⊞

Traditional pub, dating from the 1820s, named after Sir Hugh Macintosh who commissioned the building of the adjacent docks. Formerly part of a courthouse, the original ceiling can be seen through skylights in the lounge. A real community pub, it is deservedly popular with customers of all ages. Very lively on weekend eves but enjoy the friendly banter at lunchtimes. Home of Goole and District Motorbike Club – the 'wobbly goolies' – the group is very supportive of local charities. No garden, but pavement tables are provided for outdoor drinking. Sunday lunches are served.

❀◐⇌♣P

HEDON

Shakespeare Inn

9 Baxtergate (200 yds off A1033)

12-11; 12-10.30 Sun

☎ (01482) 898371

John Smith's Bitter; Tetley Bitter; Theakston Best Bitter; guest beers ⊞

Friendly, one-roomed local in East Yorkshire's smallest town, noted for its food, particularly eve meals (not served Sat or Sun) and tea-time specials. Brewery memorabilia and old photographs of Hedon, through the ages, are interesting. A real fire in the corner creates a cosy atmosphere. There is a pleasant seating area in front of the pub with floral displays. Transport from Hull is by EYMS buses 76 and 78.

⋒❀◑♣P

HESSLE

Haze

5-7 Swinegate

11-3, 5-11; 11-11 Sat; 12-10.30 Sun

☎ (01482) 648559

Black Sheep Best Bitter; Flowers IPA; Taylor Landlord; Tetley Dark Mild; guest beer ⊞

Hessle lies in the shadow of the Humber Bridge. The pub, which overlooks the church, is a conversion of a former wine bar and retains a comfortable, welcoming atmosphere with stone floors and a large open fireplace. A split-level dining area serves a full range of home-made dishes, including vegetarian and speciality fish dishes. Photos and memorabilia of old Hessle feature. Celtic folk music and quiz nights are popular events. The pub takes the Anglo-Saxon name for Hessle.

❀◑⇌♣

HOWDEN

Barnes Wallis
Station Road (B1228)
⏲ 12-2 (not Mon), 5 (7 Mon)-11; 12-11 Sat; 12-10.30 Sun
☎ (01430) 430639 website: www.barneswallis.co.uk
Black Sheep Best Bitter; Hambleton Bitter; guest beers [H]
The pub stands next to Howden Station, one mile north of the small market town of Howden with its fine 14th-century minster. Barnes Wallis, the famous inventor, had local associations and features in the intriguing pub display of photos. A friendly, open-plan inn with the best range of beers for miles around; the three guest beers from independent breweries change frequently. Live music is performed once a month. Summer barbecues are held in the sheltered garden.
♨❀♿⇌♣P🍺

HULL ✻

Bay Horse Hotel
115-117 Wincolmlee
⏲ 11-11; 12-10.30 Sun
☎ (01482) 329227
Bateman Mild, XB, XXXB, seasonal beers [H]
Homely, two-roomed, street-corner local, purchased by Bateman's in 1990. The bar has old photographs of the city's two Rugby League teams, while the lounge, which doubles as a dining area, displays brewery memorabilia. Home-cooked food is a speciality; try the home-made pies. No food is served on Sat. The pub plays host to a number of games team. This community pub, close to the city centre, always offers a warm welcome.
♨◐⊟♿♣P

Editorial Inn
48 Spring Bank
⏲ 11-11; 12-3, 7-10.30 Sun
☎ (01482) 327738
Tetley Bitter; guest beers [H]
Excellent free house near the Hull Daily Mail offices. Up to three guest beers are served. The pub comprises a comfortable front area and narrow bar, while diners sit at the rear. A number of interesting articles from the local paper archives are featured. Good lunchtime food is offered (no meals Sat). A quiz and curry night are held weekly (Tue). ❀◐♿⇌♣

Gardeners Arms
35 Cottingham Road
⏲ 11-11; 12-10.30 Sun
☎ (01482) 342396
Tetley Bitter; guest beers [H]
Local CAMRA Pub of the Year runner-up for two consecutive years, popular with both the local community and nearby university. Six guest ales, mainly from independents, are served in the two bars. The huge back bar has several pool tables and contrasts sharply with the friendly front public bar, with original matchwood ceiling. Good value food is served 12-3 and 5-7 Mon-Fri, 12-6 at weekends. Excellent choice of quiz nights; films (Mon), general knowledge (Wed) and music (Thu). A large front patio is ideal for summer drinking. ❀◐⊟♣P

Hole in the Wall
115 Spring Bank
⏲ 12-11; 12-10.30 Sun
☎ (01482) 580354
Beer range varies [H]
Recent (Aug 2001) conversion in the Spring Bank area of the city. The pub offers an excellent, ever-changing range of six ales, mainly sourced from independents. Featuring wooden floors throughout, the spacious front bar has plenty of standing room and comfortable leather seating and is ideal for conversation, while sport enthusiasts prefer the rear bar where a large-screen TV and pool table dominate. Pool leagues are hosted Mon-Wed and a quiz night is held (Thu). A patio area is planned (summer 2002). Bus routes 13 and 15 pass regularly. ❀♿

Minerva Hotel
Nelson Street (near marina and Victoria Pier)
⏲ 11-11; 12-10.30 Sun
☎ (01482) 326909 website: www.hull-local.co.uk
Taylor Landlord; Tetley Bitter; Young's Special; guest beers [H]
Overlooking the Humber estuary and Victoria Pier this famous pub, built in 1835, is a great place to watch the ships. Superb photos and memorabilia are a reminder of the area's maritime past. The central bar

INN BRIEF

BEVERLEY

Dog & Duck Inn
33 Ladygate
11-4, 7-11; 11-11 Sat; 12-3, 7-10.30 Sun
(01482) 862419
Greene King Abbot; John Smith's Bitter; guest beer [H]
Solid public house, just off the main Saturday market, in the same family for 30 years. Accommodation is available.

BRIDLINGTON

New Crown Inn
158 Quay Road
11.30-11; 12-10.30 Sun
(01262) 401874
John Smith's Bitter; guest beers [H]
Substantial Victorian pub opposite the Town Hall. The large wooden-floored bar and games room prove popular with all ages.

HUGGATE

Wolds Inn
Driffield Road
12-2, 6.30-11; closed Mon; 12-2.30, 6.30-10.30 Sun
(01377) 288217
Taylor Landlord; Tetley Bitter; guest beers [H]
Family-run inn, dating back to the 16th century, with a wood-panelled restaurant and bar.

HULL

Kingston Hotel
25 Trinity House Lane
11-4.30, 7-11; 11-11 Fri & Sat; 12-4.30, 7-10.30 Sun
(01482) 223993
Mansfield Dark Mild, Riding Bitter [H]
Historic, Grade II listed, basic town pub, dating from 1882, overlooking Holy Trinity Church and the former market place.

New Clarence
77 Charles Street
12-11; 12-10.30 Sun
(01482) 320327
Greene King Abbot, Old Speckled Hen; Taylor Landlord; Tetley Bitter; guest beers [H]
Handy for the new theatre and very popular for its wide range of food. One room with U-shaped bar.

Rugby Tavern
5 Dock Street
(01482) 324759
Samuel Smith OBB [H]
U-shaped, one-roomed pub with comfortable seating and a wooden façade. Popular for lunchtime food (Mon-Sat) and busy at weekends.

serves a variety of rooms including a tiny snug. Evening meals are served Mon-Thu (6-9); home-made food and huge haddocks complete an enticing menu. The pub is connected to the new millennium tourist site by a footbridge at the mouth of the River Hull. Local CAMRA Pub of the Year 2000 and 2001.
♨❀◐◑⊟♣

Old Blue Bell
Market Place (down alley next to covered market)
✪ 11-11; 12-10.30 Sun
☎ (01482) 324382
Samuel Smith OBB Ⓗ
Historic pub, dating from the 1600s, hidden away but worth seeking out. The multi-roomed interior comprises a central passage with a large, long bar immediately to the right, a tiny wood-panelled snug to the left, and a small, comfortable lounge directly ahead. A popular place for local societies, it boasts a fine collection of bells. Children are welcome in the homely snug. Pool is played upstairs.
Q❀◑⊟♣⚟

Olde Black Boy ☆
150 High Street
✪ 12-11; 12-10.30 Sun
☎ (01482) 326516
Tetley Bitter; guest beers Ⓗ
Attractive, 14th-century listed building in the heart of the old town. The black front room snug and window with carved head over the fireplace are of special interest and the rear bar has recently returned to rich chestnut varnished walls. The front upstairs bar is open on Friday and Saturday evenings only. The rear upstairs room houses a pool table. Up to five guest ales are available at weekends, plus two ciders from the Weston's range.
♨Q⊟♣●

Olde White Harte ☆
25 Silver Street
✪ 11-11; 12-10.30 Sun
☎ (01482) 326363
Banks's Bitter; McEwan 80/-; Marston's Pedigree; Theakston Old Peculier; guest beer (occasional) Ⓗ
Historic 16th-century courtyard pub, once the residence where the Governor of Hull resolved to deny Charles I entry to the city. Award-winning floral displays, superb dark woodwork, stained glass windows and sit-in fireplaces feature. It is situated in the old town, down an alleyway, at the heart of the commercial centre. An impressive staircase leads to the upstairs rooms including the 'Plotting Room'. An occasional guest beer replaces Pedigree. Ideal for a quiet drink as there is no raucous music or TV. There is a covered, heated outdoor drinking area.
Q❀◑

Queen's Hotel
Queens Road (off Beverley Rd, 1 mile N of centre)
✪ 12-11; 12-10.30 Sun
☎ (01482) 470241
Banks's Bitter, seasonal beers; Mansfield Riding Bitter; Marston's Pedigree Ⓗ
The Queen's Hotel first appears in White's Directory of 1867. It is thought to have been named after Queen Victoria who had visited Hull on several occasions. It is a typical symmetrical building of the time. The internal layout has been slowly eradicated over the years, but fortunately a separate lounge and bar still remain. The sizeable lounge is decorated with local photographs. The bar is much more basic and contains a pool table. The clientele is very mixed with students chatting happily with locals. Regular bus services 5, 15 and 16 pass the pub to and from the city centre.
❀⊟♣P

St John's Hotel
10 Queens Road (off Beverley Rd, A1079, 1½ miles N of centre)
✪ 12-11; 12-10.30 Sun
☎ (01482) 343669
Banks's Bitter; Camerons Strongarm; Mansfield Dark Mild, Riding Bitter; Marston's Pedigree Ⓗ
Classic, street-corner local, boasting one of the least altered interiors in the city. Attracting a diverse cross-section of drinkers, it can get busy weekend eves. The welcoming front corner public bar complements a quiet back room with original bench seating. A larger, basic third room, with juke box, doubles as a family area (until 8pm) and leads to a secluded beer garden. Bring your own food or order a takeaway (menus provided). A major bus route (Beverley Road) passes nearby.
Q♘❀⊟♿♣P

KILHAM

Star Inn
Church Street
11.30-2, 6-11; 11-11 Sat; 12-10.30 Sun
(01262) 420619
John Smith's Bitter; Theakston Mild; guest beer Ⓗ
Traditionally renovated four-roomed pub with a central bar, it boasts a piano and high quality restaurant.

LANGTOFT

Ship
Scarborough Road
12-2.30 (5 Sat), 7-11; 12-5, 7-10.30 Sun
(01377) 267243
John Smith's Bitter; guest beer Ⓗ
Cosy, friendly local with a reputation for good food. Children are welcome in the games room and restaurant. Caravan site nearby.

NAFFERTON

King's Head
22 Middle Street
4.30 (12 Sat)-11; 12-10.30 Sun
(01377) 254417
Black Sheep Special; John Smith's Bitter Ⓗ
Built in 1750, a calico works until it became a pub around 1810. In the centre of the village and sympathetically renovated in 2001.

PATRINGTON

Hildyard Arms
1 Market Place
12-11; 12-10.30 Sun
(01964) 630234
Draught Bass; Tetley Bitter; guest beer Ⓗ
Former coaching inn, a central bar serves all rooms: a public bar, restaurant area and games room. Excellent food.

Missing?

If a pub is not listed in the Guide that you think is worthy of consideration, please let us know at GBG, CAMRA, 230 Hatfield Road, St Albans, Herts, AL1 4LW or camra@camra.org.uk. All recommendations are forwarded to CAMRA branches, which are responsible for choosing pubs.

Tap & Spile

169-171 Spring Bank

12-11; 12-10.30 Sun

☎ (01482) 323518

Black Sheep Best Bitter; Rooster's Yankee; Taylor Landlord; Yorkshire Terrier; guest beers Ⓗ

Victorian, street-corner local, formerly owned by the original Hull Brewery. It stocks four regular ales, up to eight guests, Hoegaarden on draught and traditional cider (Weston's Old Rosie). Popular live music nights – folk (Sun), acoustic (Mon), blues (Tue) and jazz (Thu) – draw drinkers from all over the city. A main core, with pool table, is complemented by two no-smoking areas. Food is available Mon-Sat eves (5-7) and Sun lunchtime (12-3). Bus routes 13 and 15 serve the pub.

◐ ♣ ⊁

Three John Scotts

Lowgate

11-11; 12-10.30 Sun

☎ (01482) 381910

Bateman Mild; Black Sheep Special; Courage Directors; Hop Back Summer Lightning; Shepherd Neame Spitfire; Theakston Best Bitter; guest beers Ⓗ

Wetherspoon's outlet opened in 2001 in the former general post office building next to the Guildhall. The imposing 1901 building also incorporates 50 flats and a Riley's Snooker Centre. The name originates from three clergymen, grandfather, father and son, who were successive vicars of St Mary's Church on the opposite side of Lowgate. Three wall plaques explain the name, the history of the site, and Hull's role in the Civil War. It is very busy at weekends. There is a heated courtyard for outdoor drinking.

Q ❀ ◐ ♿ ♣ ⊁ ⊘

LUND

Wellington Inn

19 The Green (5 miles N of Beverley)

12-3 (not Mon), 6.30-11; 12-3, 7-10.30 Sun

☎ (01377) 217294

Black Sheep Best Bitter; John Smith's Bitter; Taylor Dark Mild, Landlord; guest beer Ⓗ

The Wellington has a prime site on the green in this award-winning Wolds village. Most of the trade comes from the local farming community. It was totally renovated by the present licensee and features stone-flagged floors and beamed ceilings. There is a no-smoking room, games room and candlelit restaurant, serving an à la carte menu (eve meals Tue-Sat). Three rooms have real fires.

⛫ ❀ ◐ ♿ ♣ P ⊁

MILLINGTON

Gate Inn

Main Street

12-5 (not Mon-Fri), 7-11; 12-2.30, 7-10.30 Sun

☎ (01759) 302045

Black Sheep Best Bitter; Old Mill Bitter; John Smith's Bitter; Tetley Bitter Ⓗ

Millington, in a beautiful setting in the Yorkshire Wolds, has been inhabited since ancient times. The Gate Inn in the centre of the village has a single comfortable bar with adjoining pool room. Note the old Yorkshire map on the bar ceiling. The pub is popular with walkers as it is close to Millington Pastures and long-distance footpaths, Minster Way and Wolds Way.

⛫ ❀ ◐ ♣ P

NEWPORT

Crown & Anchor

75 Main Street

4.30 (12 Fri & Sat)-11; 12-10.30 Sun

☎ (01430) 449757

website: www.crownandanchoryorks.co.uk

Mansfield Dark Mild; Tetley Bitter; guest beer Ⓗ

Comfortable village local on the old A63 (now bypassed by the M62), it stands by the Market Weighton Canal. This friendly, multi-roomed pub offers good quality, home-cooked food Fri-Sun lunchtimes and Tue-Sun eves until 8pm. Two coal/log fires provide a warm welcome on a winter's day. The pub fields darts, cricket and football teams. Local fishing is possible in the canal and ponds. Guest beers are usually from small independents and an in-house brewery is planned for 2002. ⛫ ◐ ♣ P

NORTH NEWBALD

Tiger Inn

The Green

11-11; 12-10.30 Sun

☎ (01430) 827759 website: www.thetigerinn.com

Black Sheep Best Bitter; John Smith's Bitter; Taylor Landlord; guest beer Ⓗ

Set on a picturesque village green, this old pub has a refurbished interior with ceiling beams and polished brasses. There is a public bar, lounge bar and games room; the lounge is mainly used for dining. A substantial home-cooked menu includes house specialities, such as beef pies and haddock fried in beer and lemon batter. Close to the Wolds Way, the pub offers a warm welcome to walkers. The licensee now owns a holiday cottage in the village.

⛫ Q ❀ ◐ P

OLD ELLERBY

Blue Bell Inn

Crabtree Lane

12-4.30 (not Mon-Fri), 7-11; 12-4.30, 7-10.30 Sun

☎ (01964) 562364

Black Sheep Best Bitter; Tetley Bitter, Burton Ale; guest beers Ⓗ

This 16th-century, one-roomed inn was previously owned by Burton Constable estate. It has a games area to the rear, tiled floors, and beamed ceilings that are bedecked with horse brasses. A friendly, community-focused pub, it holds many fund-raising events. Morris dancers visit in summer and before Christmas. The patio area features attractive floral displays and hanging baskets while the large garden has a bowling green. The pub is close to the Hull-Hornsea Rail Trail Walk. ⛫ Q ❀ ▲ ♣ P

PRESTON

Cock & Bell

1 Main Street

6 (11.30 Fri & Sat)-11; 12-10.30 Sun

Castle Eden Ale; Mansfield Dark Mild; Wadworth 6X; guest beer Ⓗ

Traditional, cottage-style village pub that is 200 years old. There is a main bar, a no-smoking games room and a restaurant (only

open Sun). The large outdoor drinking area has children's play facilities and benches. The guest beer changes constantly and the licensee prides himself on the low beer prices. EYMS bus No. 277 serves Preston.
❀♣P⊬

REEDNESS

Half Moon Inn

Main Street (A161, S of Goole)
✪ 12-2 (not Dec-Easter), 7-11; 12-10.30 Sun
☎ (01405) 704484
Flowers IPA; Greene King Old Speckled Hen; guest beers (summer) Ⓗ
Comfortable village pub in a rural setting; its two well-appointed rooms are served from a single bar. The no-smoking lounge area doubles as a restaurant. Dark wood beams and red leather seating enhance the rural feel of the pub. An excellent selection of home-cooked food is available weekend lunchtimes and Wed-Sat eves. Two real ales are always stocked, supplemented by guest beers in summer. Camping facilities are provided at the rear of the pub for caravans and tents; handy for the Blacktoft Sands RSPB reserve located nearby.
⛰Q❀◐◑⊞♿⛺♣P⊬🚆

RYEHILL

Crooked Billet

Pitt Lane (400 yds off A1033, E of Thorngumbald)
✪ 11-11; 12-10.30 Sun
☎ (01964) 622303
Burtonwood Bitter, Top Hat, guest beer Ⓗ
Unspoilt, 17th-century coaching inn with a stone-flagged floor and comfortable upholstered seating areas, horse brasses and historical pictures of the pub adorn the walls. This welcoming, two-roomed inn, with a real fire is a peaceful retreat, served by hourly Hull-Withernsea EYMS bus No. 76. The guest beer is from Burtonwood's monthly rotating list. Freshly prepared home-cooked food (not served Tue eve) is offered. The pub is home to cricket and darts teams and a Scrabble club.
⛰Q◐◑♣P

SKERNE

Eagle Inn ☆

Wandsford Road
✪ 12-2 (not Mon-Fri), 7-11; 12-3, 7-10.30 Sun
☎ (01377) 252178
Camerons Bitter Ⓗ
This classic pub is a gem. It is a plain, white-painted village local surrounded by mature trees. The unspoilt, homely interior comprises a public bar with a coal fire and a matchboard ceiling, and a more comfortable parlour. Drinks are brought to your table from a cellar off the entrance corridor. They are dispensed from a Victorian cash register beer engine which serves a spectacular cone head above the glass. Outside WCs complete this time-warp pub. ⛰Q❀⊞♣P

SNAITH

Downe Arms

15 Market Place
✪ 12-11; 12-10 Sun
☎ (01405) 860544
Banks's Bitter; Camerons Strongarm; Marston's Pedigree; guest beer Ⓗ
The pub is named after Lord Downe, a local landowner. The market place façade with its paired, rounded sash bay windows is worth viewing. Inside unusual whiskies and a fine collection of whisky water jugs add atmosphere, enhanced by four well-used hand engines. Excellent food includes a Sunday carvery. There is a Sunday evening singalong (organ and all). Listen to Jaguar talk here on weekdays while customers' beloved cars are ministered to by the local expert. ❀◐◑P

SUTTON UPON DERWENT

St Vincent Arms

Main Street (follow B1288 past Elvington)
✪ 11.30-3, 6-11; 12-3, 7-10.30 Sun
☎ (01904) 608349
Fuller's Chiswick, London Pride, Ⓗ **ESB, seasonal beer;** Ⓖ **John Smith's Bitter; Taylor Landlord; Wells Bombardier; guest beers** Ⓗ
Quintessential country inn, family-owned and run, it plays an integral part in village life. A striking, white building, it has several separate rooms. On the right is a cosy bar – little changed over the years and often busy with groups of regulars. To the left is a smaller bar/dining room and two further dining areas. Note the large Fuller, Smith and Turner mirror. The pub offers the complete Fuller's range, two are served on gravity. York CAMRA Pub of the Year 2002.
Q❀◐◑⛺P

Yorkshire (North)

(Including parts of Cleveland)

APPLETREEWICK

New Inn

Main Street
✪ 12-3 (not Mon or Tue; 4 summer Sat), 7-11; 12-3 (4 summer), 7-10.30 Sun
☎ (01756) 720252
Daleside Bitter; John Smith's Bitter; guest beer (summer) Ⓗ
Walkers, (motor)cyclists, and tourists are all welcome at this family-run 'small pub with a big heart', that also enjoys a good local trade. The emphasis is on foreign beer with three draught Belgian beers always available, alongside a wide range of bottled beers from around the world. The landlord is a keen mountain biker and can offer information on routes both on- and off-road. A 'bike livery' behind the pub provides a workshop, bike-wash and changing facilities. Good value, home-cooked food is served. The guest beer is from Daleside. ⛰❀🛏◐⛺♣P

BEDALE

Three Coopers

2 Emgate
✪ 11-11; 12-10.30 Sun
☎ (01677) 422153
Black Sheep Best Bitter; Jennings Bitter, Cumberland Ale; guest beer (summer) Ⓗ
Situated a few yards off the busy main street near the market cross, a feature is made here of the bare brick walls, stone and wood floors and wooden furniture. Although the bar is opened out, it is partitioned into three

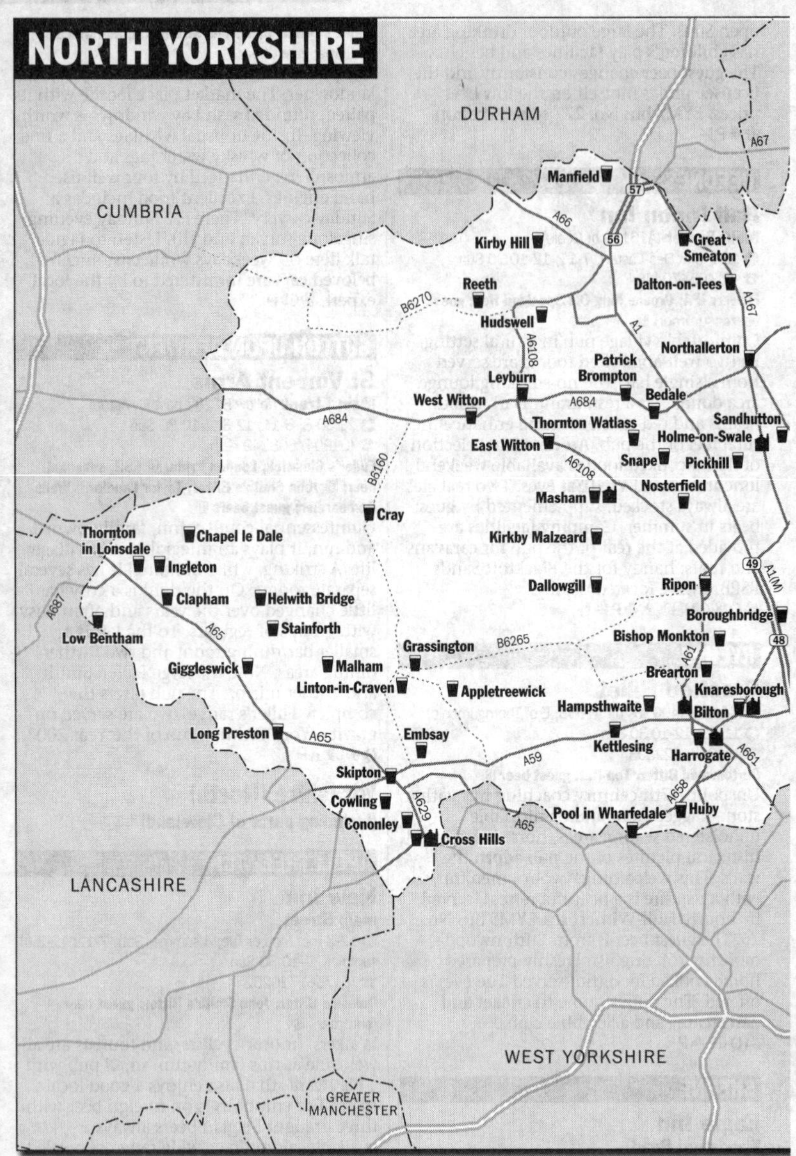

distinct drinking areas. It organises fortnightly steak nights (Wednesday – book in advance) but otherwise does not serve food. There is a garden at the rear. ⛼♣✓

BISHOP MONKTON

Lamb & Flag Inn

Boroughbridge Road (off A61)

12-3, 5.30-11; 12-3, 7-10.30 Sun

☎ (01765) 677322

Tetley Bitter; guest beer H

This two-roomed, cosy, friendly country pub is filled with unusual brasses, toby jugs, glasses and knick-knacks. It has a peaceful garden at the rear and tables in a suntrap at the front. The menu offers high quality food at reasonable prices. The centre for many clubs and societies, it is an active fund-raiser for the cricket team. The village stages an annual duck race on August bank holiday on the picturesque stream. A second guest beer is stocked in summer.

⛼Q❀◑♣P

Mason's Arms

St John's Road (off A61)

12-3, 6.30-11; 12-3, 6.30-10.30 Sun

☎ (01765) 677427

Black Sheep Best Bitter; John Smith's Bitter; Tetley Bitter; guest beer H

Set in a delightful village, the pub overlooks a stream which is home to some unusual species of ducks. The pub, which made an appearance in TV's Touch of Frost, has a cosy interior with beamed ceilings and open fires. It has a pool room with TV and a dining area where an extensive à la carte menu is served. The guest beers are usually from Rudgate and Daleside; the landlord's son brews for Rudgate.

⛼Q❀◑♿♣P

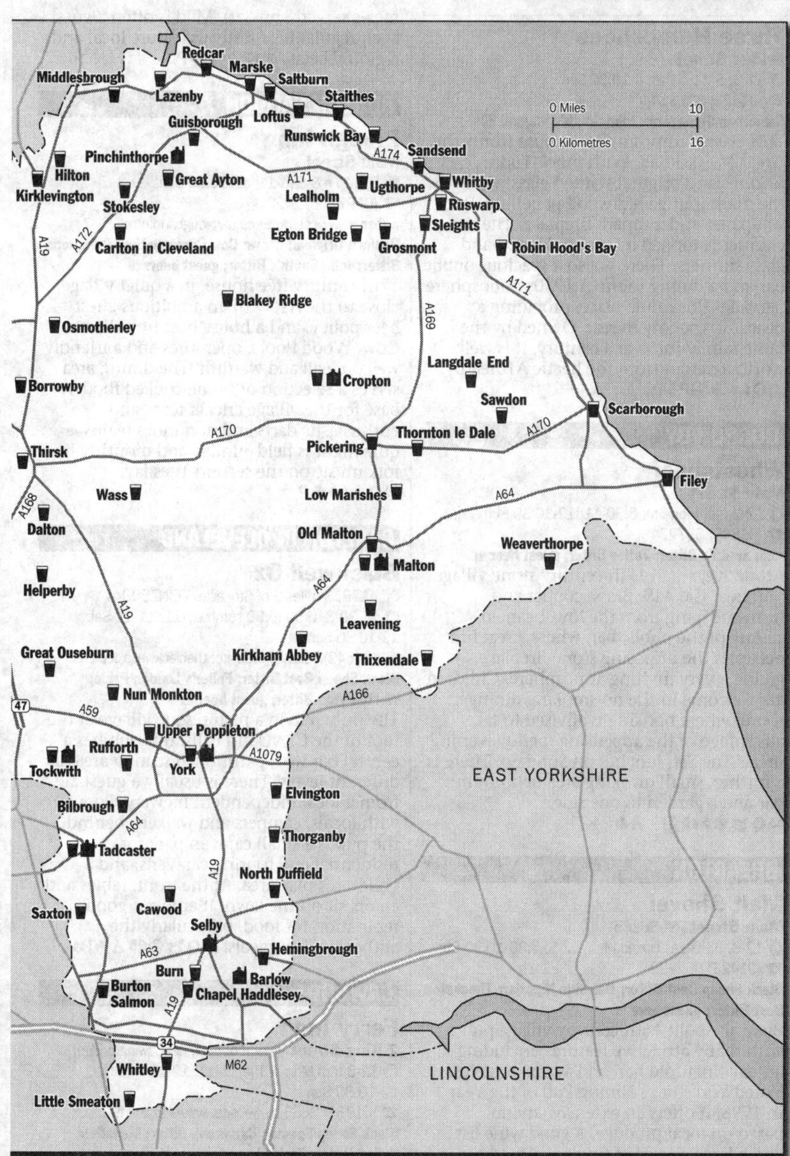

BLAKEY RIDGE

Lion Inn

6 miles N of Hutton le Hole on Castleton road
OS679997
11-11; 12-10.30 Sun
☎ (01751) 417320 website: www.lionblakey.co.uk
Greene King Old Speckled Hen; John Smith's Bitter; Theakston Best Bitter, Black Bull, Cool Cask, Old Peculier H

Remote inn, dating from the 16th century, located high on the North Yorkshire Moors. Low, beamed ceilings, open fires and a variety of drinking areas all contribute to the welcoming atmosphere. A large percentage of the customers come for the food, which is served in generous portions in the bar and restaurant areas. Surprisingly, despite its isolated setting, the Lion is the venue for very popular monthly live music.
P

BOROUGHBRIDGE

Black Bull

6 St James Square
11-11; 12-10.30 Sun
☎ (01423) 322413
Black Sheep Best Bitter; John Smith's Bitter; guest beer H

This historic inn near the town centre is very attractive – white painted with Georgian-style bay windows and bedecked with hanging baskets in summer. The main bar is cosy, with a brick inglenook, low, beamed ceiling and copper-topped tables; the adjacent snug has another open fire. Down a wood-panelled corridor is a very popular, highly-rated, spacious restaurant (booking advised at weekends). Food is served all day summer weekends.
Q

Three Horseshoes ☆
Bridge Street
✪ 11-3, 5-11; 12-3, 6-10.30 Sun
☎ (01423) 322314
Camerons Strongarm; John Smith's Magnet Ⓗ
This classic, imposing roadhouse fronts the Great North Road. With mock-Tudor features and original stained glass windows, the main lounge has wood panelling, flock wallpaper and a superb fireplace. The bar counter is topped by unusual wood and glass shutters. There is also a spacious public bar and a dining room. A 1930s atmosphere pervades the whole place, providing a peaceful, friendly retreat. Owned by the same family for over a century, it is well worth a detour from the hectic A1 nearby.
♔Q⇌◑◐ⒸP

BORROWBY

Wheatsheaf
Main Street
✪ 12-2 (not Mon-Fri), 5.30-11; 12-10.30 Sun
☎ (01845) 537274
John Smith's Bitter; Tetley Bitter; guest beer Ⓗ
Attractive, small 17th-century stone village pub near the A19. Brass, copper and ironware hang from the low, beamed ceiling of the public bar, where a real fire occupies the imposing stone fireplace, giving a very inviting atmosphere. Children are welcome in the no-smoking dining room, where booking is advised to take advantage of the appetising menu (evening meals Tue-Sat, lunches on Sunday). There is a further, small drinking area behind the bar and a garden to one side.
♔Q♘❀⇌◐Ⓒ♿▲♣P⚟

BREARTON

Malt Shovel
Main Street (off B6165)
✪ 12-3, 6.30-11; closed Mon; 12-3, 7.30-10.30 Sun
☎ (01423) 862929
Black Sheep Best Bitter; Daleside Nightjar; Theakston Best Bitter; guest beer Ⓗ
Busy, unspoilt 16th-century village pub with many attractive features, including an oak linenfold bar, and a mix of tables. Voted Yorkshire's Dining Pub of the Year in 1998, it offers an extensive menu based on local produce. A good wine list and a large choice of single malts add to the appeal of this good value pub. Heaters on the patio allow you to sit out even on cooler days.
♔Q♘❀◑◐♣P

BURN

Wheatsheaf
Main Road (A19, 3 miles S of Selby)
✪ 12-11; 12-10.30 Sun
☎ (01757) 270614
John Smith's Bitter; Taylor Landlord; Tetley Bitter; guest beers Ⓗ
Roadside inn, built in 1896, which retains a narrow bar passage, pool room and huge open fire. Agricultural and aeronautical memorabilia reflect the rural and WWII associations of the village – Burn aerodrome was a bomber base. It also boasts a large collection of Dinky toys. Home-cooked food is especially popular Sunday lunchtime (eve meals served Thu-Sat). Mild is often a guest beer; regular beer festivals feature local and regional beers. ♔Q❀◑◐♣P

BURTON SALMON

Plough Inn
Main Street
✪ 5 (11 Fri & Sat)-11; 12-10.30 Sun
☎ (01977) 672422
website: www.selbynet.co.uk/plough/inn.html
Banks's Original; Brown Cow Constellation; Camerons Bitter; John Smith's Bitter; guest beers Ⓗ
17th-century free house, in a quiet village close to the A1, with an ambitious guest beer policy, and a house beer from Brown Cow. Wood floors, open fires and a friendly welcome all add warmth. The dining area serves a selection of home-cooked food. A base for the village cricket team and enthusiastic darts and dominoes teams, a quiz night is held Sunday and monthly live folk music on the second Tuesday.
♔Q❀◑◐♣P

CARLTON IN CLEVELAND

Blackwell Ox
Off A172, 3 miles S of Stokesley OSNZ5004
✪ 11.30-3, 6.30 (5.30 summer)-11; 11-11 Sat; 12-10.30 Sun
☎ (01642) 712287 website: theblackwellox.co.uk
Black Sheep Best Bitter; Fuller's London Pride; Worthington Bitter; guest beer Ⓗ
The only pub in a picturesque village at the foot of the Cleveland Hills, this pub has a central bar with partitioned seating areas at different levels. There is usually a guest ale from a local independent brewery. Popular with locals, campers and walkers, behind the pub is a small caravan park for residential and touring caravans, and a children's play area. At the front, tables and chairs sit on the lawn. It enjoys a good reputation for food, particularly the authentic Thai meals. ♔Q♘❀◑◐▲♣P⚟

CAWOOD

Ferry Inn
2 King Street (S side of river, near swing bridge)
✪ 12-3 (not Mon or Tue), 5-11; 12-11 Fri & Sat; 12-10.30 Sun
☎ (01757) 268515 website: www.ferryinn.f9.co.uk
Black Sheep Special; Camerons Bitter; Mansfield Riding Bitter; Taylor Landlord; guest beers Ⓗ
Low ceilings and inglenooks lend a cosy atmosphere to this friendly, historic, village inn, with a terrace and garden overlooking the river. The village has connections with Cardinal Wolsey who, as Archbishop of York, resided at Cawood Castle. Although the menu today is not as sumptuous as the Great Feast of 1464 – see details in the bar – it is still exceptional value. The guest beer is often local. ♔Q❀⇌◑◐▲♣P

CHAPEL HADDLESEY

Jug Inn
Main Street
✪ 12-3, 6-11; 12-11 Sat; 12-10.30 Sun
☎ (01757) 270307
website: www.selbynet.co.uk/jug/inn.html
Brown Cow Bitter; John Smith's Bitter; guest beers Ⓗ
300-year-old pub on the bank of the River Aire. Privately owned, it is renowned for its

guest beers. A small bar serves both the lounge and public bar, each features a collection of jugs. Local folk groups meet here on Wednesday evenings for impromptu entertainment. An extensive menu is based on local produce, including game and fish. The large garden backs on to the river. ⌂Q❀◐◑⊟P

CHAPEL LE DALE

Hill Inn

⏲ 12-3, 6-11 (closed winter Mon; 12-11 summer); 12-10.30 Sun
☎ (01524) 241256
Black Sheep Best Bitter, Riggwelter; Theakston Best Bitter; guest beers 🄷
Beloved of generations of hikers and potholers – well-worn paths run from here to both Whernside (Yorkshire's highest peak) and Ingleborough (its best-known). Soft furnishings are unheard of in the bar that features plenty of woodwork and some exposed limestone. The restaurant has recently been extended in pursuit of the food trade as well as its traditional custom. It hosts a monthly folk evening (last Fri). The nearest public transport is Ribblehead Station, two miles. ⌂Q❀◐◑⛺P⊬

CONONLEY

New Inn

Main Street
⏲ 12-2.30, 5.30-11; 11-11 Sat; 12-10.30 Sun
☎ (01535) 636302
Taylor Golden Best, Best Bitter, Landlord, Ram Tam 🄷
Attractive, low-beamed Taylor's tied house at the centre of a quiet Dales village. The traditional exterior, with stone-mullioned windows, complements the well laid-out, recently refurbished interior. There is a small, but pleasant garden. If catching the train south, allow plenty of time to get over the level crossing. It is served by hourly buses (78A/67/67A) from Keighley and Skipton. ⌂❀◐◑⇌♣

CRAY

White Lion

⏲ 11-11; 12-10.30 Sun
☎ (01756) 760262 website: www.whitelioncray.com
Moorhouses Premier, Pendle Witches Brew; guest beers 🄷
Small, welcoming pub below Buckden Pike dating from the mid-1600s, formerly a farm-cum-drovers' inn. The main stone-flagged bar is warmed by a log fire and decorated with ancient artefacts and tools. There is an alcove to the rear and a small dining area in which children are welcome. An extensive menu is offered with evening 'early bird' discounts. Two guest beers often come from breweries such as Cottage, Goose Eye, Black Sheep or Rooster's.
⌂Q♨❀⛟◐◑⛺♣P⊬

CROPTON

New Inn

Woolcroft
⏲ 11-11; 12-10.30 Sun
☎ (01751) 417330 website: www.croptonbrewery.co.uk
Cropton King Billy, Two Pints, Honey Gold, Scoresby Stout, Balmy Mild, Monkmans Slaughter; guest beers 🄷
Situated near the moors, the Heritage Coast and Pickering, the New Inn is a good stopping-off point, and the accommodation makes it an ideal base for exploring the area. Locals and visitors mingle in the cosy bar, sampling beers from the outstanding brewery sited in the grounds. The cider varies. Downstairs is a large family room which is also the venue for the annual beer festival, held in November.
Q♨❀⛟◐◑⛺♣●P⊓

DALLOWGILL

Drovers' Inn

On minor road, 2 miles W of Laverton OS210720
⏲ 12-3 (not winter Mon-Fri), 7-11; closed Mon; 12-3, 7-10.30 Sun
☎ (01765) 658510
Black Sheep Best Bitter; Hambleton Bitter; Old Mill Bitter 🄷
Cosy pub, high on the moors above Nidderdale, between Ripon and Pateley Bridge, the inn is very busy in summer with walkers and campers. Affording fantastic views of Nidderdale, this pub is also used by hunters on local shoots, as reflected in the memorabilia. Good English pub food is served, with a busy Sunday lunch trade. Darts teams play in the Dales league. An open coal fire makes for a cosy atmosphere.
⌂Q❀◐◑♿⛺♣P

DALTON

Moor & Pheasant

Dalton Moor
⏲ 12-11; 12-10.30 Sun
☎ (01845) 577268
John Smith's Bitter; guest beer 🄷
Formerly the Railway Inn (the London-Edinburgh line passes close by, but the station is now closed), this pub lies on the outskirts of the village, five miles south of Thirsk. A small front bar with a pool table shares a servery with the larger lounge, with open fire, that doubles as a dining area, serving good value meals (no food Sun eve). Outside is a large play area for children and a private static caravan site. ⌂❀◐◑⊟♣P⊓

EAST WITTON

Cover Bridge Inn

On A6108, 3/4 mile N of village
⏲ 11-11; 12-10.30 Sun
☎ (01969) 623250
website: www.thecoverbridgeinn.co.uk

INDEPENDENT BREWERIES

Black Sheep Masham
Brown Cow Barlow
Cropton Cropton
Daleside Harrogate
Franklin's Bilton
Hambleton Holme-on-Swale
Malton Malton
North Yorkshire Pinchinthorpe
Old White Bear Cross Hills
Rooster's Knaresborough
Rudgate Tockwith
Selby Selby
Samuel Smith Tadcaster
York York

Black Sheep Best Bitter; Taylor Landlord; Theakston Best Bitter, Old Peculier; guest beers Ⓗ
Dating from at least the 15th century and retaining many original features in several rooms, this inn enjoys a splendid location on the Cover near its confluence with the Ure. When you have puzzled out the escutcheon door latch you are met by a cosy atmosphere, log fires and bench seating. The sacked abbey of Jervaulx and ruins of Richard III's castle of Middleham are nearby, as well as good walks. It is served by a Bedale-Leydale bus (Mon-Fri) and Richmond-Ripon bus (Mon-Sat).
⩕Q❀⇔◑◐▲♣P⊬

EGTON BRIDGE

Horseshoe Hotel

Bottom of hill, Rosedale/Goathland, road jct
❂ 11.30-3, 6.30-11 (11.30-11 summer); 12-3, 7-10.30 Sun
John Smith's Bitter; Theakston Best Bitter; guest beer Ⓗ
Overlooking the River Esk, this old country house hotel stands in a large garden, which takes the overspill from the bars in summer. The bar is in two parts, with stone floors, fires and old wood settles. In good walking country – tackle the stepping-stones before drinking! A beer from Durham Brewery is often available. Buses stop about 200 yards away. ⩕Q❀⇔◑◐♿≥♣P

ELVINGTON

Grey Horse

Main Street
❂ 12-2.30 (not Mon, Tue or Thu), 5.30-11; 12-11 Sat; 12-10.30 Sun
☎ (01904) 608335
Black Sheep Best Bitter; John Smith's Bitter; Taylor Landlord; guest beers Ⓗ
Small pub where two rooms are served from a central bar. In winter the wood-burning stoves add to the comfortable atmosphere. A regular quiz is staged (Thu) and live music on Friday evening. In the lounge are photographs of the WWII bombers that used to fly from the airfield next to the village, now the Yorkshire Air Museum. The guest beers are changed regularly. No meals are served Monday evening.
⩕❀◑◐▲♣P

EMBSAY

Elm Tree

5 Elm Tree Square
❂ 11.30-3, 5.30-11; 12-3, 7-10.30 Sun
☎ (01756) 790717
Goose Eye No-Eyed Deer; Tetley Bitter; guest beers Ⓗ
This village local, popular for both food and ale, has a large main bar and a smaller side bar, used mainly by diners. Formerly a coaching inn, it is well sited for exploring the nearby moors or visiting the Embsay and Bolton Abbey Steam Railway. Note the worn mounting steps at the front. Three guest beers are normally available. Hourly daytime buses run from Skipton. Q❀⇔◑◐P

FILEY

Imperial Vaults

20-22 Hope Street
❂ 11-11; 12-10.30 Sun
☎ (01723) 512185
John Smith's Bitter; Tetley Bitter; guest beers Ⓗ
Sympathetically restored town-centre pub with traditional wood and stone floors, it is within easy reach of Filey beach and Brigg, which ends the Cleveland Way walk. Popular with walkers, birdwatchers and campers, food is served in the summer season (April-Sept). Guest ales are changed on a regular basis; quizzes are staged on Thursday and Sunday evenings. ◑◐♿▲≥♣

GRASSINGTON

Foresters Arms

20 Main Street
❂ 11-11; 12-10.30 Sun
☎ (01756) 752349
Black Sheep Best Bitter; Taylor Best Bitter; Tetley Mild, Bitter; guest beers Ⓗ
Very popular village-centre local that also welcomes tourists. On entering, the bar is to the left, beyond is the pool area and TV, switched on for major sporting events. Games include shove-ha'penny and devil among the tailors; join in the quiz (Mon). Another large seating area leads to the dining room, where home-cooked food includes a take-away menu. The accommodation is all en-suite with colour TV. Up to three guest beers are stocked.
⩕❀⇔◑◐♣P✔

INN BRIEF

BILBROUGH

Three Hares
Main Street
12-3, 7-9.30; closed Mon; 12-4 (closed eve) Sun
(01937) 832128
Black Sheep Best Bitter; Taylor Landlord; guest beers Ⓗ
200-year-old, converted blacksmith's shop with central servery to bar and eating areas. Award-winning beer and food.

CLAPHAM

Flying Horseshoe
6 (12 Fri & Sat)-11; 12-10.30 Sun
(015242) 51229
Black Sheep Best Bitter; Tetley Bitter; guest beers Ⓗ
Country hotel in its own grounds with a campsite, opposite the station.

COWLING

Bay Horse
161 Keighley Road
4 (11 Mon, Fri, Sat & summer)-11; 12-10.30 Sun
(01535) 632797
Tetley Mild, Bitter; guest beer Ⓗ
Village community pub with open-plan main bar and two smaller rooms. The guest is usually from Goose Eye.

CROSS HILLS

Old White Bear
6 Keighley Road
11.30-11; 12-10.30 Sun
(01535) 632115
Boddingtons Bitter; Old White Bear Bitter; guest beer (occasional) Ⓗ
Large, multi-roomed brew-pub, circa 1735, at the heart of village life. Good value food is served.

DALTON-ON-TEES

Chequers Inn
12-3, 5.30-11; 12-11 Sat; 12-10.30 Sun
(01325) 721213
John Smith's Bitter; guest beers Ⓗ
Dating back to the 1840s, it hosts regular gourmet evenings and a quiz (Wed eve).

GIGGLESWICK

Hart's Head
Belle Hill
12-2.30, 5.30-11; 11-11 Sat; 12-10.30 Sun
(01729) 822086
Black Sheep Best Bitter; Jennings Cumberland Ale; Tetley Mild, Bitter; Theakston Black Bull; Taylor Landlord; guest beer Ⓗ
Welcoming, 17th-century coaching inn, modernised but retaining four drinking areas, and offering an imaginative menu.

GREAT AYTON

Buck Inn
1 West Terrace (A173, 200 yds from bridge)
⊙ 11-11; 12-10.30 Sun
☎ (01642) 722242
Black Sheep Best Bitter; Boddingtons Bitter; Flowers Original Ⓗ
18th-century coaching inn, opposite the River Leven, green and Norman church. Traditionally arranged, four rooms are set around a central bar. Charity events are organised for mountain search and rescue, with quizzes (Sun and Tue). Theme nights are staged occasionally on Saturday, with live music. Wander round this fine village, feed the ducks and try Suggitt's ice cream.

Tile Sheds
46 Newton Road
⊙ 11 (10 Sat)-11; 10-10.30 Sun
☎ (01642) 722306
Camerons Strongarm Ⓗ
Traditional drinkers' pub, with a separate lounge and bar, and the only beer garden in the village. Note the boxing pictures in the bar, and Americana in the lounge, which hosts live music every Saturday evening. Call in and enjoy a quiet pint after a walk or ride to Roseberry Topping. Meals are served 11-7 (10-6 Sunday).
❀◑⊟♿⇌♣P⊡

GREAT SMEATON

Bay Horse
On A167
⊙ 12-2 (not Mon or Tue), 6-11; 11-11 Sat; 12-10.30 Sun
☎ (01609) 881466
John Smith's Bitter; guest beers Ⓗ
Small, 18th-century free house in the middle of a row of roadside cottages in an attractive village setting. This former local CAMRA Rural Pub of the Year has three linked rooms: a soft furnished lounge, with central fireplace and beams, a bustling little bar, and a games room. An attractive, enclosed garden to the rear has a small play area. No evening meals are served Monday.
❀◑⊟♿♣⊡

GROSMONT

Crossing Club
Front Street (off A171, via Egton)
⊙ 12-3 (not winter), 7-11; 12-3 (not winter), 7-10.30 Sun
☎ (01947) 895040
Durham Magus; guest beers Ⓗ
Brilliant, comfortable conversion of a former Co-op delivery bay, undertaken by village volunteers, complete with its own level crossing gate inside – Grosmont Station is next door. Usually at least three real ales from independents are available, with a mild regularly on tap. Members are proud of their club, as proved by their hospitality, non-members are welcome – just ring the bell and push the door. Children are allowed in until 9.30pm. Bar snacks are available. ⇌♣P⊡

GUISBOROUGH ❄

Tap & Spile
11-13 Westgate
⊙ 11.30-11; 12-10.30 Sun
☎ (01287) 632983
Big Lamp Bitter; Jennings Cumberland Ale; Theakston Best Bitter; guest beers Ⓗ
Old pub, on the main street of this historic market town, which was the original capital of Cleveland. The bar area features a wood floor and beamed ceilings. A no-smoking/family room is at the rear; a pool table and small snug area are added attractions. The yard behind the pub, with shaded tables, is very inviting in summer. Four guest ales change constantly. Live music is staged on Wednesday evening, a quiz on Tuesday. ❀◑♣

HARROGATE ❄

Coach & Horses
16 West Park (A61, opp. West Park Stray)
⊙ 11-11; 12-10.30 Sun
☎ (01423) 568371
Black Sheep Best Bitter; Tetley Bitter; guest beers Ⓗ
Highly popular pub, enjoying a good regular following of all ages. Always busy, and buzzing with conversation – no music or TV is necessary. Bus and rail stations are just a short walk away. Recently refurbished, without spoiling its character, it has been

GREAT OUSEBURN
Crown Inn
Main Street
5-11; 12-11 Sat; 12-10.30 Sun
(01423) 330430
Black Sheep Best Bitter; John Smith's Bitter; Taylor Landlord Ⓗ
In a picturesque village, busy early evenings, serving good food. Wartime memorabilia features in this historic pub.

GUISBOROUGH
Anchor
Belmangate
11-11; 12-10.30 Sun
(01287) 632715
Samuel Smith OBB Ⓗ
Old-fashioned local on the outskirts of town: a bar, two other rooms and a garden. Lunches served Thu-Tue.

HAMPSTHWAITE
Joiner's Arms
High Street
11.30-2.30, 5.30-11; 11.30-11 Sat; 12-10.30 Sun
(01423) 771673
John Smith's Bitter; Tetley Bitter; guest beer Ⓗ
Busy village inn with a restaurant attached.

HARROGATE
Shepherd's Dog
141 Otley Road
11-11; 12-10.30 Sun
(01423) 533031
Draught Bass; Stones Bitter Ⓗ
Large, lively open-plan pub, busy at lunchtime for food; live music, excellent choice of wines and quizzes feature.

KETTLESING
Queen's Head
11-1.45, 6.30-11; 12-3.30, 7-10.30 Sun
(01423) 770263
Black Sheep Best Bitter; Theakston Old Peculier; guest beer Ⓗ
Nestling in the bottom of a pretty village, a long-established eating house.

KIRKBY MALZEARD
Henry Jenkins
Main Street
12-3 (not Mon, or Tue-Fri winter), 6-11; 12-11 Sat; 12-3, 6-11 (12-11 summer) Sun
(01765) 658557
Black Sheep Best Bitter; John Smith's Bitter; Tetley Bitter Ⓗ
Welcoming local in a picturesque village. Meals Tue-Fri, plus weekends in winter.

opened up to create a more spacious interior and better disabled access. The U-shaped bar serves three drinking areas. Framed caricatures of members of the pub's golfing society are hung on one wall. Evening meals are served Mon-Thu.
Q◐♿⇌⊘

Gardener's Arms ☆
Bilton Lane (off A59)
✪ 12-3, 6-11; 12-3, 7-10.30 Sun
☎ (01423) 506051
Samuel Smith OBB ⊞
Built in the 1500s, with thick stone walls, wood panelling, and a large stone fireplace, it has a tiny snug. Very popular in summer, the excellent garden by a stream attracts much wildlife. It stands on an old bridle path, a route used by Oliver Cromwell after destroying Knaresborough Castle. Fishing tickets are available. No evening meals are served on Sunday or Wednesday in winter.
♨Q♉❀◐▲P

Old Bell Tavern
6 Royal Parade
✪ 12-11; 12-10.30 Sun
☎ (01423) 507930
website: www.markettowntaverns.co.uk
Black Sheep Best Bitter; Caledonian Deuchars IPA; Taylor Landlord; guest beers ⊞
This 1999 restaurant conversion was enlarged in 2001 by extending into the former Farrah's toffee shop next door. The new, no-smoking, area displays memorabilia from this old well-known Harrogate business, while the original bar area retains its collection of old brewery adverts. Eight real ales concentrate on northern breweries, usually including local products, complemented by two foreign draught beers and a good range of Belgian bottled beers. Top quality food is served in the bar and upstairs restaurant.
Q◐⇌⊬

Tap & Spile
Tower Street (opp. multi-storey car park)
✪ 11-11; 12-10.30 Sun
☎ (01423) 526785
Big Lamp Bitter; Theakston Best Bitter, Old Peculier; guest beers ⊞
Formerly a Camerons house, now well established as a quality ale house, the pub has three drinking areas, one of which is no-smoking, linked by a central bar. Popular with all ages, the interior is a mix of wood panelling and exposed brick walls, displaying many old photos of Harrogate. Regular weekly live music adds to the atmosphere of this often lively pub. Lunches are served Mon-Sat. ❀◖⇌♣●⊬

HELPERBY

Half Moon
Main Street
✪ 3-11 (not Mon), 7-11; 12-11 Sat; 12-10.30 Sun
☎ (01423) 360270
Tetley Bitter; guest beers ⊞
This small, traditional pub has served the village of Helperby for at least 150 years. The main room is furnished with settles, and in winter the real fire is a welcome sight. A further drinking area is located to the right of the bar and there is also a small snug. The guest beers are chosen from a wide range. Daleside Half Moon is Daleside Bitter, rebadged.
♨❀♣P

HELWITH BRIDGE

Helwith Bridge
OS811695
✪ 11-11; 12-10.30 Sun
☎ (01729) 860220
Greene King Old Speckled Hen; Marston's Pedigree; Theakston Best Bitter; Webster's Yorkshire Bitter; guest beers ⊞
Friendly, stone-flagged pub, full of character, backing on to the River Ribble, affording good views of the Settle-Carlisle railway and Pen-y-Ghent. Recently partially divided to create a cosy alcove, railway paintings and photographs decorate the walls and a roaring fire is guaranteed in winter. Good value food is usually available all day. Guest beers are mainly from the Scottish Courage guest list. ♨❀◐▲♣P

HEMINGBROUGH

Crown
Main Street
✪ 12 (2 Mon)-11; 12-10.30 Sun
☎ (01757) 638434
John Smith's Bitter; Tetley Bitter; guest beers ⊞
This excellent village local offers something for everyone. There is a comfortable lounge area, large-screen TV for sports, a restaurant, a well-used function room and a pleasant garden. It plays host to a number of village teams and there is always plenty going on, including quiz nights, karaoke and folk evenings. The guest beer is often from one of the local independents. ❀◐P

HILTON

Falcon
Seamer Road (2 miles off A1044, at High Leven crossroads)
✪ 11.30-11; 12-10.30 Sun
☎ (01642) 592228
Flowers Original; Marston's Pedigree; guest beers ⊞
Much-extended village pub where a strong emphasis is put on food, but the bar area remains popular with local drinkers. The licensee has a long-standing reputation in the area for serving excellent real ale. Guest beers are often from local micros, with North Yorkshire Brewing Company ales making frequent appearances. The restaurant draws customers from a wide area, many of them to enjoy the range of good value daily specials. Q❀◐♿♣P

HUBY

New Inn
Main Street
✪ 5.30-11; 12-3, 6-11 Sat; 12-3, 6.30-10.30 Sun
☎ (01347) 810393
Black Sheep Best Bitter; John Smith's Bitter; Taylor Landlord; Tetley Bitter; guest beers ⊞
Historic local, formed from three 500-year-old cottages, it has a spacious dining room extension to the rear, and many fine features remain, notably ceiling beams and a particularly splendid Yorkshire range in the old kitchen area. The pub's decor reflects its past use by Canadian airmen during the war, and its present custom – the

racing, hunting and shooting fraternity. Traditional food is a speciality, but it maintains a focus for local community activities. ⚑Q◑◐⊟♣P⊬

HUDSWELL

George & Dragon

OS145003
⊙ 12-3, 6.30-11; 12-3, 7-10.30 Sun
☎ (01748) 823082
Draught Bass; Black Sheep Best Bitter; guest beer Ⓗ
Homely country inn where a large terrace offers fantastic panoramic views over the Swale Valley. Home-made food is available every day, except Monday. Bar games, including shove-ha'penny, and books are available for old and young alike. Children are very welcome, as are well-behaved dogs. ⚑Q❀◑◐♣⊬

INGLETON

Wheatsheaf

22 High Street
⊙ 12-11; 12-10.30 Sun
☎ (015242) 41275
Black Sheep Best Bitter, Special; Moorhouses Pendle Witches Brew; Tetley Bitter Ⓗ
At the top end of the village, the Wheatsheaf is handy for the finish of the Waterfalls Walk. One long, narrow bar is divided into different areas, plus a restaurant. Very popular with tourists, who come especially for the accommodation or the food, Ingleton is served by infrequent bus No. 580 to Settle and the 80 and 80A services to Lancaster. Birds of prey have been spotted in the pub garden.
⚑❀⊭◑◐⛺♣P

KIRBY HILL

Blue Bell

On B6265, Boroughbridge-Ripon road
⊙ 12-4.30 (not Mon-Fri), 6 (5 Fri; 7 Sat)-11; 12-3.30, 7-10.30 Sun
☎ (01423) 324180
Greene King Old Speckled Hen; John Smith's Bitter; Tetley Bitter; guest beers Ⓗ
Traditional village inn beside the old Great North Road, heading out of Boroughbridge. A cosy lounge area, with open fire, and a public bar are both served by a central servery, offering up to six real ales. This pub offers sensibly-priced accommodation in an ideal location to tour the Dales, Ripon, York and Harrogate, with easy access from the nearby motorway. ⚑❀⊭◑◐⊟♣P

KIRKHAM ABBEY

Stone Trough Inn

⊙ 12-2.30, 6-11; closed Mon; 12-10.30 Sun
☎ (01653) 618713 website: www.stonetroughinn.co.uk
Black Sheep Best Bitter; Malton Golden Chance; Taylor Landlord; Tetley Bitter; guest beers Ⓗ
Country pub with loads of character: exposed beams, low ceilings, log fires and stone-flagged floors. It enjoys a beautiful setting overlooking Kirkham Priory and the River Derwent. In warm weather you can sit outside and admire the views of the valley. The pub is well known for its award-winning food, served in the bar and restaurant. The house beer is brewed by Malton. ⚑Q❀◑◐♣P⊡

KIRKLEVINGTON

Crown

Thirsk Road (A67, near A19, Crathorne interchange)
⊙ 5 (12 Sat)-11; 12-10.30 Sun
☎ (01642) 780044
Castle Eden Ale; John Smith's Magnet; Ⓗ
Old whitewashed pub in a quiet village, bypassed by the busy A19. The warm, welcoming interior is divided into two drinking areas, each with its own real fire. One area, with a pool table, is popular with younger drinkers; the other, used for both drinking and dining, boasts an ornate wooden fire surround. All meals are prepared and cooked to order. A little off the beaten track, this pub is well worth searching out.
⚑❀◐⊟♣P

KNARESBOROUGH

Blind Jack's

18a Market Place
⊙ 11-11; 12-10.30 Sun
☎ (01423) 869148
Black Sheep Best Bitter; Daleside Greengrass; Taylor Landlord; Village White Boar; guest beers Ⓗ
Superb, cosy, town-centre pub, over three storeys, with lots of little rooms. With a traditional atmosphere and always busy, one room is no-smoking. A diverse range of beers means this pub caters for the tastes of all ale lovers. Within walking distance of the train and bus stations and town-centre car parks, you will always receive a warm welcome here.
Q⇌⊬⊡

Mitre Hotel

4 Station Road
⊙ 4 (11 Sat)-11; 12-3, 7-10.30 Sun
☎ (01423) 863589 website: the-mitre.bizhosting.com
Beer range varies Ⓗ
This large pub stands almost on the railway platform. Warm and welcoming, there is plenty of space inside. It offers a choice of guest ales, with a commitment to local breweries; the house beer is brewed by Rooster's. Regular live music includes jazz and excellent bands at least twice a week. A twice-yearly beer festival offers up to 20 real ales. Bed and breakfast accommodation is available, but parking is limited. Pool is played here.
❀⊭⇌♣P

LAZENBY

Half Moon

High Street (off A174, by Wilton works)
⊙ 11-11; 12-10.30 Sun
☎ (01642) 452752
Beer range varies Ⓗ
Located beneath the Eston Hills, the view from the patio at the rear of the pub is spectacular. The Half Moon is an Enterprise Inns free house, a traditional village inn with an excellent reputation for home-cooked food, which is served daily (12-9). You can eat in the no-smoking dining area where children are welcome. The pub keeps five cask ales that vary on a daily basis.
⚑❀◑◐♿⛺P

LEALHOLM

Board Inn

Village Green OS762077

11-3, 7-11 (11-11 Sat spring & summer); 12-3, 7-10.30 (11-11 spring & summer) Sun

(01947) 897279

Camerons Strongarm; guest beer H

Built in 1740, it has recently been extended to provide a restaurant, new guest accommodation and new toilet facilities. This traditional country inn has three rooms, a restaurant, games room and a bar. The large garden borders a river, and quoits is played on the adjacent village green (do not try to park there). Ghosts have been seen in the bar, even by the sober. The pub sponsors the local football club.

LEAVENING

Jolly Farmers

Main Street

12-3 (not Mon), 7-11; 12-3, 7-10.30 Sun

(01653) 658276

John Smith's Bitter; Taylor Landlord; Tetley Bitter; guest beers H

In rolling countryside, between York and Malton, on the edge of the Yorkshire Wolds, this former York CAMRA Pub of the Year dates from the 17th century. A village local, it has been extended, but retains the cosiness of its original multi-roomed layout. The restaurant offers a varied menu, specialising in locally-caught game dishes. Guest beers often include strong ales from independent breweries. Accommodation is in a holiday cottage.

LEYBURN

Black Swan Hotel

Market Place

11.30-11; 12-10.30 Sun

(01969) 623131

Black Sheep Best Bitter; John Smith's Bitter; Taylor Landlord; guest beer (summer) H

The spacious bar, with its comfortable seating, stocks a good choice of real ales. The earliest record of its liquor licence goes back to 1713. A fascinating photo in the bar shows the pub's exterior in 1870 when it was known as the Cornmarket. Friendly staff help create a cheerful atmosphere. Accommodation varies from inexpensive, basic single rooms to luxury en-suites. A wide range of food is served in the bar; the Sunday carvery is especially good value. The garden is safe for children.

LITTLE SMEATON

Fox

Main Street

12-3 (not Mon-Thu; 12-4 Sat), 7-11; 12-5, 7-10.30 Sun

(01977) 620254

Black Sheep Best Bitter; John Smith's Bitter; Taylor Landlord H

Visit this attractive inviting free house and you will be rewarded with a superb view of the tranquil Went Valley. Built in 1927, one door along from the original premises (now a private residence), this immaculate country pub is also the meeting place of the local parish council. Doncaster CAMRA Pub of the Season, summer 2001, the Fox is strictly a drinking pub and that's exactly the way its customers like it.

LOFTUS

White Horse

73 High Street

12-11; 12-10.30 Sun

(01287) 640758

John Smith's Bitter; guest beer H

Long-established, terraced pub at the eastern end of town, just off the market place. Refurbished, it has a large L-shaped room with a central bar, a real fire and beamed ceilings. It enjoys a strong local patronage, with darts and pool teams competing in the local leagues. No food unless you are a B&B guest; the accommodation includes a family room.

LONG PRESTON

Maypole Inn

11-3, 6 (5 Sat)-11 (11-11 summer Sat); 12-10.30 Sun

(01729) 840219 website: www.maypole.co.uk

INN BRIEF

LANGDALE END

Moorcock Inn

7 (11 summer)-11 (closed winter Mon & Tue); 11-3, 7-11 (11-11 summer) Sat; 12-3, 7-10.30 Sun

(01723) 882268

Beer range varies H

Remote, sympathetically renovated pub near Dalby Forest Drive. Home-cooked food uses local produce. Cricket in summer.

LINTON-IN-CRAVEN

Fountaine Inn

The Green

11-11; 12-10.30 Sun

(01756) 752210

Black Sheep Best Bitter; John Smith's Bitter; Taylor Landlord; Tetley Bitter H

Low, beamed, 17th-century inn serving food all day, idyllically set on the green in this historic village.

MIDDLESBROUGH

Isaac Wilson

61 Wilson Street

11-11; 12-10.30 Sun

(01642) 247708

Courage Directors; Shepherd Neame Spitfire; Worthington Bitter; guest beers H

Wetherspoon's pub, near the station, converted from the county court. Busy Fri and Sat eves. Cask Marque accredited.

NORTHALLERTON

Tithe Bar

2 Friarage Street

12-11; 12-10.30 Sun

(01609) 778482

Black Sheep Best Bitter; Hambleton Bitter; Taylor Landlord; guest beers H

Attractive, modern but traditional town-centre bar with excellent brasserie, stocking over 25 Belgian beers.

PICKERING

Bay Horse

Market Place

11-11; 12-10.30 Sun

(01751) 472526

Greene King Old Speckled Hen; Tetley Bitter; guest beer H

Friendly local near the station. Guest beer comes from the Tapster's Choice range. Can be noisy at weekends.

REETH

King's Arms

High Row

11-11; 12-10.30 Sun

(01748) 884259

Black Sheep Best Bitter; John Smith's Bitter; Taylor Landlord; Theakston Best Bitter, Old Peculier; guest beer H

Overlooking the green, the pub boasts a splendid inglenook. Food is served all day in summer.

Castle Eden Ale; Moorhouses Premier; Taylor Landlord; Tetley Bitter Ⓗ
On the village green, opposite the maypole, this welcoming village local has won many awards. The tap room boasts carved bench seating dating from 1875. The cosy lounge has a list of the pub's licensees since 1695 and old photos of the village showing a quieter A65. Good value food (served all day Sun) can be eaten in the pub or in the no-smoking dining room. Dogs are welcome in the tap room. ♨Q❀⇔◑◗≠♣●P

LOW BENTHAM

Punch Bowl

⌚ 12-3 (not Mon), 6.30-11; 12-4, 7-10.30 Sun
☎ (015242) 61344
Everards Beacon; Worthington Bitter; guest beer Ⓗ
Small country pub, 400 years old, run by and for locals (but visitors are welcome). Various nooks and crannies, warmed by two open fires, include a cosy bar and a room down some steps with extra seating where games are played. The no-smoking restaurant is open at weekends (no food is served Mon eve). Buses 80 and 80A stop nearby. ♨❀◗⛺♣⚡

Sun Dial

⌚ 11-3, 5-11; 11-11 Fri & Sat; 12-10.30 Sun
☎ (015242) 65132 website: www.sundialinn.co.uk
Beer range varies Ⓗ
The Sun Dial remains what it has always been – a village local. It comprises a small, homely bar and an even smaller games room, which becomes a dining room in summer. Note the old sundial that serves as an inn sign. It hosts a weekly quiz on Wednesday evening. Four draught beers often include a brew from Jennings or Everards and there is always a mild on tap. ❀◑◗♣P

LOW MARISHES (NEAR MALTON)

School House Inn

Just off A169, Malton-Pickering road
⌚ 11.30-3, 6-11; 12-10.30 Sun
☎ (01653) 668247
Black Sheep Best Bitter; Hambleton Stallion; Tetley Bitter; guest beer Ⓗ
Cosy, multi-roomed pub offering excellent food. This wonderful unspoilt inn is a little off the beaten track, but worth finding. Eat in the large dining area or drink on the patio. Children (and dogs) are welcome. Darts and pool are played in the small, but not too cramped, back room. The guest beer is usually from Hambleton. ♨Q❀◑◗⊟♣P

MALHAM

Lister Arms

⌚ 12-3, 7-11; 12-11 Sat; 12-10.30 Sun
☎ (01729) 830330 www.listerarms.co.uk
Boddingtons Bitter; Taylor Landlord; guest beers Ⓗ
Early 18th-century pub, just off the village centre. A tiled entrance leads to the main bar area, which faces the garden to the rear – a suntrap in summer. The front room looks towards the village. The restaurant that seats 70, offers good quality food to match the overnight accommodation. Up to four guest beers are complemented by a good range of foreign bottled beers, plus a draught cider in summer. Internet access is available here. ♨❀⇔◑◗⛺♣●P

MALTON

Crown Hotel (Suddaby's)

12 Wheelgate
⌚ 11-11; 12-4, 7-10.30 Sun
☎ (01653) 692038 website: www.suddabyscrown.co.uk
Malton Double Chance, Golden Chance, seasonal beers; John Smith's Bitter; guest beers Ⓗ
Five generations of the Suddaby family have run the hotel since 1879 – the building's façade is Grade II listed and many architectural and historic features have been preserved. The hotel has nine bedrooms including two en-suite in the brewery annexe. Malton Brewery, in the courtyard, regularly supplies many other outlets in the area. Live music evenings, including jazz, folk and piano recitals, are staged in the conservatory and seasonal beer festivals are held. Lunches are served on Saturday (snacks Mon-Fri); evening meals on request. ♨Q♉❀⇔◗≠♣P⚡

MANFIELD

Crown Inn

Vicars Lane (500 yds from B6275)

RUNSWICK BAY

Royal Hotel
11-3, 6-11; 11-11 Sat & August; 12-10.30 Sun
(01947) 840215
Black Sheep Best Bitter; John Smith's Bitter Ⓗ
Old seaside hotel: a large front bar, quiet back bar, upstairs dining room with good views over the bay.

SAXTON

Greyhound
Main Street
11.30-3, 5.30-11; 11-11 Sat; 12-10.30 Sun
(01937) 557202
Samuel Smith OBB Ⓗ
Excellent 13th-century village inn, Grade II listed: three small rooms, real fires and stone-flagged floors.

SCARBOROUGH

Alma Inn
1 Alma Parade
11.30-11; 12-10.30 Sun
(01723) 375587
Malton Golden Chance; Tetley Bitter; Theakston XB; guest beers Ⓗ
Local with snug, bar and lounge, near rail station and shopping centre. Good value meals (no food Sun).

Golden Ball
Sandside
11.30-11 (winter hours vary); 12-10.30 Sun
(01723) 353899
Samuel Smith OBB Ⓗ
Multi-roomed pub on seafront by harbour with a wood-panelled lounge and children's room. Phone for winter opening hours.

SKIPTON

Cock & Bottle
30 Swadford Street
11-11; 12-10.30 Sun
(01756) 794734
Boddingtons Bitter; Castle Eden Ale; Tetley Bitter; guest beers Ⓗ
Refurbished 18th-century coaching inn with a single, split-level bar offering two guest beers from Enterprise Inns' portfolio.

SLEIGHTS

Salmon Leap Hotel
6 Coach Road
11.30-11; 12-10.30 (closes afternoons in winter) Sun
(01947) 810233
Tetley Bitter Ⓗ
Old-fashioned family hotel, with a large bar and dining room overlooking River Esk and the garden.

⏲ 5.30 (12 Sat)-11; 12-10.30 Sun
☎ (01325) 374243
Village White Boar, Bull; guest beers Ⓗ
Attractive, 18th-century inn situated in a quiet village. Consisting of a main lounge and a games room, the design of the bar allows both areas to be served. The mix of locals and visitors gives the pub a friendly atmosphere. Guest beers come from micro-breweries countrywide. Snacks are available.
⛫Q❀◖◗♣P⊡

MARSKE

Frigate
Hummers Hill Lane (opp. Marske Cricket Club)
⏲ 11 (12 Fri & Sat)-11; 12-10.30 Sun
☎ (01642) 484302
John Smith's Magnet Ⓗ
Well-established, friendly, local estate pub, comprising a lounge, bar and snug. Regular quiz nights enjoy strong support, while live music is staged in the lounge (Tue eve). Pool and darts are played in the bar, with teams competing in local leagues. The lounge doubles as a function room. The pub is connected with the Frigate Walk (Whitby-Marske), providing a welcome watering-hole after the 18-mile trek, on the Sunday before May Day.
Q⛾❀⊟⥱♣P⊡

MASHAM

Black Sheep Brewery Visitors Centre
Wellgarth, Crosshills (follow tourist signs on A6108)
⏲ 11-11; closed Mon (closed Tue Jan & Feb); 12-5.30 Sun
☎ (01765) 680101 website: www.blacksheep.co.uk
Black Sheep Best Bitter, Special, Riggwelter, seasonal beer Ⓗ
Visiting this attraction is a pleasant way of spending a few hours. Whether just calling in for a beer, enjoying a meal, snack or coffee, touring the brewery or browsing in the 'sheepy shop' in this spacious and historic former maltings, it should provide a fascinating insight into this successful small regional brewery. It is a popular venue for events ranging from plays to Victorian fairs. Families are welcome during the day. Ring to check times of tours. The small garden overlooks lower Wensleydale.
❀◖◗♿P

White Bear
12 Crosshills
⏲ 11-11; 12-10.30 Sun
☎ (01765) 689319
Caledonian Deuchars IPA; Theakston Best Bitter, Black Bull, Old Peculier; guest beer Ⓗ
Solid Yorkshire stone inn on the edge of an historic market town, the unspoilt public bar has a friendly, local feel. The spacious, bare-boarded lounge is popular for meals and occasional live jazz sessions. The cosy interior is warmed by open fires in winter and there is a large patio at the front for summer drinking. Admire the attractive stained glass window behind the bar of a cooper at work. This characterful pub in a scenic part of Wensleydale is worth a visit.
⛫❀◖◗⊟P

MIDDLESBROUGH ❊

Doctor Brown's
135 Corporation Road (opp. UGC cinema)
⏲ 12-11; 12-10.30 Sun
☎ (01642) 213213
Beer range varies Ⓗ
This large, end-of-terrace pub has changed hands several times in recent years. Divided into three areas, the pub can be partitioned for party bookings. It hosts regular live music on Fridays and Saturdays, and has large-screen Sky TV for football matches. Extremely popular on match days, the pub has also featured on away team fans' web-sites. Three or four beers often include an unusual or seasonal beer. The outdoor drinking area is under shady trees on the pavement. ❀◖♿⥱

Hogshead
14 Corporation Road (facing Cleveland Centre)
⏲ 11-11; 12-10.30 Sun
Boddingtons Bitter; Caledonian Deuchars IPA; Hook Norton Old Hooky; guest beers Ⓗ
Now owned by the Laurel Pub Co., this standard, comfortable Hogshead pub is in a pedestrianised area of the town centre. Popular with daytime shoppers and office workers, a pavement café-style area is set out in summer. It offers a wide selection of guest beers, with good value four-pint jugs for at least one beer. Bottled Belgian beers are also stocked. It hosts regular beer festivals and at least one annual real cider/perry festival. Children are not admitted. Q❀◖◗♿⥱⍻

Star & Garter
14 Southfield Road (opp. university students union)
⏲ 11-11; 12-10.30 Sun
☎ (01642) 245307
Beer range varies Ⓗ
Converted from a dockers' club, this pub is a former CAMRA Pub Preservation award winner. The large lounge houses a large-screen TV for football matches, which are always popular, although the far corner provides a quieter area. The beer range is constantly changing, with four on offer, often from smaller breweries. It holds regular beer festivals. There are no handpulls in the bar, but real ale is served from the lounge. Outdoor drinking is in a section of the car park.
❀◖◗⊟⥱♣P

NORTH DUFFIELD

King's Arms
The Green, Main Street (off A163)
⏲ 4 (12 Sat)-11; 12-10.30 Sun
☎ (01757) 288492
Black Sheep Best Bitter; John Smith's Bitter; guest beers Ⓗ
Traditional, 18th-century village pub, with an outdoor children's play area, overlooking the village green and duck pond. The hosts offer a warm welcome and provide one of the best selections of real ale in the area, with frequently changing guest beers. Indoor sports fans are catered for and there is a quiz on Sunday evening. Food is served in the no-smoking dining area Wed-Sat evenings, and lunchtime at the weekend.
⛫❀◖◗♣●P⍻✔

NORTHALLERTON ❄

Station Hotel

2 Boroughbridge Road

12-2.30 (not Sat), 5 (7 Sat)-11; 12-3, 7-10.30 Sun

☎ (01609) 772053

website: www.stationhotel.northallerton.com

Adnams Broadside; Bateman XB; Greene King IPA; Tetley Bitter; guest beers H

The hotel boasts a fine, well-maintained Edwardian frontage including an etched window in the main bar, proclaiming its former name of the Railway Hotel. The front bar is light and airy; the lounge bar doubles as a (no-smoking) dining area at lunchtime, and a quiet bar at other times. A function room is available for small gatherings. Two beer festivals are held every year, and the main bar typically hosts a couple of live music evenings a month.

NOSTERFIELD

Freemasons Arms

On B6267

12-3, 6-11 (closed Mon); 12-3, 7-10.30 Sun

☎ (01677) 470548

Black Sheep Best Bitter; Taylor Best Bitter, Landlord; Tetley Bitter H

This old stone inn is a prominent feature on the main road through the village. It has a stone-flagged bar area, low, heavily beamed ceilings and two open fires. Opened up long ago, it retains the feeling of separate areas. A plethora of fascinating memorabilia mainly relate to the Great War and motorcycling. It attracts customers from far and wide because of its reputation for quality cuisine, but it is definitely a pub with food rather than a restaurant with beer. No children admitted.

NUN MONKTON

Alice Hawthorn

The Green (off A59, York-Harrogate road)

12-2, 6-11; 12-10.30 Sun

☎ (01423) 330303 website: www.alicehawthorn.co.uk

Flowers IPA; Marston's Pedigree; Tetley Bitter; guest beers H

At the end of a country lane, this cosy country pub offers excellent food and drink. Enjoy the view of the maypole and the duck pond on the village green, or huddle around a log fire in winter. The pub is a firm favourite with the fishing and boating fraternity from the nearby rivers Ouse and Nidd. Walkers are most welcome and local routes can be supplied on request. Outside are patio tables and a children's playground.

OLD MALTON

Royal Oak

47 Town Street

12-2.30 (not Mon), 5-11; 12-11 Sat & summer; 12-10.30 Sun

☎ (01653) 692503

website: www.royaloak@maxpages.com

Tetley Bitter; guest beers H

Traditional two-roomed village pub with a warm, friendly atmosphere. Centrally located near local moorland, the seaside and York's tourist attractions, it features cosy, beamed bars, an open fire and brasses adorning the wood-panelled walls. The garden provides a pleasant outdoor drinking area. Home-cooked food (eve meals Tue-Sat) and two guest ales, regularly featuring a Durham brew, are added attractions at local CAMRA's joint Rural Pub of the Year 2001.

OSMOTHERLEY

Golden Lion

6 West End (1 mile E of A19 at Northallerton jct)

12-4, 6-midnight; 12-midnight Sat; 12-10 Sun

☎ (01609) 883526

Hambleton Bitter; John Smith's Bitter; North Yorkshire Fools Gold; Taylor Landlord; Tetley Bitter H

Situated at the end of the Lyke Wake Walk, the pub overlooks the ancient cross of this picturesque village in the National Park. It is popular with locals and walkers for its food, all of which is made on the premises, except the bread, but drinkers are always made welcome. The bar area has simple decor of whitewashed walls and exposed beams, with many mirrors giving an illusion of size, while candles provide a lovely, warm and intimate atmosphere.

PATRICK BROMPTON

Green Tree

12-3 (not winter; 12-2.30 Fri), 6 (7 Sat)-11; 12-3, 7-10.30 Sun

☎ (01677) 450262

Black Sheep Best Bitter; Taylor Landlord; guest beer (summer) H

Cosy, Grade II listed, village pub overlooking the main A684 Wensleydale road at the eastern edge of the village, next to the parish church gates. There is a simple, but welcoming bar with brick-built bar and chimney breast housing a real fire. The restaurant is a little larger, but still imparts a country pub atmosphere. Home-cooked meals are served in both rooms most days, with vegetarian options and a children's menu.

PICKHILL

Nag's Head

$1^1/_2$ miles off A1 between Bedale and Masham exits

11-11; 12-10.30 Sun

☎ (01845) 567391

website: www.nagsheadpickhill.co.uk

Black Sheep Best Bitter; Hambleton Bitter; John Smith's Bitter; guest beers H

Coaching inn with a well-deserved reputation for good food and warm hospitality in the centre of a tiny village, just off the A1. The cosy bar, separate from the lounge and restaurant, retains a local pub atmosphere. It is decorated with a frieze of ties snipped from their owners (including a Lord Mayor of London)! A distinctive draughts board is laid into the stone-flagged floor; the TV is for rugby only. Outdoor games include bowls, quoits and a nine-hole putting green.

POOL IN WHARFEDALE

Hunter's Inn

Harrogate Road (A658)

11-11; 12-10.30 Sun

☎ (0113) 284 1090

Theakston Best Bitter; Tetley Bitter; guest beers H

Detached, single-storey roadside country inn, on a main bus route with ample parking. Popular and busy, its open-plan interior combines barside and table seating. It offers a large range of well-priced ales, Saxon cider and a good selection of wines. Food is available at lunchtime; children are welcome until 9pm. Pool is played here. ♨❀◖♣●P

REDCAR

Plimsoll Line

138 High Street

11-11; 12-10.30 Sun

☎ (01642) 495250

Courage Directors; Greene King Abbot; Hop Back Summer Lightning; Shepherd Neame Spitfire; Theakston Best Bitter; guest beers Ⓗ

Relatively new addition to the Wetherspoon's chain, the building was formerly a hardware store at the top end of the High Street. The theme is nautical – the pub getting its name from a Mr Plimsoll, who was a frequent visitor to Redcar. The pictures around the spacious split-level large room relate to local history, but chrome-legged high bar stools and tables give a modern feel. The dining area, which is no-smoking, leads to an outside seating area. Q❀◖◗♿≠●⚟▯✔

RIPON

One-Eyed Rat

51 Allhallowgate

12-3.30 (not Mon-Wed), 6 (5.30 Fri)-11; 12-11 Sat; 12-3, 7-10.30 Sun

☎ (01765) 607704 website: www.oneeyedrat.co.uk

Black Sheep Best Bitter; Taylor Landlord; guest beers Ⓗ

Characterful local situated in a terrace on one of the oldest streets in town, near the market square. It features many nostalgic items including old bottles, labels and rugby memorabilia. There are always four guest beers from independent breweries and specialist bottled beers from many countries, plus a range of fruit wines. In summer, the garden, complete with pool table, is opened, giving views over open countryside; bar billiards is available indoors, too. ♨Q❀▲♣●

Wheatsheaf

Harrogate Road (by southern roundabout on city bypass)

12-3 (not Mon), 7-11; 12-3, 7-10.30 Sun

☎ (01765) 602410

Greene King IPA; Tetley Bitter Ⓗ

Small, cosy local in what was once quarrymen's cottages. The two-roomed interior is divided by an open fire with one side a quiet area and the other the bar which features a lovely carved wood back and dummy drawers at the front. From the outside the pub is notable for the distinct lean towards what once was the quarry, and is now the sunken garden. ♨❀♣P

ROBIN HOOD'S BAY

Victoria Hotel

Station Road

12-3, 6-11; 12-11 Fri & Sat and summer; 12-10.30 Sun

☎ (01947) 880205

Camerons Bitter, Strongarm; guest beers Ⓗ

Impressive Victorian building on the cliff overlooking Robin Hood's Bay and the village below. Views from the hotel are spectacular, especially from some of the hotel's nine en-suite bedrooms. The comfortable bar bears a collection of guest ale pump clips. There is a no-smoking family room and a dining room; the hotel enjoys a well-deserved reputation for the quality of its home-cooked food. Cleveland CAMRA Pub of the Year 1999, and Pub of the Season 2001, it is excellent for families. ♨Q♉❀⛟◖◗♣

RUFFORTH

Tankard Inn

Main Street (B1224, 4 miles W of York)

12-3, 6-11; 12-11 Sat; 12-4 (3 winter), 7-10.30 Sun

☎ (01904) 738621

Samuel Smith OBB Ⓗ

The 1930s remodelling of this outstanding local shows how a pub can retain the essential elements of a past era and continue to be a popular village inn. Two delightful rooms, in which the original, small curved counter in the public bar has been successfully replicated in the lounge. Both have leaded windows, bench seating and open fires. A daily specials board lists home-cooked food (no food Sun eve or Mon). The outside drinking area has children's play equipment. ♨❀◖◗⊟♣P

RUSWARP

Bridge

High Street (B1416)

12-3 (not Mon-Fri), 7 (6 Fri)-11; 12-6, 7-10.30 Sun

☎ (01947) 602780

John Smith's Bitter; Theakston XB; guest beer Ⓗ

Traditional village ale house of two bars, with a pool room on the right. Step down from the pavement into the bar. Enjoy good views of the river and occasional live music. Try the railways (Esk Valley and miniature steam train) in summer, or row a boat to Sleights. It is an easy walk across the fields to Whitby. ♨❀≠♣

SALTBURN

Saltburn Cricket, Bowls and Tennis Club

Marske Mill Lane (by Leisure Centre)

8 (2 summer Sat)-11; 12-3, 8-10.30 Sun

☎ (01287) 622761

Tetley Bitter; guest beers Ⓗ

Friendly, private sports club, fielding cricket, tennis and bowls teams in local leagues. It has a spacious, well-furnished lounge and a games room; both areas afford a magnificent view of the cricket field. The club is open all day on match days. Casual visitors are welcome, without joining. It stocks a large range of guest beers, sometimes local brews, and hosts occasional beer festivals. It was voted Cleveland CAMRA Pub of the Season in 1997, '99 and 2001. ❀▲≠♣P▯

SANDHUTTON

King's Arms

On A167, 4 miles W of Thirsk

☺ 12-2.30 (not Mon), 5.30-11; 12-4, 6.30-11 Sat; 12-4, 6.30-10.30 Sun
☎ (01845) 587263
John Smith's Bitter; Taylor Landlord; Theakston Cool Cask; Village White Boar Ⓗ
Homely, friendly, warm and comfortable, this is a splendid, traditional village inn. It affords easy access to the North Yorkshire moors and dales. Well used by the locals, it offers a good selection of real ales and an extensive menu of home-cooked meals, served in the dining room, lounge and public bar (no food Mon). Pool and darts are played in the public bar.
🝓Q❀0◗🝓🝓♣P

SANDSEND

Hart Inn
East Row (A174)
☺ 11-11; 12-10.30 (12-3, 6-10.30 winter) Sun
☎ (01947) 893304
Camerons Strongarm; Theakston Best Bitter Ⓗ
Traditional village pub; the cottage next door used to be the stables. The single downstairs room bears the original beamed ceiling around the bar; upstairs is a dining room. It is rumoured to have been built by monks, as a stopping-off place during the building of Whitby Abbey. It stands just across the road from the beach and is supposed to have been named after a hart that fell down a precipice in Mulgrave Woods. 🝓Q❀0◗P

SAWDON

Anvil Inn
Main Street (off A170)
☺ 11.30-2.30 (3 Sat), 7-11; 12-3, 7-10.30 Sun
☎ (01723) 373746
Theakston Best Bitter; guest beers Ⓗ
Warm, friendly, restored blacksmith's shop where original anvils, old photos and artefacts adorn the stone walls. It boasts a huge log fire and a dining area providing excellent value, home-cooked food. Barbecues feature during the summer. It is conveniently located for outdoor pursuits, the moors, forest and open country walking. 🝓Q🝓❀🝓0◗🝓♣P🝓

SCARBOROUGH ❊

Cellars
35-37 Valley Road
☺ 3 (12 Sat)-11 (11-11 summer); 12-10.30 Sun
☎ (01723) 367158
website: www.scarborough-brialene.co.uk
Black Sheep Special; Tetley Bitter; guest beers Ⓗ
Small, cosy family-run pub located in the cellars of an elegant Victorian building, converted into self-contained holiday flats, a short walk from the South Bay beach, the Spa complex and town centre. Sporting memorabilia adorn the lounge area. Bar meals are available from midday to early evening, plus traditional lunch on Sunday. Above the pub is a restaurant offering fine cuisine. A patio and gardens offer outside drinking. Two guest ales are usually on offer. ❀🝓0◗♿🝓⇌P

Cricketers
119 North Marine Road
☺ 12 (3 winter Mon)-11; 12-10.30 Sun
☎ (01723) 365864
Taylor Landlord; Tetley Bitter; York Yorkshire Terrier; guest beers Ⓗ
Scarborough's best-kept secret, located on a clifftop, overlooking North Bay, with good views of the castle. It is opposite the cricket ground (second home to Yorkshire CC) and gets busy on match days. Good value, home-cooked food is based on local ingredients; a full menu is available every day until 9pm – specialities include steak and ale pie. The large upstairs family room hosts children's entertainment in summer; a children's menu is also available. A large-screen TV is switched on for sport.
🝓❀0◗♿🝓⇌♣P

Highlander
15-16 The Esplanade
☺ 11-11; 7-10.30 Sun
☎ (01723) 373426 website: www.highlandhotel.com
Tetley Bitter; Webster's Green Label; guest beers Ⓗ
This pub is attached to the Highlander Hotel and offers a lounge and a cellar bar. Superb views of the South Bay can be seen from the patio area. The lounge bar sports a huge collection of malt whiskies and tartan decor. Showcased in an extension to the rear of the pub is a steam engine, Island Chief. Wm Clark's Mild, brewed in Wakefield, is available throughout the year, as well as two guest ales. 🝓Q❀🝓0🝓⇌

Indigo Alley
4 North Marine Road
☺ 3 (12 Sat)-11; 1-10.30 Sun
☎ (01723) 381900
Beer range varies Ⓗ
After becoming run-down and eventually closed as the Nottingham Hotel, this pub has been given a name change and a new lease of life by the present owners and is now a lively, popular local. It stocks six constantly changing guest ales and Belgian Leffe beer on draught, alongside fruit beers and fruit wines. Live music is performed four nights a week and it even stages the occasional play! It has been local CAMRA Pub of the Year for the last three years.

Old Scalby Mills Hotel
Scalby Mills Road
☺ 11-11; 12-10.30 Sun
☎ (01723) 500449
Daleside Old Legover, Monkey Wrench; guest beers Ⓗ
Popular with walkers and tourists in a seafront location, the building was originally a watermill and has seen many uses over the years. Old photographs and prints chart its history. Soak up the superb views of the North Bay and castle from the sheltered patio. The Cleveland Way Walk reaches the seafront at this point and there is a Sea-life Centre nearby. The pub holds a children's certificate. Q🝓❀🝓🝓♣

Scholar's
Somerset Terrace
☺ 12-3, 6-11; 12-11 Fri, Sat & summer; 12-10.30 Sun
☎ (01723) 360084
website: www.yorkshirecoast/bedfordhotel.co.uk
Beer range varies Ⓗ
Part of the Bedford Hotel, the pub has a recently-extended bar offering a maximum of four handpumped ales, with regular appearances of York and Durham beers. The hotel was the birthplace of Edith Sitwell's brother, the author, poet and art critic, Sir

Sacheverell Sitwell. Good value, home-cooked food is available until early evening. Live jazz is performed on Tuesday evening. ⛟◐♿⇌

Tap & Spile

94 Falsgrave Road

⏲ 11-11; 12-10.30 Sun

☎ (01723) 363837

Big Lamp Bitter; Everards Tiger; Taylor Landlord; Theakston Old Peculier; guest beers Ⓗ

Sympathetically restored coaching inn, not far from the centre, comprising three rooms, including a no-smoking lounge, plus a large patio. Local memorabilia is displayed. A recently extended menu offers excellent value meals at lunchtime (Tue-Sun), Thursday and Friday evenings and all day Saturday. Barbecues are held on the patio on summer Sunday afternoons. Live music, (performed Thu eve and Sun afternoon), is often blues-oriented. This thriving, busy local has a good atmosphere; TV sport is watched in one bar. Q❀◐⛺⇌P⚡

SKIPTON

Narrow Boat

38 Victoria Street (alleyway off Coach St)

⏲ 12-11; 12-10.30 Sun

☎ (01756) 797922

website: www.markettowntaverns.co.uk

Black Sheep Best Bitter; Taylor Landlord; guest beers Ⓗ

Skipton's permanent beer exhibition is furnished with old church pews and decorated with old brewery posters, mirrors and two eye-catching, canal-themed murals. Piped music, gaming machines and juke boxes are conspicuous by their absence. Smoking is only permitted in the upstairs minstrels' gallery. Charity events are held here, giving it a community atmosphere. It stages live jazz (Tue) and folk music (Sun), and stocks up to six ever-changing guest beers, mainly from local breweries, plus bottled and draught Belgian and German beers. Q❀◐♿⇌♣⚡

Railway

13-15 Carleton Street

⏲ 11-11; 12-10.30 Sun

☎ (01756) 793186

Tetley Mild, Bitter; guest beer Ⓗ

Friendly, traditional, two-roomed, street-corner local, decorated on a railway theme, with a large collection of water jugs in the lounge. The tap room is popular with racing enthusiasts in the afternoons and dominoes players in the evenings. The affable licensee takes great pride in his cellarmanship and welcomes visiting drinkers. The rotating guest beer is from the Tapster's Choice range. ⇌♣

SLEIGHTS

Plough Inn

180 Coach Road OS866068

⏲ 11-3, 5.30-11; 12-3, 5.30-10.30 Sun

☎ (01947) 810412

John Smith's Bitter; Marston's Pedigree; Theakston Black Bull Ⓗ

17th-century coaching inn, long and narrow, with an L-shaped bar near the front, a lounge in the middle and a dining room behind. The large garden at the back has seats for 30. Some people say there is a ghost here. Good for walking, it stands at the edge of the village near one of the wilder parts of the moors, affording fine views of the Esk Valley. Bed and breakfast accommodation is available at the pub, or for the more hardy, there are several local campsites. ♨Q❀⛟◐⛺⇌P

SNAPE

Castle Arms Inn

⏲ 12-3, 6-11; 12-3, 7-10.30 Sun

☎ (01677) 470270

Black Sheep Best Bitter; Hambleton Bitter; John Smith's Bitter; guest beer Ⓗ

Snape sits quietly, two miles off the Bedale-Masham road. The village is divided by a stream – the inn stands on the north bank. Nearby is the Thorpe Perrow Arboretum. Snape's castle, once home to Catherine Parr, is still inhabited. This 14th-century inn boasts a splendid fireplace and stone-flagged floor. With food available Wed-Sat, the Castle Arms provides a wide choice of meals in the restaurant and very comfortable, modern accommodation. ♨Q❀⛟◐⛺♣P

INN BRIEF

STAINFORTH

Craven Heifer

12-2, 7-11 (12-11 summer Sat); 12-10.30 Sun

(01729) 822599

Thwaites Mild (summer), **Bitter, Reward** (summer) Ⓗ

Cosy, two-roomed Thwaites tied house at the hub of the village, incorporating the shop and post office.

STAITHES

Royal George Inn

High Street

11-11; 12-10.30 Sun

(01947) 841432

Tetley Dark Mild, Bitter Ⓗ

Small, village-centre pub in a 17th-century building. Rare outlet for mild in this part of the country.

THIRSK

Golden Fleece

Market Place

11-2.30, 6-11; 12-3, 7-10.30 Sun

(01845) 523108

Hambleton Bitter, Goldfield, Stud Ⓗ

The cosy lounge and Paddock Bar serve a selection of local ales and traditional bar meals.

UGTHORPE

Black Bull Inn

11.30-2.30 (not Mon), 6.30-11; 12-3, 7-10.30 Sun

(01947) 840286

Tetley Bitter; Theakston Old Peculier Ⓗ

Old village pub with bar, snug, pool room and restaurant and original beamed ceilings. Quoits played in summer.

UPPER POPPLETON

Lord Collingwood

The Green

11.30-3, 6-11; 11-11 Sat; 12-10.30 Sun

(01904) 794388

Banks's Bitter; Camerons Bitter; Mansfield Cask Ale; guest beers Ⓗ

Attractive, friendly Tudor-style pub, overlooking the village green, with a single, comfortable, L-shaped bar.

WASS

Wombwell Arms

12-3 (11.30-3.30 Sat), 6.30-11; 12-4, 7-10.30 (closed winter) Sun

(01347) 868280

Black Sheep Best Bitter; Taylor Landlord; guest beers Ⓗ

Welcoming 18th-century inn which has a small, cosy bar. Traditional country food is served in three dining rooms.

STAITHES ❄

Captain Cook Inn
60 Staithes Lane
11-11; 12-10.30 Sun
☎ (01947) 840200
website: www.capitaincookinn.co.uk
Hoskins & Oldfield Bitter; John Smith's Magnet; guest beers Ⓗ
Built as the Station Hotel, it was renamed in the 1960s after the closure of the railway line. Admire the views across Staithes Beck towards Boulby Cliffs, which, at 660 feet, are the highest in England. The two guest beers generally come from East Midlands micro-breweries or from regional brewers. Evening meals are served Fri-Sun. This lovely olde-worlde fishing village, the home of Captain Cook, has a museum dedicated to him. A beer festival is held during Lifeboat week in the summer. Children are welcome in the games room.
Q❀◐♣

Cod & Lobster Inn
High Street (near harbour)
12-11; 12-10.30 Sun
☎ (01947) 840295
Camerons Strongarm; Greene King Abbot; John Smith's Bitter; guest beer (summer) Ⓗ
It stands right on the seafront, so be careful which door you use when the sea is high. A former landlady's ghost sometimes appears to warn of bad weather, and on a really rough day it is impossible to open the doors. It has one small bar, but drinkers spill out on to the seawall in fine weather. Dominoes is played here. If you are lucky, you might be served fish for dinner, freshly caught by the landlord. No dogs are admitted. ❀◐♣

STOKESLEY

Spread Eagle
39 High Street (near Town Hall)
11-11; 12-10.30 Sun
☎ (01642) 710278
Camerons Strongarm; Marston's Pedigree; guest beer Ⓗ
Small, unspoilt, town-centre pub with a friendly, relaxed atmosphere. Excellent home-cooked food is available all day from an interesting menu, with meat, game and poultry from the family butcher, 'real' vegetables and imaginative salads (booking advisable at peak times). An enclosed garden leads down to the River Leven. In the front room, only the real fire is permitted to smoke. Live music is staged on Tuesday evening, otherwise this is a quiet pub with occasional subdued piped music.
Q❀◐

TADCASTER

Angel & White Horse
Bridge Street
11-3.30, 5-11; 12-3.30, 7-10.30 Sun
☎ (01937) 835470
Samuel Smith OBB Ⓗ
In the town centre, this is Samuel Smith's brewery tap, an old coaching inn with late-Georgian façade. The large single bar, with fine wood panelling and furnishings, affords good views of the brewery yard and stables at the rear. Brewery tours, which start from the pub, include a visit to the tack room and the chance to inspect the famous grey shire horses which haul Sam's dray around local outlets. ❀◐♣

THIXENDALE

Cross Keys
12-3, 6-11; 12-3, 7-10.30 Sun
☎ (01377) 288272
Jennings Bitter; Tetley Bitter; guest beers Ⓗ
Thixendale lies at the heart of the Yorkshire Wolds at the junction of several dry valleys. Inhabited since the Stone Age, many tracks established by Roman times are still used today by walkers on their way to the Cross Keys which is an unspoilt, unpretentious village local serving award-winning beer. The single bar also offers good value, home-cooked food. Children are welcome in the garden. ❀◐♣

THORGANBY

Ferryboat Inn
1 mile NE of village OS697426
12-3 (extended in summer), 7-11; 12-3, 7-10.30 Sun
☎ (01904) 448224
Old Mill Bitter; guest beers Ⓗ
Quiet, remote, family-run inn situated beside the River Derwent. The public rooms comprise a main bar and large family room, which looks out on to the attractive garden, sloping down to the river – a perfect setting for sunny summer afternoons. Unsurprisingly, given its position, the pub is popular with anglers and boaters. Guest beers come from local breweries, often Rooster's. Well worth the effort of seeking out. Q❀♣P

THORNTON IN LONSDALE

Marton Arms
1/4 mile N of A65/A687 jct
12-11; 12-10.30 Sun
☎ (015242) 41281 website: www.martonarms.co.uk
Black Sheep Best Bitter; Dent Bitter; Oakhill Best Bitter, Mendip Gold; Taylor Golden Best; guest beers Ⓗ
In a hamlet containing a parish church, old stocks and little else, the pub relies almost entirely on tourists attracted by the 16 handpumps, although there are other interesting beverages, notably Belgian specialities. Behind the 1679 datestone and old oak door there has been recent modernisation: a flagged passage leads to a bar dominated by white wood and bus and rail memorabilia. Ten minutes' walk from the start of the Ingleton Waterfalls Walk, buses 80 and 80A run along the main road.
❀◐P

THORNTON LE DALE

New Inn
12-2.30, 6.30-11; 12-3, 6.30-10.30 Sun
☎ (01751) 474226
Black Sheep Best Bitter; John Smith's Bitter; Taylor Landlord Ⓗ
Family-owned and run inn, restored to create the feel of yesteryear. Dating to around 1720, when it was a coaching house, the inn overlooks the ancient village stocks and market cross. An ideal touring

base for the North York moors, countryside and coast, it prides itself on freshly-cooked food, with a wide range of specials. All bedrooms are en-suite and feature hand-made pine furniture.
Q P

THORNTON WATLASS

Buck Inn

On village green
11-11; 12-10.30 Sun
(01677) 422461
website: www.smoothhound.co.uk/hotels/buckinn
Black Sheep Best Bitter; John Smith's Bitter; Theakston Best Bitter; guest beers

This delightful Wensleydale inn overlooks the village green and its 100-year-old cricket pitch with unusual boundaries; outside, the front door acts as a position for deep third man. A small comfortable bar has settles, old bottles and a gem of a bar servery. An excellent menu is served in the bar and informal no-smoking dining area. Sunday lunchtime trad jazz is performed fortnightly. The large garden has a children's play area and quoits pitches.
P

TOCKWITH

Spotted Ox

Westfield Road (off B1224)
11-3, 5.30-11; 11-11 Fri & Sat; 12-10.30 Sun
(01423) 358387
Tetley Bitter; guest beers

Situated in a village 'twixt York and Wetherby in the area famed for the Battle of Marston Moor (visit the local memorial). The Spotted Ox is a perfect example of a community local attracting regular visitors from a wide area. An ever-changing range of guest beers and an extensive menu of home-cooked food, including daily specials, served by friendly staff, all contributed to the licensee being presented with a York CAMRA Pub of the Season award.
P

WEAVERTHORPE

Star Inn

Main Street (off A64 at Sherburn traffic lights)
12-4 (not Mon & Tue), 7-11; 12-4, 7-10.30 Sun
(01944) 738273 website: www.starinn.net
Camerons Bitter; John Smith's Bitter; Tetley Bitter; guest beers

One of Susan Nowak's favourite rural pubs, listed in all issues of her Good Pub Food and Pub Super Chef publications. With good en-suite accommodation, it is ideally situated for visiting the Yorkshire coast, moors and National Park. Bar/restaurant lunches are available daily except Mon and Tue, dinner is served Wed-Mon evenings, specialising in game, seafood and vegetarian dishes. Traditional guest ales usually hail from Durham, Hambleton or Slaters (Eccleshall) breweries.
Q A P

WEST WITTON

Fox & Hounds

Main Street (A684, 3½ miles W of Leyburn)
12-4, 7-11 (may vary summer); 12-4, 7-10.30 Sun
(01969) 623650
Black Sheep Best Bitter; John Smith's Bitter; Tetley Burton Ale; guest beers

In a village on a limestone terrace of Penill Beacon, this 15th-century outpost of Jervaulx Abbey has been a pub for 300 years. Inside the Grade II listed building a stone fireplace divides the cosy drinking area. Meals are served here or in the dining room, boasting an impressive chimney arch, complete with bread oven. Each August, Witton feast includes the 'Burning of Bartle' when a straw effigy is paraded through the village before being set alight. Daily bus services run from Leyburn and Hawes. A P

WHITBY

Tap & Spile

New Quay Road (opp. bus and rail stations)
12-11; 12-10.30 (12-4.30, 7-10.30 winter) Sun
(01947) 603937
Black Sheep Best Bitter; Courage Directors; Theakston Cool Cask; guest beers

The pub benefits from views over the quayside and River Esk, in this historic port. Once called the Cutty Sark, it was converted to a Tap & Spile in Victorian style with bare floorboards. It has a snug on one side of the central bar and a no-smoking room that are suitable for families. A varying range of ales includes up to six guests, plus two ciders. It hosts live music regularly and is a mecca in Whitby's folk week. Food is served 12-7 (4 Sun). Q

WHITLEY

George & Dragon

Doncaster Road (A19)
11.30-3, 5-11; 11.30-11 Fri & Sat; 12-10.30 Sun
John Smith's Bitter

Comfortable pub, built in the late 1930s, just a stone's throw from the old George & Dragon Hotel which was then demolished. Open fires in the lounge and public bar ensure a warm welcome for winter visitors. An extensive garden/children's play area behind the pub houses an aviary and is

INN BRIEF

YORK

Derwent Arms
39 The Village
11.30-3, 5.30-11; 11-11 Fri & Sat; 12-10.30 Sun
(01904) 413498
Greene King Abbot; John Smith's Bitter; guest beers
Suburban pub with village local feel, opposite the green; a comfortable bar and plush lounge.

Sun Inn
The Green, Acomb
11-11; 12-10.30 Sun
(01904) 798500
John Smith's Bitter; Wells Bombardier; guest beers
Traditional-style pub, much improved by a recent sprucing-up, attracting a good mixture of locals and passing trade.

York Beer & Wine Shop
28 Sandringham Street
11 (6 Mon; 10 Sat)-10; 6-10 Sun
(01904) 647136
Taylor Landlord; guest beers
Draught beer and cider in any quantity and many bottle-conditioned beers. Mouth-watering cheeses and ice cream too.

home to peacocks. In late spring and summer the grounds are ablaze with hundreds of bedding plants. ⛺❀◐◑⊟♣P

YORK ❊

Ackhorne

9 St Martins Lane (up cobbled lane at foot of Micklegate)

⏲ 12-11; 12-10.30 Sun

☎ (01904) 671421 website: www.ackhorne.com

Caledonian Deuchars IPA; Rooster's Yankee; guest beers 🄷

Veritable oasis, providing a refuge from the bustle of the city centre. The bare-boarded bar is spacious, with comfortable bench seating and original stained glass windows; a carpeted snug area displays pictures of Civil War hero, Sir Thomas Fairfax. A recent innovation is the tiny garden, a real suntrap. Interesting guest beers, often from local micro-breweries, change with reassuring frequency; a range of foreign bottles is also stocked. No food is served Sunday. York CAMRA Pub of the Year 2001. Q❀◐⇶♣●

Blue Bell ☆

53 Fossgate

⏲ 11-11; 12-10.30 Sun

☎ (01904) 654904 website: www.bluebellyork.co.uk

Adnams Bitter; Camerons Strongarm; Greene King Abbot; John Smith's Bitter; Wells Bombardier; guest beer 🄷

This tiny pub has York's only perfectly surviving Edwardian interior and is of sufficient importance to merit Grade II* listed status. It owes its fittings and panelling to a 1903 refurbishment, although the building has been a public house for a good deal longer. The bench-seated public bar, drinking corridor and cosy lounge provide a welcoming haven from the busy tourist spots close by and it is very much a local. Good value sandwiches are available 11-6 Mon-Sat. ⊟♣

Golden Ball ☆

2 Cromwell Road

⏲ 4 (12 Fri & Sat)-11; 12-10.30 Sun

☎ (01904) 652211 website: www.goldenballyork.com

Greene King Ruddles Best Bitter; Marston's Pedigree; John Smith's Bitter, Magnet; guest beers 🄷

Victorian street-corner pub, with an impressive glazed brick façade. It has recently been added to CAMRA's National Inventory of pubs with interiors of outstanding heritage interest. An inter-war refurbishment by John Smith's left the internal layout of this lively, community local as a public bar, unusual bar-side alcove and rear lounge. Recently, an extra public room with bar billiards and TV was created from former living accommodation. Live music is staged (Thu and Sun). Q❀◐⛺♣

Last Drop Inn

27 Colliergate

⏲ 11-11; 12-10.30 Sun

☎ (01904) 621951 website: www.thelastdropinn.co.uk

York Stonewall, Bitter, Yorkshire Terrier, Centurion's Ghost Ale, seasonal beers; guest beers 🄷

York Brewery's first tied house is only two years old, but seems to have been here much longer. The large, plain, glass windows allow a good view into this skilfully converted former solicitor's office. These alterations were effected using mostly quality, local materials, which give a feeling of permanence. Modern gimmickry is notable by its absence – a rare phenomenon for a new pub. Food, made mostly from local ingredients, is served daily until 3pm. Live music is staged (Mon and Tue). Q❀◐

Maltings

Tanners Moat (below Lendal Bridge)

⏲ 11-11; 12-10.30 Sun

☎ (01904) 655387 website: www.maltings.co.uk

Black Sheep Best Bitter; guest beers 🄷

Having won a plethora of awards, the Maltings remains committed to maintaining its high standards. It cannily exploits its position as one of the area's only true free houses to provide a selection of six guest beers, mostly from micro-breweries. Unsurprisingly, with its proximity to the station and businesses, this draws an eclectic clientele. The regular beer festivals are enormously popular, as is the food, served in huge portions, 12-2 (4 at weekends). The ciders vary. ◐⇶●

Phoenix Inn

75 George Street

⏲ 11-11; 12-10.30 Sun

☎ (01904) 652594

John Smith's Bitter; Wells Bombardier; guest beers 🄷

Situated just inside the city walls, the Grade II listed Phoenix dates back to the 1830s. Current owners, the Unique Pub Company refurbished it so sensitively recently that it won the CAMRA/English Heritage Conservation category of the Pub Design Awards 2001. At the front of this fine local is a bare-boarded public bar, frequented by dominoes players. A corridor with a small drinking lobby off it leads to a comfortable lounge, extended into former living accommodation. ❀⊟♣

Royal Oak

18 Goodramgate

⏲ 11-11; 12-10.30 Sun

☎ (01904) 653856

website: www.royal-oak-pub-york.co.uk

Greene King Abbot; Tetley Bitter, Burton Ale; guest beers 🄷

The incumbents of this small, stylish town pub recently celebrated 25 years' occupancy – for most of which time they have featured in this Guide. The building's Tudor look is due to a 1934 revamp by local brewers John J. Hunt, but there has been a pub on the site since 1783. Cosy and intimate, there are three small drinking rooms off a staggered corridor. It is widely known for its food – including home-baked bread – available from 11 (12 Sun) until 8pm daily. Q☕◐◑⚟

Swan Inn ☆

16 Bishopgate Street

⏲ 4 (12 Sat)-11; 12-10.30 Sun

☎ (01904) 634968

Greene King Abbot; Taylor Landlord; Tetley Bitter; guest beers 🄷

Classic, street-corner local with a 'West Riding' layout, unusual for the city. The entrance corridor leads to a drinking lobby with a servery and two rooms, also served from the main bar. A Tetley Heritage inn, one of three York pubs recognised by CAMRA as having national historic interest, this popular local gets extremely busy most

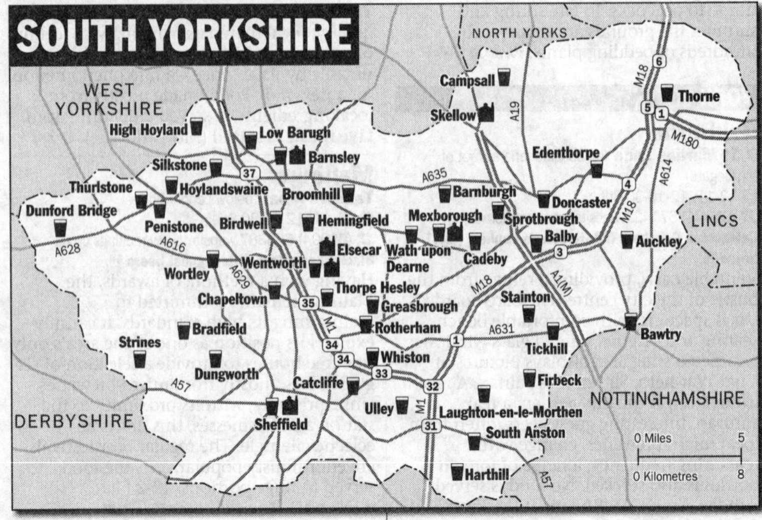

evenings. A paved, walled garden (large by York's standards) has a pleasant, sunny aspect. ❀⊟⇌♣

Tap & Spile

29 Monkgate

☼ 11.30-11; 12-10.30 Sun

☎ (01904) 656158

Black Sheep Best Bitter; Caledonian Deuchars IPA; guest beers Ⓗ

Imposing Flemish-style building, purpose-built as a pub in 1897. The main bar and smaller, raised area (with darts and TV) both have bare boards. There is a carpeted lounge, formed when partitions were skilfully introduced recently, which has bookshelves and an elegant fireplace. High ceilings create an airy feel throughout. The long bar has eight handpumps where local brewers, particularly Rooster's, are often featured. Note the thriving hop bine outside; last year's crop was used for a special brew. ❀◐♣♠P✔

Three-Legged Mare

15 High Petergate

☼ 11-11; 12-10.30 Sun

☎ (01904) 638246

website: www.thethreeleggedmare.co.uk

York Stonewall, Bitter, Yorkshire Terrier, Centurion's Ghost Ale, seasonal beers; guest beers Ⓗ

York Brewery's second tied house was opened in the summer of 2001. The styling is cool, restrained, modern, and completely free of electronic gimmicks. The single bar leads to a conservatory, which is atmospherically candlelit at night. This in turn leads outside to a replica of the device after which the pub is named – a three-posted gallows. The downstairs toilets are accessed via a tightly twisting spiral staircase. Sandwiches and baked potatoes are served until 4pm daily. Q❀♿

Yorkshire (South)

AUCKLEY

Eagle & Child

24 Main Street

☼ 11.30-3, 5-11; 11.30-11 Sat; 12-4, 7-10.30 Sun

☎ (01302) 770406

Barnsley Bitter; John Smith's Bitter; Theakston Cool Cask; guest beer Ⓗ

Popular, traditional village local. Darwin beers are a permanent feature here, together with a rotating guest beer, Springhead being the most regular. Meals are served every day in a no-smoking area. There is a quiz on Monday evening and occasional ceilidhs are an added attraction at this local CAMRA Pub of the Year 2000 runner-up. Q❀◐◑⊟P

BALBY

Winning Post

Warmsworth Road

☼ 12-11; 11-11 Sat; 12-10.30 Sun

☎ (01302) 853493

John Smith's Bitter; guest beer Ⓗ

Spacious community local, serving the estates at the top end of Balby, run by a capable licensee who was literally brought up in the trade. The pub opened in 1956 and retains a traditional two-roomed layout. It comprises a tap room, with pool and darts, and a large, comfortable lounge, hosting regular quiz nights, with a quiet area to the rear. The landlord's Sunday lunches come highly recommended (no other food is served). Guest beers are sold at competitive prices. ❀⊟♣P

BARNSLEY ✻

Courthouse Station

24 Regent Street (opp. rail/bus interchange)

☼ 11-11; 12-10.30 Sun

☎ (01226) 779056

Shepherd Neame Spitfire; Tetley Bitter; Theakston Best Bitter; guest beers Ⓗ

Still Barnsley area's only Wetherspoon's, giving the town a changing and reasonable choice of keenly-priced beers. The building has had several identities hence the name, and now features a drinking area with a very small (open-plan!) no-smoking section, and secluded corners behind the long single bar, plus a raised drinking platform. Very busy before and after matches, it remains the closest and best choice for the discerning football fan. Q❀◐◑♿⇌P⅟✔

George & Dragon

Summer Lane (at Dodworth Rd roundabout head for hospital)

12-3, 7 (6 Sat)-11; 12-11 Fri & summer Sat; 12-4, 7-10.30 Sun

☎ (01226) 205609

John Smith's Bitter; guest beers H

One of town's most popular real ale outlets, warm and friendly, this is a local where you can hear yourself talk. Its two rooms are on different levels, with the high level housing a pool table. It is popular with darts and pool teams who meet here regularly. Pictures of Summer Lane in the early 20th century adorn the walls and teapots make a large collection on the shelves. Outside drinking is on seats in the car park. ❀ ≠ (Interchange) ♣ P

Keresforth Hall

Keresforth Hall Road, Kingstone

11-2, 7-11; 12-3, 7-10.30 Sun

☎ (01226) 284226

Beer range varies H

About half a mile from the nearest bus stop and one and a half miles from the town centre, the walk is very worthwhile to this pleasing quarter of Barnsley. With open rural views across to Stainborough Low and Wentworth Castle, the main 1930s rebuilt house provides for all: dining room; lounge bar with usually two real ales, a conservatory, plus a large function hall. Children are well catered for with a slide, swings and playhouses in a split-level garden. Q ❀ ◐ ◑ ♿ P ⊬

BAWTRY

Turnpike

High Street

11-11; 12-10.30 Sun

☎ (01302) 711960

Greene King Ruddles Best Bitter; Marston's Pedigree; John Smith's Bitter; guest beer H

Friendly, market place pub; the interior has wood panelling, and part-flagstoned floor. The L-shaped bar has four open sections down one side and another for meals, which are good value, with a varied menu (eve meals served Wed and Thu). It has been in this Guide for the last 16 years, and has won local CAMRA Pub of the Season three times. A frequent bus service runs through the day and parking is easy in the market place. ❀ ◐ ◑

BIRDWELL

Cock Inn

Pilley Hill (off A61)

12-3, 7-11; 12-3, 7-10.30 Sun

☎ (01226) 742155

Draught Bass; John Smith's Bitter; guest beer (occasional) H

Popular village local, the Cock is stone built and traditional in style with two main rooms, the larger featuring a slate floor, exposed beams, brassware and an open fire. The smaller room is comfortable and more peaceful. A popular bar menu includes daily specials (no meals Sun eve, book Sun lunch). Quizzes are held Monday and Thursday evening. Book for the occasional gourmet nights (Wed); garden barbecues are held in summer. ❀ ◐ ◑ P

BROOMHILL

Old Moor Tavern

Everilgate Road

11-11; 12-10.30 Sun

Black Sheep Best Bitter; Marston's Pedigree; John Smith's Bitter; guest beers H

Just off the A1/M1 link road, this is an easily accessible village pub. In the middle of a developing wetlands project, it makes a useful watering-hole for birdwatchers, naturalists, walkers and, of course, locals. The provision of good honest food is an art which has been honed by the landlord and his wife over many years. Q ❀ ◐ ◑ ♿ P

CADEBY

Cadeby Inn

Main Street

11-11; 12-10.30 Sun

☎ (01709) 864009

John Smith's Bitter; Taylor Landlord; Tetley Bitter; Theakston Cool Cask; guest beer H

The inn was a farmhouse for over 200 years, before being converted to a pub in 1975. The interior features three open fires, oak-beamed ceilings, a large lounge with a no-smoking room, and a smaller bar with stone-flagged floor. The pub attracts many diners, and a daily lunchtime carvery is offered. The large front garden is popular with families. The Trans-Pennine Trail passes nearby and the pub is close to the Earth Centre at Conisbrough.

❀ ◐ ◑ ♣ P ⊬

CAMPSALL

Old Bells

High Street

11.30-2, 6-11; 12-3, 7-10.30 Sun

☎ (01302) 700423

Black Sheep Best Bitter; Greene King Old Speckled Hen; John Smith's Bitter H

In the tiny hamlet of old Campsall, the Old Bells, at 150-plus, is the oldest pub in Doncaster borough. It consists of a small, wood-panelled and exposed stone smoke room, a tiny snug, lounge and two restaurants, specialising in good quality, fresh food. It is popular for wedding receptions and other celebrations. Although food is obviously at the top of the agenda, this is definitely a pub that sells food; drinkers are made just as welcome as diners.

Q ◐ ◑ ♿ P

CATCLIFFE

Waverley

Brinsworth Road (B6067, 1 mile from M1 jct 33)

INDEPENDENT BREWERIES

Abbeydale Sheffield
Barnsley Elsecar
Concertina Mexborough
Crown Sheffield
Glentworth Skellow
Kelham Island Sheffield
Oakwell Barnsley
Orchard Barnsley
Port Mahon Sheffield
Wentworth Wentworth

12-4, 6-11; 11-11 Sat; 12-4, 7.30-10.30 Sun
(01709) 360906
Beer range varies H
Modern stone pub, opened in 1984 by the present licensees, it has three rooms: a small traditional tap room, a spacious lounge and a large children's room. Set back from the road, it boasts a large patio and an extensive outside play area. Four ever-changing ales are always available, sourced from brewers large and small, usually including one from Glentworth Brewery. Local CAMRA Pub of the Year winner 2000.

CHAPELTOWN

Commercial
107 Station Road
12-3, 5.30-11; 12-11 Sat; 12-10.30 Sun
(0114) 246 9066
Wentworth Needles Eye, WPA, Oatmeal Stout; guest beers H
Built by the former Stroutts Brewery in 1890, this community local caters for all tastes. The central bar serves three distinct rooms, comprising a no-smoking snug, a public bar/games room plus a comfortable lounge. The snug houses a collection of over 1,000 pump clips gathered from the four changing guest beers usually available. Popular and successful beer festivals are held each June and November.

Wharncliffe Arms
365 Burncross Road
3 (2 Fri; 12 Sat)-11; 12-10.30 Sun
(0114) 246 3807
Stones Bitter; guest beers H
Unpretentious community local, that draws a sporting clientele and hosts several clubs. A small public bar is served by the main bar, while the comfortable sunken lounge has its own servery. Built as a pub in 1878, see the collection of photographs of old Chapeltown in the lounge. A very large, enclosed rear garden has a children's play area and aviary; it stages a bonfire in November. Three changing guest beers, mostly come from established regional breweries. Small car park.

DONCASTER

Corner Pin
145 St Sepulchure Gate West
11-11; 12-10.30 Sun
(01302) 323159
John Smith's Bitter; guest beers H
Reinvigorated by tenants in their second spell at this pub and by the Unique Pub Co's guest beer policy, a sympathetic refurbishment retains the appeal of the (vanishing) traditional boozer. It offers two weekly changed and one regular guest beer. The central bar serves the lounge and bar areas. It supports darts teams and, unusually, an angling club; its friendly atmosphere attracts a good mix of customers. What a street-corner pub should be, confirmed by local CAMRA as Pub of the Year 2002.

Leopard
1 West Street
11-11; 12-10.30 Sun
(01302) 363054
John Smith's Bitter; guest beer H
Large, street-corner pub boasting a superb tiled exterior recalling its former ownership by Warwicks and Richardson's Brewery. A wide variety of music is played on the juke box in both the lively bar/games room and the more comfortable and (usually) subdued lounge. An upstairs music room hosts regular gigs, featuring local and nationally-known bands. Doncaster's only regular outlet for local Glentworth beers (one is always available), it was local CAMRA Pub of the Year 2000. The car park has tables for outdoor drinking.

Masons' Arms
Market Place
11-11; 11-5, 8-11 Mon; 12-4.30, 8-10.30 Sun
(01302) 364391
Taylor Landlord; Tetley Bitter; guest beer H
Despite a recent change of management, the Masons' Arms has kept the character that has made it a Guide perennial. This traditional market place pub is a little over 200 years old and has maintained its multi-roomed layout. The public bar is an outstanding example of its type and is

INN BRIEF

BARNBURGH

Coach & Horses
High Street
12-5, 7.30-11;
12-10.30 Sun
(01709) 892306
John Smith's Bitter; Tetley Bitter H
Three rooms and a lobby in an unspoilt 1930s pub, where wood, glass and brass abound.

BARNSLEY

Shaw Inn
Racecommon Road
4 (12 Fri & Sat)-11;
12-4, 7-10.30 Sun
(01226) 294021
John Smith's Bitter; guest beers H
Imposing roadside pub, on the edge of town, serving a varied menu, specialising in steaks and seafood.

BRADFIELD

Old Horns Inn
Towngate
12-11; 12-4, 5.30-11 Mon, Tue & Thu;
12-10.30 Sun
(0114) 285 1207
Courage Directors; John Smith's Magnet; Stones Bitter; Theakston Best Bitter; guest beer H
Village local dating from 1833, with a single L-shaped lounge bar. Food is served lunchtime and evening.

DONCASTER

Cumberland
Thorne Road, Wheatley Hills
11-11; 12-10.30 Sun
(01302) 360000
Draught Bass; Flowers Original; Marston's Pedigree; H **Whitbread Trophy Bitter** P
Friendly old pub: a large L-shaped room with good food served at one end, with a no-smoking section.

Tut 'n' Shive
6 West Laithe Gate
11-11 (midnight Fri & Sat); 12-midnight Sun
(01302) 360300
Black Sheep Best Bitter; Boddingtons Bitter; Marston's Pedigree; guest beers H
Eccentric decor, but excellent ale and cider as recognised by the Cask Marque award. Food, music and TV sports.

DUNFORD BRIDGE

Stanhope Arms
Windle Edge Road
12-3, 7-11; not Mon (12-11 summer);
12-10.30 Sun
(01226) 763104
Black Sheep Best Bitter; Taylor Landlord; guest beer H
Set in moorland, this former shooting lodge offers a warm welcome. Restaurant and bar meals available.

complemented by two quieter, comfortable rooms (the back room is the HQ of the local morris men). The lunchtime sandwiches are good value. Q⊟≹

Plough

8 West Laith Gate

✪ 11-11; 12-3, 7-10.30 Sun

☎ (01302) 738310

Barnsley Bitter; Draught Bass 🄷

This ex-Hewitts of Grimsby pub has been unchanged for many years, keeping features lost from many other town-centre outlets that have attempted to keep pace with a fickle younger generation. Note the stained glass windows in the comfortable lounge at the rear. The beer garden is reputed to be the smallest in Yorkshire. A quiet oasis in the centre of Doncaster, you can relax here after shopping or meet friends for the evening. Q✿⊟≹♣

Salutation

14 South Parade

✪ 12-11; 12-10.30 Sun

☎ (01302) 340705

Tetley Dark Mild, Bitter; guest beers 🄷

Coaching inn dating from 1745, the pub is now an ale house, consisting of a large open room divided into cosier drinking areas. There is a large function room upstairs, complete with its own bar, and a patio to the rear for outside drinking. A variety of guest beers is always on offer, along with inexpensive meals (eve meals Mon-Fri). On Tuesday evening the quiz usually draws a good crowd. ✿◐≹♣P

DUNGWORTH

Royal Hotel

Main Road

✪ 5.30 (12 Sat)-11; 12-10.30 Sun

☎ (0114) 285 1213

website: www.royalhotel-dungworth.co.uk

Tetley Bitter; guest beer 🄷

Village local in the Bradfield Dale, north-west of Sheffield, affording panoramic views of the Loxley Valley – binoculars are provided. Built as a pub around 1813, it is compact, with comfortable seating in and around the bar area, plus another room to the left of the entrance. Ask to see the home-cooked pie menu for evening meals or Sunday lunch. Longer opening hours apply in summer. Regular buses run from Hillsborough. ♨✿⇐◑♣P

EDENTHORPE

Beverley Inn

117 Thorne Road

✪ 12-3, 5 (6 Sat)-11; 12-3, 7-10.30 Sun

☎ (01302) 882724

John Smith's Bitter, Magnet; guest beer 🄷

Popular, family-owned and run local, with a 200-year history. A rotating guest beer complements the John Smith's range. The no-smoking restaurant hosts a steak night on Friday and offers an à la carte menu on Saturday evening; there is also a popular Sunday carvery, the emphasis being on home-cooked meals. Monday is quiz night. Accommodation is in 14 rooms with a two-star rating. ⛾✿⇐◐P

FIRBECK

Black Lion

9 New Road

✪ 11.30-11; 12-10.30 Sun

☎ (01709) 812575

Greene King Ruddles County; John Smith's Bitter; Stones Bitter; guest beers 🄷

17th-century pub which has been pleasantly modernised, in a quiet, rural village. Its rooms are full of photos of local people and scenes and famous visitors. It stands close to the ancient monument of Roche Abbey. A quiz night is held on Tuesday and karaoke on Thursday. Known for its food which includes a lunchtime carvery, children are welcome until 9pm when dining. Occasional cabaret nights are staged in the restaurant. Formerly a Duncan Gilmour house, it stocks a range of changing guest ales. ✿◐P

GREASBROUGH

Prince of Wales

9 Potter Hill

✪ 11-4, 7-11; 12-3, 7-10.30 Sun

☎ (01709) 551358

John Smith's Bitter; 🄿 **guest beer** 🄷

Friendly, street-corner local serving a low-

HOYLANDSWAINE

Rose & Crown

Barnsley Road

12-11; 12-10.30 Sun

(01226) 762227

Marston's Pedigree; Tetley Bitter 🄷

Cosy, unspoilt village local with unrivalled views; a rare outlet for Pedigree.

ROTHERHAM

Woodman

Midland Road, Masbrough

12-3, 7-11; 12-2, 7-10.30 Sun

(01709) 512128

Draught Bass; Stones Bitter; guest beer 🄷

Former Bentley's pub, close to Rotherham FC ground with good public transport, 20 years in this Guide.

SHEFFIELD: *CENTRAL*

Brown Bear

109 Norfolk Street

12-11; 12-10.30 Sun

(0114) 272 7744

Samuel Smith OBB 🄷

Close to the theatre, both physically and spiritually, plastered with posters from local and national productions.

Red House

168 Solly Street

12-2.30 (not Sat), 5.30 (7.30 Sat)-11; 3-10.30 Sun

(0114) 272 7926

Adnams Bitter; Greene King IPA; guest beers 🄷

Former Ward's house with a splendid view, a haunt of folk musicians some eves. Weekday lunches.

NORTH

Rock House

168-172 Rock Street, Pitsmoor

1-4 (not Mon-Thu), 8-11; 1-4, 8-10.30 Sun

(0114) 272 4682

Draught Bass; John Smith's Bitter; guest beer (occasional) 🄷

A warm Scottish welcome awaits at this small community local; wide range of whiskies and a guest beer from Fisherrow.

SOUTH

Old Mother Redcap

Prospect Road, Bradway

11.30-3.30, 5.30-11; 11-11 Sat; 12-10.30 Sun

(0114) 236 0179

Samuel Smith OBB 🄷

Popular, modern farmhouse-style building, with a single L-shaped lounge. It sells the cheapest beer in Sheffield.

priced, ever-changing guest beer in its traditional tap room and comfortable lounge. China plates depict the local mining industry, alongside a large collection of jugs. Up to 50 malt whiskies are stocked as well as some unusual beers for the area. This Guide regular has twice been local CAMRA Pub of the Season. A chip shop next door is one of four local takeaways, and it is well served by public transport. ⊟♣⊽

HARTHILL

Beehive

16 Union Street (opp. church)

⊛ 12-3 (not Mon), 6 (7 Sat)-11; 12-3, 7-10.30 Sun

☎ (01909) 770205

Taylor Landlord; Tetley Bitter; guest beer Ⓗ

Lively, friendly, traditional pub in an historic village. Two rooms are for drinking and dining; a back room houses a full-sized snooker table, home to the famous Harthill morris dancers and monthly folk club (first Fri). The function room hosts many other local clubs and events. Good home-cooked food is based on local produce; a Braille menu is available and children are welcome, if dining, until 9pm. Rother Valley Country Park is close by, offering camping and very good walks. Q❀◐◑♿♣P

HEMINGFIELD

Elephant & Castle

Tinglebridge Lane (off M1 jct 36, at B6096)

⊛ 11-11; 12-10.30 Sun

☎ (01226) 755986

Eastwood & Sanders Nettlethrasher; John Smith's Bitter; Tetley Bitter; guest beers Ⓗ

17th-century village inn, which has been sympathetically refurbished to a very high standard. By the canal, it is a perfect spot to relax on a summer's day. Inside is a split-level seating area, the upper level is no-smoking. A large bar front area has window seats overlooking a beautiful fountain. Both food and beer are served in tip-top condition. This local CAMRA Pub of the Season is well worth a visit.

❀◐◑♿⇌(Wombwell) ♣P⊬

HIGH HOYLAND

Cherry Tree

Bank End Lane OS410026

⊛ 11-3.30, 5-11; 11-11 Sat; 12-10.30 Sun

☎ (01226) 382541

Eastwood & Sanders Nettlethrasher; John Smith's Bitter Ⓗ

The semi-circle central bar serves a lounge on either side, each boasting an open fire and beamed ceilings. This very popular venue is used by clubs of walkers and cyclists because of the location; its magnificent views look out to Cawthorne Park, and nearby Cannon Hall, inside the pub a mural shows all the buildings and the names of the residents of High Hoyland when the collage was executed in 1999.

⌂Q❀◐◑P

LAUGHTON-EN-LE-MORTHEN

St Leger Arms

4 High Street

⊛ 12-11; 12-10.30 Sun

☎ (01909) 562940

Barnsley Bitter; Boddingtons Bitter; Whitbread Trophy Bitter Ⓗ

Handy for walkers visiting Roche Abbey, this friendly village pub is popular with locals. A small bar area, for drinkers only, has a games section to one side, including a TV and pool. Good, moderately-priced food is served in the busy restaurant (all day Sat and Sun); all food is home made and cooked to order, children are allowed in the restaurant to dine until 9pm. The outside drinking section has a grassy play area for children.

❀◐◑♣P⊽

LOW BARUGH

Millers

Dearne Hall Road (off M1 jct 37/38)

⊛ 11.30 (5 Tue)-11; 11.30-2.30, 5-11 Wed & Thu; 12-10.30 Sun

☎ (01226) 382888

Barnsley Bitter; Taylor Landlord; Wells Bombardier; guest beers Ⓗ

Built in the 1800s at the end of a row of cottages that were provided for millworkers, the River Dearne runs behind the pub. The public bar features a mural in raised red brick, showing a clay pigeon shooter and his gun dog, linking the two fireplaces. The lounge has a large raised open fire with a smaller lounge/dining area to the side. With a football team, plus darts and its own clay pigeon club, it is a popular venue for clubs and societies to hold their meetings.

⌂Q❀◐◑⊟♿♣P

MEXBOROUGH

Concertina Band Club

9a Dolcliffe Road (off High St)

⊛ 12-4, 7-11; 12-2, 7-10.30 Sun

☎ (01709) 580841

Concertina Club Bitter, Bengal Tiger; John Smith's Bitter; guest beers Ⓗ

Originally the home of the local concertina band, photos relate the prize-winning band's history. The club is now family-owned, drawing a good local membership and welcoming to visitors. In 1992 a small brewery was installed to produce its own ales alongside the popular guest beers. There is a large bar, and a spacious lounge/concert room where regular games of bingo are played. A small TV and pool room has a serving hatch to the bar.

⇌♣⊽

Falcon

12 Main Street

⊛ 11.30-11; 12.30-3.30, 7-10.30 Sun

☎ (01709) 513084

Old Mill Bitter; guest beers Ⓗ

Town-centre, double-fronted pub, where the original leaded windows overlook a paved seating area at the front. Originally called the Old Mason's Arms, it closed for some time and was eventually bought by Old Mill Brewery in 1990. After refurbishment it reopened as the Falcon, and is now a lively pub, with raised seating areas in a large lounge and a smaller tap room offering pub games. Guest beers are from the Old Mill range.

❀⊟⇌♣

PENISTONE

Cubley Hall
Mortimer Road
11-11; 12-10.30 Sun
☎ (01226) 766086
Tetley Bitter; guest beers H
Originally a moorland farm on the Pennine packhorse routes of the 1700s, Cubley Hall evolved into a fine Victorian gentleman's residence, then a children's home, when resident ghost Flora was said to appear at the bedside of sick children. Sympathetically refurbished under the present owners, original mosaic tiles, oak panelling, stained glass and elaborate ceiling mouldings create a rich ambience. The guest rooms are new. Family-friendly – ample grounds include a children's play area. The area is criss-crossed with footpaths. Good food. P

ROTHERHAM

Alma Tavern
27 Westgate
11-4, 7-11; 11-11 Fri & Sat; 12-4, 7-10.30 Sun
☎ (01709) 839857
Barnsley Bitter, IPA, seasonal beers; guest beers H
A welcome back to an old pub which has spent over 10 years in the real ale wilderness; acquired by Country Inns who have refurbished it well and provided six handpulls. The pub has a single, split-level room with bare polished floors; the bar area is decorated with hop bines. A warm welcome and a traditional atmosphere are guaranteed. Q (Central) ♣P

Blue Coat
The Crofts (behind new Town Hall)
11-11; 12-10.30 Sun
☎ (01709) 539500
Theakston Best Bitter; Wentworth Black Zac; guest beers H
Rotherham's second Wetherspoon's is hidden behind the town hall. Originally a school building, donated to the town by the Ancient Order of the Feoffees of Rotherham, the name of the pub is taken from the colour of the school uniform. Previously a keg-only pub/nightclub called Feoffees, it is handy for Rotherham's nightlife, but is also busy at lunchtime with the local business community. A family room is available for children's use until 6pm.
Q (Central)

Cat & Cabbage
Carlisle Street
11-3.45, 6-11; 12-10.30 Sun
☎ (01709) 365266
John Smith's Bitter, Magnet; guest beers H
This former keg nightspot has returned to the real ale scene with a vengeance, under the guidance of the current managers (who are CAMRA members). They put on three cask beers regularly, plus one or two other guest beers. This single-roomed pub offers a warm welcome to all, as well as lively entertainment and pool. An adjoining room is used for meetings. It was a recent CAMRA Pub of the Season winner. ♣P

Moulder's Rest
110-112 Masbrough Street (near Millmoor football ground)
4-11; 12-5, 7-11 Sat; 12-5, 7-10.30 Sun
☎ (01709) 560095
John Smith's Bitter; guest beer H
Built in the early 1800s, the Moulder's Rest occupies a prominent corner position, within easy reach of the town centre, and is well served by public transport. This traditional pub comprises a busy tap room, popular for pub games, and a spacious lounge. Good value food and accommodation is available. A regular in this Guide, it has twice been local CAMRA Pub of the Season. Evening meals are served Mon-Thu (6.30-8). (Central) ♣P

Rhinoceros
35-37 Bridgegate
11-11; 12-10.30 Sun
☎ (01709) 361422
Theakston Best Bitter; guest beers H
Open-plan, town-centre pub, close to All Saints Square. Offering good value beer and food as standard in Wetherspoon's pubs, this is a typical conversion from a furniture salesroom. No music, but conversation is appreciated here. Beer festivals are held regularly. The no-smoking area is extensive. Note the old pictures of Rotherham on the way to the toilets. Nearby is the 15th-century Chapel of Our Lady on the Bridge, one of only three in Britain.
Q (Central)

SHEFFIELD: *CENTRAL*

Banker's Draft
1-3 Market Place
11-11; 12-10.30 Sun
☎ (0114) 275 6609
Boddingtons Bitter; Courage Directors; Greene King Abbot; Taylor Landlord; Tetley Bitter; guest beers H
Taking its name from the fact that it occupies a former financial institution, this is a typically spacious Wetherspoon's conversion. A solid, unpretentious watering-hole between the High Street and the markets, it is the best bet for a good pint at a reasonable price in the very centre of the city. (Midland) (Castle Sq)

Devonshire Cat
49 Wellington Street
11.30-11; 12-10.30 Sun
☎ (0114) 279 6700 website: www.devonshirecat.co.uk
Bateman XB; Black Sheep Best Bitter; Fuller's London Pride; H **Kelham Island Pale Rider;** G **Theakston Old Peculier;** H **guest beers** H/G
Younger sibling to Sheffield's Fat Cat (see below) it combines a modern drinking experience with a wide range of real ale and cider and an impressive selection of bottled beer from Britain, Belgium, Germany and the rest of the world. A spacious, open-plan, air-conditioned corner of a new building, it is situated in the fashionable Devonshire quarter, cleverly mixing traditional pub values with a pavement café aesthetic. A beer club offers discounts and special events. (West St)

Fat Cat
23 Alma Street
12-3, 5.30-11; 12-11 Fri & Sat; 12-3, 7-10.30 Sun
☎ (0114) 249 4801 website: www.thefatcat.co.uk
Kelham Island Bitter, Pale Rider, seasonal beers; Taylor Landlord; H **guest beers** H/G
Set among the survivors of Sheffield's

cutlery industry in an area where factories are being converted into modern city apartments, the pub's wide range of beers includes a selection from the Kelham Island Brewery in the car park next door. It combines the warmth of a traditional pub with elements of modern thinking, including a no-smoking area and award-winning home-made food with an emphasis on vegetarian and vegan options (eve meals Mon-Fri).
⚭Q♨❀◑◐⊖(Shalesmoor) ♣P⚟⊓

Hogshead

25 Orchard Street, Orchard Square
⚙ 11-11; 11-10.30 Sun
☎ (0114) 275 5016
Boddingtons Bitter; Greene King Abbot, Old Speckled Hen; Hook Norton Old Hooky; Marston's Pedigree Ⓗ **guest beers** Ⓗ/Ⓖ
Refurbished as part of the initiative to revive city-centre commerce, the airy, pine-clad interior provides an alternative real ale drinking arena. Handily located at the heart of Sheffield, it provides a convenient stop for lunchtime or an after-work drink. The summer weather brings drinkers out on to the pleasant verandah, extending from the café-style lower level. It operates a 'try before you buy' policy.
❀◑◐♿⇶(Midland) ⊖(Cathedral)

Red Deer

18 Pitt Street
⚙ 11.30 (11 Fri)-11; 12-3, 7-11 Sat; 7.30-10.30 Sun
☎ (0114) 272 2890
website: www.red-deer-sheffield.co.uk
Black Sheep Best Bitter; Fuller's London Pride; Marston's Pedigree; Taylor Landlord; Wells Bombardier; guest beers Ⓗ
This traditional, cosy pub nestling among buildings of the red brick university, is set behind the bustling circuit drinkers' home strait. Popular with academics, students, and local workers, the real ale is complemented by a varied lunchtime menu of home-cooked favourites. Memorabilia from breweries old and new includes frosted windows from both Gilmour's and Tetley.
⚭◑⊖(West St/University)

Rutland Arms

86 Brown Street (near Midland Station)
⚙ 11.30-11; 12-10.30 Sun
☎ (0114) 272 9003
website: www.rutlandarms-sheffield.co.uk
Adnams Bitter; Barnsley Bitter; Black Sheep Best Bitter; Greene King Abbot; Marston's Pedigree; guest beers Ⓗ
Street-corner pub where the exterior shows off its Gilmour's heritage. Inside, the space has been well used, with the bar surveying an eclectically decorated room – Art Deco meets the East in a traditional English pub. In the city's cultural industries quarter, the customers are as varied as the decor. The walled garden provides a pleasant drinking space and has won numerous awards, as indeed has the pub itself from local CAMRA. Home-cooked evening meals are served Mon-Fri until 7.45pm.
❀◑◐⇶(Midland) ⊖P

Ship Inn

312 Shalesmoor
⚙ 12-3, 7 (6 Fri; 6.30 Sat)-11; 12-3, 6.30-10.30 Sun
☎ (0114) 281 2204
Hardys & Hansons Best Bitter Ⓗ
Behind a Tomlinson's tiled façade lies a spacious, high-ceilinged pub, with a satisfyingly snug and shadowy pool room. The traditional decor is dotted with items that bring a nautical flavour to this pub, one of a small selection of Kimberley houses in Sheffield. The calm, relaxed atmosphere is occasionally punctuated by the click of dominoes or the early CD juke box. Lunches are served on weekdays.
◑⊖(Shalesmoor) ⊓

Wetherspoon's

16-18 Cambridge Street
⚙ 11-11; 12-10.30 Sun
☎ (0114) 263 9500
Boddingtons Bitter; Courage Directors; Greene King Abbot; Hop Back Summer Lightning; Theakston Best Bitter Ⓗ
With an interesting mix of styles, ranging from 1970s retro to a stark, modern design, this is the ideal establishment for the real ale fan to work on converting trendy lager-drinking friends to the good stuff. A plaque by the door refers to this as the Corn Law Rhymer, however this is the only place where the pub is referred to by this political name rather than plain Wetherspoon's.
❀◑◐♿⇶(Midland) ⊖(City Hall)

SHEFFIELD: *EAST*

Carlton

563 Attercliffe Road
⚙ 11-3, 7 (7.30 Sat)-11; 11.30-3.30, 7.30-11 Fri; 7.30-10.30 Sun
☎ (0114) 244 3287
John Smith's Bitter, Magnet Ⓗ
Former Gilmour's pub, dating from 1862 with a deceptively small frontage. A free house for the last 13 years, a comfortable lounge around the main bar, leads to a pool room at the rear. Entertainment at weekends may include a singalong with the landlord at the organ or karaoke. Once at the heart of a busy shopping centre, it remains a community pub, redolent of a bygone era complete with a swear box. It is handy for the Don Valley Stadium.
Q⊖(Attercliffe/Woodbourne Rd) ♣⊓

Cocked Hat

75 Worksop Road
⚙ 11-11; 11-3, 7-11 Sat; 12-2, 7-10.30 Sun
☎ (0114) 244 8332
Marston's Bitter, Pedigree, seasonal beers Ⓗ
Corner pub, dating from the 1840s, completely refurbished in traditional style, when Marston's acquired it in the mid-1980s. Stall seating at the end of the bar is reserved for diners at lunchtime (Mon-Fri), while a raised area boasts one of Sheffield's few bar billiards tables. The bar area displays an impressive collection of bottled beers and pictures of old Attercliffe. Lying in the shadow of the Don Valley Stadium, it is patronised by sports personalities, and is handy for the Five Weirs Walk.
⚭Q❀◑⊖(Attercliffe) ♣✔

SHEFFIELD: *NORTH* ❄

Cask & Cutler

1 Henry Street, Shalesmoor
⚙ 12-2 (not Mon), 5.30-11; 12-11 Fri & Sat; 12-3, 7-10.30 Sun

☎ (0114) 249 2295
Beer range varies Ⓗ
Excellent, award-winning free house next to the Shalesmoor tram stop. 2001 Sheffield CAMRA Pub of the Year (third time) and runner-up in Yorkshire, for the second time, it continues to champion small independent breweries, offering eight varying guests, alongside a cider, a perry and a selection of Belgian bottled beers. The house brewery (Port Mahon) opened in 2001 in time for the popular annual November beer festival and at least one house beer is normally available.
♨Q❀⊖ (Shalesmoor) ●⚟▯

Gardener's Rest
105 Neepsend Lane
⏲ 3 (12 Fri & Sat)-11; 12-10.30 Sun
☎ (0114) 272 4978
Taylor Golden Best, Porter, Best Bitter, Landlord; Ⓗ **guest beers** Ⓗ/Ⓖ
Situated in the shadow of the closed Stones Brewery, this friendly free house is one of several along this stretch of the River Don. Up to six guest beers (two on gravity) join four Taylor beers and four draught Belgian beers. The main room houses a bar billiards table, displays local artwork and stages live music; the no-smoking dram shop features brewery memorabilia. The new conservatory opens on to the secluded riverside garden.
Q❀♿⊖ (Infirmary Rd) ♣●⚟▯

Hillsborough Hotel
54-58 Langsett Road
⏲ 4.30-11; closed Mon-Wed; 4.30-10.30 Sun
☎ (0114) 232 2100
website: www.hillsboroughhotel.com
Crown HPA, Loxley Gold, Stannington Stout; guest beers Ⓗ/Ⓖ
Opened in 1999 following refurbishment, this is a recent CAMRA/English Heritage design award-winner. A conservatory is the hotel's latest structural addition. Beers from the new five-barrel Crown Brewery in the basement have already won CAMRA awards at both local and regional levels and are supplemented by a range of guests. Up to 16 beers are available each weekend, eight on handpull and others in jugs direct from the cellar.
Q❀⇌⊖ (Langsett/Primrose View) ●P⚟

New Barrack Tavern
601 Penistone Road, Hillsborough
⏲ 12-11; 12-10.30 Sun
☎ (0114) 234 9148
Barnsley Bitter, IPA; Abbeydale Moonshine; John Smith's Magnet; guest beers Ⓗ
Three-roomed roadside pub, handy for Hillsborough on match days, with programmes and fanzines available. The reasonably-priced local beers add to the five ever-changing guests from small independent breweries. A varying guest cider is stocked, along with a large selection of bottled continental beers (seven on draught) and more than 70 malt whiskies. It hosts popular live music (Sat) and speciality food evenings (Wed); home-made food includes vegetarian options.
❀◐⊟⊖ (Bamforth St) ♣●⚟

SHEFFIELD: *SOUTH*

Archer Road Beer Stop (off-licence)
57 Archer Road (opp. Esporta sports club)
⏲ 11-10; 12-2, 6-10 Sun
☎ (0114) 255 1356
Beer range varies Ⓗ
Small real ale off-licence stocking up to four frequently changing draught beers from independent breweries, plus an extensive range of bottle-conditioned beers and world classics. A generation of real ale enthusiasts have enjoyed the carry-out service and helped the Beer Stop, formerly Small Beer, retain a continuous presence in this Guide. The management may have changed but the commitment to provide the best ales from around the world is as strong as ever.

Castle Inn
Twentywell Road, Bradway
⏲ 12 (11 Fri & Sat)-11; 12-10.30 Sun
☎ (0114) 236 2955
Black Sheep Best Bitter; Boddingtons Bitter; Fuller's London Pride; Taylor Landlord; Tetley Bitter; guest beer Ⓗ
Stone-fronted pub at the end of a row of Victorian cottages, probably built for the workers who constructed the Bradway railway tunnel. Consisting of a large lounge, with adjoining restaurant and a tap room, it is popular at mealtimes, although this is essentially a pub which serves food (Sun-Fri) rather than a restaurant serving beer. A smart, community pub where newcomers comment on the warmth of the welcome; it is a little hard to find, but worth seeking out.
❀◐◑⇌ (Dore) ♣P

Prince of Wales
150 Derbyshire Lane
⏲ 11-11; 12-10.30 Sun
☎ (0114) 255 0960
Flowers Original; Stones Bitter; guest beers Ⓗ
Traditional local where a single L-shaped lounge is split into small areas. A strong emphasis is placed on family entertainment, with special events arranged for children, usually held in the garden; this is home to Piggy, a huge English White who enjoys real ale. Guest beers come from the smaller independents, often local. Quizzes and karaoke nights are very popular, and the regulars are passionate about football.
❀♿♣P

Sheaf View
25 Gleadless Road
⏲ 12-11; 12-10.30 Sun
☎ (0114) 249 6455
Abbeydale Moonshine; Barnsley Bitter, IPA; John Smith's Magnet; guest beers Ⓗ
Unusually-shaped, 19th-century pub that experienced periods of dereliction in the 1990s. After extensive renovation it reopened in May 2000 as a free house, and is run on similar lines to the owner's award-winning New Barrack Tavern. Ales from local breweries are complemented by four constantly changing guests from independents, real cider and a good range of draught and bottled continental beers, all at realistic prices.
Q❀♿♣●P▯

White Lion
615 London Road
12-11; 12-10.30 Sun
☎ (0114) 255 1500
Marston's Pedigree; Tetley Bitter, Burton Ale; guest beers [H]
Popular pub in the Heeley Bottom area, formerly a Tetley house, it now forms part of the small Just Williams group, which has a strong commitment to real ale and good cellar management. Drinkers can choose between the no-smoking lounge, two delightful snugs or the other rooms, that tend to be livelier with music and games. Note the original tiled corridor and windows with misspelt Windsor Ales. This is, sadly, one of the few pubs of real character in Sheffield. ❀♣●⊁✔

SHEFFIELD: WEST

Ball Inn
171 Crookes
11-11; 12-10.30 Sun
☎ (0114) 266 1211
Boddingtons Bitter; Castle Eden Ale; Flowers Original; Marston's Pedigree; guest beers [H]
Large, suburban pub with a bay-windowed frontage and entrance porch, approached across a cobbled forecourt with outdoor seating. Inside, two rooms are in typical ale house style of bare floorboards, exposed brick walls and wood panelling. To the rear is a further seating area and a games room with two pool tables. Up to five guest ales mostly come from established regional brewers. A popular community pub, it attracts the local student population. ❀◐♣●

Noah's Ark
94 Crookes
12 (11 Sat)-11; 12-10.30 Sun
☎ (0114) 266 3300
Boddingtons Bitter; Castle Eden Ale; Flowers IPA; John Smith's Magnet; Tetley Bitter; guest beers [H]
Busy, community pub in a popular student area. Extended a couple of years ago to provide various seating areas around a central bar, its welcoming decor features dark wood, exposed brickwork, and old pictures of Crookes. It was one of the first Whitbread pubs in the city to reintroduce real ale (in the 1980s). It now stocks at least two guests, mainly from regional brewers. Although having a pool table and TV, it is still more of a pub for conversation. Evening meals are served 5-7. ❀◐◑♣

Porter Brook
565 Ecclesall Road
11-11; 12-10.30 Sun
☎ (0114) 266 5765
Boddingtons Bitter; Greene King Abbot; Wadworth 6X; guest beers [H]
Five-year-old Hogshead pub, converted from a house on the banks of the River Porter. Quickly established as the leading real ale venue on the Ecclesall Road scene, it offers up to 10 cask beers, including guests from established regional brewers and local micros. Furnished in typical ale house style with bare floorboards and exposed brickwork, it attracts a wide-ranging clientele and can be crowded, especially weekend evenings. Meals are served all day until 9pm. ❀◐◑⊁

Sportsman
569 Redmires Road
11.30-3, 5-11; 11.30-11 Fri & Sat; 12-3, 5-10.30 Sun
☎ (0114) 230 1935
John Smith's Bitter; Taylor Landlord; Tetley Bitter [H]
One of the highest pubs in Sheffield on the edge of the city, affording fine views over the Rivelin Valley. This one-roomed pub comprises an L-shaped lounge around a central bar. Converted from a farmhouse over 100 years ago to serve the workers building the nearby Redmires Reservoir, it retains a country pub atmosphere, although just a 20-minute bus ride from the city centre. It hosts a popular quiz (Tue) and a local pianist plays on Thursday. Meals are served Tue-Sat (eve meals 6-8). Q❀◐◑▲P⊁

Star & Garter
82-84 Winter Street
11-11; 12-10.30 Sun
☎ (0114) 272 0694
Tetley Bitter; Greene King Abbot; guest beer [H]
Open-plan corner pub in the shadow of the university arts tower. The central bar has a pool table at one end and darts at the other. Busy at lunchtime and early evening with staff and students from the university and St George's Hospital, later it reverts to a traditional community pub with thriving

INN BRIEF

WEST

Old Grindstone
3 Crookes
11-11; 12-10.30 Sun
(0114) 2366 0322
Tetley Bitter; Wadworth 6X; guest beers [H]
Busy, spacious corner pub in a student area. A raised games area has snooker. Cask Marque accredited.

SPROTBROUGH

Ivanhoe Hotel
Melton Road
11-11; 12-10.30 Sun
(01302) 853130
Samuel Smith OBB [H]
Popular pub next to the village cricket pitch. No food Sun eve. Conservatory doubles as a family room.

STAINTON

Three Tuns
Stainton Lane
11.30-3, 5-11; 12-3.30, 7-10.30 Sun
(01709) 812775
Barnsley Bitter; John Smith's Bitter, Magnet; Wentworth Best Bitter [H]
Welcoming village local with two dining areas serving high quality, home-cooked food.

THORPE HESLEY

Mason's Arms
Thorpe Street
12-3, 5.45-11; 12-3, 7-10.30 Sun
(0114) 246 8079
John Smith's Bitter; Theakston Best Bitter, Cool Cask, Old Peculier; guest beer [H]
Once owned by Tennant Bros' of Sheffield; good beer and good food in a quiet village.

TICKHILL

Carpenter's Arms
Westgate
12-3, 6-11; 12-5, 7-10.30 Sun
(01302) 742839
Jennings Cumberland Ale; John Smith's Bitter; Wells Bombardier [H]
Traditional village pub with family room, conservatory and award-winning garden. Meals available.

WHISTON

Sitwell Arms
Pleasley Road (A618)
12-11; 12-10.30 Sun
(01709) 377003
Tetley Bitter; guest beers [H]
Friendly village local, originally a farm and ale house, centuries old in parts. Wheelchair access, food, garden.

games teams and popular quiz nights (Thu and Sun). A large-screen TV is used for important football matches. Note the etched windows. The guest beer changes weekly.

Walkley Cottage
46 Bole Hill Road
11-11; 12-10.30 Sun
(0114) 234 4968
Black Sheep Best Bitter; Taylor Landlord; Tetley Bitter; guest beers H
Large, suburban roadhouse with two rooms; the good-sized tap room has a snooker table and large-screen TV. The comfortable L-shaped lounge has a food servery and no-smoking area at mealtimes. Built for Gilmour's between the wars with a large car park, the extensive garden affords good views over the Rivelin Valley. Up to four guest beers are sourced from regional brewers and local micros. This lively local stages a popular quiz (Thu). Evening meals are served 6-8 (not Sun). P

SILKSTONE

Silkstone Lodge
Cone Lane (just off A628, towards Silkstone Common)
6.30-midnight; 12-midnight Sat; 12-midnight Sun
(01226) 791094
John Smith's Bitter; Wentworth WPA (occasional), **Best Bitter, Black Zac** H
Large, comfortable, chalet-style former working men's club in the village of Silkstone, staging live music events, regular jazz and quizzes. The stone interior has several bar areas and a large function room. The full-sized snooker table is used for regular matches as is the crown green outside. Excellent home-cooked Sunday lunches are served. There is a chance of meeting Zac, the black labrador, who has a real ale named after him!
Q (Silkstone Common) P

SOUTH ANSTON

Loyal Trooper
34 Sheffield Road (off A57, 3 miles from M1 jct 31)
12-3, 6-11; 12-11 Sat; 12-3, 7-10.30 Sun
(01909) 562203
Taylor Landlord; Tetley Bitter; guest beers H
Village local in the old part of Anston, reputedly so-named after being used to house soldiers. Partly dating back to 1690, it comprises three rooms: public bar, snug and lounge (known as the Dragoons Room). A function room upstairs caters for local groups, including Anston folk club. Children are welcome for meals; good value, home-cooked food is served Mon-Thu (6-8 eves). Anston Stones Nature Reserve and Lindrick golf course are close by. Local CAMRA Pub of the Year 2002.
Q P

STRINES

Strines Inn
Bradfield Dale, Bradfield (signed 2 miles from A57) OS222906
10.30-11; (10.30-3, 6-11 winter); 12-10.30 (12-3, 6-10.30 winter) Sun
(0144) 285 1247
website: www.thestrinesinn.freeserve.co.uk
Beer range varies H
Originally a manor house, built in 1275, most of the current building dates from the 1550s. An inn since 1771 and although never owned by a brewery, it became a genuine free house in 2002. The beer range should reflect this new-found freedom. An isolated pub, in walking country, its three drinking areas include a no-smoking room. Coffee Pub of the Year runner-up 2002, award-winning home-made meals are served all day in summer (phone for other times). P

THORNE

Canal Tavern
South Parade (A614, by flyover bridge)
11.30-3, 5.30-11; 11.30-11 Fri & Sat; 12-10.30 Sun
(01405) 813688
Draught Bass; John Smith's Bitter; Tetley Bitter; Wells Bombardier; guest beer H
Dating back to 1822, the hostelry stands on the Stainforth & Keadby Canal, which is very popular with boaters. Pictures of Thorne and maps of its windmills line the walls, and there are over 50 items on the menu to line your stomach walls. Dave and Dawn Merrington run this true free house where the array of pump clips behind the bar signals the variety of previous guest beers. (South) P

THURLSTONE

Huntsman
136 Manchester Road (A628)
6 (12 Fri & Sat)-11; 12-10.30 Sun
(01226) 764892
website: www.pub-explorer.com/thehuntsman
Taylor Landlord; guest beers H
The plain exterior of this Clark's terraced pub belies the quality inside, where something is bound to delight you. It could be the real fires, the excellent home-cooked food, or the variety of guest beers, with six handpumps in regular use and many more on the pub's beer festival weekends. One guest beer is always from Clark's and there is a house ale. Meals are served 6-8.30, all day Fri and Sat (until 8.30), and until 4pm Sun.

TICKHILL

Scarbrough Arms
Sunderland Street
11-3, 6-11; 12-3, 7-10.30 Sun
(01302) 742977
Greene King Abbot; John Smith's Bitter, Magnet; guest beers H
A constant Guide entry since 1990, this excellent three-roomed, stone pub has won several local CAMRA awards, including Doncaster Pub of the Year 1997. Originally a farm, the building dates back to the 16th century, though structural changes have inevitably taken place over the years. The pub's wonderfully cosy, timber-panelled snug is a delight. Other attractions include its two rotating guest beers, oversized lined glasses and interesting food (served Tue-Sat). Q P

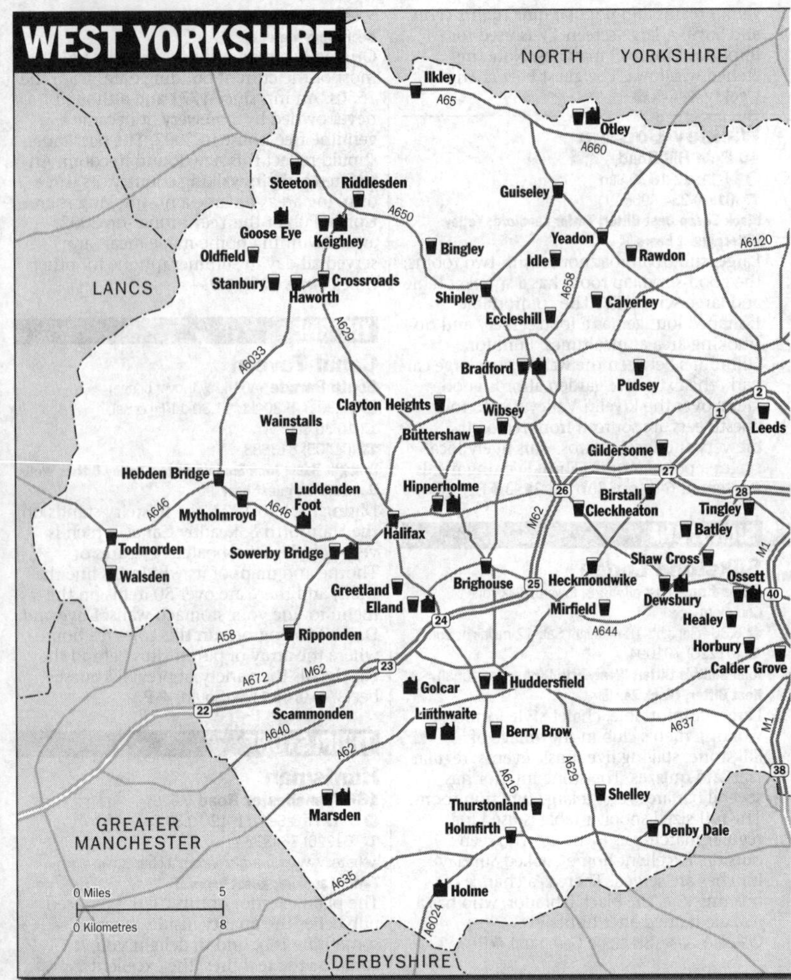

ULLEY

Royal Oak

12 Turnshaw Road (off A618, near M1 jct 31)
11-3, 6-11; 11-3, 6-10.30 Sun
(0114) 287 2464
Samuel Smith OBB H

Parts of this pub are over 300 years old, but later extensions fit in with its olde-worlde charm. Set in a picturesque, rural village, the beamed interior is hung with brasses and saddles, reflecting local horse-riding and farming activities. Popular with walkers and diners, it has extensive gardens and good children's facilities both outside and in the family room. Close to Ulley Reservoir Country Park (walking and water sports), it serves the only real Sam Smith's in the area and excellent home-cooked food.

WATH UPON DEARNE

Church House

Montgomery Square
11-11; 11-10.30 Sun
(01709) 875918
Courage Directors; Theakston Best Bitter; guest beers H

Situated in the centre of Wath upon Dearne, this impressive building was originally built for the local landowner in the 1870s. The interior is now fully air-conditioned and thoroughly modern. The single bar serves two floors and in typical Wetherspoon's fashion, the toilets are upstairs. There is always a cask beer for sale at the grand price of 99p, and also beers from the local Wentworth Brewery.
Q P

WENTWORTH

George & Dragon

85 Main Street
11 (10 Sat)-11; 10-10.30 Sun
(01226) 742440
Stones Bitter; Taylor Landlord; Wentworth WPA; guest beers H

Very popular, traditional pub at the heart of a conservation village. The main feature of the pub is the stone floor; the earliest part of the building dates from the 16th century. A new addition is the steak and seafood restaurant (open Wed-Sun eves) in the Hoober Room upstairs. Guest beers are sourced from micro-

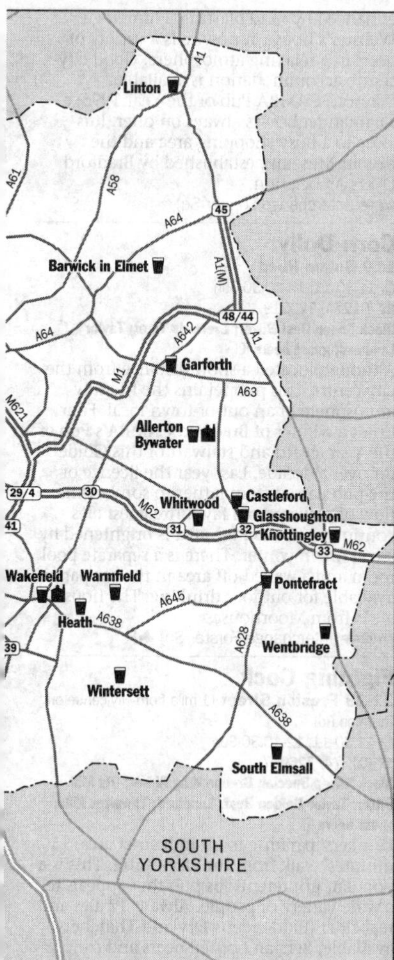

breweries, with always two beers from Wentworth. A recent CAMRA Rotherham Pub of the Year, it is easily accessible by public transport.
⛫Q❀◐♣●P

WHISTON ❊

Golden Ball

7 Turner Lane (off A618, 1½ miles from M1 jct 33)
⏲ 12-11; 12-10.30 Sun
☎ (01709) 726911
Draught Bass; Stones Bitter; Taylor Landlord; guest beers Ⓗ
Partly dating back 500 years, this former coaching inn, is renowned for its range of cask beers, but prices can be high. Extended during the 1970s and '80s, using traditional materials to retain its olde-worlde character, the pub is replete with exposed beams and brasses. In a conservation area close to the village dyke and an historic 13th-century thatched manorial barn, this frequent local CAMRA Pub of the Season is a consistent Guide entry. A large garden in a picturesque village and good food are added attractions.
⛫❀◐♣P⊬

WORTLEY

Wortley Arms

Halifax Road (A629)
⏲ 12-11; 12-10.30 Sun
☎ (0114) 288 2245
Abbeydale Absolution; Archers Golden; Barnsley Bitter; Taylor Dark Mild, Landlord; Theakston Old Peculier Ⓗ
Cosy, rambling, multi-roomed old village hostelry, oozing with understated character and charm, boasting an enormous inglenook, wood panelling, and exposed stonework, inlaid with a coat of arms. It stocks a range of malt whiskies and bottled Belgian beers. The house beer is light and refreshing, but its origin is a closely-guarded secret. Half a mile (uphill) from the Trans-Pennine Trail, in excellent walking country, it is served by buses from Penistone and Sheffield. ⛫Q⛮❀⇔◐⊟P⊬

Yorkshire (West)

ALLERTON BYWATER

Boat Inn

Boat Lane
⏲ 11.45-3.30, 6-11; 11.45-11 Sat & summer; 12-10.30 Sun
☎ (01977) 552216 website: www.boatpub.co.uk
Boat Man in the Boat, seasonal beers; Taylor Landlord; Tetley Bitter Ⓗ
This pub has an attractive setting beside the River Aire. It is run by Brian Lockwood, former Great Britain Rugby League captain, note the rugby mementos decorating the main bar. In addition to a dining area and family room there is an extensive garden with a children's play area. The award-winning Boat Brewery is located behind the pub. Booking for meals is advised.
⛮❀◐♿▲P

BARWICK IN ELMET

New Inn

17 Main Street
⏲ 12-11; 12-3, 7-10.30 Sun
☎ (0113) 281 2289
John Smith's Bitter; guest beer Ⓗ
This former cottage tavern lies in what was once the kingdom of Elmet. Over 250 years old, it was a stopover on the run to York. It was an ale house until 1969 when it was granted a spirit licence. The entrance leads into a cosy snug with a low ceiling and beams and a bar, which also serves the tiny tap room. A comfortable separate room makes up the accommodation. The guest beer is often from a Yorkshire micro-brewery. No lunchtime meals are served on Sat. Q◐⊟♣

BERRY BROW, HUDDERSFIELD

Berry Brow Liberal Club

6 Parkgate (A616, 2 miles S of Huddersfield)
⏲ 12-2 (not Tue & Thu), 8-11; 12-11 Sat in football season; 12-2, 8-10.30 Sun
☎ (01484) 662549
John Smith's Bitter; guest beers Ⓗ
Two guest beers from independent brewers are always available at this compact CIU-affiliated village club. There are three distinct drinking areas served from an L-shaped bar. Photographs of the area dating from the early 20th century adorn the walls.

Two snooker tables are to be found on the first floor. Parking may be difficult, but the village is well served by public transport. ⇌♣

BINGLEY

Brown Cow

Ireland Bridge (over the river from Bingley church)
✪ 12-3, 5-11; 12-11 Sat; 12-10.30 Sun
☎ (01274) 564345
Taylor Golden Best, Best Bitter, Landlord; guest beers Ⓗ
Extensively refurbished in 2001 following severe flooding, this riverside pub is popular for its quality food and range of beers. Up to five Timothy Taylor beers are complemented by varied guests often from local breweries. Quiz nights and Irish music feature during the week. Opening hours may be extended during the summer months. ⚔❀◖◗♿⇌P

Myrtle Grove

141 Main Street
✪ 11-11; 12-10.30 Sun
☎ (01274) 564681
Black Sheep Special; Greene King Abbot; Hop Back Summer Lightning; Shepherd Neame Spitfire; Taylor Landlord; guest beers Ⓗ
Busy recent pub conversion on the main road between Bradford and Keighley. Originally a cinema, then a supermarket before Wetherspoon's turned the empty premises into a popular one-roomed venue for all ages. Ideally placed for both trains and buses, this pub features a large glass frontage, raised no-smoking area and a number of small booths. It often has eight or more real ales on tap. Myrtle Park and Bingley Theatre are both nearby.
Q◖◗♿⇌⊬✔

BIRSTALL

Black Bull

5 Kirkgate (off A652, near A643)
✪ 12-11; 12-3.30, 7-10.30 Sun
☎ (01274) 873039
Boddingtons Bitter; Whitbread Trophy Bitter; guest beer Ⓗ
Dating from the 17th century, this inn stands opposite St Peter's Church at the heart of a large parish. The pub became the natural place for functions such as auctions, elections and as a magistrates' court (the last trial was held in 1839). The courtroom upstairs retains the wood panelling, magistrate's box and prisoner's dock, while the snug below is popular for small meetings or a quiet drink. Addlestone's cloudy cider is on handpull. Local CAMRA Pub of the Year 2001. Evening meals are served Tue-Sat (6-9) – advisable to book at weekends. ❀◖◗●P

BRADFORD ❊

Castle Hotel

20 Grattan Road (off Westgate)
✪ 11.30-11; closed Sun
☎ (01274) 393166
website: www.thecastlehotel.britain-uk.com
Banks's Bitter; Barnsley Bitter; Fuller's ESB; guest beers Ⓗ
This imposing stone pub was built in 1898 complete with castellated battlements enhanced by sand blasting. Formerly a Webster's house, it now sells a variety of beers in a relaxing atmosphere. Good city-centre accommodation is available. Bradford CAMRA Pub of the Year 1995; a Salamander beer is always on offer. It is close to a busy shopping area and the Colour Museum, established by Bradford Dyers Association.
⇌(Interchange/Forster Sq)

Corn Dolly

110 Bolton Road
✪ 11.30-11; 12-10.30 Sun
☎ (01274) 720219
Black Sheep Best Bitter; Everards Tiger; Taylor Landlord; guest beers Ⓗ
Although located a short distance from the city centre, this pub retains the friendly atmosphere of an out-of-town local. Four times a winner of Bradford CAMRA's Pub of the Year award and stalwart of this Guide for over a decade. Last year the licence of the pub passed from father to son but the flow of new and old favourite guest ales continues. The lounge area is brightened by a real fire in winter. There is a separate pool room and a walled-off area in the car park is available for outdoor drinking. The house ale is from Moorhouses.
⚔❀⇌(Interchange/Forster Sq) ♣P

Fighting Cock

21-23 Preston Street (1 mile from city centre off Thornton Rd)
✪ 11.30-11; 12-10.30 Sun
☎ (01274) 726907
Black Sheep Special; Greene King Abbot; Old Mill Bitter; Taylor Golden Best, Landlord; Thwaites Mild; guest beers Ⓗ
Drinkers' paradise in an industrial area, 15 minutes' walk from the city centre. This is a popular, unpretentious pub that appeals to a wide variety of people. Always 12 ales and real cider (Biddendens Dry and Thatchers) available, Belgian bottled beers and fruit wines are also stocked. The pub divides into three areas, so it is possible to avoid the crush around the bar. Sandwiches and hot lunches are served weekdays (12-2.30) and hot meals are offered all day Saturday.
⚔◖♣●

Goldsborough

118 Bolton Road
✪ 11.30-11; 12-10.30 Sun
☎ (01274) 740138
Old Mill Bitter; Taylor Landlord; Tetley Bitter; guest beers Ⓗ
Pleasant pub on the fringe of the city centre, good transport links are close by. A pool table, big-screen TV and juke box provide entertainment but do not dominate the L-shaped bar. Large sofas, complete with low-level tables ensure a comfortable visit. The strong Bradford City FC connection means the pub is busy at times. No food is served on Sun. There is a patio for outdoor drinking. ❀◖⇌(Interchange/Forster Sq) P

Haigy's

31 Lumb Lane
✪ 5 (12 Fri & Sat)-1am; closed Sun
☎ (01274) 731644
Black Sheep Best Bitter; Greene King Abbot; Tetley Bitter; guest beers Ⓗ
This pub is handy for Valley Parade, the

home of Bradford City FC and temporary ground of Bradford Bulls Rugby League Club. It makes up one of the corners of Westgate's real ale golden triangle, the others being the Melborn Hotel and New Beehive Inn. The pub has areas to suit most customers: a comfortable lounge, large pool room and a disco with an unusual feature – a video wall. The range of quality ales includes one Ossett beer, usually on tap.
❀⇌(Interchange/Forster Sq) ♣P

Melborn Hotel

104 White Abbey Road (B6144, 1/2 mile from city centre)
⏲ 12 (4 Wed-Fri)-11; 12-10.30 Sun
☎ (01274) 726867
Tetley Bitter; guest beers Ⓗ
Built in 1935 for the Melbourne Brewery, this genuine free house is gradually being restored to its former glory by an owner dedicated to traditional standards and quality ale. Look out for Melbourne breweriana in glass cases. Busy in the evening, it has a large traditional tap room and even larger music room featuring live folk and blues music six nights a week. The guest beers are exclusively from Yorkshire and northern small brewers.
❀⇆⊟⇌(Forster Sq) P

New Beehive Inn ☆

171 Westgate (B6144)
⏲ 12-11 (2am Fri & Sat); closed lunch, 6-10.30 Sun
☎ (01274) 721784
Kelham Island Bitter; Taylor Landlord; guest beers Ⓗ
This multi-roomed, Edwardian gaslit free house was built in 1901. The genuine interior comprises a drinking hallway and three original rooms with wood panelling. The front bar has 12 handpumps, a collection of toby jugs and an old photograph of the pub above the fireplace. A variety of live music is performed in the cellar bar on Fridays and some Saturdays. Stonehouse cider is available and guest beers include Salamander and Lloyds.
⛰❀⇆⊟⇌(Forster Sq) ♣●P

Queen Hotel

863 Thornton Road, Fairweather Green (B6145)
⏲ 12-11; 12-10.30 Sun
☎ (01274) 542898
Beer range varies Ⓗ
Originally a desirable private house, it was converted to a pub in the early 1900s. Now a busy local, this two-roomed free house with local stone and slate flooring has plenty of character. It was Bradford CAMRA Pub of the Year 1997, under previous ownership, but the present licensees have kept up the tradition of serving a wide range of ever-changing guest ales. Regulars include Taylor, Moorhouses, Goose Eye and Salamander. ⛰❀◑◗♣P

Sir Titus Salt

Windsor Baths, Morley Street (by Alhambra Theatre)
⏲ 11-11; 12-10.30 Sun
☎ (01274) 732853
Boddingtons Bitter; Shepherd Neame Spitfire; Taylor Landlord; Theakston Best Bitter; guest beers Ⓗ
This spacious Wetherspoon's conversion has one long bar. It is very popular with a mixed variety of customers, ranging from mature couples to students from the nearby university and colleges. There is upstairs seating which overlooks most of the pub area. An application for a children's certificate is underway. Often very busy on Friday and Saturday nights as the pub is well placed for theatregoers and clubbers. Weston's Old Rosie cider is stocked. A very small patio is available for summer drinking. Q❀◑◗♿⇌(Interchange) ●⊬✓

BRIGHOUSE

Crown

6 Lightcliffe Road, Waring Green (off A644)
⏲ 11-11; 12-10.30 Sun
☎ (01484) 715436
Courage Directors; Tetley Bitter; Theakston Mild Ⓗ
In an area of stone terraces up the hill from the town centre, is this welcoming pub with three comfortable lounge areas and a separate games room. A TV dominates the bar area but not the whole pub. There are displays of china decorating the walls. Enjoy the tunes from the piano player every Saturday night. ♣P

Globe

66 Rastrick Common, Rastrick
⏲ 11.45-11; 12-10.30 Sun
☎ (01484) 713169
Tetley Bitter; Wells Bombardier Ⓗ
Only five minutes' walk from the town centre, this roadside inn is popular with all sections of the community. There are two rooms: the main bar plus a separate restaurant (with no-smoking area). Good value, home-cooked meals are served in both rooms (not available Mon eve). The pleasant conservatory overlooks the garden.
⛰❀◑◗⇌♣P

Red Rooster

123 Elland Road, Brookfoot (A6025)
⏲ 5 (4 Fri)-11; 12-11 Sat; 12-10.30 Sun
☎ (01484) 713737
Black Sheep Best Bitter; Rooster's Yankee; guest beers Ⓗ

INDEPENDENT BREWERIES

Anglo Dutch Dewsbury
Boat Allerton Bywater
Briscoe's Otley
Clark's Wakefield
Eastwood & Sanders Elland
Egyptian Dewsbury
Fernandes Wakefield
Golcar Golcar
Goose Eye Keighley
Halifax Hipperholme
Linfit Linthwaite
Ossett Ossett
Rat & Ratchet Huddersfield
Red Lion Ossett
Riverhead Marsden
Ryburn Sowerby Bridge
Salamander Bradford
Taylor Keighley
Tigertops Wakefield
Turkey Goose Eye
Upper Agbrigg Holme
West Yorkshire Luddenden Foot

Small, stone-built pub on the inside of a sharp bend on the A6025 road out of Brighouse. It has been opened out but the former four-roomed layout is apparent. Popular with real ale drinkers, bikers and cyclists, it stocks six changing guest beers and a traditional cider from Saxon. Two-pint glasses are available for particularly thirsty customers (or the Cropton drinker). There is a small patio garden. ❀♣♣P

BUTTERSHAW

Beehive Inn
583 Halifax Road
⏲ 11-11; 12-10.30 Sun
☎ (01274) 678550
Ansells Best Bitter; Tetley Bitter; guest beers 🄷
Lively, homely local where children are welcome until 7.30pm. A pool table dominates the side room and there is a large TV screen for sporting events in the lounge. Guest beers change weekly, many are from local breweries such as Salamander, Daleside and Taylor. Slaters (Eccleshall) from Staffordshire is also a regular. Entertainment includes a disco held every Friday and karaoke on Saturday.
♿♣

CALDER GROVE

Navigation
Broad Cut Road (400 yds off Denby Dale road over canal bridge)
⏲ 12-11; 12-10.30 Sun
☎ (01924) 274361
Eastwood & Sanders Bargee, Best Bitter, Nettlethrasher; Tetley Bitter 🄷
An island is the unusual setting for this two-roomed pub. The River Calder flows on one side and the Aire and Calder Navigation Canal on the other. This makes it a popular venue for boaters, particularly in the summer months. The pub has a quiet lounge where no children are allowed. There is, however, a separate no-smoking family room with a soft play adventure playground. Children are also well catered for in the large garden with its excellent playground facilities.
♨Q♉❀◐◑♣P⚟

CALVERLEY

Thornhill Arms
18 Town Gate
⏲ 11-11; 12-10.30 Sun
☎ (0113) 256 5492
Courage Directors; John Smith's Bitter; Theakston Cool Cask; guest beers 🄷
There has been a building on this site since the 17th century. The current building, of traditional Yorkshire stone, is a former coaching inn close to the church, an underground passage reputedly links the two. This is a smart pub in a commuter village between Leeds and Bradford. Once multi-roomed, it has been opened out but retains several distinct drinking areas. It is plushly decorated and some of the comfy settles retain their bell pushes (non-functional). The car park entrance/exit is at an acute angle to a busy main road. No evening meals are served Sat-Mon.
❀◐◑♿♣P

CASTLEFORD ❄

Glassblower
15 Bank Street (near jcts 31 and 32 of M62)
⏲ 11-11; 12-10.30 Sun
☎ (01977) 520390
Greene King Abbot; Hop Back Summer Lightning; Shepherd Neame Spitfire; Taylor Landlord; Theakston Best Bitter; guest beers 🄷
Converted from an old post office, the Glassblower is a large, bustling town pub, with an extensive beer garden at the rear and a children's certificate. It has a comfortable interior, with pictures of the town's history displayed. In addition to the regular cask ales, a good range of six to eight rotating guests from around the country are stocked. Bi-annual beer festivals take place in the spring and at Hallowe'en.
Q❀◐◑♿⇌⚟●

CLAYTON HEIGHTS

Old Dolphin
192 Highgate Road (A647, Bradford side of Queensbury)
⏲ 12-11; 12-3.30, 5.30-11 Mon, Tue & Thu; 12-10.30 Sun

INN BRIEF

BATLEY

Wilton Arms
4 Commercial Street
11-11; 12-10.30 Sun
(01924) 479996
Stones Bitter; Tetley Bitter; guest beer (occasional) 🄷
Capture Rugby League history with memorabilia in the tap room where the pub's active sporting teams socialise. Home-made food is available Mon-Sat.

BRADFORD

Old Bank
69 Market Street
11-11; 12-10.30 Sun
(01274) 743680
Boddingtons Bitter; Castle Eden Ale; Marston's Pedigree; Tetley Bitter; guest beers 🄷
Barclays Bank conversion in city centre with a two-level layout. Large selection of real ales served. Near Interchange Station.

Steve Biko Bar
D floor, Richmond Building, Richmond Road
11 (7 Sat)-11; 7-10.30 Sun
(01274) 233257
Courage Directors; John Smith's Bitter; Theakston Cool Cask, XB, Old Peculier; guest beers 🄷
University bar open to general public. Four guest beers and snacks are available; it can be noisy.

CASTLEFORD

Early Bath
Wheldon Road
7-11 (all day on match days); 12-3, 7-11 Sun
(01977) 518389
Daleside Old Legover; John Smith's Bitter; Samuel Smith OBB 🄷
Friendly, two-roomed local displaying wealth of Rugby League memorabilia. Amazingly cheap beer and incredible Art Deco function room.

GILDERSOME

Old Griffin Head
Branch Road
11.30-3, 5.30-11; 11-11 Fri & Sat; 12-10.30 Sun
(0113) 253 3159
Boddingtons Bitter; Castle Eden Ale; Taylor Landlord; Whitbread Trophy Bitter 🄷
Village local with a brisk lunchtime food trade. Has a traditional country pub feel with low beams.

HALIFAX

Sportsman Inn
Bradford Old Road, Swalesmoor
12-2.30, 6-11 (midnight Fri); 12-midnight Sat; 12-10.30 Sun
(01422) 367000
Taylor Landlord; Tetley Bitter; Theakston Old Peculier; guest beer 🄷
Hilltop pub with large family room, dry ski slope, karting, virtual golf and adventure playground. No food Mon. Fine views.

☎ (01274) 882202
Beer range varies Ⓗ
This 300-year-old coaching inn offers a welcoming atmosphere. The house beer (Fat Boy Bitter) is from Goose Eye Brewery and regular guest beers include Kelham Island, Durham, Phoenix, Salamander and Ossett. A good selection of meals and sandwiches are served including vegetarian and diabetic choices. The garden has a play area and barbecue facilities. The pub has witnessed some momentous events: Cromwell stayed here during the Civil War; John Foster, a local mill owner, performed here, creating the world-renowned Black Dyke Mills Band; and the 'cat's eye' was invented in the pub by Percy Shaw. ⌂❀◐◑P

CLECKHEATON

Marsh

28 Bradford Road (A638)
✪ 12-3 (4 Sat), 7-11; 10-5, 7-11 Fri; 12-5, 7-10.30 Sun
☎ (01274) 872104
Old Mill Mild, Bitter, Bullion, seasonal beer Ⓗ
All ages are drawn to this triangular-shaped ex-Tetley pub refurbished in Old Mill's house style. The popular games room has exposed brickwork decorated with embedded bottles. The remodelled lounge has a dais and some attractive woodwork and glass. It is a focal point for the local community who relax with dominoes, darts and pool or the Wednesday quiz, or sit and take in the convivial atmosphere. Located out of the town centre, the bus station is nearby. There are picnic benches in the yard for outdoor drinking. ❀♣P

CROSSROADS

Quarry House Inn

Bingley Road, Lees Moor OS054380
✪ 12-3, 7-11; 12-3, 7-10.30 Sun
☎ (01535) 642239
Taylor Golden Best, Landlord; Tetley Bitter Ⓗ
A converted farmhouse, this family-run pub is set in open countryside and benefits from extensive views. The bar is a former pulpit, set in small, cosy surroundings. Twice local CAMRA Pub of the Season, it welcomes families at all times; coaches are accommodated by appointment. The restaurant provides a 'global' menu, with excellent soups; the mixed grill is a speciality (Wed eve). Meals reflect seasonal availability, including game (booking is advisable Sun lunch). ❀◐◑♿▲P

DENBY DALE

Dunkirk Inn

231 Barnsley Road (A635, midway between Holmfirth and Barnsley)
✪ 12-3 (not Mon, or winter Tue & Wed), 5.30-11; 12-11 Sat; 12-10.30 Sun
☎ (01484) 862646 website: www.dunkirkinn.co.uk
Taylor Landlord; Tetley Bitter; Theakston Cool Cask; guest beers Ⓗ
A pleasantly-situated rural pub that is popular with ramblers and cyclists. Formerly three separate rooms now linked together: a restaurant serves good home-made fare. There is a well-proportioned lounge, plus a games room with pool table. An eccentric collection of branded advertising mugs dotted around provides a focal talking point. Guest beers (often five at once) are selected from a variety of breweries. There is limited public transport from Huddersfield (bus routes 236 and 237). ⌂❀◐◑♣P

DEWSBURY

Leggers Inn

Robinson's Boatyard, Savile Town Wharf, Mill Street East (off B6409, S of town centre)
✪ 11.30-11; 12-10.30 Sun
☎ (01924) 502846
Everards Tiger; guest beers Ⓗ
Idiosyncratic upstairs bar with very low beams, adorned with interesting objects. Once the hayloft of the stables where horses rested after towing barges along the Calder and Hebble Navigation Canal, it still overlooks a busy canal basin, now with residential moorings and a trip boat. The Egyptian (formerly Sunset) Brewery brews downstairs and two of its beers are on tap, with four other ales including one from Rooster's. Good value snacks and sandwiches are available all day. It is worth

---

HAWORTH

Fleece Inn
67 Main Street
12-11; 12-10.30 Sun
(01535) 642172
Taylor Golden Best, Best Bitter, Landlord, Ram Tam Ⓗ
Popular with locals and visitors, this former coaching inn has a stone-flagged bar and three distinct drinking areas.

HUDDERSFIELD

Dusty Miller
2 Gilead Road, Longwood
5 (12 Sat)-11; 12-10.30 Sun
(01484) 651763
Eastwood & Sanders Best Bitter; Taylor Best Bitter, Landlord; Tetley Bitter; guest beers Ⓗ
Friendly, multi-roomed free house with two pool rooms. Two rotating guest beers served.

IDLE

New Inn
58 High Street
12-11; 12-10.30 Sun
(01274) 613136
Taylor Landlord; Tetley Mild, Bitter Ⓗ
At top of aptly-named street. Food served lunchtimes. Big-screen TV for Sky Sports.

KEIGHLEY

Albert
Bridge Street
11-11; 12-10.30 Sun
(01535) 602306
Taylor Golden Best, Best Bitter, Landlord Ⓗ
Large town-centre pub; the imposing interior features a horseshoe bar and two distinct seating areas.

LEEDS: *NORTH*

Pack Horse
208 Woodhouse Lane
11-11; 12-10.30 Sun
(0113) 245 3980
Tetley Bitter; guest beers Ⓗ
Fine interior that has been partially opened out and modernised, but still retains much of its Victorian multi-roomed character.

LEEDS: *WEST*

Beech Hotel
8 Tong Road, Lower Wortley
11-11; 12-3, 7-10.30 Sun
(0113) 263 8659
Tetley Bitter Ⓗ
Community local with genuine Irish connections, comprises a main bar, a basic smoke room and a pool room.

the 20-minute walk from the rail station.
⛰❀♣P

Station Hotel

Crackenedge Lane (by the market)
⏲ 11-11; 11-4, 7.30-11 Mon & Tue; 12-3, 7.30-10.30 Sun
☎ (01924) 450727
Stones Bitter; Worthington Bitter Ⓗ
Traditional town-centre pub with interesting architectural features: an original glass entrance, carved wooden snob screens in the side lounge and ornate glass canopies in the tap room. Originally the hotel served the old Dewsbury central station that once stood opposite. Now the pub trade is boosted by a bustling twice-weekly market (Wed and Sat). Local sports teams hold regular meetings at the pub and there is a folk club on Saturday night. Evening meals are offered Wed-Sat. ◐▯⇌♣

West Riding Licensed Refreshment Rooms

Railway Station, Wellington Road (ring road)
⏲ 11-11; 12-10.30 Sun
☎ (01924) 459193
Black Sheep Best Bitter; Taylor Landlord; guest beers Ⓗ
This lively pub is part of the 1848 Grade II listed station building. Access is from the car park or station platform. There are usually up to eight beers on tap including those from its own Anglo Dutch Brewery and other small brewers. Some bottled Belgian speciality beers are available. Regular live music is hosted and an annual festival is held in July. This pub is a popular stop on the Trans-Pennine Ale Tour. Lunchtime food is served daily and evening meals on Tue and Wed. ⛰❀◐♿⇌P

Woodman Inn

6 Hartley Street, Batley Carr (A652)
⏲ 11-11; 11.30-3, 5.30-11 Tue, Wed & Thu; 12-4, 7-11 Sat; 12-4, 7-10.30 Sun
☎ (01924) 463825
Tetley Mild, Bitter; guest beer Ⓗ
Featuring a memorial stone marked 1680, this is thought to be the town's oldest pub. Formerly owned by Edward Roberts & Son of Farnley Tyas and then Bentleys Yorkshire Breweries, it has been a free house since 1984 and still boasts the same licensees. Extended to include a large tap room, it retains all the inviting character of a thriving back-street local. Bar snacks are served lunchtime Mon-Fri. Darts and dominoes are played.
❀▯⇌♣P

ECCLESHILL

Royal Oak

39 Stony Lane
⏲ 11-11; 12-10.30 Sun
☎ (01274) 639182
Taylor Landlord; Tetley Mild, Bitter Ⓗ
Traditional local on the main street of one of Bradford's old villages. The 18th-century building was converted to a pub around 1900. The tap room has darts and dominoes and the lounge has a friendly feel with regular quizzes. Try the heated patio on cool summer eves. A rare outlet for Tetley Mild in Bradford.
❀▯♣P

ELLAND

Barge & Barrel

10-20 Park Road (A6025)
⏲ 12-11; 12-10.30 Sun
☎ (01422) 373623
Black Sheep Best Bitter; Eastwood & Sanders Bargee, Best Bitter, Nettlethrasher; guest beers Ⓗ
Large canalside/roadside pub with a central horseshoe-shaped bar. Many interior walls have been removed while some have been replaced with glazed screens. A raised seating area on the canal frontage doubles as a stage for live music (occasional Sun eves). One regular and four changing guest beers, perry, plus one of the Saxon ciders, are offered. Evening meals are served Tue-Sat. ⛰❀◐♣●P

GARFORTH

Gaping Goose

41 Selby Road (A63, 200 yds E of A642 jct)
⏲ 11.30-11; 12-10.30 Sun
☎ (0113) 286 2127
Tetley Mild, Bitter Ⓗ
This Grade II listed roadside local deservedly makes a splendid watering-hole for the mature drinker and many clubs and organisations gather here. It has been a pub for over 100 years and was originally called the White Swan. The name changed when an observant customer remarked that the swan on the sign looked more like a goose. The Goose offers a quiz (Tue) and money-off nights on its Mild and Bitter. ⛰Q❀▯P

GLASSHOUGHTON

George V WMC

Holliwell House, 124 Front Street
(A639/B6136 jct near Freeport Designer Outlet)
⏲ 11-11; 12-10.30 Sun
☎ (01977) 552775
John Smith's Bitter; Taylor Landlord; Tetley Bitter Ⓗ
CAMRA members showing their card can be signed in at this popular and comfortable working men's club. Building works (due in late 2002) should see full disabled access and new cellarage. The club has a large concert room and a bar lounge. Events held most nights of the week include live entertainment Friday and Saturday. At the rear is a large, secure children's play area and garden. Bar prices represent extremely good value. ❀▯♣P

GREETLAND

Druids Arms

2-4 Spring Lane (off Rochdale Road, B113, at Community Centre)
⏲ 12-3, 5-11; 12-11 Sat; 12-10.30 Sun
☎ (01422) 372465
website: www.druidsarms@btinternet.com
Taylor Golden Best, Best Bitter, Landlord; guest beers Ⓗ
Popular village free house, also known as the Rat. It is difficult to spot, but well worth seeking out. Customers help choose the three guest beers and local micro-breweries feature strongly. Theme beer weeks are held with menus, tasting notes and real ales, so far, from London, Scotland, Ireland and even France. Cider is stocked during the summer. Two real fires warm the pub in winter, while the outdoor terrace offers

impressive views across the valley. There is a pub piano and occasional live music. ♨❀♿♣P

GUISELEY

Ings

45A Ings Lane (off A65, at Guiseley Town FC)
11-11; 12-10.30 Sun
☎ (01943) 873315
Taylor Landlord; Tetley Bitter; guest beer Ⓗ
Backing on to fields, the Ings is handy for walking to Otley Chevin and Guiseley Moor. Airedale and Wharfedale Motorcycle Club meets here twice a month on Wednesday evenings and for ride-outs on Sunday mornings. A local walking club also leaves from here (Sun) for the Yorkshire Dales. There is a music quiz (Tue) and a general knowledge quiz (Thu). The well-appointed lounge boasts two open fires and there is a heated outdoor patio and secure garden. No lunchtime meals are served at the weekend. ♨❀(≠P

HALIFAX

Brown Cow

569 Gibbet Street, Highroad Well
11.30-11; 12-10.30 Sun
☎ (01422) 361640
Boddingtons Bitter; Castle Eden Ale; Taylor Landlord; guest beer Ⓗ
Roadside inn that is very much a community pub appealing to regulars of all ages. It is open plan, but has four distinct drinking areas. Sports-oriented Sky TV features in the games area and the pub has its own golf society and Sunday football team, while members of other teams regularly meet here. An unusual display of cow milk jugs is suspended from ceiling beams. Dominoes and shove-ha'penny are played. Lunchtime meals are served Mon-Fri. ❀(♣

Commercial

23 Lower Skircoat Green (1 mile S of centre)
12-2, 5-11; 12-3, 7-10.30 Sun
☎ (01422) 365078
Tetley Bitter; guest beers Ⓗ
You will be guaranteed a warm welcome when you call at the Commercial. The inn retains many of its original features. It has one of the few remaining 1950s Whitaker's fireplaces with the famous 'Cock of the North' embellishment. With plenty of on-street parking, it is an ideal starting point for a scenic walk along the Calder and Hebble Navigation Canal or a ramble through the North Dean woods. ❀

Pump Room

35 New Road
12-11; 12-10.30 Sun
☎ (01422) 381465
Black Sheep Best Bitter; Caledonian Deuchars IPA; Taylor Golden Best, Landlord; guest beers Ⓗ
Originally the Druids, this two-roomed beamed pub is adorned with brewery and other ephemera. A stone-floored bar space leads to a raised carpeted seating area featuring a large-screen TV. A separate pine-floored room has alcoved seating. Quiz night is Thursday (free supper to participants) and a gallon of beer is presented to the winners. Regular fund-raising events are held for the pub's chosen charities. Three guests are stocked, one is always from Ossett, and Biddendens cider is served. Trestle tables to the front of the pub provide an outdoor area for drinking. ❀≠♣P

Shears Inn

Paris Gates, Boys Lane (behind flats opp. football ground)
11.45-11; 12-10.30 Sun
☎ (01422) 362936
Taylor Golden Best, Best Bitter, Landlord, Ram Tam; Theakston Black Bull; guest beer Ⓗ
Lodged in the valley next to Hebble Brook and dominated by one of the few remaining working textile mills, the Shears has been an inn for many a year. It takes some finding at first, but is well worth the effort and is a popular lunchtime venue for workers and for locals in the evening. Basically one room but the central chimney piece and seating alcoves create more intimate areas. Home to soccer and cricket teams. No meals are served Sunday. ♨❀(≠♣P

Three Pigeons Ale House

1 Sun Fold, South Parade
12-11; 12-10.30 Sun
☎ (01422) 347001
website: www.threepigeons.demon.co.uk
Black Sheep Best Bitter; Eastwood & Sanders Best Bitter; Taylor Best Bitter, Landlord; guest beers Ⓗ
This 1930s Art Deco pub has won several awards. It comprises three rooms plus a central octagonal drinking area with a unique ceiling mural. The enthusiastic owners host regular initiatives including guest beers from specific breweries or regions, and milds, 'meet the brewer' eves, plus an annual light-hearted brewers' awards ceremony. Occasional live jazz and games nights are held. Three guest beers and over 30 different rums are available. Food is served on weekdays and the Monday curry night is a popular event. Enjoy a game of cribbage, bar skittles, shut the box or toad in the hole. ♨❀(≠♣⊘

Windmill Tavern

1 Park Square, The Hough, Northowram (off A6036)
12-11; 12-10.30 Sun
☎ (01422) 202464
Old Mill Bitter; Taylor Best Bitter, Landlord; Tetley Bitter; guest beers Ⓗ
This friendly, open-plan pub is built on the site of the old Windmill Brewery. The decor features a fish tank and fishing memorabilia. There is a quiz night (Thu) and the local motorcycle club meets on the last Saturday of every month. Awarded local CAMRA Pub of the Season March 2002, the Windmill caters for small functions and has an area to the front for outdoor drinking. ❀P

HAWORTH

Haworth Old Hall

Sun Street (opp. park)
11-11; 12-10.30 Sun
☎ (01535) 642709
Jennings Bitter, Cumberland Ale, Cocker Hoop, Sneck Lifter, seasonal beer; Tetley Bitter Ⓗ
Circa 1612, this former manor house, with

mullioned windows and low ceilings, is warm and comfortable. Children are welcome throughout the three rooms; the Tudor Room is no-smoking. Pictures show views of the surrounding area; two rooms have large inglenooks while the bar area is wood-panelled with a stone-flagged floor. Toilets, including a wheelchair WC, are in the former stables (indoors). Good quality, home-cooked food includes steaks and seasonal specials that change monthly. Meals are served all day Sat and Sun (12-9). ⚓ ♣ ≠ (K & WVLR) P ⊬ ✔

HEALEY

Brewer's Pride

Low Mill Road, Healey Road (at the bottom of Healey Road, 1½ miles from Ossett centre)

11-3, 5-11; 12-11 Fri & Sat; 12-10.30 Sun

☎ (01924) 273865

Ossett Excelsior; Taylor Landlord; guest beers Ⓗ

Popular free house next to Ossett Brewery with a choice of eight beers. The pub is within five minutes' walk of the Calder and Hebble Canal or can be reached by bus route 121 from Wakefield. Home-cooked food is available Mon-Sat lunchtimes and Wed evening. The pub holds a beer festival late in the year with over 30 beers on sale. The local folk club meets here (Thu) with live music on the first Sunday of each month. Awarded Wakefield CAMRA Pub of the Season in 1999 and 2000. Q

HEATH

King's Arms ☆

Heath Common

11.30-3, 5.30-11; 11.30-11 Sat; 12-10.30 Sun

☎ (01924) 377527

Clark's Traditional, seasonal beers; Taylor Landlord; Tetley Bitter Ⓗ

Built in the early 1700s and converted into a pub in 1841, the King's Arms became a member of the Clark's Brewery chain of ale houses in 1989. The pub, with its three gaslit, oak-panelled rooms, conservatory and extensive gardens, is surrounded by 100 acres of common grassland. The pub offers an excellent selection of real ale and serves good food. Q P

HEBDEN BRIDGE

Fox & Goose

9 Heptonstall Road (A646 jct)

11.30-3, 7-11; 12-3, 7-10.30 Sun

☎ (01422) 842649

Daleside Blonde; guest beers Ⓗ

The ever-changing ales from independent breweries make an on-going beer festival in this traditional, sociable pub. Its three rooms, free from juke box or bandits, include a pool table, small bar and huge pump clip collection. Czech and German bottled beers and 30 malt whiskies are also stocked in this cosy pub celebrating 13 consecutive years in this Guide. Q ≠ ♣

HECKMONDWIKE

Old Hall

New North Road

11.30-11; 12-10.30 Sun

☎ (01924) 404774

Samuel Smith OBB Ⓗ

Built in 1472 as a timber structure, this Grade I listed building is one of only four remaining aisled manor houses in the country. Many original timbers may still be seen in the upstairs gallery. The main hall, reputed to be haunted, has a 16th-century Royalist acorn ceiling and the walls are adorned with Tudor portraits. Joseph Priestley, one of the discoverers of oxygen, once lived here. Lively quiz nights are held Tue and Thu. Food is served daily (except Sun eve). ♣ P ⊬

HIPPERHOLME

Brown Horse

Denholme Gate Road, Coley (A644)

11-11; 12-3, 7-10.30 Sun

☎ (01422) 202112

Boddingtons Bitter; Taylor Landlord; Tetley Bitter; Wells Bombardier Ⓗ

The only Brown Horse pub in Yorkshire, this white-painted, roadside inn is deservedly popular for its food (served daily at lunchtime and early eve Mon-Fri). It has four comfortable drinking/dining areas (with an impressive display of collectables) plus an attractive conservatory and garden. The valley-head location affords fine views. P ⊬

HOLMFIRTH

Farmer's Arms

2-4 Liphill Bank Road, Burnlee (off A635)

5 (12 Sat)-11; 12-10.30 Sun

☎ (01484) 683713

Black Sheep Best Bitter; Eastwood & Sanders Bargee; Fuller's London Pride; Tetley Dark Mild, Bitter; guest beers Ⓗ

Friendly local close to Compo's Café in Holmfirth's 'Summer Wine' country. Owned by White Rose Inns and run by a very experienced licensee, the beer range reflects a commitment to top quality choice, enterprise and value. The layout is straightforward, with several partitioned seating areas adjoining the bar and an area for darts and games. A warm and cosy atmosphere predominates. Q P

Rose & Crown (Nook)

7 Victoria Square

11.30-11; 12-10.30 Sun

☎ (01484) 683960

Taylor Best Bitter, Landlord; Tetley Bitter; Theakston Best Bitter; guest beers Ⓗ

This family-owned free house has featured for the past 25 years in this Guide. There have been very few changes to this traditional local, tucked away among the huddle of buildings in Holmfirth's town centre. Down-to-earth and unpretentious, the pub's several rooms are served from a central bar. A folk group meets here monthly. A sound beer range includes regulars, guests and a mild, typically either Tetley or Moorhouses Black Cat. ♣

HORBURY

Boon's

6 Queen Street (1 mile from M1 jct 40)

11-3, 5-11; 11-11 Fri & Sat; 12-10.30 Sun

☎ (01924) 280442

Clark's Classic Blonde; John Smith's Bitter; Tetley Bitter; guest beers Ⓗ

Just off the High Street, this one-roomed pub is furnished in traditional style with a central bar. It is the most successful pub within the small tied estate owned by Clark's Brewery. A large patio with a children's play area extends at the back of the pub and plays host to the annual beer festival. 🙞❀♣

HUDDERSFIELD ❊

Fieldhead

219 Quarmby Road, Quarmby

✪ 4 (12 Fri & Sat)-11; 12-10.30 Sun

☎ (01484) 654581

Tetley Bitter; guest beers 🄷

Large, prominent building dominating a suburban housing estate some three miles from the town centre. It has an imposing exterior and spacious interior with generous seating. There is a lounge, pool room and the games area was once a tap room. Presiding over all is an equally spacious bar, whose horseshoe-like contour is a highly distinctive feature. Usually three beers are available and music-lovers can enjoy live entertainment most Tuesday and Friday evenings. ❀♣P

Marsh Liberal Club

Glenfield, 31 New Hey Road, Marsh (A640)

✪ 12-2, 7-11; 12-11 Sat; 12-10.30 Sun

☎ (01484) 420152

Taylor Golden Best, Dark Mild, Best Bitter; Theakston Best Bitter; guest beers 🄷

An impressive Grade II listed building houses this thriving club, which was the CAMRA Yorkshire Club of the Year 2001. Three guest beers are usually on offer from independent micros. Among the wide choice of rooms is the carrot-festooned bar, a lounge and a no-smoking family room (children are welcome in the lounge or family room until 9pm). The snooker room is a major attraction inside, while crown green bowling is popular outside in the summer. Cards, darts and dominoes are also played. Wheelchair ramp access and a disabled WC are available. Show this Guide or a CAMRA membership card to be signed in. ❀♿♣P⅍

Rat & Ratchet

40 Chapel Hill (A616, below ring road)

✪ 12 (3.30 Mon & Tue)-11; 12-10.30 Sun

☎ (01484) 516734 website: www.ratandratchet.co.uk

Greene King Abbot; Pictish Brewers Gold; Taylor Dark Mild, Landlord, Ram Tam; guest beers 🄷

Popular brew-pub with an admirable record for the quality and variety of its ales. Several seating areas exist, all adorned with drinking-related memorabilia. The excellent choice of up to 14 beers (including a 'Rat' beer brewed on the premises) is arguably one of the widest selections locally, making it a regular entry in this Guide. Lunches are served Wed-Sat; Wednesday is curry night attracting students and locals. ❀◐⇌♣P

Syngenta Sports & Fitness Club

509 Leeds Road (A62)

✪ 12-11; 12-10.30 Sun

☎ (01484) 421784

Taylor Best Bitter; Tetley Bitter; guest beer 🄷

Set back off the Leeds road (A62), this CAMRA award-winning club (formerly known as the Zeneca Club) is well worth visiting. It is served by a regular bus service. The club has a spacious bar, large no-smoking area, snooker hall, conservatory, and a patio for outdoor drinking and watching the crown green bowling. Excellent value food is served at lunchtimes. Show this Guide or CAMRA membership card to gain entry. ❀◐♣P

IDLE ❊

Albion Inn

25 New Line, Greengates (A657)

✪ 12-11; 12-10.30 Sun

☎ (01274) 613211

Barnsley Bitter; Taylor Landlord; Tetley Dark Mild, Bitter 🄷

Popular roadside inn on the main Leeds-Keighley road. This compact local has a friendly atmosphere. The L-shaped lounge is decorated with Old Bradford memorabilia and is served by an L-shaped bar. The games room (during a darts match) can be very busy and cramped. Service is from a small bar. ⊞♣

Idle Working Mens' Club

23 High Street

✪ 12-4 (5 Sat), 7 (7.30 Mon-Thu)-11; 12-5, 7-10.30 Sun

☎ (01274) 613602 website: idleworkingmensclub.com

Tetley Mild, Bitter; guest beers 🄷

Popular club that attracts members because of its name. Souvenir merchandise is available to buy. The club comprises a concert room, lounge and games room. The concert room hosts live entertainment on Sat and Sun eves. The lounge offers a quieter alternative. The downstairs games room has two full-sized snooker tables, plus big-screen TV. A different guest beer is sometimes available in the games room. Show this Guide or CAMRA membership to be signed in. Car parking is difficult but bus routes 610/612 pass close by. ♣

Symposium Ale & Wine Bar

7 Albion Road (near village green)

✪ 12-2.30, 5.30-11; 12-11 Fri & Sat; 12-10.30 Sun

☎ (01274) 616587

Back Sheep Best Bitter; Taylor Landlord; guest beers 🄷

This market town tavern pub offers regular promotions; each fortnight different northern independent breweries' beers appear alongside the regulars. There is a good range of bottled foreign beers plus a wide selection of wines. Promotions extend to the excellent meals provided. Loyalty schemes are in operation. A separate no-smoking room is available and can be used for small meetings. Bradford CAMRA 2002 Pub of the Year. Q◐◑⅍

ILKLEY

Bar T'at

7 Cunliffe Road

✪ 12-11; 12-10.30 Sun

☎ (01943) 608888

Black Sheep Best Bitter; Caledonian Deuchars IPA; Taylor Landlord; guest beers 🄷

Friendly, two-level bar converted from a china shop in 1999, located in the town centre behind Betty's Tea Rooms, close to a large car park. A wide range of bottled and draught continental beers complement the guest ales. These usually include beers from small Yorkshire breweries, such as Daleside, Ossett and Rooster's, and frequently a stout. The bar is decorated with brewery memorabilia. Newspapers are provided and dogs are welcome. Q❀◑⇌⊬

Riverside Hotel

Riverside Gardens, Bridge Lane

✪ 11-11; 12-10.30 Sun

☎ (01943) 607338

Samuel Smith OBB; Tetley Bitter; Thwaites Bitter Ⓗ

Smart hotel in a parkland setting, with a popular riverside patio. The two-roomed bar is comfortable and welcoming to families; there is also an outdoor play area. The hotel has a fish and chip shop attached, with additional ice cream sales. Although opening is limited in winter months, it opens daily at 10am for tea and coffee. This is a perfect starting or finishing point for the Dalesway long-distance path. The Riverside Hotel features for the fifth consecutive year in this Guide. ♨Q◑⇌P

KEIGHLEY ✲

Boltmakers Arms

117 East Parade

✪ 11-11; 12-10.30 Sun

☎ (01535) 661936

Taylor Golden Best, Best Bitter, Landlord Ⓗ

Small, one-roomed, popular local on two levels, it features pictures of Victorian pub interiors and distilling and brewing processes. As there is little space, games are limited, but the pub fields a football team in the local league. The TV in the back area shows major sporting events, while the fire in the front is cosy on cold winter evenings. Over 50 malt whiskies are stocked. Sandwiches are available.

♨⇌♣

Brewery Arms

Longcroft

✪ 11 (4 Tue)-11; 12-10.30 Sun

Goose Eye Barmpot; Taylor Golden Best, Best Bitter; guest beers Ⓗ

Situated on Worth Way opposite Morrison's supermarket, this comfortable and relaxed free house has a large open bar with a raised seating area and a smaller side room with a pool table. The emphasis is on cask beer with up to seven guest ales usually on offer. Hot and cold snacks are served all day.

❀⇌P

Cricketers' Arms

23 Coney Lane

✪ 11.30-11; 12-10.30 Sun

☎ (01535) 669912

Eastwood & Sanders First Light; Moorhouses Black Cat, Premier; guest beers Ⓗ

Originally three cottages, built in 1828, this compact, friendly, single-roomed free house was imaginatively refurbished by the former Worth Brewery in 1999. The walls have been taken back to the original stone, brass ship's portholes adorn the doors and the part-carpeted, part-polished floor interior features tram-style seating complete with luggage racks. Note the Worth Brewery windows and Len Hutton on the pub sign. The three guest beers come mostly from micros in the north of England. Q♿⇌♣

Friendly

2 Aireworth Street

✪ 12-11; 12-5, 7-11 Sat; 12-10.30 Sun

☎ (01535) 672136

Taylor Golden Best, Best Bitter Ⓗ

Friendly by name, friendly by nature, this two-roomed local is one of Keighley's small terraced pubs. No theme needed here, just good Yorkshire hospitality – if this pub did not exist, it would probably not be built today. A bright, relaxed place with 1960s background music, this Taylor's tied house serves the beers in oversized glasses. The view from the upstairs ladies' is awesome, owing to the steep stairs. ⊡

KEIGHLEY TO OXENHOPE AND BACK

Keighley & Worth Valley Railway Buffet Car

The Station, Haworth (stations also at Keighley, Ingrow West, Oakworth & Oxenhope)

✪ Sat, Sun & Bank Hols, March-Oct; Dec 26th-Jan 1st

☎ (01535) 645214; talking timetable (01535) 647777

website: www.kwvr.co.uk

Beer range varies Ⓗ

Impressive steam railway buffet car providing changing views of the Worth Valley. The line has been run by volunteers for over 30 years – far longer than it was run by British Rail. The railway (and particularly Oakworth Station), was used as the location for the original film version of The Railway Children. The round trip takes about 90 minutes, or passengers can buy a Day Rover and spend all day on the train. It usually sells two beers from independent breweries.

Q⛺⇌(Keighley) ⊬⊡

KNOTTINGLEY

Steampacket Inn

Bendles, 2 Racca Green (A645)

✪ 12-11; 12-10.30 Sun

☎ (01977) 677266

John Smith's Bitter; guest beer Ⓗ

Busy locals' pub situated next to the Aire and Calder Canal. Recently the lounge area has been refurbished and quizzes take place here every Thursday evening. Ample space as there is a separate public bar, a pool room and a function room. Darts and dominoes are popular. It was awarded Wakefield CAMRA Pub of the Season (winter) 2001/2.

♨❀⊟♿♣P

LEEDS: *CITY*

City of Mabgate

45 Mabgate

✪ 11-11; 12-3, 7-10.30 Sun

☎ (0113) 245 7789

Boddingtons Bitter; Taylor Landlord; Whitbread Trophy Bitter; guest beers Ⓗ

Regular award-winner for the quality of its ales, it has up to four guest beers, always including one from the Rooster's/Outlaw Brewery. With its future now secure, a minor refurbishment has enhanced this hostelry's charms. Its crowning glory still remains, though, the superb glazed tiling to the exterior. The plethora of Leeds Rugby League decoration and memorabilia signals the landlord's allegiance. Weekday lunches are served.

♨❀◑⊟♣

Duck & Drake

43 Kirkgate

⊙ 11-11; 12-10.30 Sun

☎ (0113) 246 5806

Old Mill Bitter; Taylor Landlord; Theakston Best Bitter, Old Peculier; guest beers Ⓗ

The quintessential example of an ale house. With up to seven guest beers in addition to its regular beers, the pub – Leeds CAMRA Pub of the Season (winter) 2001/2 – offers the city's widest choice of real ale and cider on draught. It is a basic two-roomed pub with a central bar. The front room is actually the lounge, the back room acting as the public bar – here can also be found the dartboard and TVs, both large-screen and standard size. Jazz can be heard on Mon and Thu nights while Sun lunchtime also has a music session. Bar snacks available weekday lunchtimes. ⚔⊟≹♣●

Horse & Trumpet

51-53 The Headrow (next door to City Varieties Theatre)

⊙ 11-11; 12-10.30 Sun

☎ (0113) 243 0338

Tetley Bitter; guest beers Ⓗ

Ex-Festival Ale House, serving up to four guest beers, decorated in the usual style – various shades of brown, bare wooden floors, and plenty of breweriana. Plaques on the wall record that the pub was officially reopened by trumpeters of the 1st Battalion Prince of Wales's Own Regiment of Yorkshire. The small snug has its own access to the bar. The rest of the pub has been opened out, but three separate drinking areas are identifiable. ◑≹⊁

North Bar

24 New Briggate

⊙ 12-1am (2am Fri & Sat); 12-10.30 Sun

☎ (0113) 242 4540 website: www.northbar.com

Beer range varies Ⓗ

Situated at the top end of Leeds, near Leeds' old boundary stone, the North Bar. Blink and you will miss the narrow, completely glass frontage. Inside it is similarly unassuming, with plain walls and a long, simple bar – but what a bar. Alongside the handpump which dispenses an unusual guest beer is a forest of fonts. These, along with fridges groaning with bottles, provide a foreign beer feast unparalleled in the city. Also of note are some strange pickled eggs, real art and interesting music. ◑

Palace

Kirkgate (next to parish church)

⊙ 11-11; 12-10.30 Sun

☎ (0113) 244 5882

Draught Bass; Tetley Bitter, Burton Ale; guest beers Ⓗ

Ex-Festival Ale House serving up to six guest ales, handy for the bus station, decorated in the typical style – dark wood panelling, exposed brick and plaster with plenty of ephemera. Formerly a three-roomed pub, of which traces are still visible, with two bars, it is now opened out into one room. Some Melbourne Brewery windows are still visible as is some of the original tiling in places. Its 18th-century roots as a merchant's house are evident in the fabric of the building, and in the cellars; a long passageway extends down to the River Aire. The pub is reputedly haunted. There is a heated beer garden to the rear, and tables to the front. ❀◑

Prince of Wales

Mill Hill

⊙ 11-11; 12-10.30 Sun

☎ (0113) 245 2434

Black Sheep Best Bitter; Greene King Old Speckled Hen, Ruddles County; John Smith's Bitter Ⓗ

Bustling, traditional pub in the shadow of Leeds Station. An eclectic mix of artefacts adorn the lounge with its four banqueting tables. The games room, designed by Andy Gibney, defies description – it is unique! On Saturday evening live bands pack out the lounge, and Leeds United home games also see the pub filled to capacity. The Prince of Wales Special Ale is always competitively priced. A lived-in look works splendidly for this hostelry. In summer there is an outdoor pavement area for drinking. ❀◑≹♣

Victoria Family & Commercial Hotel

28 Great George Street

⊙ 11-11; 12-10.30 Sun

☎ (0113) 245 1386

Black Sheep Best Bitter; Tetley Dark Mild, Bitter; guest beers Ⓗ

Opened in 1865 to provide accommodation for people attending the new assizes court at Leeds Town Hall, it was restored to some of its former glory in 1997. The long, narrow main bar area has some splendid wood and glass screens which separate the seating into cubicles. There are two further rooms, Bridget's Bar and the Albert Room (no-smoking), both of which are available for meetings and functions. The marvellous exterior is worth taking the time to view. ◑≹⊁

Whitelock's First City Luncheon Bar ☆

6-8 Turks Yard (off Briggate)

⊙ 11-11; 12-10.30 Sun

☎ (0113) 245 3950

Greene King Ruddles Best Bitter; John Smith's Bitter; Theakston Best Bitter, Old Peculier; guest beers Ⓗ

Whitelock's started life as the Turk's Head in 1715, although the building pre-dates this. The current name derives from the family who held the licence for 90 years until 1944. The last alterations were carried out in 1886 and now both the interior and exterior are protected by preservation orders. The pub comprises a main bar with restaurant area and outdoor drinking passage which leads to a secondary bar/private function room with three handpumps. Up to four rotating guest beers are available and real cider is served April-Sept. ⚔Q❀◑⊟≹●

Wrens

59-61 New Briggate

⊙ 11-11; 6-10.30 Sun

☎ (0113) 245 8888

Flowers Original; Taylor Landlord; Tetley Dark Mild, Bitter, Burton Ale Ⓗ

Three-roomed pub with strong links to the nearby Grand Theatre; opening hours on Sunday evening depend on performance times. The central bar dominates, with a wooden-floored public bar and no-smoking theatre bar; take a look at the memorabilia. The history of this hostelry and the

surrounding area is chronicled in the passageway which leads from the Merrion Street entrance to a comfortable lounge. Theatre patrons are able to order refreshments to beat the inevitable crush during the interval.
Q◑◐⊟♣⊬

LEEDS: *NORTH* ❄

Eldon
190 Woodhouse Lane
⏲ 11-11; 12-10.30 Sun
☎ (0113) 245 3387
Draught Bass; Tetley Bitter; guest beers Ⓗ
The combination of a fine range of ales and proximity to the university makes the Eldon popular with students and locals alike. Once a multi-roomed corner pub, it has been extended and opened out and is now split-level with wood flooring and a variety of seating. The guest beers change regularly due to the high throughput and a mild is normally available. A large TV near the bar shows most major sporting events. ◑◐♿

New Roscoe
Bristol Street, Sheepscar
⏲ 11-11; 12-10.30 Sun
☎ (0113) 246 0778
Tetley Bitter; guest beers Ⓗ
Formerly a club, then an Indian restaurant, the building was transformed in 1988 into a three-roomed modern pub in the style of the late lamented Old Roscoe. Farewell and Hail, written by CAMRA's Barrie Pepper, chronicles the history of both houses. Roscoe Special is brewed for the pub by Briscoe's. The large concert room gets very busy with live bands; the back room is quieter and more comfortable and has a large-screen TV. The lively front bar opens on to a games area with three pool tables.
❀◑⊟♣P

LEEDS: *SOUTH*

Grove Inn
Back Row, Holbeck
⏲ 12-11; 12-10.30 Sun
☎ (0113) 243 9254
Adnams Broadside; Caledonian Deuchars IPA; John Smith's Bitter; guest beers Ⓗ
Popular beer-drinker's paradise situated among modern office blocks on the edge of the city centre. First mentioned in a survey of the City of Leeds in 1850, it has since been extended to four rooms off a traditional West Riding corridor. There is a quiet front room, a side room, a tap room with wood-burning stove, and the concert room where a variety of live music is performed. The fine range of guest beers always includes one from Batemans Brewery. Leeds CAMRA Pub of the Year 2001. There are benches on the pavement for outdoor drinking. ♨❀◑⊟⇌♣

LEEDS: *WEST* ❄

Highland
36 Cavendish Street (down steps to left of Sentinel Towers on Burley Rd)
⏲ 11.30-11; 12-10.30 Sun
☎ (0113) 242 8592
Taylor Landlord; Tetley Mild, Bitter Ⓗ
Small, friendly local dwarfed by the surrounding buildings, this triangular-shaped pub would have originally been at the end of two rows of terraced houses; now long-demolished. The narrow main room has the bar along one side and contains a collection of black and white photographs of trams. At the wider end of the pub a doorway leads to a seating area with a large TV. The brick-built exterior features some attractive leaded stained glass windows. There are benches on the pavement for summer drinking. ❀♣

Old Vic
17 Whitecote Hill, Bramley (400 yds from A657/B6157 jct)
⏲ 4 (2 Fri; 11 Sat)-11; 12-3, 7-10.30 Sun
☎ (0113) 256 1207
Black Sheep Best Bitter; Taylor Landlord; Tetley Bitter; guest beers Ⓗ
Popular, suburban local, originally a vicarage, hence the name. This spacious, three-roomed pub is served by a central bar and comprises a lounge, two games rooms and a function room. The landlord is keen to foster a community spirit. Pool and dominoes are popular and quiz eves (Thu) can be busy. Three changing guest beers are usually available. ♨Q❀♿♣P

West End House
26 Abbey Road, Kirkstall (A65)
⏲ 11.30-11; 12-10.30 Sun
☎ (0113) 278 6332
Beer range varies Ⓗ
Former brewery tap of the now-defunct Kirkstall Brewery (Whitbreads), this Victorian, roadside pub has been extended in recent years to provide an enlarged dining area. Food is served daily (except Sun eve). It has an excellent location next to Kirkstall Leisure Centre, close to Abbey House Museum and the 12th-century Kirkstall Abbey, and is very popular after fixtures at nearby Headingley cricket and rugby grounds. Quiz nights are held Tue and Thu. ❀◑◐⇌(Headingley)

LINTHWAITE

Sair Inn
139 Lane Top (top of Hoyle Ing, off A62)
OS100143
⏲ 7 (5 Fri; 12 Sat)-11; 12-10.30 Sun
☎ (01484) 842370
Linfit Mild, Bitter, Cascade, Special, English Guineas Stout, seasonal beers Ⓗ
This brew-pub has won national acclaim as CAMRA's 1997 Pub of the Year. Perched on a hillside with superb views of the Colne Valley, its popularity, awards, and recommendations are widespread. The small bar overlooks a quartet of separate, cosy rooms, one is no-smoking; in winter ample fires provide extra warmth. There is a generous selection of beers (up to 10) plus seasonal specials. Weston's cider is served. The pub's history dates back to the 1800s with the current brewery having over 20 years' experience. ♨Q❀♣⊬

LINTON

Windmill
Main Street
⏲ 11-3, 5-11; 11-11 Sat & summer; 12-10.30 Sun
☎ (01937) 582209

John Smith's Bitter; Theakston Best Bitter; guest beer Ⓗ
Imposing stone building (over 700 years old) that was once the village blacksmith's. Now an attractive, classic pub with a friendly welcome and good quality beer and food. The beamed interior is on two levels, the upper area features a handsome grandfather clock. There are several fireplaces dotted around creating a warm, cosy environment in the winter months. The pub is named after a windmill that used to stand nearby. Conveniently the No. 99 bus from Leeds to Wetherby stops right outside. ⚜Q❀◑P

MARSDEN

Riverhead Brewery Tap

2 Peel Street (off A62)
✪ 4 (11 Sat)-11; 12-10.30 Sun
☎ (01484) 841270
Riverhead Sparth Mild, Butterley Bitter, Deer Hill Porter, Cupwith Light, March Haigh Special Ⓗ
This brew-pub, converted from a grocery store, has won deserved popularity among locals and visitors since opening in 1995. Located in an area close to the Pennine Way and Peak District, the surrounding countryside's landmarks are commemorated in the pub's many regular beers. Additional brews feature at Christmas, Easter and other times, plus Saxon Ruby Tuesday cider. A large ground-floor room is supplemented by two additional upstairs rooms for private functions. Q⇌●

MYTHOLMROYD ❄

Hinchcliffe Arms

Cragg Vale, Hebden Bridge (off B1638)
✪ 11.30-2, 5.30-11; closed Mon; 12-10.30 Sun
☎ (01422) 883256 website: www.hinchliffearms.com
Barnsley Bitter; Greene King Old Speckled Hen; Taylor Landlord; Theakston Best Bitter; guest beers Ⓗ
Large pub with an imposing entrance, set in a delightful secluded valley, overlooked by the local church, St John's in the Wilderness. Built as a pub, it was purchased by the local Hinchcliffe family to provide their estate workers with an outlet for their wages. A cosy lounge, with a panoramic painting over the bar, is supplemented by an intimate restaurant in which children aged 14-plus are welcome (meals are served Tue-Sat 12-2, 6-9, Sun 12-6). Popular with walkers, the Calderdale Way passes the door. Caravans only are permitted at the camping site. ⚜❀⇆◑◗ÅP

OLDFIELD

Grouse Inn

Harehills Lane OS011383
✪ 11.30-3, 5.30-11; 11-11 Sat; 12-10.30 Sun
☎ (01535) 643073 website: www.thegrouseinn.co.uk
Taylor Golden Best, Best Bitter, Landlord Ⓗ
Quiet, comfortable inn in open countryside where the silence is only disturbed by conversation. One room serves as a tap room/games room with a tiled floor, bare stone walls and a wood-burning stove. The oak-panelled lounge has a display of pictures, some for sale. It offers extensive views across open moorland and the reservoir to Wuthering Heights of Brontë fame. The restaurant with a coffee/smoking lounge off, serves a good, weekly changed menu; meals served all day Sunday until 9pm. Children are welcome throughout the inn.
⚜❀◑◗♿ÅP

OSSETT ❄

Red Lion

273 Dewsbury Road (old Gawthorpe-Flushdyke road, parallel with bypass)
✪ 12-11; 12-10.30 Sun
☎ (01924) 273487
Rooster's Yankee; John Smith's Bitter; guest beers Ⓗ
Set in a largely industrial area of town, this squat, but well-proportioned, stone building with its traditional flagged roof still has a farmhouse feel. The pub is cosy with low ceilings and plenty of nooks in which to settle. There are at least four cask beers from independents. Generous portions of real food are available daily; indeed on Sundays it is a totally food-oriented pub. ◑◗P

OTLEY

Black Bull

Market Place (near bus station)
✪ 11-11; 12-10.30 Sun
☎ (01943) 462288
Taylor Best Bitter, Landlord; Tetley Bitter Ⓗ
This excellent pub dates back in part to the 16th century. Sympathetically refurbished, it retains a medieval feel with a stone fireplace, stone-flagged floor and low ceiling. English Civil War paintings adorn the walls. It is said that in 1648 a party of Cromwell's Ironsides drank the tavern dry. Now a single bar serves an L-shaped drinking area divided into three distinct alcoves. It tends to be busy at weekends.
⚜❀◑

Bowling Green

18 Bondgate (near bus station)
✪ 12-4, 7-11 (Mon & Tue are variable in winter); 2.30-10.30 Sun
☎ (01943) 461494
Beer range varies Ⓗ
This imposing former courthouse, built in 1757, became a pub in 1825. The L-shaped main bar is crammed full of weird objects – look out for the skeleton by the pool table. Beers from Briscoe's, brewed in converted outbuildings behind the pub, are always available. An annual beer festival is held in September. No children are permitted in the pub. An outdoor area, to the front, is used for summer drinking.
⚜❀♣

Red Lion

43-45 Kirkgate (near market square)
✪ 11-11; 12-4, 7-10.30 Sun
☎ (01943) 462226
Courage Directors; Greene King Ruddles County; John Smith's Bitter; guest beer Ⓗ
Traditional, late 19th-century town-centre pub that caters for the more mature drinker. The open-plan front lounge provides three quiet drinking areas served by a small rear bar. Dominoes are played in the back room and there is a TV. The upstairs meeting room is popular with local clubs and there is a quiz night (Tue). The guest beer changes weekly.
Q◑♣

Royalty

Yorkgate OS206440
11-11; 12-10.30 Sun
(01943) 461156
Black Sheep Best Bitter; Taylor Landlord; Tetley Bitter H

Isolated pub perched on top of Otley Chevin, offering fine views across Airedale and Wharfedale. A cosy tap room, comfortable lounge and family room (part of which is no-smoking) cater for all tastes. The pub name derives from the name of the land on which it stands. Caravans are allowed at the campsite. Meals are served until 8pm Mon-Sat (9pm summer) and 6pm Sun. The attractive location means the pub and garden tend to be busy during sunny holiday periods.
P

Whitakers

47 Kirkgate (near market square)
11.30 (11 Fri & Sat)-11; 12-10.30 Sun
(01943) 462580
Black Sheep Best Bitter; Tetley Bitter; guest beer H

Popular, late 18th-century town-centre pub. It has been refurbished to provide a long, narrow, split-level drinking area. Two real fires create a cosy atmosphere. Lunchtime meals are served until 3pm (5pm Sat and Sun) and good value chilli on Mon eve. The house beer is from Goose Eye. The enclosed garden at the rear is well patronised in summer.

PONTEFRACT

Robin Hood

4 Wakefield Road (off A645)
11.30-3.30 (4.30 Fri & Sat), 7-11; 12-3.30, 7-10.30 Sun
(01977) 702231
John Smith's Bitter; Tetley Bitter; guest beers H

Friendly, welcoming pub at Town End traffic lights. The Robin has a busy public bar and three other drinking areas; quizzes are held on Tue and Sun eves and regular beer festivals are hosted. Traditional pub games are played; there are darts and dominoes teams. It was awarded Wakefield CAMRA Pub of the Year 1998.
(Tanshelf/Baghill)

PUDSEY

Bankhouse

42 Bankhouse Lane
12-3, 5.30-11; 12-11 Sat; 12-10.30 Sun
(0113) 256 4662
Black Sheep Best Bitter; Taylor Landlord; Tetley Bitter H

Comfortable, 18th-century pub overlooking Tong Valley Country Park. The central bar serves a cosy lounge and smaller drinking area. There is a small, separate dining room. Good food is served daily (Sun meals until 7.30pm). It was once a haunt of the Yorkshire and England cricketing legend, the late Sir Len Hutton, who was born nearby. The ceilings and walls are adorned with a panoply of china and metalware. A weekly quiz is held (Mon eve).
P

Royal Hotel

30 Station Street, Greenside
12-11; 12-10.30 Sun
(0113) 256 4085
Thwaites Bitter H

Originally called the Station Hotel, built in 1879 to serve passengers of the long-gone Greenside Station, it is still a grand pub, its fixtures and fittings mercifully very much intact. Many rooms lead off a fine wood-panelled corridor. You can play 'spot the difference' between the twin red and green lounges, watch big-screen TV in the bustling tap room or stand and sup at the central bar. It is a meeting place for ukulele enthusiasts and fledgling bands. Children enjoy the good selections of pop and sweets on sale.
P

World's End

Booths Yard, Lowtown
11-midnight; 12-10.30 Sun
(0113) 255 1634
website: www.margarethare.yahoo.com
Theakston Best Bitter, Old Peculier; guest beer H

Lively free house built in 1983, although it looks much older. This two-bar pub is split over no less than five levels, but all are similarly decorated with bare boards, stone walls and wooden furniture. The pub hosts many events from live jazz and folk to music quizzes and other music nights throughout the week. The interesting beer

INN BRIEF

LEEDS: *WEST*

Railway
Calverley Bridge, Rodley
12-11; 12-10.30 Sun
(0113) 257 6603
Black Sheep Best Bitter; Tetley Bitter H
Next to the Leeds-Liverpool Canal, this friendly local has a family room. Greene King Old Speckled Hen is available Christmas and summer.

MIRFIELD

Airedale Heifer
53 Stocksbank Road
12 (3 winter Mon-Thu)-11; 12-10.30 Sun
(01924) 493547
Eastwood & Sanders Bargee; Tetley Bitter; guest beer H
Recently refurbished pub with food served lunchtimes only.

MYTHOLMROYD

Shoulder of Mutton
38 New Road
11.30-3, 7-11; 11-11 Sat; 12-10.30 Sun
(01422) 883165
Black Sheep Best Bitter; Boddingtons Bitter; Castle Eden Ale; Flowers IPA; Taylor Landlord H
Streamside local by station, popular with diners. Coin counterfeiting equipment is displayed.

OSSETT

Fleece
Spa Street
12-11; 12-10.30 Sun
(01924) 273685
John Smith's Bitter; Tetley Bitter; guest beers H
Quiet, three-roomed pub situated between Ossett and Horbury with a small garden. Live music is staged.

PONTEFRACT

Tap & Barrel
13 Front Street
11.30-11; 12-10.30 Sun
(01977) 699918
Daleside Bitter; Greene King Old Speckled Hen; Theakston Cool Cask, Old Peculier H
Pontefract's only genuine free house. Recently refurbished, it has a large lounge and public bar. Live music Sat and Sun.

RAWDON

Princess
Apperley Lane
12-11; 12-10.30 Sun
(0113) 250 2495
Black Sheep Best Bitter; Taylor Landlord; Tetley Bitter; guest beer (occasional) H
Friendly, two-roomed local, open plan with L-shaped lounge and TV room. Sun meals are served 12-7.

range (always includes Daleside) and late bar ensure that the pub is rarely quiet. No eve meals are served on Sunday. ❀◐◑

RIPPONDEN ❄

Butchers Arms

143 Rochdale Road

⏲ 12-3 (not Mon), 5-11; 12-11 Sat; 12-10.30 Sun

☎ (01422) 823100

Black Sheep Special; Greene King Abbot; Mansfield Cask Ale; Orkney Red MacGregor; Taylor Landlord Ⓗ

Comfortable, homely pub, with mullioned windows, set on a fringe of moorland. Its elevated position affords spectacular views across the Pennine Hills. Several rooms are sited at differing levels. The dining room is highest, and there is a strong emphasis on food. Pool is played, and regulars watch sport on Sky TV in the bar. A collection of Belgian beer glasses is displayed. ❀◐◑♣P

SCAMMONDEN

Brown Cow

Saddleworth Road, Deanhead (B6114, 2½ miles S of Barkisland)

⏲ 12-3 (not Mon-Thu), 7-11; 12-3, 7-10.30 Sun

☎ (01422) 822227

website: www.thepubs/browncowscammonden.hem

John Smith's Bitter, Magnet; guest beers Ⓗ

Despite its remote location on the Pennine Moors, this ex-coaching house is a thriving concern, with remarkably fine beer quality, ample food and a separate restaurant (no meals Mon). Old fire-fighting paraphernalia and an odd clock collection adorn the walls, and the pub's history back to 1838 has been meticulously researched by its keen licensee, the 24th here. The pub can be reached by limited public buses – 900 service from Huddersfield and 556-559 from Halifax. Two permanent beers are complemented by two rotating guests. ♨Q❀◐◑♿⛺♣P⚟

SHAW CROSS

Huntsman

Chidswell Lane

(near Dewsbury, 400 yds from A653/B6128 jct)

⏲ 12-3 (not Mon), 7-11; 12-3, 7-10.30 Sun

☎ (01924) 275700

Black Sheep Best Bitter; Taylor Landlord; guest beer Ⓗ

Situated on the edge of the village and next to a working farm, this pub boasts extensive views over open countryside. Originally two 17th-century farm cottages, the inn has recently been extended and has three linked rooms decorated with brasses and bric-à-brac; there is an old Yorkshire range. The house beer is brewed by Highwood. Lunchtime meals are served Tue-Sat. ♨❀◐P

SHELLEY

Three Acres Inn

37/41 Roydhouse (off B6116) OS214124

⏲ 12-3, 7-11; 12-10.30 Sun

☎ (01484) 602606 website: www.threeacres.co.uk

Adnams Bitter; Banks's Bitter; Taylor Landlord; guest beer Ⓗ

Rural coaching inn nestling below Emley Moor Mast, with attractions such as Bretton Park and the National Mining Museum nearby. It is widely renowned for highly imaginative menus, an extensive wine list, and the speciality foods sold in its own on-site shop. It offers a multi-roomed layout and accommodation in 20 en-suite rooms. There are limited bus services, 233 from Huddersfield (four daily Mon-Sat). The accent is firmly on quality dining so public bar facilities are limited. ♨❀🛏◐◑P

SHIPLEY ❄

Fanny's Ale & Cider House

63 Saltaire Road (A657)

⏲ 11.30 (5 Mon)-11; 12-10.30 Sun

☎ (01274) 591419

Taylor Landlord; Theakston Cool Cask; guest beers Ⓗ

Formerly a pet shop and a beer shop before becoming a fully licensed free house, it has a cosy, nostalgic atmosphere downstairs, enhanced by gaslights, a log fire and old brewery memorabilia. It stocks a range of foreign bottled beers with additional selections on draught. Usually seven real ales are on offer. The pub is close to the historic village of Saltaire. The opening of an upstairs room has increased the available drinking areas. ♨Q⇌(Saltaire)♣🍎

Shipley Pride

1 Saltaire Road (A657)

⏲ 11.30 (11 Sat)-11; 12-10.30 Sun

☎ (01274) 585341

Taylor Landlord; Tetley Bitter; guest beers Ⓗ

This former Hammonds house (built in 1870) is a traditional local, comprising two rooms linked by a central bar. The rectangular lounge features wood panels and stained glass windows served by a semi-circular bar; the games room has two pool tables that are popular with locals. Guest beers include ales from Ossett and Daleside. Weekly quiz nights are held (Thu). Meals are served weekday lunchtimes. Bradford CAMRA Pub of the Season 2001, summer. ❀◐⇌(Saltaire/Shipley)♣P

SOUTH ELMSALL

Brookside Commercial Social Club

35 Barnsley Road (near bus and rail stations)

⏲ 11.30-4, 6.30-11; 11-5, 6.30-11 Sat; 11-2, 6.30-10.30 Sun

☎ (01977) 643530

John Smith's Bitter; Old Mill seasonal beers; guest beers Ⓗ

An oasis for real ale in the town centre. This popular club caters for all ages and takes pride in its support for independent breweries. Over 100 guest brews have been served at Wakefield CAMRA's Club of the Season 2001/2, winter. CIU-affiliated, CAMRA members can be signed in on production of a membership card or by showing a copy of this Guide. Limited parking. ♿⇌(South Elmsall/Moorthorpe)♣P

SOWERBY BRIDGE ❄

Alma Inn

Cottonstones, Mill Bank

(1¼ miles off A58 at Triangle pub)

⏲ 5.30 (12 Sat)-11; 12-10.30 Sun

☎ (01422) 823334

Taylor Golden Best, Landlord; Tetley Bitter; guest beer Ⓗ

This popular, family-friendly, country inn has stone-flagged floors and a real fire in an open-plan setting. Over 90 Belgian beers are stocked, and tutored tastings can be arranged. Two main festivals are hosted annually: 'Rushbearing' (first weekend in Sept) when the rush cart visits, and Octoberfest (second Sun in Oct), these are very busy periods. A regular bus service from Halifax stops at the door. Weekend meals are served 12-9, no meals Mon or Tue eves. ♨❀◑♿▲♣P

Ram's Head
26 Wakefield Road

12-2 (3 Sat), 5-11; 12-3, 6-10.30 Sun

☎ (01422) 835876

Ryburn Best Bitter, Humpty, Rydale Bitter, Luddite, Stabbers H

A warm, cosy atmosphere is created in this compact bar lounge and L-shaped drinking/dining area with beamed ceilings, plenty of woodwork and stone fireplaces. Etched glass windows provide a reminder of Webster's Brewery. Five Ryburn beers (brewed in the cellar beneath the pub) are normally on offer, interspersed occasionally with other ales from the company's range; all at competitive prices. Home-cooked food is available until 9pm. The no-smoking area (until 9pm) is not exclusive to diners. Join in the singalongs on Sat eve. ♨Q❀◑♣⁄

White Horse
Burnley Road, Friendly (A646, 3/4 mile from centre)

12-11; 12-10.30 Sun

☎ (01422) 831173

Eastwood & Sanders Nettlethrasher; Tetley Mild, Bitter H

Popular local by the Halifax to Burnley road, with award-winning window box displays. The comfortable lounge was once two rooms. Photographs and certificates show the generosity of the customers in aid of muscular dystrophy; there are also pictures of old Sowerby Bridge, and a 1944-45 excise licence. The small, busy tap room has trophies displayed. There is a drinking area to the front of the pub, and an enclosed seating area overlooking the car park. ❀♣P

Burton to the Baltic

Benjamin Wilson's Burton beer was better known in Russia, where he did a large trade, than it was in the metropolis. The Empress Catherine, and the grand old savage Tsar Peter, freely drank the beer at their respective courts long before it became popular at St James's under the four Georges.

Dr Bushman, 1852.

STANBURY

Wuthering Heights
Main Street

12-3.30 (not Mon), 7-11; 12-11 Sat; 12-4, 7-10.30 Sun

☎ (01535) 643332

Goose Eye Brontë; Taylor Golden Best; Tetley Bitter; guest beer H

Lively and friendly, this traditional village free house has two distinct rooms. The comfortable main bar is subdivided using partitions and there is a cosy dining section to one side, offering good value food with vegetarian options (no food Mon). The separate games room is at the rear. An hourly bus, No. 664 from Keighley, passes during the day (Mon-Sat).
❀⇌◑♣P

STEETON

Steeton Hall
Station Road

11-11; 12-10.30 Sun

☎ (01535) 655676

website: www.honeycombe.co.uk/steetonhallhotel

Black Sheep Best Bitter; Jennings Bitter; Taylor Best Bitter H

Part of the Honeycombe Leisure Group, this 16th-century house has a glass conservatory and several other public rooms decorated with a mix of old photographs and paintings of the local area. A comfortable pub/restaurant, it has a recently refurbished function room and nine bedrooms, and serves excellent food at reasonable prices.
❀⇌◑♿⇌(Steeton & Silsden) P

TINGLEY

British Oak
407 Westerton Road

5.30 (1.30 Fri; 11 Sat)-11; 12-10.30 Sun

☎ (0113) 253 4792

Boddingtons Bitter; Castle Eden Bitter; John Smith's Bitter; guest beer H

Single-roomed, open-plan pub, with a central island bar, that is decorated throughout in shades of pink. Once in a rural setting, it is now surrounded by housing, with more on the way. Comfortable banquette seating is set around most of the walls with a mixture of upholstered stools and chairs around the tables. A pool table dominates one corner of the pub, along with a large-screen TV. Organised entertainment includes karaoke (Sat), a music quiz (Sun), plus Play Your Cards Right and quiz (Mon). ❀P

TODMORDEN ❊

Masons Arms
1 Bacup Road (A6033/A681 jct)

3 (12 Sat)-11; 12-10.30 Sun

☎ (01706) 812180

Barnsley Bitter; Tetley Bitter; guest beers H

Friendly locals' pub at the junction of two valleys. The high valley sides and the adjacent railway viaduct seem to dwarf the pub. The entrance corridor and two flanking rooms open out to face the bar.

The lounge area, with unusual tables, is believed to have once been a mortuary. Pictures and descriptions of local historical interest are displayed. The guest beers are mainly from smaller breweries. ❀⇌♣

WAINSTALLS

Cat i' th' Well Inn

Wainstalls Lane

✪ 12-3 (not winter Mon-Fri); 7 (6 Sat & summer)-11; 12-3, 7 (6 summer)-10-30 Sun

☎ (01422) 244841

Castle Eden Bitter; Taylor Golden Best, Best Bitter, Landlord Ⓗ

Overlooked by some mysterious white-painted rocks, and tucked into a steep Pennine valley below the hilltop village of Wainstalls, the 'Caty' is a quiet, relaxing retreat. Very popular with walkers, it was hard hit by the 2001 outbreak of foot-and-mouth disease. There are three cosy, panelled drinking areas and superb views over Luddenden Dene to the moors beyond. A weekly quiz is held (Mon). Q❀♣P

WAKEFIELD ❊

Fernandes Brewery Tap

5 Avison Yard, Kirkgate (500 yds from Kirkgate Station)

✪ 5 (11 Fri & Sat)-11; 12-10.30 Sun

☎ (01924) 369547

Fernandes Malt Shovel Mild, Ale to the Tsar, Double Six; guest beers Ⓗ

Housed in the original malt kiln, built in 1822 by Louis Fernandes (closed 1929), the premises became the malt store and conditioning room for Beverley's Brewery until 1968. It was bought in 1994 by the James family, when they transferred their home-brew shop. A micro-brewery was installed in 1997, using the Fernandes name and the brewery tap opened in 1999. Local CAMRA Pub of Year 1999-2001 and Yorkshire Pub of the Year 2001, it has won many Pub of the Season awards. The pub features an extensive collection of brewery memorabilia. Biddendens cider is served.
Q⇌(Westgate/Kirkgate) ●

Harry's Bar

107b Westgate (200 yds from Westgate Station)

✪ 3-11; 4-10.30 Sun

☎ (01924) 373773

Black Sheep Best Bitter; Ossett Silver King; Taylor Landlord; guest beers Ⓗ

Small, one-roomed pub, hidden just off Westgate, but certainly not aimed at the 'Westgate Run' crowd. A must for those who enjoy a quiet drink. The pub was named after the landlord's father-in-law, Harry Murphy, who played rugby for Great Britain and Wakefield Trinity in the 1940s and '50s; the walls display photos from his playing days. No one-armed bandits or juke box, but live music is performed Tue and Wed eves.
♛❀◐♿⇌

Henry Boon's

130 Westgate (100 yds from Westgate Station)

✪ 10.45-11 (1am Fri & Sat); 11.30-10.30 Sun

☎ (01924) 378126

Clark's Classic Blonde, seasonal beer; Taylor Landlord; Tetley Bitter Ⓗ

Friendly, wood-floored, city-centre pub on the 'Westgate Run' so it tends to be crowded at weekends. Wood casks are spread around the bar and there is a thatched canopy above. Live music is played Thursday evening; other attractions include a juke box, pool table and two function rooms. The pub caters for all age groups. ⇌♣

O'Donoghues

60 George Street

✪ 5-11; 1-10.30 Sun

☎ (01924) 291326

Hop Back Summer Lightning; Ossett Excelsior; Taylor Best Bitter; guest beers Ⓗ

Situated only 200 yards off Westgate (south side) but not aimed at the 'Westgate crowd', this pub is a traditional ale house with a reputation as an outlet for Ossett Brewing Company. Live music eves are a regular feature. A selection of Sunday newspapers is provided for drinkers to read. Please note no lunchtime opening Mon-Sat.
♛⇌(Westgate/Kirkgate)

Redoubt ☆

28 Horbury Road

✪ 12 (11 Sat)-11; 12-10.30 Sun

☎ (01924) 377085 website: www.theredoubt.co.uk

Taylor Landlord; Tetley Mild, Bitter Ⓗ

Tetley Heritage pub consisting of four cosy

INN BRIEF

RIDDLESDEN

Marquis of Granby Inn
Hospital Road
4 (12 Fri & Sat)-11; 12-10.30 Sun
(01535) 607164
Black Sheep Special; Webster's Green Label, John Smith's Bitter Ⓗ
Comfortable, three-roomed canalside pub, handy for East Riddlesden Hall.

RIPPONDEN

Old Bridge
Priest Lane
12-3, 5.30-11; 12-11 Sat; 12-10.30 Sun
(01422) 822595
Black Sheep Best Bitter; Taylor Golden Best, Best Bitter, Landlord; guest beer Ⓗ
Picturesque, whitewashed free house by the old packhorse bridge. The building dates from the 14th century. Eve meals Mon-Fri.

SHIPLEY

Branch
105 Bradford Road
11-11; 12-10.30 Sun
(01274) 584495
Black Sheep Best Bitter; Marston's Pedigree; Tetley Bitter, Burton Ale; guest beers Ⓗ
A central, rectangular bar dominates this local, adorned with brewery memorabilia. Up to three guest ales are usually stocked.

SOWERBY BRIDGE

Puzzle Hall Inn
21 Hollins Mill Lane
12-11; 12-10.30 Sun
(01422) 835547
Greene King IPA, Abbot; Jennings Cumberland Ale Ⓗ
Former home of the Puzzle Hall Brewery. Very popular, with regular jazz, live bands and games eves. Curry night Wed.

THURSTONLAND

Rose & Crown
3 The Village
12-2, 5.30-midnight; 12-midnight Sat; 12-10.30 Sun
(01484) 661872
Black Sheep Best Bitter; Taylor Landlord; Tetley Dark Mild, Bitter Ⓗ
Multi-roomed pub with a pool table and impressive collection of Tetley shire horse memorabilia.

TODMORDEN

Top Brink
Brink Top, Lumbutts
12-3 (not Mon-Fri), 6-11; 12-10.30 Sun
(01706) 812696
Boddingtons Bitter; Castle Eden Ale; Flowers Original; guest beer Ⓗ
This family-run pub has three rooms around the bar, with attractive brassware. Busy with diners at peak periods.

rooms, two of which are available mid-week for private functions – at no charge. The family room is available until 8pm. The pub fields its own football and cricket teams as well as having strong Rugby League connections. One of the oldest pubs in the city, it has had the same name since 1882 and has changed little since. A rare outlet for Tetley Mild in Wakefield.
Q ❀ ≋ (Westgate) ♣P

Wakefield Labour Club (Red Shed)
18 Vicarage Street
(by market car park)
11-4 (not Mon-Thu), 7-11; 12-5, (closed eve) Sun
☎ (01924) 215626
Ossett Pale Gold; guest beer ⊞
The club has provided a base for Wakefield's labour movement for many years. Unlike other labour clubs, it has continued as a socialist club and has been the backbone of organisational support for workers involved in a whole range of industrial struggles, playing a vital part in the lives and history of the people of Wakefield. This small, friendly, wooden club has become a favourite with traditional ale drinkers, stocking a variety of beers from independent breweries. It holds a clutch of CAMRA awards including national joint Pub of the Year 2000. There is a barbecue area for outdoor drinking.
❀ ≋ (Westgate/Kirkgate) P

WALSDEN

Cross Keys
649 Rochdale Road (A6033)
12-11; 12-10.30 Sun
☎ (01706) 815185
Black Sheep Best Bitter; Taylor Landlord; Wells Bombardier; guest beers ⊞
This stone-built pub is part of a row of roadside cottages. The lounge, extended with a conservatory, is separated from the canal towpath at the back of the pub by a small, enclosed drinking area. There is a busy tap room with pool and pub games and a separate smaller old-fashioned room. Bar snacks and traditional English meals are served; bed and breakfast accommodation is available.
❀ ≋ ♣

WARMFIELD

Plough
45 Warmfield Lane (400 yds from A655)
12-3, 5-11; 12-11 Sat; 12-10.30 Sun
☎ (01924) 892007
John Smith's Bitter; Theakston Best Bitter, Old Peculier ⊞
Unspoilt, 18th-century inn overlooking the Lower Calder Valley, with a low-beamed ceiling and a huge open fireplace. It has been extensively, yet sympathetically, refurbished by the owners. Good quality bar meals and snacks are served. There is a paved seating area at the front of the pub with an adjacent children's play area.
Q ❀ ♣P

WENTBRIDGE

Blue Bell
Great North Road
11.30-3, 5-11; 12-10.30 Sun
☎ (01977) 620697
Taylor Landlord; Tetley Bitter ⊞
Situated in the picturesque village of Wentbridge on the old A1, this former coaching inn was rebuilt in 1633. An original pub sign hangs in the entrance. The inn stands at the head of Brockadale, the smallest of the Yorkshire Dales. Noted for its excellent range of food, with several vegetarian options, it is comfortably furnished with Mousey Thompson chairs and tables, in a warm, friendly atmosphere. Q ❀ P

WINTERSETT

Angler's Retreat
Ferrytop Lane (between the villages of Crofton and Ryhill) OS382157
12-3, 7-11; 12-11 Fri & Sat; 12-3, 7-10.30 Sun
☎ (01924) 862370
Barnsley Bitter; John Smith's Bitter; Samuel Smith OBB; Theakston XB; guest beer (summer) ⊞
Cosy, two-roomed rural pub; the bar has a stone-flagged floor and open fireplace, the lounge displays old photographs of the area, a plate collection and two stuffed birds in glass cases. Handy for birdwatchers, anglers and walkers, the Anglers Country Park is close by. The guest beer pump is only in action in the summer months. Take routes 195 and 196/7 from Wakefield bus station.
❀ P

INN BRIEF

WAKEFIELD

White Hart
77 Westgate End
12-11; 12-10.30 Sun
(01924) 375887
Boddingtons Bitter; Greene King IPA, Old Speckled Hen; Tetley Bitter; Theakston Cool Cask, Old Peculier ⊞
Traditional pub with stone floors and olde-worlde atmosphere. Caters for all age groups.

WHITWOOD

Rising Sun
Whitwood Common Lane
11.30-11; 12-10.30 Sun
(01977) 554766
Taylor Landlord; Tetley Bitter ⊞
Converted from a former miners' institute and cottages designed by the famous architect, Charles Voysey. Noted for excellent food.

WIBSEY

Gaping Goose
5-6 Slack Bottom Road
(off Buttershaw Lane)
4 (2 Sat)-11; 2-10.30 Sun
(01274) 601701
Black Sheep Best Bitter; Taylor Landlord; Tetley Bitter; guest beer (occasional) ⊞
Popular, village free house offers a comfortable lounge with games-oriented tap room. Limited parking.

YEADON

Albert Inn
81 High Street
12 (11.30 Fri & Sat)-11; 12-10.30 Sun
(0113) 250 0420
John Smith's Bitter; Taylor Landlord; Tetley Bitter; ⊞
Busy local on corner site with long, narrow lounge and small games room. Close to Yeadon Tarn.

Check it out

Pubs in the Good Beer Guide may change ownership and the facilities listed could alter. If a visit to a pub involves a long journey, it's advisable to check before leaving that full meals, family facilities, accommodation or camping sites are still available.

STYLE MONITOR

Scottish Beer

JUST AS MONKS call their Lenten beers 'liquid bread', it's tempting to call traditional Scottish ales 'liquid porridge'. They are beers brewed for a cold climate, a country in which beer vies with whisky (uisge breatha – water of life) for nourishment and sustenance.

Brewers blend not only darker malts such as black and chocolate with paler grains, but also add oats, that staple of many foodstuffs in the country. In common with the farmer-brewers of the Low Countries and French Flanders in earlier centuries, domestic brewers in Scotland tended to use whatever grains, herbs and plants were available to make beer. The intriguing use of heather in the Fraoch range of ales recalls brewing practice in Scotland from bygone times.

CALEDONIAN
80/-
BREWERY
"THE REVERED STANDARD BEARER OF THE SCOTTISH BREWING RENAISSANCE."

Caledonian maintains two traditions: it brews an 80 Shilling ale and serves it through a tall font

Concentrate

The industrial revolution arrived later in Scotland than in England, and industry tended to concentrate in the Lowland belt around Alloa, Edinburgh and Glasgow. As a result, brewing remained a largely domestic affair for much longer and – as with early Irish ales – made little use of the hop, which could not grow in such inhospitable climes.

Brewing developed on a commercial scale in the Lowlands in the early 19th century at the same time as many French emigres, escaping the revolution, settled in the Scottish capital. They dubbed the rich, warming local ales 'Scottish Burgundy'. Real wine from France, always popular in Scotland as a result of the Auld Alliance, became scarce during the Napoleonic Wars, and commercial brewing grew rapidly to fill the gap and to fuel the needs of a growing class of thirsty industrial workers.

Different

Traditionally, Scottish ales were brewed in a different manner to English ones. Before refrigeration, beer was fermented at ambient temperatures far lower than in England. As a result, not all the sugars turned to alcohol, producing rich, full-bodied ales. As hops had to be imported from England at considerable cost, they were used sparingly. The result was a style of beer markedly different to English ones: vinous, fruity, malty and with only a gentle hop bitterness.

Many of the new breed of ales produced by micro-brewers in Scotland tend to be paler and more bitter than used to be the norm. For the true taste of traditional Scottish ales you will have to sample the products of the likes of Belhaven, Broughton, Caledonian and Traquair.

Complexities

The language of Scottish beers is different, too. The equivalent to English mild is called Light (even when it's dark in colour), standard bitter is called Heavy, premium bitter Export, while strong old ales and barley wines (now rare) are called Wee Heavies.

To add to the complexities of the language differences, many traditional beers incorporate the word Shilling in their names. A Light may be dubbed 60 Shilling, a Heavy 70 Shilling, an Export 80 Shilling, and a Wee Heavy 90 Shilling. The designations stem from a pre-decimalisation method of invoicing beer in Victorian times. The stronger the beer, the higher the number of shillings.

Until recent times, cask-conditioned beer in Scotland was served by air pressure. In the pub cellar a water engine, which looks exactly the same as a lavatory cistern but works in reverse, used water to produce air pressure that drove the beer to the bar. Sadly, these wonderful Victorian devices are rarely seen, and the Sassenach handpump and beer engine dominate the pub scene.

GLAMORGAN

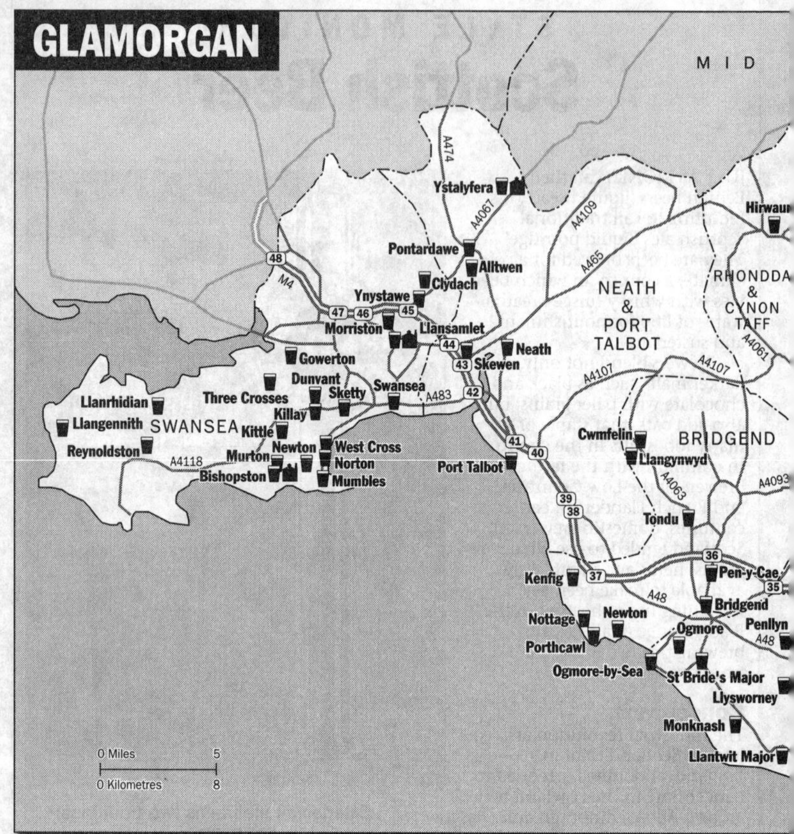

Authority areas covered: Bridgend UA, Caerphilly UA, Cardiff UA, Merthyr Tydfil UA, Neath & Port Talbot UA, Rhondda, Cynon, Taff UA, Swansea UA, Vale of Glamorgan UA

ABERCARN

Old Swan

55 Commercial Road

12.30 (11.30 Fri & Sat)-11; 12-10.30 Sun

☎ (01495) 243161

Courage Best Bitter; H/G guest beer H

Welcoming, roadside pub with a well-refurbished bar area, leading on to a comfortable lounge. Courage on gravity is a popular choice, known by the locals as 'cold tea'. A great supporter of a local charity, the pub has a strong community spirit and the atmosphere is enhanced by a real fire. The relatively local game of 'corks' is played here, among the more usual pub games. A convenient bus stop is just outside. ♨♣

ABERDARE

Cambrian Inn

Seymour Street

11-4, 7-11; 11-11 Fri & Sat; 12-10.30 Sun

☎ (01685) 879120

Beer range varies H

Fine, pleasant town pub, just a short stroll away from the centre. Well decorated and furnished, it draws a range of customers from near and far. The pub sign outside portrays a picture of 'Caradog' or Griffiths Rhys-Jones, a famous music conductor from the town of Aberdare. A range of lunchtime meals is available daily. ⫏≠♣

Whitcombe Inn

Whitcombe Street

3 (12 Sat)-11; 12-10.30 Sun

☎ (01685) 875106

Beer range varies H

Small, pleasant street-corner pub, just off the town centre, offering a good welcome. Behind its etched windows, the interior has basic furnishings with brick walls and floorboards made cosy by the real fire. Something of a real ale oasis in the town, Fuller's London Pride is a welcome regular accompanied by a good range of guest beers. Darts and pool are available in the back room and live music on Wednesday and Friday nights. ♨≠♣

ALLTWEN

Butchers Arms

Alltwen Hill (just off main road to Neath, A474)

12-3, 6.30-11; 12-3, 7-10.30 Sun

☎ (01792) 863100

Courage Directors; Everards Original; John Smith's Bitter; Wadworth 6X; guest beer H

Welcoming, well-run, genuine free house situated high above the Swansea Valley, with a separate restaurant where the locally-renowned meals are home made by the chef, who has served the pub for 12 years (no food Sun eve). The hearth, with its real fire and gleaming copper artefacts,

complements the brick-fronted bar and substantial dark wood furniture. A strong guest ale usually accompanies the four regular beers. Unusually, half pints are served in goblets. A large selection of whiskies is available. ⌂❀◑P

BISHOPSTON

Joiners Arms

50 Bishopston Road

⌚ 11.30-11; 12-10.30 Sun

☎ (01792) 232658

Courage Best Bitter; Marston's Pedigree; Swansea Bishopswood Bitter, Three Cliffs Gold, Original Wood; guest beers Ⓗ

The Joiners has been licensed since the 1860s and is home to the popular Swansea Brewing Company. It is an attractive, stone-built village pub and has an interesting spiral staircase in the bar. There is also a rear lounge and good value food is served in both bars. It is a regular venue for CAMRA visits and occasional beer festivals are held. It was the South and Mid Wales CAMRA Pub of the Year in 1999. ⌂Q❀◑⊟♣P

BLACKWOOD

Rock & Fountain

St David's Avenue, Woodfieldside (from High St take turn opp. Argos, follow road down to river)

⌚ 12 (3 Mon)-11; 12-10.30 Sun

☎ (01495) 223907

Beer range varies Ⓗ

This small, traditional pub is popular with the locals. It is best described as a country inn, based in a market town by a river. The building, originally a counting house for the mining industry, dates from the 1820s. The bar is divided into three areas, one is for non-smokers. Wooden floors and a real fire enhance the friendly atmosphere. Good quality, reasonably-priced food is served, including 'real chips' (no meals on Sun eve or Mon). Diversions include a quiz night (Tue) and live entertainment (occasional Sat). The Sirhowy Valley walk passes the pub. Benches are provided to the front for summer drinking. ⌂Q❀◑♣P⊬

BONVILSTON

Red Lion

On A48

⌚ 11.30-3, 5-11; 12-3.30, 7-10.30 Sun

☎ (01446) 781208

Brains Bitter, SA Ⓗ

This regular Guide entry is situated halfway between Cardiff and Cowbridge on the A48. A 17th-century pub, it is open plan with two bars catering for three separate drinking areas. Photos and paintings, past and present, of this public house adorn the walls alongside the abundant brasses. The outside area consists of a neat, enclosed garden to the rear and car park to the side. Good quality meals are available (except Sun and Mon eves).

Q❀◑♣P✓

BRIDGEND ✻

Haywain

Coychurch Road, Brackla

⌚ 11.30-11; 12-10.30 Sun

☎ (01656) 669945

Greene King Old Speckled Hen; Shepherd Neame Spitfire; Worthington Bitter; guest beers Ⓗ

Large, bustling estate pub decorated with old farming implements. It is popular for lunches, particularly attracting custom from the nearby trading and industrial estates. Evening meals are offered Mon-Sat, 5-9. The Haywain is about one mile from the centre of Bridgend.

❀◑P

Two Brewers

Brackla Way, Brackla (off Coychurch Rd)

⌚ 12-11; 12-10.30 Sun

☎ (01656) 661788

Brains Bitter, SA Ⓗ

Large, modern estate pub with a comfortable public bar and lounge. A separate function room seats 44. The rooms have high ceilings with exposed roof trusses and main beams. Darts and pool are played. Smoking is allowed in all areas. Meals are served 12-7; there is a patio for outdoor drinking.

ᘓ❀◑⊟♣P✓

INDEPENDENT BREWERIES

Brains Cardiff
Bryn Celyn Ystalyfera
Bullmastiff Cardiff
Carters Machen
Lord Raglan Cefn Coed y Cymmer
Swansea Bishopston
Tomos Watkin Llansamlet

Wyndham Arms
Dunraven Place
11-11; 12-10.30 Sun
☎ (01656) 663608
Brains Arms Park, SA; Theakston Best Bitter; Worthington Bitter; guest beers H
Wetherspoon's revival of an old town-centre hotel, the comfortable interior has much original wood panelling and displays interesting photographs and paintings of old Bridgend and district. Wetherspoon's curry club range and other meals are available daily 11-10 (12-9.30 Sun). The upstairs has recently been refurbished as a Wetherlodge. Wheelchair WC.
Q

CARDIFF

Chapter Arts Centre
Market Road, Canton (next door to Butchers Arms)
6-11 (midnight Fri & Sat); 7-10.30 Sun
☎ (029) 2030 4400 website: www.chapter.org
Beer range varies H
This former school is now a thriving local arts centre and a previous local CAMRA Pub of the Year. It caters for a mixed clientele of all ages. The bar boasts a wide range of whiskies and continental beers. Four real ales are offered from independent breweries. Work by local artists displayed in the bar, adds to the bohemian atmosphere.

Butchers Arms
29 Llandaff Road, Canton (B4267)
11-11; 12-10.30 Sun
☎ (029) 2022 7927
Brains Dark, Bitter, SA H
Traditional local with a strong Welsh flavour. A wealth of rugby memorabilia is on display. The pub retains its characterful arched windows, with the Brains logo evident. The bright, lively public bar has pew seating and a dartboard, while the lounge is small and homely. The Butchers Arms is located next to the Chapter Arts Centre. Q

Cayo Arms
36 Cathedral Road, Pontcanna
12-11; 12-10.30 Sun
☎ (029) 2039 1910
Tomos Watkin Whoosh, BB, Merlin's Stout, OSB, seasonal beers H
Cardiff's first Tomos Watkin pub has continued to consolidate its reputation as one of the best alternatives to the ubiquitous Brains establishments. It was voted local CAMRA Pub of the Year within six months of opening, a feat it repeated in 2002. It is conveniently situated for the Millennium Stadium and the Glamorgan County Cricket Club and attracts a mixed clientele of locals, business people and real ale enthusiasts. There is a well-appointed patio area and a fully-equipped conference room available. A regular guest beer is being considered. Meals are served 12-8 daily.
P

Cornwall
92 Cornwall Street, Grangetown
12-11; 12-10.30 Sun
Brains Dark, Bitter, SA; guest beer H
Popular community street-corner local. Both the pub and road it is in, are named after the HMS Cornwall, though after a recent refurbishment it has lost some of its nautical character. The original two rooms have been knocked through but two distinct drinking areas remain. It is particularly busy on match days at nearby Ninian Park, as the pub lies on the main walking route from the city centre. The guest beer is restricted to a Brains seasonal offering.
(Grangetown)

INN BRIEF

ABERAMAN

Blaengwawr Inn
373 Cardiff Road
11-11; 12-10.30 Sun
(01685) 871706
Cains Bitter; guest beers H
Lively, bustling, single-bar village pub, situated on the main road. Live entertainment on offer most weekends.

BRIDGEND

Coach
37 Cowbridge Road
11.30-11; 12-10.30 Sun
(01656) 649231
Draught Bass; Hancock's HB; Worthington Bitter; guest beer H
Friendly, family-run, quiet award-winning pub near Bridgend College. Sparklers are not used. No food Sun eve.

Five Bells Inn
Ewenny Road
11.30-11; 12-10.30 Sun
(01656) 653222
Draught Bass; Worthington Bitter H
Cosy pub on busy road junction. It offers a splendid public bar, adjoining games area, with a quiet lounge bar.

Old Castle/Yr Hen Gastell
90 Nolton Street
11-11; 12-10.30 Sun
(01656) 652305
Hancock's HB; Worthington Bitter H
Old-fashioned, largely unspoilt town pub. The wooden handpump is used for cask-conditioned cider in summer.

CARDIFF

Goat Major
33 High Street
11.30-11.30; 12-5 Sun
(029) 2033 7161
Brains Dark, Bitter, SA, seasonal beers H
Traditional Brains pub with food served every lunchtime. Seasonal beers offered.

Three Horse Shoes
Merthyr Road
12-11; 12-10.30 Sun
(029) 2030 4445
Brains Dark, Bitter, SA, seasonal beer H
Welcoming local beside busy A470. Lively bar with TV and pub games, contrasts with quiet, comfortable lounge. Cask Marque accredited.

Cottage
25 St Mary Street
11-11; 12-10.30 Sun
(029) 2033 7195
Brains Dark, Bitter, SA H
Comfortable, traditional lounge bar with ornate wooden exterior. Long, narrow layout reflects the street's medieval origins.

CWMFELIN

Cross Inn
Maesteg Road
11.45-11; 12-10.30 Sun
(01656) 732476
Brains Buckley's IPA, Bitter; Wye Valley Butty Bach H
Friendly local on the busy A4063. It has a traditional benched public bar and a smart lounge.

GOWERTON

Commercial Hotel
Station Road
12-11; 12-3, 6-10.30 (12-10.30 summer) Sun
(01792) 872072
Brains Buckley's Best Bitter, SA, seasonal beers H
Busy village local near Gowerton railway station. Convenient for cyclists using the Clyne Valley cycle track.

Fox & Hounds

Old Church Road, Whitchurch
❂ 11-11; 12-10.30 Sun
☎ (029) 2069 3377
Brains Dark, Bitter, SA, seasonal beers; guest beers Ⓗ
Enlarged in recent years, the Fox retains a cosy atmosphere as a locals' pub as well as developing a popular and convivial family restaurant and garden. Part of the eating area is a designated no-smoking section. The 'village' bar remains traditional and bustling, with a strong following for sporting events. Quiz night is Sunday. Guest beers are usually from established independent and family brewers. A beer festival is held in early July, as part of the Whitchurch festival and carnival celebrations.
❀◑♿⇌(Whitchurch) P⊬

Glamorgan Council & Staff Club

17 Westgate Street (opp. Millennium Stadium)
❂ 11-11; 12-10.30 Sun
☎ (029) 2023 3216
Black Sheep Best Bitter; Brains Dark; Bullmastiff Gold, seasonal beer Ⓗ
Victorian, red-brick building of great character, previously the office/home of the clerk of the peace and clerk of the county council of Glamorgan. The club was established in 1963. It is a favoured watering-hole on match days with four bars on two floors. A pool room and dartboard are upstairs. The busy, friendly atmosphere makes it a popular venue. A copy of this Guide or a CAMRA membership card will gain admission. Q⛐⊟⇌(Central) ♣

Glass Works

4 Wharton Street (close to indoor market)
❂ 11.30-11; 12-6.30 Sun
☎ (029) 2022 2114
Fuller's ESB; Greene King IPA, Abbot, Old Speckled Hen; guest beers Ⓗ
This popular venue is now open for Sunday trade and is part of the Greene King empire. Once a city-centre shop, it has been converted to form a split-level pub. Visit during 'happy hour' (weekdays 5-7) when there is a 25 per cent reduction on all cask beers. A two-for-one price offer on meals is also sometimes available; meals are served 11.30-7 (7.30 Thu-Sat) and 12-3 Sunday. Invariably an interesting rotating range of up to four guest beers is offered at any time. Beware, it sometimes becomes uncomfortably noisy in the evening as there are loudspeakers in every corner, rendering normal conversation impossible.
◑⇌(Central) ⊬

Griffin

Church Road, Lisvane
❂ 11-11; 12-10.30 Sun
☎ (029) 2074 7399
Draught Bass; Flowers IPA; Fuller's London Pride; Marston's Pedigree; Wadworth 6X; guest beer Ⓗ
The pub comprises a bar area with flagstones, a large fireplace with a TV and two separate raised dining areas. A long central bar links the areas. A guest beer complements a range of well-known real ales. The relaxed atmosphere and local reputation for good food makes this a popular pub. There is a small rear patio which overlooks the large car park.
❀◑♿P✔

New Dock Tavern

188 Broadway, Roath
❂ 12-11; 12-4, 7-10.30 Sun
☎ (029) 2047 1221
Brains Dark, Bitter, SA Ⓗ
Street-corner local; it is basic and simply furnished, but clean and tidy. One side of the triangular bar serves the public bar and

HIRWAUN

Glancynon Inn
Swansea Road
11-11; 12-10.30 Sun
(01685) 811043
Fuller's London Pride; Greene King Old Speckled Hen; guest beers Ⓗ
Welcoming, old coaching inn, dating back to 1870. Split-level bar and comfortable lounge.

LLANTRISANT

New Inn
Swan Street
12-11; 12-10.30 Sun
(01443) 222232
Worthington Bitter; guest beer Ⓗ
Traditional pub set in ancient hilltop town. Well-kept guest beers offered. Photographs of old Llantrisant in the bar.

LLANTWIT MAJOR

Llantwit Major Social Club
The Hayes, Colhugh Street
11.30-3 (not Wed), 6.30-11; 7-10.30 Sun
(01446) 792266
Hancock's HB; Worthington Bitter; guest beer Ⓗ
Large club near town hall attracting a wide range of ages. Normal CIU rules apply, non-members must be signed in.

MERTHYR TYDFIL

Tregenna Hotel
Park Terrace
12-3, 5.30-11; 12-4, 7-10.30 Sun
(01685) 723627
Draught Bass; guest beer Ⓗ
Pleasant lounge bar in family-run three-star hotel which is ideally placed for exploring the nearby Brecon Beacons National Park.

MORRISTON (SWANSEA)

Red Lion Hotel
49 Sway Road
11-11; 12-10.30 Sun
(01792) 773206
Beer range varies Ⓗ
This pub has one cask available from a local brewery at all times. Lunch and evening meals served (except Sun eve).

MUMBLES

Mumbles Rugby Club
588 Mumbles Road
7 (12 Sat; not Wed)-11; 12-3 Sun
(01792) 368989
Worthington Bitter; guest beers Ⓗ
Friendly club with one or two guest beers, usually micros. Membership not required for entry.

NEWTON (PORTHCAWL)

Jolly Sailor
Church Street
11-11; 12-10.30 Sun
(01656) 782403
Brains Dark, Bitter, SA, seasonal beers; guest beers (summer) Ⓗ
Fine, old nautically themed pub with genuine ships' fittings. Former smugglers' tunnel now bricked up. Live music on Sunday.

NOTTAGE (PORTHCAWL)

Rose & Crown
Heol y Capel
11-11; 12-10.30 Sun
(01656) 784850
Courage Best Bitter, Directors; guest beers Ⓗ
Rustic, almost 'Dickensian' ambience in the best sense. Smartly kept old pub with accommodation, pleasantly modernised.

PORTHCAWL

Royal Oak
1 South Road
11.30-11; 12-10.30 Sun
(01656) 782684
Draught Bass; Worthington Bitter; guest beer (occasional) Ⓗ
Comfortable, characterful pub on the fringe of the shopping area. Famed for its generous food portions; no food Sun eve.

another side the snug. There is a third room which is used for occasional meetings and functions. The decor has a nautical theme and features Cardiff docks. Located just off the Newport road, it is worth the journey of a mile or so east of the city centre. A warm welcome is assured.
⊟♣

Olde Butchers Arms

22 Heol y Felin, Rhiwbina
⏲ 12-11; 12-10.30 Sun
☎ (029) 2069 3526
Brains SA; Greene King Old Speckled Hen; Marston's Pedigree; Tetley Bitter Ⓗ
Popular and lively pub with a central bar. Entertainment includes a regular quiz night, jazz (Thu) and a much-used skittle alley. A pool table and TV in one area contrast with the quieter section on the other side of the pub. The landlord has a display of Cardiff City memorabilia. There is a pleasant beer garden at the rear, and ample parking. Under 21s are restricted at weekends.
Q❀◐◑♿♣P

Owain Glyndŵr

St John's Square
⏲ 12-11 (usually extends to midnight Fri & Sat); 12-10.30 (may vary) Sun
☎ (029) 2022 1980
Beer range varies Ⓗ
In the heart of the city, by St John's Church, the Owain Glyndŵr forms part of the larger RSVP pub but has a totally different atmosphere. The fine guest beers, brown woodwork and slightly bohemian, Welsh character are unusual in Cardiff. Variable pricing makes the pub very good value Sun-Thu. It is most expensive on rugby international days. Music is played but it does not spoil the quiet ambience. A real cider is frequently available, usually Weston's Old Rosie. Outdoor drinking is possible on the pedestrianised street.
❀◐◑♿⇌(Central/Queen St) 🍎

Pendragon

Excalibur Drive, Thornhill
⏲ 11-11; 12-10.30 Sun
☎ (029) 2061 0550
Brains Dark, Bitter, SA Ⓗ
Modern estate pub set on a rise with its own green belt and fine mature monkey puzzle trees. The pub has a central bar area with three separate sections, a quiet lounge, lively bar with pool and TV, and a function room. A beer garden and children's play area have fine views over Cardiff. The large car park is linked by its own driveway to the main estate road. Hard work, and dedication to good beer, has turned this pub around. Q❀◐◑⊟♿♣P✔

Vulcan

10 Adam Street (opp. the prison)
⏲ 12-11 (6 Sat); may stay open later for special events in Cardiff; 12-6 Sun
☎ (029) 2046 1580
Brains Dark, Bitter Ⓗ
Quiet pub close to the city centre, it is a fine example of a traditional local of a style which has all but vanished. A large front public bar has a sawdust-covered floor and traditional Brains stained glass windows. The pictures and artefacts displayed reflect the city's maritime past. To the rear is a small lounge served via a hatch. The pub attracts a loyal following of mature customers, many of whom originally came from the now-demolished area of Newtown, and they often travel some distance to visit. Lunches are served Mon-Fri.
Q◐⊟⇌(Central)

Westgate

49 Cowbridge Road East
⏲ 12-11; 12-10.30 Sun
☎ (029) 2030 3926
Brains Dark, Bitter, SA Ⓗ
A landmark 1930s red-brick, two-bar pub on a busy junction. This one-time flagship of the estate of local brewers, Brains, was designed by the famous architect, Sir Percy Thomas. The large lounge bar features plaster reliefs of the signs of many long-vanished Brains' pubs. Close to the Millennium Stadium and the city centre, on event days it can become very busy and entry may be restricted. The pub has a skittle alley, a rare amenity for the city centre. Meals are served weekdays.
◐◑⊟⇌(Central)

INN BRIEF

SWANSEA

Singleton Hotel
1-2 Dillwyn Street
11-11; 12-10.30 Sun
(01792) 412132
Greene King Old Speckled Hen; guest beers Ⓗ
City-centre pub with live music Tue and Sat, and karaoke Fri and Sun. Sun lunches only. Unique Pubco outlet.

TONDU

Llynfi Arms
Maesteg Road
12 (2 Mon & Tue)-4, 7-11; 12-3, 7-10.30 Sun
(01656) 720010
Draught Bass; Worthington Bitter; guest beers Ⓗ
Roadside pub with lively bar and comfortable lounge, encircled by working model railway. Lunches served Wed-Sun, eve meals Wed-Sat.

UPPER CHURCH VILLAGE

Farmers Arms
St Illtyd's Road
11-11; 12-10.30 Sun
(01443) 205766
Brains Bitter; guest beers Ⓗ
Oldest pub in the parish. It still retains a country pub feel. Popular with all ages, and types.

WEST CROSS

West Cross Inn
43 Mumbles Road
11-3.30, 5.30-11; 11-11 Sat; 11-3, 7-10.30 (11-10.30 summer) Sun
(01792) 401143
Greene King Old Speckled Hen; Tomos Watkin OSB; Worthington Bitter Ⓗ
Popular pub/restaurant in a splendid position on the edge of Swansea Bay, on old Mumbles railway route.

Check it out

Pubs in the Good Beer Guide may change ownership and the facilities listed could alter. If a visit to a pub involves a long journey, it's advisable to check before leaving that full meals, family facilities, accommodation or camping sites are still available.

CLYDACH (SWANSEA)

Carpenters Arms

High Street (B4603)
⏲ 11-11; 12-10.30 Sun
☎ (01792) 843333
Brains Dark, seasonal beers; guest beers Ⓗ

Popular, stone-fronted pub with a busy public bar, and a split-level lounge/restaurant. Throughout the year seasonal beer festivals are organised, with ales from regional brewers. Traditional pub games are played and it is also used for meetings by the local cyclists group. A pleasant patio beer garden is available and ample parking.
❀◐◑⊟♣P

CRAIG PENLLYN

Barley Mow

1½ miles N of A48 OS978773
⏲ 12-2.30 (not Mon or Tue), 6-11; 12-3, 7-10.30 Sun
☎ (01446) 772558
Hancock's HB; guest beers Ⓗ

This old established inn retains a special atmosphere. The real ale is always in good condition and the pub continues to supply some of the finest guest beers. The bar meals are reasonably priced and of excellent quality. Families are welcome and there is plenty of parking space in the large car park opposite. The pub is heated in winter by roaring log fires and a small beer garden at the rear is a welcome summer facility.
⩓Q❀◐◑⊟♣P⍻

CWMAMAN

Falcon Inn

1 Incline Row OS008998
⏲ 11-11; 12-10.30 Sun
☎ (01685) 873758 website: www.thefalconinn.net
Beer range varies Ⓗ

Nestled in the Aman Valley, this pub is close to the village but feels almost isolated. The picturesque setting by the river, ensures its popularity in the summer. Three beers are usually on offer at any one time, Robinson's Old Tom is a favourite in the winter. The extension, using wood and stone from a local chapel, proceeds at a leisurely pace. The pub is hard to find, but well worth the effort. Once visited, it is never forgotten.
❀⊟P

DUNVANT

Found Out Inn

Killan Road (up hill towards Three Crosses)
⏲ 12-3.30 (not Mon), 5.30-11; 12-3, 7-10.30 Sun
☎ (01792) 203596
Flowers Original; guest beer (occasional) Ⓗ

This village local was rebuilt in the 1960s when the old inn was demolished. The pub was originally called the Dunvant Inn but was nicknamed the Found Out from the time when local colliers went straight from work to the pub on paydays, only to be found there by their wives and chased home! The pub is immaculately kept and the bar has darts, pool table, juke box and TV. Good value food is served and a quiz is held (Tue). A ramp is available for wheelchair access.
Q❀◐◑⊟♣P

GELLIHAF

Coal Hole

Bryn Road
⏲ 12-3, 6.30-11; 11-11 Fri & Sat; 12-10.30 Sun
☎ (01443) 830280
Hancock's HB; guest beers Ⓗ

This comfortable, friendly one-bar pub, formerly a private house, has extensive views over the Rhymney Valley. Although rather food-based, this pub is well worth a visit, with the two guest ales changing weekly. Drinkers are made to feel very welcome. A courtesy bus is available for use by customers in the local area. No meals are served on Sunday evening. ◐◑P⍻

GILFACH FARGOED

Capel

Park Place
⏲ 12-4, 7-11; 12-11 Fri & Sat; 12-4, 8-10.30 Sun
☎ (01443) 830272
Draught Bass; Brains SA; John Smith's Bitter; guest beers Ⓗ

Large, friendly, traditional Valleys pub featuring many original features including a long bar and extensive wood panelling – there is even a gaslight. The beams bear witty anecdotes and are festooned with hops. The pub offers a comfortable no-smoking room together with overnight accommodation. Look out for the large decorated cast-iron weighing scales in the lobby. It is a focus of the local community with pool, cricket, quizzes and a mini annual beer festival. A rare surviving example of a style once common in the former mining valleys. Guest beers are usually from small independent craft brewers. Lunches are served at weekends.
Q⇄◐⊟≹⍻

GILFACH GOCH

Griffin Inn

Hendreforgan (½ mile off A4093) OS988875
⏲ 7 (12 Sat)-11; 12-10.30 Sun
☎ (01443) 672247
Brains SA; guest beer (occasional) Ⓗ

Nicknamed 'the Bog', this traditional, unspoilt, remote, three-roomed pub is filled with many china, brass, mining, old military and hunting artefacts with some period furniture and a resident ghost – former landlord, 'Bill the Bog'. Outside benches, for summer use, afford views of the surrounding hills and wildlife, including the pair of resident peacocks. The lively atmosphere, with the old stone fireplace newly reopened, gives visitors a warm welcome. The large car park is accessed by an uneven road. ❀⊟♣P

GROESFAEN (PONTYCLUN)

Dynevor Arms

Llantrisant Road (A4119) OS061810
⏲ 11-11; 12-3, 7-10.30 Sun
☎ (029) 2089 0530
Draught Bass; Hancock's HB; Marston's Pedigree; guest beer Ⓗ

Popular, roadside village pub, it is comfortable and well decorated on the inside while on the outside it is colourfully signposted and painted in traditional pub colours. Ever-changing

guest beers are stocked from various brewers. An area is set aside for darts, dominoes and cards and either live music or a quiz is held on Sunday evening. A dining area enhances the open-plan bar facilities and a varied menu offers good value meals with special prices for senior citizens on Monday (no food Sun eve).
✿◑♣●P

KENFIG

Prince of Wales

Maudlam OS804818
⏲ 11.30-4, 6-11; 11.30-11 Sat; 12-10.30 Sun
☎ (01656) 740356 website: www.princeofwales.co.uk
Draught Bass; Worthington Bitter; guest beer (occasional) Ⓖ
Historic pub nearly four centuries old with exposed stone walls and a large open fireplace. It is a former town hall (upstairs is complete with ghostly harmonium player) of the drowned city of Kenfig. It is believed that the Maid of Sker (immortalised by RD Blackmore of Lorna Doone fame) first met her harpist lover here. Renowned for Bass on gravity, no handpumps are used. The pub may stay open throughout the afternoon if busy. The garden adjoins a nature reserve.
♨Q✿◑▲P

KILLAY

Railway Inn

553 Gower Road, Upper Killay
⏲ 11-11; 12-10.30 Sun
☎ (01792) 203946
Marston's Pedigree; Shepherd Neame Spitfire; Swansea Deep Slade Dark, Bishopswood Bitter, Original Wood; guest beers Ⓗ
The pub was built in 1864 when the railway was constructed through the Clyne Valley. The railway closed in the 1960s but happily the pub still stands, an unspoilt gem with railway memorabilia and a good selection of ales. The pub is a major outlet for the Swansea Brewing Company and holds occasional beer festivals. It was Swansea CAMRA Pub of the Year in 2000. The old railway route is now a popular walk, and a cycle track.
♨♉✿⊟♣P

KITTLE (SWANSEA)

Beaufort Arms

18 Pennard Road
⏲ 11.30-11; 12-10.30 Sun
☎ (01792) 234521
Brains Buckley's Best Bitter, SA, Rev James, seasonal beers Ⓗ
Reputedly the oldest pub in Gower, it has won awards for its community focus. A Brains tenanted house with three bars and a function room, the oldest part of the pub has a beamed ceiling and early stonework. There is a large car park and outdoor seating, plus a children's play area. Piped music is played and a juke box provided. Quizzes are held (Mon) and the pub hosts a local ladies' darts team. An extensive menu is served daily (11.30-9.30 Fri-Sun).
♉✿◑⊟♣P✔

LLANGENNITH

King's Head

⏲ 11-11; 12-10.30 Sun
☎ (01792) 386212
Felinfoel Double Dragon; Fuller's London Pride; Tomos Watkin BB, OSB; guest beer (summer) Ⓗ
Historic pub on the village green, extended over the centuries as adjoining farm buildings have been incorporated. There are splendid views of nearby beaches which are within walking distance for the energetic. The pub is popular with visitors to nearby caravan and camping sites, especially in the holiday periods, and a games room is available. Food is served all day. Note the old pictures in the bar, including those of Phil Tanner, the legendary Gower folk singer. ♨Q✿◑⊟▲♣P

LLANGYNWYD

Old House/Yr Hen Dŷ

On top of the hill, W of A4063 OS858889
⏲ 11-11; 12-10.30 Sun
☎ (01656) 733310 website: www.oldhouse-llan.co.uk
Flowers IPA, Original; Worthington Bitter; guest beer Ⓗ
Extremely popular, atmospheric thatched pub, one of the oldest in Wales (circa 1147). Much extended, its large windows afford views across the Bryncynan Valley. Booking is advised for Sunday and evening meals in the excellent restaurant. The festive tradition 'Mari Lwyd' is depicted on the pub sign and performed each New Year. Locals dress up (in a horse's head for example) and visit houses, singing and drinking on the way. Wil Hopcyn (1701-41), the poet, used the pub. He courted Ann Thomas, the maid of Cefn Ydfa, and wrote the song Bugeilio r Gwenith Gwyn about her. Read about them in the pub. There is an adventure playground, and the garden incorporates a helicopter landing pad. ♨Q♉✿◑▲P✔

LLANRHIDIAN

Greyhound Inn

Oldwalls
⏲ 11-11; 12-10.30 Sun
☎ (01792) 391027
Fuller's London Pride; Marston's Pedigree; Tomos Watkin BB, OSB; guest beer Ⓗ
Free house with an excellent atmosphere situated on the main north Gower road. There is usually a guest beer and the food is popular – especially local fish. Families are welcome in the games room and food is served all day in the bars and the restaurant. There is also a function room.
♨Q♉✿◑⊟▲♣P

LLANSAMLET

Plough & Harrow

57 Church Road (next to church)
⏲ 12-11; 12-10.30 Sun
☎ (01792) 772263
Tomos Watkin Whoosh, Merlin's Stout, OSB, seasonal beers Ⓗ
Brewery tap for Tomos Watkin ales, the first Watkin pub in Swansea, situated just off the busy road at the junction of Llansamlet lights. The Plough nestles in the shadow of the parish church. A bright, cheery, open-plan pub with a large, cosy log fire at one

end which adds to the warmth of the welcome. As well as the brewery beers, the pub sells a tempting menu for the weary traveller. A pleasant alternative to the town pubs. Live music is performed (Sun) and a quiz hosted (Wed). ⛰❀◐◑♿⇌P

LLANTWIT MAJOR ❄

King's Head

East Street

✪ 11-11; 12-10.30 Sun

☎ (01446) 792697

Brains Dark, Bitter, SA, seasonal beers; Worthington Bitter Ⓗ

Very pleasant town-centre local, this two-bar pub comprises a large public bar with pool table, sports on a large-screen TV and bench seating. Dominoes or another game is often played by the real fire in winter. This room also houses live music and karaoke on weekend nights. The lounge, by contrast, is carpeted and upholstered, and tends to be slightly more peaceful. Bar meals comprise good value, home-cooked grub. A children's menu is available, and if desired, the small, separate no-smoking dining room can be used. ⛰❀◐⊟▲♣

Old Swan Inn

Church Street (opp. Town Hall)

✪ 12-11; 12-10.30 Sun

☎ (01446) 792230 website: www.oldswaninn.com

Beer range varies Ⓗ

This small town pub has suffered mixed fortunes for quite some years. Happily, under its current owners, it has once again become a first-class venue for real ale drinkers. There is a constantly changing range of three or four ales, normally including one session beer. The range tends to be different to other guest beer houses in the area. The staff are knowledgeable and helpful, and will happily remove sparklers on request. Food is served all day in summer and generally 12-3 and 6-10 in winter. Ring the pub for further details. Meals are top quality and value and include 11 varieties of mashed potato. ⛰❀◐◑⊟♣P

LLYSWORNEY

Carne Arms

On B4268, off A48

✪ 12-11 (closed 3-5 during winter); 12-10.30 Sun

☎ (01446) 773553 website: www.thecarnearms.co.uk

Usher's Best Bitter, Founders Ale Ⓗ

White-walled, friendly local situated at the southern end of the village on the B4268, 3¼ miles from Llantwit Major (according to the milestone outside). At the far end of the car park, children can be kept amused in the safe play area or animal garden. A covered Mediterranean-style patio guards the main entrance to the two-roomed pub, both rooms boast inglenooks and were used during the war as soup kitchens. Main meals are served in the lounge, and special themed menus are regularly offered. There is a no-smoking area from Fri-Sun. ⛰Q❀◐◑⊟♣P⚡

MACHEN

White Hart Inn

Nant Ceisiad (100 yds N of A468, under railway bridge) OS203892

✪ 12-3, 6.30-11; 12-11 Sat; 12-10.30 Sun

☎ (01633) 441005

Hancock's HB; guest beers Ⓗ

Convivial country inn enjoyed by drinkers and diners alike. Fine wood panelling (much salvaged from the luxury liner Empress of France) adorns the walls throughout. This room also has a welcoming real fire in the winter. Leading off from the main bar is a comfortable ante-room and a large function room, the latter opens for Sunday lunches and the regular beer festivals. The in-house brewery (Carters) has expanded and its products are often on sale at the bar. ⛰❀⇄◐◑P

MERTHYR TYDFIL ❄

Dic Penderyn

102-103 High Street

✪ 11-11; 12-10.30 Sun

☎ (01685) 385786

Brains Arms Park, SA; Theakston Best Bitter; Worthington Bitter; guest beer Ⓗ

This busy Wetherspoon's pub is named after one of the leaders of the Merthyr riots of 1833. He was later executed and has become a local hero. The premises have been converted from a very large 19th-century general store. There is a pleasant room dedicated to the famous Welsh composer, Joseph Parry, where his family records are displayed. There are also many historic photographs of Merthyr when it was a major iron-producing town. The railway and bus stations and a large car park are nearby. Q◐◑♿⇌●⚡✔

MISKIN

Miskin Arms

Hensol Road (180 yds off B4264, opp. war memorial in village)

✪ 11.30-11; 12-10.30 Sun

☎ (01443) 224346

Hancock's HB; guest beer Ⓗ

First mentioned by name as the Miskin Arms in local records dating from 1741. This pleasantly decorated listed building not only serves guest beers, but also daily curries from 'around the world'. The pub incorporates Mayfields restaurant, well known for its first-class, adventurous evening meals. Lunches are offered Mon-Sat, evening meals Tue-Sat. A wooden decking area outside the lounge overlooks the patio, which is adjacent to the car park and beer garden. Suggestions for new guest beers are always welcomed by the proprietors. ❀◐◑♿▲⇌P

MONKNASH

Plough & Harrow

Off B4265, between Marcross and Broughton

✪ 12-11; 12-10.30 Sun

☎ (01656) 890209

website: www.theploughandharrow.com

Draught Bass; Ⓖ **Hancock's HB; Shepherd Neame Spitfire; Tomos Watkin OSB; Wye Valley HPA;** Ⓗ **guest beers** Ⓗ/Ⓖ

This consistently excellent pub has won the Vale CAMRA Pub of the Year award for several years running. The atmosphere has to be experienced to be believed, as it is unlike all but a few other pubs in the UK, which is why it reached the final four in the

National CAMRA Pub of the Year awards a few years ago. There are up to 12 ales and three ciders on sale, although the range is slghtly reduced in winter. Good food is served all day Mon-Fri and lunches at weekends. If you only visit one Vale pub make sure it is this one.
⚓❀◑⊟♣●P

MOUNTAIN ASH

Jeffreys Arms

Jeffrey Street

⊙ 12-11 (may vary in winter); 12-10.30 Sun
☎ (01443) 472976

Worthington Bitter; guest beer Ⓗ

Popular and lively village pub, set in a quiet side street not far from the main road. Photographs of Mountain Ash in bygone times adorn the walls of the pleasantly-furnished public bar, while the lounge offers customers a greater degree of comfort. The pub was recently refurbished. Upstairs is a spacious function room and restaurant, the latter offering a good menu of home-cooked food (booking is advisable). Wheelchair access is possible on the ground floor only. The pub has an attractive beer garden.
❀⊟♿⇌♣

MUMBLES ❊

Park Inn

23 Park Street

⊙ 12-2.30 (not Mon), 4.30-11; 12-11 Sat; 12-10.30 Sun
☎ (01792) 366738

Swansea Three Cliffs Gold; Worthington Bitter; guest beers Ⓗ

Former Swansea CAMRA Pub of the Year, the Park has a long-established reputation for a good selection of guest ales (usually five, including Welsh beers). Good value, home-cooked meals are available and there is always an appetising selection of specials on offer. Theme nights such as Spanish evenings and regular open mike music nights are popular with both locals and visitors alike. There are some interesting pictures displayed of the pub in years gone by. A light-hearted quiz is held weekly (Thu). Addlestone's cider is stocked.
Q◑♣●

Victoria Inn

21 Westbourne Place

⊙ 12 (11.30 Sat)-11; 12-10.30 Sun
☎ (01792) 360111

Draught Bass; Greene King Old Speckled Hen; Worthington Bitter; guest beer (occasional) Ⓗ

Lovely old back-street, corner local dating from the mid-19th century, as the name implies. The pub has been attractively renovated, retaining the stained glass windows and making a feature of the old pub well which was undoubtedly the water source in the days when the pub brewed its own beer. The pub is single-roomed, although there are two distinct sections – the bar area has darts and TV, while the other end is a little quieter. The Bass is served 'flat' on request.
❀♣

MURTON

Plough & Harrow

88 Oldway

⊙ 11-11; 12-10.30 Sun
☎ (01792) 234459

Courage Best Bitter, Directors; guest beers Ⓗ

One of the oldest pubs in Gower, which has been enlarged and renovated in recent times. It still retains its character and manages to combine its popular food trade with its tradition as a village local. The bar has darts, TV and a pool table, and is popular with younger customers, while the lounge is a comfortable place to enjoy a quiet chat or a bar meal. Quiz night is on Tuesday. Q❀◑♣P

MWYNDY

Barn at Mwyndy

Down lane opp. Corner Park Garage on A4119
OS056816

⊙ 11-3, 5-11; 11.30-11 Sat; 12-10.30 Sun
☎ (01443) 222333

Worthington Bitter; guest beers Ⓗ

Converted 16th-century long barn with an intriguing array of farming and fishing memorabilia (note the coracle). There is a split-level bar, the lower area has a thatched canopy and the upper area a log fire in winter. Amenities include an excellent, no-smoking restaurant (reservations advised), conference facilities, a beer garden, children's play area and a large car park. Regular beer festivals are hosted and an enthusiastic pétanque team plays frequently. Up to six guest beers are served. Local CAMRA Pub of the Year 2001. Reputedly sightings of a female ghost upstairs! ⚓❀◑♿P

NEATH

Highlander

2 Lewis Road (on Stockhams roundabout on A474)

⊙ 12-2.30, 6-11; 12-11 Sat; 12-3.30, 7-10.30 Sun
☎ (01639) 633586

Draught Bass; Hancock's HB; guest beers Ⓗ

Popular, genuine free house, this imposing building is situated between the British Legion and the Methodist church, about 200 yards from the Neath River bridge. It is a comfortable, one-bar town pub with plenty of wood, an elevated eating area downstairs plus an upstairs restaurant. It enjoys a well-deserved reputation locally for good value food. A wide variety of guest ales is sourced from all over the country (and occasionally further afield), three are usually on offer. ◑⇌

Star Inn

83 Pen-y-dre (near Courage Gnoll rugby ground)

⊙ 12-11; 12-10.30 (12-3, 6-10.30 winter) Sun

Draught Bass; Hancock's HB; guest beer Ⓗ

Popular, old back-street local where strangers are welcome and where the new landlord runs a splendid pub. Beer is dispensed from 1940s beer engines. It is very busy when Neath RFC play at home and for Six Nations games. Lunches are served Mon-Sat; quiz night is Sunday. The beer garden has a boules piste and a children's play area. Charities are well supported. Neath Canal and a national cycle track are nearby. A trouble-free,

genuine free house, it is often described as a real pub.
Q❀◑⇌♣P⊬

NEWTON (GOWER)

Newton Inn

New Well Lane (opp. garage)
12-11; 12-10.30 Sun
☎ (01792) 365101
Draught Bass; H/G Fuller's London Pride; Marston's Pedigree; Worthington Bitter H

Popular village local refurbished about 10 years ago but retaining bar and lounge areas in a semi open-plan layout. The pub offers very competitively-priced meals and is popular with diners at lunchtimes and early evenings. The bar has a big-screen TV which is much-used for sporting events. The draught beers, particularly the Bass, can be drawn straight from the cask on request. Quizzes are held on Monday and Wednesday. Tables outside the pub on the roadside are available for summer drinking. ❀◑▶⊟

NORTON

Beaufort

1 Castle Road (turn by Norton House Hotel, off Mumbles Rd)
11.30-11; 12-10.30 Sun
☎ (01792) 401319
Draught Bass; Worthington Bitter; guest beer H

Village local dating from the 18th century, with traditional public bar and smaller, comfortable lounge, recently refurbished. Both rooms have real fires. The bar has darts and a TV and a quiz is held every Tuesday. There are photographs of the annual Mumbles Raft Race on the walls including one splendid picture of a raft built to replicate the pub itself! The Beaufort retains its friendly charm. ⋒Q❀⊟♣

NOTTAGE (PORTHCAWL) ❋

Farmer's Arms

Lougher Row
11.30-midnight; 12-10.30 Sun
☎ (01656) 784595
Greene King Abbot, Old Speckled Hen; Worthington Bitter; guest beers H

Popular, rambling pub by the village green. Live music is staged most nights in one of the bars. Good lunchtime food is served 12-2 (12.30-2.30 Sun) and evening food Mon-Sat, 6.45-9.15. Caravans are allowed on the nearby campsite. ❀◑▶⊟▲P

OGMORE

Pelican In Her Piety

Ewenny Road
11.30-11; 12-10.30 Sun
☎ (01656) 880049 website: www.pelicanpub.co.uk
Draught Bass; Fuller's London Pride; Greene King Old Speckled Hen; Wadworth 6X; Young's Special H

An excellently refurbished roadside public house with a newly-improved patio at the front, affording great views of the ruins of Ogmore Castle opposite. Welcoming both to its locals and visitors, with a warming log fire in winter, this pub rightly prides itself on its top quality ales (all served without sparklers) and its food. A great deal of charity work goes on, in aid of an autistic children's charity. The pub name was just the Pelican for many years, but has reverted to its original title (an heraldic symbol), under its current owners. ⋒Q☎❀◑▶♣P

OGMORE-BY-SEA

Sealawns Hotel

Slon Lane (on coast road)
12-3, 6-11; 12-3, 7-10.30 Sun
☎ (01656) 880311
Felinfoel Double Dragon; Tomos Watkin OSB; Worthington Bitter H

Originally a 16th-century cottage, this premises was a country club before it was converted to an hotel. Situated at the eastern end of Ogmore, with the car park stretching down to the Bristol Channel, in good weather Devon can be easily seen plus six other counties. There is a large, enclosed garden with a fresh lobster/crayfish tank on the patio visible from the à la carte restaurant which boasts three chefs – dine by candlelight. A welcoming open fire greets you during the winter months. Barbecues are held in summer.
⋒Q❀⇔◑▶⊟P

PANT

Pant-Cad-Ifor

By mountain railway
12-11 (12-3, 7-11 winter Mon); 12-10.30 Sun
☎ (01685) 723688
Hancock's HB; Worthington Bitter; guest beers H

The Pant-Cad-Ifor (Ivor's Chair in the Hollow) is a plush, bustling village pub situated near the Brecon Mountain Railway. Popular with locals and visitors alike, the pub offers a fine range of guest ales, a real cider and good food from the restaurant. Pleasant decor and a real fire welcome people in. The beams are festooned with a bewildering array of pump clips showing past guest beers. ⋒❀◑▶P

PENLLYN

Red Fox Inn

Off A48 at Pentre Meyrick cross
12-2.30 (3 Sat), 7-11; 12-3, 7-10.30 Sun
☎ (01446) 772352
Tomos Watkin Whoosh, OSB H

This charming country inn continues to enjoy a fine reputation for the quality of its real ale and excellent cuisine. It is now in its third year of business since reopening (with the help and support of CAMRA) and is gaining in popularity. It is a friendly local with much character. In winter it boasts a roaring log fire around which chestnuts are roasted and enjoyed by all. In front is a large patio with a beautiful floral display while at the rear, a large orchard beer garden is a safe haven for children (who are very welcome but must be accompanied by adults). ⋒Q❀◑▶♣P

PEN-Y-CAE

Tŷ'r Isha

OS903824
11-11; 12-10.30 Sun
☎ (01656) 725287
Brains Buckley's Best Bitter, SA, seasonal beers; Greene King Abbot H

Comfortable conversion of an old Welsh

long-house, originally a farm, then a court house. The cellars were once cells and stables. The surrounding gardens include a children's playground. It is located near, and south of, junction 36 of the M4. Take the little lane that runs along the southern side of Sainsbury's and the McArthur Glen designer village. Down the hill, just before it bends sharply to the left, the pub is down a short drive on the right. Meals are served Mon-Thu 12-9 (9.30 Fri and Sat), and Sun 12-6.
P

PONTARDAWE

Pontardawe Inn

123 Herbert Street

12-11; 12-10.30 Sun

(01792) 830791 website: www.come.to/gwachel

Brains Dark, Buckley's Best Bitter, Rev James, seasonal beers or guest beers H

This attractive two-bar village inn, with a riverside location, is locally known as the Gwachel. An interesting selection of local history is displayed in the bar. There is a large car park, family play area and boules court. Colourful hanging baskets are displayed during the summer (2001 prize winner of Neath Port Talbot in Bloom). Live music is performed (Fri and Sat eves) and the landlord holds regular beer festivals during the year. Wheelchair WC. No food Tuesday or Sunday evenings.
P

PONTLLANFRAITH

Crown

Bryn View

12-3, 5-11; 12-11 Fri & Sat; 7-10.30 Sun

(01495) 223404

Courage Best Bitter; John Smith's Bitter; guest beers H

Two-roomed pub surrounded by roads on all sides. It comprises a basic public bar and a spacious lounge and dining area and has been recently refurbished. There is a large car park and an outside drinking area with children's play equipment. It can get busy with families at weekends and on fine summer evenings. Regular quiz nights (Tue) are hosted by the landlord.
P

PONTYPRIDD

Llanover Arms

Bridge Street

12-11; 12-3, 7-10.30 Sun

(01443) 403215

Brains Dark, Bitter, SA; Worthington Bitter; guest beer H

Opposite the renowned Ynysynharad Park and adjacent to the A470, this 18th-century town pub has been kept by the same family for over a century. Once slaking the thirst of chainmakers and bargees, it is now the favoured watering-hole of discerning drinkers from near and far. The enterprising guest ale policy is much appreciated as is demonstrated by their rapid turnover. There is a small bar, snug and vestry – each area has its devotees who appreciate the olde-worlde setting and convivial atmosphere.
P

PORTHCAWL

Lorelei Hotel

36-38 Esplanade Avenue

5 (12 Sat)-11; 12-10.30 Sun

(01656) 788342 website: www.loreleihotel.co.uk

Draught Bass; G **Shepherd Neame Spitfire; Wye Valley Butty Bach; guest beers** H

Enterprising bar in a small hotel that runs several beer festivals each year. Situated just off the seafront, the bar is small but comfortable with a dining area to the rear of the premises. Neath and Bridgend CAMRA Pub of the Year 2000, it is well worth visiting this oasis of real ale in a mainly keg seaside town. Beers on gravity are not kept in the bar so ask what is available. Beers from Bullmastiff Brewery regularly feature. Sunday lunch is served and evening meals Mon-Sat (6-9pm).

PORT TALBOT

Lord Caradoc

69-72 Station Road

11-11; 12-10.30 Sun

(01639) 896007

Draught Bass; Brains Dark, SA; Greene King Abbot; Hop Back Summer Lightning; Theakston Best Bitter; guest beers H

Typical open-plan Wetherspoon's pub with an L-shaped bar situated in the centre of Port Talbot, two minutes' walk from the railway station. It has the usual range of five beers on all the time and occasionally stocks two different guest ales. It offers a beer garden (situated at the back exit), a no-smoking section, wheelchair facilities and a separate dining area. Food is served all day with special offers on certain meals. It is the only pub in the town worth drinking in.
Q

QUAKERS YARD

Glan Taff

Cardiff Road (A4054 between Abercynon and Treharris)

12-4, 7-11; 12-4, 7-10.30 Sun

(01443) 410822

Courage Best Bitter, Directors; John Smith's Bitter; guest beers H

Comfortable inn displaying a large collection of water jugs, boxing memorabilia and photographs of local and historical interest. This well-appointed pub enjoys a warm and friendly atmosphere on the side of the River Taff and close to the Taff Trail. Walkers and cyclists break their journey for refreshments, to sample a cool, refreshing glass of beer and the good food that is served (no meals Sun eve). This is a long-standing Guide entry and well worth a visit. Q P

REYNOLDSTON

King Arthur Hotel

Higher Green

12-11; 12-10.30 Sun

(01792) 390775

Draught Bass; Felinfoel Double Dragon; Worthington Bitter H

Imposing pub and hotel/restaurant popular with both locals and tourists. The King Arthur is named after Arthur's Stone, a prehistoric monument situated on the nearby Cefn Bryn Hill. The hotel is in a most pleasant spot in the middle of the Gower Peninsula and has a large outdoor drinking area. It is reputedly haunted by two ghosts. Meals are served in the bar, the restaurant, the family room and also outside. ⋔Q☺❀⊭◐ ▶ ⊞⋀♣P

RHYMNEY

Farmers Arms

Brewery Row

✪ 12-11; 12-10.30 Sun

☎ (01685) 840257

Boddingtons Bitter; Brains Bitter; Fuller's London Pride; guest beer Ⓗ

Friendly, spacious, comfortable pub and restaurant, traditionally furnished. Originally a farmhouse, it was taken over by the former Rhymney Brewery which opened in 1839 to slake the thirst of iron workers and miners. Later extended to provide a function room for up to 40 people, the furnishings and bric-à-brac reflect a farming theme, together with Rhymney Brewery memorabilia and interesting old photographs. It is popular with locals and train-spotters alike. Traditional card games are played, especially cribbage. Good, reasonably-priced food is served and there is a separate dining area. Regular guest beers are stocked.
❀◐▶ ⇌(Valley Lines) ♣P✔

RISCA

Commercial

Commercial Street, Pontyminster (B4591)

✪ 11-11; 12-10.30 Sun

☎ (01633) 612608

Beer range varies Ⓗ

Large pub at the southern end of Risca. The one bar is divided into two distinct areas. The comfortable lounge has plenty of seating, carpeted floor and small TV, while the public bar with lino floor has darts, pool table and fruit machines, plus a larger TV. A patio is available for outdoor drinking. No food is served. Regular ales come from Tomos Watkin and Wye Valley breweries.
❀♣

Fox & Hounds

Park Road

✪ 11-11; 12-10.30 Sun

☎ (01633) 612937

Beer range varies Ⓗ

Bustling village pub situated away from the main road, with fine views over the local park grounds. Pleasantly decorated, the single bar offers guest ales from predominantly local micro-breweries, with the next beers due displayed on a blackboard in the bar. A pool table at one end and a large TV screen at the opposite end cater for all sports fans. Bar meals are available and a beer festival is usually held between Christmas and New Year. ❀◐▶♣P

RUDRY

Maenllwyd Inn

At crossroads SE of Rudry

✪ 11-11; 12-10.30 Sun

☎ (029) 2088 2372

Courage Best Bitter, Directors; Theakston XB; guest beer Ⓗ

Charming country inn, parts of which date back 400 years. With low, beamed ceilings and grey stone walls (the Welsh equivalent being maenllwyd), it was originally a farmhouse at the time of the Civil War. There have been reported sightings of two ghosts; one is a legless cavalier (not due to drink, but the floor level was once lower). An extensive menu is offered daily.
⋔Q☺❀◐▶P

ST BRIDE'S MAJOR

Farmers Arms

Wick Road (B4265)

✪ 12-2.30, 6-11; 12-3.30, 6-10.30 Sun

☎ (01656) 880224

Courage Best Bitter; Usher's Best Bitter, Founders Ale, seasonal beers Ⓗ

Locally known as the pub on the pond for reasons that become obvious when you get there. This is an extremely popular pub and restaurant where you can expect good beer and food with a friendly welcome. Booking is advisable for the restaurant, especially at weekends. The pub is decorated in traditional style, with plenty of china and glass jugs in evidence. Despite its popularity with tourists and passing trade, there is still a lively local scene in evidence. If you do go for a stroll to the pond, remember that swans can be quite vicious! ⋔Q❀◐▶P

ST HILARY

Bush Inn

Off A48, E of Cowbridge

✪ 11.30-11; 12-10.30 Sun

☎ (01446) 772745

Draught Bass; Greene King Old Speckled Hen; Ⓖ **Hancock's HB;** Ⓗ **guest beer** Ⓖ

Marvellous 400-year-old thatched inn in an attractive vale village. Do not be fooled by the tiny bar as you go in, as there is another larger one to the left and an intimate restaurant to the right. There is also a pleasant outside drinking area for warm weather. A display of hops around the fireplace makes a very cosy winter atmosphere when the fire is lit. Please ask which beers are available rather than rely on the pump clips. Well known for excellent food (no meals Sun eve), it is also one of the rare outlets for the locally produced 'real crisps'. Weston's Old Rosie cider is stocked.
⋔Q❀◐▶●P

SIGINGSTONE

Victoria Inn

E of B4268

✪ 11.45-3, 6.30-11; 12-3, 7-10.30 Sun

☎ (01446) 773943

Tomos Watkin Whoosh, OSB, seasonal beers Ⓗ

Situated off the B4268 behind the disused Llandow airfield, this pub was once called the Moor's Head but changed its name during Queen Victoria's jubilee year. A small front bar, with an open fire and a large print of Queen Victoria's jubilee procession, leads into a much larger L-shaped room with plates and brasses on the walls and a bust of Queen Victoria in the corner. Meals are served in the main bar and also upstairs in the beamed restaurant.
Q❀◐▶P

SKETTY (SWANSEA)

Vivian

6 Gower Road
12-11; 12-10.30 Sun
(01792) 516194
Brains Buckley's Best Bitter, SA, Rev James H
Long-standing Guide entry situated on Sketty Cross. A Brains managed house, it has been refurbished and is now a one-bar pub. Lots of wood, and walls adorned with a mixture of modern art and pictures of old Swansea, it still retains some stained glass windows. Lunches are served daily and evening meals Mon-Fri, 6-8. The large-screen TV is used for sporting events. There is a relaxed atmosphere with piped music. Enjoy a pint in the pretty, walled beer garden. Wheelchair WC.

SKEWEN

Crown

216 High Street (village centre)
12-11; 12-10.30 Sun
(01792) 411270
Brains Dark, Bitter, SA H
This friendly inn has a central village location, and a traditionally-furnished locals' bar where horse racing is popular at afternoon sessions. There is a separate, comfortable, split-level lounge bar with a big TV screen for major sporting events. Live music is staged every Friday evening for the more mature ear. There is also an upstairs snooker room. The rear walled courtyard has recently been developed and offers seating for about 30. This pub offers the best range of Brains' beers in the area.

SWANSEA

Bank Statement ☆

57-58 Wind Street
11-11; 12-10.30 Sun
(01792) 455477
Brains Dark, SA; Theakston Best Bitter; Worthington Bitter; guest beers H
Former bank converted into a large city-centre Wetherspoon's. Located in the heart of the lively Wind Street pub, club and restaurant area, it is quiet during the day, but tends to become very busy in the evening, especially at the weekends. It offers cheap prices and a selection of two regularly changing guest ales. Good value food is available throughout the day. Wheelchair WC. Q (High St)

Brunswick Inn

3 Duke Street
12-11; 12-10.30 Sun
(01792) 456676
Greenalls Bitter; Swansea Deep Slade Dark; H **guest beers** G
Long-established pub on the fringe of the city centre. It was attractively refurbished about 10 years ago and boasts much woodwork and many rural pictures, providing a cosy atmosphere. Popular for food, especially lunches; evening meals are served 6-8.30 Mon-Sat. Subdued piped music is played. A quiz is hosted every Monday and live music twice monthly. Guest beers are served straight from the barrel. It is a Scottish Courage pub.

Eli Jenkins Ale House

24 Oxford Street
11-11; 12-10.30 Sun
(01792) 630961
Badger Tanglefoot; Draught Bass; Worthington Bitter; guest beer H
Large, modern city-centre outlet named after a character in Under Milkwood by Dylan Thomas. There are wooden alcoves and niches throughout and the walls are adorned with memorabilia, such as old books, and some references to Dylan Thomas. Meals are served 11.30-7 Mon-Sat, and 12-3.30 on Sunday. It can get very busy at lunchtime. The guest beer is changed frequently. Piped music is played. Wheelchair WC.

Queen's Hotel

Gloucester Place
11-11; 12-10.30 Sun
(01792) 521531
Brains Buckley's Best Bitter; Theakston Best Bitter, Old Peculier; guest beers (occasional) H
Genuine free house on the edge of the city centre and marina. This is a one-bar outlet with strong local support. The walls have many photographs depicting the maritime history of the area and the pub co-hosts the sea shanty festival in July. Weekly quizzes are hosted (Sun and Wed). Live music is staged on bank holiday Monday; selective juke box music is played at other times. It is a rare regular outlet for Old Peculier. A small TV room is available for sporting events.

Westbourne Hotel

1 Bryn-y-mor Road
12-2.30, 5.30-11; 12-11 Fri & Sat; 12-2.30, 7-10.30 Sun
(01792) 476637
Draught Bass; Hancock's HB; guest beer H
Comfortable Enterprise Inn house with an internal layout that manages to retain two separate areas and bars including a dartboard. The guest beer changes regularly and is often of high gravity. Good value food is served at lunchtime, and on weekday evenings (6-8). It is a short walk from the city centre and convenient for the rugby and cricket grounds. Unobtrusive background music makes this pub a welcome haven. There is a small raised garden area to the front. Wheelchair WC.

THREE CROSSES

Poundffald Inn

12-11; 12-10.30 Sun
(01792) 873428
Brains SA; Greene King Abbot, Old Speckled Hen; Marston's Pedigree; Worthington Bitter; guest beer (occasional) H
This popular village local has a traditional public bar with a welcoming fire in winter – it was awarded Real Fire Pub of the Year 2001. There is an interesting collection of horse bits, and other rural implements. The name Poundffald refers to the old circular animal pound that was incorporated into the lounge. The 'ffald' half of the name is the Welsh word for pound and so we have the name in both languages together. The lounge is food-oriented and meals are offered all day. P

TREFOREST

Otley Arms
Forest Road
11-11; 12-10.30 Sun
☎ (01443) 402033 website: www.otleyltd.co.uk
Bullmastiff Gold; Cains Bitter; guest beers H
Since the Commercial became the Otley in 1975, this once small, end-of-terrace pub has expanded through a series of arches into the two adjacent properties, giving it a Tardis-like feel. Though well-frequented by students from the nearby university, it is still popular with locals, everyone appreciating the keenly-priced ales and lunchtime food. Sports fans are well catered for with multiple TVs (which often show different events simultaneously). Guest beers may not be available during university breaks. ◑≋♣P

TYLE GARW

Boar's Head Hotel
600 yds off A473, down Coed Cae Lane, over level crossing
12-11; 12-5, 7-10.30 Sun
☎ (01443) 225400
Brains SA, Rev James; guest beers H
Built in 1875, the pub once served the workforce from the local railway, iron ore mine, tin works and 'Cambrian' forge. Now it has modern industrial units and a housing estate as neighbours. It is thought to be haunted by George Owen who was landlord at the pub in the 1920s. Despite recent refurbishments, the pub still retains that warm, friendly, welcoming atmosphere where customers of all ages drink together. The landlord has set a target of 200 different real ales a year.
⚲❀⇌◑◗⊟⩓≋(Pontyclun) ♣P

YNYSTAWE (SWANSEA)

Millers Arms
634 Clydach Road (next to school)
11.30-3, 6-11; 11.30-11 Sat; 12-3, 7-10.30 Sun
☎ (01792) 842614
Adnams Bitter; Taylor Landlord; Wells Bombardier H
Welcoming roadside pub now a regular Guide entry. It is well known for its good food, served in the bar and adjoining restaurant. The beer list is unusual for the area and is proving popular with locals. Note the teapot collection on top of the bar. There is a car park at the rear of the pub, and for public transport users there is a frequent bus service from the city centre on routes 5, 120 and 122 – all of which stop outside. Q◑◗P⚟

YSTALYFERA

Wern Fawr Inn
47 Wern Road
7-11; 12.30-3, 7-10.30 Sun
☎ (01639) 843625
website: www.bryncelynbrewery.co.uk
Bryn Celyn Buddy Marvellous, Cwrw Celyn, Oh Boy, Rave On, Feb 59, seasonal beers H
Public house that is home to Bryn Celyn Brewery (est. 1999), the name translates as Holly Hill. All the brewery beers relate to the singer Buddy Holly – the landlord is a big fan. The pub consists of a cosy lounge and bar that display a large collection of bygone domestic and industrial curios. It is well worth finding just to sit by the old stove and listen to 1960s music being played. Be warned, this pub is very hard to leave – it is just too good.
⚲❀⊟♣⊓

YSTRAD MYNACH

Royal Oak
Commercial Street
12-3, 5.30-11; 12-11 Sat; 12-3, 7-10.30 Sun
☎ (01443) 862345
Draught Bass; Hancock's HB H
Unmistakable 'Brewers Tudor' style pub on a busy road junction. There are some noteworthy examples of acid-etched windows, displaying the former owners – Giles & Harrap, the long-defunct Merthyr Tydfil brewers. There is a separate dining area with good food and a busy public bar which includes discrete areas. An interesting selection of old photographs of the area is displayed. Join the quiz on Thursday. No food is served on Sun eve. ❀◑◗≋♣P

Beer: a gracious and salutary influence

Upon both mind and body, then, beer exercises a gracious and salutary influence. It civilises and sustains; it feeds and refreshes; it soothes and humours. As an influence no other drink can compare with it in humanity and companionability. It adjusts the human machine to its optimum working conditions.

Anon, 1934.

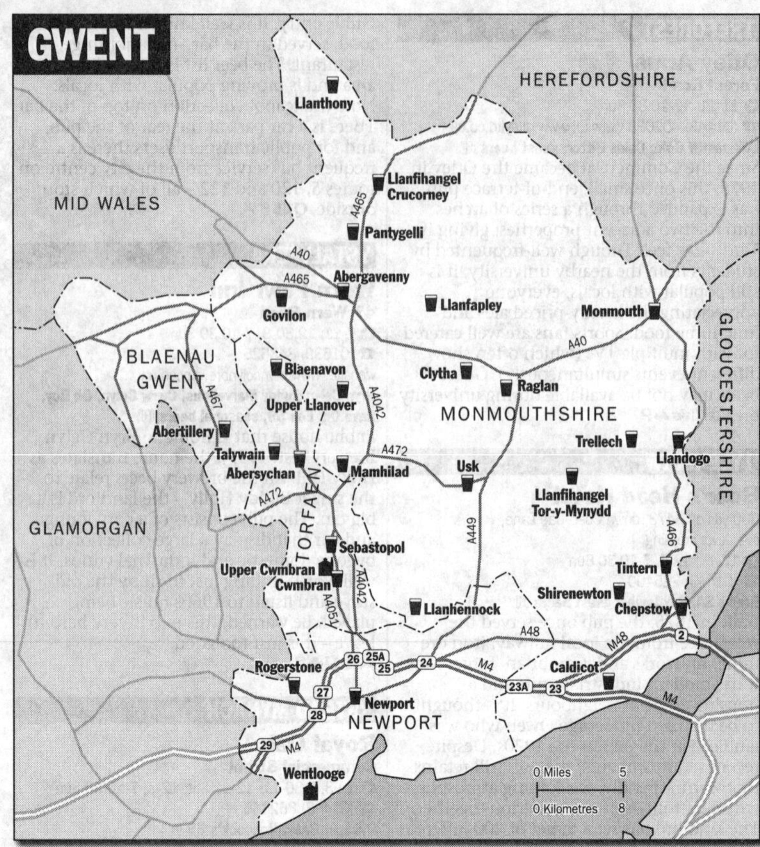

Authority areas covered: Blaenau Gwent UA, Monmouthshire UA, Newport UA, Torfaen UA

ABERGAVENNY

Coliseum

Lion Street (just off High St)
11-11; 12-10.30 Sun
(01873) 736960
Draught Bass; Brains Arms Park, SA; Greene King Abbot; Shepherd Neame Spitfire; Theakston Best Bitter; guest beers Ⓗ

Once the Coliseum cinema, this recent addition to the Wetherspoon's chain has brought new life to the town-centre beer scene. Despite having no electric music, the large drinking area with its high ceiling helps create a loud and vibrant atmosphere. Note the paintings inspired by the locality that were specially commissioned for the pub. By far the poshest pub toilets in town!

Somerset Arms

Victoria Street (at the jct with Merthyr Rd)
12-11; 12-10.30 Sun
(01873) 852158
Draught Bass; Worthington Bitter; guest beer Ⓗ

One of a dying breed – the pub with a separate public bar and lounge. The bar is decorated in warm colours and is a hive of activity and conversation. Darts is popular and TV features sporting action, while the landlord's legendary CD collection provides background music. The lounge provides a more intimate atmosphere and also acts as the dining room for the much-praised home-cooked food. On warm days the patio provides a quiet, secluded outdoor drinking area.

ABERSYCHAN

White Hart

2 Broad Street
12-11; 12-10.30 Sun
(01495) 772924
Draught Bass; guest beers Ⓗ

Historic former hotel with a cosy front bar featuring an old serving hatch. This is the haunt of the Temperance hillwalking club. Another, more spacious, bar and a pool room (to the rear) are popular with younger folk. Besides a skittle alley, there is also a cellar bar used as an occasional music venue. The Chartists are thought to have used the former cellar ovens to store gunpowder prior to their ill-fated march to Newport in 1839. Guest ciders are served.

BLAENAVON

Pottery

Llanover Road (off Ton Mawr Rd)
12-3 (not Mon & Tue), 6.30 (not Mon; 7 Tue)-11, 12-11 Fri & Sat; 12-10.30 Sun
(01495) 790395
Brains Bitter; guest beer Ⓗ

Named after the former Blaenavon blue pottery, once a local speciality, this pleasant pub has built a fine reputation for good beer and food. Diners select from a well-balanced

menu that includes home-made dishes and sauces. Lunches are served 12-2 (book on Sun) and evening meals Wed-Sun, 7-9.30. While the front bar is popular with diners, the public bar caters mainly for the wet trade. Enjoy the wonderful mountain views glimpsed beyond the garden play area. Competitively priced Brains Bitter sells alongside a frequently changing guest beer.
❀◐◑⊟♿♣P

CALDICOT

Cross Inn

1 Newport Road

11-11; 12-10.30 Sun

☎ (01291) 420692

Draught Bass; Courage Best Bitter; Wells Bombardier; guest beer Ⓗ

Popular, fairly basic pub at the crossroads in the village centre. It has a busy local trade, especially at weekends. The lounge is based around a central fireplace and has a raised area where bands play (Thu eve). The smaller bar is games-oriented, pool and darts predominating. Guest beers tend to be of higher gravity and are generally unusual for the area. Cider is served in summer.
♨❀⊟♣●P

CHEPSTOW

Castle View Hotel

16 Bridge Street

12-11; 12-10.30 Sun

☎ (01291) 620349 website: www.hotelschepstow.co.uk

Wye Valley HPA Ⓗ

Handsome old house converted to a hotel in 1950. The bar, with its single handpump, welcomes locals as well as visitors exploring this historic town's attractions. These include the oldest (1067) stone-built castle in Europe, just across the road. 19th-century visitors could explore some 50 inns within the town walls, but today this lounge bar is a rare font of dependable ale in a much reduced pub community in this part of town. Good quality meals add to the appeal. Q❀⛟◐◑⇌

Chepstow Athletic Club

Mathern Road

7 (12 Sat)-11; 12-2.30, 7-10.30 Sun

☎ (01291) 622126

Boddingtons Bitter; Brains SA; Flowers IPA, Original; guest beers Ⓗ

Clear contender for the ugliest building in Chepstow award, but once inside this 1960s monolith there is a striking and very friendly contrast. The large, comfortable lounge sports two features vital to this popular club's membership – two TV screens and six handpumps, all working hard for their living. No food, but the smart function room upstairs serves ale and meals for booked events. CAMRA members are welcome (show card at bar). The 50p visitor's fee is quickly recouped through refreshingly low bar prices. A patio overlooks the sports field. ❀⇌P

CLYTHA

Clytha Arms

On B4598, between Raglan and Abergavenny

12-3 (not Mon), 6-11; 11-11 Sat; 12-4, 7-10.30 Sun

☎ (01873) 840206

website: www.lineone.net/~one.bev

Draught Bass; Bullmastiff Gold; Felinfoel Double Dragon; guest beers Ⓗ

Superb CAMRA award-winning country inn. This former Dower house has extensive grounds which are well used by families. An outbuilding is the venue for occasional beer festivals. Inside, the range of facilities includes pub games (such as table skittles) and newspapers. Check out the unusual decor in the toilets! Eight handpumps dispense top quality ales and a real cider or two. The bar and restaurant menus offer a wide and innovative choice of home-produced meals (no food on Sun eve or Mon). ♨Q❀⛟◐◑⊟♣●P⊓

CWMBRAN ✲

Commodore Hotel

Mill Lane, Llanyravon (off Llanfrechfa Way, behind Crow's Nest pub)

11-11; 11-3, 6-11 Sat; (Mary O'Brien's: 5 [2 Fri; 12 Sat]-11); 7-10.30 (Mary O'Brien's 12-10.30) Sun

☎ (01633) 484091

Brains Arms Park, SA; Cwmbran Crow Valley Bitter Ⓗ

Friendly, family-run residential hotel providing a comfortable base for those on business travel, visitors to regional tourist attractions, as well as locals. The Pilliners lounge is spacious and relaxing while, downstairs, Mary O'Brien's bar is livelier and offers a variety of evening entertainment. Good value bar meals are served or savour the tasty à la carte dishes in the Willows restaurant. Beers listed sometimes give way to guests from other independent breweries. ❀⛟◐◑⊟♣P

GOVILON

Bridgend Inn

Church Lane

12-4 (not winter Mon), 7-11; 12-4, 7-10.30 Sun

☎ (01873) 830177

Draught Bass; Brakspear Bitter; guest beers Ⓗ

Set in the heart of the village, both literally and figuratively, the pub is popular with walkers along the picturesque canal set within the national park, and is also favoured by music lovers. The landlord is a musician and there are jazz/folk sessions every Friday evening. Two ever-changing guest beers supplement the regular ales to keep the clientele content. This is a first-time entry in the Guide supported by strong local lobbying. ❀◐◑⊟♣P✔

LLANDOGO

Sloop Inn

On A466

12-2.30, 6-11; 11.30-11 Sat; 12-10.30 Sun

☎ (01594) 530291

Wye Valley Dorothy Goodbody's Traditional Bitter; guest beer Ⓗ

Attractively situated between the steeply wooded valley side and the River Wye, the Sloop is named after the vessels which used to ply their trade to Bristol. The nautical theme extends to the bar which has old

INDEPENDENT BREWERIES

Cwmbran Upper Cwmbran

Warcop Wentlooge

masts supporting the roof beams while a large log fire warms the room. The smaller lounge has good views of the river and the four guest rooms offer good value accommodation. The mainly local trade is supplemented by passing visitors.
⛰✿🛏◐ ⊟♣P

LLANFAPLEY

Red Hart Inn

Old Monmouth Road (B4233 E of Abergavenny)
✪ 7-11 (not Mon); 12-2, 7-11 Sat; 12-2 (closed eve) Sun
☎ (01600) 780227 website: www.redhartinn.co.uk
Draught Bass; Cottage Golden Arrow; guest beer Ⓗ
Old family-run pub in pleasant rural surroundings. A dining area leads from the small bar area, as does a separate pool room. There is another larger dining area for busier occasions. A wide variety of home-cooked food is available. At least one Cottage Brewery beer is usually on tap (sometimes two). A pergola outside provides an ideal place to relax and enjoy the view on warm, sunny days.
⛰Q✿◐♣P

LLANFIHANGEL CRUCORNEY

Skirrid Inn

Hereford Road (off A465, 4 miles N of Abergavenny)
✪ 12-3, 6-11; 12-11 Sat; 12-10.30 Sun
☎ (01873) 890258
Draught Bass; Usher's Best Bitter, Founders Ale Ⓗ
Reputedly the oldest pub in Wales, this massively built hostelry is steeped in history and tradition. Solid walls, heavy flagstone floors and a huge stone fireplace in the main bar set the tone. Add to this a garden with lovely views, imaginative food (snacks and full meals) and excellent good value accommodation and you begin to get the feel of this famous pub. Judge Jeffreys ordered hangings here – you can order a first-class pint.
⛰Q✿🛏◐ ⊟♣P

LLANFIHANGEL TOR-Y-MYNYDD

Star Inn

Follow signs for Llansoy OS459023
✪ 11.30-3 (not Mon), 6.30-11; 12-3, (closed eve) Sun
☎ (01291) 650256
Marston's Pedigree; Tetley Burton Ale; guest beer (occasional) Ⓗ
Very friendly, even by country pub standards. The cosy interior has a dining area, a small lounge (with a huge log fire in winter) and from this leads the public bar. It is the centre of activity in the hamlet, with fund-raising for charity and splendid hog roasts held in fine weather. The grounds have a camping and caravan site, while there is a cottage to let for up to five people. There is a supper licence at the pub until midnight. ⛰Q✿🛏◐ ⊟⛺♣P

LLANHENNOCK

Wheatsheaf Inn

Approx 1 mile off main Caerleon-Usk road OS353927
✪ 11-11; 11-4, 6-11 Mon & Wed; 12-4, 7-10.30 Sun
☎ (01633) 420468
Draught Bass; Worthington Bitter; guest beer Ⓗ
Charming rural pub of character perched on a hill with fine views of the Usk Valley and southern parts of the county. It is worth spending time to examine various artefacts in the interior including a model of an old Rhymney Brewery hobby horse and an impressive coat of arms (origin unknown). Darts and boules have a strong following. Outside, admire the old railway semaphore signal in the car park, and note the iron rings where horses were tethered.
⛰✿◐⊟♣P

LLANTHONY

Half Moon

Off A465 at Llanfihangel Crucorney OS286279
✪ 11-3 (not winter Mon-Thu), 6-11 (phone to check winter eves); closed Tue; 12-3, 7-10.30 Sun
☎ (01873) 890611

INN BRIEF

ABERGAVENNY

King's Arms
29 Nevill Street
11.30-3, 7-11; 12-2, 7-10.30 Sun
(01873) 855074
Marston's Pedigree; John Smith's Bitter; Wadworth 6X Ⓗ
Oldest surviving pub in town, dating from the 16th century. A fine 17th-century royal coat of arms adorns the wall.

King's Head
59 Cross Street
10.30 (10 Fri)-3, 7-11; 10.30-11 Sat; 12-3, 7-10.30 Sun
(01873) 853575
Wells Bombardier; guest beer Ⓗ
Comfortable single-room pub next to the market hall, very busy at weekends. Bombardier is a rarity in the area.

ABERSYCHAN

Buck Inn
8 Station Street
12-11; 12-10.30 Sun
(01495) 772152
Greene King Abbot Ⓗ
Friendly pub with an open-plan bar and function/games room. The Abbot Ale has a good following.

ABERTILLERY

Commercial
Market Street
12-3 (not Mon), 6.30-11; 12-11 Fri & Sat; 12-10.30 Sun
(01495) 212310
Worthington Bitter; guest beer Ⓗ
Popular pub offering a haven in a real ale desert. Large public bar and two lounge bars used by diners.

CWMBRAN

Bush Inn
Graig Road
12-3 (not Mon), 7 (12 Sat)-11; 12-10.30 Sun
(01633) 483764
Cwmbran Crow Valley Bitter Ⓗ
Cosy hillside pub with split-level interior. Superb views on a clear day. Showcases beers from nearby Cwmbran Brewery.

Mount Pleasant Inn
Wesley Street
4 (12 Sat)-11; 12-3, 7-10.30 Sun
(01633) 484289
Greene King Abbot; Marston's Pedigree; Usher's Best Bitter Ⓗ
Pleasant, comfortable inn with a friendly atmosphere. 'Early bird' food available and Sunday lunch.

NEWPORT

Handpost
Bassaleg Road
11-11; 12-10.30 Sun
(01633) 264502
Ansells Best Bitter; Draught Bass; Tetley Burton Ale; guest beer Ⓗ
Large single-room pub just outside the town centre. Live jazz staged on Thu. No-smoking area available.

UPPER LLANOVER

Goose & Cuckoo
11.30-3, 7-11; 11-11 Fri & Sat; closed Mon; 12-10.30 Sun
(01873) 880277
Beer range varies Ⓗ
Remote rural pub in beautiful countryside. Two miles along a narrow lane off the A4042, well worth finding – a stunner!

❋ symbol next to a main entry place name indicates there are Inn Brief entries as well.

Bullmastiff Gold, Son of A Bitch; guest beer (summer) Ⓗ
Remote, traditional pub and restaurant a few yards beyond Llanthony Priory, in the Ewyas Valley. The Offa's Dyke path passes along the mountain ridge nearby. The views and walks make the pub popular with hikers and horse riders. The bar area features a flagstone floor and a bar billiards table. The pub has been an outlet for the Bullmastiff Brewery for many years. Addlestone's cider is available. Ring to check opening times, particularly in winter. ♨Q♉❀⇋◑◗▲♣●P⊬

MAMHILAD

Star Inn

Folly Lane (off A4042(T) at roundabout)
⊛ 11.30-3, 6-11; 11-11 Sat & summer; 12-3, 7-10.30 Sun
☎ (01495) 785319
Draught Bass; Hancock's HB; guest beers Ⓗ
Attractive rural pub situated opposite St Illtyd's Church which claims to have the oldest yew trees in Wales. It is handy for those walking the Monmouthshire & Brecon Canal. Enjoy a mouth-watering meal in the small dining room, or relax with a pint in this intimate, cosy inn. Dried hops, drinking vessels and a variety of other items hang from the low, beamed ceilings. The two guest ales are usually from independent breweries. The tempting food is made with fresh ingredients and comes highly recommended. A holiday cottage is available to let. ♨❀⇋◑◗⊞P

MONMOUTH

Green Dragon

St Thomas Square (adjacent to Monnow Bridge/300 yds from bus station)
⊛ 11-11; 12-10.30 Sun
☎ (01600) 712561
Draught Bass; Hancock's HB; Marston's Bitter, Pedigree; guest beer Ⓗ
In summer window boxes, overflowing with floral displays, bring a blaze of colour to this prominent pub facing the 13th-century, fortified Monnow Bridge. This comfortably furnished two-bar pub, features decorative plaster mouldings on the ceiling and prints on the walls. The pub is always a buzz of activity, with a strong local following, live music (Wed and Fri eves) and a daily 'happy hour' (3-7). A good selection of home-cooked fare is normally available (no food on Tue eve). ❀◑◗⊞P

Old Nag's Head

Granville Street (off St James Square – follow signs to leisure centre)
⊛ 12-3, 6 (5 Fri)-11; 12-11 Sat; 12-10.30 Sun
☎ (01600) 713782
website: www.theoldnagshead@aol.com
Brains Rev James; Fuller's London Pride Ⓗ
Late 18th-century inn originally built into a medieval town gate, part of the town's historic defences. It boasts an unspoilt, traditional layout above street level, with a small locals' bar at the front. A quiet back bar is more spacious, with flagstone floors and seated bay windows, making an interesting feature. A games room (with pool, crib and darts) and separate family room adjoin. A daily 'happy hour' offers good value in the early evening. Good food is well presented and reasonably priced. Sunday lunches are a speciality (no meals on Sun eve). ♉❀◑◗⊞♣

NEWPORT ✻

Godfrey Morgan

158 Chepstow Road, Maindee (approx. 1 mile from town centre)
⊛ 11-11; 12-10.30 Sun
☎ (01633) 221928
Brains Dark, SA; Greene King Abbot; Theakston Best Bitter; Worthington Bitter; guest beers Ⓗ
Named after a member of the once powerful Morgan family, this Wetherspoon's pub is housed in the former Maindee cinema. The interior is much larger than the frontage suggests. Pictures of movie stars with local connections decorate the walls. The drinking area at the front leads to a larger room with the bar. Two separate no-smoking sections are available, as is wheelchair access from the car park. Q◑◗♿P⊬⊘

Olde Murenger House

53 High Street
⊛ 11-3, 5.30-11; 11-11 Fri & Sat; 7-10.30 Sun
☎ (01633) 263977 website: www.murenger.com
Samuel Smith OBB Ⓗ
A black and white timber building dating back to the early 1500s which stands out among the dreary pubs and architecture of Wales' newest city. The name of the pub comes from the murage which was a tax levied for the upkeep of the town walls and the person responsible for collecting the payment was the murenger. Originally built as the town house of the local gentry, the Herberts, it later became a pub (the Fleur-de-Lys) before acquiring its present name in Victorian times. The pub was in a near-derelict state before Yorkshire brewery, Samuel Smith refurbished it. Popular with all ages it does get busy at weekends. The beer is still drawn up to the bar from oak casks. A split-level interior (with a good juke box) offers more seats and tables to the rear of the pub. An outstanding pub amid a ghetto of superpubs. ◑⇶

Red Lion

47 Stow Hill
⊛ 11-11; 12-10.30 Sun
☎ (01633) 264398
Draught Bass; John Smith's Bitter; Usher's Best Bitter; seasonal beer; guest beer (occasional) Ⓗ
This popular locals' bar has a great location close to the town-centre shopping and nightlife; very handy for both railway and bus stations after a steep five-minute climb. The pub tends to get very busy when major sporting events are shown on the large-screen TV. It was the founding place of Gwent CAMRA during the 1970s. Look out for the old barrels and handpumps which are now ornaments. Pub games, such as shove-ha'penny, are played. Occasional live music is performed. There is a meeting room available and a small paved area serves as a garden. ♨❀◑⇶♣

St Julian Inn

Caerleon Road (outskirts of Caerleon)
⊛ 11.30-11; 12-10.30 Sun
☎ (01633) 243548

Courage Best Bitter; John Smith's Bitter; guest beers Ⓗ

Situated on the main road between Newport and Caerleon, this Guide regular still remains one of the best real ale outlets in the area. A mixed clientele enjoys darts, pool, skittles and quizzes, as well as the many sporting events shown on the large-screen TV. The attractive balcony, which overlooks the Roman village of Caerleon and the River Usk, is an ideal place to spend a relaxing summer evening. Usually four real ales are available. Families are welcome. No food is served on Sun. ❀◐◑♣P

PANTYGELLI

Crown Inn

Old Hereford Road (off A465, 4 miles N of Abergavenny)

12-3 (not Mon), 6.30-11 (12-11 summer Sat); 12-3, 7-10.30 Sun

☎ (01873) 853314

Draught Bass; Fuller's London Pride; Hancock's HB; Ⓗ **guest beers** Ⓗ/Ⓖ

Defying the trend of decline in the country pub, the Crown goes from strength to strength. While serving several hamlets as a local, many regulars come from further afield to provide a strong trading base. Nestling between the Skirrid and Sugar Loaf mountains in the National Park, walkers and pony trekkers are attracted to drink, eat and stay here, while the flower-decked patio acts as a magnet to those travelling by car. ♨❀⇌◐◑▲♣P

RAGLAN

Ship Inn

8 High Street

11.30 (12 Mon)-11; 12-10.30 Sun

☎ (01291) 690635

Draught Bass; guest beers Ⓗ

This is a rural pub with a difference as it is open all day. An attractive 16th-century former coaching inn with an old water pump outside in the cobbled forecourt, the pub was originally called the Sheep Inn, but the name was changed in the 19th century. Set in a quiet village close to the church, Raglan Castle is just across the main road. Rumour has it that the pub fireplace was taken from the castle ruins following a siege in the Civil War. A genuine free house with distinct areas, a newly created dining section has not encroached on the drinking space at the bar counters. This friendly and welcoming pub has a bus stop nearby (Newport-Monmouth and Abergavenny-Monmouth services) but as this is rural Monmouthshire there is no evening service. ❀◐◑⊟♣

ROGERSTONE

Tredegar Arms

157 Cefn Road (1 mile from M4 jct 27)

12-3, 6.30-11; 12-11 Thu-Sat; 12-3, 7-10.30 Sun

☎ (01633) 664999

Draught Bass; Courage Best Bitter; guest beer Ⓗ

Traditional pub, popular with locals, and handily placed to refresh visitors to local attractions such as the Sirhowy Valley Walk, 14 locks and Cwmcarn Forest drive. The interior has original flagstones and ceiling beams, and includes a public bar, lounge and dining room, with an area set aside for under 14s. The award-winning food is recommended with good lunches (book for Sunday) and a mouth-watering range of evening meals. Barbecues are held in summer. ❀◐◑⊟P⊭

SEBASTOPOL

Sebastopol Social Club

Wern Road

12-4, 7-11; 1-11 Sat; 12-3, 7-10.30 Sun

☎ (01495) 763808

Cwmbran Deryn Du; Greene King IPA; guest beers Ⓗ

This former private residence became the Comrades of the Great War Club in the 1920s. It billeted men of the Durham Light Infantry during WWII. An upstairs room hosts the Torfaen jazz society (Wed and Fri eves). Skittles and crib are played. Children are welcome in the lounge. The steward aims to sell 100 different beers each year, a target achieved inside nine months in 2001. Four guest beers are usually available. Card-carrying CAMRA members and those with a copy of this Guide are welcome. ☋❀⊟♣P

SHIRENEWTON

Carpenters Arms

Usk Road (B4235) OS485943

12-2.30, 6-11; 12-3, 7-10.30 Sun

☎ (01291) 641231

website: www.chepstow.co.uk/adverts/carps

Flowers IPA; Fuller's London Pride; Marston's Pedigree; Wadworth 6X; guest beers Ⓗ

This 400-year-old pub used to be three separate premises – a blacksmith's and carpenter's were merged into the original pub to create a charming building with seven rooms, flagstone floors and low beams (mind your head!). Many items of bric-à-brac hang on the walls and ceilings, and two log fires provide warmth in winter. The whitewashed exterior is given added colour in the summer by an attractive display of hanging baskets. Good home-cooked food is served (no meals on Sun eve). Over 50 malt whiskies are available. ♨Q☋❀◐◑♣P

Tredegar Arms

The Square

12-3 (may vary), 6 (12 Sat)-11; 12-4, 7-10.30 Sun

☎ (01291) 641274

Draught Bass; Hancock's HB; guest beers Ⓗ

Situated at the heart of the village, next to the church. The public bar is mainly frequented by locals and is decorated with old farming implements and pictures of the pub through the ages and in all weathers, from deep snow to summertime when a floral display covers the front. The smaller lounge is popular with diners from near and far – the pub enjoys a good reputation for its food. ♨Q❀⇌◐◑⊟♣P

TALYWAIN

Globe Inn

Commercial Road

7 (12 Sat)-11; 12-10.30 Sun

☎ (01495) 772053

Brains Dark, Bitter; guest beer Ⓗ

Traditional locals' pub and a stalwart supporter of the real ale cause. A distinctive 'Globe' sign hanging over the entrance announces its presence. Inside the small public bar has a welcoming real fire in cold weather. Popular live weekend entertainment takes place in the lounge which has a pool table situated unobtrusively at the rear. Good local trade and thriving sports teams competing in local leagues help make this a genuine community hub. Guest cider is served in summer. ⛰❀⊟♣

TINTERN

Cherry Tree

Forge Road (off A466 at Royal George Hotel)
OS526001
⊙ 12-2.30, 6.30-11; 12-11 Sat; 12-10.30 Sun
☎ (01291) 689292 website: www.thecherry.co.uk
Hancock's HB; guest beer Ⓖ

A short distance up the wooded Angidy Valley from Tintern with its famous ruined abbey, this is the only Welsh pub to have been in every edition of this Guide. An old Hancock's Toastmaster sign indicates its position and some steep steps lead up from the small car park, passing a newly decked and covered patio area and the suntrap garden. The cosy single room has a warming fire and small corner bar – the beer comes straight from the cask in the adjoining cellar. Tasty food is served (all day on Sat and Sun). This is an excellent community local with traditional pub games. ⛰❀◐♣♣P

Wye Valley Hotel

On A466
⊙ 11-3, 6-11; 12-3, 7-10.30 Sun
☎ (01291) 689441 website: www.wyevalleyhotel.co.uk
Wye Valley Bitter, Butty Bach; guest beer (summer) Ⓗ

Smart hotel on the main road at the north end of the village. It was originally built in 1835 as an ale house called the Carpenters Arms, but was extended and renamed in 1909. The bar has a large collection of old beer bottles on display. The hotel offers a good standard of food and accommodation and is popular for short breaks to explore the local area. Outdoor drinking is possible on the forecourt. ❀⇌◐P

TRELLECH

Lion Inn

On B4293, Chepstow-Monmouth road
⊙ 12-3, 6 (7 Mon; 6.30 Sat)-11; 12-3 (closed eve) Sun
☎ (01600) 860322
Bath SPA; guest beers Ⓗ

Split-level pub with a small bar and a raised dining area, it is a regular outlet for Bath Ales. Regulars can request their choice of future guest beers on a blackboard. Quiz and cribbage teams are run, plus a whisky club. The Lion Inn is very popular with walkers and those interested in archaeology; there is a dig nearby, plus the ancient Trellech Standing Stones. The menu is extensive and some unusual and exotic dishes are to be found. ⛰☺❀◐⊟♣P

USK

Greyhound Inn

1 Chepstow Road (off Twyn Square)
⊙ 12-3, 6-11; 12-3, 7-10.30 Sun
☎ (01291) 672074
website: www.greyhoundinn.freeserve.co.uk
Black Sheep Best Bitter; guest beers Ⓗ

Situated a short distance from the main square, this was once a major junction of roads in the days of stagecoaches but is now a quiet back road. The single L-shaped room with photographs and other items of local interest is a peaceful haven for the mainly local clientele. Normally three guest beers are on sale to accompany the wholesome home-cooked food. ❀◐P

King's Head Hotel

18 Old Market Street
⊙ 11-11; 12-10.30 Sun
☎ (01291) 672963
Badger Tanglefoot; Fuller's London Pride; Taylor Landlord Ⓗ

Fine, town-centre hotel which has been a stalwart supporter of real ale for many years. The lounge where it is served is pleasant and relaxing with a huge log fire and comfortable armchairs. There is plenty of bric-à-brac which has been collected over the years – much of it is connected with the landlord's passion for fishing. The food is of a very high standard and, as you would expect, fish features prominently on the menu. With excellent accommodation too, the King's Head is definitely worth a visit. ⛰⇌◐♣P

Nag's Head

Twyn Square
⊙ 11-3, 5.30-11; 12-3, 6.30-10.30 Sun
☎ (01291) 672820
Brains Buckley's Best Bitter, SA, Rev James Ⓗ

Located in the main square, this pub is better known for its fine food but drinkers are very welcome. It has been run by the same family for over 35 years. The charming 500-year-old building comprises a bar with original beams and a small snug with fine etched windows. To the rear, the family room doubles as a no-smoking area while pavement tables and chairs allow customers to enjoy a drink overlooking the square. The pub prides itself on selling almost entirely Welsh produce and the menu is highly regarded (it is advisable to book at weekends). Q☺❀◐⊬✔

Wholesome

The only genuine and wholesome beverage in England is London porter and Dorchester table beer; but as for your ale and your gin, your cider...and all the trashy family of made wines, I detest them as infernal compositions contrived for the destruction of the human species.

Tobias Smollet, 1721-71.

MID WALES

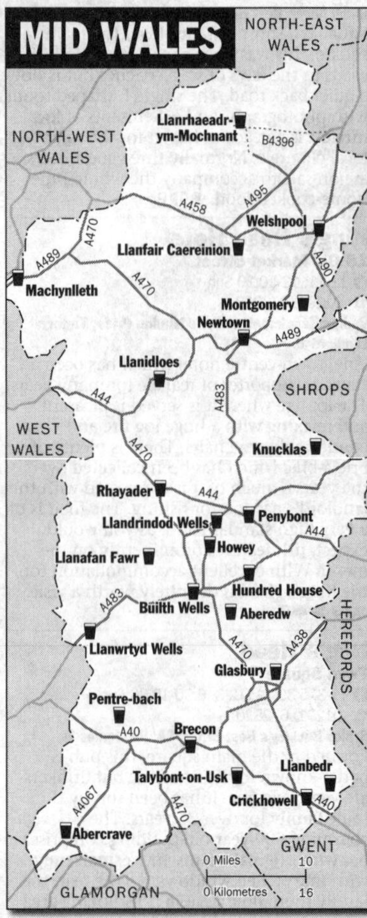

ABERCRAVE

Copper Beech Inn

133 Heol Tawe (off A4067)

11 (12 winter)-11; 12-10.30 Sun

(01639) 730269

Beer range varies H

Large single-bar, residential inn, situated on the southern edge of the Brecon Beacons National Park. A constantly changing range of up to five real ales is always on offer, it usually includes at least one beer from both Wye Valley and Shepherd Neame. Food is available all day up to 9.30pm including daily specials. The main menu specialises in home-made chilli, curry and rice dishes. Children accompanied by adults are welcome at all times. Live music is provided regularly on Fri eves. Q P

ABEREDW

Seven Stars

On minor road off B4567, Builth Wells to Erwood

12-2.30 (may vary winter), 6.30-11; 12-3, 6-10.30 Sun

(01982) 560494

Brains Rev James; Wye Valley Butty Bach; guest beers H

The pub was saved from closure about 10 years ago following years of neglect. The floor of the bar is part quarry-tiled with sturdy, sensible wooden tables, exposed stonework, low beams and a real fire. Accommodation has recently been added, together with the Llywellyn bar (site of an old smithy) and named after the last native Prince of Wales. Legend has it that his horse was shod with reversed shoes by the smith to enable him to escape his pursuers. This ruse, if true, was unsuccessful because Llywellyn was killed at nearby Cilmeri. The pub has a reputation for good food and was the 1997 regional CAMRA Pub of the Year.

Q

BRECON

Bull's Head

86 The Struet

12-2.30, 7-11; 12-3, 7-10.30 Sun

(01874) 622044

Beer range varies H

Situated overlooking the River Honddu, just below the cathedral, the Bull offers a constantly changing choice of real ales. It stocks a good range of bottled foreign and British beers and Addlestone's cider. There are two bars but three distinctive drinking areas. Well worth visiting while in town, and take a look at the monthly magazine the pub publishes.

George

George Street (off The Struet)

11-11; 12-10.30 Sun

(01874) 623422

Greene King Abbot; Tetley Burton Ale; guest beer H

Smartly refurbished, family-run hotel with an upmarket bar, separate bistro and a conservatory giving an interesting view of old Brecon. The hotel is set back from one of the main roads through the town. There is an imaginative menu which features local ingredients and offers vegetarian and children's choices. Enjoy a pint in the courtyard garden.

P

Old Boar's Head

14 Ship Street (by the river)

11.30-2.30, 5.30-11 (longer in summer); 11-11 Fri & Sat; 12-4.30, 7-10.30 Sun

(01874) 622856

Fuller's London Pride, ESB; guest beers H

A rare local outlet for Fuller's Brewery, this riverside pub offers two distinct bars: a spacious rear one with a pool table, and a smarter, wood-panelled locals' bar to the front. Photographs of flooded Brecon adorn the walls of the pub. Opening hours may be extended in summer.

P

CRICKHOWELL

Bear Hotel

High Street

11-3, 6-11; 12-3, 7-10.30 Sun

(01873) 810408 website: www.bear-hotel.co.uk

Draught Bass; Greene King Old Speckled Hen; guest beer (occasional) H

Originally a 15th-century coaching inn, now a multi-award-winning hotel. It is set in a small town close to the Brecon Beacons National Park. The low, beamed bar area features a welcoming log fire in the winter months. Universally popular, the Bear has an extensive inventive menu. Crickhowell is an ideal base for exploring the Black Mountains. ⛼Q🚼❀🛏◑◐⊞P

HOWEY

Drovers' Arms

Off A483, $1\frac{1}{2}$ miles S of Llandrindod Wells
⏲ 12-2.30 (not Tue), 7-11; 12-2.30, 7-10.30 Sun
☎ (01597) 822508 website: www.drovers-arms.co.uk
Beer range varies Ⓗ
Stylish, red-brick Victorian building, housing a pleasant two-bar inn. It is on the original drovers' route, with a 13th-century cellar. Some woodcarving in the charming bar is reputedly part of a staircase from Penybont Hall. The house beer, Drovers Ale, is brewed by Wood of Wistanstow, Shropshire. Occasionally, it is replaced by ales from other small breweries. Excellent, traditional food is prepared using Welsh produce where possible. Home-made puddings, with Welsh and English cheeses, complement the main courses. Book for Sunday lunch. The Drovers' Arms has won a huge array of awards and has been a regular entry in the Guide since 1987.
⛼Q❀🛏◑◐⊞⛺♣P

HUNDRED HOUSE

Hundred House Inn

Adjacent to A481 - Builth Wells-New Radnor road
⏲ 11-11 (Easter to late autumn); 12-10.30 Sun
☎ (01982) 570231
Greene King Abbot; Worthington Bitter; guest beers Ⓗ
Former drovers' inn set in a prominent position with fine views of the surrounding uplands. The ground floor is a series of connected rooms. The public bar and lounge retain original fireplaces. The games room and no-smoking restaurants (supper licence) are later additions, but the joins do not show too much! The pub has ample parking and en-suite accommodation. The Hundred was an ancient Anglo-Saxon administrative subdivision of the shire or county, their origins now lost in the mists of time. A more detailed explanation of a Hundred is on display in the public bar.
⛼Q❀🛏◑◐⊞♿⛺♣P

KNUCKLAS

Castle Inn

100 yds off B4355 in village centre
⏲ 12-2.30 (ring bell if closed), 6.30-11; 12-2.30, 7-10.30 Sun
☎ (01547) 528150
Draught Bass; guest beer Ⓗ
Dating back to the 16th century, this inn was once home to one of Oliver Cromwell's generals. Now it houses the village post office (Tue and Thu mornings). Wood-panelled rooms, settles and excellent home cooking provide a good place to stop on the Offa's Dyke path. Knucklas lies on the 'Heart of Wales' railway line and an attractive viaduct overlooks the village. Accommodation and a restaurant adjoin the pub. ⛼❀🛏◑◐⛺≋♣P

LLANAFAN FAWR

Red Lion

On B4358, Newbridge on Wye-Beulah road
⏲ 12-2 (closed Jan-Mar), 6-11; 12-2, 6-10.30 Sun
☎ (01597) 860204
Worthington Bitter; guest beers Ⓗ
Dating from 1188, the pub still retains an olde-worlde character. The huge beams, despite being in place for over 500 years, are thought to be secondhand. Other materials have been recycled; the shaped stones around the fireplace and the large floor slates probably came from Llanafan church. A booklet describing the history of the pub and local area is on sale (produced by the current owners). A yew in the churchyard opposite is one of the oldest trees in Britain, thought to be at least 2,200 years old. The pub offers an excellent, varied menu and live outdoor music. It hosts the world amateur tippet competition. Two self-catering cottages and camping facilities are available. ⛼Q🚼❀🛏◑◐⊞♿⛺♣P⚟

LLANBEDR

Red Lion

OS241204
⏲ 12-2.30 (not winter Mon & Tue), 7-11; 12-11 Sat; 12-3, 7-10.30 Sun
☎ (01873) 810754
Brains Buckley's Best Bitter; guest beers Ⓗ
Set in a small village in the scenic Black Mountains, this pub was originally owned by local brewer Facey's of Abergavenny, then Roberts of Aberystwyth, then Hancock's of Cardiff before becoming a free house. Situated next to the church, this charming pub is the heart of the local community as well as being popular with hillwalkers. Opening hours may be extended in summer. Winter weekday lunchtime hours may vary, so please ring first. ⛼Q🚼❀◐⛺♣P

LLANDRINDOD WELLS

Conservative Club

South Crescent
⏲ 11-2, 5.30-11; 11-11 Fri & Sat; 12-10.30 Sun
☎ (01597) 822126
Worthington Bitter; guest beers Ⓗ
The club stands next to the Glen Usk hotel, overlooking the Temple Gardens, whose lawns fill with marquees and costumed onlookers during the town's Victorian festival. The 'Con' has a large, well-decorated lounge, TV room, rear games bar, snooker (two) and pool tables, a small patio at the front and a very pleasant outlook. The ever-present Worthington Bitter is accompanied by up to four changing guest beers every week. Lunches are very popular and the Con sometimes stages evening entertainment. Non-members must be signed in to this quiet, comfortable haven.
Q❀◑♿≋♣

Llanerch 16th-Century Inn

Llanerch Lane (by police station)
⏲ 11.30-2.30, 6-11; 11.30-11 Sat; 12-10.30 Sun
☎ (01597) 822086
Hancock's HB; guest beers Ⓗ
Originally Llanerchderion - 'resting place by the glade for coaches' - the 16th-century Llanerch was built as a staging post, and still retains many of its original features such as a Jacobean staircase and an inglenook in the lounge bar. With a large garden and orchard at the front and views of the Cambrian foothills at the rear, it has

easy access to the railway station and town centre. Boules is played in summer. A vigorous guest beer policy is operated, many from smaller craft breweries. The inn, with its many-roomed, split-level interior, has a no-smoking lounge up to 8pm. The inn has its own drive, car park and cycle storage, but limited wheelchair access.
Q☋❀⇌◑♿≹♣P⁄

Royal British Legion Club

Tremont Road (A483, between hospital and fire station)
⊙ 7 (12 Sat)-11; 12-10.30 Sun
☎ (01597) 822558
Ansells Best Bitter; Draught Bass; Worthington Bitter; guest beers Ⓗ

This friendly club is just north of the town centre. It offers a comfortable lounge and a games room with snooker, pool, darts, quoits, dominoes and now skittles after acquiring a portable mat, which is available for hire. Weston's Old Rosie cider is stocked. Non-members are welcome at South and Mid Wales CAMRA's Club of the Year 1999 and 2000. ☋◑♿≹♣●P

LLANFAIR CAEREINION

Goat Hotel

High Street (A458)
⊙ 11-11; 12-10.30 Sun
☎ (01938) 810428
Brains Rev James; guest beers Ⓗ

Well-appointed beamed inn, with a friendly clientele. The lounge is full of comfortable armchairs and settees, and is dominated by a large real fire and inglenook. A number of Old Weston's cider photographs decorate the walls. The restaurant and games area (with pool table) have changed places over the last year. The restaurant provides home-cooked food. ♨❀⇌◑♣P

LLANIDLOES

Mount Inn

18 China Street
⊙ 11-3, 5.30-11; 11-11 Sat; 12-10.30 Sun
☎ (01686) 412247
Draught Bass; Worthington Bitter Ⓗ

Excellent town-centre inn with two basic public bars, a separate TV and games room, and a plush, comfortable lounge. One bar has a tiled floor while the other has a listed stone floor, originally from a castle which stood on this site. This bar also has an attractive stove and two settles. Food is served in the lounge. ♨Q❀⇌◑⊟♣P

Royal Head

⊙ 12-11; 12-10.30 Sun
☎ (01686) 412583
Draught Bass; Courage Directors; Theakston Old Peculier Ⓗ

Once two pubs, this comfortable establishment is in the centre of town. Both bars are welcoming with wooden beams; one has a large inglenook with subdued lights, the other is brighter with a pool table. The main bar has a number of TV sets and is popular with sports fans. Reasonably-priced accommodation is available.
❀⇌◑⊟P

LLANRHAEADR-YM-MOCHNANT

Hand Inn

⊙ 12-11; 12-10.30 Sun
☎ (01691) 780413
Wadworth 6X; Greene King Abbot Ⓗ

Charming multi-roomed village pub with wooden beams. Tiled floors feature and the bar is dominated by an impressive inglenook and real fire. Inglenooks are also found in the smaller, comfortable lounge, and the separate TV area. A large function room is available and the restaurant area is no-smoking. The inn offers reasonably-priced accommodation.
☋❀⇌◑⊟Ⲁ⁄

LLANWRTYD WELLS

Neuadd Arms

The Square (A483, Builth Wells-Llandovery road)
⊙ 11.30-11 (may close afternoons); 12-3, 7-10.30 Sun
☎ (01591) 610236
website: www.a1tourism.com/uk/neuaddarms.html
Felinfoel Double Dragon; Hancock's HB; guest beers Ⓗ

Situated on the picturesque 'Heart of Wales' railway line, the smallest town in Wales offers regular beer festivals in January (Saturnalia) and November (Mid-Wales) as well as hosting the world Bog-Snorkelling Championship in August. The Neuadd Arms is a large, imposing hotel, extended in Victorian times. The bar and lounge provide distinct drinking areas. The food must be tried, it is highly recommended (particularly the curry).
♨Q❀⇌◑⊟Ⲁ≹♣P⁄

Stonecroft

Dolecoed Road (off A483)
⊙ 12 (5 winter Mon-Thu)-11; 12-10.30 Sun
☎ (01591) 610332
website: www.a1tourism.com/uk/stonecraft.html
Brains SA; Wye Valley Butty Bach; guest beers Ⓗ

Open-plan Victorian pub, popular with locals and visitors alike; a good base for touring scenic Powys. The attractive patio garden has a barbecue area. Families are welcome at this beer festival venue. Food is available all day. Accommodation is in the adjoining independent youth hostel. The song 'Sospan Fach' was composed nearby.
♨❀⇌◑Ⲁ≹♣P

INN BRIEF

BUILTH WELLS

Barley Mow
1 West Street
11-11; 11-10.30 Sun
(01982) 553648
Hancock's HB Ⓗ
Pleasant farmers' pub with friendly atmosphere. Good food is available.

GLASBURY

Harp Inn
11-3, 6-11; 12-3, 7-10.30 Sun
(01497) 847373
Brains SA; guest beers Ⓗ
Attractive pub overlooking the River Wye. Former CAMRA Welsh village Pub of the Year.

NEWTOWN

Sportsman
Severn Street
11-11; 12-10.30 Sun
(01686) 625885
Tetley Bitter, Burton Ale; Theakston Best Bitter Ⓗ
Popular town-centre pub with characterful beams and three drinking areas.

MACHYNLLETH

Skinners Arms
Main Street (A487)
⏲ 11-11; 12-10.30 Sun
☎ (01654) 702354
Burtonwood Bitter; guest beer Ⓗ
Town-centre, timbered local, with a plush, comfortable stone-walled lounge bar and a no-smoking eating area. This is set around an impressive stone inglenook. The public bar has a friendly, comfortable feel with a wood floor, subdued lighting and a pool table. A good selection of food is provided in the lounge and bar snacks in the public bar. Evening meals are served 6-8.15 (not Sun eve). A patio garden is available.
✿◑ ⊟≢♣

Wynnstay Arms Hotel
Maengwyn Street (off A487)
⏲ 11-11; 12-10.30 Sun
☎ (01654) 702941 website: www.wynnstay-hotel.com
Beer range varies Ⓗ
Very friendly, small bar in a town-centre hotel. The main room is beamed with a large open log fire creating an excellent setting. Small rooms off to the side are quiet and offer a relaxing retreat if you want to escape from the crowd. Guest beers are served from a wide range of breweries.
♨Q✿🛏◑≢♣P⊭

MONTGOMERY

Dragon Hotel
Off B4385
⏲ 11-3, 6-11; 12-3, 7-10.30 Sun
☎ (01686) 668359 website: www.dragonhotel.com
Beer range varies Ⓗ
Excellent plush bar in a 17th-century coaching inn. This hotel is a two-star establishment in the town centre. The bar walls are covered with bric-à-brac and the beams and masonry are reputedly from the local castle which was destroyed by Cromwell. The hotel has good facilities, including an indoor, heated swimming pool and a function room catering for 20-100 people. The bar stages jazz (Wed eve) and the beer range includes guests from independent breweries including Wood's.
Q🛏◑♣P

NEWTOWN ❄

Bell Hotel
30 Commercial Street (B4568)
⏲ 12-2 (3 Tue; not Wed), 5-11 (midnight Fri); 12-midnight Sat; 12-3, 7-10.30 Sun
☎ (01686) 625540
Greene King Old Speckled Hen; Six Bells Big Nev's; guest beer Ⓗ
Edge-of-town local hosting live music at weekends. The Bell is popular with a wide range of customers. Six Bells beers are supplied to the hotel without fish finings, making them vegetarian. The comfortable lounge is separate from the more basic public bar which has a pool table. The pub is the home of the Dragonfire Rocket project which explains some of the cartoons on the bar. 🛏◑♣P

Cross Guns
32 Park Street (off A483)
⏲ 12.30-3, 7-12.30; 12-10.30 Sun
☎ (01686) 625546
Theakston Best Bitter; guest beer Ⓗ
Very pleasant, many-roomed, beamed pub offering guest beers from independent breweries. The beams are hung with a large collection of water and milk jugs. A large patio area behind the pub offers an outside drinking venue, and a large function room, with a capacity of 200, is available. Meals include Indian dishes that have won local awards. ✿🛏◑⊟≢♣P

Railway Tavern
Old Kerry Road (off A483)
⏲ 12-2.30, 6.30-11; 11-11 Tue, Fri & Sat; 12-10.30 Sun
☎ (01686) 626156
Draught Bass; Worthington Bitter; guest beer Ⓗ
Unspoilt, small, one-bar local near the railway station. This popular, friendly pub has beams and a stone wall. Highly successful darts and dominoes teams compete as can be seen by the number of cups and trophies adorning the shelves and walls. The pub can be very busy on match nights. Beware of the cellar hatch which is right in front of the dartboard! 🛏≢♣

PENTRE-BACH

Shoemakers Arms
Signed 'country pub' from Sennybridge OS908328
⏲ 12-3 (not Mon & Tue), 6-11 (may open longer in summer); 12-3, 7-10.30 Sun
☎ (01874) 636508
Beer range varies Ⓗ
'The road to Pentre-bach is always open', according to the roadsigns on the way here. A little further along, one encounters the Eppynt firing range so the pub is a safe place to stop! Originally four cottages, this 18th-century pub was saved from closure by the local community who purchased it. After an extensive refurbishment, the pub reopened and is once again the focus of the community. Two real ales are on sale, usually from regional breweries. The Shoemakers Arms is set in glorious Mid Wales, on the edge of the Brecon Beacons National Park. A varied menu is available. Quoits is played. ♨Q✿◑⊟♿♣P

PENYBONT

Severn Arms
At A44/A488 jct
⏲ 11-2.30, 6-11; 12-3, 7-10.30 Sun
☎ (01597) 851224
Draught Bass; Courage Best Bitter; Brains SA; guest beers Ⓗ
18th-century coaching inn and a stop-off point between Hereford and Aberystwyth. It is named after John Cheesment Severn, the second squire of Penybont Hall, who married Mary Price, the daughter of the first squire. It was he who had the first pub built in Penybont. The Severn Arms has a spacious bar, which has access to a large rear garden. A games room, quiet secluded lounge and a restaurant, the Cheesements, complete the picture. The pub has six miles of fishing rights on the River Ithon (free to residents). Wales and Border Counties trotting racing takes place twice yearly on a nearby course.
♨✿🛏◑⊟♿⛺P

RHAYADER

Crown Inn
North Street
11-11; 12-3, 7-10.30 Sun
(01597) 811099
Brains Bitter, Rev James; guest beers H
This 16th-century building has always been a pub. Although horses were stabled here it was never a coaching inn; it was linked with the hiring of horses (livery) instead. Despite changes made in the 1970s, much of the internal timbering is still visible and the linen-fold bar front panelling came from a demolished chapel. A pictorial history of recent Rhayader, with text, lines the walls of both bars, and reference is made to a former, less fastidious owner (1953-1978), which prompted a comment from CAMRA – 'We recommend the beer but with strong reservations about the standard of cleanliness'. Backgammon is played.
Q❀⇌◑♿♣P⅟

TALYBONT-ON-USK

Star Inn
On B4518
11-3, 6.30-11; 11-11 Sat; 12-3, 6.30-10.30 Sun
(01874) 676635
website: www.members.lycos.co.uk/starinn/starinn.htm
Beer range varies H
From the road this pub looks like an ordinary terraced pub but it turns out to be a welcoming, canalside inn which features an island bar and a large fireplace. Thanks to a sympathetic refurbishment very little has changed. Beer is served in jugged glasses. Up to 12 real ales and a cider are available in the summer. Regular beers include Double Dragon, Wye Valley and Old Peculier. A blues festival is held during the second weekend of August. Throughout the winter months a quiz night is held on Monday. A former CAMRA regional Pub of the Year winner, the Star has served beers from many different breweries through the years and their pump clips are displayed on the bar. There is a bus stop nearby for the Abergavenny-Brecon service but being rural Wales there is no evening service.
❀⇌◑▲♣●

WELSHPOOL

Royal Oak Hotel
Severn Street (off A483)
11-3, 5.30-11; 11-11 Fri & Sat; 12-10.30 Sun
(01938) 552217
Worthington Bitter; guest beer H
Plush, town-centre, 300-year-old coaching inn, which was formerly the manor house of the Earls of Powys. There are two bars; the comfortable, quiet Oak bar with a real fire and relaxing atmosphere and the Ostler bar with pool, music and TV. The hotel has a separate restaurant where the food is highly recommended. Q⇌◑≹

Reflections on Perfection

It's late at night
I sit and think of things I could have done
On summer days, before they're gone
Bask in the blazing sun.

But I have found a certain peace
Regardless of the weather
The comfort overwhelms me
Like soft and downy feather.

To find the words that may describe
This wondrous joy of life
Just seems a task impossible
'Complete and utter strife'.

But strive I will that you may know
The pleasures I attain
Among the cosy taverns, warm lit,
Sheltered from the rain.

It's poetry and love within
That fills me full of cheer
My love, my deep affection
For a perfect pint of beer.

LD Pearce, *Making Matters Verse*, Janus, 1996

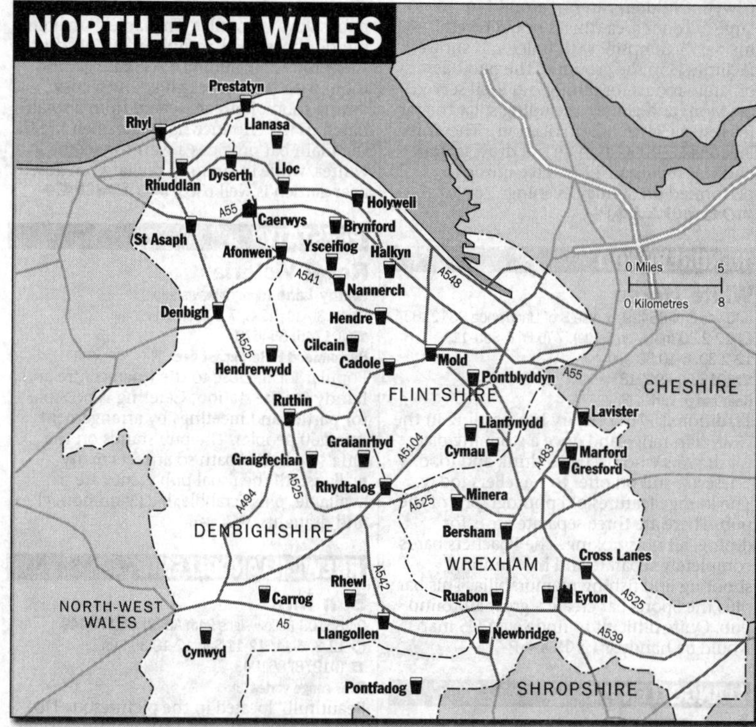

Authority areas covered: Denbighshire UA, Flintshire UA, Wrexham UA

Denbighshire

CARROG

Grouse Inn

On B5437 OS113435
12-11; 12-10.30 Sun
☎ (01490) 430272
Lees Bitter, seasonal beers H

Originally a farm and brewhouse, the Grouse is the last remaining of four pubs that once served Carrog, a hamlet transformed by the coming of the railways in the 1860s. The railway is still evident and the western terminus of the Llangollen preserved line is a short walk away. This warm, cosy village pub has a games room, intimate lounge/dining room, and superb views of the Dee Valley from the bar and patio. Evidence of the pub's many brewery awards are displayed throughout. Food is available 12-10 every day and there is guesthouse accommodation nearby (ask at the pub for details).
❀◑ ⛺ ≠ (Llangollen railway) ♣P

CYNWYD

Blue Lion

On B4401, 2 miles SW of Corwen OS056411
12-3, 6-11; 12-11 Fri & Sat; 12-10.30 Sun
☎ (01490) 412106
Marston's Bitter; Plassey Bitter H

Friendly, traditional pub in the centre of this small village, near Cynwyd Forest and Waterfall, popular attractions for hikers and summer visitors. The public bar has a painted stone floor, and the peaceful rear lounge (where meals are served) displays a fine selection of old dinner plates. The River Dee lies 400 yards away and is spanned by a narrow road bridge. It is close to a youth hostel. ⩸◑

DYSERTH

New Inn

Waterfall Road (off A5151, 4 miles S of Rhyl) OS055796
12-11; 12-10.30 Sun
☎ (01745) 570482
Banks's Original, Bitter; Mansfield Riding Bitter; Marston's Pedigree H

This three-roomed inn, close to the local waterfall, has been sympathetically refurbished after being flooded four times in November 2000. Brewery prints line the walls of two of the rooms, while brass plates decorate the third. The pub's reputation for superb food and an excellent choice of ale attracts customers from far and wide. Duck races are held on bank holidays at the waterfall.
⩸Q❀◑ ♣P

GRAIGFECHAN

Three Pigeons

On B5429, 3 miles S of Ruthin OS147545
12-3, 5.30-11; 12-11 Sat; 12-10.30 Sun
☎ (01824) 703178
Draught Bass; Enville Bitter; Hancock's HB; Plassey Fusilier H/G

Spacious, rural pub, a new balcony affords fine panoramic views over the Vale of

INDEPENDENT BREWERIES

Plassey Eyton
Travellers Inn Caerwys

Clwyd. Children can run around in the large outdoor area (this is not allowed inside). A campsite with toilet and shower facilities is in the grounds. The pub has separate rooms for dining (no food served on Mon) and games, including splat the rat (to test the level of intoxication). The Three Pigeons is situated on an old drovers' trail and was rebuilt in 1777. Live music is performed on Sunday evenings.
⩩Q❀◑♿▲♣P⚟

HENDRERWYDD

White Horse

600 yds E of B5429, 1 mile S of Llandyrnog OS121634
⌚ 12-2.30 (not Mon & Tue), 7 (6 Fri & Sat)-11; 12-2.30, 6-10.30 Sun
☎ (01824) 790218
Beer range varies Ⓗ

Traditional 17th-century inn nestling in the Clwydian range and once a stopping place for drovers who needed a drink and food. These are still on offer to travellers today. The lounge features old photographs of the pub. There are three separate areas for dining, all no-smoking. The Poachers bar is completely separate and has hunting, shooting and fishing memorabilia. This bar plus the Sports bar create a great all-round pub. Quite difficult to find so an OS map would be handy. ⩩❀◑▲♣P

LLANGOLLEN ❊

Corn Mill

Dee Lane
⌚ 12-11; 12-10.30 Sun
☎ (01978) 869555
Boddingtons Bitter; Plassey Bitter; Taylor Landlord; guest beers Ⓗ

Upmarket conversion of a former mill building on the River Dee. The large ground-floor bar has up to five cask ales, while the upstairs bar is reserved for diners. The spectacular outdoor terrace, on stilts above the water, runs the entire length of the building, past the (functioning) water wheel, and beyond to form a perfect location for watching the river (and canoeists). Q❀◑♿

Sun

49 Regent Street (A5)
⌚ 12-11 (may close weekday afternoons); 12-10.30 Sun
☎ (01978) 860233 website: www.thesuninn.8m.com
Beer range varies Ⓗ

Five years on from its rescue, this classic pub proves real ale and real music mix perfectly. The large slate-floored main room hosts music up to five evenings a week, featuring weekly folk and jazz nights alongside more mainstream bands at weekends. A small snug with its own serving hatch provides a quieter refuge. Up to six cask ales are served, usually from within a 100 mile radius. Awarded local CAMRA Pub of the Year 2001.
⩩◫▲●

Wynnstay Arms

20 Bridge Street
⌚ 12-3 (4 Sat), 7 (6 Fri & Sat)-11; 12-3, 7-10.30 Sun
☎ (01978) 860710
Greene King IPA, Abbot; Tetley Burton Ale Ⓗ

Historic 16th-century coaching inn on a quiet riverside street, this friendly locals' pub is always popular. The largely unaltered interior boasts a charming layout of several small rooms, including a separate games room with its own juke box and a cosy dining room. Both are served from a small hatch in the entrance hall. The open fire in the main bar provides a warm welcome in winter, while in summer the large enclosed beer garden is well used. ⩩Q❀⇆◑◫♣

PRESTATYN

Royal Victoria

Sandy Lane (opp. railway station)
⌚ 11.30-11; 12-3, 7-10.30 Sun
☎ (01745) 854670
Burtonwood Bitter; guest beer Ⓗ

Popular local, close to the town centre and handy for the station. Catering is possible for parties and meetings by arrangement (max 60 people). The pub stands on the Offa's Dyke footpath so attracts many walkers. All the usual pub games are available, plus Scrabble, backgammon, chess and draughts. ❀▲⇌♣

RHEWL (LLANGOLLEN)

Sun Inn

On B5103 (follow signs from A542) OS178449
⌚ 12-3, 6-11; 12-11 Sat; 12-10.30 Sun
☎ (01978) 861043
Beer range varies Ⓗ

Beautifully located in the picturesque Dee Valley, this wonderful 14th-century former drovers' inn is popular with locals and visitors alike. A perfect spot to take advantage of the surrounding hills and moors. Three characterful rooms – the main room with its open fire, a small rear snug and the intimate public bar – are served from a small central bar and hatch. The good value, home-made food is highly recommended. ⩩Q❀◑◫▲♣P

RHUDDLAN

King's Head

High Street (corner of Princes Rd, by new mini roundabout) OS025782
⌚ 11-11; 12-10.30 Sun
☎ (01745) 590345
Mansfield Dark Mild; Marston's Bitter Ⓗ

Modern town-centre pub with a restaurant in a side conservatory (meals served 9.30-3.30, 7-9.30 Wed-Sun). The public bar has an interesting selection of photos depicting the history of local sports teams and there is a comfortable lounge bar. Close to the historic castle and parliament building remains. Regular buses link Rhuddlan with Rhyl, Dyserth, St Asaph and Denbigh.
❀◫♣P

RHYL

Sussex

Sussex Street
⌚ 11-11; 12-10.30 Sun
☎ (01745) 362910
Cains Mild; Courage Directors; Greene King Abbot; Plassey Bitter; Shepherd Neame Spitfire; Tetley Bitter; guest beers Ⓗ

Wetherspoon's conversion of an existing pub that was also known as the Sussex. The building was originally the local old

comrades club. The result is a pleasantly airy, comfortable pub that is appreciated for its excellent selection of ales and food. Located in an established pedestrian area, it is popular with shoppers and visitors. It tends to be busy at weekends especially eves. The town's history is told through a series of wall plaques. The fenced front patio is ideal for summer drinking.
Q❀◑▶≠⅟✔

Swan
13 Russell Road
⏲ 11-11; 12-10.30 Sun
☎ (01745) 336694
Thwaites Mild, Bitter, seasonal beers; guest beer Ⓗ
Welcoming, two-roomed pub close to the town centre. Reputed to be the oldest pub in town, the frontage bears the name Wilderspool Ales which no longer exists. The bar has a display of old electric substation nameplates. The homely, long lounge bar has many pictures of old Rhyl. The Swan has darts, pool and dominoes teams and organises fund-raising charity fun days in summer.
◑⊟≠♣🍎

RUTHIN

Wine Vaults
2 Castle Street (in town square) OS123582
⏲ 12-11; 12-10.30 Sun
☎ (01824) 702067
Robinson's Best Bitter, seasonal beers Ⓗ
Town-centre pub with an Irish theme, old Guinness posters are mounted on the walls of the main bar and sports bar. Not that the Guinness sells as well as the excellent Robinson's bitter. The locals are sports-oriented and regular promotional events take place. A verandah serves as a garden and overlooks the historic courthouse (AD 1401) now converted into a bank. Ruthin Castle is nearby. A good locals' pub; food is not available.
❀⊟Å♣

ST ASAPH

Kentigern Arms
High Street (A525, close to A55) OS036743
⏲ 12-3, 7-11; 12-3, 7-10.30 Sun
☎ (01745) 584157
Courage Directors; John Smith's Bitter; Theakston Best Bitter; guest beer Ⓗ
17th-century free house located a short distance from the cathedral (home to the North Wales Music Festival in September). The nearby River Elwy gives the place its Welsh name of 'Llanelwy'. A quiz team of doctors play home league games (they go under the name 'quacks'). A no-smoking area is set aside. ⛫◑⊟Å♣P⅟

Plough
The Row OS033745
⏲ 12-11.30; 12-10.30 Sun
☎ (01745) 585080
Plassey Bitter; guest beers Ⓗ
Large pub with a racing theme, the bar has tables named after racehorses. The restaurant on the first floor is set either side of the staircase; one serving Italian dishes, the other English. It was awarded Best Seafood Restaurant, North Wales 2000-01. The ground floor has several small seating areas and plenty of standing room.
Q◑▶♿P⅟

Flintshire

AFONWEN

Pwll-Gwyn
Denbigh Road (A541) OS127717
⏲ 12-2, 7-11 (not Mon); 12-3, 6-11 Sat; 12-3, 7-10.30 Sun
☎ (01352) 720227
Tetley Bitter; guest beer Ⓗ
This 18th-century coaching inn was once owned by Chester Northgate Brewery. It is now a spacious, roadside pub with one large bar and two dining rooms, both no-smoking. Food features strongly and there is

INN BRIEF

Denbighshire

DENBIGH

Old Vaults
40 High Street
11-11; 12-10.30 Sun
(01745) 815142
Draught Bass; Greene King IPA, Abbot Ⓗ
Town-centre pub, close to Town Hall, library and museum. Denbigh Castle is also nearby. Popular with locals.

GRAIANRHYD

Rose & Crown
4 (1 Fri & Sat)-11; 1-10.30 Sun
(01824) 780727
Flowers IPA; Marston's Pedigree Ⓗ
Friendly, busy local with masses of bric-à-brac. Good value food served and the best Pedigree for miles.

LLANGOLLEN

Bridge End
Mill Street
12-11; 12-10.30 Sun
(01978) 860634
Robinson's Best Bitter Ⓗ
Lively, bustling locals' pub next to the Steam Railway station. Other Robinson's beers are sometimes available.

Flintshire

LLOC

Rock Inn
St Asaph Road
12-11;
12-10.30 Sun
(01352) 710049
Burtonwood Bitter; guest beer Ⓗ
Two-roomed inn with separate restaurant. Teapots of diverse shape and size hang from beams in the main bar.

Wrexham

MINERA

Tyn-y-Capel
Church Road
(off B5426 from Coedpoeth)
12-11;
12-10.30 Sun
(01978) 757502
Tetley Bitter; guest beers Ⓗ
Much refurbished former drovers' pub, with wood floors and whitewashed walls. Stunning views of the surrounding area.

NEWBRIDGE

Black Lion
Park Road
7 (11 Sat)-11;
12-10.30 Sun
(01978) 823878
Lees Bitter Ⓗ
Unspoilt and unpretentious old community pub.

PONTFADOG

Swan Inn
On B4500 7
12-3, 7-11;
12-3, 7-10.30 Sun
(01691) 718273
Brains SA; guest beer Ⓗ
Welcoming pub in the picturesque Ceiriog Valley. Guest beer usually comes from a local independent.

✻ symbol next to a main entry place name indicates there are Inn Brief entries as well.

an extensive menu and specials board, with separate lunchtime and evening menus. There is usually at least one guest beer alongside the ubiquitous Tetley's.
⌂❀◐◑♿▲P

BRYNFORD

Llyn-y-Mawn

On B5121, 1 mile from Holywell OS181748
☉ 12-3, 5.30-11; 12-11 Sat; 12-10.30 Sun
☎ (01352) 714367
John Smith's Bitter; guest beers Ⓗ
Charming village pub, close to the A55 and town of Holywell, the site of St Winefrede's well. Parts of the building date back to the 14th century when it may have been a travellers' hostel. It has two cosy bars and a dining room which is especially busy at the weekend. It is a short distance from the moors and Holywell golf course on which sheep roam freely. ⌂❀◐◑⊟▲P

CADOLE

Colomendy Arms

Village Road (off A494) OS205629
☉ 7 (6 Thu; 4 Fri; 12 Sat)-11; 12-10.30 Sun
☎ (01352) 810217
Shepherd Neame Master Brew Bitter; guest beers Ⓗ
Hidden-away, rustic, red-bricked local close to Loggerheads Country Park, it offers the best beer for miles around. A small lounge caters for the less extrovert but the pine-panelled bar, with its wood and tiled floor, and warmed by a healthy fire, is the place to be. Here it is easy to forget about the cares of the world as you engage in the most sociable of conversations with the genial owners and regulars. Quite splendid.
⌂❀▲♣P

CILCAIN

White Horse

The Square (1 mile S of A541) OS177652
☉ 12-3, 6.30-11; 12-11 Sat; 12-10.30 Sun
☎ (01352) 740142
Banks's Bitter; guest beers Ⓗ
Picturesque, whitewashed pub in an attractive village in the foothills of Moel Famau in the Clwydian Range. The public bar has a traditional quarry-tiled floor and welcomes dogs and walkers. Meals are served in the cosy split-level lounge (12-2 and 7-9) from an imaginative menu, plus specials. There are photographs of the village and exterior signs from long-defunct breweries. Awarded local CAMRA Pub of the Year 2001. Under 14s are not admitted. It is on the Holywell to Mold bus route.
⌂Q❀◐◑⊟♣P

CYMAU

Talbot

Cymau Lane
☉ 12-4 (not Mon-Thu), 7-11; 12-4, 7-10.30 Sun
☎ (01978) 761410
Hydes Bitter, Ⓟ **seasonal beers** Ⓗ
An uncomplicated, no-nonsense, whitewashed village local which has featured in the Guide for many years. From the outside porch, take your pick, to the left, often echoing to the sound of rattling dominoes, is a tile-floored public bar with darts and TV, while to the right is a quieter, more intimate lounge. A central bar serves both rooms. Hope Mountain Country Park is close by and affords spectacular views across the Cheshire Plain. Q⊟♣P

HALKYN

Britannia

Pentre Road (off A55, jct 32B) OS211711
☉ 11-11; 12-10.30 Sun
☎ (01352) 780272
Lees GB Mild, Bitter, seasonal beers Ⓗ
500-year-old former coaching inn on the Chester to Holyhead road, recently listed as a Grade II building. Situated in a picturesque stone hamlet yet less than 400 yards from the main A55, this four-roomed pub has an attached conservatory restaurant offering tea, coffee, snacks and sandwiches as well as more formal meals lunchtime and evening. Enjoy the idyllic views over the Dee Estuary from both the conservatory and patio areas. ⌂Q❀◐◑⊟♿♣P

HENDRE

Royal Oak

Denbigh Road (A541) OS191677
☉ 7 (12 Sat)-11; 12-10.30 Sun
☎ (01352) 741466
Black Sheep Best Bitter; Worthington Bitter Ⓗ
Roadside pub with many local community activities including Welsh classes, quizzes, singing and chess club. There are two bars and a pool room, the lounge has the original hooter from the local Olwyn Goch mine which has been returned to the village after 25 years. The bar has a collection of old bottles from long-defunct local breweries. The pub is the starting point (and often finishing point!) for walks in the nearby Clwydian Hills, one of which follows the old Mold to Denbigh railway line. Good value weekend lunches and special meal promotions are offered (Wed meal and a pint for £3.99). ⌂Q❀◐◑⊟▲♣P

HOLYWELL

Glan-yr-Afon Inn

Milwr (off A5026, 1 mile S of Holywell, follow signs to Dolphin) OS195739
☉ 12-3, 5.30-11; 12-10.30 Sun
☎ (01352) 710052
Tetley Bitter; guest beers Ⓗ
Renovated Welsh long house extended to provide accommodation. There are seven guest bedrooms, some with disabled facilities. Regular beer festivals are held with different themes such as Welsh beers. The food is excellent and Pepe, the Spanish landlord, hosts a Spanish language circle every last Thursday of the month. There is a quiz every Wednesday and the pub fields football and darts teams. A real rural gem.
⌂Q☕❀⛟◐◑⊟♿P

LLANASA

Red Lion

Signed from A5151 at Trelawnyd OS105815
☉ 12-11; 12-10.30 Sun
☎ (01745) 854291
Courage Directors; Webster's Yorkshire Bitter; guest beer Ⓗ
Delightful two-bar inn with a separate no-smoking restaurant, open fires and

traditional atmosphere. The games area houses a pool table. Two regular beers are served alongside a guest ale (weekends). Llanasa is not far from the resort town of Prestatyn. ♨Q❀🛏◐◑♿⛺♣P

LLANFYNYDD

Cross Keys

On B5101 OS280566
⏲ 7-11; 12-3.30, 7-10.30 Sun
☎ (01978) 760333
Beer range varies Ⓗ

This 300-year-old pub may only boast one handpump but, as the beer is always from an independent brewery (usually local), this is not a problem. The entrance leads to a basic but cosy quarry-tiled bar, while the plusher lounge with its unusual raised area has superbly carved settles. Lunchtime food is available on Sunday, evening meals are offered daily. Dominoes and crib are played. Parking is only accessible from the direction of Ffrith. ♨Q❀◑🚂♣P

MOLD

Y Pentan

3 New Street
⏲ 11-11; 12-10.30 Sun
☎ (01352) 758884 website: www.y-pentan.co.uk
Marston's Pedigree; guest beer Ⓗ

Busy, town-centre pub commemorating the 19th-century Welsh language novelist Daniel Owen. His shop formed part of the premises and the pub is named after one of his books, the Hob. A smattering of pictures and prints depicting his life and times decorate the walls of the smaller of the two rooms. Convivial, with plenty of seating and sensible level MTV; in stark contrast, but quite separate and not intruding, the second room – effectively Mold's disco – is an open, loud, brash, bare-floored, lively club affair with a massed bank of TVs. Evening meals are served Mon-Thu.
◐◑♿

NANNERCH

Cross Foxes

Village Road (off A541) OS167695
⏲ 6-11; 1-11 (Sat & summer); 12-10.30 Sun
☎ (01352) 741293
Beer range varies Ⓗ

Traditional village pub, a free house, with low, beamed ceilings and a welcoming atmosphere. The public bar has an open fire and tiled floor and the extended lounge (with piano) is decorated with brassware. The restaurant is only open at weekends, with a full menu plus a wide range of filled baguettes. A curry and pint eve every Tuesday is a popular feature. Fly fishing is available nearby and the regular Denbigh to Mold bus stops outside.
♨Q◐◑🚌♿P

PONTBLYDDYN

New Inn

Corwen Road (B5104)
⏲ 12-11; 12-10.30 Sun
☎ (01352) 771459
Beer range varies Ⓗ

Up to three ales on offer means that this 19th-century pub is an oasis of choice in an area dominated by national brands. The bar offers pool and TV, and there is an upstairs dining room (no food served on Mon). The lounge tends to be more peaceful apart from the popular Tuesday folk night. The landlord, being aware of the pub's position, does not stock any strong beers. Booking is advisable for Sunday lunch.
♨👶❀◐◑🚌♣

RHYDTALOG

Liver Inn

A5104/A5430 crossroads OS235550
⏲ 12-2 (not Mon), 5.30-11; 12-2, 5.30-11 Sun
☎ (01824) 780244
Tetley Bitter; guest beer Ⓗ

This impressive inn stands at the crossroads on the edge of Llandegla Moor. Inside there are various pictures of the pub adorning the walls. The pub is popular with local groups and walkers, who stray from the nearby Offa's Dyke footpath. The food is well recommended and superb value. There are several drinking areas and a pool table. The beers are served from a cosy bar and the guest policy is very interesting. A separate function room is available for hire.
♨Q❀◐◑⛺♣P🚭

YSCEIFIOG

Fox Inn

Signed from A541 Denbigh to Mold road OS151715
⏲ 6 (12 Sat)-11; 12-3, 7-11 Sun
☎ (01352) 720241
Beer range varies Ⓗ

Attractive country pub with inviting real fires in the two bars. The separate games area serves as a post office in the morning. The building is over 300 years old and has a number of aged tape decks and other vintage equipment. It is advisable to book for the popular Sunday lunch. The pub holds a beer festival for St David's Day. There is a request list for guest beers (Cains Mild is often available). A number of the locals have personalised glasses painted by the wife of the licensee. Weston's First Quality cider is stocked.
♨👶❀🚌⛺♣🍎

Wrexham

BERSHAM

Black Lion Inn

Y Ddol (off B5097)
⏲ 12 (11.30 Sat)-11; 12-10.30 Sun
☎ (01978) 365588
Hydes Light, Bitter, seasonal beers Ⓗ

Known locally as the Hole-in-the-Wall, the pub stands in an attractive hamlet, below road level, on the bank of Clywedog (next to Bersham heritage centre). It is a sympathetic renovation of a parlour-style pub with a side off-shoot and a separate pool room with darts. Convivial, cosy and popular with hikers, it is halfway along the Clywedog Valley industrial trail. The garden overlooks the wooded riverside. Runner-up in the 1999 Hydes Best-Kept Cellar competition. Hot snacks are available throughout the day.
♨❀🚌♣P✔

CROSS LANES

Kagan's Brasserie (Cross Lanes Hotel)

On A525, 1 mile from Marchwiel
11-11; 12-10.30 Sun
(01978) 780555 website: www.crosslanes.co.uk
Plassey Bitter

Large lounge set around a central bar in a mansion formerly known as Maes-y-Nant. Attached to an upmarket hotel in six acres of gardens, it is reached via a grand entrance hall containing fine panelling and a 1618 staircase rescued from Emral Hall, Worthenbury. Old prints and paraphernalia include a photo of the last survivor of the Charge of the Light Brigade. An interesting layout, includes a formal drawing room and a small, varnished-floored barside and a flagged dining area. P

EYTON

Plassey Leisure Park

The Plassey (off B5426, signed from A483)
11-11 (may vary in winter); 12-10.30 Sun
(01978) 780905
Plassey Bitter

Atop a wooded hillock, this one-time Victorian dairy farm is now fully dedicated to the leisure industry. With a caravan park attached, there is plenty here for the family from craft shops, boutiques, salons and garden nurseries to nature trails, a blacksmith's and a swimming pool. Most importantly, it is the home of Plassey Brewery whose products (occasionally including Cwrw Tudno and Dragon's Breath) may be sampled in the restaurant, the Treetops bar (summer only) or in the club house of the on-site golf course. P

GRESFORD

Griffin

Church Green
3-11; 3-10.30 Sun
(01978) 852231
Greenalls Mild, Bitter

This quiet pub, situated in a border village, is very popular with locals, who enjoy a few games of dominoes or darts. A bright interior features various local pictures and a collection of cigarette cards on the walls. A true local, this is one of a very few pubs in the area that does not serve food and concentrates on Greenalls. Note the huge tortoise shell in the fireplace. P

LAVISTER

Nag's Head

Chester Road (B5445)
12-3 (not Mon-Wed), 5.30-11; 11.30-11 Sat; 12-10.30 Sun
(01244) 570486
Draught Bass; Boddingtons Bitter; Taylor Landlord; guest beer

A plaque on the bar claims this pub to be the birthplace of CAMRA in 1971. On the old Chester road, this extended pub is very popular with locals and tourists. A children's play area, camping facilities and a bowling green are provided to the rear. Beer is served from a central bar, with a pool table and dartboard to one side, and comfortable seating by an open fire to the other. Tasty meals are served in the no-smoking dining area. P

MARFORD

Red Lion

Marford Hill
12-2 (not Mon & Tue), 5-11; 12-11 Sat; 12-10.30 Sun
(01978) 853562
Burtonwood Bitter; guest beer

This friendly pub, a former coaching inn, is presided over by a real ale-loving landlord. Attractively decorated throughout, it is divided into two distinct areas. The split-level, partitioned lounge features interesting old prints of surrounding villages, while the bar, with a splendid brick fireplace, has TV and pool. Thai food is a speciality; it is essential to book at weekends. P

RUABON

Wynnstay Arms

High Street
11.30-3, 5.30-11; 12-11 Sat; 12-3.30, 7-10.30 Sun
(01978) 822187
Robinson's Hartleys XB, Best Bitter, seasonal beers

This red-brick hotel with large wrought-iron inn sign lies opposite St Mary's Church. Named in honour of the socialite William-Wynn's family, the pub comprises an unassuming bar, restaurant, library and function room. However, the highlight is the attractive, comfortably furnished, wood-panelled lounge and adjacent reception area that feature local period photographs, various brasses plus a collection of porcelain shire horses. The Welsh Football Association was founded here in 1876. No evening meals are served on Sun. P

Porter

Look at its goodly colour
here!
Where else can you find such
good beer?
So brown and stout and
healthy, too!
The porter's health I drink
to you!

Yes, hurrah! The hops and
hurrah! The malt,
They are life's flavour and
life's salt.

Canzone del Porter
[The Porter Song] from the opera Marta, 1847.

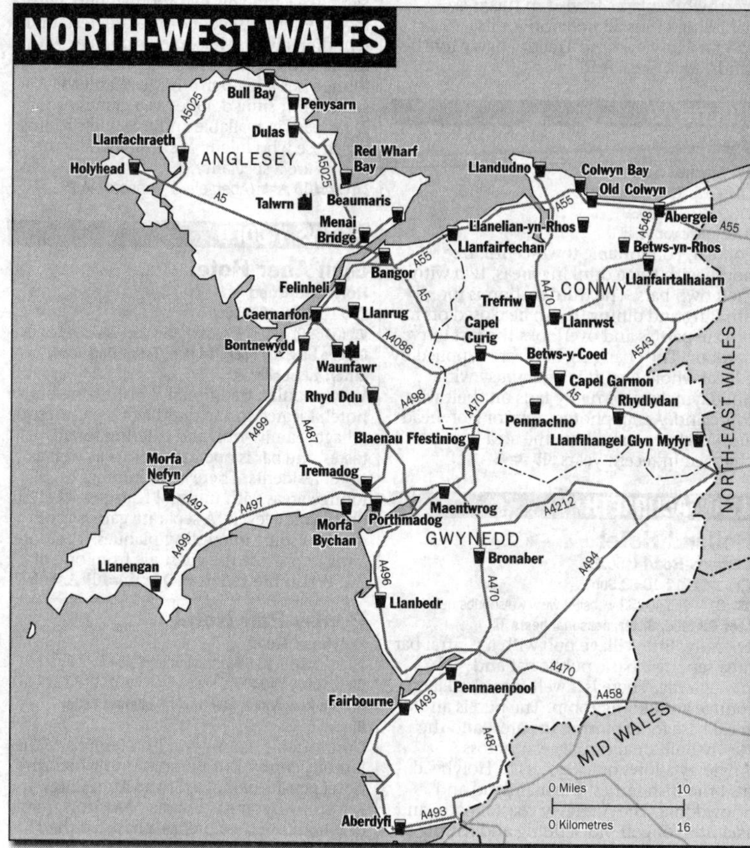

Authority areas covered: Anglesey UA, Conwy UA, Gwynedd UA

Anglesey/Ynys Môn

BEAUMARIS

George & Dragon

Church Street (B5109)

11-11; 12-10.30 Sun

(01248) 810491

Robinson's Best Bitter, seasonal beers Ⓗ

Welcoming local in the centre of the town and a short walk from the Menai Straits, castle and other historic buildings. According to tradition, this timber-framed inn was built in 1410 but architectural details suggest a date in the more settled, prosperous days of Queen Elizabeth I. In the 1970s a remarkable series of wall paintings came to light during repair work. These have been restored and can be viewed on request.

Olde Bull's Head Inn

Castle Street

11-11; 12-10.30 Sun

(01248) 810329

Draught Bass; Hancock's HB; Worthington Bitter; guest beer Ⓗ

Grade II listed building that was the original posting house of the borough. In 1645 General Mutton, a Parliamentarian, commandeered the inn while his forces lay siege to the castle which is a mere stone's throw away. The Royalists surrendered on 25th June, 1646. Dr Samuel Johnson and Charles Dickens were famous guests and each individually-designed bedroom is named after a Dickens' character. The beamed bar has a large open fire and many antiques to create a genuine olde-worlde atmosphere. The inn has an excellent restaurant and brasserie (with wheelchair access). Limited parking available.

DULAS

Pilot Boat Inn

On A5025

11-11; 12-10.30 Sun

(01248) 410205

Robinson's Best Bitter, seasonal beers Ⓗ

Friendly, rural family pub with a play area and converted double-decker bus to keep the children amused. Originally a cottage-type building now much extended, the lounge has an unusual bar (created from half a boat). The pub is much used by walkers, the Anglesey coastal path passes through the car park. There are many

INDEPENDENT BREWERIES

Bragdy Ynys Môn Talwrn

Snowdonia Waunfawr

worthwhile places to visit in the area, including Mynydd Bodafon for its spectacular views and Traeth Lligwy for the sands. ❀◐ ⊟♿⛺♣P

HOLYHEAD

79

79 Market Street
☼ 11-11; 12-10.30 Sun
☎ (01407) 763939
Beer range varies Ⓗ
Popular, comfortable town-centre free house with three drinking areas, two with their own bars. The third section is for drinking and dining, it can be closed off for private parties and overlooks the fast ferry harbour. The changing beers are supplied by a local wholesaler. It is often busy with holidaymakers, or rugby fans on their way to Ireland. Aerial photographs of Holyhead and Anglesey show how the area has changed in recent years. ◐⇌♣

LLANFACHRAETH

Holland Hotel

Cemaes Road (A5025)
☼ 11-11; 12-10.30 Sun
☎ (01407) 740252 website: www.welshpubs.net
Lees GB Mild, Bitter, seasonal beers Ⓗ
Friendly, little village pub with a central bar area serving a basic public bar and passageway. There is a well-furnished larger lounge and dining room. The pub is an ideal base for exploring the area, and the newly-built dual carriageway across Anglesey allows quick access to Holyhead and the Irish ferries, the mainland and Snowdonia. The Anglesey coastal path, and facilities for golf, horseriding and fishing are all nearby. There are some intriguing historic and prehistoric sites to visit.
Q❀⛟◐ ⊟♣P

PENYSARN

Bedol

Off A5025
☼ 12-11; 12-3, 7 (12 summer)-10.30 Sun
☎ (01407) 832590
Robinson's Hatters Mild, Best Bitter, seasonal beers Ⓗ
Welcoming, family-run pub with a large lounge and smaller bar/games room, in a small village near the north coast of Anglesey. Purpose-built in 1984 as a free house, it is now a Robinson's tied house which rotates the whole range of their beers (except dark mild). The Bedol (Welsh for horseshoe) is a community pub with regular functions and a strong local following, supplemented in season by visitors attracted by historic sites, beaches and the industrial heritage trail. ♨Q❀◐⊟⛺♣P

Conwy

ABERGELE

Bull Hotel

Chapel Street
☼ 11-3, 5.30-11; 11-11 Fri & Sat; 12-10.30 Sun
☎ (01745) 832115 website: www.abergelebull.co.uk
Lees GB Mild, Bitter, seasonal beers Ⓗ
One of the oldest buildings in Abergele, registered as a place of worship by Welsh mormons in 1849, prior to setting off for Salt Lake City. This two-roomed pub, with a recently refurbished, no-smoking restaurant (children always welcome) is popular with locals and visitors. The large, homely lounge has a log-burning stove and the small front snug doubles as a games room. A car park is available and five guest rooms for those who might overindulge. Theme nights are a speciality.
♨Q⛟◐⛺⇌(Abergele & Pensarn) ♣P

BETWS-Y-COED

Glan Aber Hotel

Holyhead Road
☼ 11-11; 12-10.30 Sun
☎ (01690) 710325 website: www.betws-y-coed.co.uk
Greene King Old Speckled Hen; Tetley Dark Mild, Bitter; guest beer Ⓗ
Very popular, traditional Welsh stone-built hotel, located in the middle of a picturesque village. Family-run, and catering for all tastes, the bar is open to visitors as well as hotel residents. There are a number of lounge areas with unusual features, located on separate levels. A separate games room displays some interesting plaques. The hotel aims to provide the guest ale from one of the Welsh breweries. ♨Q♉❀⛟◐⛺⇌♣P

Pont-y-Pair Hotel

Holyhead Road
☼ 11-11; 12-10.30 (11 summer) Sun
☎ (01690) 710407
Greene King Abbot; Marston's Pedigree; Tetley Bitter Ⓗ
Comfortable, family-run hotel opposite the famous Pont-y-Pair Bridge (from which the hotel gets its name) over the Afon Llugwy. A warm welcome is offered to visitors, many of whom use the hotel as a base for their varied activities around Snowdonia. Enjoy a good selection of freshly-cooked meals, served in the bar areas and lounge or in the no-smoking dining room. There is a small pool room at the rear. Tiny car park available with spaces for only three cars.
Q❀⛟◐⛺⇌♣P

BETWS-YN-RHOS

Wheatsheaf Inn

☼ 12-3, 6.30-11; 12-3, 6.30-10.30 Sun
☎ (01492) 680218
Greene King IPA, Ruddles Best Bitter; Wadworth 6X Ⓗ
Originally built in the 13th century, and licensed in 1640 as a coaching inn, this free house features brass-strewn oak beams, stone pillars and an original hayloft ladder. It offers a quiet, cosy front lounge where light snacks and bar meals are served and a separate public bar. The split-level rear extension provides an à la carte restaurant, and a function room (with bar and dance area). Disabled facilities are at the rear of the function room. There is a small beer garden available, and bed and breakfast accommodation in four guest rooms.
Q❀⛟◐♿♣P

CAPEL CURIG

Bryn Tyrch Hotel

☼ 12-11; 12-10.30 Sun
☎ (01690) 720223
Castle Eden Ale; Flowers IPA; Wadworth 6X Ⓗ
Situated in a walker's paradise, this old pub

is located at the top end of the village, and has a convenient, large car park located across the A5 road. There is an interesting front lounge that is full of character, popular with walkers and climbers, a distinct, quiet no-smoking room, and a separate no-smoking restaurant. Make your choice from the extensive food menu, displayed on large blackboards. A small TV room to the rear boasts a pool table.
Q P

CAPEL GARMON

White Horse Inn

12-4 (not Mon-Fri), 6-11; 12-4, 6-10.30 Sun
(01690) 710271
website: www.betws-y-coed.co.uk/acc/white-horse
Tetley Bitter; guest beer H

Well off the beaten track, this stone-built, 400-year-old pub can be found in the centre of a small village. The two cosy rooms are full of character, with beamed ceilings, and open fires contributing to the warm, comfortable atmosphere. The pub has a reputation for good food; bar meals are served, together with an extensive menu in the no-smoking restaurant. Six guest rooms are available. ♣P

COLWYN BAY

Wings Social Club

Station Square
11-3, 7-11; 11-11 Sat; 12-3, 7-10.30 Sun
(01492) 530682
Lees GB Mild, Bitter H

Social club open to visitors and their families, with CAMRA members particularly welcome. The large, L-shaped lounge has a raised stage area for live entertainment. The club also has a billiards, pool and darts room in addition to a separate TV room. Proud winner of CAMRA's Regional Club of the Year 2000, it is close to the railway station and the main road bus services. There is a small charge for admission.
Q ♣

LLANDUDNO

Links Hotel

Conway Road (A470)
11-11; 12-10.30 Sun
(01492) 879180
Lees GB Mild, Bitter, seasonal beers H

Large two-roomed pub, purpose-built in 1898 as an urban roadside hotel. It offers a football themed public bar and a lounge bar/restaurant with fascinating old photographs showing the development of the building and locality. There is a spacious conservatory, where children are welcome, and an extensive outdoor play area. This friendly, family-run hostelry has ample room and good car parking facilities. It enjoys a consistent local trade and is well patronised by holidaymakers. Lined glasses are a bonus. ♣P

Snowdon Hotel

11 Tudno Street
12-11; 12-10.30 Sun
(01492) 872116 website: www.snowdonhotel.co.uk
Courage Directors; Tetley Burton Ale; Theakston Best Bitter; guest beers H

Popular pub just off the main shopping centre. A lounge, with an open coal fire and TV, surrounds a central bar. A relatively separate pool area has another TV. Dominoes and darts are played in the games room which is decorated with memorabilia from the days of the tall ships. Regular independent ales come from the Weetwood Brewery and up to two other guests may be on hand. 'Happy hour' is 4-7 and a doubles bar operates 12-9.
♣

LLANELIAN-YN-RHOS

White Lion Inn

Off B5383
11.30-3, 6-11; 12-3, 6-10.30 Sun
(01492) 515807 website: www.whitelioninn.co.uk
Marston's Bitter, Pedigree; guest beer H

Next to the church, in the hills above the coast, this is an attractive, family-run, traditionally furnished inn. It has been extended to accommodate a no-smoking area for diners, and boasts a slate-floored bar, a tiny snug and a lounge partly dating back to the 16th century. White lion statues are a feature, as is the collection of jugs hanging from the ceiling beams. The comfortable leather suite in front of a real log fire is especially inviting in winter.
Q ♣P

LLANFAIRFECHAN

Virginia Inn

Mill Road
12-11; 12-3, 7-10.30 Sun
(01248) 680584
Theakston Mild H

Owned and run by the same family for 30 years, this busy, basic, terraced pub (built around 1880) is situated in the upper village. It is a pleasant and typical local, next to the fast-flowing River Ddu and the village smithy. A quarry-tiled hallway leads to a small bar and three rooms all furnished with interesting period items. The old till and genuine Allsopp's Burton mirror, above the fireplace, are worthy of note. The beer is served from a vertical stillage. Q ♣

LLANFAIRTALHAIARN

Black Lion Hotel

12-3, 7-11; 12-3, 7-10.30 Sun
(01745) 720205
Robinson's Hatters Mild, Best Bitter P

Situated beside the Afon Elwy, the pub is a popular summer tourist venue, and is used by locals all year. The carpeted public bar has a pool table, dartboard, TV and games machines; darts and pool teams play regularly. Occasional weekend entertainment is staged in the extended lounge; this area is ideal for bar snacks or full meals. The separate no-smoking restaurant seats 40, and there is a small snug/cocktail bar. In warmer weather, customers can use the large outdoor areas and picnic tables. If you require accommodation, five guest rooms are available.
Q ♣P

LLANFIHANGEL GLYN MYFYR

Crown Inn

On B5105
⏲ 7 (12 Sat)-11; closed Mon; 12-5, 7-10.30 Sun
☎ (01490) 420209
Beer range varies [H]

A warm welcome awaits in this lovely old inn situated beside the Afon Alwen. The front bar has an open fire, normally lit, and a slate floor. Across the corridor is the pool room (with portable TV). Children are welcome in the pub, and in the terraced gardens beside the river, where in summer bar meals are served. Permits are available for trout fishing (rights owned by the licensee). The beers are from breweries in the Principality, or independents. Camping facilities are provided in the pub grounds.
♨Q✿🛏◗▲♣P

LLANRWST

Pen-y-Bryn

Ancaster Square
⏲ 11-11; 12-10.30 Sun
☎ (01492) 640678
Black Sheep Best Bitter; Greene King Abbot; guest beer [H]

Popular, traditional stone-built terraced pub, owned by Enterprise Inns, located in the town square. The hospitable landlord offers a warm welcome, and the regulars are friendly. One long bar serves the large, comfortable open-plan, timber-floored front area, and there is a smaller, secluded section to the rear. An original inglenook was uncovered during alterations in May 1994. There is a pleasant rear garden and play area to amuse the children.
✿◖⇌

OLD COLWYN

Plough

282 Abergele Road
⏲ 12-3, 6-11; 12-4, 7.30-10.30 Sun
☎ (01492) 515387
Boddingtons Bitter; Greenalls Bitter; guest beers [H]

The Plough is a traditional pub. A one-level lounge surrounds the bar, with cosy, quiet areas. Two guest ales usually come from independent breweries. A separate games room also offers TV and the quiz on Thursday evening is very popular. This pub is the quenching-place for the local Colwyn male choir and the walls display a pictorial account of the choir's history. Lunchtime meals are offered (with concessions to senior citizens) and Sunday lunch is a speciality. It has convenient access to local bus services. Q◖♣

Red Lion

385 Abergele Road
⏲ 5 (4 Fri; 12 Sat)-11; 12-10.30 Sun
☎ (01492) 515042
Boddingtons Bitter; Flowers IPA; Theakston Mild; guest beers [H]

Popular town pub with a wide lounge area warmed by a real coal fire. The local history of the area is depicted in framed pictures around the walls, including a description of the origins of the pub. There is a separate games room with TV and a rear yard with picnic tables. With up to four ales from independent brewers, it boasts many CAMRA awards for its dedication to real ale. The pub is well served by the local buses.
♨✿⊟♣

Sun

383 Abergele Road
⏲ 12-3, 5-11; 12-11 Fri & Sat; 12-10.30 Sun
☎ (01492) 517007
Mansfield Dark Mild, Riding Bitter; Marston's Bitter, Pedigree; guest beer [H]

Small town pub dating from 1844. It is the only original pub building in Old Colwyn, all the others have been rebuilt. A central bar serves a lounge area and a games room, which also has TV. The lounge, which has a welcoming real coal fire, is decorated with a local artist's paintings. The pub's main custom is beer drinkers. Situated in the centre of town, it is handy for local transport. ♨♣

PENMACHNO

Eagles/Ty Uchaf

⏲ 7 (1 Sat)-11; 1-10.30 Sun
☎ (01690) 760177
website: www.eaglespenmachno.co.uk
Greene King Ruddles Best Bitter; John Smith's Bitter; guest beer [H]

Delightful, traditional village pub, recently attractively redecorated. With a wood-burning stove in the lounge, a warm welcome awaits visitors. The piano is another focal point, with the pub itself being the centre of many village activities in this isolated area. A separate room is available, for drinking or dining, and is no-smoking, with its own bar. Only lined glasses are used here! The bunkhouse accommodation costs around £10 a night.
♨Q✿🛏♣⚡⊟

RHYDLYDAN

Giler Arms Hotel

⏲ 11-2.30, 6.30-11 (11-11 summer); 12-10.30 Sun
☎ (01690) 770612
Marston's Pedigree; Tetley Bitter; guest beers [H]

Friendly country hotel situated in the Hiraethog, in seven acres of grounds. It offers a coarse fishing lake, a small campsite and pleasant gardens beside the River Merddwr. Welcoming bars are well stocked, the comfortable lounge has a large open stove, and the 60-seater restaurant overlooks the lake. Children are welcome. The separate public bar, and small pool room are popular with the locals. A genuine free house, the landlord chooses interesting guest beers, and holds an annual summer beer festival. Accommodation is available with seven guest rooms. ♨Q✿🛏◖◗⊟▲♣P

Gwynedd

ABERDYFI/ABERDOVEY

Penhelig Arms Hotel

Terrace Road
⏲ 11-3.30, 6-11 (11-11 summer); 12-3.30, 6-10.30 Sun
☎ (01654) 767215
Tetley Bitter; guest beers [H]

Archetypal, small, friendly seaside hotel standing beside the Penhelig harbour, with superb views across the Dyfi Estuary. The building is of historical interest – today the 'Little Inn' has

grown into a delightful hotel with a well-earned reputation. Located in a self-contained part of the building is the rather stylish, nautically-themed Fisherman's public bar, with a designated no-smoking area. The excellent restaurant serves delicious food including fish specialities. The hotel has 14 bedrooms.
♨Q❀⇌◑Å≠P⊬

BANGOR ❄

Belle Vue
Holyhead Road
11 (12 Sat)-11; 12.30-10.30 Sun
☎ (01248) 364439
Boddingtons Bitter; Bragdy Ynys Môn Medra or Amnesia; Flowers IPA; Marston's Pedigree Ⓗ
Traditional town pub situated near Bangor University, frequented by students, lecturers and locals. A good range of beers includes local Bragdy Ynys Môn brews. There is a wood-panelled lounge, and the bar boasts an old Welsh range and a piano. Regular quiz nights and outdoor summer music events are recent features at the pub. Generous helpings of home-made food are served at lunchtime when a no-smoking area is available. Sunday hours may vary outside term time.
❀◑⊟Å≠⊬

Black Bull/Tarw Du
107 High Street
11-11; 12-10.30 Sun
☎ (01248) 387900
Courage Directors; Greene King Abbot; Theakston Best Bitter; guest beers Ⓗ
Wetherspoon's pub in a converted church and presbytery, at the top of the High Street. It offers spacious drinking areas (large no-smoking section) with an outdoor patio overlooking Upper Bangor and the university. A good selection of real ales is served. It is very busy during term time, especially at weekends. A lift is available for disabled access. Note the interesting pictures displayed showing the history of the university and the Menai Bridge.
Q❀◑♿≠⊬✔

Castell
Off High Street, Glanrafon (opp. cathedral)
12-11; 12-10.30 Sun
☎ (01248) 355866
Boddingtons Bitter; Marston's Pedigree; Wadworth 6X; guest beers Ⓗ
A former Hogshead pub, this spacious one-roomed house is popular with locals and students. It serves six guest beers and four draught ciders. The menu, served 12-9 (12-7 Fri and Sat) includes specials. A no-smoking area is available at mealtimes. Newspapers are provided. ◑♿≠●

Globe Inn/Glôb
Albert Street Upper Bangor (off Holyhead road, near post office)
11-11; 12-10.30 Sun
☎ (01248) 362095 website: www.tafarnyglôb.com
Beer range varies Ⓗ
Small, traditional hostelry full of locals and students. This is a family-run pub serving good value, home-made food with plenty of variety. There is a wood-panelled bar, pool room and a cosy snug. The guest beer range is varied, often chosen from the local brewery Bragdy Ynys Môn. Pool, dominoes and backgammon are played. ◑Å≠♣

Tap & Spile
Garth Road (off old A5, follow pier signs)
12-11.30; 12-10.30 Sun
☎ (01248) 370835
Draught Bass; Greene King IPA; guest beers Ⓗ
Very popular, multi-levelled pub overlooking the pier and Menai Straits. It has a back-to-basics feel with no upholstered seats. Be prepared for big-screen TV and fruit machines. The Tap & Spile attracts locals and university students.
⇌◑♣

INN BRIEF

Anglesey/Ynys Môn

BULL BAY

Bull Bay Hotel
11-11; 12-10.30 Sun
(01407) 830223
Lees GB Mild, Bitter, seasonal beers Ⓗ
Residential hotel with an all-year trade of locals and visitors. Fishing and golf available nearby.

Conwy

TREFRIW

Old Ship Hotel
12-3, 6-11 (12-11 Sat & summer); 12-10.30 Sun
(01492) 640013
Banks's Bitter; Marston's Pedigree; guest beer Ⓗ
This village pub is a free house: welcoming front rooms with an open fire, and a rear dining room.

Gwynedd

BANGOR

Albion Hotel
158 High Street
12-11; 12-10.30 Sun
(01248) 370577
Burtonwood Bitter; guest beer Ⓗ
Old coaching inn on the High Street just past the cathedral. Shows Sky Sports.

Eryl Môr Hotel
2 Upper Garth Road
11-11; 12-10.30 Sun
Beer range varies Ⓗ
Residential hotel overlooking Bangor pier and the Menai Straits. Lunches and evening meals are served.

BONTNEWYDD

Newborough Arms
On A487, Porthmadog-Caernarfon road
11-11; 12-10.30 Sun
(01286) 673126
Felinfoel Dragon Bitter; Tetley Mild, Bitter; guest beer Ⓗ
Village pub on holiday route to Porthmadog and the Lleyn Peninsula; multi-roomed with a restaurant. Cask Marque accredited.

BRONABER

Rhiw Goch
12-11; 12-10.30 Sun
(01766) 540374
Tetley Bitter; guest beer Ⓗ
Spacious pub, comprising three large rooms and a games area. Food is served all day; adjacent ski slope, log cabins and bike hire.

CAERNARFON

Alexandra Hotel
North Road
11-11; 12-10.30 Sun
(01286) 672871
Draught Bass; Boddingtons Bitter; Flowers IPA; guest beer Ⓗ
Free house of original style on roundabout past Safeway's supermarket. Friendly local offering a variety of beers.

BLAENAU FFESTINIOG

Queen's Hotel/Gwesty r Frenhines

High Street

11-11; 12-10.30 Sun

(01766) 830055

website: www.marketsite.co.uk/queens

Tetley Bitter; guest beer H

Situated in the centre of town, beside the railway station(s), this family-run hotel was completely refurbished in 1996. It now offers a public front lounge bar, which is pleasantly decorated, and 'Buffers', a separate bistro-style restaurant. Morning coffees, afternoon teas and bar meals are available all day. The hotel has 12 bedrooms, attractively furnished, together with the usual facilities. Families are welcome. Full disabled facilities are provided.

CAERNARFON

Black Boy Inn

Northgate Street (near the marina)

11-11; 12-10.30 Sun

(01286) 673023

Draught Bass; guest beers H

16th-century pub within the town walls between the marina and the castle. A public bar and small lounge are both warmed by roaring fires. Good value food is served. Limited parking is available. The Welsh Highland Railway starts in Caernarfon. This historic town is well worth a visit; ending with a welcome pint at the Black Boy Inn. Outdoor drinking is on the (traffic-free) street.

Q (Welsh Highland Rlwy) P

FAIRBOURNE

Fairbourne Hotel

11-3, 6-11; 11-11 Sat; 12-10.30 Sun

(01341) 250203

McEwan 80/-; John Smith's Bitter; guest beer (summer) H

This large, 17th-century residential hotel is renowned for excellent food, a friendly atmosphere and 20 comfortable bedrooms. The lounge bar is attractive, with subdued lighting and plenty of quiet corners, where bar meals are served. The terrace bar (no-smoking until 9pm) provides an ideal area for families. The restaurant has beautiful views over the gardens and the estuary, and offers a comprehensive menu. This is the only outlet for McEwan's beers in the county. Full disabled facilities available. Q P

FELINHELI

Gardd Fôn

Beach Road (off main road, by the Menai Straits)

11-11; 12-10.30 Sun

(01248) 670359

Burtonwood Bitter; guest beer H

Nautically-themed, 18th-century, friendly pub, busy in summer and at weekends when locals are joined by numerous visitors. The new bistro (no-smoking) offers excellent food, booking is advisable at weekends. Splendid views of the Menai Straits can be enjoyed from the outdoor drinking area opposite the pub. Note the lovely brasses and church pews. Frequent bus services run from Bangor and Caernarfon (routes 5 and 5A); limited parking. Q P

LLANBEDR

Tŷ Mawr Hotel

Take Cwmbychan turn in centre of village, on left

11-11; 12-10.30 Sun

(01341) 241440

Draught Bass; Worthington Bitter; guest beers H

Small country hotel set in its own grounds; the modern lounge bar has a slate-flagged floor and a cosy wood-burning stove in winter. The corner bar sometimes has unobtrusive background music playing. Interesting flying memorabilia points to connections with a local airfield nearby. French windows lead on to a verandah and landscaped terrace with outdoor seating. Popular with locals, walkers and real ale enthusiasts; dogs and children are welcome. Good value meals are offered with occasional theme nights. An interesting range of guest beers is stocked.

P

LLANENGAN

Sun Inn

From Abersoch, through village, pub on left OS294268

12-3 (not winter), 6-11; 12-11 Sat; 12-3, 6-10.30 Sun

(01758) 712660

Robinson's Hatters Mild, Best Bitter, Frederics H

Surprisingly large pub with distinct drinking areas. Good quality food is always available. It stands on the road to Porth Neigwl (Hell's Mouth) with its sweeping sandy beach that is loved by surfers. The beautiful National Trust gardens at Plas yn Rhiw are a few miles away towards the end of the Lleyn Peninsula. It should be noted that the pub does not open weekday lunchtimes in the winter. No dogs are allowed in the garden which incorporates a covered area for chillier weather. Q P

LLANRUG

Glyntwrog Inn

On A4086, towards Llanberis approx 1/2 mile past Spar shop

11-11; 12-10.30 Sun

(01286) 671191

Greene King IPA; guest beer H

New entry in this Guide, this spacious pub is situated just outside the village on the A4086. It offers a games room, comfortable no-smoking area and children's playground. Popular with locals, meals are served lunchtime and evening. It is handy for Llanberis, Padarn Lake and Snowdonia National Park. The pub is served by bus services 83 and 88 from Caernarfon and route 86 from Bangor.

P

MAENTWROG

Grapes Hotel

On A496 towards Harlech

11-11; 12-10.30 Sun

(01766) 590208

Beer range varies Ⓗ
Welcoming, 13th-century former coaching inn, a Grade II listed building with a sizeable public bar, large verandah/diner and smaller lounge warmed by a real fire. A dining/drinking section is no-smoking and doubles as a family room. A quiet atmosphere prevails apart from the juke box in the public bar. Stone walls feature and the pub is furnished with pitch-pine pews and settles, some salvaged from chapels. Excellent value, home-cooked food with seafood specialities offered – but try the ultimate challenge of house spare ribs! It is a popular central point for hillwalking, on a bus route, and not far from the Ffestiniog Railway. Local CAMRA Pub of the Year 2001.
(Ffestiniog Rlwy) P

MENAI BRIDGE

Liverpool Arms Hotel
St George's Road (between post office and pier)
11-3, 5.30-11; 7-10.30 Sun
(01248) 713335
Flowers IPA, Original; guest beers Ⓗ
Newly extended accommodation provides first-rate bed and breakfast (12 rooms) with an excellent reputation for home-cooked food and Sunday lunches. Meals are served daily at lunchtime and on Sunday evening. This 150-year-old pub has several rooms and a conservatory served from three central bars. Popular with locals, the sailing fraternity and students, a different guest beer is offered every few days. Old maps, antiquities and local photos adorn the walls. The pub makes a good base for touring Anglesey and Snowdonia. The narrow gauge Welsh Mountain Railway from Caernarfon to Rhyd Ddu in Snowdonia is within easy reach. Sailing and fishing are popular locally.
Q

Victoria Hotel
Telford Road (over suspension bridge towards town centre)
11-11; 12-10.30 Sun
(01248) 712309
Draught Bass; guest beers Ⓗ
Overlooking the beautiful Menai Straits, this residential hotel (19 rooms) has a lovely garden and patio area. A large function room is licensed to midnight (and for weddings) and regular live music is a feature. There is easy access to Snowdonia, the North Wales coast, and the Welsh Highland Railway from Caernarfon. The local independent brewery Bragdy Ynys Môn supplies the hotel with excellent Welsh bitters. Wide-screen TV for sports is available. The resorts and beaches of Anglesey are all accessible, and sailing on the Menai Straits and many golf courses are close at hand. Fishing is popular locally.
Q P

MORFA BYCHAN

Tafarn Glanaber
Beach Road
12-3, 6.30-11 (11-11 summer); 12-10.30 Sun
(01766) 514917
Beer range varies Ⓗ
Large, friendly free house situated among the Black Rock Sands camp and caravan sites in a handy location close to the beautiful, popular sandy beaches and the golf course. The spacious room has comfortable seating areas and an additional indoor section for families. Outside, there is a garden and children's play area. With a varying beer range, occasional live music and an extensive menu of good value food, this pub attracts tourists, so it can be very busy in high season. P

MORFA NEFYN

Cliffs Inn
Beach Road OS283408
12-3, 6 (7 winter)-11; 12-3, 6-10.30 (not winter eves) Sun
(01758) 720356
Greene King Old Speckled Hen; guest beer Ⓗ
Particularly popular in summer, this spacious pub has a sun lounge overlooking the bay. Located on the clifftop with a panoramic view of the beach round to Porth Dinllaen (once planned as main mail port for Ireland, but this was never developed and it remains sheltered and tranquil). An excellent range of reasonably-priced food is offered, including vegetarian dishes. Dedicated disabled parking is available. The guest beer is normally from a Welsh brewery. Welsh is spoken. Self-catering accommodation is provided.
Q P

PENMAENPOOL

George III Hotel
11-11; 12-10.30 Sun
(01341) 422525 website: www.george-3rd.co.uk
Greene King Ruddles Best Bitter; John Smith's Bitter; guest beer (summer) Ⓗ
This family-owned and run residential hotel (built circa 1650) is situated beside the tollbridge crossing the Mawddach Estuary, adjacent to the old railway line (now a cycle route). The Cellar bar with slate floor, oak-beamed ceiling, and panelled benches is ideal for families, with a children's certificate and menu and no-smoking policy. Home-made hot and cold bar food is served. There is a separate Dresser bar lounge, and a restaurant, with fine views. Disabled access/toilet facilities are available.
Q P

PORTHMADOG

Ship Inn/Llong
Lombard Street (near park and harbour)
11-11; 12-4 (not winter) Sun
(01766) 512990
Greene King IPA, Old Speckled Hen; Tetley Dark Mild, Bitter, Burton Ale; guest beer (varies) Ⓗ
Two-roomed local with public bar and no-smoking lounge, with a further separate dining area at the rear. Both bars are attractively adorned with nautical memorabilia, early photographs and prints. The landlord has several awards for cellarmanship and stocks a large range of beers. An annual beer festival is staged in March. The menu offers plenty of choice; children are welcome only if dining. A

superb selection of over 80 malt whiskies is offered. ⩕Q◑⊟⋏≹♣⚟

Spooner's Bar

Harbour Station

⏲ 11-11; 12-10.30 Sun

☎ (01766) 516032 website: www.festrail.co.uk

Banks's Original; Marston's Bitter, Pedigree; guest beers Ⓗ

Popular bar forming part of the terminus of the world famous Ffestiniog Railway, with narrow gauge steam trains running from Easter to the end of October. The fine range of home-cooked food includes a varied vegetarian selection. Accompanied children are welcome. Beer festivals are held regularly throughout the year, but particularly to coincide with special events on the railway (see website) and bank holiday weekends.

❀◑♿≹(Ffestiniog Rlwy) P⚟

RED WHARF BAY (TRAETH COCH)

Ship Inn

1½ miles off A5025, near Benllech

⏲ 11-3.30, 6.30-11 winter; 11-11 summer; 12-10.30 Sun

☎ (01248) 852586

Friary Meux Bitter; Tetley Bitter, Burton Ale; guest beer Ⓗ

Renowned for its good food (daily menu changes) and location, with superb views over the bay, this warm, cosy, old pub has superb log fires in the winter, and the exposed beams add to the character. Red Wharf Bay saw boat building between 1700 and 1820 and was once a busy port in the days of sail. The main cargoes were fertiliser and coal. The pub was then known as the Quay, today it is busy with locals and holidaymakers, bustling in summer. The beer garden affords panoramic views across the bay. Enjoyable walks can be found nearby. Try the local Welsh bitter from Bragdy Ynys Môn in summer.

⩕Q♉❀◑⋏P⚟

RHYD DDU

Cwellyn Arms

Foot of Snowdon (on A4085 Caernarfon-Beddgelert road)

⏲ 11-11; 11-10.30 Sun

☎ (01766) 890321 website: www.snowdoninn.co.uk

Worthington Bitter; guest beers Ⓗ

This beamed, 200-year-old pub at the foot of Snowdon, serving an extensive menu of tasty food, is open 365 days a year. It offers large bunkhouse accommodation and camping in a beautiful national park location, 15 minutes' walk from the pub; ideal for walkers and climbers. Up to six guest beers are on tap. The Welsh Highland Railway is due to reach Rhyd Ddu by autumn 2002. It is served by Sherpa bus route 95. Local CAMRA Pub of the Year 2000.

⩕Q♉❀⛀◑⋏≹(Welsh Highland Rlwy) P

TREMADOG

Golden Fleece

The Square

⏲ 11.30-3, 6-11; 12-3, 6-10.30 Sun

☎ (01766) 512421

Draught Bass; guest beer Ⓗ

Situated in the old market square of Tremadog, this old coaching inn is now a friendly local. On the main bus routes, nearby attractions range from rock-climbing to narrow gauge railways. The large lounge has a no-smoking area at the rear, and there is a snug which may occasionally be reserved for local regulars. There is also an extensive covered area with well-designed decking and bench seating. An additional bistro is located upstairs, booking is advised. Children are welcome. The food is good value. Try your hand at pool, a small table is to the rear. ⩕Q❀⛀◑⚟

WAUNFAWR

Snowdonia Parc

On A4085, Caernarfon-Beddgelert road

⏲ 6 (12 Sat & summer)-11; 12-10.30 Sun

☎ (01286) 650409

website: www.snowdonia-park.co.uk

Mansfield Dark Mild; Marston's Bitter, Pedigree; Snowdonia Welsh Highland Bitter, seasonal beers Ⓗ

Brew-pub located in the heart of Snowdonia with its own campsite (reduction for CAMRA members). It offers good food
and home-brewed beers, plus live entertainment on Saturday evening. The Welsh Highland Railways stops outside the pub. There is plenty to keep children amused as there is a playground in the garden, and another play area inside the pub. The Sherpa bus from Caernarfon stops close by (routes 89 and 95).

Q♉❀◑⊟⋏≹(Welsh Highland Rlwy) ♣P⚟

On-licence

Of all the strange bills that they'd pass'd
To make people act with propriety,
They've managed to make one at last,
That is causing some fun in society.

For in every street you go through,
Lane, alley, or any such crevices,
Each beer-shop writes up in full view,
'Allowed to be drunk on the premises'.

John Labern, circa 1855.

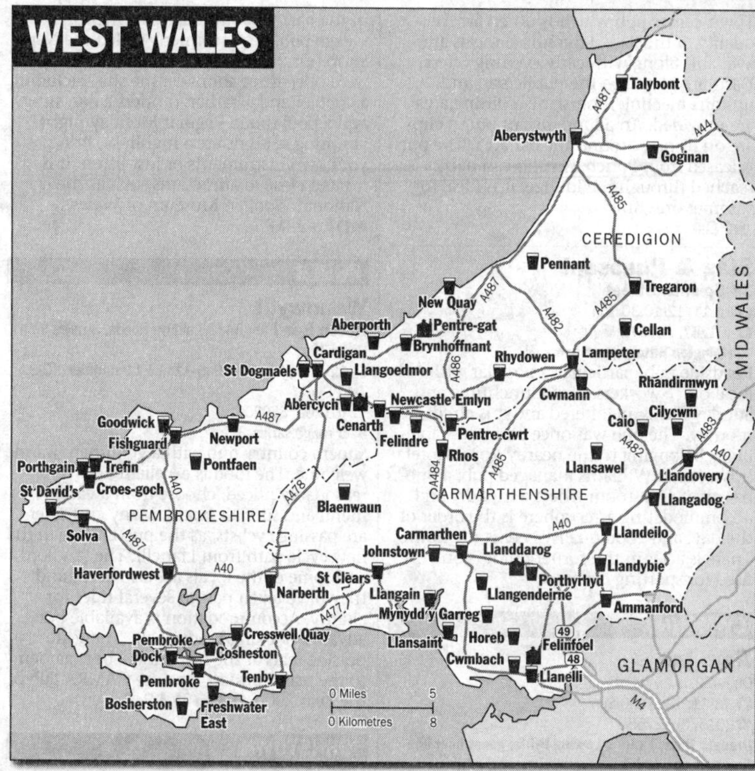

Authority areas covered: Carmarthenshire UA, Ceredigion UA, Pembrokeshire UA

Carmarthenshire

AMMANFORD

Wernolau

31 Pontamman Road (from Ammanford-Neath road, 50 yds past Murco garage on right)
✪ 5.30-11; 12-10.30 (7 winter) Sun
☎ (01269) 592598
Brains Buckley's Best Bitter; guest beers Ⓗ

The excellent choice here of five varying guest ales is popular with locals. This was originally a mine manager's house and was built in the 17th century. Five acres of landscaped grounds and woodland surround this residential hotel (open to non-residents). There is a Victorian theme including open fires in winter. A large function room caters for weddings. Meals are available and families welcome. The Lions Club and Round Table meetings are held here regularly. ♨Q❀⇔◗⚠

BLAENWAUN

Lamb Inn

8 miles N of St Clears, on road to Tegryn OS237271
✪ 5.30 (12 Sat)-11; 12-10.30 Sun
☎ (01994) 448440
Brains Rev James; guest beer Ⓗ

Interesting country pub, set in the heart of rural west Wales. Definitely worth paying a visit if you are in the area. The pub is an Aladdin's Cave, full of interesting bric-à-brac and a resident parrot for extra amusement. Live entertainment is laid on during the summer season. The pub has a friendly, convivial atmosphere and a warm welcome is assured. Interestingly, if you call on the first Monday of the month you can have a haircut while sipping your pint. Limited food available. ❀⚠♣P

CAIO

Brunant Arms

✪ 12 (6 Mon)-11; 12-10.30 Sun
☎ (01558) 650483
Greene King Old Speckled Hen; Tomos Watkin Whoosh; guest beers Ⓗ

In the centre of the village, near the Dolau Cothi Goldmines, this pub is the sole survivor; Caio once had five inns. Pool and quiz teams meet here. Good quality home-cooked food is available. There is a nearby pony-trekking centre and it is easy to call at the pub en route and tether the horses to a rail outside. A legendary Welsh wizard is buried in the church opposite. Three guest beers are usually available, including one from the Cottage Brewery. ♨❀⇔◐◗⚠P

CARMARTHEN

Queen's Hotel

✪ 12-11; 12-10.30 Sun
☎ (01267) 231800
Draught Bass; Worthington Bitter; guest beer Ⓗ

INDEPENDENT BREWERIES

Bragdy Ceredigion Pentre-gat
Coles Llanddarog
Felinfoel Felinfoel
Nag's Head Abercych

Town-centre pub which is noted for the quality of the Bass. Lunchtime meals are available along with early evening offers. Darts are played in the public bar, and upstairs meeting rooms and a dining area are provided. An abundance of pump clips are on display around the bar area. The pub is leased from Punch. A patio can be reached through the lounge, it is ideal for summer drinking.
✿◐⊟≠

Stag & Pheasant

34 Spilman Street
⏲ 11-11; 12-10.30 Sun
☎ (01267) 236278
Worthington Bitter; guest beers Ⓗ
Roadside pub, particularly popular with local office workers. Good lunchtime and Sunday meals are offered and it is child-friendly. The pub was once part of a stable block belonging to the nearby Royal Hotel. It is a James Williams managed pub; a one-bar open-plan room where a friendly and accommodating atmosphere is the order of the day, and good quality beer is the norm. There is a TV in the corner but it is only used for sporting events. ◐≠

CWMANN

Ram Inn

On A482, outskirts of village
⏲ 11-11; 12-10.30 Sun
☎ (01570) 422556
Draught Bass; Fuller's London Pride; guest beer Ⓗ
Do not miss this award-winning pub (former CAMRA Best Pub in Wales and fourth in GB). You will always find a warm welcome as testified by President Carter and other celebrities who have left evidence of their visits. The pub consists of two cosy, traditional bars, a restaurant and a large beer garden. The landlord is proud to have been associated with the Ram for 23 years.
♨Q✿◐◗♣P

CWMBACH

Farriers

Trimsaran Road
⏲ 11-11; 12-10.30 Sun
☎ (01554) 774256
Draught Bass; Worthington Bitter; guest beer Ⓗ
Small pub with an attractive garden, a popular drinking area in summer as it overlooks a stream. The main entrance to the pub is via steps leading down to a suspended walkway. A good reputation for food is enjoyed with a varied and interesting menu. The owner is a keen golfer and the memorabilia reflects this. The Farriers is situated on the Trimsaran to Furnace (Llanelli) road; parking is possible opposite the pub. Q✿◐◗

FELINDRE

John y Gwâs

Opp. school and church
⏲ 2 (12 Sat)-11; 12-10.30 Sun
☎ (01559) 370469
Brains Rev James; Greene King Old Speckled Hen; guest beer Ⓗ
The pub name translates from Welsh as 'John the Servant', and relates to a previous owner (in the 1950s) whose portrait hangs in the bar. A traditional, cosy, friendly, village pub, it was formerly called the New Shop Inn. Built in the early 1800s, there were once three shops on the site, including a cobbler and a barber. It offers a bar, snug and a pool room. Regular Monday night jamming sessions are a highlight, bring your own instruments or just listen. It is located close to attractions such as the National Woollen Museum of Wales.
♨Q◗♿▲♣P

HOREB

Waunwyllt

Horeb Road (off B4309 at Five Roads, 3 miles from Llanelli)
⏲ 12-3, 7 (6.30 Fri & Sat)-11; 12-11 summer; 12-3, 7-11 Sun
☎ (01269) 860209
Beer range varies Ⓗ
Superb country pub with a genuinely warm welcome. The food is excellent and reasonably priced; choose from a varied menu and specials board. Many customers are passing cyclists, as the pub is close to the new cycle path from Llanelli. The landlord and some of the locals are also keen, and they have taken part in several rides for charity. Accommodation is available but advance booking is advisable. There are outside seats at the front and a beer garden to the rear. Carmarthenshire CAMRA Pub of the Year 2000. Q✿⇋◐◗▲P

JOHNSTOWN

Friends Arms

St Clears Road (jct of Johnstown-Picton Hill)
⏲ 11-11; 12-3, 7-10.30 Sun
☎ (01267) 234073
Ansells Mild; Tetley Bitter, Burton Ale Ⓗ
There has been a pub on this site for 400 years, alongside a blacksmith's with attached stables and a nearby tollhouse (which is still standing). The smith was owned by John Thomas in 1841 who took 60 years to become landlord. It is a community local which raises a great deal for charity every year. The pub has low beams and plenty of brassware adorns the walls. Q✿♣

LLANDEILO

Castle Hotel

113 Rhosmaen Street
⏲ 11-11; 12-10.30 Sun
☎ (01558) 823446
Tomos Watkin Whoosh, BB, Merlin Stout, OSB, seasonal beers Ⓗ
This was originally the home of Tomos Watkin Brewery, now relocated in Swansea. It is a multi-roomed pub with an increasing reputation for good food. It is close to several local tourist attractions including the National Botanical Gardens at Llanarthne. For more ideas, the local tourist office is based in the large council car park behind the Castle Hotel. Locals are very friendly and will make all visitors welcome. There is live music on Fri eve. Q✿◐◗≠

White Horse

125 Rhosmaen Street (off main street through arch)
⏲ 11-11; 12-10.30 Sun

☎ (01558) 822424
Wadworth IPA; Wells Bombardier; guest beers Ⓗ
Popular with all ages, this multi-roomed pub occasionally hosts live bands. It is a charming, 16th-century, Grade II listed coaching inn. A good range of beers is usually available. While ordering, note the caricatures of locals on the bar front. A pleasant courtyard at the front of the building has outdoor seating, or opt for the beer garden at the rear. The main council car park is located just behind. No food is served.
⛼❀⇌♣✓

LLANDOVERY

Castle Hotel
King's Road
✪ 11-11; 12-3, 7-11 Sun
☎ (01550) 720343
Wadworth IPA; Worthington Bitter; guest beer Ⓗ
Originally built in the 18th century, the pub has recently undergone extensive refurbishment. It is close to the castle (hence the name) and the livestock market. The nearby car park has ample space for visitors. There are 23 rooms which include two heritage rooms that boast four-poster beds. All the rooms have en-suite accommodation. There is an annual drovers' festival in Llandovery in September. The town is situated on the River Towy.
⇌P

LLANDYBIE

Ivy Bush
18 Church Street
✪ 12-4 (not Mon or Tue; 4.30 Sat), 6 (6.30 Sat)-11; 11-11 Fri; 12-2 Sun
☎ (01269) 850272
Tetley Burton Ale; guest beer Ⓗ
The oldest pub in the village, dating back nearly 300 years. Recently refurbished to an open-plan layout, it has lost none of its local appeal. Darts and cards are played on Wednesday. An interesting selection of cigarette cards and militaria are on display. Children and dogs are welcome. It is situated near the Heart of Wales railway line. No food served, just good honest ale.
⇌P

LLANELLI

Baldy's Bar
2 Prospect Place (off A476, near jct with A484)
✪ 11.30-11; 12-10.30 Sun
☎ (01554) 755121
Brains Buckley's Best Bitter; Tomos Watkin Whoosh; guest beer Ⓗ
Popular local with a strong sport-loving clientele. This pub was previously called the Lemon Tree but is now named after the new owner's hairstyle. It features interesting exterior artwork, and the interior has recently been refurbished. It is now open plan but retains the feel of separate bars. The bowling green situated to the rear of the pub is now disused but houses a marquee for beer festivals. The pub was once the Buckley's brewery tap and mementos of this once proud company are to the rear of the pub. ❀

LLANGENDEIRNE

Smiths Arms/y Gof
On main Carmarthen-Pontyberem road
✪ 12-2.30 (not winter Mon-Fri), 6.30-11.30; 12-2.30, 6.30-11.30 Sun
☎ (01269) 871554
Brains Dark; guest beer Ⓗ
Situated in a pretty village, with splendid views of the river (the Gwendraeth Fawr), this friendly pub is on the main road. The bar area includes a games room where pool and darts can be played. The lounge has a large dining area with a no-smoking section. Tasty meals are offered and prove excellent value. Pump clips cover the walls, giving testament to the ever-changing range of guest ales available. The pub is the focal point of the village. ❀⚟

LLANSAINT

King's Arms
13 Maes yr Eglwys
✪ 12-2.30, 6.30-11; 12-2.30, 6.30-10.30 Sun
☎ (01267) 267487
Worthington Bitter; guest beers Ⓗ
Welcoming, 200-year-old pub with a roaring log fire, situated close to the village's 11th-century church. An interesting collection of jugs adorns the low beams and local photographs hang on the walls. It is rumoured to be built from stone

INN BRIEF

Carmarthenshire

CENARTH

Three Horseshoes
11-11 (closed winter eve); 12-10.30 (closed winter eve) Sun
(01239) 710119
Brains Dark, Buckley's Best Bitter; Ⓗ **Greene King Abbot;** Ⓖ **guest beer** Ⓗ
Picturesque riverside inn popular with anglers and tourists. Its garden overlooks the Cenarth Falls.

CILYCWM

Neuadd Fawr Arms
OS753401
11-3, 6-11 (can vary, phone first); 12-10.30 Sun
(01550) 721644
Beer range varies Ⓗ
Four miles north of Llandovery, a traditional local pub with interesting interior.

LLANGADOG

Telegraph
Station Road
5.30-11; 12-3, 6-11 Sat; 12-3, 7-10.30 Sun
(01550) 777727
Beer range varies Ⓗ
No-frills inn near station; rotating guest from smaller breweries and Black Rat cider. Campsite nearby; limited B&B and food available.

LLANGAIN

Tafarn Pantydderwen
Old School Road
12-3, 6-11; 12-11 Sat; 12-10.30 Sun
(01267) 241560
Flowers Original; guest beer Ⓗ
Country pub set in the middle of the village. The restaurant dominates, but real ale drinkers are made welcome.

LLANSAWEL

Black Lion
5 (11 Sat)-11; 12-10.30 Sun
(01558) 685263
Beer range varies Ⓗ
The main bar is on two levels in a traditional black and white building. One handpump usually serves a Cottage ale.

ST CLEARS

Corvus
Station Road
11-11; 12-10.30 Sun
(01994) 230965
Courage Best Bitter; Worthington Bitter; guest beer Ⓗ
Busy, two-bar locals' pub in the centre of the village. It is reputedly haunted.

recovered from the lost village of St Ishmael's. Children are welcome and the food is good; handy for Carmarthen Bay holiday park. ♨❀⊨◐◑▲♣P

MYNYDD Y GARREG

Prince of Wales

$1^1/_2$ miles from Kidwelly bypass
✪ 7 (5 Sat)-11; 12-3 Sun
☎ (01554) 890522
Beer range varies Ⓗ
Small, isolated pub that is worth finding. Take a look at the extensive movie memorabilia. There is a small, no-smoking restaurant serving delicious food (Mon-Sat eve and Sun lunch). The pub does a good trade in take-home beer. Bring your own containers. Bullmastiff beers regularly feature and there is an ever-changing choice of ales from small local breweries. In fact, the Prince of Wales offers the most extensive range of real ales in the area. Children under 14 are not admitted. Pembrey Country Park, Kidwelly Castle and Kidwelly Industrial Museum are close to this comfortable, welcoming hostelry. ♨Q❀◐◑

NEWCASTLE EMLYN

Bunch of Grapes

Bridge Street (opp. provisions market)
✪ 12-11 (closed winter Mon); 12-3, 7-10.30 Sun
☎ (01239) 711185
Blackawton Best Bitter; Courage Directors; Theakston Old Peculier Ⓗ
Charming, 17th-century listed town pub with one main bar. It retains exposed oak beams, a huge inglenook and timber floors. An unusual indoor garden has a grapevine growing over the roof. An excellent range of guest ale is served to accompany the fine food. The live music (Thu eve) is popular with all age groups. ♨❀◐◑▲♣

Coopers Arms

Station Road (A484)
✪ 12-3.30, 5.30-11; 12-3, 7-10.30 Sun
☎ (01239) 710323 website: www.pub-explorer.com
Bragdy Ceredigion Barcud Coch; guest beer Ⓗ
This pub prides itself on its excellent cellar which is second to none. A new, improved 32-seat restaurant is now complete, superb food is served and a full selection of wines. The quality local beer is available on pump, in bottles and also in take-away plastic containers. This pub is now a retail outlet for Ceredigion Brewery (bottles). See the permanent exhibition by local artists, the paintings are for sale. Q❀◐◑▲♣P⚟

PENTRE-CWRT

Plas Parke Inn

On B4335 between Llandysul and Newcastle Emlyn
✪ 2.30-11; 12-10.30 Sun
☎ (01559) 362684
Draught Bass; guest beer Ⓗ
Friendly village meeting place with a choice of three bars and cosy nooks and crannies. Gazebos in the garden provide sheltered outdoor seating in summer, whatever the weather. Evening meals and Sunday lunch are served in the 40-seat restaurant, which has a reputation for gargantuan helpings. Close to a local beauty spot, Alltcafan Bridge, it is much frequented by fly fishermen on the River Teifi and is handy for the canoeing centre at Llandysul, a rapidly growing sport. The Henllan Falls and the National Woollen Museum of Wales are close by. ♨❀◐◑▲♣P

PORTHYRHYD

Mansel

Banc y Mansel (off A48, Drefach-Llanddarog road)
✪ 6 (2 Sat)-11; 12-4 Sun
☎ (01267) 275305
Greene King IPA; guest beers Ⓗ
Friendly local pub with wood fires in each room. It is an 18th-century former coaching inn on the A48. The games room to the rear, where you can play pool and darts, used to be a killing room for pigs but the limestone slabs have been broken up and used in the fireplace. Low beams have been added to create a homely atmosphere; they are adorned with a fine collection of jugs. A warm welcome is assured. ♨Q◑⊟▲♣P

RHANDIRMWYN

Royal Oak

Signed from A483 in Llandovery
✪ 11.30-3, 6-11 (times can vary); 12-2, 7-10.30 Sun
☎ (01550) 760201
Beer range varies Ⓗ
Remote stone-flagged pub of great character with excellent views of the valley. It was built as a hunting lodge for the local landowner. Darts, pool and crib are played. The pub is close to the Llyn Brianne Dam so it attracts ramblers and birdwatchers. There is an extensive selection of whiskies and bottled beers. Food is good and the ever-changing guest list is popular. There are three to four guest ales in winter, and up to six in summer. Local CAMRA Pub of the Year 2001 and 2002, it was South and Mid Wales Regional Pub of the Year 2001.
♨Q❀⊨◐◑▲♣P

RHOS

Lamb Inn

On A484, Carmarthen-Newcastle Emlyn road
✪ 12-2.30 (not Wed), 5.30-11; 12-11 Fri & Sat; 12-10.30 Sun
☎ (01559) 370055
Banks's Original; Greene King Old Speckled Hen; Worthington Bitter; guest beer (occasional) Ⓗ
Spacious country inn, overlooking the Teifi Valley, with flagstoned floors and interesting interior and exterior brickwork. There has been a pub here for 300 years. It was extended in the 1970s, then known as 'the little Ritz in Wales', and has undergone a recent, attractive refurbishment. Spend an hour browsing among the curios, including a collection of bottled beers. The children can play in what must be the smallest 'fun' village jail, HM Prison Rhos. The bottled beers regularly include Wychwood Hobgoblin. ♨❁❀⊨◐◑♣P⚟

Ceredigion

ABERPORTH

Ship Inn

West Street (B4333, facing beach)
✪ 12-2, 5-11 (12-11 summer); 12-10.30 Sun
☎ (01239) 810822

Fuller's London Pride (summer); **Greene King IPA, Abbot** (summer); **guest beer** (occasional) Ⓗ
Lively village hostelry in summer, but naturally quieter out of season. The Ship has one large, refurbished bar with a seafaring theme, together with covered outside seating areas affording excellent views of Cardigan Bay, where dolphins are sometimes seen. Tasty, reasonably priced food is sold and occasional live music performed. Public car parking is located opposite. The pub is served by Aberystwyth-Cardigan buses (limited service eve and Sun).

ABERYSTWYTH

Hen Orsaf

Alexandra Road
11-11 (opens 10 Mon-Sat for tea & coffee); 12-10.30 Sun
☎ (01970) 636080
Boddingtons Bitter; Courage Directors; Greene King Abbot; Shepherd Neame Spitfire; Wadworth 6X; guest beers Ⓗ
The name means 'old station' and a classy Wetherspoon's conversion has restored the GWR's listed building of 1924 to its former glory. Linked ground floor rooms include the former booking office, but perhaps the choicest spot is the glass-roofed concourse, now an attractive 'beer patio'. There is generous toilet provision on the first floor and a fully specified disabled toilet on the ground floor. Three to four guest beers are available at all times and include some highly enterprising choices. Standard Wetherspoon's policies apply (no under-18s, except for daytime family dining, full menu until one hour before closing). Handy for trains, buses, taxis and public car parks; like many pubs in town, it can get very busy on weekend evenings.
Q

Ship & Castle

1 High Street
12-11; 12-10.30 Sun
☎ (01970) 612334
Beer range varies Ⓗ
This small, street-corner pub in the heart of the old town should be the first call for discerning beer drinkers in Aberystwyth. Six Bells Full Moon (4.5% ABV) is brewed specially for a local wholesaler; the other five beer pumps present a constantly changing range mainly from micros in Wales and borders, although more mainstream beers are sometimes seen. Midweek beer festivals are held twice a year (April and October). Addlestone's cider on handpump is occasionally partnered by a farm cider. Though sometimes quiet during the day, the place is never dull. Sunday lunch (12-4) draws the crowds for its quality and good value, no other meals are served. Live Irish music is performed on Wednesday evening.

CARDIGAN

Black Lion/Llew Du

High Street
10-11; 12-10.30 Sun
☎ (01239) 612532
Tomos Watkin Whoosh, OSB, seasonal beers Ⓗ
Historic coaching inn in a busy, characterful town. It dates back to the 12th century, but the present building is 18th century. There is a main drinking area, a small panelled snug and a rear dining section. It is a welcome outpost for this Swansea-based brewery, through which it has regained its leading position among the town's pubs.

CELLAN

Fishers Arms

On B4343, S end of village
4.30 (11 Sat)-11; 12-10.30 Sun
☎ (01570) 422895
Beer range varies Ⓗ
Very much the centre of village life, this popular pub offers a relaxed and friendly atmosphere. The house beer, Fishers Ale, is from Brains, and a second cask beer is also offered – generally either Taylor Landlord or Greene King Old Speckled Hen, though others have also appeared. The beamed and flagstoned interior is adorned with fishing and hunting paraphernalia, and the area offers excellent fishing and hillwalking. Buses from Lampeter and Tregaron, while hardly frequent, permit an afternoon or early evening visit, (Mon-Sat service).
Q P

INN BRIEF

Ceredigion

ABERYSTWYTH

Downies Vaults

33 Eastgate
11-11; 12-10.30 Sun
(01970) 625446
Banks's Original, Bitter, Ⓟ **Mansfield Riding Bitter** Ⓗ
Pleasantly modernised town-centre pub named after a bygone local worthy. One main room, with a warm, welcoming atmosphere.

Fountain

Trefechan
12 (2 Mon-Fri Jan & Feb)-11; 12-10.30 Sun
(01970) 612430
Boddingtons Bitter; Brains Dark; guest beer Ⓗ
Characterful, two-roomed pub, once a brewery tap. The guest beer generally comes from large regional breweries.

BRYNHOFFNANT

Brynhoffnant Inn

12-3 (not Mon), 5-11 (12-11 summer); 12-10.30 Sun
(01239) 654961
Felinfoel Double Dragon; Hancock's HB; Worthington Bitter; guest beer (summer) Ⓗ
Friendly, cosy inn with no-smoking restaurant. Glorious coastal scenery is close. The garden has a play area.

Pembrokeshire

COSHESTON

Cosheston Brewery

12-4, 6.30-11; 12-4, 6.30-10.30 Sun
(01646) 686678
Worthington Bitter; guest beers Ⓗ
Extended village local with games room and restaurant.

FISHGUARD

Fishguard Arms

11-3, 6-11;
12-3, 7-10.30 Sun
Beer range varies Ⓗ
Small locals' pub. Welcoming bar with an open fire. Two rotating real ales are served and no keg beer.

GOODWICK

Rose & Crown

11-11;
12-10.30 Sun
Worthington Bitter; guest beer Ⓗ
Picturesque pub close to the ferry and enjoying harbour views. It has a no-smoking restaurant.

GOGINAN

Druid Inn

On A44, 7 miles E of Aberystwyth
11-11; 12-10.30 Sun
☎ (01970) 880650 website: www.goginan.co.uk
Banks's Bitter; Brains Bitter; guest beer (occasional) H

True free house, on a main trunk route across Wales, in a former lead-mining village – the local Llywernog Mining Museum displays the industrial heritage. The L-shaped main bar is pleasantly decorated, with one part used mainly for dining. Locally made love spoons are on display and several reference books are on hand to settle pub arguments. The village website details guest beers and events. The guest beer (usually available in summer, and at other busy times) may come from an established regional or a Welsh or borders micro; Cottage beers have also often been seen. Regular buses run from Aberystwyth (Mon-Sat daytime, including bank holidays). Q ❀ P

LAMPETER

Castle Hotel

High Street
11-11; 12-10.30 Sun
☎ (01570) 422554
Brains Buckley's IPA, SA, seasonal beer H

Recently acquired by Brains, this attractive town-centre hotel is a useful showcase for the Cardiff brewery's ales. Refurbished throughout, the modernised bar is spacious and comfortable, and the hotel's prominent position in this small university town makes it an ideal base for touring. Bus services link Lampeter to railheads at Aberystwyth and Carmarthen. ❀ P

King's Head

14 Bridge Street (A482)
11-11; 12-10.30 Sun
☎ (01570) 422598
Beer range varies H

Friendly, two-bar local on the main street of this small town, popular with locals, students and lecturers from the nearby university. The regularly changing beers (one or two) come from independent breweries from all over Britain. Good value, tasty food is available, including Sunday lunch. The small car park is behind the pub, also nearby is a free public car park.
❀ P

LLANGOEDMOR

Penllwyndu

4 miles E of Cardigan, on B4570 OS241458
3-11; 3-10.30 Sun
☎ (01239) 682533
Brains Buckley's Best Bitter; Tetley Burton Ale; guest beer H

Quiet, friendly, country pub with a good atmosphere. An excellent example of an old-fashioned rural ale house: the public bar has a traditional slate floor and is oak beamed with a large open inglenook fire. The games room (pool and darts) is down steps from the public bar. The beer garden (with children's play area) has views to the Preseli Hills. Caravans are not allowed at the local campsite. ❀ P

MPs reneged on Full Price policy

Steven Byers MP, Secretary of State for Trade and Industry Dec 1998 – April 2001.

'We will...make sure that a pint of beer is a pint of beer.'
Hansard 22 July 1999.

'I compliment my Hon. Friend on raising this matter over a number of years to try to get a fair deal for the British beer drinker. I am delighted that we have been able to find space in the White Paper to take up his best proposals. This is a good example of a government working for everyone, including beer drinkers, unlike the Conservative government who worked just for the few.'
Hansard 22 July 1999.

NEW QUAY

Cambrian Hotel

New Road (B4342)
12-11; 12-10.30 Sun
☎ (01545) 560295
website: www.smoothhound.co.uk/hotels
Brains Buckley's Best Bitter; Felinfoel Double Dragon; Worthington Bitter H

At first glance, the Cambrian could be taken for nothing more than a small hotel, but a cosy bar awaits at the back, reached either through the restaurant at the front or by its own side door. Winter trade is often sparse midweek, with just two beers on to ensure quality, but weekend live music attracts customers. In summer, the large holiday complex across the road provides custom, and a guest beer may appear; look out for the pub's own beer festival. A separate lounge provides a quiet refuge away from the main bar. Buses from Carmarthen terminate opposite, (Mon-Sat daytime); Aberystwyth-Cardigan buses also call (limited Sun and eve service). ❀ P

PENNANT

Ship Inn

300 yds S of B4577 OS513631
6 (12 Sat)-11; closed Mon; 12-3, 7-10.30 Sun
☎ (01545) 570355
Beer range varies H

For most of the 20th century this was a timeless, unchanged rural ale house – one licensee spent 60 years here (see newspaper cutting in the bar). The present owners have extended and changed the pub, creating a new games-cum-family room, but much of the place's character remains. Built in 1754 and claiming smuggling connections with the nearby old port of Aberarth, it is a village local which embraces visitors from the nearby caravan park in summer. Just one real ale is available at all times, sourced from a west Wales wholesaler; mainly session beers up to 5% from regional brewers and micros throughout the UK. No full meals, but sandwiches are made to order in summer. A quiz is held on the first Sunday in the month. ♨Q☕❀▲♣P

RHYDOWEN

Alltyrodyn Arms

At A475/B4459 crossroads
⏲ 12-11; 12-4 Sun
☎ (01545) 590319
Beer range varies Ⓗ

A frequent CAMRA award-winner including Welsh Pub of the Year 2001, this family-run village pub sells a constantly changing range of real ales (usually four or five available) from regional and micro-breweries. Dating from Elizabethan times, the pub attracts locals, tourists and beer fans and it is the hub of local charitable activities. The main bar, with roaring fire and hundreds of mugs dangling from the beams, is flanked by a dining room and a games room. Real cider is served in summer. ♨❀⇔◑◗▲♣●P

TALYBONT

White Lion/Llew Gwyn

On A487, 7 miles N of Aberystwyth
⏲ 11-11; 12-10.30 Sun
☎ (01970) 832245
Banks's Original, Bitter Ⓗ

One of two Lions facing the village green, this welcoming pub functions well both as a local and as an ideal stop-off point for the traveller. Serious drinkers head for the traditional front bar, with a slate floor, bench seating and TV. The rear lounge is plain and quiet, but some fascinating photographs of the area and a local history display lend interest. The family/pool room, dining room, and beer garden complete the picture. Curries feature heavily on the menu, and can also be supplied to take away. Buses from Aberystwyth to Machynlleth call outside (limited eve and very limited Sun service).
Q☕❀⇔◑◗⊟♿▲♣P⊓

TREGARON

Talbot Hotel

The Square
⏲ 11-11; 12-10.30 Sun
☎ (01974) 298208
Boddingtons Bitter; Felinfoel Double Dragon; Marston's Pedigree Ⓗ

Comfortable old drovers' inn at the heart of a small upland market town. The public bars adjoin the main hotel building and comprise two small, cosy rooms at the front with a larger main bar at the back. There is a regular programme of live music in the function room, and local arts festivals tend to revolve around the pub. Glorious walking country abounds, and fishing, birdwatching and pony-trekking can all be enjoyed locally. Buses from Aberystwyth and Lampeter run Mon-Sat daytime.
♨Q❀⇔◑◗▲♣P

Pembrokeshire

ABERCYCH

Nag's Head

⏲ 11-3, 5.30-11; 11-11 Sat; 12-10.30 Sun
☎ (01239) 841200
Flowers Original; Nags Head Old Emrys; Worthington Bitter; guest beers Ⓗ

Well-restored old smithy, boasting a beamed bar, riverside beer garden and a micro-brewery. Its Old Emrys Ale is not always available. The bar area is furnished with an interesting collection of old medical instruments, railway memorabilia and a range of timepieces giving the time in different parts of the world. Space is also found for an extensive collection of bottled beers. ♨Q☕❀◑◗P

BOSHERSTON

St Govan's Inn

Signed from Pembroke
⏲ 11-3, 7-11 (11-11 summer); 12-3, 7-10.30 Sun
☎ (01646) 661311
Hancock's HB; Worthington Bitter; guest beers Ⓗ

A relatively modern pub, it takes its name

INN BRIEF

Pembrokeshire

HAVERFORDWEST

George's
Market Street
10.30-10.30; closed Sun
Marston's Pedigree; Wye Valley Bitter; guest beer Ⓗ
Reached through a small Celtic Arts shop at the front. Enjoy the relaxing atmosphere, fine ales and excellent food.

NARBERTH

Angel Inn
High Street
11-3, 5.30-11; 7-10.30 Sun
Worthington Bitter; guest beer Ⓗ
Cosy, modernised town-centre pub, popular for food. It has a separate public bar.

PEMBROKE

Royal George
2 The Quay
11-3, 5-11; 11-11 Sat; 12-3, 7-10.30 Sun
(01646) 682751
Worthington Bitter; guest beers Ⓗ
Pleasant pub in the shadow of the castle on the site of the old town wall.

TENBY

Hope & Anchor
St Julian Street
12 (11 summer)-11; 12-10.30 Sun
(01834) 842131
Worthington Bitter; Brains Rev James; guest beer Ⓗ
Friendly local close to the harbour.

TREFIN

Ship Inn
OS838325
12-3, 6-11; 11-10.30 Sun
Worthington Bitter; guest beer Ⓗ
Village local with separate dining area, situated on unclassified road through village.

❊ symbol next to a main entry place name indicates there are Inn Brief entries as well.

from the saint who built a chapel on the cliffs close by. The pub is on the coast path and close to the internationally renowned Bosherston lily ponds. The pub is frequented by climbers who find the local high cliffs irresistible. A short distance away is a safe sandy beach. The pub serves a variety of food to complement its range of real ales. Q❀◐◑⊟▲♣P

CRESSWELL QUAY

Cresselly Arms

Follow signs for Lawrenny
⊙ 12-3, 5-11; 7-10.30 Sun
☎ (01646) 651210
Worthington Bitter; guest beer Ⓗ

Situated on a tributary of the western Cleddau, the Cresselly was originally a one room bar. It has now been sympathetically extended without losing any of the character and charm of this friendly local. Beer is still dispensed from barrels on the back of the bar. The pub is the hub of the community and is the meeting place for most of the local sports teams. Pembrokeshire CAMRA Pub of the Year 2001. ♨Q❀P

CROES-GOCH

Artramont Arms

On A487 through road
⊙ 7-11 (12-3, 6-11 summer); 12-3, 6-10 Fri & Sat; 12-3, 7-10.30 Sun
☎ (01348) 831309
Brains SA; guest beer Ⓗ

Friendly village local with a large public bar and a separate lounge and dining area. There is a no-smoking area for drinkers and a pleasant beer garden. Interesting, varied menu; food is served lunchtime and evening. The pub acts as the central focus for village activities. ♨❀◐◑⊟P⊬

FISHGUARD ✻

Royal Oak

Market Square (town centre roundabout, on A487)
⊙ 11-11; 12-10.30 Sun
☎ (01348) 872514
Hancock's HB; guest beers Ⓗ

Charming, friendly, comfortable pub claiming historic connections (French forces surrendered here following the last invasion of mainlaind Britain in 1797). Some fascinating memorabilia dates back to this time. This pub is full of character and offers a separate public bar and attractive beer garden. Home-cooked meals are served at affordable prices from a varied menu. Camping facilities are available nearby. The local folk-singing fraternity meet here on Monday evening. ♨◐◑⊟▲♣

FRESHWATER EAST

Freshwater Inn

⊙ 12-3, 6.30-11 (12-11 summer); 12-3, 7-11 Sun
☎ (01646) 672828
Theakston Old Peculier; guest beers Ⓗ

Overlooking the beautiful Freshwater East Bay, this pub lies on the Pembrokeshire coast path and within the Pembrokeshire National Park. The Freshwater started life as a club to avoid the Sunday drinking laws in Wales. When Sunday drinking came in, the pub was extensively altered to provide both a popular local, and a comfortable inn for visitors to the area. The pub has a superb location, with stunning views from the bar and restaurant. Relax over a good meal and excellent pint in a wonderful setting. Q❀◐◑♿▲♣P

HAVERFORDWEST ✻

Pembroke Yeoman

St Thomas's Green, Hill Street
⊙ 11-11; 12-3, 7-10.30 Sun
☎ (01437) 762500
Flowers IPA; Worthington Bitter; guest beers Ⓗ/Ⓖ

This well-supported, comfortable town local attracts a wide range of customers. It is very popular with all age groups and is a meeting place for a variety of local organisations. The guest ale can be served by jug or handpump and the sparkler will be removed on request. Enjoy the peaceful atmosphere, fine beers and traditional pub games. An imaginative menu is on offer. ♨◐◑♣

NARBERTH ✻

Kirkland Arms

East Gate, St James Street
⊙ 11-11; 11-10.30 Sun
☎ (01834) 860423
Felinfoel Best Bitter, Double Dragon; guest beer Ⓗ

Comfortable, two-bar local on the edge of a one-way traffic system. No food is served other than barbecues for special occasions. Enjoy the exceptional beer quality. There are separate public and lounge bars and the pub has its own car park. If walking, it is the first stop-off point for a pint after a lengthy trek from the railway station. Camping facilities are available nearby. ⊟▲⇌P

NEWPORT

Castle Hotel

Bridge Street (A487 through road)
⊙ 11-11; 12-10.30 Sun
☎ (01239) 820742
Wadworth 6X; Worthington Bitter; guest beer Ⓗ

This friendly, popular local, has an attractive bar with a real fire and a wealth of wood panelling. There is an extensive separate dining area serving food at all sessions. A large off-street car park is situated at the rear of the hotel. ♨♉❀⇔◐◑▲P

Llwyngwair Arms

Bridge Street (A487 through road)
⊙ 11-11; 12-10.30 Sun
☎ (01239) 820267
Worthington Bitter; guest beer Ⓗ

This popular local has not been altered for some considerable time. It has a separate dining area that serves inexpensive food all day in summer (more restricted hours in winter). Curries are a speciality. Car parking is available through an archway on the opposite side of the road. ♨Q◐◑▲P

PEMBROKE DOCK

First & Last

London Road (entrance to town on A477)
⊙ 11-11; 12-10.30 Sun
☎ (01646) 682687

Worthington Bitter; guest beer 🄷

Large, friendly, local pub on the outskirts of the town offering a good variety of guest ales and value-for-money bar food. Live music is staged on Saturday evening, plus a quiz night on Sunday. The pub is close to local castles and within easy reach of the Pembrokeshire coastal path – well worth the short diversion. ❀◑ ⇌♣P

Station Inn

Apley Green, Dimond Street (follow signs to railway station)

✪ 11-3, 6.30-11; 12-3, 7-10.30 Sun

☎ (01646) 621255

Beer range varies 🄷

Housed in a Victorian railway station with the trains still running on the adjoining lines. This town-centre pub is a short distance from the Irish ferry terminal. The bar features a range of ales and its restaurant specialises in local fish and organic meats. A range of bar meals is also available. Every Tuesday a new beer is on tap and beer festivals are held in March, June and November. ♨Q❀◑♿⇌P

PONTFAEN

Dyffryn Arms ☆

On B4313, Gwaun Valley road OS027341

✪ hours vary

☎ (01348) 881305

Draught Bass or Tetley Burton Ale 🄶

This bar resembles a 1920s front room where time has stood still. The beer is still served by the jug through a sliding hatch. Conversation is the main form of entertainment. The landlady is in her eighties and there is a superb, relaxed atmosphere in this pub. It lies in the heart of the scenic Gwaun Valley between the Preseli Hills and Fishguard (Abergwaun). ♨Q❀⛺♣

PORTHGAIN

Sloop Inn

Near quay in heart of village

✪ 11.30-3, 6-11 (11-11 summer); 12-4, 6-10.30 Sun

☎ (01348) 831449

Brains SA; Felinfoel Double Dragon; Worthington Bitter 🄷

This sympathetically modernised old inn has served both the locally-based fishing industry and the now-defunct quarrying and stone exporting industries. The pub features quarrying and shipping ephemera as part of its decor. Holding hoppers for stone can be seen on the opposite side of the harbour. It is a very popular pub with locals and visitors, and has a good variety of beers and reasonably-priced food, produced locally where possible. ♨❀◑♣P

ST DAVID'S

Farmers Arms

Goat Street (on road leading from Old Cross Square to St Justinians) OS751253

✪ 11-11; 12-10.30 Sun

☎ (01437) 720328

Felinfoel Double Dragon; Flowers Original; Wadworth 6X; Worthington Bitter 🄷

19th-century stone hostelry that retains many old features. It is popular with local farmers, fishermen and youngsters, with many tourists calling in during the summer season. The pub serves an interesting range of good, wholesome home-cooked food. Definitely worth a visit. ♨Q❀◑⊟⛺

ST DOGMAELS

White Hart

Finch Street (B4546 through village)

✪ 12-2.30 (not Tue), 7-11; 12-3, 7-10.30 Sun

☎ (01239) 612099

Wadworth IPA; guest beer 🄷

Cheery, welcoming, small village pub with a good local following. It is on the right-hand side of the road when entering St Dogmaels from Cardigan. The guest beers change on a regular basis and are often from breweries not represented locally. Three guest ales are served in summer and two in winter. The landlord is a great rugby enthusiast. The opening hours extend in the summer and the pub is a good stop-off point if walking the Pembrokeshire coastal path. ♨◑⊟⛺♣

SOLVA

Harbour Inn

On A487 through road adjoining harbour car park

✪ 11-11; 12-10.30 Sun

☎ (01437) 720013

Draught Bass; Worthington Bitter; guest beer 🄷

This delightful seaside hostelry retains a traditional atmosphere, having remained unaltered for a considerable time. It is used as a base for many community activities and is very popular with locals. Camping facilities are close by for both tents and caravans. Enjoy a quiet, relaxing pint in this attractive, unspoilt local. Entertainment is organised on an ad hoc basis. ♨Q❀⇔◑⛺

MPs reneged on Full Price policy

Dr Kim Howells MP, Minister for Competition and Consumers, July 1998 – April 2001

'However, when I order a pint, I am determined that I will get a full pint. The Hon.Gentleman's colleagues talked out the legislation that related to a full pint. They do not want fairness for consumers – they are ready to allow the breweries to continue cheating them.'

Hansard 14 March 2001.

BORDERS

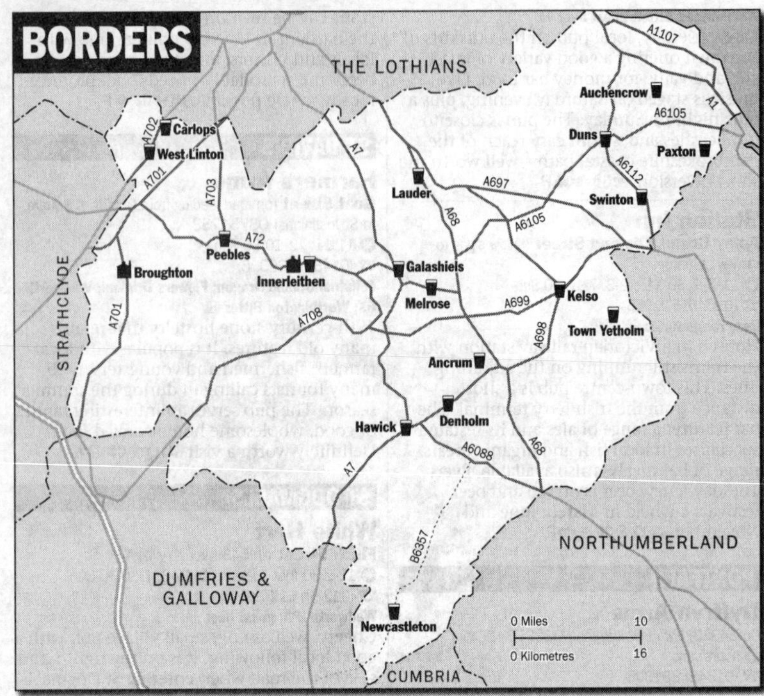

Authority area covered: The Borders UA

ANCRUM

Cross Keys Inn ☆

The Green (B6400, off A68)

6-11 (midnight Thu); 5-1am Fri; 12-midnight Sat; 12.30-11 Sun

☎ (01835) 830344

Draught Bass; Caledonian Deuchars IPA; guest beers Ⓗ

Friendly village local with a bar that remains nearly untouched from the refurbishment by Jedburgh Brewery in 1908. It retains the pine panelling through into the gantry, has compact but comfortable seating, and tables made from old sewing machine bases. The spacious back lounge has been sympathetically refurbished and retains overhead tramlines from the former cellar. A good, varied menu is supplemented by daily specials such as wild boar or pheasant in season. Lunches served weekends only. Families are welcome (children's certificate). ⛫Q❀◑⊟♣P

AUCHENCROW

Craw Inn

On B6438, follow signs from A1

12-2.30, 6-11 (midnight Fri); 12-midnight Sat; 12.30-11 Sun

☎ (018907) 61253

Beer range varies Ⓗ

Village inn, circa 1680. The beamed bar has bench seating at one end and wooden tables and chairs by the log-burning stove at the other. The two beers usually come from smaller breweries, and change regularly. The no-smoking rear of the inn affords rural views and is divided into a lounge-cum-eating area and restaurant; traditional furniture gives a select feel. Local produce is used in many dishes on the wide-ranging menu. Families are welcome (children's certificate). ⛫Q❀⇌◑♿♣P⊬

CARLOPS

Allan Ramsay Hotel

Main Street (A702)

12 (12.30 Sun)-midnight

☎ (01968) 660258

website: www.allanramsayhotel.co.uk

Caledonian Deuchars IPA; guest beer Ⓗ

Hotel in a small village beside the Pentland Hills, originally a flax mill dating from 1792. Several rooms have been knocked through into a single area, retaining many original features, with tartan upholstery giving a Scottish feel. The bar is inlaid with pre-decimal pennies. Local myth suggests witches leapt from two stones either side of the road near the pub; Carlops gets its name from the Gaelic for witch's leap. Meals are available 12-9; children welcome. The guest rooms were upgraded in 2000. ⛫❀⇌◑Å♣P

DENHOLM

Auld Cross Keys Inn

Main Street (A698)

11-2.30 (not Mon), 5-11 (midnight Fri); 11-midnight Sat; 12.30-11 Sun

☎ (01450) 870305

Draught Bass; guest beer Ⓗ

18th-century inn by the village green. The cosy main bar has a low ceiling, real fire and a pool table; the scarlet macaw and Robinson's Golly provide conversation pieces. Through the back is an upmarket lounge (with children's certificate) and dining area, which, Tardis-style, opens through to a large function room. Quizzes, folk music sessions and concerts are regular

events. The high teas are highly recommended; no food Mon.
⛰❀🛏◐◑⊟♣P

Fox & Hounds Inn

Main Street (A698)
⊙ 11-3, 5-midnight (1am Fri); 11-1am Sat; 12.30-midnight Sun
☎ (01450) 870247
Wylam Gold Tankard; guest beer Ⓗ
Village local, circa 1750, overlooking the green. The main beamed bar is light and comfortable, a real fire gives it a cosy feel in winter. Above the fire is the odd stuffed animal head and other memorabilia. The separate dining area, where children are welcome, has a coffee-house feel to it. In summer the courtyard is used for sheltered outdoor drinking. Guest beers are usually from smaller breweries. No evening meals are served winter Sundays.
⛰❀🛏◐◑⊟♿⅄♣P

DUNS

Whip & Saddle

Market Square
⊙ 11-11 (midnight Fri; 1am Sat); 12.30-11.30 Sun
☎ (01361) 883215
Belhaven 80/-; Caledonian Deuchars IPA; guest beer (summer) Ⓗ
This town-centre bar, dating from around 1790, has an airy interior due to the light wood floor and leaded windows, which offer views across the square. The pub has modern decor, its bright vibrant colours contrasting with the 1950s photos of local interest. Children are welcome in the upstairs lounge-cum-dining room which is pleasantly decorated (no meals Sun). River Whiteadder angling permits are available.
◐⅄♣⊬

GALASHIELS

Ladhope Inn

33 High Buckholmside (A7, 1/2 mile N of centre)
⊙ 11-3, 5-11; 11-11 Wed; 11-midnight Thu-Sat; 12.30-midnight Sun
☎ (01896) 752446
Caledonian Deuchars IPA; guest beer Ⓗ
Comfortable, friendly local with a vibrant atmosphere. Originating from around 1792, this inn has been altered considerably inside and comprises a single room with an alcove. The main area has a practical feel with TVs and modern slot machines and is decorated with whisky jugs. The alcove has a historical theme, displaying old photographs and a large map of the Borders area. The guest beer changes regularly; toasties are available. Children are welcome.
❀⅄♣

Salmon Inn

54 Bank Street
⊙ 11-11 (midnight Thu; 1am Fri & Sat); 12.30-11 Sun
☎ (01896) 752577
Caledonian Deuchars IPA; Tetley Burton Ale; guest beer Ⓗ
Comfortable, friendly pub, bearing a mixture of old and modern decoration. The bar is decorated with old photographs of the Galashiels area; the curvature of the room gives the impression of two rooms; towards the back is more seating and a games machine. It is popular with the locals at lunchtime for meals, when a children's certificate applies (no food Sun). It stands opposite the fountain and gardens, close to the shopping area. ❀◐◑⅄♣

HAWICK

High Level Bar

11 Green Terrace (SW edge of town)
⊙ 11-2.30 (not Tue or Thu), 5-11; 11-1am Fri & Sat; 12.30-11 Sun
☎ (01450) 377469
Beer range varies Ⓗ
Popular community local on a hillside in the heart of a residential area. The fine public bar has wood-panelled walls, wood floors, bar and gantry. The regulars have a strong interest in horses and rugby, creating a lively atmosphere on most race days. The lounge is half-filled by a pool table and also has a dartboard. Snacks are available. Children are welcome in the back bar. ⊟♣

INNERLEITHEN

Traquair Arms Hotel

Traquair Road
(B709, off A72)
⊙ 12-11; 11-midnight Fri & Sat; 11.30-11.30 Sun
☎ (01896) 830229
website: www.traquair-arms-hotel.co.uk
Broughton Greenmantle, Merlin's Ale; guest beer Ⓗ
Elegant, 18th-century family-run hotel. The plush lounge is decorated with prints of local interest and has a tank of goldfish. The log fires in the lounge and adjacent dining room help create a cosy Borders atmosphere. Good home-cooked Scottish dishes from local produce are served 12-9 daily. The guest beer is usually from Traquair Brewery. Children are welcome. The no-smoking area is the tea room.
⛰❀🛏◐◑⅄P⊬

KELSO

White Swan

Abbey Row
⊙ 11-midnight (1am Thu-Sat); 11-midnight Sun
☎ (01573) 224348
Caledonian Deuchars IPA; Tetley Bitter; guest beer (summer) Ⓗ
This family-run hotel has a long, low-ceilinged, lively, modernised bar with bare floorboards. Originally two rooms, now knocked into one and extended, it lies between traditional old town houses and boasts views to the ruins of Kelso Abbey and the graveyard. Pool is played in the back area. Drinks can be taken into the café at the front, where meals are served (11-4). The pub is close to all the main amenities and shopping areas of Kelso.
⛰❀🛏◐⅄♣

MELROSE

Burt's Hotel

Market Square
⊙ 11-2, 5 (6 Sun)-11
☎ (01896) 822285
Caledonian Deuchars IPA, 80/-; guest beer Ⓗ

INDEPENDENT BREWERIES

Broughton Broughton
Traquair Innerleithen

Elegant, family-run hotel in the main square. The decor of the plush lounge bar reflects the hunting and fishing interests of many of the clientele. The restaurant is expensive but serves award-winning food; the bar menu offers a cheaper option. A comfortable seating area by the entrance is reserved for non-smokers. Close by is the famous Melrose Abbey and the Teddy Bear Museum. Real ale may not be available during Melrose 7's rugby week. Children's certificate.
⛰Q⇌◑⛺P⚟

King's Arms Hotel
High Street
⏲ 11 (12 Sun)-midnight
☎ (01896) 822143
Tetley Bitter, Burton Ale; guest beer Ⓗ
Coaching inn, dating from 1793, with two separate rooms, near the rugby ground. The bar has a wood floor and church pew seating, and is decorated with rugby memorabilia and old local photographs. There is a large-screen TV for sporting events, and the room can get smoky. The contrasting lounge (where a children's certificate applies until 8pm) is comfortably furnished and has a lovely old carved door set into the ceiling. ⛰Q⇌◑⊟⛺♣

PAXTON

Cross Inn
Off B6460
⏲ 11-2.30, 6.30-midnight; closed Mon; 12.30-2.30, 6.30-midnight Sun
☎ (01289) 386267
Beer range varies Ⓗ
Pleasant village pub, circa 1870s, now reverted to its original name following the restoration of an old cross outside. Until recently it was the Hoolit's Nest, reflecting the vast number of owls, in all sorts of guises, which watch the bar. The bar counter has a mahogany top and wood panelling; there is also a small, comfortable dining room. One of the two beers is often from Broughton. Fishing permits are available. Children's certificate.
❀◑♿♣P

Black Velvet

Black Velvet, equal parts of Guinness and Champagne, was created in memory of Prince Albert, husband of Queen Victoria, who died in 1861. The Champagne represented the nobility, the stout the 'common classes'.

PEEBLES

Bridge Inn
Portbrae
⏲ 11 (12 Sun)-midnight
☎ (01721) 720589
Caledonian Deuchars IPA; Courage Directors; guest beer (summer) Ⓗ
Cheerful town-centre local: the ground floor of the Tudor-style building contains a bright, single bar. The mosaic-floor in the entrance bears the pub's original name of the Tweedside Inn; it is also known locally as the Trust. The comfortable bar is decorated with memorabilia of outdoor pursuits; a selection of jugs and bottles also catch the eye. ⛺♣

SWINTON

Wheatsheaf Hotel
Main Street
⏲ 11-2, 6-11 (11.30 Fri & Sat; not winter Mon eve); 12.30-3.30, 6.30-10.30 (not winter eve) Sun
☎ (01890) 860257
website: www.wheatsheaf-swinton.co.uk
Caledonian 80/-; guest beer Ⓗ
This well-appointed hotel, with an award-winning restaurant, dates from the 1850s. There are three large, comfortable dining and lounge areas, one being a conservatory. The food is not cheap but is excellent, offering an extensive choice, with much local produce and children's portions (no food Mon eve). A small, dimly-lit snug bar has an oak-topped counter, church pews and photos of local legend, Jim Clark, the racing driver. The guest beer is often from Broughton. ⛰Q❀⇌◑⊟♣P

INN BRIEF

LAUDER

Eagle Hotel
1 Market Place
11-11 (midnight Thu-Sat); 12.30-11 Sun
(01578) 722255
Caledonian Deuchars IPA; guest beer Ⓗ
Friendly hotel with locals' bar. A stone wall and ornate bar are features of the comfortable lounge. Good food.

NEWCASTLETON

Liddesdale Hotel
Douglas Square
11-2.30, 5-midnight (1am Fri & Sat); 11-midnight (1am Fri & Sat) summer and winter Sat; 12-11 Sun
(01387) 375255
Greene King Old Speckled Hen Ⓗ
Small hotel with split-level bar. Food is served in the comfortable upper level, while the lower level is more functional.

TOWN YETHOLM

Plough Hotel
High Street
11-2.30, 5-11 (midnight Thu; 1am Fri); 11-1am Sat; 12.30-midnight Sun
(01573) 420215
Greene King Old Speckled Hen Ⓗ
Friendly village local. The small dining room is no-smoking; the menu, with daily specials, is quite extensive.

WEST LINTON

Gordon Arms Hotel
Dolphinton Road
11-midnight (1am Fri & Sat); 11-midnight Sun
(01968) 660208
Caledonian Deuchars IPA; guest beer Ⓗ
Airy, L-shaped, homely public bar with stone walls and fine cornice. Imaginative food is served in the attractive restaurant.

Check it out

Pubs in the Good Beer Guide may change ownership and the facilities listed could alter. If a visit to a pub involves a long journey, it's advisable to check before leaving that full meals, family facilities, accommodation or camping sites are still available.

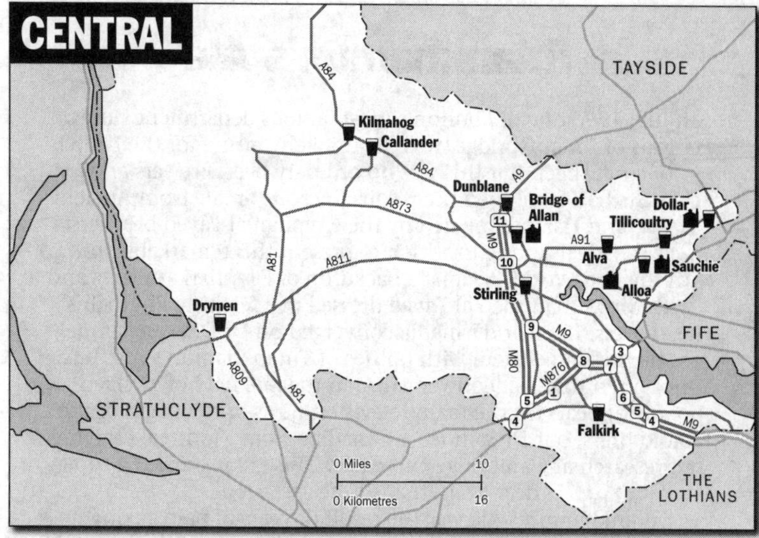

Authority areas covered: Clackmannan UA, Falkirk UA, Stirling UA

ALVA

Cross Keys
Stirling Street

11-11 (midnight Thu; 1am Fri & Sat); 11-11 Sun
(01529) 760409
Beer range varies H

Busy local with a well-appointed lounge bar. It tends to be noisy on Friday and Saturday evenings. The pub enjoys a very busy food trade due to its inexpensive, good quality bar meals (booking is recommended at weekends). Three handpumps dispense ale from local and national brewers. This is a good walking area with Alva Glen and the Ochil Hills on the doorstep.

BRIDGE OF ALLAN

Hydes Bar, Queen's Hotel

11-midnight (1am Fri & Sat); 10-midnight Sun
(01786) 833268
Caledonian Deuchars IPA; Fuller's London Pride; Tetley Bitter H

Close to Stirling University, Hydes Bar is located to the rear of the hotel. The bar has recently been refurbished with modern style furniture to create a bistro atmosphere. Close to the rail station, it is convenient for Stirling and the Trossachs. Popular with students and tourists as well as locals, it tends to be quiet during the day but busy in the evenings and weekends. Food is available in the bar brought through from the main hotel.

CALLANDER

Waverley Hotel
88-94 Main Street

11-midnight (1am Fri & Sat); 11-midnight Sun
(01877) 330245
website: www.thewaverleycallander.com
Arran Dark, Light; Harviestoun Bitter & Twisted, Schiehallion; guest beers H

The Claymore Bar, in the hotel, stocks guest beers from Houston and Heather breweries in addition to the regulars. It has two drinking areas with a dining section screened off by a steel framework. Located at the gateway to the Trossachs, it is very popular with tourists and walkers. Two beer festivals are held annually (in Sept and Dec), for a week each. Lunches are served all year but check availability of evening meals in winter.

DOLLAR

Strathallan Hotel
6 Chapel Place

5-midnight (1am Fri); 12-1am Sat; 12-midnight Sun
(01259) 742205
Fuller's London Pride; Harviestoun Bitter & Twisted; guest beer H

Small, country hotel with bistro-style restaurant and a small, cosy lounge run by cheerful staff. An outlet for local Harviestoun beers, it may stock special brews when they are available. The National Trust's Castle Campbell is a short walk away and dates back to the 15th century, it was burned by Cromwell's troops in the mid-17th century, but is still worth a visit. Pleasant walks can be taken in Dollar Glen, if you feel like burning up some energy before a pint. Q P

DRYMEN

Winnock Hotel
The Square

11-midnight (1am Fri & Sat); 12-midnight Sun
(01360) 660267 website: www.winnockhotel.com
Caledonian 80/-; Taylor Landlord; Tetley Bitter; guest beers H

Pleasant, 300-year-old hotel at the centre of a village near the eastern side of Loch Lomond. No real ale is dispensed in the

INDEPENDENT BREWERIES

Bridge of Allan Bridge of Allan
Devon Sauchie
Eglesbrech Falkirk
Forth Alloa
Harviestoun Dollar

Tutankhamun's Ale

In July 1996 one of London's most famous department stores, Harrods of Knightsbridge, was the unlikely setting for the launch of a new beer. But this was no ordinary beer. Brewers and scientists had combined their skills to create an ale from Ancient Egypt, and Harrods, owned by the Egyptian al-Fayed brothers, was the ideal setting in which to present this remarkable link with the Old World. Against a backdrop of Egyptian artefacts and with Mr Mohammed al-Fayed dressed in a fetching Pharoah's head-dress, the world's media converged on Dr Delwen Samuel as she presented them with bottles of Tutankhamun's Ale. It is not often that someone engaged in the rare field of archaeo-botany appears on the main television news or the pages of the tabloid press, but Dr Samuel, a Canadian from Montreal carrying out research at Cambridge University, was talking about a topic dear to journalists' hearts: beer.

Tutankhamun's Ale was the result of years of painstaking research by archaeologists, archaeo-botanists, Egyptologists and brewers. The end result not only gave us a glimpse of what beer from the Old World may have tasted like but it also deepened our knowledge of life in those days, the importance of beer to those societies and its role in turning nomadic people into settled communities. Until Dr Samuel and her colleagues from the Egypt Exploration Society at Cambridge University presented their recreation of Egyptian ale, the received wisdom of historians was that beer had been a bi-product of bread making in the Old World. Now history was turned on its head. It was beer, not bread, that came first, and it was alcohol that had convinced the ancients to stop wandering the fertile valleys of the Nile and the Euphrates, and settle down to grow grain.

Roger Protz, *The Taste of Beer*, Weidenfeld, 1998.

public bar but the main stone-walled lounge bar, from which the restaurant leads, sports five handpumps. It is well-known for its food, Sunday night ceilidhs and murder mystery weekends. There is a pétanque pitch in the grounds. ♣P

DUNBLANE

Dunblane Hotel
10 Stirling Road
11-midnight (1am Fri & Sat); 12-midnight Sun
☎ (01786) 822178
Greene King Abbot, Old Speckled Hen; Tetley Burton Ale; guest beers H
Well-appointed bar in a comfortable hotel with interesting old brewery mirrors on the walls. It is very popular with tourists and locals and a good centre for golfing. The lounge bar has a splendid view over the River Allan. Three frequently changing guest ales are on tap. ♿P

Tappit Hen
Kirk Street (opp. Cathedral)
11-12.30am (1.15am Fri & Sat); 12.30-12.15am Sun
☎ (01786) 825226
Belhaven Sandy Hunter's Ale, 80/-; guest beers H
Real pub for discerning drinkers with eight ales on tap at any time. Its traditional single bar room is partitioned into two areas, the walls are decorated with hundreds of pump clips. The town, with an imposing Cathedral, is in an ideal position to visit Gleneagles and the Highlands. A tappit hen is a jug or pitcher.
♣

FALKIRK

Goose on Newmarket
Upper Newmarket Street
10-11 (midnight Sat); 12.30-11.30 Sun
☎ (01324) 618701
Draught Bass; Caledonian Deuchars IPA, 80/-; Highgate Dark; Taylor Landlord H
Recently refurbished, traditional Scottish pub with a clear and bright atmosphere, good ventilation and high ceilings, now transformed as a Six Continents outlet. On two floors with no-smoking areas on each and no music, there are long bars, both of which dispense ale and food. Prices of food and drink are much lower than average. Tends to be quiet during the week but fills up at the weekend.
Q ♿ (Grahamston)

Wheatsheaf Inn

16 Baxter's Wynd

11-11 (12.30am Fri & Sat); 12.30-4.30, 7.30-11 Sun

(01324) 623716

Arran Dark; Caledonian Deuchars IPA; Houston Peter's Well H

This building has always been a public house, starting off as a coaching inn in the 18th century, it has retained much of its character over the years. The bar is long and narrow with stools and small tables round the walls, which are decorated with caricatures of local worthies and old brewery mirrors.The pub stocks a good selection of whiskies. Well used by locals, the atmosphere is peaceful as there is no intrusive music or TV.

Q ≉ (Grahamston & Falkirk High)

KILMAHOG

Lade Inn

At A84/A821 jct, 1 mile W of Callander

12-2.30, 5.30-11; 12-11 Sat; 12.30-10.30 Sun

(01877) 330152 website: www.theladeinn.com

Broughton Greenmantle; Caledonian 80/-; guest beers H

Located in an idyllic position at the gateway to the Trossachs, this welcoming inn offers excellent facilities. The lounge bar doubles as a restaurant and has the feeling of a 'bothy'. The furnishings are rustic, but comfortable and the decor consists of various instruments and artefacts displayed on the walls.
A ceilidh is held every Saturday evening in the public bar. Two guest ales change frequently.

SAUCHIE

Mansfield Arms

7 Main Street

11-midnight; 12.30-11 Sun

(01259) 722020

Devon Original, Thick Black, Pride H

This pub consists of a typical public bar, well used by locals, it offers a very comfortable atmosphere. The lounge/restaurant attracts families and those looking for good value, quality meals. Behind the pub is the compact brewery where three standard ales are made, they are sold only at their own premises. Tours can be arranged.

P

STIRLING

Birds & Bees

Easter Cornton Road, Causewayhead

11-3, 5-midnight; 11-1am Fri & Sat; 12.30-midnight Sun

(01786) 473663

Beer range varies H

Busy and popular with local residents, the pub has a rural setting and feel, although close to town (30 minutes) and University (15 minutes). It is a converted farm building whose history is reflected in the interior design. Note the unusual fleece-covered sheep seats and milk-churn bar stools, while the walls feature odd wrought-iron birds and bees. A large restaurant and outside seating provide a good view of the nearby Wallace Monument. The pub has regular 'happy hours'. P

Hogshead

2 Baker Street

11-midnight (1am Fri & Sat); 11-midnight Sun

(01786) 448722

Caledonian Deuchars IPA, 80/-; guest beers H

Busy, noisy pub that is popular with locals and students. Staff actively encourage sampling the choice of the several ales before purchase. A rustic, light interior features wooden floorboards, old pine tables and old farm implements on the walls. Food is served 11-9 and there is a quiz night every Tuesday. It is situated close to the town centre.

Portcullis Hotel

Castle Wynd (next to Stirling Castle Esplanade)

11.30-midnight; 12.30-midnight Sun

(01786) 472290 website: www.portcullishotel.com

Orkney Dark Island; guest beer H

Originally a grammar school, built in 1787, the Portcullis is softly lit by candles and a real log fire and has a quiet, calming atmosphere. It features a walled garden for outdoor drinking in ancient surroundings. Good quality food is served. There are four en-suite rooms available and reservations are recommended. Q P

TILLICOULTRY

Woolpack Inn

Glassford Square

11-midnight (1am Fri & Sat); 12.30-11 Sun

(01259) 750332

Beer range varies H

Old drovers' inn dating back to 1784, with a basic bar area, a small lounge to the rear and a small room with no bar. This cheerful pub is very popular with hillwalkers in summer and tends to be busy at weekends. Beers are sourced from both large and small breweries all over the UK, ales from Scottish breweries such as Cairngorm or Isle of Skye feature. This hostelry is an ideal starting (or finishing) point for a walk in the Ochil Hills. Q

Drunken Primates

Brehm asserts that the natives of north-eastern Africa catch the wild baboons by exposing vessels with strong beer, by which they are made drunk. On the following morning they (the baboons) were very cross and dismal; they held their aching heads with both hands, and wore a most pitiable expression: when beer was offered them, they turned away in disgust.

Charles Darwin, *The Origin of Species,* 1859.

DUMFRIES & GALLOWAY

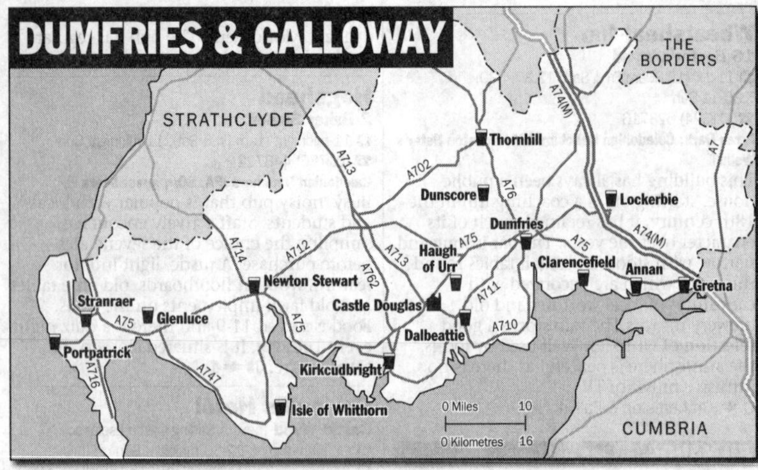

Authority area covered: Dumfries & Galloway UA

ANNAN

Bluebell Inn

10 High Street

11-11 (midnight Thu-Sat); 12.30-11 Sun

☎ (01461) 202385

Theakston Best Bitter; guest beers Ⓗ

Busy riverside pub in a pleasant rural market town. A former coaching inn, it is built of sandstone and is easily identified by the large blue bell above the front door. It serves a varied selection of real ales and offers a pool table, darts and a large-screen TV. A courtyard serves as a garden in summer. This lively, friendly local usually has three guest beers. A previous local CAMRA Pub of the Year, it is a regular in this Guide.

CLARENCEFIELD

Farmers Inn

Main Street (B724)

11-2.30, 6-11.30 (12.30am Fri); 12-12.30am Sat; 12.30-11.30 Sun

☎ (01387) 870675

website: www.smooth.hound.co.uk/hotels/farmersinn.html

Sulwath Cuil Hill; guest beers Ⓗ

Late 16th-century coaching inn with a varied history. The current version opened in 1983 with the original bar area still in use. It was the post office, and also housed the village's first telephone exchange. Robert Burns was a customer when he came on a visit to the Brow Well for health reasons. The world's first savings bank at Ruthwell, the 8th-century Ruthwell Cross, Caerlaverock Castle and nature reserve are all nearby, as is championship Powfoot golf course. Good salmon and sea trout fishing can be had on the River Nith and Annan.

Q P

DALBEATTIE

Pheasant Hotel

1 Maxwell Street

10.30-midnight (including Sun)

☎ (01556) 610345

Beer range varies Ⓗ

Town-centre hotel situated on the corner at the end of the main street in the granite Burgh of Dalbeattie. The bar is a large, open area with a pool table and big-screen TV which regularly shows live football. There is good walking and fishing available locally, and the Solway coast is close at hand. There is one real ale available, usually from the Sulwath Brewery.

DUMFRIES

New Bazaar

39 Whitesands

11-11 (midnight Thu-Sat); 11-11 Sun

☎ (01387) 268776

Belhaven St Andrew's Ale; McEwan 80/-; Sulwath Knockendoch; guest beers Ⓗ

Traditional pub with superb Victorian bar affording excellent views across the River Nith to the Camera Obscura. Dating from 1836, the Camera Obscura is located in a converted windmill and offers a panoramic view of Dumfries. An absolute must is a walk over the superb Devorgilla Bridge, where you can visit the Old Bridge Museum and Robert Burns Centre. There are usually two guest ales on tap. Q

Robert the Bruce

Castle Street

11 (12.30 Sun)-midnight

☎ (01387) 270320

Caledonian 80/-; guest beers Ⓗ

Former episcopalian church originally consecrated in 1817 and sold 50 years later to local methodists. It remained empty and roofless for many years before a sympathetic conversion by Wetherspoon's. With its relaxed atmosphere it has quickly established itself as a favourite meeting place, handy for the town centre. Typical Wetherspoon's fare is provided with some guest beers from Scottish breweries.

Ship Inn

97-99 St Michael Street (opp. St Michael's Church)

11-2.30, 5-11; 12-2.30, 6.30-11 Sun

☎ (01387) 255189

Greene King Abbot, Ⓐ **Old Speckled Hen; McEwan 80/-; Marston's Pedigree; Taylor Landlord; Theakston XB** Ⓗ

Very friendly and welcoming two-roomed free house with six pumps selling a variety of beers of varying strengths. On display are a small collection of toby jugs and other lovely artefacts including an old-fashioned working till. Very handy for lovers of Robert Burns as his mausoleum is in St Michael's churchyard opposite and the house he lived in (now Burns House Museum) is only a short walk. Q≠⊁

Tam O'Shanter

113-117 Queensbury Street

⏲ 11-11 (midnight Fri & Sat); 12.30-11 Sun

☎ (01387) 254055

Caledonian Deuchars IPA; guest beers H

The 'Tam' is a 17th-century former coaching inn named after one of Rabbie Burns' famous poems. The bar is small, and decorated with prints of old Dumfries, a corridor leads to the small no-smoking room that retains the original hearth, while the back room displays a number of brewery mirrors. Guest beers include Belhaven and Houston with a fine selection of brews from both sides of the border. Q≠♣

DUNSCORE

George Hotel

Main Street (B729)

⏲ 5 (12 Fri-Sun)-midnight

☎ (01387) 820250

Beer range varies H

This focal point of village life caters for clubs with interests as diverse as bridge and investments, and occasional 'bothy' nights are held when locals and visitors bring their own talents and guitars, accordions and spoons and storytelling. Kirkpatrick McMillan, inventor of the bicycle, lived and worked nearby and enthusiasts gather regularly to cycle the route, which passes the hotel, and find well-earned refreshment. Meals are served Fri-Sun. ❀⇔◐◑♿P⊁

GLENLUCE

Kelvin House Hotel

53 Main Street (off A75)

⏲ 11-3, 6-11.30 (midnight Fri & Sat); 12.30-11.30 Sun

☎ (01581) 300303

website: www.anglofrance.co.uk/kelvin/index

Orkney Red MacGregor; guest beers H

This small, friendly hotel was built in 1770 and is situated near Luce Bay in a village bypassed by the busy A75 road. The hotel's restaurant is renowned for its traditional Scottish fare, including local seafood and game dishes. The single guest beer changes regularly as can be seen from the display of pump clips above the bar. The lounge is warmed by a real fire. ♨❀⇔◐◑▲⊁

GRETNA

Solway Lodge Hotel

97-99 Annan Road

⏲ 11-11 (including Sun)

☎ (01461) 338266

Tetley Bitter H

Comfortable hotel on the main road into town. Gretna is known as the Gateway to Scotland and the Solway Lodge is less than 10 minutes' walk from the border. It is popular with wedding parties with the famous old blacksmith's shop and museum at Gretna Green within strolling distance. Good value bar meals are served, and a no-smoking restaurant is open in the evenings. ♉❀⇔◐◑♿▲≠(Gretna Green)

HAUGH OF URR

Laurie Arms Hotel

On B794, 1 mile S of A75

⏲ 11.45-2.30, 5.30-11 (midnight Thu-Sat); 11.45-3.30, 6-midnight Sun

☎ (01556) 660246

Beer range varies H

Attractive country inn, situated on the main street of a quiet village in the Urr Valley. A warm welcome is guaranteed in the bar which features a large fireplace of local Dalbeattie granite. A wide selection of meals is available in both the bar and restaurant. There are up to four real ales, with regular beers from Black Sheep, Houston and Orkney. Look out for the saucy postcard selection in the toilets. Bus service 501 between Dumfries and Castle Douglas stops outside. ♨❀◐◑P

ISLE OF WHITHORN

Queen's Arms Hotel

22 Main Street

⏲ 12-3 (not winter Mon-Thu), 6.30-11 (midnight Fri); 11-midnight Sat; 12.30-midnight Sun

☎ (01988) 500369

Sulwath Knockendoch, Galloway Gold; guest beers H

This pub has been sympathetically restored by an enthusiastic landlord. It features comfortable seating, stone-clad walls, a separate pool room and a well-appointed restaurant. Real ales are only served in the bar where the regular Sulwath beers are complemented by an ever-changing guest which is often a national brand. The restaurant bar has traditional Scottish tall founts, but these dispense keg beer. ♨Q⇔◐◑

Steampacket Inn

Harbour Row (A750)

⏲ 11-11 (11-2.30, 6-11 winter); 12-11 Sun

☎ (01988) 500334

Theakston XB; guest beer H

This attractive harbourside inn has a small public bar with stone-clad walls, a large fireplace and flagstone floor. There is a larger lounge, with a pool room off. Picture windows allow good views of the harbour which attracts sailing craft from near and far. Both the Isle of Man and the Lake District can be seen from this picturesque, historic village. The menu features mainly local produce. ♨Q♉❀⇔◐◑♣

KIRKCUDBRIGHT

Masonic Arms

19 Castle Street

⏲ 11 (12.30 Sun)-midnight

☎ (01557) 330517

Taylor Landlord; guest beers (summer) H

A friendly local with an assured welcome from the three resident labradors! Unusually, the bar front and table are made from old barrels. Situated in the centre of this historic town, close to the harbour on the Dee Estuary, it affords access to some

INDEPENDENT BREWERY

Sulwath Castle Douglas

wonderful walks including a visit to the splendid McLellan's Castle. ⛫♣

Selkirk Arms Hotel

High Street

11 (12 Sun)-midnight

☎ (01557) 330402

website: www.selkirkarmshotel.co.uk

Greene King Old Speckled Hen; Sulwath Criffel; guest beers (summer) Ⓗ

A friendly, warm and welcoming three-star hotel which serves good quality food. It has a comfortable lounge with an impressive plaque depicting the life of John Paul Jones, a local man who founded the US navy. Robert Burns is thought to have written his Selkirk Grace in this hotel. The real ales are served in the lounge bar but are brought through to the public bar on request. It is close to the Dee Estuary and the historic fishing harbour, and there are some superb walks in the area. Q❀⇔◐◑P

NEWTON STEWART

Creebridge House Hotel

Minigaff (old main road, E of river)

12-2.30, 6-11.30 (midnight Sat); 12.30-11 Sun

☎ (01671) 402121 website: www.creebridge.co.uk

Beer range varies Ⓗ

This superb country house hotel sits in three acres of idyllic gardens and woodland. Built in 1760 as the home of the Earl of Galloway, it has been beautifully converted and is renowned for fine food and warm hospitality. The three real ales (four in summer) are served in the Bridge bar, usually two from the local Sulwath Brewery. Meals are served in the adjacent brasserie and in the more formal garden restaurant. ❀⇔◐◑♣P

PORTPATRICK ✻

Downshire Arms Hotel

12-14 Main Street

11-12.30 (1am Thu-Sat); 12.30-midnight Sun

☎ (01776) 810300

website: www.downshire-arms-hotel.co.uk

Beer range varies Ⓗ

Former coaching inn (circa 1880), conveniently situated on the village's main street. Two real ales, from the Sulwath and Houston breweries, are served in the Seafarer's bar. This is dominated at one end by a pool table and giant-screen TV, but also features nautical memorabilia and a collection of spirit miniatures. While only a restricted menu is available in the bar, the Mariner restaurant is noted for its local game and seafood dishes. ⛫Q⇔◐◑♣

Liquor for a King

I'm very fond of water,
I drink it noon and night;
Not Rechab's son or daughter
Had therein more delight.

At luncheon, too, I drink it,
And strength it seems to bring:
When really good, I think it
A liquor for a king.

But I forgot to mention –
'Tis best to be sincere –
I used an old invention
That turns it into beer.

Lord Neaves

THORNHILL

Buccleuch & Queensberry Hotel

112 Drumlanrig Street

11-midnight (1am Thu-Sat); 12.30-midnight Sun

☎ (01848) 330215 website: www.buccleuchhotel.co.uk

Caledonian 80/-; guest beers Ⓗ

Occupying a commanding position in the town centre, the hotel offers a varied menu with that something special, which draws customers from far and near. The main lounge is decked with fishing gear and trophies, reflecting the interest of both locals and visitors and constitutes most of the bar-side chat along with golf and shooting which are all available locally. It is well situated for visitors to historic Drumlanrig Castle. ⛫Q⇔◐♿P

INN BRIEF

DUMFRIES

Globe Inn

56 High Street

11-11 (midnight Thu-Sat); 12-midnight Sun

(01387) 252335

Caledonian 80/- Ⓗ

Established in 1610, this town-centre inn is internationally famous for its Robert Burns connections.

LOCKERBIE

Somerton House Hotel

35 Carlisle Road

11-11 (midnight Thu-Sat); 11-11 Sun

(01567) 202583

Beer range varies Ⓗ

Comfortable hotel close to the M74, but within walking distance of the town centre.

PORTPATRICK

Harbour House Hotel

Harbour Square

11-11.15 (11.45 Fri & Sat); 12.30-11 Sun

(01776) 810456

Houston Killellan; guest beer Ⓗ

Harbour-front hotel which is popular for lunch and eve meals. Opening hours are extended to 1am for live music most summer weekends.

STRANRAER

Ruddicott Hotel

London Road

12-2.30, 5-11 (midnight Thu-Sat); 12.30-11 Sun

(01776) 702684

Beer range varies Ⓗ

Small, family-run hotel close to the football ground and the ferry terminal. Screens separate the bar from the eating area.

Missing?

If a pub is not listed in the Guide that you think is worthy of consideration, please let us know at GBG, CAMRA, 230 Hatfield Road, St Albans, Herts, AL1 4LW or camra@camra.org.uk. All recommendations are forwarded to CAMRA branches, which are responsible for choosing pubs.

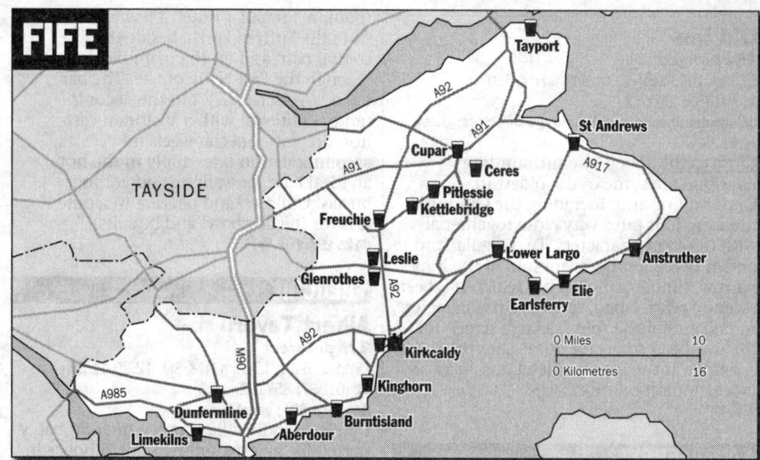

Authority area covered: Fife UA

ABERDOUR

Aberdour Hotel

38 High Street (A921)

4-11; 3-11.45 Fri; 11-11.45 Sat; 12-11 Sun

☎ (01383) 860325 website: www.aberdourhotel.com

Adnams Broadside; Caledonian Deuchars IPA; guest beers H

Small, family-run, traditional hotel in a popular tourist and commuter area. The lounge is used more as a restaurant (open 6-9 eve) specialising in seafood. Lunches are served weekends. The hotel started life as a coaching inn and despite extensive modernisation, many of the original features remain. One handpump is in use during winter, two in spring, sometimes four in summer, and a small beer festival is run in the first week of August to coincide with the Aberdour Gala. P

Cedar Inn

20 Shore Road (off A921)

11-2.30, 5-midnight; 11-midnight Sat; 12-midnight Sun

☎ (01383) 860310

Caledonian Deuchars IPA; guest beers H

On the north shore of the Forth, Aberdour is renowned for its 'silver sands'. This family-run hotel can be found in a quiet side street, a short walk from the scenic harbour. The public bar has a mega TV and pool table; a smaller side bar and no-smoking conservatory are more peaceful. It also has a quiet lounge and a restaurant. One regular, and three guest beers are sold, changing on an almost daily basis. P

ANSTRUTHER

Dreel Tavern

16 High Street (A917)

11-midnight; 12.30-11 Sun

☎ (01334) 310727

Orkney Dark Island; guest beers H

This old stone building in the East Neuk of Fife features crow-step gables and a pantile roof. Previously called the Railway Tavern, it started life as a 16th-century coaching inn, reputedly visited by James V; the beamed ceiling certainly looks old enough. The public and lounge bars are separated by an open fire and a conservatory provides dining/family space. It is very busy serving good quality meals. One regular and two guest beers are served from three handpumps. Joint winner of CAMRA Kingdom of Fife Pub of the Year 2001.

CERES

Ceres Inn

The Cross (B939)

12-3, 5-midnight (1am Fri); 12-midnight Sat; 12.30-midnight Sun

☎ (01334) 828305 website: www.ceresinn.uk

Beer range varies H

Pleasant, low-ceilinged bar, restored to its original state with beams and stone walls, in the 1990s. Situated at a crossroads, it probably started life as a coaching inn. One of two villages in Scotland with a village green, Ceres hosts the oldest Highland Games each June, when competitors try to throw the Ceres Stone, which is kept in the bar. The beer range, from two handpumps, varies continuously, showcasing Harviestoun and other small local breweries. Meals in the restaurant include high teas at the weekend. Q P

DUNFERMLINE

Commercial Inn

13 Douglas Street

11-2.30, 5.30-midnight; 11-midnight Fri & Sat; 11-midnight Sun

☎ (01383) 733876

Courage Directors; McEwan 80/-; Theakston Old Peculier; guest beers H

Busy, town-centre pub with bouncers on the door weekend evenings. The interior is typical of a branded pub with a wood and sawdust floor, simulated distemper on the walls and a multitude of blackboards listing the cask and bottled beers. Four ales from the ScotCo range are supplemented by four guest ales. Good value meals are served throughout the day, including all-day breakfast.

INDEPENDENT BREWERY

Fyfe Kirkcaldy

Old Inn

15a Kirkgate

11 (12.30 Sun)-11 (midnight Fri & Sat)

(01383) 736652

Caledonian Deuchars IPA; Courage Directors; guest beers

Close to the abbey, the surrounding buildings are some of the oldest in Dunfermline and, including the Old Inn, there are four pubs very close together all with different characters. Two regular and one or two guest beers are sold in the long, narrow, timber-panelled bar which has been recently refurbished, retaining its character. At one end of the room, a large screen for the overhead projector dominates the space. A lounge at the rear is quieter and has a more modern interior.

EARLSFERRY

Golf Tavern (19th Hole)

5 Links Road (southern edge of Elie golf course)

11-2, 5-11; 11-1am Fri & Sat; 11-midnight Sun

(01333) 330610 website: www.the19th.freeola.com

Caledonian Deuchars IPA, 80/-; guest beer (summer)

Superb, timber-panelled public bar boasting old-fashioned gas lamps at each end of the counter, a gas cigar lighter on the bar and two magnificent etched mirrors on one wall. The lounge bar has exposed stonework with an open fire and a golfing theme. It is home to the 19th Acoustic Music Club which meets on the first and third Thursday of each month. A small room to the rear is used for pool and darts. Opening hours may vary in winter.

ELIE

Braid's Bar at the Victoria Hotel

High Street (A917)

11-1am; 12-midnight Sun

(01333) 330305 website: www.the-vic.com

Caledonian Deuchars IPA, 80/-; guest beers

Narrow, timber-panelled bar and a pool room in a popular hotel, a few yards from the Firth of Forth, beside the Fife coastal path and on the main bus route through the East Neuk of Fife. The bar has a large-screen TV but the decor is more traditional with a Victorian cast-iron fireplace. Special weekend accommodation rates apply in the hotel, an ideal base for walking and golfing breaks. Children and pets are welcome (ask for the dog bowl and biscuits).

FREUCHIE

Albert Tavern

2 High Street

11-2, 5-11; 12-1am Fri & Sat; 12.30-11 Sun

(01337) 857192

Belhaven 80/-; guest beers

Family-friendly village pub which probably started life as a two-up-two-down house in the 18th century. An old photograph shows the tavern sometime in the 19th century. The 'two down' are the bar and lounge with beamed ceilings and wainscotting in the bar. One room upstairs is a small restaurant seating about 20. Three handpumps offer one regular and two guest beers at weekends and one guest during the week. Kingdom of Fife CAMRA Pub of the Year 2002.

GLENROTHES

Golden Acorn

1 North Street

11 (12.30 Sun)-midnight

(01592) 751175

Courage Directors; guest beers

Wetherlodge with one large bar situated beside the town bus station in a 1970s building, rather than the usual old bank. Beers from independent Scottish brewers are usually available and the low prices attract a varied clientele of all ages. No music or TV, it gets extremely busy Thursday evening through the weekend. Accommodation is available in the hotel above; breakfast is served in the bar. The patio is next to the car park.

INN BRIEF

BURNTISLAND

Crown Tavern

17 Links Place

11 (12.30 Sun)-midnight

(01592) 873697

Beer range varies

Two-roomed traditional town pub, off the main street beside Burntisland Links.

CUPAR

Golf Tavern

11 South Road

11.30-midnight (1am Fri & Sat); 12-11.30 Sun

(01334) 654233

Beer range varies

Small, traditional bar with a modern interior, part of a terrace on the main road south out of Cupar. Lunches are served.

KINGHORN

Auld Hoose

6-8 Nethergate

(steps lead down to Nethergate from A921)

12 (12.30 Sun)-midnight

(01592) 891074

Broughton Ghillie; Caledonian 80/-; guest beers

Busy local situated on a steep side street, handy for the station and Kinghorn beach. The bar has a TV and pool table and stages dominoes competitions at the weekend.

LOWER LARGO

Railway Inn

1 Station Wynd

11 (12.30 Sun)-midnight

(01333) 320239

Taylor Landlord; guest beers

One-roomed pub, situated below redundant railway arches near the small harbour. The Crusoe Hotel with its Alexander Selkirk exhibition is nearby.

ST ANDREWS

Central Bar

77-79 Market Street

11 (12.30 Sun)-11.45 (1am Fri & Sat)

(01334) 478296

Caledonian Deuchars IPA; Greene King Old Speckled Hen; McEwan 80/-; Theakston Best Bitter, Old Peculier; guest beers

Town-centre pub, popular with students and locals. Large windows and old mirrors give a Victorian feel. The pavement tables are an excellent place to relax. Good value meals are served all day until 10pm.

✻ symbol next to a main entry place name indicates there are Inn Brief entries as well.

KETTLEBRIDGE

Kettlebridge Inn

9 Cupar Road

11.30-2.30, 5-11; 4.30-midnight Fri & Sat; 12.30-11 Sun

(01337) 830232

Belhaven 80/-; guest beers H

Small, one-roomed local beside a busy trunk road in the scenic Howe of Fife. It stocks one regular beer and three guests from a variety of independent brewers. Opening hours can vary, depending on how busy the pub is. A patio behind the pub allows for outdoor drinking. Tayside CAMRA Pub of the Year 1999.

KINGHORN

Ship Tavern

2 Bruce Street (A921)

12 (12.30 Sun)-midnight

(01592) 890655

Caledonian Deuchars IPA; Inveralmond Independence; guest beers H

One of the older buildings in Kinghorn, one door lintel is dated 1668. It was built as a mansion for 'Bible Bruce' who printed bibles for King James VI. The unobtrusive entrance door, facing the main road opens into a fine timber-panelled interior, with a long bar counter and ornate gantry. The small jug bar is one of the finest surviving traditional interiors in Fife. One guest and two regular beers are offered from the three handpumps. Good value bar meals are available lunchtime and early evenings in summer.

KIRKCALDY

Harbour Bar

471-473 High Street

11-2.30, 5-11; 11-midnight Thu-Sat; 12.30-midnight Sun

(01592) 264270

Beer range varies H

Quiet, unspoilt local in a tenement building, with a timber-panelled bar; see the murals depicting the town's whaling history. The ornate gantry offers a fine range of malt whiskies. Six handpumps offer ales from all over the country, changing on a daily basis, including some from the Fyfe Brewing Company which is housed in premises at the rear. CAMRA Scottish Pub of the Year 2000, runner-up British Pub of the Year 2000 and joint winner of the Kingdom of Fife Pub of the Year 2001.

LESLIE

Burns Tavern

184 High Street

12 (11 Fri & Sat; 12.30 Sun)-midnight

(01592) 741345

Taylor Landlord; guest beers H

Typical Scottish two-roomed main street pub, with a public bar on two levels: the lower level is lively and friendly, the upper level has a large-screen TV and pool table. The lounge bar is more spacious and quieter, except Thu-Sun evenings when karaoke and regular pub quizzes are held. One guest, generally from a small independent brewery, and two regular beers are served. Basic bar snacks are available at lunchtimes but there is no set menu.

LIMEKILNS

Ship Inn

Halkett's Hall (promenade)

11-11 (midnight Thu-Sat); 12.30-midnight Sun

(01383) 872247

Belhaven 70/-, 80/-; guest beers H

Single-roomed pub in an historic village with a classic painted exterior but rather unexpected interior, the colours being more typical of a bistro than a bar. Meals are available lunchtime and early evening; specials are listed on the blackboard inside. The benches outside on the pavement provide a good location to enjoy the fine views across the River Forth on a warm summer evening.

PITLESSIE

Village Inn

Cupar Road

11-midnight (1am Fri & Sat); 11-2.30, 5-midnight winter; 12.30-1am Sun

(01337) 842156

Caledonian Deuchars IPA; guest beers H

With its traditional external appearance, the public bar is quite a surprise, featuring bare stonework and an open fire; the overall feel is bothy-like with wooden tables for dining. The interesting menu combines the traditional and exotic, cooked to order. The pub has several rooms, one featuring a Rayburn cooker, with others providing space for families and games, and a large function room at the rear. One regular and two guest beers are kept. It closes 2.30-5 in winter. Quiz night is held every second Wednesday. P

ST ANDREWS

Aikman's Cellar Bar

32 Bell Street

6-midnight (1am Fri); 11-1am Sat; 6-midnight Sun

(01334) 477425 website: www.cellarbar.co.uk

Beer range varies H

Small basement lounge bar below a continental-style bistro, mainly frequented by students. Opening hours outside term times can vary. The rolled copper bar top was salvaged from the White Star liner Oceanic (same shipping line as the Titanic). Around 300 real ales are sold each year, together with a variety of continental bottled beers. A week-long beer festival at Easter offers 20 ales. Ask for cask ales in the bistro upstairs and the staff will oblige.

Whey Pat Tavern

2 Argyle Street (just outside the old town wall)

11 (12.30 Sun)-11.30 (11.45 Fri & Sat)

(01334) 477740

Beer range varies H

Town-centre pub on a busy road junction at a site where there has been a hostelry for a few centuries. Unusually for St Andrews, this friendly, welcoming pub is popular with students, academics and townspeople alike. The three beers often feature small Scottish independent breweries such as Harviestoun, Inveralmond and Orkney. Some unusual soups and excellent sandwiches are served at lunchtime, with a vast range of 'help yourself' pickles and mustards. ♿♣

TAYPORT

Bell Rock Tavern

4-6 Dalgleish Street (near harbour)
11 (12.30 Sun)-midnight (1am Thu & Fri)
☎ (01382) 552388
Taylor Landlord; guest beer Ⓗ

Friendly, small, town local whose main bar is on three levels, each with a separate theme. Artefacts include charts of the River Tay and old photographs of Dundee, Tayport and the Tay ferries which last ran in 1966. One real ale is served throughout the year, increasing to two in the summer and over the festive season. Excellent value home-cooked meals, such as mince and tatties are available at lunchtimes, ideal for walkers on the nearby Fife coastal path. ♣

College Arms (1995)

Step through the door, escape the noise
(The curséd motor car)
And once inside a pleasing atmosphere.
There's businessmen and nice old boys
And this long polished bar
With pumps and cask dispensing wondrous beer.

There's blokes in boots from building sites.
There's students from the school
And office girls, some noisy some demure.
There's fruit machines with flashing lights
(Thank heaven there's no pool)
And condoms in the toilets...to be sure.

It's mentioned in the Good Beer Guide (1996)
An accolade indeed
And well deserved, the Guv'nor never shirks.
He serves his well kept ales with pride
And surely must succeed
He has such dedication and it works.

Tradition's what it's all about
A place to take one's ease.
To sit with friends and sup a drink or two.
Praise be to those who dish it out
Who try so hard to please
Let's drink to that...so cheers, may God bless you.

LD Pearce, *Making Matters Verse*, Janus, 1996

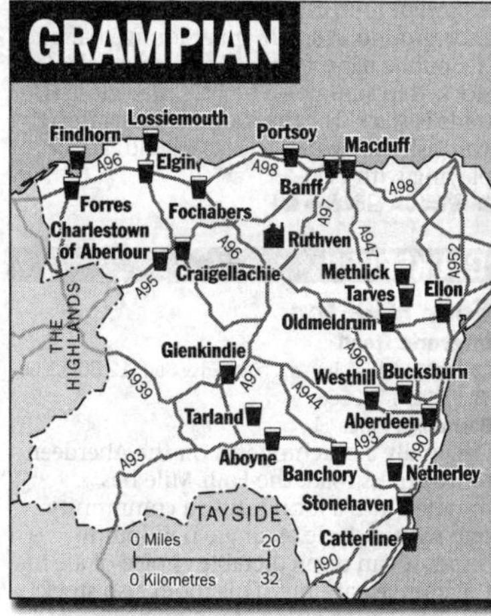

Authority areas covered: Aberdeenshire UA, City of Aberdeen UA, Moray UA

ABERDEEN

Cameron's Inn (Ma's)
Little Belmont Street

11-midnight (1am Fri & Sat); 12.30-11 Sun

(01224) 644487

Beer range varies

Recently acquired by Belhaven, this ancient inn boasts the most character-filled tiny snug bar in the city, and is the longest-serving outlet for real ale in Aberdeen since it was re-introduced to the area in 1976. The open-plan rear lounge bar offers a great contrast to the listed public bar.

Carriages
Brentwood Hotel, 101 Crown Street

11-2.30, 5-midnight; 6-11 Sun

(01224) 626490

website: www.brentwood-hotel.demon.co.uk

Boddingtons Bitter; Castle Eden Ale; Flowers Original; guest beers

Situated in the basement of the city-centre Brentwood Hotel, this bar is of peculiarly English character, and offers one of the biggest and most varied selections of real ale in Aberdeen. Because it is part of an hotel, the busiest times are midweek, making this a good bet to get a seat on Friday and Saturday nights. The adjoining busy restaurant serves traditional food in the evenings. Limited parking behind the hotel.

P

Globe Inn
13-15 North Silver Street

12 (12.30 Sun)-midnight

(01224) 624258

Houston Peter's Well; guest beer

Recently expanded to include letting rooms, this convivial, open-plan pub, with a plethora of musical instruments decorating the lounge, stages a variety of musical events on a weekly basis, including folk sessions. Note the unusual stained glass light fitting. It boasts the nicest gents in the city, with a prominent fireplace! Convenient for both the theatre and music hall, the Globe enjoys a substantial lunchtime food trade.

Moorings
2 Trinity Quay

11-midnight (1am Fri & Sat); 12.30-midnight Sun

(01224) 587602

Beer range varies

One-roomed dockside haven for rock and real ale; following no trends and much the better for it – a true example that any style of pub can dispense quality ale. The five handpumps tend to stick to Scottish independents, but can offer just about anything. Live music at weekends can become rather overpowering. It is convenient for the Maritime Museum, multiplex cinema and ferry terminal.

Old Blackfriars
52 Castlegate

11-midnight; 12.30-11 Sun

(01224) 581922

Belhaven 80/-, St Andrew's Ale; Caledonian Deuchars IPA, 80/-; Inveralmond Ossian's Ale; guest beer

Belhaven's flagship north-eastern outlet, mimicking the ambience of a high quality continental café, with its well-balanced mixture of bar and restaurant. The eclectic decor includes some back-lit stained glass from Dunecht House, and has religious overtones. This multiple local CAMRA award-winner serves food throughout its split-levels until 9pm (8pm Fri and Sat). Annual real ale and Czech beer festivals are held.

Old Town School
Little Belmont Street

11-midnight (1am Fri & Sat); 11-midnight Sun

(01224) 626490

Boddingtons Bitter; Caledonian 80/-; guest beer

Fairly standard Hogshead conversion of a former school, recently refurbished. Unfortunately it now offers a reduced selection of ales. It features an unusual upstairs cellar, visible from the balconied drinking area. Food is served until 9pm, and is also available on the flagged patio. Service can be slow at busy periods.

Prince of Wales
7 St Nicholas Lane

10-midnight; 12.30-11 Sun

(01224) 640597

Draught Bass; Caledonian 80/-; Theakston Old Peculier; guest beer

Fine old pub, with an impressive long bar and a bank of eight handpumps, it also boasts two old gantries, one of which was inherited from the long-vanished Lemon Tree pub. A seated lounge area at the front complements a large stone-floored space at the back with separated seating. The bar area retains its pendant lighting, keeping the traditional feel. Regular promotions showcase selected Scottish independent breweries' beers. In addition to lunches, toasted and plain sandwiches are available every day. Local CAMRA Town Pub of the Year 2002.

Q

INDEPENDENT BREWERY

Borve Ruthven

Under the Hammer
11 North Silver Street
5 (2 Sat)-midnight (1am Thu & Fri); 6.30-11 Sun
☎ (01224) 640253
Caledonian Deuchars IPA; Inveralmond Ossian's Ale; guest beer Ⓗ
Compact and intimate cellar wine bar, next to the city auction rooms, it tends to get busy with theatregoers relaxing around showtime, but charges highly for the privilege of using its facilities. The ever-changing art displays on the walls can be purchased. The large notice board shows extensive listings of forthcoming attractions in the town. It is also convenient for the music hall. ⇌

ABOYNE

Boat Inn
Charleston Road (N bank of River Dee, near bridge)
11-2.30, 5-11; 11-midnight Sat; 11-11 Sun
☎ (013398) 86137
Draught Bass; guest beer Ⓗ
Popular riverside inn where food is emphasised in the lounge, which features a log-burning stove and a spiral staircase leading to an upstairs drinking area and dining room. Junior diners can request to see the model train traverse the entire pub at picture-rail height, upon completion of their meal. Accommodation is provided in a self-catering flat and there is a campsite a mile outside the village. Guest beers usually come from Scottish independent breweries.
♛Q❀⇄◑◐⊟♿⛺♣P

Charleston Hotel
Ballater Road
11-11 (midnight Sat); 11-11 Sun
☎ (013398) 86475
Draught Bass; Greene King Old Speckled Hen; Harviestoun Bitter & Twisted Ⓗ
Attractive, small hotel at the centre of a Victorian tourist village, overlooking the showground. A small, quiet lounge bar and the public bar offer three ales, and cider is stocked in summer. The bars may close if trade is slack. For the football fans among you, ask the owner, a local legend, about playing with Pele!
♛❀⇄◑◐⊟♿⛺♣●P

BUCKSBURN

Four Mile Inn
Inverurie Road
11-11 (11.30 Thu; midnight Fri & Sat); 12.30-11 Sun
☎ (01224) 712588
Beer range varies Ⓗ
Originally a coaching inn on the Aberdeen to Inverness road, the Four Mile has mutated into a local rarity: a community pub with cask ale. A single handpump dispenses an unpredictable choice of ale in the lounge bar only. This room also stocks an imaginative range of malt whiskies to welcome the weary traveller.
⊟P

CATTERLINE

Creel Inn
By harbour OS868781
12-2.30, 6-11 (midnight Fri & Sat); closed Tue; 12-2.30, 5.30-11 Sun
☎ (01569) 750254
Beer range varies Ⓗ
Superb seafood (lobster a speciality) is the main selling point of this traditionally-built converted cottage in a tiny coastal village. The low ceiling and small windows give an intimate atmosphere to the three areas of bar, lounge and restaurant. Accommodation is provided in converted fishing cottages adjacent to the inn (reservations recommended). There is also a caravan park nearby.
♛❀⇄◑◐⊟♣P

INN BRIEF

ABERDEEN

Atholl Hotel
54 Kings Gate
11.30-2.30, 5-11 (11.30 Fri & Sat); 12-2.30, 5-11 Sun
(01224) 323505
Courage Directors; Taylor Landlord Ⓗ
Plush lounge bar in an impressive granite building, with a restrained and refined ambience. Meals served lunchtime and eve.

Grill ☆
213 Union Street
10-midnight (1am Fri & Sat); 12.30-midnight Sun
Caledonian 80/-; Isle of Skye Red Cuillin; McEwan 80/- Ⓗ
Superb, traditional National Inventory pub, once a men-only establishment; unspoilt despite alterations to provide female toilet facilities.

Number 10 Wine Bar
10 Queens Terrace
11-midnight; 12.30-11 Sun
(01224) 631928
Caledonian Deuchars IPA, 80/-; Fuller's London Pride; Taylor Landlord; guest beers Ⓗ
Vaulted cellar bar, popular with the local business community. Food includes breakfasts served from 9am. Draught cider stocked.

BANCHORY

Scott Skinners
North Deeside Road
11-2.30, 5-midnight (11 Mon); 11-2.30, 5-11 Sun
(01330) 824393
Beer range varies Ⓗ
Converted Victorian house, comprising a restaurant and combined public/lounge bar offering three varying guest beers.

BANFF

Ship Inn
Deveronside
11-midnight (12.30am Fri & Sat); 7-11 Sun
(01261) 812620
Courage Directors Ⓗ
Unspoilt historic inn, complete with a boat-shaped bar counter, used in the filming of Local Hero.

FINDHORN

Crown & Anchor
11-11 (11.45 Wed & Thu; 12.30am Fri & Sat); 12-11 Sun
(01309) 690243
Beer range varies Ⓗ
Situated in picturesque Findhorn Bay, this listed two-bar beamed inn dates from 1739. Meals served lunchtime and eve.

FOCHABERS

Gordon Arms
80 High Street
11.30-2.30, 5-11 (12.30am Fri & Sat); 12.30-11 Sun
(01343) 820508
Caledonian Deuchars IPA; guest beer Ⓗ
200-year-old coaching inn with a pétanque club based in the hotel. Beer available only in the public bar. Meals served.

STONEHAVEN

Ship Inn
5 Shorehead
11-midnight; 12.30-midnight Sun
(01569) 762617
Caledonian 80/-; Orkney Dark Island; guest beer Ⓗ
Welcoming pub, built in 1771, and set in a picturesque harbour location. No food Sun eve.

TARLAND

Aberdeen Arms
The Square
12-2.30, 5-midnight (12-midnight Sat); 12-11 Sun
Beer range varies Ⓗ
Traditional, listed, unspoilt village pub, normally supplying Inveralmond beer from its single handpump. Meals available.

CHARLESTOWN OF ABERLOUR

Mash Tun

8 Broomfield Square

✪ 12-11 (11.45 Thu; 12.30am Fri & Sat; 12-2.30, 5-11 winter Mon-Fri); 12.30-11.45 Sun

☎ (01340) 881771

Beer range varies Ⓗ

Dating from 1896 as the Station Bar, this round-ended building is a former local CAMRA Country Pub of the Year. It keeps one beer in winter and up to three in summer, plus several malts and some unusual bottled beers. On the Speyside Way long-distance footpath, its good value food includes Mexican dishes as a speciality. The disused railway station platform, with its views of the River Spey, makes an ideal location for an alfresco pint. ❀◑▲P

CRAIGELLACHIE

Highlander Inn

Victoria Street

✪ 11-2.30, 5-11 (11.45 Wed & Thu; 12.30am Fri); 11-12.30am Sat; 12-11 Sun

☎ (01340) 881446

Isle of Skye Red Cuillin Ⓗ

Small downstairs hotel lounge bar, where the beer is overshadowed by the selection of over 80 malt whiskies. The heavy summer tourist trade in the Spey Valley is enticed by the excellent local cuisine. The inn runs an outdoor bar at the local Couthie Do event in May, and hosts frequent live music. ⇆◑P

ELGIN

Flanagan's

Shepherds Close, 48a High Street (end of narrow alleyway opposite Farmfoods)

✪ 11-12.30am (1.30am Fri & Sat); 12-12.30am Sun

☎ (01343) 549737

Beer range varies Ⓗ

Difficult to find, down a narrow alleyway leading off the main shopping street, this long, dimly-lit but lively city-centre bar is bedecked with a plethora of Irish memorabilia. Up to three beers are on offer in the bar, regularly featuring Scottish beers; they are also available on request in the upstairs Tapas restaurant. It stands close to the ruins of Elgin Cathedral, considered in its day the most beautiful in Scotland (open to the public). ◑⇌

Muckle Cross

34 High Street

✪ 11-11.45 (1.30am Fri & Sat); 12.30-11.45 Sun

☎ (01343) 559030

Caledonian 80/-; Courage Directors; Theakston Best Bitter; guest beers Ⓗ

This Wetherspoon's outlet was converted from a former Halfords store as opposed to the usual bank premises. A long, wide walk-through bar offers a selection of five ales. It has re-invigorated the local drinking scene. Meals are served all day. ◑♿⇌⊬✔

Sunninghill Hotel

Hay Street

✪ 12-11 (midnight Fri & Sat); 12-11 Sun

☎ (01343) 547799

Taylor Landlord; Tetley Burton Ale; guest beers Ⓗ

Small, family-run hotel, just outside the city centre, near the railway station and Moray College. The excellent food can be almost as tempting as the five real ales on offer. A children's certificate ensures custom for the conservatory. A large selection of whiskies also entices some travellers slightly off the beaten track to this turn-of-the-century hostelry.

❀⇆◑⇌P

ELLON

Tolbooth

23 Station Road

✪ 11-2.30, 5-11 (midnight Thu & Fri; 11.45 Sat); 6.30-11 Sun

☎ (01358) 721308

Draught Bass; guest beers Ⓗ

Converted from two semi-detached houses, this split-level pub has a spacious conservatory on the lower level. Up to three guest beers are available, but no food other than lunchtime sandwiches is served. The predominantly mature clientele find things fairly quiet, as children are not allowed at any time. An upstairs attic lounge opens on Friday evenings.

Q❀♿♣

FINDHORN ❊

Kimberley Inn

✪ 11-11 (11.45 Thu & Fri; 12.30am Sat); 12.30-11.45 Sun

☎ (01309) 690492

Tetley Bitter; guest beers Ⓗ

Popular, friendly bar with two no-smoking areas; the patio affords fine views over Findhorn Bay, esteemed for water sports. Famed for its food, the bar has a children's certificate until 8pm. Orkney, Fuller's and Marston's beers feature regularly on the guest list.

♨Q❀◑♿▲♣⊬

FOCHABERS ❊

Red Lion Inn

67 High Street

✪ 11-11.30 (1am Fri & Sat); 12.30-midnight Sun

☎ (01343) 820455

Beer range varies Ⓗ

Situated on the main street, in the middle of the village, this local has up to two ales available in the public bar, which can be taken into the lounge. Handy for fishermen and walkers traversing the Speyside Way, it serves keenly-priced food. A caravan site is nearby.

♨◑⊟♿▲♣

FORRES

Carisbrooke Hotel

Drumduan Road (1/4 mile off A96, E end of town)

✪ 11-midnight (1.30am Fri & Sat); 12-midnight Sun

☎ (01309) 672585

Boddingtons Bitter; guest beers Ⓗ

Small, but friendly, family-run hotel on the eastern outskirts of town. The compact bar and larger lounge offer good food at competitive prices, and the quality of accommodation attracts families with children. Regular activities include barbecues on the patio and quiz nights, and the hotel specialises in golfing breaks.

♨❀⇆◑⊟♣P

GLENKINDIE

Glenkindie Arms

11-11 (1am Fri; midnight Sat); 11-11 Sun
(019756) 41288 website: www.glenkindiearms.co.uk
Beer range varies

This tiny drovers' inn, some 400 years old, was formerly used as a Masonic lodge, evidence of which can still be seen. The cosy bar and small dining room provide an enormous selection of excellent cuisine – all produce is sourced locally. No food served Mon in winter. Two beers are available in summer, one in winter. Convenient for the Castle Trail and Lecht ski area, it is advisable to check winter opening times before travelling.

LOSSIEMOUTH

Clifton Bar

5 Clifton Road
11-2.30, 5-midnight (12.30am Fri & Sat); 12.30-midnight Sun
(01343) 812100
McEwan 80/-; Tetley Bitter; Theakston Old Peculier; guest beer

Two-roomed bar overlooking the River Lossie and the harbour area, near the marina. The bar is popular with RAF personnel from the local base. An adjacent guesthouse in the same ownership offers accommodation. Visit the toilet to make a deposit in the 'wishing well'! The licensees concentrate on selling excellent ales and staunchly refuse to provide meals.

MACDUFF

Knowes Hotel

78 Market Street
12-midnight (12-2, 5-midnight winter Mon-Fri); 12.30-11 Sun
(01261) 832229
Beer range varies

Spacious, detached, family-run hotel, dated 1879 but frequently extended, it stands on an elevated site affording tremendous panoramic views of the Moray Firth. The beer range usually comprises one national brand and one Scottish micro-brew. The food is excellent. Nearby, Macduff Aquarium is of family interest, with its unusual open-air central tank.

METHLICK

Gight House Hotel

Sunnybrae (1/2 mile N of river)
12-2.30, 5-midnight (12-midnight Sat); 12-11 Sun
(01651) 806389
website: www.gight-house@freeuk.com
Beer range varies

This former free kirk manse, built in 1850, is reputedly haunted by a former minister. The attractive beamed lounge bar offers at least two guest beers while the two conservatories overlook a colourful one-acre garden, complete with a putting green and pétanque pitch. It has a well-earned reputation for home-cooked meals, predominantly made with local produce. A clay pigeon lodge, fishing and golf facilities can be found nearby.

Ythanview Hotel

Ellon Road
11-2.30; 5-11 (1am Fri; 12.30am Sat); 12.30-11 Sun
(01651) 806235
Beer range varies

Family-run hotel overlooking the river, with a smart lounge and cheery public bar. An impressive array of trophies displays support for local football, cricket and fishing teams, and there are regular theme nights and live music. Good value, home-cooked food is proffered; the landlord's curry is especially challenging. On the Castle Trail, Haddo House and Fyvie Castle are both nearby.

NETHERLEY

Lairhillock Inn

Off B979 (signed), 3 miles S of B9077
11.30-2.30, 5-11; 11-midnight Sat; 12-midnight Sun
(01569) 730001 website: www.lairhillock.co.uk
Courage Directors; Taylor Landlord; guest beers

Set in the heart of the countryside, but reasonably close to town, the emphasis here is on quality and friendliness. The public bar, with its log fire, provides convivial surroundings for drinking, while the lounge and conservatory are for diners. Whatever the season, this is a popular venue for families with children. The house beer comes from Isle of Skye.

OLDMELDRUM

Redgarth Hotel

Kirk Brae (off A947, towards golf course)
11-2.30, 5-midnight; 12-2.30, 5-11 Sun
(01651) 872353
Beer range varies

Traditional, wood-panelled lounge bar in an imposing position at the top of the village, it benefits from panoramic views of the eastern Grampian mountains. The landlord, a former national Publican of the Year, offers an imaginative selection of guest ales and a varied home-cooked menu. Occasional 'brewers in residence' evenings are an added attraction. A no-smoking room is available for diners or meetings. Local CAMRA Country Pub of the Year 2002.

PORTSOY

Shore Inn

49 Church Street
11 (10 summer)-11 (midnight Thu; 12.30am Fri & Sat); 11-11 Sun
(01261) 842831
Beer range varies

This 18th-century inn, at the oldest harbour on the Moray coast, bears a nautical theme. Up to three ales are kept in summer, only one in winter, selected from Fuller's and local micro-breweries. The pub runs an outdoor bar for the annual boat festival – the Shore Out. An extensive evening menu is produced, and the bar has a children's certificate (children welcome until 8pm).

STONEHAVEN ❄

Marine Hotel
9-10 Shorehead
11-midnight (1am Fri & Sat); 12-midnight Sun
☎ (01569) 762155
website: www.marinehotel@hotmail.com
Inveralmond Ossian's Ale; Taylor Landlord; guest beers H

Former Scottish CAMRA Pub of the Year whose picturesque harbour-front location makes for an appealing pint, particularly outdoors in summer. The downstairs bar consists of a simple, but busy, wood-panelled bar, contrasting with a comfortably furnished lounge, complete with huge fire in winter. The main upstairs restaurant specialises in fresh local produce, especially fish dishes. Addlestone's cider is stocked.

TARVES

Aberdeen Arms Hotel
The Square
12-2.30 (not Mon), 5-11; (12-1am Fri; 12-midnight Sat); 12-11 Sun
☎ (01651) 851214
Beer range varies H

Small, family-run hotel in a village conservation area. Note the fine mirrors in the public bar where a children's certificate operates until 8pm. Regular folk sessions feature bagpipes and zither! The cuisine ranges from north-east to far east and is extremely good value. It is handy for Tolquhon Castle and the 17th-century Pitmedden Gardens designed by Sir Alexander Seddon with their elaborate flowerbeds, fountains and pavilions.

WESTHILL

Shepherd's Rest
Straik Road, Arnhall Business Park
11-11; 12.30-11 Sun
☎ (01224) 740208
Courage Directors; guest beers H

A recent addition to the Chef & Brewer chain, a huge menu ensures that food dominates the proceedings. The kit-built interior is well done, with differing areas surrounding the bar. The guest beers on offer tend to be ales not available anywhere else in the region. Accommodation is in the large commercial lodge adjoining the pub.

The Mountain Brewery

O, hail to the Mountain that giveth
The porter so rich and so pure,
That the Nobles and Lords might partake of,
As well as the humble and poor!
The French folk may boast of their Brandies,
The Hollanders talk of their Gin,
But give me the stout from the Mountain,
And then I'll feel happy within.

God speed to the New Mountain Brewery,
May its orders be many and great,
For its porter's the height of perfection;
The Doctors pronounce it 'first-rate'!
Then stop drinking inferior liquors,
And Caffrey's Pure Porter begin –
And I'm sure you will always be healthy,
For you'll always feel happy within.

T Rafferty, Belfast, 1897,
on the opening of Thomas Caffrey's
Mountain Brewery

HIGHLANDS & ISLANDS

Authority areas covered: Highland UA, Orkney Islands UA, Shetland Islands UA, Western Islands UA

ARDGOUR

Inn at Ardgour

A861, at the Corran Ferry
10-11 (1am Fri & Sat); 12-11 Sun
(01855) 841225 website: www.ardgour.biz
Beer range varies

Family-run, 18th-century village inn at the entrance to the Great Glen. All 10 en-suite rooms benefit from views over Loch Linneche. Popular with locals, the inn is ideally located for walking, fishing, climbing, sailing and watching wildlife, and makes a good base for exploring the West Highlands. Bar meals are served all day. Beers are from the Isle of Skye Brewery; 50 malts are stocked. The comfortable lounge has an open fire. P

AVIEMORE

Old Bridge Inn

Dalfaber Road (100 yds from Cairngorm ski road jct)
11-midnight (1am Fri); 12.30-11 Sun
(01479) 811137
Beer range varies

This converted cottage, recently enlarged, is situated just to the south of the village, on the road leading to the Strathspey Steam Railway. It is popular with walkers, climbers and skiers. It features at least one beer from the nearby Cairngorm Brewery. The pub has a children's certificate. Q P

AVOCH

Station Hotel

Main Street
11-2.30, 5-11 (midnight Fri); 11-11 summer; 11-11.30 Sat; 12.30-11.30 Sun
(01381) 620246
Beer range varies

Large family-run pub, a meeting place for many local clubs, it has only had two owners in the last 75 years. A spacious conservatory provides an attractive environment to enjoy the popular menu. Red kites (the RSPB's big success story) can often be seen from the child-friendly garden. Other local attractions include dolphin watching at Chanory Point, a spectacular golf course by the Moray Firth and many well-signed walks.
P

BALLACHULISH

Laroch Bar

Off main road through village
11-12.30am (1.30am Thu-Sat); 12.30-12.30am Sun
(01855) 811900
Beer range varies

When the Laroch was opened in 1990 it was the first pub in Ballachulish for over 50 years, with a new bar being added two years ago. The modern building is situated in a pretty Argyllshire village, strung along the edge of Loch Leven and close to the awesome Glencoe. The beers are from the Isle of Skye Brewery on a rotation basis.
P

CARRBRIDGE

Cairn Hotel

On B9153 (formerly A9)
11.30-midnight (1am Fri & Sat); 12.30 (12 summer)-11 Sun

☎ (01479) 841212
Beer range varies Ⓗ
Busy pub, with an adjoining hotel at the centre of the village, catering for locals as well as skiers, walkers and birdwatchers. The two beers are mainly Scottish, and include brews from Isle of Skye and Black Isle. In addition to bar meals, soup and toasties are available all day; evening meals are served 6-8.
♨❀⇔◑◐ ⇌P⊬

DRUMNADROCHIT

Benleva Hotel

At southern end of village, off A82
⊙ 11 (12 Sun)-midnight
☎ (01456) 450080 website: www.benleva.co.uk
Beer range varies Ⓗ
400-year-old, extended manse with a large walled garden, recently extensively refurbished. It is convenient for the tourist attractions of Urquart Castle and the Loch Ness Monster – a short footpath leads to the banks of Loch Ness, and it is ideally situated for touring the Great Glen and the Glen Affric natural Caledonian pine forest. Two Scottish beers are stocked, one of which will be from the Isle of Skye Brewery. The menu changes daily and features locally-sourced food. The spectacular sweet chestnut tree by the front entrance is reputedly the second oldest in Britain and is a former hanging tree.
♨Q❀⇔◑◐ ⊟⅄♣P

FORT WILLIAM

Grog & Gruel

66 High Street
⊙ 11 (12 winter)-midnight (1am Thu-Sat); closed lunch, 5-midnight Sun
☎ (01397) 705078 website: www.grogandgruel.co.uk
Beer range varies Ⓗ
In the shadow of Britain's highest mountain, in one of Scotland's main tourist areas, this bare-floored ale house with church pew seating, keeps up to six beers in summer, reducing to two in winter. Owned by the same family that owns the famous Clachaig Inn, it holds beer festivals at Easter, October and Christmas, often specialising in Highland beers. Busy with tourists in summer, it is also popular with locals. Home-cooked food is available in the upstairs dining room or from the more limited bar menu (no meals Sun lunch).
❀◑◐ ⅄⇌

Nevisport Bar

Tweedale (N end of High St)
⊙ 11.30-11.30 (1am Fri & Sat); 11.30-11.30 Sun
☎ (01397) 704921
Beer range varies Ⓗ
A warming open fire welcomes winter visitors to this large but cosy bar, which is at the north end of Fort William and convenient for Glen Nevis and Aonach Mor. Popular with winter sports enthusiasts in winter, and climbers and walkers in summer, the informal lounge-style bar displays large pictures of mountain scenery and mountain sports paraphernalia. Mainly Scottish beers are served, often from the Isle of Skye Brewery.
♨♉◑◐ ♿⅄⇌

GAIRLOCH

Old Inn

Opp. harbour
⊙ 11-1am (11.30 Sat); 12.30-11 Sun
☎ (01445) 712006 website: www.theoldinn.co.uk
Beer range varies Ⓗ
This family-run hotel, in a delightful setting on the magnificent Wester Ross coast at the foot of the Flowerdale Glen, is popular with walkers and climbers. It boasts a pottery, walkers' lodge and a natural climbing wall in the grounds. Do not miss the murals in the main bar and the spectacular painting by Lincoln Rowe. Eight beers, mainly Scottish, are served in summer (three in winter). A bistro and restaurant offer a home-cooked menu specialising in seafood and game.
♨♉❀⇔◑◐ ⊟⅄♣P⊡

GLENCOE

Clachaig Inn

On old road, 2 miles SE of village OSNN1256
⊙ 11-11 (midnight Fri; 11.30 Sat); 11-11 Sun
☎ (01855) 811252
website: www.glencoescotland.co.uk
Caledonian 80/-; Heather Fraoch Heather Ale; Tetley Bitter, Burton Ale; guest beers Ⓗ
A glacier inching its way off Rannoch Moor scoured out the landscape of this awe-inspiring, historic glen. This old coaching inn nestles by a small wood behind the heritage centre. The large stone-floored bar plays host to many climbers and walkers who refresh themselves on wooden benches and warm up by cast-iron stoves. There is also a no-smoking room and a lounge. It keeps up to nine guest beers and a range of malt whiskies. Live music is staged weekends.
♨Q♉❀⇔◑◐ ⊟♿⅄P⊬

Kinghouse Hotel

Off A82, 10 miles SE of village OS259546
⊙ 11-12.30am; 12.30-12.30am Sun
☎ (01855) 851295 website: www.kingy.com
Caledonian 80/-; Orkney Dark Island; guest beer (summer) Ⓗ
One of Scotland's oldest inns stands in splendid isolation between the rugged grandeur of Glencoe and the desolation of Rannoch Moor. Its name derives from its role as a garrison for the troops of George II after the Battle of Culloden. Despite its remote situation, the small public bar is well known to climbers, walkers and other outdoor types; a larger lounge is at the front. Outside, the view of Buachaille Etive Mor is one of the most photographed in Scotland.
♨Q♉❀⇔◑◐ ⊟⅄P

INDEPENDENT BREWERIES

Atlas Kinlochleven
Black Isle Munlochy
Cairngorm Aviemore
Far North Melvich
Hebridean Stornoway
Isle of Skye Uig
Newtonmore & Kingussie Kingussie
Orkney Quoyloo
Valhalla Baltasound

HOSWICK

Barclay Arms Hotel

OS416240

✪ 12.30-3 (not Mon-Fri); 6.30-1am;12.30-3, 6.30-1am Sun

☎ (01950) 431226

Beer range varies Ⓗ

Friendly, coastal village inn, built into the hillside. The 1970s lounge bar, with full-height windows, overlooks a Shetland rarity – namely a stand of trees. Live music is provided most weekends. A convenient base for visiting the local archaeological sites of Jarlshof, Mousa and Scatness. Accommodation is available, but without breakfast. A very varied guest beer policy is pursued and the bar displays a collection of rare drinks trays. ⇆◑⊡♣P

INVERGARRY

Invergarry Hotel

✪ 12-2.30, 6-11 (midnight Fri); 12.30-2.30, 6-11 Sun

☎ (01809) 501206 website: www.invergarry.net

Beer range varies Ⓗ

Fully modernised coaching inn, dating from the Victorian era. It is conveniently situated on the main route to Skye, at an access point to the Great Glen cycle route and close to the proposed Great Glen walkway. These premises were once owned by John Anderson, the good friend of Rabbie Burns. Usually two Scottish beers are served, one from the Isle of Skye Brewery. Local shinty players use the hotel as their main meeting place. Saturday afternoons can be quite lively. ♨☕⇆◑♿♣P

INVERIE

Old Forge

Accessible by ferry from Mallaig

✪ 11-midnight (including Sun)

☎ (01678) 462267 website: www.theoldforge.co.uk

Beer range varies Ⓗ

The most remote pub in mainland Britain is reached by ferry or by a 15-mile hilly walk from Kinloch Hourn. In a spectacular setting on the shore of Loch Nevis, it provides an ideal base for walking the 'Rough Bounds' of Knoydart; moorings welcome waterborne visitors. An essential hub of the local community, it has two pumps serving mainly Isle of Skye beers. Specialities on the all-day menu include locally-caught seafood. An informal atmosphere prevails – dress code is wellies, waterproofs and midge cream. The landlord can arrange local accommodation. ♨Q❀◑⛺

INVERNESS

Blackfriars

93-95 Academy Street

✪ 11-midnight (12.30am Fri; 11.45 Sat); 12.30-11 Sun

☎ (01463) 233881

website: www.blackfriars.50megs.com

Black Isle Red Kite; Courage Directors; McEwan 80/-; Marston's Pedigree; Theakston Best Bitter, Old Peculier; guest beers Ⓗ

Traditional, town-centre pub: one spacious room, with a large standing area at the bar and ample seating in comfortable alcoves around the room. Three guest ales often showcase Black Isle and Isle of Skye breweries. Belgian and German bottled beers are also stocked. Inexpensive meals are home cooked, using local produce; a vegetarian choice is always available. Children are welcome. Live entertainment most nights features traditional music and local bands. ◑⇌

Clachnaharry Inn

17-19 High Street (A862, on outskirts of town)

✪ 11-11 (midnight Thu-Sat); 12.30-11.45 Sun

☎ (01463) 239806

Adnams Broadside; Courage Directors; Isle of Skye Red Cullin, Ⓗ **Blaven; McEwan 80/-;** Ⓗ/Ⓖ **guest beers** Ⓗ

Friendly, family-run, 17th-century coaching inn overlooking the north railway line and Caledonian Canal sea lock. The lounge and garden afford fine views of Ben Wyvis beyond the Beauly Firth. Families are welcome and bar meals are served all day. Up to three beers are served by gravity from wooden casks; house beers come from the Isle of Skye Brewery. Local CAMRA Town Pub of the Year 2001 and 2002, it was CAMRA Scottish Pub of the Year 2001. ♨Q❀◑⊡⛺

Number 27

27 Castle Street (below castle)

✪ 11-11 (midnight Thu; 1am Fri; 11.45 Sat); 12.30-11 Sun

☎ (01463) 241999

Beer range varies Ⓗ

Bright, friendly, modern pub in the shadow of the castle. The bar has a comfortable seating area where beers on tap usually include an English bitter, plus a local ale often from Black Isle or Isle of Skye; only one beer is kept in winter. Meals, served in the attractive dining area and the main bar, are prepared using fresh local produce, including game and salmon in season. A large-screen TV shows sporting events. ◑⇌

KINGUSSIE

Royal Hotel

29 High Street

✪ 11-midnight (1am Thu-Sat); 12.30-midnight Sun

☎ (01540) 661898

Beer range varies Ⓗ

Large, 52-roomed hotel, specialising in coach parties, located in an attractive holiday area. It is the main outlet for the attached Newtonmore & Kingussie Brewery (formerly Iris Rose). An ideal spot for hillwalking and birdwatching in the Cairngorms, other attractions include the award-winning Highland Folk Museum and the Wildlife Park at Kincraig. Up to 12 handpumps are in use in summer (three in winter) and at the increasingly popular beer festival (Nov). The large bar and dining area are supported by locals, providing a basic menu all day in summer. It hosts regular live music. ❀⇆◑♿⛺⇌P⍻

KIRKWALL

Bothy Bar (Albert Hotel)

Mounthoolie Lane (100 yds from harbour along Junction Rd)

✪ 11-11 (1am Thu-Sat); 12-1am Sun

☎ (01856) 876000

Orkney Red Macgregor, Dark Island Ⓗ

The bar is a popular meeting place, partly because the Albert Hotel also houses a nightclub. However, it is generally possible to have an unrushed drink in front of a large open fire or join in with the conversation at the bar. It is convenient for the harbour and ferry terminal.

Westend Hotel

14 Main Street

11-11 (midnight Sat); 12.30-11 Sun

(01856) 872368

Orkney Dark Island

Cosy bar on the first floor of an hotel, used by locals and residents alike. The Westend began life as a town house and then became the local hospital from 1845 until 1927. Lunches are served Mon-Sat.

NAIRN

Invernairne Hotel

Thurlow Road

11-11.30 (1am Thu-Sat); 11-11.30 Sun

(01667) 452039 website: www.golf-vacations.co.uk

Beer range varies

Family-run Victorian hotel, set in secluded gardens overlooking the Moray Firth. A path to the beach runs through the garden. In winter there is an open log fire in the baronial-style oak-panelled lounge. Real ales usually come from the Isle of Skye Brewery. Excellent cuisine is based on fresh local produce. An ideal base for the Whisky Trail and close to both championship golf courses, the hotel has a children's certificate.

NETHY BRIDGE

Heatherbrae Hotel

Dell Road (off B970)

5-11 (1am Fri); 12-1am Sat; 12-11 Sun

(01479) 821345

website: www.nethybridge.com/heatherbraehotel.htm

Cairngorm Ruthven Brew, Stag

Busy, welcoming pub, forming part of a small hotel that is popular with locals, birdwatchers, walkers, fishermen, golfers and skiers. All meals are served in the dining room adjoining the bar. Bunkhouse accommodation is available nearby.

ONICH

Nether Lochaber Hotel

By E terminal of Corran Ferry, 200 yds from A82

11-2.30; 5-11 (midnight Fri & Sat); 12.30-2.30, 6-11 Sun

(01855) 821235

Draught Bass

This delightful, little, cosy bar, tucked away at the rear of a family-run hotel, welcomes both locals and tourists. It stands beside the slipway for the Corran Ferry. Once a Temperance hotel, not allowed to serve alcohol, the bar was built on to the rear of the building and was only accessible from an outside door. Glencoe and the Ben Nevis mountain range are close by.

ROSEMARKIE

Plough Inn

High Street

11-11.30 (12.30am Fri); 11-2.30, 6-11.30 (12.30am Fri) winter; 12.30-11.30 Sun

(01381) 620164

Beer range varies

Beautiful old country pub, in a pretty seaside village on the old coaching route to the famous Duthas Stone in Tain. This gem is the tap for the Black Isle Brewery which supplies all the real ales. Unmissable, with its distinctive leaning gable, it has a cosy wood-lined bar with an ancient marriage stone lintel (dated 1691) over the fireplace. Two attractive gardens lead to a sandy beach, with signposted walks on the shore and through the local beauty spot, the Fairy Glen. The menu specialises in seafood and fresh local produce.

SCOUSBURGH

Spiggie Hotel

11-11 (midnight Wed-Sat); 12.30-11 Sun

(01950) 460409 website: www.spiggie.co.uk

Valhalla Simmer Dim; guest beers

Family-run hotel, with a children's certificate, situated above the Spiggie trout loch and convenient for exploring the archaeological sites of Jarlshof and Scatness. The traditional public bar features a stone and wood floor. The locally-sourced menu always includes a vegetarian option. Of the two ales on offer, in summer one is always from Valhalla; the other is usually from further afield. Cask cider is an occasional summer visitor.

SLIGACHAN

Sligachan Hotel

A850/A863 jct

9am-midnight; 9am-11 Sun

(01478) 650204

website: www.sligachan.demon.co.uk

Beer range varies

Situated next to the Cuillin Hills, this superb, family-run, 19th-century hotel lies in some of the most spectacular walking and climbing country in Britain. There is a fully-equipped campsite opposite, and children are welcome. Eight ales are available during the summer, with a reduced range in winter. Bar meals are excellent value. The hotel hosts an autumn real ale and music festival. Local CAMRA Country Pub of the Year 2001.

STRATHCARRON

Strathcarron Hotel

11-11 (including Sun)

(01520) 722227

Beer range varies

This traditional, small 100-year-old Highland hotel enjoys a spectacular situation at the head of Loch Carron. Right next door to a station on the Inverness-Kyle railway, it makes an ideal base for touring Wester Ross. On the road to Skye, Plockton and the famous Eilean Donan Castle, it is popular with visitors from Britain and abroad who enjoy Highland beers from Isle of Skye, Black Isle, Orkney and Cairngorm breweries. The food is home cooked; seafood is a speciality in summer.

STROMNESS

Ferry Inn

John Street (100 yds from ferry terminal)
9am-midnight (1am Thu-Sat); 11-midnight Sun
(01856) 850280 website: www.ferryinn.com
Orkney Dark Island H

Nearest pub to the ferry terminal for the thirsty traveller, the Ferry Inn is popular all year round. The divers who come to look at the remains of the German fleet at Scapa Flow swell the numbers and can provide a lively atmosphere. Originally a Temperance hotel, it is now endorsed by the Cyclist Tourist Club.

Stromness Hotel

15 Victoria Street (pierhead)
11-11 (1am Fri & Sat); 12-11 Sun
(01856) 850298 website: www.stromnesshotel.com
Orkney Red MacGregor, Dark Island H

The beer is served in the first-floor lounge that commands a fine view of Stromness harbour. If you tire of watching boats, there are beer, jazz and rock festivals, but even when empty this large bar has soul. In winter, free food and cheap beer are laid on to entice locals in. Once the season starts the atmosphere becomes very cosmopolitan, with visitors arriving from all over the world. Q

THURSO

Central Hotel

Traill Street
11-11.45 (1am Fri & Sat); 12.30-11.45 Sun
(01847) 893129
Beer range varies H

Town-centre hotel, two miles from Orkney ferry terminal at Scrabster, on the spectacular Pentland Firth coast. It attracts many families with children who enjoy the soft play area and bouncy castle, accessed from the large upstairs bar/restaurant. No children are admitted to the downstairs bar, which, with a large-screen TV, is popular with locals and frequented by Caithness rugby club. The food is mainly home made and served from 9am-8.30pm (takeaways available).

ULLAPOOL

Ferry Boat Inn

Shore Street
11 (12.30 Sun)-11
(01854) 612366 website: www.ferryboat-inn.com
Beer range varies H

This family-run, 18th-century inn, on the shore of Loch Broom, is a short stroll from the Western Isles ferry terminal. The small, comfortable bar, with a welcoming fire in winter, has an old-fashioned style; the atmosphere is friendly and informal. The bar and restaurant afford glorious views across the loch to the mountains of Wester Ross. Local fresh produce is served in the bar all year round and the restaurant is open from spring to late autumn. Local CAMRA Pub of the Year 2002.
Q

WATERNISH

Stein Inn

Stein (north of Dunvegan on B886, 4½ miles from Fairy Bridge
4-11 (midnight Fri); 12-midnight summer; 12.30-11 Sun
(01470) 592362 website: www.steininn.co.uk
Isle of Skye Red Cuillin; guest beers H

This traditional Highland hostelry, in a picturesque setting on the shores of Loch Bay, is the oldest inn on the Isle of Skye. The small bar has recently been extended and includes a central fireplace. Local seafood is served (Easter-Oct) in the bar and restaurant, both boasting fine views over the loch to Rubha Maol. The large garden is on the shore. Facilities for seafarers include council moorings, showers, food supplies (by arrangement), and message relay services.
Q P

WORMADALE

Inn on the Hill at Westings Hotel

On A971, 10 miles NW of Lerwick OS402464
12-2 (3 Sat), 5-11; 12-3, 5-11 Sun
(01595) 840242
website: www.westings.shetland.co.uk
Beer range varies H

Small hotel with tremendous sea views, situated near the summit of Wormadale Hill at the head of Weisdale Voe. One beer from Valhalla plus two guests are served in the Palm Shack, while the Library Bar is no-smoking. Evening food only from 7.15-8.15.
P

A Pint of Plain

When your health is bad and your heart feels strange,
And your face is pale and wan,
When doctors say that you need a change,
A PINT OF PLAIN IS YOUR ONLY MAN.

Flann O'Brien, *A Pint of Plain, from At Swim-Two-Birds* (1939).
Plain was a Dublin term for Porter.

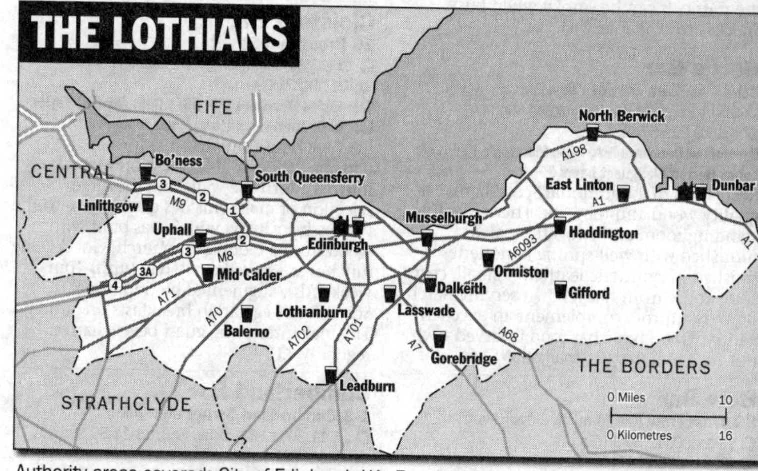

Authority areas covered: City of Edinburgh UA, East Lothian UA, Midlothian UA, West Lothian UA

BALERNO

Johnsburn House

64 Johnsburn Road (off A70, on NW side of village)
12-3 (not Mon), 6.30-midnight (1am Fri); 12-1am Sat; 12.30-midnight Sun
☎ (0131) 449 3847
Caledonian Deuchars IPA; guest beers H

Grade B listed baronial mansion dating from 1760, originally owned by Professor Adam Fergusson who reputedly brought together the two great men of Scottish literature, Robert Burns and Sir Walter Scott. The low-ceilinged, cosy bar has a convivial atmosphere with varied memorabilia and exposed beams. A passageway leads to a dining room, beyond which a corridor leads to further rooms for diners. It enjoys a good reputation for award-winning meals. Children's certificate. Q P

BO'NESS

Anchor Tavern

54 North Street (opp. bus station)
11 (12.30 Sun)-11 (11.30 Fri & Sat)
☎ (01506) 824717
website: www.bo-ness.org.uk/html/history/anchor
Caledonian Deuchars IPA; Orkney Dark Island H

Built in 1891 and in its early days a popular haunt for sailors of all nationalities, it remains a popular local watering-hole, offering a good selection of ales, lagers and whisky. It bustles with regular activity every time there is a quiz night, major football or rugby match, and more frequently because of customer parties and social events. It is also a gathering point for local business people and visiting steam enthusiasts.

DALKEITH

Black Bull

1 Lothian Street (behind shopping precinct)
11-11.30 (midnight Thu-Sat); 12.30-11.45 Sun
☎ (0131) 663 2095
Caledonian Deuchars IPA; guest beer H

Perfect example of a 'Gothenburg', with a busy, vibrant public bar, boasting fine arched windows, cornice work and a well-crafted gantry. The large TV makes it a popular venue for sporting events. The fire is not real; so be warned! The more modern lounge (which holds a children's certificate) is popular at lunchtimes and can be a welcome refuge from the bar at busy times. Disabled access is via the side door. The pool room leads off the bar. Inexpensive lunches are served.

EAST LINTON

Bridgend Hotel

3 Bridge End (off A1)
12-2, 7-11 (1am Thu); 12-1am Fri & Sat; 12-midnight Sun
☎ (01620) 860202
website: www.scoot.co.uk/bridgend_hotel/
Hadrian & Border Rampart; guest beer H

Village pub with a public bar and a comfortable lounge. Ownership connections to the Hadrian & Border Brewery mean their beers are usually stocked. The stained glass windows and rooftop statue hint that the pub was once the Red Lion. The bar has a light wood counter, musical instruments around the walls and a pool table. The lounge-cum-dining room (eve meals Fri-Sun) has a display of poaching pictures and is decorated in a plaid decor.

EDINBURGH

Bennets Bar ☆

1 Maxwell Street, Morningside
11-midnight; closed Sun
☎ (0131) 447 1903
Belhaven 70/-, 80/-; guest beers A

Couthy back-street boozer in the douce suburb of Morningside, except that it is only yards from one of the city's busiest road junctions. The walls are adorned with old photographs of Edinburgh, including one of the eponymous family's first pub, now demolished, in Market Street. During the summer you can sit outside and watch

INDEPENDENT BREWERIES

Belhaven Dunbar
Caledonian Edinburgh
Fisherrow Edinburgh

the traffic. It can be smoky when busy. Snacks are available. ❀

Bert's Bar

29-31 William Street (West End)
11-11 (midnight Thu-Sat); closed Sun
☎ (0131) 225 5748
Caledonian Deuchars IPA, 80/-; Marston's Pedigree; Tetley Burton Ale; guest beers H

Recreation of a traditional Scots' bar with quality wood and tilework. There is ample standing room and two sitting areas, furnished with well-sprung banquettes finished in synthetic leather. A small, cosy snug at the front has its own serving hatch. Brewery mirrors complement an excellent gantry. Good basic bar food is served – why not try a pie? ◐≡ (Haymarket) ♣

Bow Bar

80 West Bow (Old Town, off Grassmarket)
12-11.30; 12.30-11 Sun
☎ (0131) 226 7667
Belhaven 80/-; Caledonian Deuchars IPA; Taylor Landlord; guest beers A

One-roomed bar in the heart of the Old Town, close to the temporary home of the Scottish parliament, dedicated to traditional Scottish air pressure dispense. Rare, old brewery mirrors, advertising ephemera and a map showing the original 33 Scottish counties adorn the walls. The five interesting guest beers are complemented by a superb range of malts. Those of a nervous disposition should not look at the pub sign. Q≡ (Waverley)

Cask & Barrel

115 Broughton Street (eastern edge of New Town)
11-12.30am (1am Thu-Sat); 12.30-12.30am Sun
☎ (0131) 556 3132
Draught Bass; Boddingtons Bitter; Caledonian Deuchars IPA, 80/-; Flowers IPA; guest beers H

Spacious and extremely busy ale house drawing a mainly local clientele of all ages, ranging from business people to football fans. The interior features an imposing horseshoe-shaped bar, bare floorboards, a splendid cornice and a collection of brewery mirrors. Old barrels act as tables for those who wish to stand, or cannot find a seat. Of the five guest beers available, one is always from the Hadrian & Border Brewery (sparklers removed on request). ❀◐♿

Cloisters Bar

26 Brougham Street
11 (12.30 Sun)-midnight (12.30am Fri & Sat)
☎ (0131) 221 9997
Caledonian Deuchars IPA, 80/-; Dent Aviator; Taylor Landlord; Thwaites Bitter; A **guest beers** H

Busy ale house situated in a former parsonage. Rare old Scottish brewery mirrors adorn the walls and the large selection of malt whiskies does justice to the impressive gantry, which was built with wood from a redundant church. Good value lunches are served every day (until 4pm weekends), augmented by traditional Scottish or vegetarian breakfasts on Sunday. The four interesting guest beers change regularly. Q◐

Cumberland Bar

1-3 Cumberland Street (New Town)
11-11.30 (12.30am Thu-Sat); 11-11.30 Sun
☎ (0131) 558 3134
Caledonian Deuchars IPA, 80/-; Taylor Landlord; H **guest beers** A

Elegant, functional, New Town pub with half wood panelling. Exquisite, large, ornate brewery mirrors on the walls hang beside framed, decorative and illustrative posters. The wood finish is enhanced by dark green leather seating. Some of the beers are dispensed by traditional Scottish tall fount and the three guests are usually from smaller breweries. Children are welcome in the back room during the day. The menu includes vegetarian choices. Q❀◐✔

Golden Rule

30 Yeaman Place
11-11.30 (midnight Fri); 12.30-11 Sun
☎ (0131) 229 3413
Caledonian Deuchars IPA, 80/-; Harviestoun Bitter & Twisted; Taylor Landlord; guest beers H

Split-level, local bar in a Victorian tenement tucked away just around the corner from the Fountain Park complex. A regular entry in this Guide for over 10 years, the three guest beers, usually from smaller breweries, generally include one at 4% ABV and one at 5%. The downstairs bar, Rule 2, caters for the trendier end of the market. Lunches are available Mon-Fri. The Union Canal, soon to be refurbished, runs close by.
◐≡ (Haymarket) ♣✔

INN BRIEF

DUNBAR

Volunteer Arms
17 Victoria Street
11-11 (1am Thu-Sat); 12.30-midnight Sun
(01368) 862278
Belhaven 80/-; guest beer (summer) H
Oak-beamed friendly, boisterous bar decorated with nautical items. An RNLI flag flies outside. Meals available April-Oct.

EDINBURGH

Blue Blazer
2 Spittal Street
11 (12.30 Sun)-11 (midnight Fri & Sat)
(0131) 229 5030
Caledonian Deuchars IPA; guest beers A
Two-roomed, bare-boarded bar with original Bernard's Brewery windows. Small, cosy and convivial, although smoky at times.

Spylaw Tavern
27 Spylaw Street, Colinton
11-11 (midnight Thu-Sat); 12.30-11 Sun
(0131) 229 5030
Caledonian Deuchars IPA, 80/-; guest beer H
Light wood gives the attractive bar an airy atmosphere. Good food (12-9) in the lounge and restaurant. Cask Mark accredited.

Stable Bar
Mortonhall Park, 30 Frogston Road East
11-midnight; 12.30-11 Sun
(0131) 664 0773
Belhaven Sandy Hunter's Ale; Caledonian Deuchars 80/-; Inveralmond Ossian's Ale H
Friendly bar in an old stable block approached through a cobbled courtyard. Popular for food, and with summer campers.

GOREBRIDGE

Stobbs Mill Inn
25 Powdermill Brae
11-3, 6-11 (11.30 Thu); 11-midnight Fri & Sat; 12.30-11.30 Sun
(01875) 820202
Beer range varies H
Friendly, functional local with a tiny snug. The lounge is open for food (Fri and Sat eve and Sun lunch).

LINLITHGOW

Black Bitch
14-16 West Port
11 (12.30 Sun)-midnight
(01506) 842147
Beer range varies H
Named after the town's crest, it is one of the oldest pubs in the town. Real ale in lounge but will be brought through to the bar.

Guildford Arms

1 West Register Street (behind Burger King at E end of Princes St)
⏲ 11 (12.30 Sun)-11 (midnight Fri & Sat)
☎ (0131) 556 4312
Belhaven 80/-; [H] **Caledonian Deuchars IPA, 80/-;** [P] **Harviestoun Bitter & Twisted; Orkney Dark Island; guest beers** [H]

Busy, but orderly, city-centre pub notable for its ornate plasterwork. The high ceiling, cornices and friezes are spectacular, as are the window arches and screens, an unusual wood-panelled gallery above the main bar is also noteworthy. There are areas for standing and others with comfortable seating. The extensive range of regularly changing guest beers usually includes beers from smaller breweries. Vegetarian options are included on a varied menu (no food Sun). ◖⇌(Waverley) ♣

Leslie's Bar ☆

45 Ratcliffe Terrace (Newington, 2 miles S of centre)
⏲ 11-11 (11.30 Thu; 12.30am Fri & Sat); 12.30-11.30 Sun
☎ (0131) 667 7205
Caledonian Deuchars IPA, 80/-; Taylor Landlord; guest beers [H]

Outstanding Victorian pub, retaining its fine ceiling, cornice, leaded glasswork and half wood panelling. The island bar has a spectacular snob screen which divides the pub. Small 'ticket window' hatches allow customers to order drinks. A plaque near the fire gives further details of this busy, vibrant, but orderly pub. The two guest beers are usually from smaller breweries. Trad jazz is usually played on Monday evening. ⛰Q⊡♣⊘

Malt & Hops

45 The Shore, Leith (waterfront)
⏲ 12 (12.30 Sun)-11 (midnight Wed-Thu; 1am Fri & Sat)
☎ (0131) 555 0083
website: www.spidacom.co.uk/EDG/malthops/
Marston's Pedigree; Tetley Bitter; guest beers [H]

One-roomed public bar dating from 1749, in the heart of 'new' Leith's riverside restaurant district. The superb collection of pump clips, many from now defunct breweries, indicates the ever-changing range of interesting guest beers served. The real fire is very welcoming in winter. Among the artefacts on view are an oil painting, showing Leith around 50 years ago, and the old wooden bus sign from outside. Weekday lunches include daily specials (no food at weekends). Children are welcome until 6pm. ⛰Q❀◖♣⬢

Oxford Bar ☆

8 Young Street (New Town, off Charlotte Sq)
⏲ 11-1am; 12.30-11 Sun
☎ (0131) 539 7119 website: www.oxfordbar.co.uk
Belhaven 80/-; Caledonian Deuchars IPA, 80/- [H]

Tiny, yet vibrant New Town drinking shop, retaining signs of its 19th-century parlour arrangement. Decorated with Burns memorabilia, this is where the 'Professor' holds court in Ian Rankin's novels. Over the years, this has been the haunt of many a famous and infamous character. Some nights you may rub shoulders with Rankin or other fellow authors. Alternatively visit the website and contribute to a story. Visit the Oxford Bar for a taste of New Town past. ♣

Starbank Inn

64 Laverockbank Road (foreshore, near Newhaven)
⏲ 11 (12.30 Sun)-11 (midnight Thu-Sat)
☎ (0131) 552 4141
Belhaven Sandy Hunter's Ale, 80/-, St Andrew's Ale; Caledonian Deuchars IPA; Taylor Landlord; guest beers [H]

Bright, airy, bare-boarded ale house, with an extended U-shaped layout and superb views across the Firth of Forth to Fife. The pub is proud that it does not sell any keg ales but you can try a pint of prawns with your beer! Three guest ales are usually available and the uncluttered walls sport several rare brewery mirrors. The restaurant is no-smoking; food is served until 9pm and children are welcome until 8.30pm. It hosts occasional jazz on Sunday. Q◖◗♣

Thomson's

182-184 Morrison Street
⏲ 12-11.30; closed Sun
☎ (0131) 228 5700
Caledonian Deuchars IPA, 80/-; Taylor Landlord; guest beers [A]

Award-winning refurbishment of a pub dedicated to traditional Scottish air pressure dispense and Glasgow's other architect, Alexander 'Greek' Thomson. The walls are decorated with rare mirrors from long-defunct Scottish breweries, at least one of which closed before 1920. Up to five guest beers, generally include one from either Bank Top or Oakham. Lunches are served Mon-Fri.
Q◖⇌(Haymarket)

Winston's

20 Kirk Loan, Corstorphine (off St John's Road, A8)
⏲ 11-11.30 (midnight Thu-Sat); 12.30-11 Sun
☎ (0131) 539 7077
Caledonian Deuchars IPA; Tetley Burton Ale; guest beer [H]

Run by the same licensee for many years, this comfortable lounge bar is situated in Corstorphine, a busy area of west Edinburgh about a mile from Murrayfield stadium and close to the zoo. The small, modern building houses a warm, active community pub. The one room is used by old and young alike, with children welcome until 3pm. The decor features golfing and rugby themes. Try the wonderful home-made pies (no food Sun). ◖⊘

GIFFORD

Goblin Ha' Hotel

Main Street
⏲ 11-2.30, 4.30-11; 11-midnight Fri & Sat; 11-11 Sun
☎ (01620) 810244 website: www.goblin-ha-hotel.co.uk
Caledonian Deuchars IPA; Hop Back Summer Lightning; Taylor Landlord; guest beer [H]

Large hotel in a picturesque village. The public bar is a mixture of church pew and leatherette-covered banquettes. The ceiling is low and of painted wood planking, while the gantry is a mix of glass and wood. The pool room is to the side of the bar. At the front is a comfortable lounge, mainly laid out for eating, and also a conservatory and dining room. The garden is popular with families in summer (children's certificate held). ⛫❀⇌◑⊟⅄♣

HADDINGTON

Tyneside Tavern

10 Poldrate (A6137, S of centre)
11-11 (midnight Thu; 12.45am Fri & Sat); 12.30-midnight Sun
☎ (01620) 822221 website: www.tynesidetavern.co.uk
Courage Directors; guest beers Ⓗ
Cosy, convivial local; the bar is long and narrow, with a fine stone fireplace by the door. Rustic woodwork fronts the bar counter, which boasts a mahogany top and a gantry behind. The comfortable lounge has violet walls and off-pink cloth cover banquettes; the building dates from 1819, although the interior looks more 1970s. It holds a children's certificate (children welcome until 8pm when evening meals finish). ⛫❀◑⊟♣

LASSWADE

Laird & Dog Hotel

5 High Street (A768, near river bridge)
11 (12.30 Sun)-11.30 (11.45 Thu; 12.30am Fri & Sat)
☎ (0131) 663 9219
Beer range varies Ⓗ
Comfortable village local catering for all tastes, from music-loving pool players to those who enjoy a quiet drink or meal. The pub reflects local life in its pictures and horse brasses. The food (served all day) is good and plentiful, with an extensive conservatory menu, daily specials and cheaper bar options satisfying most palates. An unusual bottle-shaped well, a real fire surrounded by armchairs and two real ales, usually from smaller breweries, are added attractions. ⛫❀⇌◑♿♣P

LEADBURN

Leadburn Inn

At A701/A703/A6094 jct
11-11 (11.45 Fri & Sat; midnight summer); 12-11 (midnight summer) Sun
☎ (01968) 672952
Beer range varies Ⓗ
Established in 1777, this large, food-oriented hostelry, with a children's certificate, has a converted railway coach which is used for parties. The functional public bar has a pot-bellied stove and a picture window looking out to the Pentland Hills. A conservatory, inhabited by a mighty grapevine, links the bar to the plush lounge. The beer range usually includes products from smaller Scottish breweries. Note the bar serves different beers to the two in the lounge.
⛫Q❀⇌◑⊟♣P⅟

LINLITHGOW ❄

Four Marys

65-67 High Street
12 (12.30 Sun)-11; 11-11.45 Thu-Sat
☎ (01506) 842171
Belhaven 70/-, 80/-, St Andrew's Ale; Caledonian Deuchars IPA; guest beers Ⓗ
Named after the four ladies-in-waiting of Mary, Queen of Scots who was born in the nearby Linlithgow Palace, it was built around 1500 as a dwelling. The pub has seen several uses through the years, such as a chemist's shop run by the Waldie family whose most famous member, David, established the anaesthetic properties of chloroform in 1847. It opened as a pub in 1975 and hosts beer festivals in May and October when 18 handpumps are used.
◑≹

Platform 3

1a High Street
11 (12.30 Sun)-midnight
☎ (01506) 847405
Caledonian Deuchars IPA; guest beers Ⓗ
Small, friendly pub on the railway station approach, originally the public bar of the hotel next door. It was purchased and renovated in 1998 as a pub in its own right and stages occasional live music. Note the interesting memorabilia displayed around the walls. The two guest beers usually come from the Caledonian range.
≹

LOTHIANBURN

Steading

118-120 Biggar Road (A702, near Hillend ski centre)
10-midnight; 12.30-11 Sun
☎ (0131) 445 1128
Belhaven 80/-; Caledonian Deuchars IPA; Orkney Dark Island; Taylor Landlord; guest beer (summer) Ⓗ
Old stone cottages converted into an attractive bar and restaurant, with large conservatory extensions. The outside drinking area affords good views of the Pentland Hills. Although it is a popular eating establishment, there is a sizeable bar area where only snacks are served. This has a real fire and a large no-smoking area. A handy place for refreshment after a walk on the hills or visit to the dry ski slope; children are welcome.
⛫❀◑P⅟

INN BRIEF

MID CALDER

Torphichen Arms
36 Bank Street
11-11 (midnight Thu-Sat); 12.30-midnight Sun
(01506) 880020
Caledonian Deuchars IPA, 80/-; Tetley Burton Ale; guest beers Ⓗ
Village local where several rooms, with original cornices, now form one L-shaped bar with public and lounge areas. Eve meals Sat and Sun.

ORMISTON

Hopetoun Arms Hotel
Main Street
11 (12.30 Sun)-11 (1am Fri & Sat)
(01875) 610298
Caledonian Deuchars IPA; guest beer Ⓗ
Village local dating from 1737; a long narrow public bar with lots of pictures and a small lounge. Children welcome.

❄ symbol next to a main entry place name indicates there are Inn Brief entries as well.

MUSSELBURGH

Levenhall Arms

10 Ravensheugh Road (B1348, near racecourse roundabout)

✪ 12 (1 winter)-11 (midnight Thu; 1am Fri & Sat); 12.30 (1 winter)- midnight Sun

☎ (0131) 665 3220

Caledonian Deuchars IPA; Tetley Burton Ale; guest beer Ⓟ

Busy pub, popular with locals, race-goers and visitors to the nearby golf course. This three-roomed hostelry dates from 1830 and was once a stopping point for the Edinburgh – London stagecoach. The public bar is half timber-panelled and carpeted, with a smaller area housing a dartboard leading off. The lounge area, with vinyl banquettes and tables, is used as a restaurant during the day. Food is served all day until 8.30 when children are also expected to leave.
Q ◐ ⊟ ⅄ ⇌ (Wallyford) ♣ P ⊁

Volunteer Arms (Staggs)

81 North High Street (behind Brunton Hall)

✪ 12-11 (11.30 Thu); 11-midnight Fri & Sat; closed Sun

☎ (0131) 665 9654

Caledonian Deuchars IPA, 80/-; guest beer Ⓗ

Three-roomed pub, run by the same family since 1858. The main bar is traditional with a tiled floor, dark wood panelling, wood and glass screens and mirrors from defunct local breweries. A superb gantry is topped with old casks. In the snug is a nascent history collection about local breweries. The rear lounge opens at the weekend. The single guest beer changes very regularly – up to four times on a Saturday. This was national CAMRA Pub of the Year in 1998.
❀ ⊟ ♣ ✔

NORTH BERWICK

Nether Abbey Hotel

20 Dirleton Avenue (A198, 1/2 mile W of centre)

✪ 11 (12 Sun)-11 (midnight Thu; 1am Fri & Sat)

☎ (01620) 892802 website: www.netherabbey.co.uk

Caledonian Deuchars IPA; guest beers Ⓟ

Sitting on the Scottish (eastern) Riviera, this comfortable, family-run hotel in a Victorian villa has a children's certificate. It has an L-shaped carpeted bar and a bistro with bare floorboards; dark wood is used in the decor. In good weather the bar expands into a sizeable outdoor area, with a retractable canvas roof. An annual real ale festival is held in February. It is handy for some legendary golf courses. Meals are served all day in summer. ♨ ❀ ⛟ ◐ ⅄ ⇌ ♣ P

Ship

7 Quality Street

✪ 11 (12 Sun)-11 (midnight Thu; 1am Fri & Sat)

☎ (01620) 890676

Caledonian Deuchars IPA; Taylor Landlord; guest beer (summer) Ⓟ

Retro-themed, open-plan bar, split into two areas by a glass partition. Recently refurbished, pine boards surround a mahogany counter which is backed by a dark stained gantry. Real ale is dispensed from founts, which look similar to those dispensing the keg beers. Nautically-themed throughout, maritime tableaux are dotted on shelves around the bar. Popular for food which is served all day, until 9pm; a children's certificate applies until 8pm. Smoking restrictions are lifted in the evening. ❀ ◐ ⅄ ⇌ ♣

SOUTH QUEENSFERRY

Ferry Tap

36 High Street

✪ 11.30 (12.30 Sun)-11.30 (midnight Thu; 12.30am Fri & Sat)

☎ (0131) 331 2000

Caledonian Deuchars IPA, 80/-; Orkney Dark Island; guest beers Ⓗ

Ground-floor bar in a 328-year-old building in the historic part of a village, dominated by bridges. The comfortable, one-roomed L-shaped bar boasts an unusual barrel-vaulted ceiling. Dark wood gives an intimate feel and numerous artefacts, many from bygone breweries, add interest. A varied selection of meals is served at lunchtime; evening meals are available on Saturday, and Wednesday and Friday in winter. ◐ ⇌ (Dalmeny) ♣ ✔

UPHALL

Oatridge Hotel

2-4 East Main Street (at A899/B8046 jct)

✪ 11 (12.30 Sun)-midnight

☎ (01506) 856465

Caledonian Deuchars IPA; guest beers Ⓗ

Originally a 19th-century coach house, the hotel still caters for the modern-day traveller as well as locals. Run by the same family for 29 years, the public bar, which serves the ale, has the feel of a village working man's pub. The large collection of ceramic vessels behind the bar once held refreshing liquids. Up to four beers regularly include Caledonian, Houston and Arran ales. Pool can be played and the bar is popular for TV sports. Evening meals are served Friday and Saturday. ❀ ⛟ ◐ ⊟ ♣ P

Beautiful Ale

And so, you see, 'twas beautiful ale, and I wished to value his kindness...and not be so ill-mannered as to drink only a thimbleful, which would have been insulting the man's generosity. And so I used to eat a lot of salt fish afore going, and then by the time I got there I were as dry as a lime-basket so thoroughly dry that ale would slip-ah, 'twould slip down sweet! Happy times! Heavenly times! Such lovely drunks as I used to have at that house!

Thomas Hardy, Far From the Madding Crow*d,* 1874.

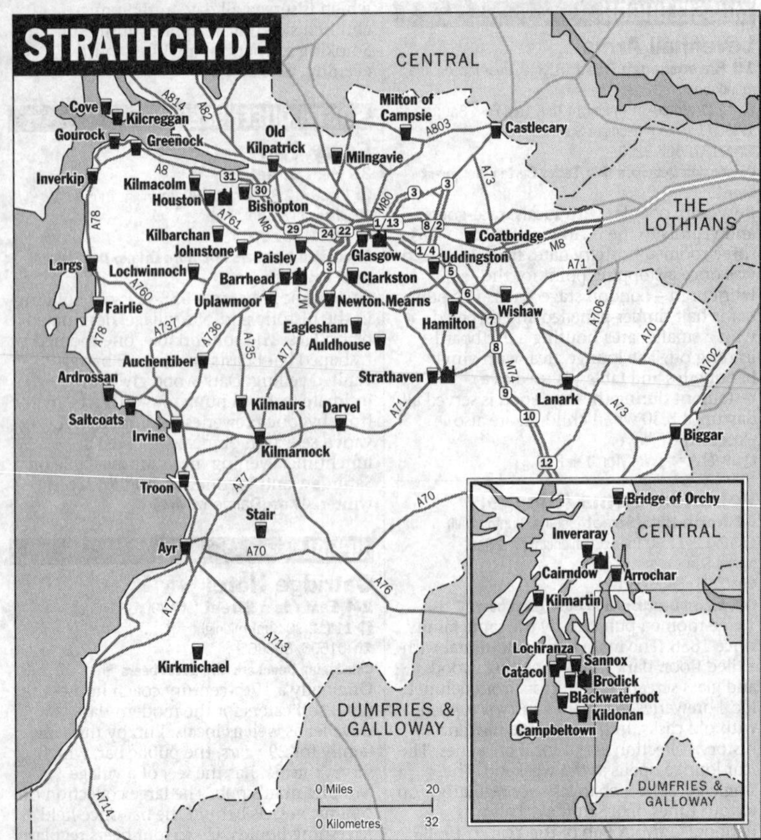

Strathclyde comprises Argyllshire, Ayrshire and Arran, Dumbartonshire, Glasgow, Lanarkshire and Renfrewshire

Argyllshire

ARROCHAR

Village Inn

On A814, 1/2 mile S of A82/A86 jct
11-midnight (1am Fri & Sat); 12-midnight Sun
☎ (01301) 702279 website: www.maclay.com
Orkney Dark Island; guest beers

Warm, friendly atmosphere in an idyllic inn, built in 1827 as the local manse. It is situated on the east shore of Loch Long, offering breathtaking views over the Arrochar Alps and the famous Cobbler. Bare floorboards and wood furniture create a rustic feel and the fireplaces are constructed with stone from Greenock esplanade and a thick section of local oak forms the mantelpiece. An ideal base for hillwalkers, it is a stop-off point on the West Highland circuit.

BRIDGE OF ORCHY

Bridge of Orchy Hotel

11-11 (midnight Fri & Sat); 12-11 Sun
☎ (01838) 400208
website: www.scottish-selection.co.uk
Caledonian Deuchars IPA, 80/-, Golden Promise; guest beers

A staging post on the road to Skye and the West Highland Way, the original hotel burnt down in 1957, was rebuilt soon after and then renovated in 1997. The Caley bar is comfortably furnished with seating that offers views across the glen to the mountains on either side. With its modern bunkhouse it provides a centre for outdoor activities, including trout and salmon fishing, splash white water rafting, walking and climbing.

CAMPBELTOWN

Commercial Inn

Cross Street
11 (12.30 Sun)-1am
☎ (01586) 553703
Caledonian Deuchars IPA; guest beer (summer)

Old coaching inn, dating back to 1774, at the end of a row of whitewashed houses in a small square towards the centre of a town once famous for its distilleries. Its busy, friendly public bar has been recently modernised with a games area and seating to one side. The walls are hung with old brewery mirrors and prints of the town in past years. The more intimate lounge is soft furnished with subdued lighting.

COVE

Knockderry Hotel

204 Shore Road (B833)
11.30-midnight; 12.30-11 Sun
☎ (01436) 842283

website: www.knockderryhotel.co.uk
Beer range varies Ⓗ
Circa 1851, this former Glasgow merchant's house, boasts one of the best local examples of works by William Leiper, Daniel Cottier and Thomas Jekyll. A stunning building, with a recurring theme of the four seasons in both stained glass and wood, it is situated in the picturesque Rosneath peninsula, offering superb views over Loch Long towards Benmore and Strone. It has a safe anchorage and large garden. Beers from Belhaven's guest list are stocked at this local CAMRA Pub of the Year 2001.
⛬❀⇔◑ ●P

INVERARAY

George Hotel
Main Street East
⏲ 11 (12 Sun)-12.30am
☎ (01499) 302111 website: www.thegeorgehotel.co.uk
Beer range varies Ⓗ
Long-established hotel, built 1775, at the heart of this historic conservation town and next to the visitor attraction, the old jail. The main bar has been well restored, keeping the original flagstone floors, stone walls and welcoming log and peat fires. The public bar, to one side, has restricted opening hours. A regular outlet for the nearby Fyne Ales micro-brewery, it offers two guest beers in summer, one in winter. Excellent meals are based on local produce.
⛬❀⇔◑ ⊟♿⛺P

KILCREGGAN

Kilcreggan Hotel
Argyll Road
⏲ 12-midnight (1am Fri & Sat); 12.30-midnight Sun
☎ (01436) 842243
Theakston Best Bitter; guest beers Ⓗ
Stone Victorian mansion, in the centre of the village at the southern tip of the rural Rosneath peninsula, affording a stunning view over the Clyde estuary to Arran. Built by a Glasgow stockbroker, it contains fine wood panelling, with stained glass windows, ornate bargeboards and balconies, and features a curious gabled and battlemented tower. Close to the pier, with a regular passenger-only ferry to Gourock, an hourly bus service runs to Helensburgh and the paddle-steamer, 'Waverley' calls on Fridays in summer.
⛬❀⇔◑ ⊟P

KILMARTIN

Kilmartin Hotel
⏲ 11 (12 Sun)-1am
☎ (01546) 510250
Caledonian 80/-; guest beer (occasional) Ⓗ
Picturesque Kilmartin Glen is one of the most important prehistoric sites in Scotland; the first burial cairns pre-date the pyramids, and, together with standing stones and early Christian grave slabs, form part of the ritual landscape of the area. The whitewashed hotel has a cosy public bar with cushioned benches and a stone wall with a gantry backed by brewery mirrors. A games room is at the back with dining rooms leading off. Guest beers are usually available in summer.
Q❀⇔◑ ⊟⛺P⚟

Ayrshire and Arran

ARDROSSAN

Lauriston Hotel
15 South Crescent Road (A738, seafront)
⏲ 11-11 (midnight summer Sats; 1am Fri); 11-11 Sun
☎ (01294) 463771 website: www.lauristonhotel.co.uk
Arran Ale, Dark, Blonde Ⓗ
Free-standing, red sandstone building, with a large conservatory at the front, which has stunning sea views. The front door leads to an extensive restaurant area, with a lounge for drinkers. The public bar has its own side entrance, with a different menu and a large-screen TV for sporting events. Beers vary between the bar, lounge and restaurant, but you can request beer from another bar; lounge beer prices are above average.
Q❀⇔◑ ⊟♿⇌(South Beach) P

AUCHENTIBER

Blair Country Restaurant
A736/B788 jct
⏲ 11-3, 5-11; 11-11 Sat & Sun
☎ (01294) 850237
Beer range varies Ⓗ
Country inn with few houses nearby so it concentrates on food, with only limited space for drinkers during main mealtimes. Its two rooms are traditionally decorated, one is no-smoking. Arran Dark is on tap frequently, with other wide-ranging guests. Well-cooked food makes it well worth the journey to visit this attractive hostelry.
Q❀◑P⚟

AYR

Chestnuts Hotel
52 Racecourse Road (A719, 1 mile S of centre)
⏲ 11 (12.30 Sun)-midnight
☎ (01292) 264393
website: www.chestnuts.hypermart.net
Beer range varies Ⓗ
The comfortable, wood-panelled lounge bar of this family-run hotel features a large collection of water jugs and golfing prints. The three real ales tend to be from the larger regionals, but beers from the local Arran and Houston breweries are sometimes available. High quality meals are served in the bar area and restaurant. The spacious garden boasts an excellent children's play area. ⛬❀⇔◑P

Geordie's Byre
103 Main Street (over river, towards Prestwick)
⏲ 11 (12.30 Sun)-11 (midnight Thu-Sat)
☎ (01292) 264925
Caledonian Deuchars IPA; guest beers Ⓗ
The landlord and landlady have been hosts of this popular pub since 1976. The rather ordinary exterior hides an Aladdin's cave of memorabilia, especially in the lounge (open

INDEPENDENT BREWERIES

Arran Brodick
Clockwork Glasgow
Fyne Cairndow
Heather Strathaven
Houston Houston
Kelburn Barrhead

Thu-Sat eve). Up to four guest ales come from far and wide, with over 300 featured in a typical year. To the landlord, spirits are a hobby as well as a profession, and well over 100 malt whiskies and 28 rums are on offer – ask for the menu.
⊟⇌(Newton-on-Ayr)

Market Inn
2 Castlehill Road
⊙ 11-12.30am; 12.30-midnight Sun
☎ (01292) 280391
Draught Bass; guest beer (occasional) Ⓗ
Once an integral part of the cattle market, this prominent, red sandstone building stands opposite the rear exit from the station. Despite refurbishment, the listed horseshoe bar and gantry have been retained, along with the original tiled floor, fireplaces and stained glass windows. The guest beer is available only rarely and is usually a seasonal ale. Meals are served in the upstairs lounge. Adequate parking can be found nearby. ◐⊟⇌

Old Racecourse Hotel
2 Victoria Park (A719, 1 mile S of centre)
⊙ 11 (12.30 Sun)-midnight (12.30am Fri & Sat)
☎ (01292) 262873
Tetley Bitter; guest beers Ⓗ
The large, comfortable lounge bar features an unusual pot still-shaped fireplace as a centrepiece. The three guest ales tend to be from the larger regionals, but the local Arran and Houston breweries are sometimes represented. High quality meals are served in the bar area or in the more formal setting of the adjacent restaurant. A pool/TV room is an added attraction. ♔Q❀⛟◐◑♿P

West Kirk
58A Sandgate
⊙ 11 (12.30 Sun)-11 (12.30am Thu-Sat)
☎ (01292) 880416
Caledonian 80/; Courage Directors; Theakston Best Bitter; guest beers Ⓗ
This Wetherspoon's conversion of a former church has retained the impressive pulpit and other architectural features. Up to four guest ales, often from Scottish breweries, are on offer. All real ales are usually offered at a promotional price. Snacks and meals are available all day, and children are welcome until 7pm. Q❀◐◑♿⇌⊁●

BLACKWATERFOOT

Blackwaterfoot Lodge
⊙ 12-3, 6.30-11; 12-11.30 Sat April-Oct; winter weekend eves only; 12-3, 6-10 Sun
☎ (01770) 860202
website: www.blackwaterfoot-lodge.co.uk
Arran Ale, Blonde Ⓗ
Small hotel near the tiny harbour and shore of this western Arran village, benefiting from stunning views across to Campbeltown Loch, Kintyre and, on clear days, Northern Ireland. Once a Temperance hotel, it now features local ales to complement the local produce on the small, but ever-changing menu. Snacks and the delicious home-cooked meals can be taken in the Mariner's bar, the conservatory dining room or the garden. Local amenities include a golf course and an hotel swimming pool, open to the public.
Q❀⛟◐◑

BRODICK

Brodick Bar
Alma Road (off Shore Rd)
⊙ 11-midnight; 12.30-midnight (summer only) Sun
☎ (01770) 302169
Arran Ale; guest beer Ⓟ
This long, white building next to the post office has two bars: the main bar has a light, airy and contemporary ambience, while the other is more traditional and food-oriented. The extensive menu is provided on blackboards in both bars. The real ale founts are unmarked, so ask what is on. This is the only real ale available in Brodick during the day on winter weekdays. ♔Q◐◑⊟

Duncan's Bar
Kingsley Hotel, Shore Road
⊙ 11-midnight (including Sun) closed winter
☎ (01770) 302531
Arran Ale, Blonde; Ⓗ **guest beer** Ⓟ
This large, comfortable bar at the side of one of the main seafront hotels has been owned and run by the Duncan family for 50 years. Offering the nearest real ale to the ferry terminal, it attracts a wide variety of locals and visitors. It is also popular for meals, and hosts regular music sessions in summer, particularly during the Arran folk festival (June). The view across the bay to Goat Fell from the front garden is spectacular. ♔Q❀⛟◐◑♿P

Ormidale Hotel
Knowe Road (off A841, W end of village)
⊙ 12-2.30 (not winter); 4.30-midnight; 12-midnight Sat & Sun
☎ (01770) 302293 website: www.ormidale-hotel.co.uk
Arran Ale, Blonde Ⓐ
This fine sandstone building, overlooking the sports field, has a small, friendly bar plus a large conservatory which is a real suntrap. The original tall founts on the boat-shaped bar serve two beers from the nearby brewery. Originally a Victorian summerhouse for the painter Herring, it was converted into an hotel in 1935 by the present owner's grandparents. It has never stopped selling real ale. It hosts discos and folk music in the conservatory (weekends), and quizzes (Tue and Thu eves).
♔Q❀⛟◐◑♣P

CATACOL

Catacol Bay Hotel
⊙ 11-1am (midnight Sun)
☎ (01770) 830231 website: www.catacol.co.uk
Arran Blonde; Draught Bass Ⓗ
This free-standing, white building nestles among the hills opposite the shore, with grand views across the Kilbrannan Sound towards Kintyre. It is adjacent to the Twelve Apostles, a listed terrace of former estate houses. Originally a manse, it has been run by the present owner for 24 years, and is ideally situated for walking and climbing. There is an abundance of wildlife – glimpses of red deer and golden eagles are not unusual.
♔♉❀⛟◐◑⊟♣P

DARVEL

Loudounhill Inn
3 miles E of Darvel on A71

12-2.30 (not Wed), 5-11 (not Tue); 12-midnight Sat; 12.30-2.30, 4.30-11 Sun
(01560) 320275
Beer range varies H
This family-owned coaching inn is situated in open country, near Loudoun Hill, a prominent volcanic feature and the site of an 11th-century battle. It has a cosy bar with an open fire, and a larger lounge/restaurant with a conservatory opening on to the garden. It is a good place to break a journey between the M74 and Ayrshire.

FAIRLIE

Mudhook
46 Bay Street (A78, 3 miles S of Largs)
11.30-11 (1am Fri & Sat); 11.30-11 Sun
(01475) 568432
Draught Bass; guest beers H
This friendly village pub enjoys a lovely position, overlooking the Isles of Cumbrae and Arran. It has two bars, plus a restaurant with a conservatory. Bar meals are available and the restaurant offers an extensive menu. There is also a garden and a large car park. At least one guest beer is always on tap. P

IRVINE

Marina Inn
110 Harbour Street
11.45-3, 5.45-midnight (11.45-midnight summer); 11.45-1am Fri & Sat; 12.30-midnight Sun
(01294) 274079
Belhaven 80/- H
This attractive harbourside lounge bar is located at the heart of Irvine's main tourist area, close to the Magnum Leisure Centre, the Scottish Maritime Museum, the Big Idea Inventor Centre and the beach park. It is very popular for food at lunchtime and early evening. It hosts regular folk jam sessions (Tue eve), and sometimes live music on Friday. The sheltered garden is a popular suntrap in summer.

KILDONAN

Breadalbane Hotel
On loop road through Kildonan
11-midnight (1am Thu-Sat); 11-midnight Sun
(01770) 820284
Arran Ale; guest beer H
This white-painted hotel sits just behind the shore in a scattered village at the southern end of the island. It enjoys extensive views, especially from the front sun lounge. The main bar has a large stone fireplace, a corner bar and a pool table. Ales are always from Scottish breweries and food is available all day. The hotel is close to beaches renowned for seal spotting. It closes for two weeks in mid-January. Q P

KILMARNOCK

Wheatsheaf
Unit 5, Portland Gate
11 (12.30 Sun)-midnight (1am Thu-Sat)
(01563) 572483
Courage Directors; Theakston Best Bitter; guest beers H
Unusually for a Wetherspoon's pub this is mostly a new building, although the shell of the original Wheatsheaf Inn can be seen at the rear. The interior is modern and open plan, displaying Robert Burns connections and local history around the walls. Children are allowed in the rear area until 6pm. It gets busy Thu-Sat eves. Close to both rail and bus stations, it lies north of the main shopping street. Q

KILMAURS

Weston Tavern
27 Main Street (A735, at the cross)
11 (12.30 Sun)-midnight
(01563) 538805
Beer range varies H
This historic pub has had a varied history, having been a school, a manse and a blacksmith's (part of the latter can still be seen at the rear). The public bar has craggy stonework and an original tiled floor, which is a listed feature. There is usually beer from the Houston Brewery. Outside the pub is the landmark 'jougs' where criminals used to be shackled and, sometimes, hanged. The rear lounge is used by various clubs.

KIRKMICHAEL

Kirkmichael Arms
3 Straiton Road (B7045, 3 miles E of Maybole)
11-2.30, 5-midnight (11-midnight summer); 12.30-midnight Sun
(01655) 750375
Beer range varies H
Well-managed country pub in a rural, south Ayrshire village, renowned for its annual international guitar festival (May). It is close to Galloway Forest Park and the coast. Excellent, well-priced, home-cooked meals are served in the bar, lounge or intimate dining room (bookable for private parties). The cosy public bar, with an exceptional mirror and a fine range of malt whiskies, is warmed by a log fire, and has a pool room. The guest beer changes regularly and tends to be higher gravity. Q

LARGS

Clachan
14 Bath Street (B7025)
11 (12.30 Sun)-midnight (1am Thu-Sat)
(01475) 672224
Beer range varies H
Single-bar, town-centre pub, normally offering Belhaven ales, alongside a good selection of whiskies. It hosts live music (Fri eve) and a quiz (Mon eve). The back door leads to the seafront opposite the pier, from where the Cumbrae ferry leaves and the paddle-steamer, 'Waverley' calls in summer. Largs is one of the main 'Costa Clyde' resorts and boasts two good golf courses and the Vikingar Centre.

LOCHRANZA

Lochranza Hotel
11 (5 winter)-1am; 11.30-1am Sun
(01770) 830223 website: www.lochranza.co.uk
Arran Dark; guest beer H
This traditional hotel is located in a very tranquil village, with spectacular views to Lochranza Castle and across the sea loch. The bar, comprising two interconnecting rooms, stocks over 100 malt whiskies. The

front of the hotel has a large, grassed area with tables, an ideal place to watch the varied local wildlife. There are good walks in the area, and the hotel is handy for the summer car ferry to Kintyre.

SALTCOATS

Salt Cot
7 Hamilton Street
11 (12.30 Sun)-midnight (1am Thu-Sat)
(01294) 465924
Beer range varies H

This is a good conversion of a former cinema, decorated with photos of its heyday, and of old Saltcoats. Children are allowed in one area, and there is a family menu. Unusually for Wetherspoon's there are no regular beers, but Theakston Old Peculier and Greene King Old Speckled Hen are frequently on tap. The pub's name comes from the original cottages at the salt pans. Q

SANNOX

Ingledene Hotel
12-midnight (reduced hours in winter); 12-midnight Sun
(01770) 810225 website: www.arran.co.uk/sannox
Arran Ale; P **guest beers** H

This detached hotel sits opposite the shore in a small village, halfway between the two Arran ferries. There are two bars, both serving an exciting range of local produce. The front sun lounge enjoys great views across the Clyde to Bute and the mainland. The guest beer rotates between Fuller's (London Pride, ESB) and Taylor's (Best Bitter, Landlord). There are spectacular views of the mountains nearby, and Sannox is at the start of a popular walk through Glen Sannox and Glen Rosa to Brodick.
Q P

STAIR

Stair Inn
(B730, 7 miles E of Ayr, 4 miles W of Mauchline)
12-3, 5-11; 12-1am Sat; 12-11 Sun
(01292) 591650 website: www.stairinn.co.uk
Beer range varies H

Family-run inn, nestling at the foot of a glen on the banks of the River Ayr. The bar, with an open log fire, is complemented by a snug. Built around 1700, it serves a district rather than a village, and is close to the historic Stair Bridge (single track on a tight corner – take care crossing). The area has many connections with Robert Burns, and is well located for walks, golf and fishing. Houston beers are regulars, and Arran beers are sometimes available. Q P

TROON

Ardneil Hotel
51 St Meddans Street
11 (12 Sun)-midnight
(01292) 311611
Draught Bass; guest beers H

Popular hotel, close to the station and in an ideal spot for all local amenities. The bar attracts all generations, locals and tourists alike. There are two restaurant areas, and a cocktail bar; the main bar includes a lower-level pool and darts area. The guest ales are usually from the Arran, Houston and Caledonian breweries. It is very popular with golfers as all the local courses are within easy reach.
P

Dan McKay's Ale House
69 Portland Street (A759)
11-12.30am; 12.30-midnight Sun
(01292) 311079
Beer range varies H

Friendly, one-roomed, town-centre lounge bar. One ale is usually from the Caledonian range; the other guests vary widely, with usually four ales in summer and three in winter. They tend to be served colder than the norm and can be pricey for the area. The rear garden is a suntrap. The pub hosts occasional live music and mini-beer festivals. A good selection of foreign bottled beers is stocked.

Piersland House Hotel
15 Craigend Road (B749, S of centre)
11-midnight (including Sun)
(01292) 314747 website: www.piersland.co.uk
Beer range varies H

Superior standard hotel, overlooking Royal Troon golf course. It has won awards for its food, and its popularity tends to restrict space for drinkers. The bar is wood panelled, with a fine fireplace. The hotel is child-friendly (children's certificate) and has gardens for adults and children alike. The quality is reflected in the ale price.
Q P

Dumbartonshire

MILNGAVIE

Talbot Arms
30 Main Street
11 (12.30 Sun)-11 (midnight Thu-Sat)
(0141) 955 0981
Draught Bass; Caledonian Deuchars IPA, 80/-; guest beers H

Popular pub near the centre of a small town, where the West Highland Way meets commuterland. Its name derives from a breed of hunting dog once raised on a nearby estate. A renovation created a single room but the atmosphere of separate bars persists with the larger public bar area having bare floorboards, simple wooden seating and a pool table, while the generally quieter, carpeted lounge area provides more seating for diners (eve meals served in summer).

MILTON OF CAMPSIE

Kincaid House Hotel
Birston Road (signed on B757) OS650759
12-midnight (1am Fri; 11.45 Sat); 12-midnight Sun
(0141) 776 2226
Orkney Raven; Taylor Landlord H

Behind the impressive, stone, castle-like hotel lies this bar with dark, wooden tables, beams with horse brasses and a fine Alloa brewery mirror. A trellis divides the lounge area with fireplace and upholstered seating from the carpeted central area with a long counter, while a pool table occupies the other end of the room. Ale and food can be ordered in the large conservatory restaurant and in the garden. ♨❀⛺◐♿♣P

OLD KILPATRICK

Ettrick

159 Dumbarton Road

⌚ 11 (12.30 Sun)-midnight (1am Fri & Sat)

☎ (01389) 872821 website: www.theettrick.com

Caledonian Deuchars IPA Ⓗ

The pub takes its name from James Hogg, the Ettrick Shepherd and friend of Sir Walter Scott and is situated on the site of the 19th-century Hogg building; prints of the original are displayed inside. The single handpump is in the small, lively, horseshoe-shaped public bar where regulars gather for quiz nights and the like, and chess. The more comfortable lounge is no-smoking while food is being served (until 8pm). ❀◐◑⊟≋P⍉

Glasgow

GLASGOW

1901 Bar & Bistro

1534 Pollokshaws Road

⌚ 11.45 (12.30 Sun)-11 (midnight Fri & Sat)

☎ (0141) 632 0161

Caledonian Deuchars IPA; guest beers Ⓗ

Situated on the ground floor of one of the first red sandstone tenements to be built in this area, it was opened in 1901 as the Old Swan Inn by Sir John Stirling Maxwell and the Provost of Pollokshaws. There is ample seating and standing room in the bare-boarded bar area, while the old lounge is now the Bistro. Five guest beers are usually available. ◐◑♿≋(Shawlands/Pollokshaws W)●

Babbity Bowster

16-18 Blackfriars Street, Merchant City

⌚ 11 (12.30 Sun)-midnight

☎ (0141) 552 5055

Houston Peter's Well; guest beers Ⓟ

This 18th-century building was named after a contemporary dance. Blending French and Scottish styles in food and decor, the uniting factor is the quality – of both the beers and the food served in the bar and upstairs restaurant. A city oasis, it hosts Saturday folk sessions and pétanque is played. The patio has flower boxes and provides rare outdoor drinking in the city, while in winter the bar has the warmth and aroma of a peat fire. It is frequented by residents, professionals and academics. ♨Q❀⛺◐◑≋(High St) ⊖(Buchanan St) ♣●P

Blackfriars

36 Bell Street, Merchant City

⌚ 12 (12.30 Sun)-midnight

☎ (0141) 552 5924

Tetley Bitter, Burton Ale; guest beers Ⓗ/Ⓟ

The raised, corner café area of this metropolitan bar looks on to the street corner. The cosy main area has subdued lighting and fine, large brass-framed mirrors; both areas have candles on the tables. Live jazz is performed on Sunday and downstairs stages films, comedy and concerts. Food, from the menu and blackboard, is served all day until 11pm; a selection of bottled and draught foreign beers is available. Residents, city workers and young people all use this bar. ◐◑≋(High St/Argyll St/Queen St) ⊖(Buchanan St) ●

Bon Accord

153 North Street (near Mitchell Library)

⌚ 11-midnight; 5-11 Sun

☎ (0141) 248 4427

Beer range varies Ⓗ

A Glasgow real ale institution since way back in the 1970s when finding a decent pint in Scotland's biggest city was about as easy as finding hen's teeth, but the 'Bon' was always there like a beacon in the night. New management has now breathed fresh life into it. Through numerous changes of management, the same cellarman has continued keeping the 10 beers in pristine condition for the past 22 years. Evening meals are served until 7pm (children welcome). ◐◑♿≋(Charing Cross/Anderston) ♣

Clockwork Beer Co.

1153-1155 Cathcart Road

⌚ 11-midnight (11 Mon; 11.30 Tue); 11-11 Sun

☎ (0141) 649 0184

Caledonian Deuchars IPA, 80/-; guest beers Ⓟ

This award-winning pub on the south side of Glasgow (local CAMRA Pub of the Year 2001) lies a short distance from Hampden Park, Scotland's national stadium. After being completely rebuilt in 1997, a five-barrel brewery was installed opposite the bar. A spiral staircase leads to an upper seated area. An extensive range of drinks includes German and Belgian bottled beers, Belgian and Czech draught beers as well as Clockwork's own ales, fruit beers and seasonal specials. ☺◐◑♿≋(Mt Florida) P⍉▯

Crystal Palace

36 Jamaica Street

⌚ 11 (12.30 Sun)-midnight

☎ (0141) 221 2624

Caledonian Deuchars IPA, 80/-; guest beers Ⓗ

This ex-furniture store is Glasgow's second largest pub where friendly staff welcome you in the spacious bars on both floors. Downstairs is all carpeted with mostly tables and chairs; upstairs the light from massive windows has been used imaginatively along with garden style furniture and sa tone slab floor, to give almost an outdoor effect. An original cage lift allows access upstairs for the disabled. It draws a varied clientele, but mainly on their way to clubs and the theatre.

Q◐◑♿≋(Central) ⊖(St Enoch) ⍉●

Lismore

206 Dumbarton Road

⌚ 11 (12.30 Sun)-11 (midnight Fri & Sat)

☎ (0141) 576 0103

Caledonian Deuchars IPA; guest beer Ⓗ

A transformation has given this pub an impressive flavour of its own. The public bar features stone walls with gantry and fittings fashioned from dark wood. Stained glass windows, specially commissioned from local artists, depict scenes from the Highland clearances, while the urinals are dedicated to the villains who enacted them. The more comfortable lounge features modern art. An informal folk group plays four evenings a week. Over 100 malt whiskies are offered.

⊟≋(Partick) ⊖(Kelvin Hall)

State Bar

148 Holland Street (near Kings Theatre)
11 (12.30 Sun)-midnight
☎ (0141) 332 2159
Caledonian Deuchars IPA; Courage Directors; Houston Killellan, McEwan 80/-; guest beers H

Well-preserved, Victorian-style pub with upholstered furniture and some original stained glass panels. The centrepiece is a fine wooden oval island bar and gantry with brass hand and foot rails. The wood-panelled walls bear a large carved Glasgow coat of arms, two distillery mirrors and photos of theatrical artists and old Glasgow. At the rear is a fireplace with mirrored shelves and an alcove with a large mirror. Hosting live blues Thursday, it is popular with city folk and theatregoers.
(Charing Cross) (Cowcaddens)

Station Bar

55 Port Dundas Street
11 (12.30 Sun)-midnight
☎ (0141) 332 3117
Beer range varies H

The now demolished Buchanan Street station gave its name to the pub (the station site is currently occupied by the Scotrail building); other trades and professions in the area are celebrated by illuminated panels over the gantry. In spite of its proximity to the city centre, the pub retains its traditional character and is justly popular. The three guest beers are often from small Scottish brewers.
(Queen St) (Cowcaddens)

Stravaigin

28 Gibson Street
11 (12.30 Sun)-11 (midnight Fri)
☎ (0141) 334 2665 website: www.stravaigin.com
Caledonian Deuchars IPA, 80/- H

Well-known eating establishment, with a restaurant downstairs. The street-level café-bar is smaller and more intimate. The pine fittings and wood floor are set off by large mirrors and assorted maritime debris. There is extra seating above the bar, although the spiral staircase can pose problems for the sturdier beer-lover. A good variety of food is available all day, ranging in styles from East Asia to north-west Scotland.
Q (Kelvin Bridge)

Tennents

191 Byres Road
11 (12.30 Sun)-11 (midnight Fri & Sat)
☎ (0141) 341 1024
Draught Bass; Broughton Old Jock; Caledonian Deuchars IPA; Fuller's London Pride; Jennings Cumberland Ale; guest beers H

Imposing, street-corner pub that has catered for generations of students at the nearby University. It can be relied upon to be very crowded when big sporting events are on the TV and it is popular with the fans of Glasgow Caledonians rugby club who play locally. Orkney Dark Island, Taylor Landlord and Cairngorm Wild Cat are also permanent beers. (Partick) (Hillhead)

Three Judges

141 Dumbarton Road
11 (12.30 Sun)-11 (midnight Fri; 11.45 Sat)
☎ (0141) 337 3055
Beer range varies H

Typical Glasgow corner tenement pub (the name derives from former owners who were keen boxing fans) whose staff and customers have resisted attempts to make it more trendy. An illuminated model of the building is mounted by one window. Up to nine beers are on offer, frequently featuring craft brewers from Scotland and north-east England. The quality can be gauged by the numerous local CAMRA awards hanging above the bar, and thousands of badges from the beers sold. (Partick) (Kelvin Hall)

Toby Jug

97 Hope Street
11-midnight; closed Sun
☎ (0141) 221 4159
Caledonian Deuchars IPA; Fuller's London Pride; Orkney Dark Island; Taylor Landlord H

Friendly, city-centre pub, which is just across the road from Central Station and very handy for catching the last train home. There is a large standing area in front of the bar with a raised seated section towards the rear where lunchtime food is served 12-4, Monday-Friday.
(Central) (Buchanan St/St Enoch)

Lanarkshire

AULDHOUSE

Auldhouse Arms

6 Langlands Road
3-11; 12.30-midnight Fri & Sun; 11.30-midnight Sat
☎ (01355) 263242
Belhaven Sandy Hunter's Ale H

The small bar has been unchanged for many years, where varnished wine casks sit behind the gantry with copper jugs above. Old photographs and plates decorate the walls around the bar area and the snugs, where the real fires are to be found. There is no public transport to the village so a trip by car is necessary. Q P

BIGGAR

Crown Inn

109 High Street
11 (12.30 Sun)-11
☎ (01899) 220116
Beer range varies H

Friendly, multi-roomed pub in the centre of an attractive borders town, which boasts the largest number of museums in the country, in proportion to the population. This 300-year-old former coaching inn features many genuine historical pictures of Biggar on the walls. The home-cooked meals are popular, and children are fed for free. 1960s music is often featured on Sunday. The snug is the designated no-smoking area.

CASTLECARY

Castlecary House Hotel

Castlecary Road
11 (12.30 Sun)-11 (11.30 Thu-Sat)
☎ (01324) 840233 website: www.castlecaryhotel.com
Draught Bass; Stones Bitter; guest beers H

Private hotel in a village on the site of one of the major forts on the Antonine Wall. Real ales are served in the Castle Lounge but can be brought through to any of the three distinct drinking areas. The main bar, the Poachers, has a central stone fireplace with a roaring fire in winter, while a large

extension has recently been completed, providing a new lounge bar and restaurant. Bar meals and high teas are highly recommended.
♨ ⛴ ❀ ⇌ ◐ ⊟ P

COATBRIDGE

St Andrews
37-38 Sunnyside Road
11-midnight; 12.30-5, 8-midnight Sun
☎ (01236) 423773
Beer range varies H
Small pub, over 100 years old, formerly called the Saloon Bar (changed when the present owners took over in 1998). A 1930s restoration added some Art Deco features while a 1960s revamp was less sympathetic, although much of the formica has now been removed. Note the two original Fowlers adverts, a 1910 local map and a Campbell, Hope and King mirror. It stocks a wide range of malts and one of the best local Belgian selections. Current CAMRA Lanarkshire Pub of the Year. ⇌ (Sunnyside)

HAMILTON

George
18 Campbell Street
11 (12.30 Sun)-midnight
☎ (01698) 424225
Beer range varies H
This family-run pub is a frequent winner of CAMRA's Lanarkshire Pub of the Year award and currently holds the West of Scotland Landlord of the Year title. The present owners took over in 1991 and immediately restored its reputation as a first-class local after a couple of years in the doldrums. Hopefully, by publication, the local licensing board will be treating all licensees equally and the pub will once again be open after midnight on Friday and Saturday.
◐ ⛺ ⇌ (Central) ⊬ ✔

LANARK

Clydesdale Inn
15 Bloomgate
11 (12.30 Sun)-midnight (1am Fri; 11.45 Sat)
☎ (01555) 678740
Beer range varies H
Formerly the Clydesdale Hotel, it was taken over in 2000 by Wetherspoon's, who made a modest change to the name but huge alterations to the interior, making it unrecognisable to anyone who visited it even a few years ago, let alone Charles Dickens who stayed here when it was a coaching inn. Many of the artefacts found in the pub are now housed in the museum along the street. Winner of the Scottish Loo of the Year award.
Q ⛴ ◐ ♿ ⛺ ⇌ ⊬ ✔

Horse & Jockey
56 High Street
11 (12.30 Sun)-midnight (1am Fri; 11.45 Sat)
☎ (01555) 664825
Beer range varies H
Public bar, with a lounge/diner at the rear, on the main street of this historic market town, where a pub has stood since 1740. The pub name and some of the decor recalls the town's connection with the Sport of Kings, although the nearby racecourse is now disused and an unusual feature is the list of previous owners on the wall. There are two handpumps in the bar, but usually only one is operational in winter. ◐ ⛺ ⇌

STRATHAVEN

Weavers
3 Green Street
12 (4.30 Tue-Thu)-midnight (1am Fri & Sat); 7-1am Sun
☎ (01357) 522647 website: www.strathaven.com
Beer range varies H
Listed building in the centre of an attractive, small town. Formerly the Crown Hotel, it reopened as the Weavers in 1980. The bar is decorated with pictures of Hollywood icons such as Marlon Brando, Liz Taylor and a big chap dressed as a gorilla. The local squash, climbing and motorcycle clubs all meet here. A range of bottled Belgian beers is also sold.

UDDINGSTON

Rowan Tree ☆
60 Old Mill Road (near Tunnock's bakery)
11 (12.30 Sun)-11.45
☎ (01698) 812678
Arran Ale; Houston Peter's Well; guest beer H
Grade B listed building boasting a superb wood-panelled interior, two fireplaces and some fine, rare mirrors including one from Whitelaw's Brewery. Reputedly the oldest pub in Lanarkshire, a former staging inn, it has a genuine olde-worlde feel that no modern fake could ever emulate. Since the present owners bought it from Maclays in 1998, it has concentrated on selling beers from local micros.
♨ ◐ ⊟ ♿ ⇌ P

WISHAW

Wishaw Malt
62-66 Kirk Road
11 (12.30 Sun)-midnight
☎ (01698) 358806
Beer range varies H
A former furniture store, it was opened by Wetherspoon's in October 1999 and overnight Wishaw changed from one of the country's most dismal beer deserts into a town worth drinking in. The bar is a large single room, but is sectioned in such a way as to give each area of the pub its own distinct feel. There is generally at least one beer from a Scottish micro on sale alongside the more usual Wetherspoon's offerings.
Q ❀ ◐ ♿ ⇌ ⊬ ✔

Renfrewshire

BARRHEAD

Cross Stobs Inn
4 Grahamston Road
11 (12.30 Sun)-11 (midnight Thu; 1am Fri; 11.45 Sat)
☎ (0141) 881 1581
Orkney Dark Island; guest beer H
Attractive coaching inn, known to locals as The Sticks, on the main road of a mature residential area of town. The spacious, yet cosy bar has ample seating, an antique sideboard and golf memorabilia. The interior is carefully unaltered – access to the lounge is via the public bar, with a window

looking into the lounge and garden beyond. An unobtrusive pool room lies off the bar and a summer football team plays friendly matches. The regular Paisley bus service stops nearby.
♨☕❀◑⊟

Waterside Inn
Glasgow Road, The Hurlet (A736)
❂ 11 (12.30 Sun)-11 (midnight Fri & Sat)
☎ (0141) 881 2822
Beer range varies [H]
Comfortable bar/lounge attached to a restaurant near the Levern Water and still famously known as Jeanie Gebbie's although the interior has been knocked through long since her day. Cosy chairs around the real fire help create a relaxed atmosphere, but the friendly, efficient staff can sometimes be overwhelmed by diners overspilling from the restaurant, which holds theme nights with musical accompaniment. A stained glass gantry and local pictures add to the ambience.
♨❀◑⊟♿P

BISHOPTON

Golf Inn
28-30 Greenock Road
❂ 12-2.30, 5-11 (midnight Fri & Sat); 12.30-2.30, 6.30-11 Sun
☎ (01505) 862303
Belhaven 80/-; guest beer [P]
A porch and swing doors lead to an uncluttered, almost austere, walnut-panelled room with an L-shaped bar on one side and chest-high drinking shelf on the opposite wall. A fruit machine is the only concession to the modern era and chilled bottled beer drinkers require the barman to visit a fridge in the cellar. A TV room and a games room leave the bar free for the main business of conversation. The lounge has its own entrance, used when busy.
Q⊟⇌P

CLARKSTON

Busby Hotel
Field Road
❂ 11 (12.30 Sun)-midnight (1am Thu-Sat)
☎ (0141) 644 4417 website: www.busbyhotel.co.uk
Beer range varies [H]
The public bar of this privately-owned hotel is on a tree-lined avenue overlooking the White Cart Water. Genuinely aged wood panelling, low level lighting and leather couches enhance a relaxed eating and drinking experience. A long bar dominates one side of the room with chalkboards promoting the ale on offer. A roomy but still cosy pub where friendly and enthusiastic staff give excellent service.
❀🛏◑◐⇌(Busby) P

EAGLESHAM

Cross Keys
1 Montgomery Street
❂ 11-midnight (11 Mon); 12.30-11 Sun
☎ (01355) 302356
Beer range varies [H]
Split-level lounge, with plenty of comfortable, recessed seating and wood panelling. Three handpumps serve mostly Scottish micro-brewery beers, that can be brought through to the adjacent public bar. A gantry with an extensive whisky collection and rural bric-à-brac add to the relaxed atmosphere in this commuter town pub. Food is served lunchtime and evenings (until 9.45) and children are allowed in until 8pm. A quiz (Thu), monthly live music in the lounge (first Sat of month) and a pool contest in the bar (Sun) provide entertainment.
◑◐⊟

GOUROCK

Spinnaker Hotel
121 Albert Road
❂ 11-11.30 (midnight Thu; 1am Fri & Sat); 12.30-midnight Sun
☎ (01475) 633107 website: www.spinnakerhotel.co.uk
Beer range varies [H]
Regular Guide entry, where Belhaven 80/- is often available alongside visiting local and national beers served from the two handpumps. Great scenery, encompassing views of the Firth of Clyde and the Cowal Hills beyond, as well as nautical activity may be enjoyed from the bay windows or outside tables. The mood is friendly and relaxed and children are welcome until 8pm when bar meals stop. The menu includes blackboard specials, vegetarian and children's choices.
Q❀🛏◑◐

GREENOCK

James Watt
80-92 Cathcart Road
❂ 11 (12.30 Sun)-11 (midnight Thu; 1am Fri & Sat)
☎ (01475) 722640
Caledonian 80/-; Courage Directors; guest beers [H]
Large, typical Wetherspoon's pub in a former post office named after one of Greenock's famous sons, the inventor, James Watt. This is a welcome oasis in a beer desert. Photographs on the walls depict scenes of shipbuilding and seafaring taken from Greenock's proud maritime heritage;

INN BRIEF

Renfrewshire

KILMACOLM

Pullman Tavern
Lochwinnoch Road
11 (12.30 Sun)-11.30 (12.30am Sat)
(01505) 874501
Draught Bass [H]
Converted railway station on the Paisley-Greenock cycle path, with a family restaurant. Cosy interior with two real fires.

PAISLEY

Bull Inn ☆
7 New Street
11-11.30 (midnight Fri & Sat); 12.30-11 Sun
(0141) 849 0472
Caledonian Deuchars IPA; Houston Peter's Well; Taylor Landlord; guest beer [H]
Old coaching inn where a large-screen TV dominates, but has three snugs at the rear.

Gabriel's
33 Gauze Street
11 (12.30 Sun)-midnight (1am Fri & Sat)
(0141) 847 8204
Tetley Burton Ale; guest beers [H]
Large tenement pub with an island bar. A raised dining area offers good quality food at reasonable prices. Children's certificate.

the whole riverside area here has now been redeveloped after the closure of the shipyards. Q◑⇌(Central)⊬●

HOUSTON

Fox & Hounds

South Street

✪ 11 (12.30 Sun)-midnight (1am Fri & Sat)

☎ (01505) 612448

website: www.houston-brewing.co.uk

Houston Killellan, Barochan, Peter's Well, Texas, seasonal beers; guest beers Ⓗ

With the Houston Brewery on site, their beers are served in all three bars of this pub. The Fox and Vixen Bar is comfortable and quiet, serving four of the beers and one guest. The Stables Bar is livelier with TV, pool table and a juke box, while the Huntsman Bar is upstairs, along with the highly commended restaurant. Food is available all day at weekends at this former local CAMRA Pub of the Year.

Q◑⊟P

INVERKIP

Inverkip Hotel

Main Street (off A78)

✪ 11 (12.30 Sun)-11 (midnight Fri & Sat)

☎ (01475) 521478 website: www.inverkip.co.uk

Beer range varies Ⓗ

Genuine local in a small village on the Clyde coast. The lounge area has adjoining alcoves, which makes for a relaxed atmosphere, although it can get very busy. The large restaurant is to the back of the building, where it is recommended to book ahead, but the menu is also available in the lounge. The hotel lies between two car ferry terminals, serving the Isle of Bute and Dunoon.

Q⇄◑⊟⇌P

JOHNSTONE

Coanes

26 High Street

✪ 11-11.30 (1am Fri & Sat); 12.30-11.30 Sun

☎ (01505) 322925

Boddingtons Bitter; Caledonian Deuchars IPA, 80/-; Orkney Dark Island; guest beers Ⓗ

This town house-style building has a cosy, local bar with fake beams and bric-à-brac. The lounge doubles as a restaurant where the eating area is on a higher level, affording a degree of privacy. The innovative menu reflects the best of Scottish produce, with the emphasis on fish. Evening meals are served 5.30-8.30, Wed-Sat; no food Sun. In late evening the dining and lounge areas merge as it tends to get busy late on, especially at weekends.

◑⊟⇌●

KILBARCHAN

Glen Leven

25 New Street

✪ 11 (12.30 Sun)-11 (midnight Wed & Thu; 1am Fri & Sat)

☎ (01505) 702481

Beer range varies Ⓗ

Friendly pub, with its own small restaurant. It hosts live music on Saturday (from 10pm onwards), a jam session on Wednesday (from 9pm) and a pub quiz on Sunday night. It is readily accessible from the Glasgow-Irvine cycle path. Backgammon is played here.

♨❀◑♿♣P

Trust Inn

8 Low Barholm

✪ 11 (12.30 Sun)-11 (11.30 Thu; midnight Fri & Sat)

☎ (01505) 702401

Caledonian Deuchars IPA; Tetley Burton Ale Ⓗ

Friendly pub in a conservation village with easy access to the Glasgow-Irvine cycle path, and a short walk from the Weavers Cottage, which is well signposted. The lounge bar has a low, beamed ceiling, intimate recesses and decorative brasses. A large TV projection screen can dominate the premises during major football and rugby matches, but when folded away, the pub's quiet, village local character is restored. Various activities during the week include a pub quiz. ◑⇌(Milliken Pk)

LOCHWINNOCH

Brown Bull

33 Main Street

✪ 12 (12.30 Sun)-11 (midnight Fri; 11.45 Sat)

☎ (01505) 843250 website: www.brownbull.co.uk

Orkney Dark Island; guest beers Ⓗ

Welcoming, low-ceilinged country pub, convenient for the Glasgow-Irvine cycle path. The licensee allows well-behaved dogs to sit under the tables but customers are requested to remember that food may be served. Evening meals are available between 5.30 and 7.30. This unspoilt inn displays local artists' paintings of farming and rural life. Castle Semple Nature Reserve is nearby. Three guest beers are usually on tap here.

♨◑♿

NEWTON MEARNS

Osprey

Stewarton Road

✪ 11 (12.30 Sun)-11

☎ (0141) 616 5071

Draught Bass; Caledonian Deuchars IPA Ⓗ

Typical vintage inn chain pub, with a strong emphasis on food, it is family-focused and child-friendly. Stone floors, wood pillars, bare brickwork and hop vines above the oak-fronted bar go a long way to create an historic pub feel. There are plenty of nooks and crannies allowing drinkers to avoid the dining crowd. Arched windows look out to generous outdoor drinking areas with benches on the grass and patios. Two real fires provide a warm welcome in winter.

♨Q❀◑♿P⊬

PAISLEY ❄

Hogshead

45 High Street

✪ 11 (12.30 Sun)-midnight (1am Fri & Sat)

☎ (0141) 840 4150

Boddingtons Bitter; Caledonian Deuchars IPA, 80/- Ⓗ

Spacious, comfortable, open-plan lounge in the town centre. It is frequented by drinkers of all ages during the week, and students at the weekend. Music can be loud. It has a raised dining area, where the popular meals are available all day.

◑♿⇌(Gilmour St)●

Last Post

2 County Square (station entrance)
11 (12.30 Sun)-midnight (1am Fri & Sat)
(0141) 849 6911
Caledonian Deuchars IPA; Shepherd Neame Spitfire; Greene King Abbot H
Typical Wetherspoon's conversion of the old post office, with a split-level drinking area. The walls are decorated with pictures of Paisley's textile and world-famous Robertson's jam-making past. Guest ales change on a daily basis. Wheelchair access is from the station entrance of the building. The usual Wetherspoon's attributes – all-day food and a no-smoking area can be enjoyed here. Q (Gilmour St)

Wee Howf

53 High Street
11-11 (11.30 Wed & Thu; 1am Fri; midnight Sat); closed Sun
(0141) 889 2095
Caledonian Deuchars IPA; Tetley Burton Ale; guest beers H
Small, town-centre pub near the University, with a warm and friendly atmosphere, featuring guest beers usually from the Arran and Houston breweries. The pub used to be called the Market Bar. The present publican has been in all of the last 15 editions of this Guide and was the first Burton Master Cellarman in Scotland. (Gilmour St)

UPLAWMOOR

Uplawmoor Hotel

66 Neilston Road (off A736)
12-2.30, 5-11 (midnight Fri & Sat); 12-midnight Sun
(01505) 850565 website: www.uplawmoor.co.uk
Beer range varies H
Parts of this hotel date from 1750, when it opened to serve travellers from Glasgow to the Clyde coast. Locals, from this highest village in Renfrewshire, are the main patrons in a basic public bar, attached to a more upmarket restaurant/hotel/cocktail bar complex. The restaurant was converted from an old barn and the cocktail bar is centred on a copper canopied open fire. Note the Burns quote.
P

Pubs and Breweries Hit By Axeing Beer Orders

In Feburuary 2002, CAMRA reacted with anger and disbelief at the Department of Trade and Industry's decision to revoke the Beer Orders. The Campaign predicted the loss of hundreds of community pubs and the closure of dozens of small brewing companies should deregulation be allowed to proceed.
Mike Benner, CAMRA's Head of Campaigns and Communications said, 'The revocation of the Beer Orders will send shock waves through the industry as there will be nothing to stop large brewers and pub chains tying up huge chunks of the market, restricting access to smaller brewers and smashing consumer choice.'

CAMRA claimed:

- That the DTI was acting against the advice of the Office of Fair Trading following its review in 2000
- That the move to allow brewers to prevent pubs from remaining pubs in the future if sold will lead to hundreds of community pub closures, particularly in rural areas where pubs are most at risk. This is despite steps by DTLR to protect rural pubs through improved planning measures and rate relief.
- That breweries will be allowed to refuse to supply beer for resale, enabling large players with key brands to force smaller wholesalers and retailers to stock all or most of their products, even if they only want one.
- That revocation will allow brewers to charge different prices to any number of different customers, as they will not be obliged to publish wholesale price lists.
- Revoking the guest beer provision will allow any brewer to buy and tie many thousands of pubs to its own products, excluding smaller brewers and wrecking consumer choice
- Lack of alternative anti-competitive controls specific to the industry will hand more brewing, distribution and retailing power to the large brewers and pub retailers.

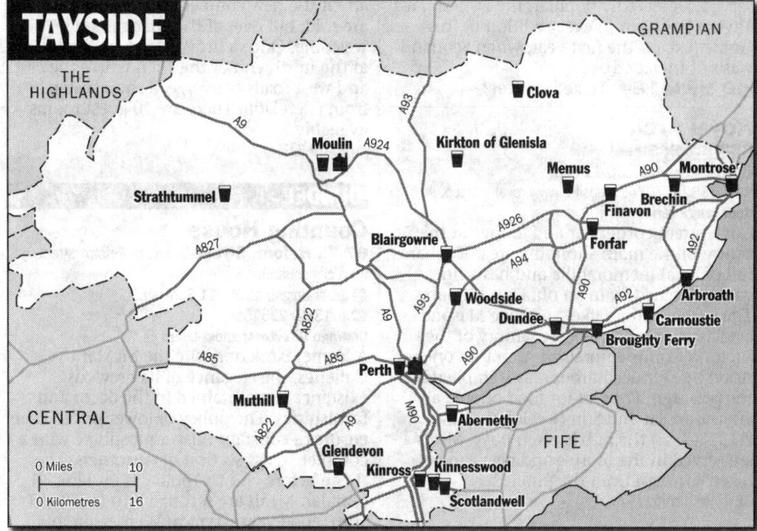

Authority areas covered: Angus UA, City of Dundee UA, Perth & Kinross UA

ABERNETHY

Cree's Inn
Main Street
11-2.30, 5-11; 11-11 Sat; 12.30-11 Sun
(01738) 850714
Beer range varies H

Lying in the shadow of a 12th-century round tower, this former farmhouse is now a homely pub situated in a quiet village which was once the ancient capital of Scotland. The building itself is now listed and renovations carried out recently have extended the lounge bar with a new restaurant and four en-suite bedrooms. A varied menu is on offer using fresh local produce to accompany the choice of up to four ales, usually two of which are Scottish. Meal times vary so it is best to contact the pub. P

ARBROATH

Lochlands Bar
14 Lochlands Street
11-midnight; (1am Fri & Sat); 12.30-midnight Sun
(01241) 873286
Beer range varies H

Classic, street-corner local with strong sporting associations; the large public bar displays a case of trophies, and the TV sets dominate when football or rugby matches are on. If you are not a fan, do not despair, as peace can be found in the small lounge where two ales are brought through from the bar. There are usually two cask beers on tap. The pub is close to the bus station.

BLAIRGOWRIE

Ericht Ale House
13 Wellmeadow
11-11 (11.45 Fri & Sat); 12.30-11 Sun
(01250) 872469
Beer range varies H

Established in 1802, this is a traditional, friendly town-centre pub. It is run by an enthusiastic landlord as is demonstrated by the ever-changing range of beers from all over Britain with up to six ales on tap and Addlestone's draught cider stocked. A large single-roomed pub, its two seated areas are split by a small, well-stocked bar. Ongoing refurbishment has included a new open fire. Occasional live music is performed at weekends.
Q

Rosemount Golf Hotel
Golf Course Road
11-11 (11.45 Fri & Sat); 12-11 Sun
(01250) 872604 website: www.rosemountgolf.co.uk
Beer range varies H

Located in a quiet area and set back from the road in its own mature gardens, it is a friendly, traditional hotel with a comfortable lounge area warmed by an open fire. As its name suggests it is very close to the golf course and is an excellent base for enthusiasts with up to 80 courses in close proximity. The hotel enjoys a good local following, with many keen walkers. Meals are served in a designated restaurant area.
P

BROUGHTY FERRY

Fisherman's Tavern
10-12 Fort Street
11-midnight (1am Fri & Sat); 12.30-midnight Sun
(01382) 775941
Belhaven St Andrew's Ale; Boddingtons Bitter; guest beers H

Long-standing flagship of good beer, it has now also won an award for its wine! The public bar is virtually unchanged from earlier days, while other drinking areas include a no-smoking room with a real fire and small garden. An annual beer festival is held in May/June. The rear lounge has wheelchair access. Lunchtime meals are

INDEPENDENT BREWERIES

Inveralmond Perth
Moulin Moulin

served. Deservedly popular, the Fisherman's Tavern has been in every edition of this Guide (except the first year, when Scotland was not included).
Q (limited service)

Royal Arch

258 Brook Street
11-midnight; 12.30-11 Sun
(01382) 779741 website: www.royal-arch.co.uk
Beer range varies
Cosy, street-corner bar and lounge at the centre of the main shopping area. The bar is full of local memorabilia and has a fine gantry rescued from an old Dundee pub. The name is more likely to have Masonic associations than to be a memory of the Victoria Commemoration Arch that once stood by Dundee harbour, as is implied by the pub sign. Popular for food offered all afternoon Sat and Sun (weekdays 11.30-2.15, 5-7.45) the pub is often busy. Meals are served in the lounge and beer can be taken through from the public bar.
(limited service)

CARNOUSTIE

Stag's Head Inn

61 Dundee Street
11-midnight (1am Fri & Sat); 12.30-midnight Sun
(01241) 858777
Fuller's London Pride; Taylor Landlord; guest beers
Large bar and lounge/function room in a totally renovated building, it is popular with locals and visiting golfers and sometimes hosts live music and karaoke. Note the tribute portrait and plaque to comedian/actor Billy Connolly who drank here in his youth while on TA exercises at Barry Buddon army range. Caravans are allowed on the local campsite. P

CLOVA

Clova Hotel

Glen Clova, near Kirriemuir, Angus
11-11 (1am Fri & Sat); 11-11 Sun
(01575) 550350 website: www.clova.com
Caledonian Deuchars IPA, 80/-
Recently refurbished, this popular centre for walking, climbing and country sports provides a high level of comfort although purists and traditionalists have doubts about the new climber's bar, where the ales are sold, but overall the changes are welcome. Once a drovers' inn, the hotel is at the north end of the Glen where the east and west roads converge, a short distance from Glen Doll. There are 10 guest rooms available.
P

DUNDEE

Counting House

67-71 Reform Street (N end of Reform Street from city square)
11-midnight; 12.30-11 Sun
(01382) 225251
Courage Directors; guest beers
A former bank opposite the McManus Galleries, the elegance of its previous existence is maintained in the decor and furnishings. The policy of lower priced beers ensures a constant busy atmosphere with a complete cross-section of customers. The 'Taste before you try' policy is proving popular. Meals are served 11-10 (12.30-10 Sun), good value, typical Wetherspoon's fare.

Drouthy Neebors

142 Perth Road (opp. Art College)
11 (12 Sun)-midnight
(01382) 322392
Beer range varies
A former car showroom turned into a Scottish theme pub, this hostelry began its life as a shrine to Dundee's anti-poet William McGonagall but now celebrates Scotland's real bard, Robert Burns. The name comes from his famous poem Tam o' Shanter and is itself a glorification of the inn, where thirsty ('drouthy') neighbours enjoy good fellowship and foaming pints ('reaming swats') of ale. The split-level bar features much dark wood, and quotes from Rabbie's works. Live music is often staged in the basement bar.

Mickey Coyle's

21-23 Old Hawkhill (W of town centre in University area)
11-3, 5-midnight; 11-midnight Fri & Sat; 7-11 Sun
(01382) 225871
Caledonian Deuchars IPA, 80/-

INN BRIEF

ARBROATH

Corn Exchange
Market Place
11-midnight (1am Fri & Sat); 12.30-midnight Sun
(01241) 432430
Caledonian 80/-; Courage Directors; guest beers
Fine Wetherspoon's refurbishment of an imposing building. Meals are served all day. Cask Marque accredited.

Old Brewhouse
1 High Street
11-midnight (1am Fri & Sat); 12-midnight Sun
(01241) 879945
Orkney Dark Island
Small bar and lounge/restaurant on the seafront. Beware of waves in stormy weather – aptly named danger point!

Viewfield Hotel
1 Viewfield Road
11-midnight (1am Fri & Sat); 12.30-midnight Sun
(01241) 872446
Beer range varies
Popular bar of a small hotel, stocking one cask ale. Spacious lounge with live music at weekends. Good food served including high teas on Sunday.

BRECHIN

Dalhousie
1 Market Street
11-midnight (1am Fri & Sat); 12-30-11 Sun
(01356) 622096
Beer range varies
Traditional high-ceilinged, basic but friendly, corner local.

CARNOUSTIE

Station Hotel
23 Station Road
11-3, 4.30-midnight; 11-11 Fri & Sat; 12.30-midnight Sun
(01241) 852447
Beer range varies
Small hotel catering for all family members. One ale is available in both bar and lounge.

DUNDEE

Bank
7-9 Union Street
11-midnight; 12.30-11 Sun
(01382) 205037
Boddingtons Bitter; guest beers
Ex-Hogshead with redecorated interior, it retains the old layout with intimate seating areas.

Named after a late 19th-century owner, who also ran a spirits business – there are some rare samples of 'MC' rum and whisky jars behind the bar. The long, split-level bar is popular for meals with university folk (served until 7pm). Its abbreviated title 'MC' once appeared in the Guinness Book of Records as the shortest pub name, but now it has adopted the full version.
◐◗ ≠ ♣

Phoenix
103 Nethergate (W of city centre towards University)
⏲ 11-midnight; 12.30-11 Sun
☎ (01382) 200014
Caledonian Deuchars IPA; Houston Peter's Well; Orkney Dark Island; Taylor Landlord Ⓗ
Popular, refurbished bar, which attracts a cross-section of university and business customers and has in the past pioneered many unusual ales but now has a good selection of regulars' favourites. A fine gantry and other features and artefacts are on display. The famous chilliburgers are still available! Food is served 12-7 Mon-Sat, 12.30-7 Sun.
◐◗ ≠

FINAVON

Finavon Hotel
N side of A90, 3 miles N of Forfar
⏲ 11-midnight (1am Fri & Sat); 12.30-11 Sun
☎ (01307) 850234
Beer range varies Ⓗ
Extensive bar in roadside hotel with intimate nooks for dining and an array of newspapers for browsers. There is a separate restaurant and no-smoking area. Famous Finavon Doocot is nearby and pictish sites Aberlemno and Dunwichen are a few miles away. A beer festival is held in July or August. Meals are served all day until 9pm.
⛰Q ❀ ◐◗ ♿ ⛺ P ⚟

GLENDEVON

Tormaukin Hotel
⏲ 11-11; 12-11 Sun
☎ (01259) 781252 website: www.tormaukin.co.uk
Beer range varies Ⓗ
The Tormaukin (meaning 'hill of the mountain hare' in old Scots) is situated in a peaceful, rural setting surrounded by the Ochil Hills. It has two comfortable lounge bars with plush seating and log fires, these combined with natural timbers and stone enhance the warm, welcoming atmosphere. An extensive menu provides an interesting choice of traditional Scottish and international dishes and there is a separate restaurant with à la carte menu. Up to three ales are served, with usually two Harviestoun ones. It is an ideal base for walking, golf and fishing. ⛰Q ❀ ◐◗ ⛺ P

KINROSS

Kirklands Hotel
20 High Street
⏲ 11-2.30, 5-11 (11.45 Sat); 12.30-11 Sun
☎ (01577) 863313 website: www.kirklandshotel.com
Beer range varies Ⓗ
In the centre of town, this traditional hotel has been fully refurnished to provide comfortable modern accommodation. It was one of the original coaching inns in Kinross. With Loch Leven nearby, a five-minute boat trip takes you to Loch Leven Castle where Mary, Queen of Scots was imprisoned by the Earl of Bothwell. Naturalists will enjoy a visit to the RSPB's Vane Farm reserve. Usually two beers are available. ⛰Q ◐◗ P

KIRKTON OF GLENISLA

Glenisla Hotel
On B591, 10 miles N of Aylth
⏲ 11-11 (12.30am Fri; 1am Sat) closed winter afternoons; 12.30-11 Sun
☎ (01575) 582223
Inveralmond Ossian's Ale, Thrappledouser; guest beers (summer) Ⓗ
This welcoming two-level bar is in a small country hotel amid splendid scenery. Refurbishment inside and out is planned by the new owner, who has a strong commitment to local beer from Inveralmond. It is an ideal base for touring, a popular centre for walking and fishing, or join in the wide range of outdoor activities, including golf and hang gliding. Alternatively, opt for indoor entertainment in the games room. ⛰❀ ◐◗ ♣ P

MEMUS

Drovers' Inn
5 miles N of Forfar, off B957
⏲ 12-2.30, 6-midnight; 12-1am Fri & Sat; closed Mon in winter – phone to check; 12.30-midnight Sun
☎ (01307) 860322
Beer range varies Ⓗ
Pleasant bar with pine-panelled walls and flagstones, separate restaurant, large garden and car park. Formerly the local post office, it serves as a shop where groceries, newspapers and vegetables can be ordered. Opening times may vary, so do phone to check. The Drovers' Inn received the Country Alliance Pub Award.
⛰❀ ◐◗ P

MOULIN

Moulin Inn
11-13 Kirkmichael Road (3/4 mile NE of Pitlochry)
⏲ 12-11 (11.45 Fri & Sat); 12-11.45 Sun
☎ (01796) 472196 website: www.moulinhotel.co.uk
Moulin Light, Braveheart, Ale of Atholl, Old Remedial Ⓗ
Established in 1695, this country inn is situated in the village square of Moulin, an ancient Scottish crossroads near Pitlochry, the 'Gateway to the Highlands'. Although extended into an hotel, it retains much character and charm. The oldest part of the building is the original inn, furnished in traditional pub style with two log fires. A good, varied choice of home-prepared local fare is available, along with its own beers, provided by the brewery in the old coach house behind the hotel. An ideal base for walking holidays, up to 16 routed walks pass nearby. 18 guest rooms are available.
⛰Q ❀ ◐◗ ♣ P

MUTHILL

Muthill Village Hotel
6 Willoughby Street
⏲ 11-11 (11.45 Fri & Sat); 12.30-11 Sun

☎ (01764) 681451
website: www.bookings@muthillvillagehot.com
Draught Bass; Inveralmond Lia Fail; Orkney Dark Island; guest beers Ⓗ
Originally an 18th-century coaching inn on the old drovers' road from the Highlands, it is a traditional, friendly local in a conservation village with over 90 listed buildings. The small 'bothy' public bar is comfortable with bare boards and a real fire; the walls are adorned with farming implements and old livestock catalogues. The adjoining restaurant bears a hunting theme. Up to four ales (two in winter) are served. Do not miss the nearby Drummond Gardens, one of the finest formal gardens in Europe.
⌂Q♨❀⇌◑◐P⚟

PERTH

Capital Asset
26 Tay Street
⌚ 11-11 (11.45 Fri & Sat); 12.30-11 Sun
☎ (01738) 580457
Caledonian Deuchars IPA, 80/-; Theakston Best Bitter; guest beers Ⓗ
Large, open-plan Wetherspoon's house with modern decoration and a small split-level seating area overlooking the River Tay. The pub takes its name from the fact that it used to be a bank and Perth was once the ancient capital of Scotland. Up to five ales are on tap. It draws a varied clientele, and can be very busy at weekends.
Q◑◐♿✔

Greyfriars
15 South Street
⌚ 11-11 (11.45 Fri & Sat); 7-11 Sun
☎ (01738) 633036
Caledonian Deuchars IPA; Taylor Landlord; guest beers Ⓗ
Small, cosy but vibrant, city-centre lounge bar with a friendly atmosphere. Up to four beers are usually available including the house beer, Friar's Tipple brewed by Inveralmond. Lunches are served in the bar and a small upstairs seated area. An ideal retreat with various nearby attractions such as a Victorian theatre, art gallery and museum, it is just a short distance from the River Tay. ◑⇚

SCOTLANDWELL

Well Country Inn
Main Street
⌚ 11-11 (11.45 Fri & Sat); 12-11 Sun
☎ (01592) 840444
website: www.thewellcountryinn.co.uk
Beer range varies Ⓗ
Located in a tranquil village that dates back to 84AD, when the Romans were in occupation, this family-run country inn provides an ideal base for outdoor pursuits and golf – the famous 'Tetley Tea Trail' is only yards from the inn. Also nearby is one of the last natural underground spring water wells still working in Scotland. Tasty meals are served.
⌂Q❀⇌◑◐⊟♣P

STRATHTUMMEL

Loch Tummel Inn
On B8019, approx. 3 miles W of Queen's View
⌚ 11-11 (may close afternoons – check in advance); 12.30-11 Sun
☎ (01882) 634272
Moulin Braveheart Ⓗ
Situated in an idyllic rural setting that boasts magnificent scenery overlooking Loch Tummel, this inn is located on part of the romantic 'Road to the Isles'. Formerly an old coaching inn, the bar area is in the former stables, and the restaurant is a converted hayloft serving the inn's own smoked salmon. Why not take in the panoramic views from Queen's View nearby. The inn closes in winter from October to mid-March. ⌂Q❀⇌◑◐P

WOODSIDE

Woodside Inn
Main Street (A94 S of Coupar Angus, NE of Burrelton)
⌚ 11-2.30, 5-11 (11.45 Fri); 11-11 Sat; 12.30-11 Sun
☎ (01828) 670254
Caledonian Deuchars IPA; Fuller's London Pride; guest beers Ⓗ
This small village pub was once used as a convalescent home for WW1 casualties. It has a small, comfortable public bar serving up to four regularly changing ales. Excellent food is served in the adjacent restaurant 11-2, 5-9 (children are welcome). ⌂◑◐♣P

INN BRIEF

Speedwell ☆
165-167 Perth Road
11-midnight; 12.30-11 Sun
(01382) 667783
Beer range varies Ⓗ
Known as 'Mennies', this pub usually has four beers on tap. It is a wonderfully preserved Edwardian bar with two sitting rooms, one no-smoking.

FORFAR

Queen Street Tavern
45a Queen Street
11-midnight; 12.30-7 Sun
(01307) 462722
Inveralmond Ossian's Ale Ⓗ
Just off the town centre, a comfortable, cosy, popular bar with panelled walls, old prints and memorabilia. It has a lounge and restaurant.

KINNESSWOOD

Lomond Country Inn
Main Street
11-11 (midnight Fri & Sat); 11-11 Sun
(01592) 840253
Beer range varies Ⓗ
Popular country inn with a fine view, overlooking Loch Leven, from the open-plan bar/restaurant.

MONTROSE

George Hotel
22 George Street
11-2, 5-11; 11-11 Sat; 12-11 Sun
(01674) 675050
Beer range varies Ⓗ
Long two-level bistro on ground floor of hotel offering up to three ales on tap.

Service

If you are unhappy with any aspect of service in a pub in the Guide, you should first complain to the manager or tenant of the pub, and then, if not satisfied, to the owner of the pub. Send a copy of your complaint, with any corrrespondence to GBG, CAMRA, 230 Hatfield Road, St Albans, Herts, AL1 4LW

NORTHERN IRELAND

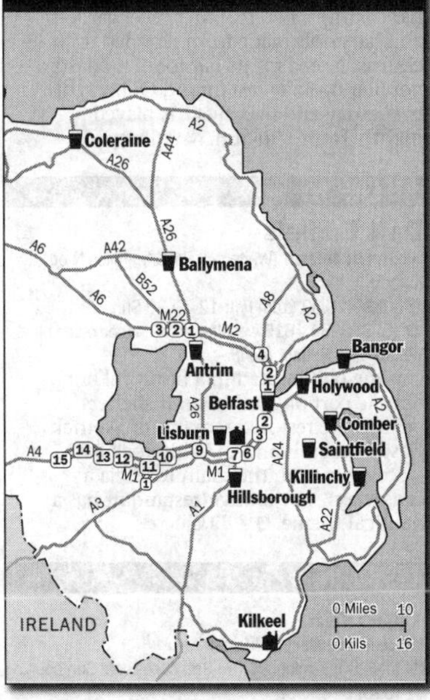

BALLYMENA

Spinning Mill

17-21 Broughshane Street

⏲ 11.30-11 (1am Fri & Sat); 11.30-1am Sun

☎ (028) 2563 8985

Courage Directors; Theakston Best Bitter; Whitewater Belfast Ale Ⓗ

The first Wetherspoon's pub in the Province provides sustenance in a real ale desert with occasional beer festivals in a cosy, friendly atmosphere. Children are now admitted to the upstairs no-smoking area beside the bar, which has the same range of beers as downstairs. Two changing guest beers are stocked from either NI or mainland breweries. ⋔Q❀◐◑⊬

BANGOR

Esplanade

12 Ballyholme Esplanade (approx. 1 mile from centre)

⏲ 11.30-11; 12.30-10 Sun

☎ (028) 9127 0954

website: www.gillespie-esplanade.com

Whitewater Glen Ale; guest beers Ⓗ

Converted three-storey house on a corner adjacent to the beach with a bar and off-licence to the rear. The patio affords wonderful views of Ballyholme Bay and Belfast Lough. Friendly staff are willing to serve the three ales in the recently refurbished lounge, and food is provided in both lounge and bar with a separate upstairs restaurant offering evening meals. The pub has its own golf society.

Q❀◐◑⊟♿

BELFAST

Beaten Docket

48-50 Great Victoria Street (opp. Europa Hotel)

⏲ 11.30-midnight (1am Thu-Sat); 11.30-10 Sun

☎ (028) 9024 2986

Beer range varies Ⓗ

20-year-old pub in one of Belfast's busiest areas at one end of the 'Golden Mile'. It serves two ales, with regular guests from across the water and is popular with the deaf community. Live music is staged downstairs on Friday evenings and upstairs on Saturday. Televised football is popular with a mixed crowd when a three-pint pitcher of ale is £4.95. Food is served 11.30-9 daily (until 6pm on Fri and Sun).

⋔◐◑≹(Gt Victoria St)

Bonaparte's

192 Cavehill Road

⏲ 11.30-11 (midnight Wed; 1am Thu-Fri); 12.30-midnight Sun

☎ (028) 9072 9292

Beer range varies Ⓗ

This attractively refurbished suburban pub sits below the city's impressive Cave Hill Country Park and is a welcome oasis. Three handpumps serve a continually changing range of guest beers, giving drinkers a taste of what is on offer from around the British Isles. The pub offers a high standard of food.

⋔◐◑⊬

Botanic Inn

23 Malone Road (500 yds from Queen's University)

⏲ 11-midnight (1am Thu-Sat); 11-midnight Sun

☎ (028) 9050 9740

Whitewater Belfast Ale Ⓗ

Large city pub catering mainly for students at the University, which is close by. Attractions include the front Sports bar including the obligatory large-screen TV. The main bar has one real ale and a very occasional guest. Entertainment plays a large part in the pub's popularity.

◐◑⊟≹(Botanic)

Crown Liquor Saloon

46 Great Victoria Street (opp. Europa Hotel)

⏲ 11.30-midnight; 12.30-10 Sun

☎ (028) 9027 9901

Whitewater Belfast Ale Ⓗ

Jewel in the crown of Belfast pubs and one of the National Trust's greatest treasures, with the finest example of high Victorian art created by Michael Flanagan in the late 1800s as the ultimate architectural fantasy of the day. The interior boasts rich, intricate carvings. ◐♿≹(Gt Victoria St)

Kitchen Bar

16-18 Victoria Square

⏲ 11.30-11 (1am Fri); 12-7 Sun

☎ (028) 9032 4901

Whitewater Belfast Ale; guest beers Ⓗ

Narrow, unspoilt building dating from the 1890s, the long, narrow bar opens into the parlour. It serves mainly English guest ales alongside the regular beers. Traditional music features on Friday with owner, Pat, occasionally bursting into song. Now under threat from developers, but there has been no news recently. Food is served 11.30-3 (until 6pm Thu-Sat, 5pm Sun).

◐◑⊟≹(Central)

INDEPENDENT BREWERIES

Hilden Lisburn

Whitewater Kilkeel

Rotterdam Bar

52-54 Pilot Street (1 mile N of city centre, off Corporation St)
11.30-1am (midnight Mon & Wed); 4-1.30am Sat; 4-midnight Sun
☎ (028) 9074 6021
Beer range varies Ⓗ
Hard to find but well worth it, this pub is sandwiched between modern apartments and Clarendon Dock and is one of the few remaining unspoilt bars. One pump dispenses various rotating ales. Live music is performed every night except Wednesday. Food is served 12-2.30 weekdays.
⛫◐⇌(Yorkgate)

COMBER

North Down House

101-103 Mill Street
12-midnight (1.30am Fri & Sat); 1-11 Sun
☎ (028) 9187 2242
Beer range varies Ⓗ
Traditional corner pub that has been updated in recent years. It now sports a lounge and pool playing area. Formerly a station pub it retains some railway-related memorabilia. North Down House is the only real ale pub in Comber, it dispenses one beer (often 4.5% ABV or stronger). Meals are served 12-5 Saturday, 1-5 Sunday.
◐⊟♿

HILLSBOROUGH

Hillside

21 Main Street
12-1am; 12-10 Sun
☎ (028) 9268 2765
Whitewater Belfast Ale Ⓗ
Halfway up the hill, this is the only real ale pub in Hillsborough to dispense regular ales and two frequently changing guests, to hold a beer festival in the summer, and be involved in the Oyster Festival in September. The atmosphere is warm and welcoming; on Sunday evening local jazz bands play. Food is offered 12-2.30 and 5-9 every day, while the upstairs restaurant is open from 7-9.30 Friday and Saturday nights. A courtyard serves as a garden.
⛫Q❀◐◑⊟♿▲

HOLYWOOD

Dirty Duck

2 Kinnegar Road (on esplanade 400 yds from railway bridge)
11-1am (11 Mon; 12.30am Tue; midnight Wed); 12.30-midnight Sun
☎ (028) 9059 6666
Beer range varies Ⓗ
Cosy, split-level pub on the shores of Belfast Lough with an apt nautical theme. Features include four handpumps, two real fires, beer garden, and barstools made from recycled milk churns. Noted for its bar food, it boasts a popular upstairs restaurant. Quiz night is Tuesday and live music is played nightly from Thu-Sun. ⛫❀◐◑⇌

KILLINCHY

Daft Eddie's

Sketrick Island (Whiterock Rd, 1½ miles N of Killinchy)
11.30-11.30 (1am Fri); 12-10.30 Sun
☎ (028) 9754 1615 website: www.dafteddies.co.uk
Whitewater Belfast Ale Ⓗ
Unique pub located in a beautiful but remote part of Co. Down. It shelters behind the restored remains of Sketrick Castle on an island in Whiterock Bay (accessible from the main road via a causeway). The lounge/restaurant has a nautical theme. Q❀◐◑⊟♿

LISBURN ❄

Taproom

Hilden Brewery, Hilden
12-2.30; 7-midnight Thu-Sat; occasional Sun opening
☎ (028) 9266 3863
website: www.networkpersonnel.org.uk/hilden
Hilden Ale, Molly Malone's Porter Ⓗ
Hilden Brewery's own licensed restaurant is located in the grounds of the Scullion family's Georgian manor. As well as the good food and ale, brewery tours can be arranged and the visitor centre reflects Hilden's linen heritage (it is only open certain Sundays, such as Easter, Father's and Mother's day). Beer festivals and concerts are hosted in the courtyard. Eve meals are offered 7-9 Thu-Sat.
⛫Q❀◐◑♿⇌(Hilden) P

SAINTFIELD

White Horse

49 Main Street
11-11; closed Sun
☎ (028) 9751 0417
Whitewater Northern Brewer, Knight Porter, seasonal beers; guest beer Ⓗ
Family-run village pub, current CAMRA Northern Ireland Pub of the Year. It runs its own annual beer festival and is one of the busiest outlets for real ale in the Province. Excellent food can be purchased in the bar or in the downstairs restaurant (an original stables conversion).
⛫Q◐◑⊟♿P⊬▯

INN BRIEF

ANTRIM

Stables
10-16 Castle Street
11.30-1am; 12-midnight Sun
(028) 9446 5189
Whitewater Belfast Ale Ⓗ
Popular pub and restaurant near the town centre. Ale is served in downstairs bar only.

COLERAINE

Old Courthouse
Castlerock Road
11.30-11 (1am Fri & Sat); 11.30-1am Sun
(028) 7032 5820
Courage Directors; Theakston Best Bitter; Whitewater Belfast Ale; guest beers Ⓗ
Wetherspoon's first conversion in Northern Ireland, a spacious one-bar pub in a former courthouse (two no-smoking areas). Children are admitted upstairs.

LISBURN

Tuesday Bell
Units 1 and 2, Lisburn Square
11.30-11.30 (1am Thu-Sat); 11.30-midnight Sun
(028) 9262 7390
Courage Directors; Hilden Ale, Molly Malone's Porter; Theakston Best Bitter; Whitewater Belfast Ale Ⓗ
New Wetherspoon's (not a conversion) that tends to be very busy. Focal point of a new shopping complex.

CHANNEL ISLANDS

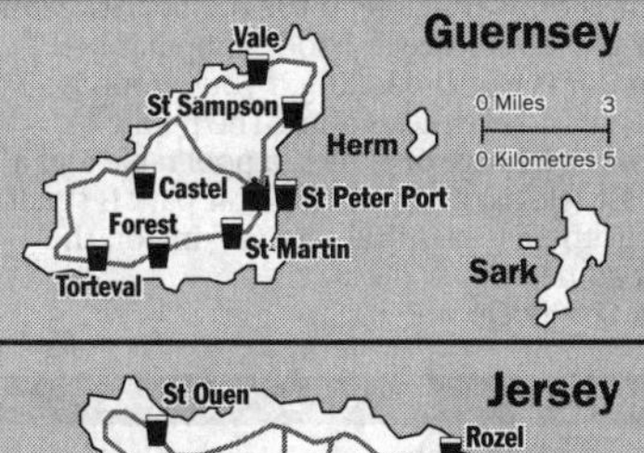

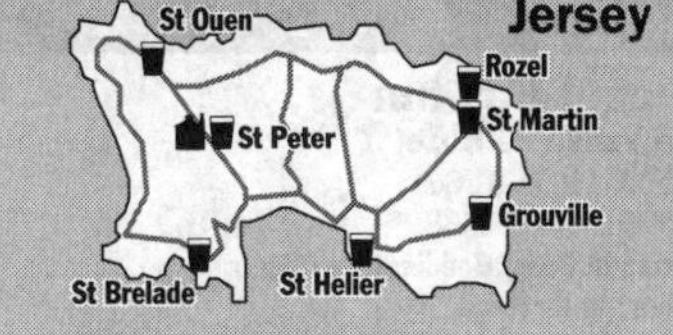

Guernsey

CASTEL ❄

Fleur du Jardin
Kings Mills
⏲ 10.30-11.45; 12-3.15 Sun ☎ (01481) 257996
Guernsey Pirates Ale, Sunbeam [H]
Country pub, with a good-sized sheltered garden, in an attractive setting. There is ample parking on site, but it can be busy during the summer. There are two bars: one small and cosy attached to the restaurant, the other large and airy; the same real ales are sold in both. The restaurant and bar menus feature fresh local produce, with daily changing specials. ♨Q⇄◐P

FOREST ❄

Venture Inn
New Road (2 minutes' drive from airport)
⏲ 10.30-midnight; closed Sun
☎ (01481) 263211
Randalls Patois, seasonal beers [H]
Popular, traditional, Guernsey hostelry, where the visitor is made to feel welcome in the lounge or busy public bars. The latter serve excellent food at lunchtime, with evening meals available Monday-Saturday during the summer and Friday and Saturday in winter. Parking is available to the front and the rear; well worth a visit. ♨◐P

ST MARTIN

Ambassador Hotel
Route de Sausmarez
⏲ 12-3, 6-11.45; 12-3.30 Sun
☎ (01481) 238356
Randalls Patois [H]
Situated just down from Sausmarez Manor, the bar area of this hotel has been renovated. An excellent range of meals is available, either in the bar or the old Guernsey conservatory. During the summer a sheltered patio area to the rear of the bar is brought into use. The bar is closed Sunday except for residents. There is limited parking to the front of the hotel. ❀⇄◐P

Queen's Hotel
La Grand Rue
⏲ 10.30-11.30; closed Sun ☎ (01481) 238398
Randalls Patois, seasonal beer [H]
The busy, locals' public bar is situated to the rear of the hotel, with access from the car park. The lounge bar, to the front, has walls adorned with posters of old film stars – Laurel and Hardy are the prime subject. Note too, the old poster for Randalls beer in the lounge bar window. Good quality food is served, with a dining area provided for non-smokers. ⇄◐P

ST PETER PORT ❄

Cock & Bull
Lower Hauteville
⏲ 11.30-2.30, 4-11.45; 11.30-11.45 Fri & Sat; closed Sun
☎ (01481) 722660
Beer range varies [H]
Popular pub, just up the hill from the town church. Five handpumps provide a changing range of beers which include Ringwood brews. A large-screen TV shows sporting events in the main bar area, but the pub is on three levels so there is plenty of choice of seating. The lower level houses a pool table. It stages regular beer festivals, some for charity, plus live music Tuesday and Thursday. Snacks are available at lunchtime.

Cornerstone Café Bar
2 La Tour Beauregard
⏲ 8am (9.30am Sat)-11.30pm; 9.30am-3.30pm Sun
☎ (01481) 713832
Courage Directors; Flowers IPA [H]
This former restaurant, has a small bar area to the front, but plenty of seating to the rear. The menu offers a wide selection of hot and cold food; it opens for breakfast. Note the collection of framed Giles cartoons and old advertising posters. Old Willy's is Randalls Pale Ale rebadged. ◐

Dog House
Rohais
(main route out of town, 200 yds from Safeway's)
⏲ 10.30-11.45; 12-3.30, 6.30-11.45 Sun
☎ (01481) 721302
Badger Tanglefoot; Randalls Patois [H]
Free house on the edge of town, specialising in live music each evening and some lunchtimes. Comfortable seating is surrounded by interesting murals. There is also a wood-panelled dining area. On Sunday a meal must be purchased to consume with alcohol, to comply with Guernsey licensing laws. Dining can be cramped when the pub is very busy. There is a patio area to the rear. ❀◐♿P

Randy Paddle
North Esplanade (opp. the tourist board office)
⏲ 10-11.45; closed Sun
☎ (01481) 725610
Badger Tanglefoot; Courage Directors [H]
Owned by the former landlady of the Drunken Duck, this is a bar which feels like a ship's cabin, in an area which would have originally housed cargo from the old sailing

INDEPENDENT BREWERIES

Guernsey St Peter Port
Randalls St Peter Port
Tipsy Toad St Peter

ships docked in the harbour across the road. It lies on the town crawl, but attracts a mixed crowd of people.

Ship & Crown

North Esplanade (opp. Crown Pier car park)
⏲ 10-11.45; 12-3.30, 6-10 Sun
☎ (01481) 721368
Guernsey Pirates Ale, Sunbeam, seasonal beers Ⓗ
Providing picturesque views of the harbour, this pub is popular with locals and tourists alike. There is a convenient public car park opposite. It appeals to all ages at different times of the day, being popular in the evening with the younger crowd, on the 'town crawl'. The walls are decorated with pictures of wartime occupation and local shipping disasters. Guernsey Braye is rebadged as Three Crowns. There is a good range of bar meals in generous portions; evening meals are served on Sunday to meet local licensing requirements. ◖

ST SAMPSON

La Fontaine Inn

Vale Road
⏲ 10.30-11.30; closed Sun
☎ (01481) 247644
Randalls Mild Ⓗ
Popular with the local community, the inn has a small public bar and a large L-shaped lounge, with its own bar and a small window further down in which to order beer from the public. A reasonably-sized car park stands to the rear, with a garden. The mild is sold as Cynfull, named after Cindy, the landlady. ❀P

VALE

Houmet Tavern

La Route du Picquerel
⏲ 10-11.45; closed Sun
☎ (01481) 242214
Guernsey Braye Ⓗ
The conservatory to the front of the lounge bar (which is designated as a no-smoking area) benefits from wonderful views of Grand Harve Bay. The friendly public bar has a range of games, including pool, darts and bar billiards. A good selection of bar meals is served in the lounge and conservatory (evening meals are available 7-8.45pm), except Mon, Thu and Sun).
❀◖◗♣●P⚡

Jersey

GROUVILLE ❊

Pembroke Inn

La Grande Route des Sablons
(by Royal Jersey Golf Club)
⏲ 11-11; 11-11 Sun
☎ (01534) 855756
Draught Bass; Courage Directors; guest beer Ⓗ
The Pembroke is a large, friendly pub. Real ale is only available in the public bar, so ask if you do not see it. Food is popular here, and it is worth booking if your group is large (no eve meals Sun). The public bar boasts a range of games, a pool table and a vast television screen. The car park is small, but there is plentiful safe parking on the road nearby.
♨Q❀◖◗⊟♿♣P

ROZEL

Rozel Bay Inn

La Vallée de Rozel
⏲ 11-11; 11-11 Sun
☎ (01534) 863438
Draught Bass; Boddingtons Bitter, Courage Directors Ⓗ
The Rozel Bay is very popular, and deservedly so. It has an extremely cosy lounge bar where three real ales are served from a small corner bar. The public bar houses a pool table and TV. There is a good pub menu and an à la carte restaurant upstairs. Evening meals are not served Sunday, except for summer barbecues. Outside is a delightful garden and a new patio area for alfresco dining. Car parking space is at a premium here.
♨Q❀◖◗⊟▲♣P

ST BRELADE

Old Smugglers Inn

Ouaisne Bay
⏲ 11-11; 11-11 Sun
☎ (01534) 741510
Draught Bass; guest beers Ⓗ
Historic pub, nestling next to Ouaisne Bay, home of the 'Agile Frog'. This busy, but cosy local, offers good beer and food. Note the distinctive carpet. A stalwart of real ale the Smugglers was until 2001, Jersey's only free house. The pub is recommended for its food and features a comprehensive menu, served in spacious dining areas. A fine beach is less than 100 yards away, and there is ample parking.
♨Q♉◖◗▲P✔

ST HELIER ❊

Lamplighter

Mulcaster Street (near bus station)
⏲ 11-11; 11-11 Sun
☎ (01534) 723119
Draught Bass; Boddingtons Bitter; Courage Directors; Theakston Old Peculier; guest beer Ⓗ
The Lamplighter is an institution on Jersey's real ale scene. Unashamedly a drinkers' pub, this was Jersey CAMRA Pub of the Year

INN BRIEF

Guernsey

CASTEL

Rockmount Hotel
Cobo Castel
10.30-11.45; 12-3.30 Sun
(01481) 256757
Randalls Patois Ⓗ
Just across the road from the beach, it has a busy lounge serving food and a public bar area.

FOREST

Deerhound Inn
Le Bourg
10.30-11.30; 12-3.30 Sun
(01481) 238585
Beer range varies Ⓗ
With a patio and garden, the inn has a no-smoking area and good food. No children admitted evenings.

ST PETER PORT

Banker's Draught
The Pollet
10-11.45; 12-3.30 Sun
(01481) 723855
Guernsey Sunbeam Ⓗ
Renamed due to the many finance houses in the vicinity. Sunbeam is rebadged as Banker's Draught. Live music Friday.

1999 and 2000, in recognition of consistently good quality and choice. The Lamplighter is the only pub in Jersey to be gaslit, lending it an intimate atmosphere in which to relax and socialise. Take time to look at the top of the pub from the outside.
◐♣●

Original Wine Bar

Bath Street
☼ 11-11; 4.30-11 Sun
☎ (01534) 871119
Beer range varies Ⓗ
Relaxed eating and drinking environment, with a variety of pastel-coloured areas. Very popular with women working in town, it offers a comprehensive wine range, but there is always a varied real ale choice, too. With usually up to four beers on tap, Tipsy Toad Jimmy's Bitter and Horny Toad alternate as regular brews. It won local CAMRA's Best Newcomer award in 1999 for its efforts in promoting real ale, and maintains a high standard. Door stewards are employed in the evenings.
Q◐♿⚟●

Prince of Wales

Hilgrove Street
☼ 10-11; 11-2 Sun
☎ (01534) 737378
Draught Bass; Wadworth 6X; guest beer Ⓗ
Busy, one-bar town pub next to the central market. An impressive bar, with stained glass inserts, dominates the room and frames a classic six-pump beer engine (but only three work). The back yard is a sun terrace, surrounding a little fountain, which offers a sanctuary from bustling St Helier. The pub services town workers and is very busy at lunchtime, when meals are available. It is less hectic in the evening.
Q❀◐

> Beware of the wily
> Martini
> And don't exceed
> two at the most
> With three you'll be
> under the table
> With four you'll be
> under the host.
>
> *Anon*

ST MARTIN

Royal Hotel

La Grande Route de Faldouet (opp. church)
☼ 9.30 (11 lounge bar)-11; 11-11 Sun
☎ (01534) 856289
Draught Bass; guest beer Ⓗ
This is a large, popular pub opposite the village church. It successfully combines a variety of drinking and dining areas, including a large public bar with games and TV, a comfortable lounge with armchairs and a roaring fire, a spacious family dining area, sun terrace, and an upstairs restaurant. The two real ales are very reliable. It is one of the most wheelchair-friendly pubs in Jersey and also caters well for children. The food is served rapidly and in generous portions (no meals Sun eve).
♨Q♉❀◐◑⊟♿⛺♣⚟

ST OUEN

Moulin de Lecq

Grève de Lecq
☼ 11-11; 11-11 Sun
☎ (01534) 482818
Draught Bass; Guernsey Sunbeam; guest beers Ⓗ
This is one of Jersey's most picturesque pubs – a must for tourists. It is a converted 12th-century watermill, with a working drive wheel behind the bar. The mill was used to generate power by the Germans during the occupation. The cosy lounge bar is warmed by a roaring fire in winter, while a large outdoor area hosts barbecues in summer, with a playground for children. In 2001, the Moulin was refurbished and became a free house, serving two regular and two guest beers.
♨Q♉❀◐◑⛺P

ST PETER

Star & Tipsy Toad Brewery

La Route de Beaumont
☼ 9-11.30; 11-11.30 Sun
☎ (01534) 485556
Tipsy Toad Ale, Jimmy's Bitter; guest beer Ⓗ
Home of the Tipsy Toad Brewery, Jersey's only remaining real ale producer. Refurbished and reopened in late 2000, the Star is smart and bright, with a variety of dining and drinking areas surrounding a central bar. All the Tipsy Toad beers are served, but the brewery is not large, and sometimes only the award-winning Jimmy's Bitter may be on tap. The main bar features a stained glass roof. Tours of the brewery are available on request. Live music is performed on Saturday evening. Meals are served Mon-Sat.
♨Q♉❀◐◑♿♣P

TORTEVAL
Imperial Hotel
Pleinmount
10.30-11.45; closed Sun
(01481) 265243
Randalls Patois Ⓗ
Newly refurbished lounge bar affording wonderful views across Rocquaine Bay. Handpumps in both lounge and public bars.

Jersey
GROUVILLE
Seymour Inn
La Rue du Puits Mahaut
11-11; 11-11 Sun
(01534) 854558
Tipsy Toad Jimmy's Bitter Ⓗ
Friendly coastal pub with a separate real ale bar in summer. Excellent for games.

ST HELIER
Dog & Sausage
Halkett Street
11-11; 11-11 Sun
(01534) 730982
Draught Bass Ⓗ
Small pub in the main shopping area, opposite McDonald's. Note the railway features. There is another bar upstairs.

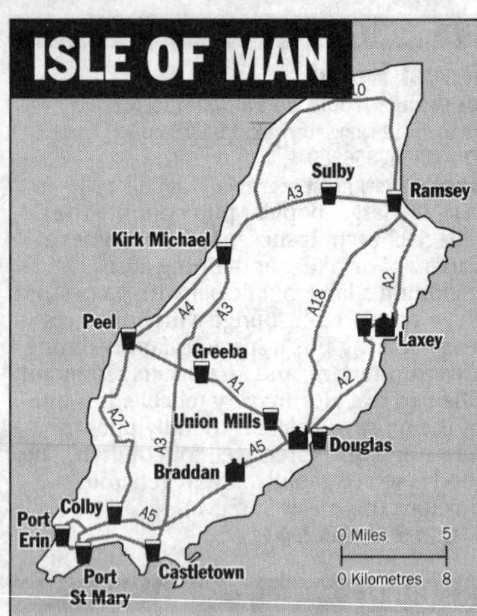

CASTLETOWN

Castle Arms (Gluepot)

The Quay

12-10.45 (midnight Fri & Sat); 12-3, 7-10.30 Sun
(01624) 824673

Cains Bitter; Okells Bitter H

Small, picturesque harbourside pub, circa 1760, in the shadow of Castle Rushen. Two rooms display nautical memorabilia. The nickname derives from the days when glue was made in the pub's cellar for use in repairing boats in the nearby harbour. Food is served 12-3, plus Thai cuisine on Friday and Saturday evenings. There is a pleasant outdoor seating area, and a private function room. Handy for Ronaldsway Airport, it lies on the Douglas to Port Erin bus route.
(IMR)

Ship

Hope Street (opp. inner harbour)

12-11 (midnight Fri & Sat); 12-3, 7-10.30 Sun
(01624) 824959

Okells Bitter H

The large basic bar acts as a lounge/games room (darts and pool). A corridor leads to the first-floor Chart Room bar, affording views of the inner harbour. It has a smart wood and tiled bar and a raised seating area for dining; an extensive bar menu is served. Prints of sailing ships adorn the walls. Across the harbour you can see the closed Castletown Brewery, now private accommodation. From the rear the pub resembles a ship, complete with a large red funnel. (IMR)

Sidings

Victoria Road (by station)

12-10 (midnight Fri & Sat); 12-3, 7-10.30 Sun
(01624) 823282

Bushy's Manannan's Cloak; Marston's Pedigree; Theakston Mild, Best Bitter; guest beers H

Large, black and white free house, next to Castletown Station, on the edge of town. The IMR line runs a regular service in summer from Douglas to Port Erin. A handsome, carved wood, long bar, with old church pews is the dominant feature of the pub. It boasts a games room, a lounge/dining area, with a stone fireplace, and a large, well-kept garden to the rear. It stocks the widest range of guest beers on the island (seven). Good value snacks are served Mon-Sat. (IMR)

COLBY

Colby Glen Hotel

Main Road (A7)

12-11 (midnight Fri & Sat); 12-3, 7-10.30 Sun
(01624) 834853

Okells Mild, Bitter H

This spacious pub sits by the main road of a rural village. Its rooms include a wood-panelled bar, a comfortable lounge, with a central stone fireplace and a games room. Diners can choose between the restaurant, which incorporates a raised carvery area and a no-smoking section, or the quaint Colby Diner attached to the pub, serving an excellent, varied menu. The No.1 bus from Douglas to Port St Mary stops nearby every half-hour.
P

DOUGLAS

Albert Hotel

3 Chapel Row (next to bus station)

10-11 (midnight Fri & Sat); 12-3, 7-10.30 Sun
(01624) 673632

Okells Mild, Bitter H

Typical back-street, busy Manx pub, full of character. A lounge bar and a basic vault, housing a pool table and Sky TV, are set around a central bar. Photographs of former Isle of Man Steampacket Co. boats and TT riders adorn the wood-panelled walls. It boasts a well-run social club, with over 100 members, and holds charity nights, including an auction. Joughs house bitter is brewed especially for the pub by Okells.
Q (IMR)

Forester's Arms

St Georges Street (near station)

12-11 (midnight Fri & Sat); 12-3, 7-10.30 Sun
(01624) 676509

Okells Mild, Bitter H

Excellent street-corner local: a traditional, characterful Manx pub, this former Castletown house retains its original brewery windows. A central bar serves several small rooms, including an old-fashioned snug. The pub is just off the central downtown area of Douglas in the finance district; the IOM Tourist Minister and Mayor of Douglas number among its clientele, which includes office workers weekday lunchtimes. It hosts lively social activities. Basic sandwiches and toasties are available during the day. Alterations are planned.
(IMR)

Old Market Tavern

2 Chapel Row (near bus station)

12-11 (midnight Fri & Sat); 12-3, 7-10.30 Sun
(01624) 675202

Bushy's Bitter; Okells Bitter H

Eye-catching blue tiles clad the exterior of this old-fashioned back-street local where a central bar serves two wood-panelled rooms. Very popular with visitors to the island, it has so far resisted selling food. The friendly licensee and regulars are keen supporters of local charities. Situated next to the Albert, the two pubs complement each other. It stays open until midnight

every night during TT fortnight. The hallway often becomes crowded evenings and weekends.
⚘⊟⇌(IMR)

Rovers Return

11 Church Street (behind Town Hall)
⏲ 12-11 (midnight Fri & Sat); 12-3, 7-10.30 Sun
☎ (01624) 676459
Bushy's Ruby Mild, Bitter, seasonal beers; guest beers Ⓗ
Previously the Albion Hotel, belonging to Castletown Brewery, now a back-street local. An outside cobbled drinking area at the front has tables and chairs in the summer. Named after the licensee's favourite Blackburn football team, a small bar serves a large basic room and three other smaller rooms, one of which is a shrine to the Lancashire club. Another room bears fire brigade memorabilia; note the unusual handpumps – fire brigade brass branch pipes which came from the former fire station nearby.
⚘ ⇌(IMR)

Saddle Inn

2 Queen's Street (on harbour)
⏲ 10-11 (midnight Fri & Sat); 12-4, 7-10.30 (12-10.30 summer) Sun
☎ (01624) 673161
Cains Bitter; Okells Mild, Bitter; guest beers Ⓗ
Small, two-roomed bar just off the quay, it retains the bare-boarded character of a local fishermen's haunt. This lively, friendly local can get very busy. Racing silks adorn the walls, alongside a large photo of Joey Dunlop, a tribute to this famous adopted son of the Isle of Man. Joey was an Irish motorcycle champion, who, having won the TT more times than any other rider, was worshipped the world over. He died in 2000, racing in Estonia, and is sadly missed. The pub hosts karaoke, and pool is played.
⇌(IMR) ♣

Terminus Tavern

Strathallan Crescent
⏲ 12-11 (midnight Fri & Sat); 12-3, 7-10.30 Sun
☎ (01624) 624312
Okells Mild, Bitter; guest beers Ⓗ
This spacious, multi-roomed black and white pub boasts bay windows overlooking the promenade at the termini of the horse tram and Manx Electric Railway. With a large outdoor seating area at the front, the accommodation includes a no-smoking family room. Old photographs feature Stan Laurel and Oliver Hardy. In summer just sit outside and watch the world go by and enjoy the panoramic views across Douglas Bay. ⊟♿⊖(MER)

Waterloo Hotel

77 Strand Street
⏲ 12-11 (midnight Fri & Sat); 12-3, 7-10.30 Sun
☎ (01624) 677468
Okells Mild, Bitter Ⓗ
Small, very basic, tile-fronted, typical Manx pub, tucked away in the main pedestrian shopping street. Its two rooms (one housing a pool table) are joined by a narrow drinking corridor displaying horse racing photographs. A collection of water jugs and plates feature in the front bar. Simple sandwiches and toasties are sold at lunchtime. This unspoilt pub is welcoming and friendly, and can get very busy and noisy; it hosts karaoke on Friday evenings.
♣

Woodbourne Hotel

Alexander Drive (off Woodbourne Rd)
⏲ 12-11 (midnight Fri & Sat); 12-3, 7-10.30 Sun
☎ (01624) 676754
Okells Mild, Bitter Ⓗ
Large Victorian, suburban multi-roomed former hotel in a residential area; worth finding for a friendly, quiet drink, among customers of all ages. Three bars serve the various rooms, which include a games room (darts and dominoes), a gentlemen-only bar (rules tend to be relaxed at times) and a large, comfortable front lounge. You could describe it as three pubs in one with three different sets of clientele, who all get on with one another. Q⊟

KIRK MICHAEL

Mitre Hotel

Main Road (A3)
⏲ 12-11 (midnight Fri & Sat); 12-3, 7-10.30 Sun
☎ (01624) 878244
Okells Mild, Bitter; guest beers Ⓗ
Large roadside village pub/restaurant, said to be the oldest on the island (circa 1789). Its large car park is an ideal spot for watching the TT races. An extensive garden and safe children's play area to the rear afford a fine panoramic view towards the mountains. A split bar serves both the lounge and dining area, and is wheelchair-friendly. An unusual pub game, shulbac, which originated in Holland, was introduced here and has been taken up by other island pubs. The adjacent former fire station is now the function room.
⚘ ⊟♿Δ♣P

LAXEY

Mines Tavern

Captains Hill (Douglas/Ramsey/Snaefell station interchange)
⏲ 12-11 (midnight Fri & Sat); 12-3, 7-10.30 Sun
☎ (01624) 861484
Bushy's Bitter; Okells Bitter Ⓗ
Adjacent to the delightful Laxey electric tram station and Snaefell mountain railway terminus, the Ramsey to Douglas bus stops nearby. This popular, family-run tourist pub is also favoured by locals. Enter the public bar from the garden and you will find a counter resembling a Manx Electric Railway car. A safe children's play area is another feature. Speciality 'sizzling platters' and home-cooked food are served daily. A trip to the summit of Snaefell (2,000 ft) and a visit to the Lady Isabella Waterwheel are recommended. ⊟⇌⊖(MER)

PEEL

Royal Hotel

25 Atholl Street (opp. bus station)
⏲ 12-11 (midnight Fri & Sat); 12-3, 7-10.30 Sun
☎ (01624) 842217

INDEPENDENT BREWERIES

Bushy's Braddan
Okells Douglas
Old Laxey Laxey

Okells Mild, Bitter Ⓗ
Faded, red-brick, three-storey pub, sandwiched between a church and a pharmacy in the town centre, it stands just off the main street, leading to the harbour and the promenade. This cosy, L-shaped local has a comfortable, attractive outdoor eating area that hosts barbecues on summer weekends, while live music nights are occasionally held in the rear lounge. A feature of the pub is a serving hatch from the bar to the small front room. Q❀▲

White House

2 Tynwald Road
12-11 (midnight Fri & Sat); 12-3, 7-10.30 Sun
☎ (01624) 842252
Bushy's Bitter; Okells Mild, Bitter; guest beers Ⓗ
Currently five real ales are stocked at this multi-roomed pub, where a snug, a public bar, music room and pool room, all surround a central bar. Local musicians meet most Saturday evenings to play Gaelic music at this popular pub, that enjoys substantial local support. A genuine free house, one of very few on the island, it also hosts occasional karaoke and 'poetry & pint' nights. Serving one of the best pints on the island (awards adorn the walls), this family-run gem serves lunchtime snacks.
❀♿▲P

PORT ERIN

Falcon's Nest Hotel

Station Road (Spaldrick Promenade jct)
12-11 (midnight Fri & Sat); 12-3, 7-10.30 Sun
☎ (01624) 834077
Okells Bitter; guest beers Ⓗ
Splendid, spacious seafront hotel with two public bars, real ale is served in the front lounge bar. It commands a fine view of Port Erin's small harbour and combines a comfortable, relaxing atmosphere with superb service. During the 19th century the hotel was the most prestigious on the island serving such distinguished patrons as Prime Minister WE Gladstone; it is now being restored to its former elegance. Children are made very welcome; good food is served in the bar or restaurant. ⇌(IMR)

PORT ST MARY

Albert Hotel

Athol Street
12-11 (midnight Fri & Sat); 12-10.30 Sun
☎ (01624) 832118
Draught Bass; Okells Bitter; guest beers Ⓗ
Small harbourside free house, recently sympathetically refurbished and extended, a wood-blocked floor and wrought-iron tables enhance its appearance. The extension includes a raised games area for pool and darts, and a bistro has been created in the former pool room. Two guest beers are always available, and it can get very busy at weekends. It has five guest rooms, and enjoys a panoramic view of the small harbour. The Douglas bus stops outside.
Q♣

RAMSEY

Swan Hotel

Parliament Square (near bus station)
12-11 (midnight Fri & Sat); 12-3, 7-10.30 Sun
☎ (01624) 814236
Okells Mild, Bitter, seasonal beers Ⓗ
Large, town-centre modern local, on the TT course. A central bar serves a spacious, comfortable lounge and a games room that supports darts and pool teams. It runs a winter quiz league and a social club for its regulars. Lunches are served Mon-Sat. It is wheelchair-accessible, including designated WCs. There is an extensive garden at the rear, and it is convenient for the MER terminus. ♿(MER)

Trafalgar

West Quay
12-11 (midnight Fri & Sat); 7-10.30 Sun
☎ (01624) 801624
Draught Bass; Bushy's Bitter; Cains Bitter; guest beer Ⓗ
Busy quayside local that also caters for visitors; no gimmicks, no frills, just good real ale, with usually one guest on tap. The good meals, with seafood a speciality, should not be missed. The friendly licensees provide free food for local sports teams at weekends. This local CAMRA Pub of the Year 1996/97 benefits from harbour views.
(MER) ♣

SULBY

Sulby Glen Hotel

Sulby Cross Roads (A3)
12-11 (midnight Fri & Sat); 12-3, 7-10.30 Sun
☎ (01624) 897240

INN BRIEF

DOUGLAS

Trafalgar
South Quay
12-11 (midnight Fri & Sat); 12-11 Sun
(01624) 618131
Okells Mild, Bitter Ⓗ
Recently reopened and attractively refurbished. First-floor drinking area has views over the harbour. Snacks weekday lunchtime.

GREEBA

Hawthorn
Main Road
12-11 (midnight Fri & Sat); 12-10 Sun
(01624) 801268
Okells Bitter; guest beers Ⓗ
Former well-known pub on the TT course has reopened primarily as a restaurant; also caters for real ale drinkers. Meals daily 12-9.

PORT ERIN

Bay
Shore Road
12-midnight (including Sun)
(01624) 832084
Bushy's Ruby Mild, Bitter, Old Bushy Tail, seasonal beers; guest beers Ⓗ
Former Guide entry, reopened by Bushy's Brewery (after being closed for 12 years) and restored with minor improvements.

RAMSEY

Mitre Hotel
Parliament Street
10-11 (midnight Fri & Sat); 12-2.30, 8-11.30 Sun
(01624) 813045
Draught Bass; Cains Bitter; Okells Bitter; guest beers (summer) Ⓗ
Long, narrow upstairs bar with panoramic views of the busy working harbour and occasionally beyond to the Lake District. Lunches served.

Bushy's Bitter, seasonal beers; Okells Bitter; guest beers Ⓗ
Pleasant, spacious, roadside hotel, situated at the centre of the village by the picturesque Sulby Straight, a very fast section of the TT course. With 11 guest rooms, it is ideally placed for motorcycle fans, or those who simply appreciate the attractive rural surroundings. Its two bars display much TT memorabilia, including signed photographs. Manx CAMRA Pub of the Year 1998 and 1999, it hosts an annual 'Battle of the Pubs' challenge, where games include wellie-throwing and canoeing. Sunday evening meals are available in summer.
♨Q❀🛏◐◑♿▲♣P✔

UNION MILLS

Railway Inn

On A1
🕐 12-11 (midnight Fri & Sat); 12-10.30 Sun
☎ (01624) 853006 website: www.therailwayinn.cjb.net
Boddingtons Bitter; Okells Mild, Bitter; guest beers Ⓗ
Village pub – a hive of social activity – serving up to three guest beers. A true free house, this former Castletown Brewery tied house has been in the same family for over 100 years, and has never had a man's name over the front door. One central bar serves the main lounge and several small rooms. Its former names include the Grapes and the Prince of Wales; look out for original memorabilia at this Manx CAMRA Pub of the Year 2000. ♨Q❀♣P

Never ask for 'a beer'...

No one goes into a restaurant and requests 'a plate of food, please'. People do not ask simply for 'a glass of wine', without specifying, at the very least, whether they fancy red or white, dry or sweet, perhaps sparkling or still. More often, they trouble to decide whether the red should be American or Australian, Italian or French, from Burgundy or Bordeaux, and choose a vineyard and year. When their mood switches from the grape to the grain, these same discerning folk often ask simply for 'a beer', or perhaps name a brand, without thinking about its suitability for the mood or moment.

What the British call 'plonk' and the American 'jug wine' is often well-made and good value, but there is more to the grape than that. It is well understood that there are 'fine wines', but less widely appreciated that beer can be equally varied, complex and noble.

The similarities between wines and beers are far greater than the difference. Wines begin with fruit (usually, but not always, the grape), while beers start with grain (customarily, but not necessarily, barley); both are made by fermentation; and many of the flavour compounds naturally formed are shared between them. Distil wine and you have brandy. Distil beer and you have whisky.

Wine was not born with a vocabulary; that came later, with the help of writers such as Saintsbury, Lichine and Johnson. Any wine-writer who has ever enjoyed beers (and most have) will confirm that some are drier, others sweeter; this one firm-bodied, that soft; one hints at pears or oranges, another at coffee or chocolate. This is not a difficult language; anyone with any interest in the tastes of foods and drinks already has a smattering of it, and it is the easiest way in which to appreciate beer, Wine-makers and brewers often prefer chemical descriptors, but those hardly reflect drink as a pleasure.

'Do you ever drink wine?' people ask me, as though beer were a prison rather than a playground. A day may pass when I do not drink wine, but never a week. Whatever is argued about other pleasures, it is not necessary to be monogamous in the choice of drink. Beer is by far the more extensively consumed, but less adequately honoured. In a small way, I want to help put right that injustice.

Michael Jackson, *Beer Companion,* Mitchell Beazley, 1993

Illustrations: John Simpson

The Breweries

A Day in the Life of a Craft Brewery

Malt Mill
Barley malt is ground in a mill at the top of the brewery. The mill has several settings: most of the malt is ground to flour, but it's blended with coarser grits and the rough husks of the grain: the husks act as a natural filter. The ground malt is known as grist, a term that gives us the old English expression 'all grist to the mill'.

The Mash Tun
Traditional ale starts its journey with an 'infusion mash'. The mash tun is like a giant tea pot and brewers 'warm the pot' with water before filling the vessel with grist and pure hot 'liquor' — the pure water used only in the brewing process. The thick porridge-like mixture stands in the mash tun for two hours while natural enzymes in the malt convert starch into fermentable sugar.

The Coppers
The sweet wort flows to the copper or boiling kettle. The liquid is boiled vigorously for up to two hours and hops are added in three stages: at the start of the boil, halfway through, and just a few minutes before the boil ends. The oils, acids and resins in the cones of the hops add bitterness to the wort and also impart citrus and resiny characteristics, too.

Paraflow
After the copper boil, the 'hopped wort' is pumped through a refrigeration unit known as a paraflow. Plates containing the boiling liquid are interleaved with plates containing cold water. The paraflow lowers the temperature of the wort prior to fermentation.

Fermenters
Now the wort prepares to meet its destiny in fermenting vessels. Yeast is mixed or 'pitched' with the wort. For ale brewing, yeast strains are known as 'top fermenting': as the yeast transforms malt sugars into alcohol and carbon dioxide it creates a thick crust on top of the liquid, rising to peaks known as cauliflowers. Brewers like to give ale 'two Sabbaths' in the fermenters to ensure a full conversion of sugar to alcohol.

Racking
When fermentation is finished, the 'green' beer is left to stand in conditioning tanks for a few days. Then the beer flows from the tanks via pipes into casks: this is known as 'cask racking'. Additional liquid brewing sugar may be added to encourage a strong second fermentation, and the beer may also be 'dry hopped' with the addition of small amounts of hops for extra flavour and aroma. Finings or isinglass, made from the swim bladders of fish, are also added: finings slowly clear the beer of yeast.

How to use The Breweries section

Breweries are listed in alphabetical order. The Independents (regional, smaller craft brewers and brew-pubs) are listed first, followed by the Nationals and finally the major non-brewing Pub Groups. Within each brewery entry, beers are listed in increasing order of strength. Beers that are available for less than three months of the year are described as 'occasional' or 'seasonal' brews. Bottle-conditioned beers are also listed: these are beers that have not been pasteurised and contain live yeast, allowing them to continue to ferment and mature in the bottle as a draught real ale does in its cask.

Symbols

A brew-pub: a pub that brews beer on the premises.

CAMRA tasting notes, supplied by a trained CAMRA tasting panel. Beer descriptions that do not carry this symbol are based on more limited tastings or have been obtained from other sources.
Tasting notes are not provided for brew-pub beers that are available in fewer than five outlets, nor for other breweries' beers that are available for less than three months of the year.

A CAMRA Beer of the Year in the past three years.

One of the 2002 CAMRA Beers of the Year, a finalist in the Champion Beer of Britain competition held during the Great British Beer Festival at Olympia in August 2002, or the Champion Winter Beer of Britain competition held earlier in the year.

The brewery's beers can be acceptably served through a 'tight sparkler' attached to the nozzle of the beer pump, designed to give a thick collar of foam on the beer.

The brewery's beer should NOT be served through a tight sparkler. CAMRA is opposed to the growing tendency to serve southern-brewed beers with the aid of sparklers, which aerate the beer and tend to drive hop aroma and flavour into the head, altering the balance of the beer achieved in the brewery.

Abbreviations

OG stands for original gravity, the measure taken before fermentation of the level of 'fermentable material' (malt sugars and added sugars) in the brew. It is a rough indication of strength and is no longer used for duty purposes.

ABV stands for Alcohol by Volume, which is a more reliable measure of the percentage of alcohol in the finished beer. Many breweries now only disclose ABVs but the Guide lists OGs where available. Often the OG and the ABV of a beer are identical, ie 1035 and 3.5 per cent. If the ABV is higher than the OG, ie OG 1035, ABV 3.8, this indicates that the beer has been 'well attenuated' with most of the malt sugars turned into alcohol. If the ABV is lower than the OG, this means residual sugars have been left in the beer for fullness of body and flavour: this is rare but can apply to some milds or strong old ales, barley wines, and winter beers.

*The Breweries Section was correct at the time of going to press and every effort has been made to ensure that all cask-conditioned and bottle-conditioned beers are included.

The Independents

*** Indicates new entry since last edition**

ABBEY ALES

Abbey Ales Ltd, The Abbey Brewery, Camden Row, Bath, Somerset, BA1 5LB
Tel (01225) 444437
Fax (01225) 443569
E-mail am@abbeyales.co.uk
Website www.abbeyales.co.uk
Tours by arrangement

⊗ Abbey Ales is the only new brewery in Bath for more than 40 years and is the initiative of brewery sales and marketing manager Alan Morgan. Bellringer, the one regular cask beer, was launched at the Bath Beer Festival in 1997 and has now won a CAMRA beer of the festival award every year since then, including Beer of the Festival, Cotswolds , July 98; Devizes May 99; Bath 2000; Runner Up Bath 2001; and a finalist in the Champion Beer of Britain 2001. Seasonal beers include Bath Star (ABV 4.5%, spring), Chorister (ABV 4.5%, autumn) and Twelfth Night (ABV 5%, Christmas). The brewery currently supplies more than 80 regular accounts within a 20-mile radius of Bath Abbey. Selected wholesalers handle deliveries nationally. One tied house, the Star Inn, Bath, is listed on the CAMRA National Inventory of Heritage Inns.

Bellringer *(OG 1042, ABV 4.2%)* ⌂◆
A notably hoppy ale which is light to medium-bodied, clean-tasting, refreshingly dry, with a balancing sweetness. Citrus, pale malt aroma and dry, bitter finish. Consistent. Amber-gold in colour.

ABBEYDALE

Abbeydale Brewery, Unit 8, Aizlewood Road, Sheffield, S Yorkshire, S8 0YX
Tel (0114) 281 2712
Fax (0114) 281 2713
E-mail
Website sales@abbeydalebrewery.co.uk

⊗ Started in 1996 by Patrick Morton, previously of Kelham Island, the brewery is located to the south of the city in the Abbeydale area, which took its name from Beauchief Abbey, a medieval monastery. It was built by men who were involved in the murder of Thomas à Becket, hence the ecclesiastical theme of the beers.

Matins *(OG 1035, ABV 3.6%)*

Bitter *(OG 1038, ABV 4%)*

Moonshine *(OG 1041, ABV 4.3%)*

Absolution *(OG 1050, ABV 5.3%)*

Black Mass *(OG 1062, ABV 6.6%)*

Last Rites *(OG 1105, ABV 11.5%)*

ADNAMS

Adnams PLC, Sole Bay Brewery, Southwold, Suffolk, IP18 6JW
Tel (01502) 727200

Fax (01502) 727201
E-mail info@adnams.co.uk
Website www.adnams.co.uk
Shop 9.30-6.30 Mon-Sat

⊗ The earliest recorded brewing on the site of Adnams was in 1345 by Johanna de Corby. The present brewery was taken over by George and Ernest Adnams in 1872 and turned into a public company in 1890. The Adnams family was joined by the Loftus family in 1902, and Adnams still has three members of the families working for the company: John Adnams, president, chairman Simon Loftus, and Jonathan Adnams, managing director. Adnams remains committed to brewing cask ale and unthemed pubs. Real ale is available in 84 of its 85 pubs, and it also supplies some 750 other outlets direct. New fermenting vessels were installed in 2001 to cope with increased demand. Seasonal beers are now available for longer periods: Regatta (ABV 4.3%, spring/summer), Fisherman (ABV 4.5%, autumn/winter), Tally Ho (ABV 7%, Christmas ▮).

Bitter *(OG 1036, ABV 3.7%)* ⌂◆
An excellent drinking beer, with the characteristic Adnams' aroma of hops, citrus fruits and sulphur. The flavour is dry and hoppy, with some fruit. The finish is long, dry and hoppy.

Regatta *(OG 1042, ABV 4.3%)*
Light, bright and crisp in flavour with a refreshing touch of bitterness.

Fisherman *(OG 1047, ABV 4.5%)*
Rich and complex, but clean and refreshing, deep copper-red ale. Roasted nuts and dark chocolate dominate the aroma, with lingering flavours of liquorice and dried fruits.

Broadside
(OG 1049, ABV 4.7%) ◆
A mid-brown beer with a well-balanced flavour of fruit, malt and hops on a bitter-sweet base. The aroma is fruity, with some underlying malt and hops. Bitter fruit finish.

ALCAZAR

Alcazar Brewing Company, 33 Church Street, Old Basford, Nottingham, NG6 0GA
Tel (0115) 942 2002
Fax (0115) 978 2282
Website www.alcazarbrewingco.com
Tours by arrangement

Alcazar Brewing Company was established in 1999 and is located immediately behind its brewery tap, the Fox & Crown brew-pub. The name Alcazar is a Spanish word meaning 'palace', which relates to the crown in the brewery tap's name. The brewery is full mash, with a 12-barrel brew length. Production to date has primarily been for the Fox & Crown, with smaller quantities sold on demand to local free houses and beer festivals. It is intended to expand the brewing operation for regular sales to the free trade as well as bottling a range of new beers for the local and export markets. Visitors are always welcome to the brewery and regular tours are conducted on Saturdays, but prior arrangements are requested. Seasonal ale: Maple Magic Winter Ale (ABV 5.5%, winter).

Alcazar Ale *(OG 1037, ABV 3.7%)*
A traditional session ale made with a blend of English and North American hops; pale, full flavoured with a fruity aroma and finish.

Black Fox *(OG 1039, ABV 3.9%)*
A dark ruby-coloured mild with distinctive fruit taste and aroma.

Nottingham Nog *(OG 1046, ABV 4.2%)*
A dark session ale brewed with five types of malt and three varieties of hops; rich and smooth with fruit tones and a palate-pleasing finish.

New Dawn *(OG 1045, ABV 4.5%)*
Golden ale made with North American hops. A fruity aroma is balanced by a crisp, malty taste.

Brush Bitter *(OG 1049, ABV 4.9%)*
An amber bitter with a well-rounded flavour, maltiness on the palate and a distinctive hoppy finish.

Vixen's Vice *(OG 1052, ABV 5.2%)*
A pale, strong ale with a rich malt flavour balanced by a clean, crisp, hop taste.

Maple Magic *(OG 1055, ABV 5.5%)*
A seasonal winter ale. An English porter with a smooth and rich balance of malt, hops and spices.

ALES OF SCILLY*

Ales of Scilly Brewery, Higher Trenoweth, St Mary's, Isles of Scilly, TR21 0NS
Tel (01720) 422419
Tours by arrangement

The brewery opened in 2001. It is a two-barrel plant, is the first brewery to be built on the islands, and is the most south-westerly brewery in Britain. It currently supplies local pubs and occasional exports to 'England'. Bottled beers are planned.

Maiden Voyage *(ABV 4%)*

Three Sheets *(ABV 4.2%)*

Scuppered *(ABV 4.6%)*

ALEWIFE

Alewife Brewery, Starston, Harleston, Norfolk, IP20 9NN
Tel (01379) 855267
E-mail AlewifeBrewery@yahoo.co.uk
Website www.alewifebrewery.co.uk
Shop Mail order service

A small brewery set up in 2000 by Jane Taylor, who had been home-brewing for 20 years. Her friends so admired her Xmas brew that they encouraged her to brew commercially. She concentrates on bottle-conditioned beers as casks are too heavy for her to handle, though she brews cask beer occasionally when she has help. She supplies one pub, several off-licences and also sells by mail order. Bottle conditioned: Harvest Ale (ABV 4.5%), Dark Skies Stout (ABV 4.6%), Festival Ale (ABV 6.5%), Hunters Moon (ABV 7%). All beers are suitable for vegetarians.

Harvest Ale *(ABV 4.5%)*
A full-bodied, amber-coloured bitter brewed using lightly crushed malts, roast barley and Wye Challenger hops. Carageen, a type of seaweed, is used to ensure beer clarity during the brewing process.

Dark Skies Stout *(ABV 4.6%)*
A smooth bottle-conditioned stout made with lashing of chocolate malt and roasted barley to give the beer a subtle bitterness.

Festival Ale *(ABV 6.5%)*
A smooth, dark, fruity ale brewed using chocolate malt and a mixture of the finest English hops including Goldings. It is matured for several months before bottling to produce a truly festive ale.

Hunters Moon *(ABV 7%)*
A reddish-coloured, mildly hopped ale.

ALTRINCHAM

Altrincham Brewing Company, Old Market Tavern, Old Market Place, Altrincham, Cheshire, WA14 4DN
Tel (0771) 2033886 (mobile)
(0161) 9277062 (pub)
E-mail dave_ward@connectfree.co.uk
Tours by arrangement

The beers are available at the pub and in free houses around Manchester.

Timperley Mild Man *(ABV 3.8%)*

Agent X *(ABV 4.1%)*

Coal Porter *(ABV 4.8%)*

ANGLO DUTCH

The Anglo Dutch Brewery, Unit 12, Savile Bridge Mills, Mill Street East, Dewsbury, W Yorkshire, WF13 6QQ
Tel/Fax (01924) 457772
Website www.anglo-dutch-brewery.co.uk
Tours by arrangement

Paul Klos (Dutch) worked as a manager for Mike Field (Anglo), who runs the Refreshment Rooms at Dewsbury Station. When they found the right location, a brewery was born. The equipment came from the Rat & Ratchet in Huddersfield. The location used to be a dyehouse and the metal beams that used to hold block and

tackle to lift lids of dye pans have been cut up and welded to make a fermenter platform. The pallet racking that makes the brewing platform came from the dye house as well. Most beers contain wheat except for Spike and Tabatha, which contain lager malt.

Whitterus Organicus *(OG 1037.5, ABV 3.8%)*
An organic version of Kletswater.

Kletswater *(OG 1039, ABV 4%)*
Pale coloured beer with a hoppy nose and a good hop and citrus fruit flavour. An excellent session beer, full-bodied and smooth with a short dry finish. Kletswater is the Dutch for waffle water.

Mild Rabarber *(ABV 4%)* ◆
Light-coloured brown mild with a malty, fruity flavour and moderate hop character. Refreshing and light bodied.

Spike's on 't' Way *(OG 1040.5, ABV 4.2%)* ◆
Pale bitter with citrus/orange flavour and dry, fruity finish.

Mitch's Epitaph *(ABV 4.1%)* ◆
Amber bitter with malty, fruity and floral overtones but not citrussy. Slightly dry.

Grizzly Ghost *(OG 1041, ABV 4.3%)* ◆
Full-bodied pale bitter.

Ghost on the Rim *(OG 1043, ABV 4.5%)* ◆
Pale, dry and fruity.

Ghoulis Organicus *(OG 1043, ABV 4.5%)* ◆

At 't' Ghoul and Ghost *(OG 1048, ABV 5.2%)* ◆
Pale golden bitter with strong citrus and hoppy aroma and flavour. The finish is long, dry, bitter and citrus.

Tabatha the Knackered *(OG 1054, ABV 6%)* ◆
Golden Belgian-style Tripel. With strong fruity, hoppy and bitter character. Powerful and warming, slightly thinnish with bitter, dry finish. Beer of the Festival at the Huddersfield Oktoberfest 2001.

ANN STREET

See Jersey.

ARCHERS

Archers Brewing & Wholesale Ltd, Penzance Drive, Swindon, Wiltshire, SN5 7JL
Tel (01793) 879929
Fax (01793) 879489
Shop 9-5 Mon-Fri; 9-12 Sat
Tours by arrangement

⊗ Under new ownership since autumn 2001, Archers is fast approaching its 25th anniversary, and has consolidated its position as one of the premier regional breweries in the south. Its position in a former weigh house adjoining the Great Western Railway makes it a Victorian landmark. The beers have gained many awards, including the gold medal at the 1996 Brewing Industry International Awards. Beers are supplied to the local free trade on a direct basis and on a national basis to pub groups, other breweries and wholesalers. The company supplies 200 free trade outlets direct and via wholesalers. Seasonal beers: Spring Ale (ABV 4.2%, March-May), Summer Ale (ABV 3.5%, June-Aug), Autumn Ale (ABV 4.5%, Sept-Oct), Winter Warmer (ABV 5.2%, Nov-Feb). Special beers: Marley's Ghost (ABV 7%, Nov-Dec), Black Jack Porter (ABV 4.6%, Nov-Jan), Dark Mild (ABV 3.6%) March-May. Bottle-conditioned beer: Archers Golden Bottle Conditioned Beer (ABV 4.7%).

Village Bitter *(OG 1036, ABV 3.6%)* ◆
A dry, well-balanced beer, with a full body for its gravity. Malty and fruity in the nose, then a fresh, hoppy flavour with balancing malt and a hoppy, fruity finish.

Best Bitter *(OG 1040, ABV 4%)* ◆
Slightly sweeter and rounder than Village, with a malty, fruity aroma and pronounced bitter finish.

Special Bitter *(OG 1044, ABV 4.3%)*
Tawny in colour, full-flavoured and well-balanced. Brewed with a blend of traditional English hops.

Golden Bitter *(OG 1046, ABV 4.7%)* ◆
A full-bodied, hoppy, straw-coloured brew with an underlying fruity sweetness. A gentle aroma, but a strong, distinctive bitter finish.

Swindon Strong Bitter (SSB) *(OG 1052, ABV 5%)*

ARKELLS

Arkell's Brewery Ltd, Kingsdown, Swindon, Wiltshire, SN2 7RU
Tel (01793) 823026
Fax (01793) 828864
E-mail arkells@arkells.com
Website www.arkells.com
Tours by arrangement

⊗ Established in 1843 and now one of the few remaining breweries whose shares are all held by one family. Managing director James Arkell is a great-great-grandson of founder John Arkell. Gradually expanding its tied estate, mainly along the M4 corridor, the brewery is committed to a continual programme of upgrading and refurbishment for its pubs. All 96 tied pubs serve real ale, which is also supplied direct to around 200 free trade accounts. Some of the malt comes from James Arkell's own farm. Fuggles and Goldings hops are used, with pale ale malt and crystal malt. There is a higher proportion of crystal malt in 3B and Kingsdown, which are 'parti-gyled', i.e. made from the same mash but then reduced with 'liquor' [water] to the required strength. Occasional/seasonal beers: Summer Ale (ABV 4%), Peter's Porter (ABV 4.8%), Noel Ale (ABV 5.5%, Christmas), JRA (ABV 3.8%).

2B *(OG 1032, ABV 3.2%)* ❖
Light brown in colour, malty but with a smack of hops and an astringent aftertaste. An ideal lunchtime beer, it has good body for its strength.

3B *(OG 1040, ABV 4%)* ❖
A medium brown beer with a strong, sweetish malt/caramel flavour. The hops come through strongly in the aftertaste, which is lingering and dry.

Kingsdown Ale *(OG 1052, ABV 5%)* ❖
A rich deep russet-coloured beer, a stronger version of 3B. The malty/fruity aroma continues in the taste, which has a hint of pears. The hops come through in the aftertaste where they are complemented by caramel tones.

ARRAN

The Arran Brewery Co Ltd, Cladach, Brodick, Isle of Arran, KA27 8DE
Tel (01770) 302353
Fax (01770) 302653
E-mail info@arranbrewery.co.uk
Website www.arranbrewery.com
Visitor centre

⊛ The brewery was opened in 2000 by Richard and Elizabeth Roberts, the plant bought from the Tipsy Toad Town House brew-pub in St Helier, Jersey. It's a 20-barrel plant arranged on two floors, with the mash tun based above the copper and fermenters. The three cask beers are also available in carbonated bottled form. Arran Ale is sold as Arran Light in bottle.

Ale *(OG 1038, ABV 3.8%)* ❖
A deep amber summer ale, typical of new wave Scottish beers. The predominance of the hop produces a bitter beer with a subtle balancing sweetness of malt and fruit.

Dark *(OG 1042, ABV 4.3%)* ❖
A well-balanced malty beer with plenty of roast and hop in the taste and a dry, bitter finish.

Blonde *(OG 1048, ABV 5%)* ■❖
A hoppy beer with substantial fruit balance. The taste is balanced and the finish increasingly bitter and dry. An aromatic strong bitter that drinks below its weight. Winner of SIBA Champion Wheat Beer of Britain, 2001.

ARUNDEL

Arundel Brewery Ltd, Unit C7, Ford Airfield Industrial Estate, Ford, Arundel, W Sussex, BN18 0HY
Tel (01903) 733111
Fax (01903) 733381
E-mail arundelbrewery@telinco.co.uk

⊗ Set up in 1992, the town's first brewery in 60 years, Arundel now supplies around 100 outlets. Under new ownership from September 1998, Arundel continues to serve and increase its range of occasional and seasonal beers. Occasional ales are on sale for one month each.

Gauntlet *(OG 1035, ABV 3.5%)*
A light, refreshing session beer. The carefully selected blend of malt and hops produce a low gravity bitter with excellent initial flavour and a pleasant bitter finish.

Castle *(OG 1038, ABV 3.8%)* ❖
A pale tawny beer with fruit and malt noticeable in the aroma. The flavour has a good balance of malt, fruit and hops, with a dry, hoppy finish.

Gold *(OG 1042, ABV 4.2%)* ❖
A light golden ale with a malty, fruity flavour and a little hop in the finish.

Classic *(OG 1045, ABV 4.5%)*
A special bitter with good hop and fruit aroma. The combination of roast malt gives way to a fruity, bitter-sweet finish.

Stronghold *(OG 1047, ABV 4.7%)*
A smooth, full-flavoured premium bitter. A good balance of malt, fruit and hops come through in this rich brew.

Black Beastie *(OG 1049, ABV 4.9%)*

Old Knucker *(OG 1055, ABV 5.5%)*

ASTON MANOR

Aston Manor Brewery Co Ltd, 173 Thimble Mill Lane, Aston, Birmingham, W Midlands, B7 5HS
Tel (0121) 328 4336
Fax (0121) 328 0139
Shop 10-6 Mon-Fri; 10-1 Sat

Aston Manor owns the Highgate Brewery in Walsall (qv). Its own plant concentrates on packaged beers, lagers and cider in plastic bottles.

ATLAS*

Atlas Brewery Ltd, Lab Road, Kinlochleven, Argyll, PH50 4SG
Tel (01855) 831111.
Fax (01855) 831122

A new brewery in a 100 year-old listed Victorian carbon bunker in the Kinlochleven aluminium smelter that closed in 1999. The 25-barrel brewery equipment was built in 1997 for the Firkin group, and has been installed by Brewing Solutions. There's also a two-barrel 'nano brewery' that will be used to experiment, innovate and 'have some fun with'. There are plans to add two more brews, one of which will be a 5% ABV pale ale.

Latitude *(OG 1036, ABV 3.5%)*
A very hoppy, bitter pale ale.

Tempest *(OG 1047, ABV 4.9%)*
A Belgian-style wheat beer, strong on citrus and hops with coriander.

B&T

B&T Brewery Ltd, The Brewery, Shefford, Beds, SG17 5DZ
Tel (01462) 815080
Fax (01462) 850841

E-mail mikebatbrewery@yahoo.co.uk
Tours by arrangement

⊗ Banks & Taylor, founded in 1981, was restructured in 1994 under the name B&T Brewery and has continued to produce an extensive range of beers, including monthly special brews together with contract brewing for wholesalers and individual public houses. 60 outlets are supplied direct and three pubs are owned. There is an extensive range of seasonal beers. Bottle-conditioned beers: Black Dragon Mild (ABV 4.3%), Edwin Taylor's Extra Stout (ABV 4.5%), Dragonslayer (ABV 4.5%), Shefford Old Strong (ABV 5%), Black Old Bat (ABV 6%), Old Bat (ABV 6%).

Two Brewers Bitter
(OG 1036, ABV 3.6%)

Shefford Bitter *(OG 1038, ABV 3.8%)*
A pleasant, predominantly hoppy session beer with a bitter finish.

Shefford Dark Mild
(OG 1038, ABV 3.8%) ◆
A dark beer with a well-balanced taste. Sweetish, roast malt aftertaste.

Black Dragon Mild *(OG 1043, ABV 4.3%)*

Dragonslayer *(OG 1045, ABV 4.5%)* ◆
A straw-coloured beer, dry, malty and lightly hopped.

Edwin Taylor's Extra Stout
(OG 1045, ABV 4.5%) ◆
A pleasant, bitter beer with a strong roast malt flavour.

Shefford Pale Ale (SPA)
(OG 1045, ABV 4.5%) ◆
A well-balanced beer with hop, fruit and malt flavours. Dry, bitter aftertaste.

Fruit Bat *(OG 1045, ABV 4.5%)*

Shefford Old Strong (SOS)
(OG 1050, ABV 5%) ◆
A rich mixture of fruit, hops and malt is present in the taste and aftertaste of this beer. Predominantly hoppy aroma.

Shefford Old Dark (SOD)
(OG 1050, ABV 5%)
SOS with caramel added for colour. Often sold under house names.

Black Bat *(OG 1060, ABV 6%)* ◆
A powerful, sweet, fruity and malty beer for winter. Fruity, nutty aroma; strong roast malt aftertaste.

2XS *(OG 1060, ABV 6%)* ◆
A reddish beer with a strong, fruity, hoppy aroma. The taste is full-flavoured and the finish strong and sweetish.

Old Bat *(OG 1070, ABV 7%)* ◆
A powerful-tasting, sweet winter beer, with bitterness coming through in the aftertaste. Fruit is present in both aroma and taste.

For Millennium Brewery
Golden Fox *(OG 1041, ABV 4.1%)*

BADGER

Hall & Woodhouse Ltd, The Brewery, Blandford St Mary, Dorset, DT11 9LS
Tel (01258) 452141
Fax (01258) 459528
E-mail info@badgerbrewery.com
Website www.badgerbrewery.com
Shop 9-6 Mon-Sat.
Tours by arrangement

⊗ The company was founded in 1777 as the Ansty Brewery by Charles Hall. Charles's son took George Woodhouse into partnership and formed Hall & Woodhouse. They moved to their present site at Blandford St Mary in 1899. Trading under the Badger name, it owns 257 pubs in the south of England including the Gribble Inn brew-pub at Oving, West Sussex (qv), and supplies 700 outlets direct. In 2000, Hall & Woodhouse bought King & Barnes of Horsham and closed the brewery. It matched some of K&B beers, which are available throughout the Badger estate as well as the former Horsham company's 57 pubs. A visitor centre was due to open in summer 2002. Seasonal ale: King & Barnes Old Ale (ABV 4.5%, winter), Champion Ale (OG 1043, ABV 4%, summer).

Sussex Bitter *(OG 1033, ABV 3.5%)*
Reasonably well-balanced, mid-brown bitter. Hints of pear fruit in the flavour.

IPA *(OG 1034, ABV 3.6%)*
A pale beer, light, refreshing and pleasantly hoppy. Served with a creamy head.

Best Bitter *(OG 1039, ABV 4%)* ◆
A fine best bitter whose taste is strong in hop and bitterness, with underlying malt and fruit. Hoppy finish with a bitter edge.

Tanglefoot *(OG 1047, ABV 5.1%)*
A full-bodied beer, pale straw in colour with a characteristic fruitiness, medium bitterness and a slightly spicy finish.

BALLARD'S

Ballard's Brewery Ltd, The Old Sawmill, Nyewood, Petersfield, GU31 5HA
Tel (01730) 821301/821362
Fax (01730) 821742
E-mail info@ballardbrewery.org.uk
Website www.ballardsbrewery.org.uk
Shop 8.30-4.00 Mon-Fri, by appointment Sat-Sun
Tours by arrangement

⊗ Founded in 1980 at Cumbers Farm, Trotton, Ballard's has been trading at Nyewood (in W Sussex, despite the postal address) since 1988 and now supplies around 60 free trade outlets. Occasional/Seasonal beers: Golden Bine (ABV 4.2%, spring), On the Hop (ABV 4.5%, Sept), Wild (ABV 4.7%). Bottle-conditioned beers: Best Bitter (ABV 4.2%), Nyewood Gold (ABV 5%), Wassail (ABV 6%), Alchemist (ABV 9.2%).

Midhurst Mild *(OG 1035, ABV 3.5%)*
Traditional dark mild, well balanced,

refreshing, with a biscuity flavour.

Trotton Bitter *(OG 1036, ABV 3.6%)* ◆
Amber, clean-tasting bitter. A roast malt aroma leads to a fruity, slightly sweet taste and a dry finish.

Best Bitter *(OG 1042, ABV 4.2%)* ◆
A copper-coloured beer with a malty aroma. A good balance of fruit and malt in the flavour gives way to a dry, hoppy aftertaste.

Nyewood Gold *(OG 1050, ABV 5%)* ◆
Robust golden brown strong bitter, very hoppy and fruity throughout, with a tasty balanced finish.

Wassail *(OG 1060, ABV 6%)* ◆
A strong, full-bodied, fruity beer with a predominance of malt throughout, but also an underlying hoppiness. Tawny/red in colour.

BANFIELD

Correspondence to: Banfield Ales, Buntingford Brewery Co Ltd, Unit 3A, Watermill Industrial Estate, Buntingford, Herts, SG9 9JS
Tel (07956) 246215
E-mail enquiries@buntingford-brewery.co.uk
Website www.banfield-ales.co.uk

Banfield started life in May 2000 in Leicestershire. Owner Steve Banfield has now set up the Buntingford Brewery Co (qv). Any future Banfield Ales will be specialist, unusual beers, brewed in Buntingford. Occasional beers only.

BANK TOP

Bank Top Brewery, Unit 1, Back Lane, off Vernon Street, Bolton, Lancs, BL1 2LD
Tel (01204) 528865
Tours by arrangement Mon-Fri evenings at the Howcroft Inn, Bolton

⊛ Bank Top was established in 1995 by John Feeney. The brewery has enjoyed gradual expansion and there were plans to relocate to the Pavilion, Ashworth Lane, Bank Top, Bolton BL1 8RZ during 2002 (same phone number). The beers are supplied to 60-80 outlets locally. Seasonal/occasional beers: Satanic Mills II Judgement Day (ABV 5%), Santa's Claws (ABV 5%, Christmas).

Brydge Bitter *(OG 1038, ABV 3.8%)*

Flat Cap *(OG 1040, ABV 4%)*

Gold Digger *(OG 1040, ABV 4%)* ◆
Golden coloured, with a citrus aroma, grapefruit and a touch of spiciness on the palate and a fresh, hoppy citrus finish.

Dark Mild *(OG 1040, ABV 4%)*

Samuel Crompton's Ale *(OG 1042, ABV 4.2%)* ◆
Amber beer with a fresh citrus-peel aroma. Well-balanced with hops and a zesty grapefruit flavour, and a hoppy, citrus finish.

The Haka *(OG 1042, ABV 4.2%)*

Old Slapper *(OG 1042, ABV 4.2%)*

Volunteer Bitter *(OG 1042, ABV 4.2%)*

Golden Brown *(OG 1042, ABV 4.2%)*

Cliff Hanger *(OG 1045, ABV 4.5%)*

Smoke Stack Lightning *(OG 1050, ABV 5%)*

BANKS'S

Wolverhampton & Dudley Breweries plc, Park Brewery, Bath Road, Wolverhampton, W Midlands, WV1 4NY
Tel (01902) 711811
Fax (01902) 329136
Website www.fullpint.co.uk
Tours by arrangement

⊛ Wolverhampton & Dudley Breweries, Britain's biggest regional brewer, successfully defeated a hostile takeover bid by the Pubmaster group in August 2001, though only by a small majority of shareholders. Pre-empting the bid, W&D's management appeased the City of London with its own get-tough stance. It sold Camerons of Hartlepool (qv) to the neighbouring Castle Eden Brewery, while Mansfield Brewery closed at the end of 2001, with Mansfield brands switched to Wolverhampton. Marston's of Burton-on-Trent (qv) remains in production. W&D has sold most of its managed pubs, and in total some 200 jobs have disappeared. Banks's was formed in 1890 by the amalgamation of three local companies. Hanson's was acquired in 1943, but its Dudley brewery closed in 1991 and its beers are now brewed at Wolverhampton, though Hanson's pubs maintain their own livery. In 1992, W&D bought Camerons Brewery and 51 pubs from Brent Walker. In 1999 W&D turned itself into a 'super regional' through the acquisition of Marston's and Mansfield. The W&D estate numbers 1,763, which makes it tempting for companies interested only in profitable retail outlets. Almost all W&D pubs serve traditional ales and they offer a 'full pint guarantee' by serving the beer in oversized glasses. There is also extensive free trade throughout the country, particularly in pubs and clubs. W&D concentrates on such key brands as Banks's Original and Bitter, and Marston's Pedigree.

Hanson's Mild *(OG 1034, ABV 3.3%)* ◆
A mid-to dark brown mild with a malty roast flavour and aftertaste.

Mansfield Dark Mild *(OG 1035, ABV 3.5%)*

Riding Bitter *(OG 1035, ABV 3.6%)*

Banks's Original *(OG 1036, ABV 3.5%)* ◆
An amber-coloured, well-balanced, refreshing session beer.

Mansfield Cask Ale *(OG 1038, ABV 3.9%)*

Banks's Bitter *(OG 1038, ABV 3.8%)* ◆
A pale brown bitter with a pleasant balance of hops and malt. Hops continue from the taste through to a bitter-sweet aftertaste.

BARGE & BARREL

See Eastwood & Sanders

BARNGATES

Barngates Brewery Ltd, Barngates, Ambleside, Cumbria, LA22 0NG
Tel/Fax (015394) 36575
E-mail barngatesbrewery@drunkenduckinn.co.uk
Website www.drunkenduckinn.co.uk
Tours by prior arrangement

☺ Barngates Brewery began operating a one-barrel brewing plant at the Drunken Duck Inn in 1997. Expansion came in 1999 when a five-barrel plant was installed, and the brewery became a separate limited company. The brewery supplies 60 local outlets in Cumbria and 15 in Lancashire. Bottle-conditioned beer: Tag Lag (ABV 4.4%).

Cracker Ale *(OG 1038, ABV 3.9%)*
Subtle hoppy aroma, clean, smooth and refreshing, developing into a long bitter finish. Satisfying and well-rounded.

Tag Lag *(OG 1044, ABV 4.4%)* ◆
A copper-coloured, fruity beer, well hopped, with a long-lasting dry finish.

Chester's Strong & Ugly *(OG 1050, ABV 5.2%)*
Slightly fruity, well-balanced roasted malt and hop flavours.

BARNSLEY

Barnsley Brewery Co Ltd, t/a Elsecar Brewing Co, Wath Road, Elsecar, Barnsley, S Yorkshire, S74 8EN
Tel (01226) 741010
Fax (01226) 741009
Tours by arrangement

☺ Established in 1994 as the South Yorkshire Brewing Co, Barnsley Bitter was reintroduced using the original yeast culture from the old Barnsley Brewery at Oakwell, closed by John Smiths in the 1970s. In 1996, South Yorkshire won the right to use the name Barnsley Brewery and changed its name. The company chairman is Robert Umbers, whose family ran the original Barnsley Brewery for three generations. Demand continues to grow, with more than 200 local outlets taking the beer direct, while others are supplied by national distributors. It is planned to reintroduce Barnsley Bitter in bottle and to buy some tied houses. Seasonal beers: Mayflower (ABV 4.5%), Ey-Up! It's Christmas (ABV 4.7%), Ginger Tom (ABV 3.9%).

Bitter *(OG 1038, ABV 3.8%)* ◆
A pale brown, creamy and smooth bitter with a hoppy and fruity aroma, and an even balance of hops and malt in the taste and in the long, dry and bitter finish.

IPA *(OG 1041, ABV 4.2%)*
A beer dominated by fruit and hops, leading to a hoppy finish. Light golden in colour with a flowery aroma.

Black Heart Stout *(OG 1044, ABV 4.6%)* ◆
A black stout with a hoppy aroma, and roasted malt flavour throughout. Chocolatey, bitter finish.

Glory *(OG 1048, ABV 4.8%)*
A stronger version of Barnsley Bitter.

BARTRAMS

Bartrams Brewery, c/o 23 Meadow Close, Felsham, Suffolk, IP30 0QS
Tel 01449 737655
E-mail captainbill@lineone.net
Tours by arrangement

⊠ Marc Bartram started his brewery in 1999 and has built up a good trade with locals. Thirty-five outlets are supplied direct. He uses a five-barrel plant purchased from Buffy's Brewery. He currently produces 10 barrels a week but hopes to double the amount. There was a Bartrams Brewery between 1894 and 1902 run by Captain Bill Bartram and his image graces the pump clips. After three years in an industrial unit, Marc is converting a barn into a brewery and retail outlet. Bottle conditioned: All beers will shortly be available. Marld and stouts are suitable for vegetarians.

Marld *(OG 1034, ABV 3.4%)*
A traditional mild.

Premier Bitter *(OG 1037, ABV 3.7%)*

Little Green Man *(ABV 3.8%)*
Made with organic ingredients.

Red Queen *(OG 1039, ABV 3.9%)*

Pierrot *(OG 1040, ABV 4%)*

Green Man *(ABV 4%)*
An organic beer, using West Country floor-malted Maris Otter malt, New Zealand hops and coriander.

Bees Knees *(OG 1042, ABV 4.2%)*

Jester Quick One *(OG 1044, ABV 4.4%)*
A darker than average best bitter that is more malty than hoppy, with hints of fruit in the aroma.

Captain's Stout *(OG 1048, ABV 4.8%)*

Captain Bill Bartrams Best Bitter *(OG 1048, ABV 4.8%)*

Damson/Cherry Stout *(OG 1048, ABV 4.8%)*

BARUM

Barum Brewery Ltd, c/o The Reform Inn, Pilton, Barnstaple, Devon, EX31 1PD
Tel (01271) 329994
Fax (01271) 321590
E-mail info@barumbrewery.co.uk
Website www.barumbrewery.co.uk
Tours by arrangement

⊠ Brewing started in 1996 and a new five-barrel plant was opened in 2001 at the Castle Inn, George Nympton, South Molton. Distribution is primarily within Devon. Seasonal beer: Gold (ABV 4%, summer). Bottle-conditioned beers: Original (ABV 4.4%), Breakfast (ABV 5%), Challenger (ABV 5.6%), Barnstablasta (ABV 6.6%).

XTC *(OG 1039, ABV 3.9%)*

Jester *(OG 1042, ABV 4.2%)*

Original *(OG 1044, ABV 4.4%)*

Breakfast *(OG 1050, ABV 5%)*

Barumberg *(OG 1051, ABV 5.1%)*

Challenger *(OG 1056, ABV 5.6%)*

Barnstablasta *(OG 1066, ABV 6.6%)*

For Thatch Inn, Croyde
Longboat *(OG 1038, ABV 3.8%)*

BATEMAN

George Bateman & Son Ltd, Salem Bridge Brewery, Wainfleet, Lincolnshire, PE24 4JE
Tel (01754) 880317
Fax (01754) 880939
E-mail jbateman@bateman.co.uk
Website www.bateman.co.uk
Shop 11-4 daily
Tours by arrangement.

⊗ A family-owned brewery established in 1874 by the present chairman's grandfather, Batemans is committed to brewing cask ale. To underscore this commitment, it opened a new brewhouse in 2002. The beers are sold throughout the country. Alongside the award-winning core brands, there is a large portfolio of seasonal and occasional beers. A visitor centre provides a good day out for all the family and includes the fascinating Brewing Experience. Batemans owns 68 pubs, all serving cask ale. Seasonal ales: Loxley's Liquor (ABV 4.7%, Jan/Feb), Excalibur (ABV 4.4%, March/April), Godiva's Gold (ABV 4%, May/June), Marie Celeste (ABV 4.6%, July/Aug), Blackbeerd (ABV 3.6%, Sept/Oct), Owd Nessie (ABV 5%, Nov/Dec). Speciality Beers: Hooker (ABV 4.5%, Feb), Victory Ale (ABV 5.2%, April and Oct), Miss Whiplash (ABV 4.2%, June), Summer Swallow (ABV 3.9%, Aug), Rosey Nosey (ABV 4.9%, Dec). Bottled-conditioned beer: Pour With Care (for Booths supermarkets: 4.5%)

Dark Mild *(OG 1032, ABV 3%)*
Characteristic orchard fruit and roasted nut nose with hops evident. One of the classic mild ales, although the lasting bitter finish may not be entirely true to type; nevertheless, a ruby-black gem.

XB Bitter *(OG 1037, ABV 3.7%)*
A mid-brown balanced session bitter with malt most obvious in the finish. The taste is dominated by the house style apple hop, which also leads the aroma.

Lincolnshire Yella Belly Organic Beer *(OG 1042, ABV 4.2%)*
Organic hops and malt combine together to produce a clean, refreshing crisp pale ale with a rich spicy hop aroma and fruity character, with vanilla as a finishing taste.

Salem Porter *(OG 1047, ABV 4.7%)*
Ruby black with a brown tint to the head. The aroma is of liquorice with a subtle hint of dandelion and burdock; the initial taste is hoppy and bitter, with a mellowing of all the elements in the finish.

Combined Harvest *(OG 1047, ABV 4.7%)*
A unique multi-grain blend of malted barley, oats, rye and wheat. Grainy tasting with a delightful floral start and finish.

XXXB *(OG 1048, ABV 4.8%)*
A brilliant blend of malt, hops and fruit on the nose with a bitter bite over the top of a faintly banana maltiness that stays the course. A russet-tan brown classic.

BATH

Bath Ales Ltd, (Admin) Hare on the Hill, Dove St, Kingsdown, Bristol, BS2 5LK
Tel Office (0117) 9071797
Fax Office (0117) 9095140
E-mail Hare@bathales.co.uk
Website www.bathales.com/co.uk
Tours by arrangement

⊗ Bath Ales began in 1995, formed by two former Smiles brewers and a Hardington brewer. They started with rented equipment at the Henstridge Brewery near Wincanton, moved premises and upgraded to a full steam, 15-barrel plant in 1999. Situated between Bath and Bristol, all beer deliveries are direct to 100-plus outlets. Wholesalers are used in a limited way. Six pubs are owned, all serving cask ale. Bottle-conditioned beer: Gem (ABV 4.8%). Seasonal/occasional beers: Spa Extra (ABV 5%), Festivity (ABV 5%), Rare Hare (ABV 5.2%).

Special Pale Ale (SPA) *(OG 1037, ABV 3.7%)*
Light-bodied, dry bitter beer. Pale and lager malts and citrus hop aroma. Long, pale, malty, bitter finish with some fruit and slight sweetness. Gold/yellow colour. Refreshing, clean and complex.

Gem Bitter *(OG 1041, ABV 4.1%)*
Malty (pale and crystal with a tiny hint of chocolate), fruity and hoppy throughout. Drier and more bitter at the end, this amber-coloured, medium-bodied bitter is well-balanced and complex.

Barnstormer *(OG 1045, ABV 4.5%)*
Mid-brown, well-balanced and smooth. Malt (roast and chocolate), hop and fruit aroma, with similar taste, with a complex malty and bitter, dry finish.

Festivity *(OG 1050, ABV 5%)*
Complex, full-bodied porter. Dark copper-brown with crystal and roast chocolate malt, hop and black cherry aroma and taste. Some sweetness but bitter and quite dry with more chocolate and roast flavour in the finish.

BATHAM

Daniel Batham & Son Ltd, Delph Brewery, Delph Road, Brierley Hill, West Midlands, DY5 2TN
Tel (01384) 77229
Fax (01384) 482292
E-mail info@bathams.com
Website www.bathams.co.uk

⊛ A small brewery established in 1877 and now in its fifth generation of family ownership, run by Tim and Matthew Batham. Batham's sympathetic programme of upgrading and refurbishment in its tied estate has been rewarded by winning CAMRA's 1996 Joe Goodwin Award for pub refurbishment for the Vine, one of the Black Country's most famous pubs and the site of the brewery. The brewery celebrated its 125th anniversary in 2002. The company has nine tied houses and supplies around 25 other outlets. Seasonal beer: XXX (ABV 6.4%, Dec-Jan).

Mild Ale *(OG 1036.5, ABV 3.5%)* ◆
A fruity, dark brown mild with a malty sweetness and a roast malt finish.

Best Bitter *(OG 1043.5, ABV 4.3%)* ◆
A pale yellow, fruity, sweetish bitter, with a dry, hoppy finish. A good, light, refreshing beer.

BATTERSEA*

The Battersea Brewery Co. Ltd., 43 Glycena Road, London, SW11 5TP
Tel/Fax (020) 7978 7978
E-mail Stephen.nockolds@btclick.com
Tours by arrangement

Founded in 2001 by Stephen Nockolds to supply pubs in London and the South-east, the five-barrel plant is used to brew beer without adjuncts or chemicals. Stephen plans to introduce a range of seasonal and other speciality beers in the future.

Battersea Bitter *(OG 1042, ABV 4%)*

BEARTOWN

Beartown Brewery Ltd, Unit 9, Varey Road, Eaton Bank Industrial Estate, Congleton, Cheshire, CW12 1UW
Tel (01260) 299964
Fax (01260) 278895
E-mail steve@beartown42.co.uk
Website www.beartownbrewery.co.uk
Tours by arrangement

Congleton's links with brewing can be traced back to 1272, when the town received charter status. Two of its most senior officers at the time were Ale Taster and Bear Warden, hence the name of the brewery. During 1999/2000 the brewery acquired two pubs, the Beartown Tap in Congleton and the White Bull in Rossendale, and in 2001 the Navigation in Stockport. The Navigation was previously an all-keg outlet and is now serving the full range of Beartown ales, plus a selection of Belgian/German and other bottled beers. The brewery also operates a private members' club at Holmes Chapel, Cheshire, where a range of the brewery's ales are served. Beartown supplies 50 outlets direct.

Ambeardextrous *(ABV 3.5%)*
Dark mild.

Bear Ass *(OG 1038, ABV 4%)* ◆
Dark ruby-red, malty bitter with good hop nose and fruity flavour with dry, bitter, astringent aftertaste.

Kodiak Gold *(OG 1038, ABV 4%)* ◆
Well-balanced, straw-coloured and very drinkable with citrus fruit and hops aroma, and sharper bitter, clean, astringent aftertaste.

Bearskinful *(OG 1040, ABV 4.2%)* ◆
A tawny, malty beer, with a clean hop finish.

Polar Eclipse *(OG 1046, ABV 4.8%)* ◆
A smooth and roasty dark stout, with light hoppy notes and dry, bitter finish.

Wheat Beer *(OG 1050, ABV 5%)* ◆
A dry and bitter wheat beer. Initial fruitiness in aroma and taste with good wheat malt flavours. Long-lasting dry aftertaste.

Black Bear *(OG 1048, ABV 5%)* ◆
Dark brown strong mild, some roast and malt flavours, with a mellow sweetish finish.

BECKETT'S

Beckett's Brewery Ltd, 10 Enterprise Court, Daneshill, Basingstoke, Hampshire, RG24 8GE
Tel/Fax (01256) 472986
E-mail beer@beckettsbrewery.co.uk
Tours by arrangement

⊠ Becketts has been brewing for more than six years and now occupies a new two-storey unit that has a bottling plant and an increased capacity of 50 barrels a week. The brewery has collected many awards for its beers and has a loyal following in and around Hampshire for the quality of its products. Seasonal beers are available under the 'Porterquack' name and range from a light mild to a Christmas ale. One Beckett's beer, a brown ale, is used in a Sainsbury's Cumberland steak and ale pie. 60 outlets are supplied direct. Seasonal ale: Porter (ABV 4.7%, Oct-March), Fortress (ABV 5%, Nov-Jan).

Old Town Bitter *(OG 1038, ABV 3.7%)* ◆
An intensely bitter, amber-coloured session beer with some pale malt, fruit and butterscotch notes. Finishes uncompromisingly bitter and dry.

Stoke Ale *(OG 1043, ABV 4.2%)*

Whitewater *(OG 1044, ABV 4.3%)*

Golden Grale *(OG 1046, ABV 4.5%)*

BEECHAM'S

Beecham's Bar & Brewery, St Helen's College, Town Centre Campus, Brook Street, St Helens, Merseyside, WA10 1PZ
Tel (01744) 623420 Fax (01744) 623400
Tours by arrangement

Beecham's Brewery is a training establishment within St Helens College of Further Education. The brewing course has a recognised certificate validated by the National Open College Network. Seasonal brews are produced.

Mild *(ABV 4.1%)*

Original Bitter *(OG 1044, ABV 4.4%)*

Epiphany *(ABV 4.8%)*

Stout *(OG 1048, ABV 5%)* ◆
Thick, creamy, silky stout with roasty and caramel aroma and flavours, some balancing hop and a residual roastiness.

Crystal Wheat Beer *(OG 1048, ABV 5%)*
Light, fruity wheat beer with an aroma of citrus fruits, clean, hoppy palate, and a dry finish.

BEER ENGINE

Beer Engine, Newton St Cyres, Exeter, Devon, EX5 5AX
Tel (01392) 851282
Fax (01392) 851876
E-mail peterbrew@aol.com
Tours by arrangement

Beer Engine, run by Peter and Jill Hawksley, started brewing in 1983 next to the Barnstaple branch railway line. The brewery is visible behind glass downstairs. It uses the finest malts from Tuckers of Newton Abbot and quality English hops from Charles Faram of Newland. Two other outlets are supplied regularly and the beers are also distributed via agencies. Seasonal beers vary from year to year, but include Porter (ABV 4.8%), and Whistlemas (ABV 7.3%).

Rail Ale *(OG 1037, ABV 3.8%)*
A straw-coloured beer with a fruity aroma and a sweet, fruity finish.

Piston Bitter
(OG 1043, ABV 4.3%)
A mid-brown, sweet-tasting beer with a pleasant, bitter-sweet aftertaste.

Sleeper Heavy
(OG 1052, ABV 5.4%)
A red-coloured beer with a fruity, sweet taste and a bitter finish.

Brewed for Agricultural Inn, Exeter
Speke Easy *(ABV 3.8%)*

BELHAVEN

Belhaven Brewing Co Limited, Dunbar, East Lothian, EH42 1RS
Tel (01368) 864488
Fax (01368) 865640
E-mail info@belhaven.co.uk
Website www.belhaven.co.uk
Shop open during tours. Tours by arrangement

Belhaven, situated on the coast at Dunbar, is on a site founded by monks some 800 years ago. The date on the lintel to the brewhouse says 1719. It's Scotland's oldest brewery and its traditional beers achieve flavour by attention to malts, rather than hops, which lead to sweetish-tasting beers. With many newer Scottish independent breweries producing hoppy beers, Belhaven claims it is the last producer of true Scottish ales. It supplies its 39 tied houses and an extensive free trade with cask beer. It also produces beers for Maclay pubs following the closure of the Alloa brewery

60/- Ale *(OG 1030, ABV 2.9%)*
A fine, but sadly rare, example of a Scottish light. This bitter-sweet, reddish-brown beer is dominated by fruit and malt with a hint of roast and caramel, and increasing hop bitterness in the aftertaste.

70/- Ale *(OG 1038, ABV 3.5%)*
A fine Scottish ale. This pale brown beer has malt and fruit and some hop throughout, and is increasingly bitter-sweet in the aftertaste.

Sandy Hunter's Traditional Ale
(OG 1038, ABV 3.6%)
A distinctive, medium-bodied beer named after a past chairman and head brewer. An aroma of malt and hops greets the nose. A hint of roast combines with the malt and hops to give a bitter-sweet taste and finish.

80/- Ale *(OG 1040, ABV 4.2%)*
The last of a noble breed of Scottish 80/-s, with malt the predominant flavour characteristic, though it is balanced by hop and fruit. Those used to hops as the lead to a beer's taste might find this complex ale disconcerting. The soubriquet 'the claret of Scotland' hints at the depth and complexity of the flavours.

St Andrew's Ale *(OG 1046, ABV 4.9%)*
A bitter-sweet beer with lots of body. The malt, fruit and roast mingle throughout with hints of hop and caramel.

For Maclay:
Wallace, Golden Scotch,
Kane's Amber Ale.

BELVOIR

Belvoir Brewery Ltd, Woodhill, Nottingham Lane, Old Dalby, Leicestershire, LE14 3LX
Tel/Fax (01664) 823455
Website www.belvoirbrewery.co.uk
Tours by arrangement

Belvoir (pronounced 'beaver') Brewery was set up in 1995 by Colin Brown, who had brewed with Shipstone and Theakston. The brewery has been lovingly constructed using mostly original equipment and artefacts recovered from traditional cask ale breweries all over the country. Time-honoured brewing methods are used incorporating only the finest ingredients. These include traditional floor-malted Maris Otter malts, and four varieties of Worcester whole hops (Bramling Cross, Challenger, Goldings and Progress). A refrigerated cold store/cellar was added in 2000. A bottled beer, Melton Red, was launched in 1999 and the acquisition of the Kitchen Brewery's bottling line will enable Belvoir to produce bottle-conditioned beers. 80-100 outlets are supplied direct. Occasional/seasonal beers: Mild Ale (ABV 3.4%), Peacock's Glory (ABV 4.7%), Old Dalby (ABV 5.1%).

Whippling Golden Bitter
(OG 1036, ABV 3.6%)

Star Bitter *(OG 1039, ABV 3.9%)*
A beer designed to replicate the bitter flavour of the old Shipstone's Bitter.

Beaver Bitter *(OG 1043, ABV 4.3%)*
A light brown bitter that starts malty in both aroma and taste, but soon develops a hoppy bitterness. Appreciably fruity.

BEOWULF

Beowulf Brewing Company, Waterloo Buildings, 14 Waterloo Road, Yardley, Birmingham, W Midlands, B25 8JR
Tel (0121) 706 4116
Fax (0121) 706 0735
E-mail cheers@beowulf.co.uk
Website www.beowulf.co.uk
Tours for small groups by arrangement

Beowulf has been brewing for more than six years and is well-established throughout central England. It remains Birmingham's only independent brewery. Close to 200 outlets serve the beers, from Scotland to southern England. There are expansion plans in hand and bottled beers will be added. Seasonal beers: Finn's Hall Porter (ABV 4.7%, autumn/winter), Dragon Smoke Stout (ABV 4.7%, autumn/winter), Grendel's Winter Ale (ABV 5.8%), Blizzard (ABV 5%, winter), Wergild cask-conditioned lager (ABV 4.3%, spring/summer), Fifty Winters (ABV 4.4%, spring/summer), Wuffa (ABV 4.5%, spring/summer), Gold Work wheat beer (ABV 5.1%, summer), Hurricane (ABV 4%, winter), Glutlusty (ABV 4.7%, autumn).

Beorma *(OG 1038, ABV 3.9%)*
A pale session ale with a malty hint of fruit giving way to a lingering bitterness.

Noble Bitter *(OG 1039, ABV 4%)* ◆
Gold colour, fruity aroma, hoppy taste with a dry finish.

Wiglaf *(OG 1043, ABV 4.3%)*
A golden bitter, with a malty flavour married to a pleasing bitterness, with three hop varieties used.

Swordsman *(OG 1045, ABV 4.5%)* ◆
Pale gold, light fruity aroma, tangy hoppy flavour. Faintly hoppy finish.

Heroes *(OG 1046, ABV 4.7%)*
Gold colour, malt aroma, hoppy taste but sweetish finish.

Mercian Shine *(OG 1048, ABV 5%)* ◆
Pale gold colour, citrus flavour with a full body and hoppy, dry finish.

BERROW

Berrow Brewery, Coast Road, Berrow, Burnham-on-Sea, Somerset, TA8 2QU
Tel (01278) 751345
Off licence 9-9
Tours by arrangement, limited numbers

⊗ The brewery started brewing in 1982. With the introduction of Topsy Turvy, its success was soon established and it remains very popular. Berrow Porter has also made its mark and is produced all year round. Millennium Mash is a newer, dark, full-flavoured ale. Berrow supplies 12 outlets direct. Seasonal beers: Christmas Ale (ABV 5%, winter), Carnivale (ABV 4.6%, Nov-Dec).

Best Bitter/4Bs *(OG 1038, ABV 3.9-4%)* ◆
A pleasant, pale brown session beer, with a fruity aroma, a malty, fruity flavour and bitterness in the palate and finish.

Berrow Porter *(OG 1047, ABV 4.6-4.7%)*

Topsy Turvy *(OG 1055, ABV 6%)* ◆
A gold-coloured beer with an aroma of malt and hops. Well-balanced malt and hops taste with a hoppy, bitter finish with some fruit notes.

BIG LAMP

Big Lamp Brewers, Grange Road, Newburn, Newcastle upon Tyne, NE15 8NL
Tel (0191) 2671689
Fax (0191) 2677387
Email brewers@biglampbrewers.freeserve.co.uk
Website www.biglampbrewers.com
Tours by arrangement

◎ Big Lamp Brewers started in 1982 and relocated in 1997 to a 55-barrel former water pumping station. It is the oldest micro-brewery in the North-east of England. Twelve outlets are supplied and two pubs are owned. Seasonal/occasional beers: Sunny Daze (ABV 3.6%), Keelman Brown (ABV 5.7%), Old Genie (ABV 7.4%), Blackout (ABV 11%) ▮.

Bitter *(OG 1039, ABV 3.9%)* ◆
A clean-tasting bitter, full of hops and malt, a hint of fruit, with a slightly dry aftertaste.

Double M *(OG 1043, ABV 4.3%)*

Summerhill Stout *(OG 1044, ABV 4.4%)* ◆
A tasty, rich, ruby stout with a lasting rich roast feel and character. A malty mouthfeel with a lingering finish.

Prince Bishop Ale
(OG 1048, ABV 4.8%) ◆
A golden-coloured, well-balanced fruity beer. Plenty of hop flavours and strong bitterness, with a spicy dry finish.

Premium *(OG 1052, ABV 5.2%)* ◆
A well-balanced, flavoursome bitter with a big nose full of hops. The sweetness lasts into a mellow, dry finish.

Embers *(OG 1055, ABV 5.5%)*

Blackout *(OG 1100, ABV 11%)* ◆
A strong bitter, fortified with roast malt character and rich maltiness. Try it for its mouthfeel and lasting bitterness.

BIRD IN HAND

Wheal Ale Brewery, Nr Paradise Park, Trelissick Road, Hayle, Cornwall, TR27 4HY
Tel/Fax (01736) 753974

Founded 1980 as Parkside Brewery, the small brewhouse is behind a large pub, the Bird in Hand, converted from Victorian stables and coach house by the entrance to the Paradise Park Bird Sanctuary. The two beers are brewed regularly and a winter warmer is available in season.

Miller's Ale *(OG 1045, ABV 4.3%)*

Old Speckled Parrot
(OG 1052, ABV 5.5%)

BITTER END

Bitter End brew-pub, 15 Kirkgate, Cockermouth, Cumbria, CA13 9PJ
Tel (01900) 828993

The brewery was founded, along with the pub, in 1995. Brewer Mike Askey was helped by Peter Yates, founder of Yates Brewery, to put together the brewing kit; Peter also supplied the brewing expertise. In 2001, Mike went into the long-distance lorry-driving business, and barmaid Nicola Farmer became Cumbria's first brewster (woman brewer) and has expanded the range. The brewery has a one-barrel capacity but there are plans to increase this to two barrels and to install a bigger gas-fired copper.

Old Neddy *(ABV 3.6%)*

Cocker Snoot *(ABV 3.8%)*

Call Out *(ABV 4.2%)*
Brewed to raise funds for Cockermouth Rescue Team.

Cuddy Lugs *(ABV 4.7%)*

Full English *(ABV 5%)*

Skinner's Old Strong *(ABV 5.5%)*

BLACK BULL

Black Bull (Haltwhistle Brewery), Market Square, Haltwhistle, Northumberland, NE14 0BL
Tel (01434) 320463

Seasonal beers: Dark Mild (ABV 3.5%), Fat Boys Bitter (ABV 3.7%), Captain O'Neills Intrepid Stout (ABV 3.8%), 1555 (ABV 4.4%), Special (ABV 4.6%), ESB (ABV 5.5%).

Bitter *(ABV 3.8%)*

Beastly Bitter *(ABV 4.5%)*

Bishop Ridley's Ale *(ABV 4.7%)*

BLACK DOG

Black Dog Brewery, St Hilda's Business Centre, Whitby, N Yorkshire, YO22 4EU
Tel (01947) 821464, (07785) 541917(m)
Fax (01947) 603301
E-mail black_dog@lineone.net
Website www.synthesys.co.uk/black-dog

The Black Dog Brewery was established in 1997. Sales grew steadily and the beers developed a loyal following but were never able to achieve a sales volume that made production viable. The brewery closed in 2001, but the Black Dog Brewery Company continues and all beers are now produced under licence by Hambleton Ales. Orders can be placed with Black Dog or Hambleton. All beers are suitable for vegetarians. Seasonal beers: Scallywag (ABV 3.6%, summer), First Out (ABV 4%, summer), Synod (ABV 4.2%, spring), Whitby Jet (ABV 5%, winter).

Scallywag *(OG 1036, ABV 3.6%)*
A light, hoppy summer session beer.

Whitby Abbey Ale *(OG 1036.7, ABV 3.8%)*
A light, hoppy bitter.

Schooner *(ABV 4.2%)*

Rhatas *(OG 1043.2, ABV 4.6%)*
A dark, malty bitter.

BLACK ISLE

Black Isle Brewery Co Ltd, Old Allangrange, Munlochy, Ross-shire, IV8 8NZ
Tel (01463) 811871
Fax (01463) 811875
E-mail greatbeers@blackislebrewery.com
Website www.blackislebrewery.com
Shop 10-6 daily, closed Sundays in winter
Tours in summer, every hour. Otherwise, any time

Launched in 1998, Black Isle Brewery is a small independent brewery in the heart of the Scottish Highlands. The five-barrel plant is based in converted farm buildings on the Black Isle. Since 2000 the brewery has focused on organic beers. One pub is owned. Bottle-conditioned beers: Wheat Beer (ABV 4.5%), Scotch Ale (ABV 4.5%), Stout (ABV 4.5%).

Yellowhammer *(OG 1042, ABV 4%)*
A classic straw coloured summer ale. Intense aroma of citrus fruits and hops, which is maintained through to the dry, bitter finish.

Red Kite *(OG 1041, ABV 4.2%)*
A crisp, amber coloured ale, steeped with Goldings hops to create a well-balanced citrus and malt flavoursome ale. Bright, amber, with a light toasted orange aroma.

Thornbush Porter *(OG 1045, ABV 4.5%)*
A dry, fruity beer with some blackcurrant and plenty of roast taste, and a long, intense, bitter finish.

BLACK SHEEP

Black Sheep Brewery plc, Wellgarth, Masham, Ripon, N Yorkshire, HG4 4EN
Tel (01765) 689227 (brewery)
680100 (visitor centre)
Fax (01765) 689746
E-mail visitor.centre@blacksheep.co.uk
Website www.blacksheep.co.uk
Bistro & Shop closed Mondays except July/Aug; closed Tuesdays in Jan & Feb. Tues 11am-5.30pm; Wed-Sat 11-11; Sundays 11am-5.30pm.
Tours by arrangement on shop opening days

Set up in 1992 by Paul Theakston, a member of Masham's famous brewing family, in the former Wellgarth Maltings, Black Sheep has enjoyed continued growth and now supplies a free trade of around 600 outlets in the Yorkshire Dales and in an 80-mile radius of Masham, but it owns no pubs. A limited number of wholesalers is also supplied. All the output is fermented in Yorkshire Square vessels; there are six slate ones and eight stainless steel Yorkshire 'round' squares. The Black Sheep complex includes video shows of the brewing process, a brewery shop, and a bistro open for snacks, lunches and evening meals every day (Wed-Sun only Jan to March). Seasonal beer: Yorkshire Square Ale (ABV 5%).

Best Bitter *(OG 1039, ABV 3.8%)*
A hoppy and fruity beer with strong bitter overtones, leading to a long, dry, bitter finish.

Special Ale *(OG 1046, ABV 4.4%)*
A well-rounded and warming bitter beer with a good helping of hops and fruit in the taste and aroma, leading to a moderately dry, bitter aftertaste.

Riggwelter *(OG 1056, ABV 5.9%)* ◆
A fruity bitter, with complex underlying tastes and hints of liquorice and pear drops leading to a long, dry, bitter finish.

BLACKAWTON

Blackawton Brewery, Unit 14, Saltash Business Park, Forge Lane, Saltash, Cornwall, PL12 6LX
Tel (01752) 848777
Fax (01752) 848999
E-mail blackawtonbrewery@talk21.com
Tours by arrangement

⊠ What was once Devon's oldest operating brewery has relocated to Cornwall. Now run independently as a family business, the brewery is once again flourishing and supplying fine ales to the free trade throughout Devon and Cornwall. A new range of bottle-conditioned beer was launched in 2001. At present Blackawton is still using the original 10-barrel plant and equipment, but the owners have plans to relocate to larger premises and increase both workforce and plant size. The brewery brews a house beer at ABV 4.8% for the Wetherspoons outlet, the Isaac Merritt in Paignton. Seasonal beers: Wheal Dream (ABV 4.1%, Easter), Shepherds Delight (ABV 4.6%, spring), Westcountry Gold (ABV 4.1%, summer), Old Fella (ABV 5%, autumn), Winter Fuel (ABV 5%, winter), Humbug (ABV 5%, Christmas), Exhibition (ABV 4.7%). Bottle-conditioned beers: Headstrong (ABV 5.2%), Winter Fuel (ABV 5%).

Original Bitter *(OG 1036, ABV 3.8%)*

44 Special *(OG 1044, ABV 4.5%)*

Headstrong *(OG 1048, ABV 5.2%)*

BLACKDOWN*

Blackdown Brewery Ltd, Units C5/C6, Dunkeswell Business Park, Dunkeswell, Honiton, Devon, EX14 0RA
Tel (01404) 891122
Fax (01404) 890097
Email swfabs@freeuk.com
Tours by arrangement

⊠ Blackdown is a purpose-built brewery, completed in 2002 by SW Fabrications, adjacent to its equipment production site at Dunkeswell. Juwards has moved from Wellington along with its founder/brewer to join Blackdown to produce both the Juwards and Blackdown range of beers. Each beer has a unique recipe, the formulation of each being selected from a choice of five hop varieties and five grains. Speciality and seasonal beers will be developed. Approximately 60 outlets are supplied.

Blackdown Bitter
(OG 1039, ABV 3.8%)

Juwards Bitter
(OG 1041, ABV 4%) ◆
A pale brown bitter with well-balanced malt and hops on the palate, and honey overtones, leading to a hoppy bitter finish.

Blackdown Gold *(OG 1044, ABV 4.3%)*

Juwards Premium *(OG 1048, ABV 4.7%)*

BLACKPOOL

Blackpool Brewery Co Ltd, The Old Dairy, George Street, Blackpool, FY1 3RP
Tel (01253) 304999
Fax (01253) 304868
Tours by arrangement

⊛ Blackpool is the first new brewery in the town for 30 years. The brewery produces up to 80 barrels a week and intends to produce a monthly beer in addition to its regular range. Seasonal beers: Lights Out (ABV 4.4%), Black Diamond (ABV 3.4%), Christmas Lights (ABV 4.3%), Crackle Porter (ABV 5%), Red Heart (ABV 4.1%).

Golden Smile *(OG 1036.5, ABV 3.7%)*
Gold-coloured beer with a hoppy aroma; well-balanced with a fruity flavour.

Bitter *(OG 1039, ABV 4%)*
A golden beer with great depth of flavour.

BPA *(OG 1041, ABV 4.2%)*
A full-bodied, malty bitter with an agreeable flowery aroma.

BLANCHFIELDS

Blanchfields of Fakenham, The Bull, Bridge Street, Fakenham, Norfolk, NR21 9AG
Tel (01328) 862560
Tours by arrangement

⊠ Blanchfields has been brewing for more than four years, mainly for the Bull and beer festivals, using a 2.5- barrel brewhouse. Awards have been won for Mild at the Peterborough Beer Festival and at Norwich with Best Bitter. Seasonal/occasional beers: White Bull Wheat Beer (ABV 4.4%, summer).

Black Bull Mild *(OG 1040, ABV 3.6%)* ◆
Light malty airs introduce this red-coloured, traditional mild. A dry fruity maltiness gives a hint of cocoa as the gentle malt base gives a counter-balance. Finish fades quickly although roasted malt remains.

Bull Best Bitter *(OG 1040, ABV 3.9%)* ◆
A moderately bitter beer with a hoppy backbone that is not apparent in the delicate malty nose. Easy on the tongue, the finish contains a subtle blend of malt, hops and bitterness.

Hi-Hop Bitter *(OG 1042, ABV 4.1%)*

Raging Bull *(OG 1048, ABV 4.9%)* ◆
A heavy feeling beer redolent of fruits of the forest. Malt mixed with sweetness remains to the bitter end. The gentle malty aroma is at odds with the depth of flavour.

BLENCOWE

Blencowe Brewing Company, c/o Exeter Arms, Barrowden, Rutland, LE15 8EQ
Tel (01572) 747247
Fax (01572) 747841
Email info@exeterarms.com
Website www.exeterarms.com
Tours by arrangement

⊠ The brewery was set up in 1998 in a barn adjacent to the pub. The two-barrel plant was bought with the intention of supplying traditional beers for sale in the Exeter Arms bar and festivals only. An expansion programme in 2001 added one extra fermenting vessel but demand still outstrips production. Seasonal beers: Fun Boy Four (ABV 4.4%, summer), Bevin Boy (ABV 4.5%, winter), Spice Boys/Choir Boys/Naughty Boys (ABV 6%, Easter and Xmas), Fruity (ABV 3.6%, spring/summer).

Farmers Boy *(ABV 3.6%)*
A wheat beer.

Beach Boys *(OG 1040, ABV 3.8%)*
Fruit on the aroma; hoppy with a bitter finish.

Danny Boys *(OG 1046, ABV 4.6%)*
A rich, dark and creamy stout.

BLEWITTS

Blewitts Brewery, Sorley Tunnel Adventure Farm, Loddiswell Road, Kingsbridge, Devon, TQ7 4BP
Tel (01548) 852485 (number for Ship & Plough: no phone at brewery)
Tours as part of Sorley Tunnel attraction

⊗ Steve Blewitt started his Kingsbridge brew-pub business in 1988 at the Ship and Plough inn. He won first prize at the Cardiff beer festival with Lights Out Stout; and first in its class and first overall at the Devon County Show for Blewitt's Wages. The brewery is now located a mile out of town at Sorley Adventure Farm where during the holiday season visitors can watch the brewing process through viewing windows.

Best *(ABV 3.6%)*

Wages *(ABV 4.5%)*

Head Off *(ABV 5%)*

Top *(ABV 5%)*

BLUE ANCHOR

Blue Anchor Inn, 50 Coinagehall Street, Helston, Cornwall, TR13 8EL
Tel (01326) 562821
Fax (01326) 565765
Tours by arrangement

⊗ Dating back to the 15th Century, this is the oldest brewery in Cornwall and was originally a monk's hospice. After the dissolution of the monasteries it became a tavern brewing its own uniquely flavoured beer called Spingo at the rear of the premises. Brewing has continued to this day and people travel from all over the world to sample the delights of this wonderful inn untouched by time. The brewery has undergone complete refurbishment and the pub is also due for improvement, with careful attention to preserving its special character. Two outlets are supplied direct. The hosts Simon and Kim Stone have owned the Blue Anchor Inn since 1993 and have done much to preserve its character. Seasonal: Spingo Bragget (ABV 6.1%, April-Sept), Spingo Easter Special (ABV 7.5%), Spingo Christmas Special (ABV 7.5%). The draught beers are also available in bottle-conditioned form.

Spingo Middle *(OG 1050, ABV 5.1%)*
A deep copper-red beer with a big fruity aroma of raisins and sultanas, a hint of

vanilla and an earthy, peppery note from the hops. The palate is nutty, with a fruit cake note. The long bitter-sweet finish has a raspberry-like fruitiness balanced by the dryness of the hops.

Spingo Special *(OG 1066, ABV 6.7%)*
Darker than Middle with a pronounced earthy character on the nose balanced by rich fruit. Fruit and peppery hops dominate the mouth, followed by a big finish in which malt, fruit and hops vie for attention.

BLUE BELL

Blue Bell Brewery Co Ltd, Blue Bell Inn, Cranesgate South, Whaplode St Catherine, Spalding, Lincs, PE12 6SN
Tel/Fax (01406) 540300
Tours by arrangement

⊗ The award-winning brewery was set up by Ken Dixon, (ex Bateman's) and Mike Pilkington (landlord of the Blue Bell). It has been in operation for two years and won the Peterborough New Brewer Beer Festival with Olde Honesty in 2000. The brewery is behind the pub in a former potato store. Ken Dixon has retired but Mike is developing sales over an ever-expanding area. 75 outlets are supplied direct.

Olde Session *(OG 1040, ABV 3.7%)*

Olde Honesty *(OG 1045, ABV 4.1%)*

Olde Fashioned *(OG 1051, ABV 4.8%)*

BLUE COW

Blue Cow Inn and Brewery, South Witham, nr Grantham, Lincs, NG33 5QB
Tel/Fax (01572) 768432
E-mail Richard@thirlwell.fslife.co.uk
Website www.thebluecowinn.co.uk
Tours by arrangement

The Blue Cow opened in 1997 and is run by Dick Thirlwell, who brews only for the pub. The equipment came from Parish Brewery at Old Somerby in Leicestershire.

Thirlwell's Cuddy *(OG 1039, ABV 3.8%)*

Thirlwell's Best *(OG 1040, ABV 3.8%)*

BLUE MOON

Blue Moon Brewery, Cock Inn, Watton Road, Barford, Norfolk, NR9 4AS
Tel (01603) 757646

Blue Moon stopped brewing for a while and its beer were contract-brewed by Buffy's. But Pete Turner has moved his kit to the Cock Inn and has expanded his range. He supplies the Cock and some 60 free trade outlets. A new brewery, Spectrum, run by Andy Mitchell, plans to brew on the Blue Moon kit.

Easy Life *(OG 1040, ABV 3.8%)* ◈
A toffee-like malt base blends well with a bitterness that slowly recedes to a slightly sweeter finish. Hop notes also slowly fade in this amber-coloured beer. The nose is a deceptively light mix of malt and hop.

Sea of Tranquillity *(OG 1042, ABV 4.2%)* ◈
Damson fruitiness introduces this copper-coloured bitter. Full of bitter-sweet richness, the long, sustained finish is at odds with the heavy malt aroma.

Moon Dance *(ABV 4.7%)*

Dark Side *(OG 1048, ABV 4.5%)* ◈
Slightly scented, with fruit, hops and malt, this dark brown strong mild has plenty of body. A caramel sweetness gives balance to the dominant malty foundation. A long finish maintains the rich blend of flavours.

Hingham High *(OG 1050, ABV 5.2%)* ◈
Rich, red and rounded, this glorious old-style ale has traces of raisins and treacle vying for attention alongside the usual hops and malt. The finish takes a dryish turn that is at odds with the early flavours.

Milk of Amnesia *(OG 1055, ABV 5.2%)* ◈
A complex beer, mid-brown coloured, but the light malty nose gives little away. The taste has a port-like fluency, cinnamon and ginger jostle with pepper and citrus as the flavours continue to hold up well.

Liquor Mortis *(OG 1075, ABV 7.5%)* ◈
Plum pudding in a glass! Dark brown and brooding with a filling malty sweetness. A dry eucalyptus background emerges as the flavours mature. All this after a heavy, malty aroma introduces this full-flavoured ale.

Total Eclipse *(ABV 8.5%)*

BOAT

Boat Brewery, Boat Lane, Main Street, Allerton Bywater, W Yorkshire, WF10 2BX
Tel (01977) 667788
E-mail ron@boatbrewery.co.uk
Website www.boatbrewery.co.uk
Tours by arrangement

◎ Conceived and constructed in 1999 for the Boat inn, the brewery has increased production and now covers the whole country. Ron Ridout, the brewer, is a keen CAMRA activist and is pleased to entertain visitors as groups or individuals. Extra capacity is being considered as the Boat inn undergoes expansion. Seasonal beer: Phesta (ABV 4.5%, winter).

Man in the Boat
(OG 1037, ABV 3.5%) ◈
A smooth, dark mild. Full in flavour for its strength. Chocolate and dark fruit in the aroma and taste lead to a satisfying dry, fruity finish.

Bomber's Moon *(OG 1038, ABV 3.8%)*

Rattler *(OG 1041, ABV 4.2%)*

Hellfire Jack *(OG 1042, ABV 4.2%)*

BODICOTE

See Plough

BOGGART HOLE CLOUGH

Boggart Hole Clough Brewing Co, Unit 13, Brookside Works, Clough Road, Moston, Manchester, M9 4FP
Tel/Fax (0161) 277 9666
E-mail mark@boggart-brewery.co.uk
Website www.boggart-brewery.co.uk
Tours by arrangement

◎ Set up by Mark Dade, former brewer at Marble, next to Boggart Hole Clough Park in North Manchester. Brewing started in 2001. With 80 or 90 free houses taking the beer, Mark has increased the brew length from 2.5 barrels to eight. He has set up a Brewery Workshop to enable visitors to learn how to design and produce beers to their own specifications. Bottle-conditioned beers: Steaming Boggart (ABV 9%), Bob Sleigh (ABV 5%).

Boggart Bitter *(OG 1038, ABV 3.8%)*

Bog Standard *(OG 1040, ABV 4%)*

Log End *(OG 1040, ABV 4%)*

Angel Hill *(OG 1042, ABV 4.2%)*

Boggart Brew *(OG 1043, ABV 4.3%)*

Dark Side *(OG 1044, ABV 4.4%)*

Sun Dial *(OG 1047, ABV 4.7%)*

Steaming Boggart *(ABV 9%)*

BORVE

Borve Brew House, Ruthven, Huntly, Aberdeenshire, AB54 4SG
Tel (01466) 760343
E-mail grgrghughes@netscapeonline.co.uk
Tours by arrangement

◎ Established in 1983, Borve moved from its original site on the Isle of Lewis five years later to a former school on the mainland. The brewhouse is adjacent. The school became a pub but that has closed due to family illness. The brewery also closed for a period but planned to resume production early in 2003. The cask beers are also available in bottle-conditioned form; Extra Strong (ABV 10%) is bottle-conditioned only. All the beers are suitable for vegans.

Borve Ale *(ABV 3.9%)*

Tall Ships *(ABV 5%)*

BOSTON EXPERIENCE

Boston Experience Ltd, Church Path, Woking, Surrey, GU21 1EL
Tel (01483) 598586
Fax (01483) 599201
Website www.boston-experience.co.uk

The Boston Experience opened in 1998, brewing American-style beer, chilled and filtered. All the beers are dispensed from cellar tanks to the bar. Beers: Babe Ruth (ABV 3.8%); Bunker Hill (ABV 4.5%); Boston Strangler (ABV 5.3%).

BRAGDY CEREDIGION

Bragdy Ceredigion Brewery, Brynderwen, Llangranog, Llandysul, Ceredigion, SA44 6AD
Tel (01239) 654099/888
Fax (01239) 654099
E-mail brian@ceredigionbrewery.fs.business.co.uk
Website www.tavernontap.co.uk
www.bestofruralwales.co.uk
Shop. Tours by arrangement

Bragdy Ceredigion Brewery is situated on the coastal belt of West Wales and housed in a converted barn on Wervil Grange Farm. A family-run craft brewery established in 1997 by Brian and Julia Tilby, it produces bottle-conditioned and cask-conditioned ales. No chemical additives are used. The bottle-conditioned beers are suitable for vegans. The full-mash, five-barrel plant uses Maris Otter floor-malted barley, with Challenger, First Gold and Fuggles hops. An organic beer with certified pale malt and organic hops was added in 2001 and a range of organic fruit beers is planned. Bottle-conditioned beers: as for cask beers, save for the Spirit of the Forest. Occasional beer: Honey Beer (ABV 5%).

Ysbryd O'r Goeden/Spirit of the Forest *(OG 1036, ABV 3.8%)*

Gwrach Ddu/Black Witch *(OG 1038, ABV 4%)*

Draig Aur/Gold Dragon *(OG 1039, ABV 4.2%)*

Barcud Coch/Red Kite *(OG 1040, ABV 4.3%)*

Blodeuwedd/Flowerface organic beer *(OG 1043, ABV 4.5%)*

Cwrw 2000/Ale 2000 *(OG 1049, ABV 5%)*

Yr Hen Darw Du/Old Black Bull *(OG 1058, ABV 6.2%)*

BRAGDY YNYS MON

Isle of Anglesey Brewery, Cae Cwta Mawr, Talwrn, Anglesey, LI77 7SD
Tel (01248) 723801
E-mail martyn@caecwtamawr.freeserve.co.uk
Tours by arrangement

◎ Martyn Lewis started brewing in summer 1999 in a converted outbuilding of a farmhouse that faces the mountains of Snowdonia. A bottling plant has been added in a former stable. All the cask beers are available in bottle-conditioned form. All the beers were due to have organic versions by summer 2002.

Medra *(OG 1039, ABV 4%)* ◆
Attractive-looking, copper-coloured, soft, malty bitter with hints of berries in the short, dry finish.

Wennol *(OG 1040, ABV 4.1%)*
The name means Swallow. Golden toned fruity beer with a lingering bitter finish.

Tarw Du *(OG 1045, ABV 4.5%)* ◆
The name means Black Bull. Inviting black porter-style beer that has an earthy flavour with some chocolate/coffee notes and a long, dry aftertatse.

Amnesia *(OG 1048, ABV 4.9%)*
Full-bodied, rich hop and malt character throughout with a delectable aftertaste.

BRAINS

SA Brain & Company Ltd, The Cardiff Brewery, Crawshay Street, Cardiff, CF10 5TR
Tel (029) 2040 2060
Fax (029) 2040 3324
Website www.sabrain.co.uk

◎ S A Brain began trading at the Old Brewery in Cardiff in 1882 when Samuel Arthur Brain and his uncle Joseph Benjamin Brain purchased a site founded in 1713. The company has remained in family ownership ever since and in 1997 bought South Wales' other leading independent, Crown Buckley, formed from the merger of the Crown Brewery of Pontyclun with Buckleys of Llanelli. The full range of Brain's and Buckley's ales are now produced at the company's Cardiff Brewery (formerly Hancock's), bought from Bass in 1999. The company owns 212 pubs, as well as having a sizeable free trade, plus interests in hotel and leisure projects in Wales and the West Country. 390 outlets are supplied direct.

Buckley's IPA *(OG 1033.5, ABV 3.4%)*

Brains Dark *(OG 1035.5, ABV 3.5%)* ◆
A dark brown mild with a pleasing, bitter-sweet mix of roast, malt caramel flavours, with a good finish. A good, traditional, satisfying mild.

Brains Bitter *(OG 1036, ABV 3.7%)* ◆
A pale beer, low aroma; malt, hops and bitterness lead to a clean, bitter finish.

Buckley's Best Bitter *(OG 1036.5, ABV 3.7%)*

Arms Park *(OG 1040, ABV 4%)* ◆
Brewed to support Cardiff Rugby Club. Faint malt and hop aroma leads to a mainly malty taste with gentle hop and fruit flavours. Finish is malty with moderate bitterness.

SA *(OG 1042, ABV 4.2%)* ◆
Low aroma, amber colour, a rounded blend of flavours. Malt, fruit and hops are accompanied by a building bitterness.

Rev James *(OG 1045.5, ABV 4.5%)* ◆
Pale brown, faint fruit, hop and malt aroma. Fruit and malt dominate the flavour with faint hop and some bitterness. Finish fades.

BRAKSPEAR

WH Brakspear & Sons plc, The Brewery, New Street, Henley-on-Thames, Oxon, RG9 2BU
Tel (01491) 570200
Fax (01491) 410254
E-mail frontoffice@brakspear.co.uk
Website www.brakspear.co.uk
Shop 9-6 Mon-Sat (9-7 Fri).

⊠ In July 2002, Brakspear announced it would close the brewery by the end of the year. Brakspear will continue in business as a pub company, while the brands have been sold to Refresh UK, which owns Wychwood of Witney. The beers will be brewed at Wychwood and Thomas Hardy in

Dorchester. Refresh says it plans eventually to build a new brewery in Oxfordshire, but as the plans for this site describe it as a 'micro-brewery' it's clear that production will be dramatically reduced in order to qualify for lower rates of beer duty announced in the 2002 budget. It's expected that many of Brakspear's brands will disappear, and Refresh will concentrate on the core beers, Bitter and Special. Brakspear currently owns or leases 103 pubs, all but one serving cask beer. The brewery warehouse was undergoing major redevelopment during 2002 and all tours are suspended for the year. There is a rolling programme of seasonal beers. Bottle-conditioned beers: Coniston Bluebird (ABV 4.2%: brewed for Coniston Brewery), Live Organic
(ABV 4.6%), Vintage Henley (ABV 5.5%). Organic beers suitable for vegans: Live Organic, Naturale Organic Lager (both ABV 4.6%).

Mild *(OG 1032, ABV 3%)*
A dry, red-brown mild with a good balance of chocolate malt and roast barley. A hint of sweetness gives way to a dry, bitter finish.

Bitter *(OG 1035.5, ABV 3.4%)*
This copper-coloured bitter is well hopped, moderately fruity and unpretentious, with a spicy bitterness and good mouthfeel. It ends fruity, dry and pungently hoppy.

Old Ale *(OG 1043.5, ABV 4.3%)*
Red/brown in colour with good body. The strong, fruity aroma is well complemented by malt and hops. Its pronounced taste of malt, with discernible sweet, roast malt flavours, gives way to fruitiness. The aftertaste is of bitter-sweet chocolate, even though chocolate malt is not used.

Special *(OG 1043.5, ABV 4.3%)*
A honey-coloured bitter, well-balanced with fruit and a good bitter hop character. Pale malt and hops lead through to an astringent finish.

Contract beer:
Bluebird (for Coniston Brewery)
(OG 1036, ABV 3.6%)

BRANDY CASK

Brandy Cask Pub & Brewery, Bridge Street, Pershore, Worcs, WR10 1AJ
Tel/Fax (01386) 552602
Tours by arrangement

Brewing started in 1995 in a refurbished bottle store in the garden of the pub. It was run as a separate business until the retirement of the brewer in 1998. Brewery and pub now operate under one umbrella, with brewing carried out by the owner/landlord. Since the change, brewing is restricted to the Brandy Cask but a return to supplying other outlets in the future is anticipated. Occasional beer: Ale Mary (ABV 4.8%).

Whistling Joe *(ABV 3.6%)*
A malty and fruity start leads into this well-balanced bitter. Hops come through and there are plenty of different flavours to savour before the final dry aftertaste.

Brandy Snapper *(ABV 4%)*
Well-balanced flowery bitter with fruity undertones, malt in the aroma and a dry aftertaste.

John Baker's Original *(ABV 4.8%)*
A balanced, subtle aftertaste emerges from a wealth of malt, roast and sweet flavours each in its right measure in this full-bodied strong bitter.

Ale Mary *(ABV 4.8%)*
A very aromatic and fruity premium bitter with a robust malty palate and lots of balancing flavours.

BRANSCOMBE VALE

Branscombe Vale Brewery, Great Seaside Farm, Branscombe, Seaton, Devon, EX12 3DP
Tel/Fax (01297) 680511
Tours by arrangement, winter only

The brewery was set up in 1992 by former dairy workers Paul Dimond and Graham Luxton in cowsheds owned by the National Trust. Paul and Graham converted the sheds and dug their own well. The NT has built an extension for the brewery to ensure future growth. Branscombe Vale currently supplies 70 regular outlets. Seasonal beers: Anniversary Ale (ABV 4.6%, Jan-Feb), Hells Belles (ABV 4.8%, winter), Summa That (ABV 5%, summer), Yo Ho Ho (ABV 6%, December).

Branoc *(OG 1036, ABV 3.8%)*
Light brown in colour, this is a good session bitter. Light fruity taste and aroma with a well-balanced bitter finish.

Draymans Best *(OG 1040, ABV 4.2%)*

BVB *(OG 1044, ABV 4.6%)*
Reddy/brown-coloured beer with a fruity aroma and taste, and bitter/astringent finish.

BREWSTER'S

Brewster's Brewing Co Ltd, Penn Lane, Stathern, Nr Melton Mowbray, Leicestershire, LE14 4HR
Tel (01949) 861868 Fax (01949) 861901
E-mail sara@brewsters.co.uk
Website www.brewsters.co.uk
Tours by arrangement

Brewster is the old English term for a female brewer and Sara Barton is a modern example. A Master of Brewing trained at Heriot Watt Brewing School in Edinburgh, she worked with Courage before striking out alone. In 2000, she won the Small Business category of Country Living magazine's Enterprising Rural Women awards. Brewster's Brewery was set up in the heart of the Vale of Belvoir in 1998 with a five-barrel plant. There are plans to upgrade to cope with increased demand. Beer is supplied direct to some 200 pubs throughout central England and further afield via wholesalers. Seasonal/occasional beers: Claudia Wheat Beer (ABV 4.5%, summer), Brewster's Stocking (ABV 5.5%, Christmas), Frau Brau Lager (ABV 5%, summer), Bellydancer (ABV 5.2%).

Hophead *(OG 1036, ABV 3.6%)*
A pale and hoppy brew, a very refreshing session beer with a fresh floral hop character.

Marquis *(OG 1038, ABV 3.8%)*
A pleasant quaffing beer with a light maltiness, balanced by a dry hoppy finish.

Monty's Mild *(OG 1040, ABV 4%)*
A full-bodied dark mild made with a blend of pale, chocolate and crystal malts as well as torrefied wheat. Lightly hopped with Progress.

Bitter *(OG 1042, ABV 4.2%)*
A well-balanced red ale with nutty malt character and aromatic hop flavour.

Vale Pale Ale (VPA) *(OG 1045, ABV 4.5%)*
A golden ale with a subtle biscuit malt flavour and citrus hop notes.

Wicked Woman *(OG 1048, ABV 4.8%)*
(Varies seasonally)

BRIDGE OF ALLAN

Bridge of Allan Brewery Ltd,
The Brewhouse, Queens Lane,
Bridge of Allan, Stirlingshire, FK9 4NY
Tel (01786) 834555
Fax (01786) 833426
E-mail brewery@bridgeofallan.co.uk
Website www.bridgeofallan.co.uk
Shop 12-4 daily, Easter to Oct.
Tours by arrangement

☺ Bridge of Allan Brewery was founded in 1997 and is located in the leafy Victorian spa town in the Forth Valley, with Stirling Castle, the Wallace Monument and the Trossochs close by. The five-barrel custom-built brewery, run by Douglas Ross, also owns two village pubs and sells to more than 75 pubs in Scotland and also distributes to England via agencies. An additional three fermenters have been installed to increase capacity. Seasonal beers: Spring Ale (ABV 4.2%, March-April), Bramble (ABV 4.2%, Sept-Oct), Bronwyn (ABV 4.4%, Dec). Other seasonals are available throughout the year on a monthly basis. Ben Nevis, Glencoe Stout and Lomond Gold are organic beers. Bottle-conditioned beer: Brig O'Allan (ABV 4.1%) only from brewery shop or via Internet.

Stirling Bitter *(OG 1038, ABV 3.7%)*
A full-flavoured beer with a nutty, fruity taste offering a relatively dry aftertaste. Bittered with Bramling Cross and Fuggles hops.

Stirling Brig *(OG 1042, ABV 4.1%)*
Brewed to commemorate the 700th anniversary of the Battle of Stirling Brig in 1297. A full-bodied, rich, malty and slightly sweet beer. A classic rich dark ruby red ale with a creamy head, typical of a traditional Scottish 80/-.

Bannock Burn *(OG 1044, ABV 4.2%)*
A light-coloured ale brewed with Maris Otter and crystal malts. A hint of torrefied wheat is added, producing a satisfying and complex flavour. A fresh dry aftertaste is supported by a fairly hoppy character.

Glencoe Wild Oat Stout *(ABV 4.5%)*
Suitable for vegetarians or vegans. Brewed in the heart of Scotland using the finest malts, pure Scottish water and wild oats. This traditional stout has a creamy, toasted oatmeal flavour and is gently hopped.

Lomond Gold *(ABV 5%)*
Suitable for vegetarians or vegans. A light-coloured beer brewed close to the banks of Loch Lomond. Clean, sharp and fresh flavoured and hopped with continental Saaz that give a hint of citrus.

BRISCOE'S

Briscoe's Brewery, 16 Ash Grove,
Otley, W Yorkshire, LS21 3EL
Tel/Fax (01943) 466515
E-mail briscoe.brewery@virgin.net

The brewery was launched in 1998 by microbiologist/chemist Dr Paul Briscoe in the cellar of his house with a one-barrel brew length. A new three-barrel brewery at the rear of the Bowling Green public house in Otley opened in 2000. The brew length increased to four barrels during 2002. The original one-barrel plant has been retained for special/occasional bottled beers. The beers are full mash, most being all malt. Eleven outlets are supplied direct. Most of the beer names are related to the brewer's other passion – long-distance running. Occasional beers: Rombalds Reviver (ABV 3.8%), Runner's Ruin (ABV 4.3%), Shane's Shamrock Stout (ABV 4.6%), Chevinbrau Pilsner-style lager (ABV 5.2%), Puddled and Barmy Ale (ABV 5.8%), Victorian Velvet (OG 1048-49, ABV 4.9%, winter).

Burnsall Classic Bitter *(OG 1040, ABV 4%)*
A full-flavoured, reddish coloured bitter with a good hop flavour.

Chevin Chaser *(OG 1043, ABV 4.3%)*
A refreshing, pale-coloured, all-malt bitter with a distinct hop finish.

Dalebottom Dark *(OG 1043, ABV 4.3%)*
A smooth and malty strong dark mild with a good hop character.

Otley Gold *(OG 1043, ABV 4.6%)*
A pale, fairly full-flavoured but soft beer brewed in the style of a lager.

Badger Stone Bitter *(OG 1044, ABV 4.4%)*
A classic English bitter, packed with the flavour of malt and hops.

Three Peaks Ale *(OG 1045, ABV 4.5%)*
A strong, pale premium bitter brewed with only pale malt and traditional hops.

Victorian Velvet *(OG 1048-49, ABV 4.9%)*
A malty, fruity and smooth copper-coloured special bitter. Small amounts are available from the brewery, bottle-conditioned around Christmas.

BROADSTONE

Broadstone Brewing Company Ltd,
Rum Runner, Wharf Road,
Retford, Notts, DN22 7ZJ
Tel (01777) 719797
E-mail broadstone.brewery@virgin.net
Website www.broadstonebrewery.com
Tours by arrangement

⊗ Alan Gill, who founded Springhead Brewery, set up Broadstone in Retford in 1999 and in the spring of 2001 moved the brewery to the same site as his Rum Runner pub. Seasonal beers: March Ale (ABV 5%, March), Mason's Field (ABV 3.6%, summer), Fletchers Ale (ABV 4.2%, spring). Alan intends to bottle Black Abbott and Gold in the near future.

Best Bitter *(OG 1038.6, ABV 3.8%)* ◆
An orange-brown session beer with a good hop backed by a malty nose that continues in the fairly bitter taste. The bitterness dries into a malty finish.

Stonebridge Mild *(OG 1041, ABV 4%)*

Charter Ale *(OG 1046.8, ABV 4.6%)* ◆
A light creamy head on a darkish brown beer. A beautiful coffee roast aroma and taste that lingers on through the hoppy, bitter finish. A fine use of amber malt.

Gold *(OG 1052, ABV 5%)*

Black Abbott *(OG 1052, ABV 5%)*

BROUGHTON

Broughton Ales Ltd,
Broughton, Biggar,
Peeblesshire, ML12 6HQ
Tel (01899) 830345
Fax (01899) 830474
E-mail beer@broughtonales.co.uk;
Website www.broughtonales.co.uk
Shop 9-5

☺ Founded in 1979, the company went into receivership in 1995 and was taken over by Whim Brewery owner Giles Litchfield along with managing director Alastair Mouat. They have created the popular Clipper IPA and the new Greenmantle Original. Expansion into new markets in England is going well. 70 per cent of production is bottled (not bottle-conditioned), much of it for export. A single tied house and 200 outlets in Scotland are supplied direct from the brewery. Seasonal/occasional beers: Winter Fire (ABV 4.2%), The Ghillie (ABV 4.5%), Border Gold (ABV 4.2%).

Greenmantle Original
(OG 1038, ABV 3.9%) ◆
This tawny beer has strong malty characteristics with a bitter-sweet finish.

Clipper IPA *(OG 1042, ABV 4.2%)*
This light-coloured, crisp, hoppy beer bears all the hallmarks of an India Pale Ale, with a strong hop character and a clean taste.

BREWED IN THE SCOTTISH BORDERS
BROUGHTON ALES
LIMITED

Scottish Oatmeal Stout
(OG 1042, ABV 4.2%) ◆
A rare pleasure, this wonderfully dry stout has a bitter aftertaste dominated by roast malt. A distinctive malt aroma is followed by a prominent roast note. Fruit is evident throughout.

Merlin's Ale *(OG 1042, ABV 4.2%)* ◆
A well-hopped, fruity flavour is balanced by malt in the taste. The finish is bitter-sweet, light but dry.

Border Gold *(OG 1042, ABV 4.2%)*
Fruity hop aroma with citrus-lime hop flavour balanced by a malty sweetness. The finish is rich malt with grapefruit bitterness.

Winter Fire *(OG 1042, ABV 4.2%)*
A rich, dark, full-bodied beer, full of malt flavour with a hint of sweetness.

The Ghillie *(OG 1043, ABV 4.5%)* ◆
A full-bodied ale. Hops, malt and fruit dominate the palate. The finish is dry and dominated by hops

The Black Douglas *(OG 1053, ABV 5.2%)*
Brewed using Maris Otter pale ale malt with the addition of roasted barley and maize, this ruby-coloured beer has a full malty flavour with a warm, strong finish.

Old Jock *(OG 1070, ABV 6.7%)*
Strong, sweetish and fruity in the finish. A classic Scottish strong ale.

BROWN COW

Brown Cow Brewery, Brown Cow Road,
Barlow, Selby, N Yorkshire, YO8 8EH
Tel/Fax 01757 618947
Website www.browncowbrewery.f9.co.uk

Brewing takes place in a converted outbuilding at the brewer's riverside home (the former Brown Cow inn). The brewery is run by Susan Simpson, who brews 5-7.5 barrels a week on the 2.5-barrel plant. The beers are always available at three local outlets and as guest ales to free houses in the area. 75 outlets are supplied direct. Seasonal beers: Maiden Century (ABV 4%, spring/summer), Nimbus Wheat Beer (suitable for vegetarians/vegans, ABV 4.8%, spring/summer), Black Diamond (ABV 5%, winter), Wassail Warmer (ABV 5%, Christmas).

Mistle Mild *(OG 1037, ABV 3.7%)* ◆
Dark, malty and softly rounded.

Bitter *(OG 1038, ABV 3.8%)* ◆
A well-hopped traditional session bitter.

Constellation *(OG 1042, ABV 4.2%)*
A house beer for pubs with individual recipes.

Simpsons No. 4 *(OG 1043, ABV 4.4%)* ◆
Dark and bitter-sweet, full of roast barley character.

Hogwort XS *(OG 1044, ABV 4.4%)*

Wolfhound *(OG 1043, ABV 4.5%)* ◆
Straw-coloured, full and rounded palate of malt and traditional English hops.

How Now *(OG 1044, ABV 4.5%)* ◆
Pale, fruity and single hopped.

BRUNSWICK

Brunswick Brewing Co, 1 Railway Terrace, Derby, DE1 2RU
Tel (01332) 290677
Fax (01332) 370226
Tours by arrangement

A purpose-built tower brewery attached to the Brunswick Inn, the first railwaymen's hostelry in the world, partly restored by the Derbyshire Historic Building Trust and bought by the present owners in 1987. Brewing began in 1991 and a viewing area allows pub-users to watch production. The beers are supplied to the inn and six other outlets. Bought by Everards in August 2002.

Triple Hop *(OG 1040, ABV 4%)*
A straw-coloured ale with a slightly sulphury aroma. An overtly bitter beer with pleasant mouth-puckering dryness.

Coming of Age *(OG 1041, ABV 4.1%)*
A tawny ale with little aroma. After initial sweetness, a lasting bitterness and a dry finish.

Second Brew/The Usual *(OG 1042, ABV 4.2%)*
A dark copper colour, it drinks vinously with a lot of mouthfeel round the rich, clean malt. Dry aftertaste with a dash of orange.

Railway Porter *(OG 1045, ABV 4.3%)*
Chocolate aroma with spicy fruit notes. A complex, full-bodied brew with distinct coffee and fruity after character.

Triple Gold *(OG 1045, ABV 4.5%)*

Old Accidental *(OG 1050, ABV 5%)*
A light vinous floral hop aroma with underlying malt notes. Well-balanced, malty beer leading to a bitter finish with warming aftertaste.

Father Mike's Dark Rich Ruby *(OG 1058, ABV 5.8%)*

BRYN CELYN

Bryn Celyn Brewery, 47 Wern Road, Ystalyfera, Swansea, SA9 2LX
Tel (01639) 843625
E-mail bryncelynbrewery@aol.com
Website www.bryncelynbrewery.co.uk
Tours CAMRA branches only

A one-quarter barrel brewery was opened in 1999 by William Hopton (owner) and Robert Scott (brewer). Capacity was increased to its present three-quarter capacity barrel in the same year. As the beer names imply, the owner is fond of Buddy Holly. Feb 59 commemorates the singer's death. Seasonal beers: Feb 59 (ABV 3.7%), Peggy's Brew (ABV 4.2%, March), May B Baby (ABV 4.5%, May), That Will Be the Sleigh (ABV 7.2%, Christmas Ale Dec/Jan).

Buddy Marvellous *(OG 1040, ABV 4%)*
Robust, tasty blend of malt and roast flavours. Hop and fruit flavours emerge along with bitterness to balance and leave a satisfying, complex finish. Moreish.

Buddy's Delight *(OG 1042, ABV 4.2%)*

Crwrw Celyn *(OG 1044, ABV 4.4%)*

Oh Boy *(OG 1045, ABV 4.5%)*
A golden beer with an enticing fruit and hop aroma. A refreshing burst of hop and fruit flavours along with underlying malt. The increasing bitterness leads to a memorable hop and fruit finish.

CHH *(OG 1045, ABV 4.5%)*
An inviting aroma, a pale brown colour with hints of red malt and hop aroma, with fruit and bitterness adding to the flavour. The finish is clean and hoppily bitter.

Rave On *(OG 1050, ABV 5%)*

Buddy Confusing *(OG 1050, ABV 5%)*

BRYSON'S

Bryson's Brews, c/o 1 Summerside, 25 Oxcliffe Road, Heysham, Lancs, LA3 1PU
Tel (01524) 852150
E-mail brysonsbrews@supanet.com

After a year of part-time brewing, George Palmer, one-time mechanical engineer and long-time home brewer, is now brewing full time. The 4.5 barrel Mossbrew plant is housed in an industrial unit near George's home. He supplies pubs locally, and uses agents to distribute further afield. 2002 saw a brew specifically for Lancaster University, which has been selling his beers since early 2001. Beer names are alliterations, after local landmarks, trades and features. Seasonal beer: Patrick's Porter (ABV 4.3%, winter), Wammellers Wheat (ABV 4%, summer).

Barrows Bitter *(ABV 4.2%)*

Acre Moss Amber *(ABV 4.5%)*

BUFFY'S

Buffy's Brewery, Rectory Road, Tivetshall St Mary, Norwich, NR15 2DD
Tel/Fax (01379) 676523
E-mail buffysbrewery@lineone.net
Website www.buffys.co.uk
Tours by arrangement

Established in 1993, the brewing capacity stands at 45 barrels, but plans are in hand to move to bigger premises. The brewery has bought its first pub, the Cherry Tree at Wickerwood, and plans to buy a second pub closer to home: the brewery will eventually move to these premises. Seasonal beers: Sleigher (ABV 4.1%, Hollybeery (ABV 6.2%, Christmas: recipe and ABV change every year.

Norwich Terrier *(OG 1036, ABV 3.6%)* Clean honey-blossom aroma gives an indication of the light refreshing hoppiness of the initial taste of this amber beer. A fruity bitterness augments the flavour. The finish is long as the bitter edge develops intensity.

Bitter *(OG 1039, ABV 3.9%)* ◆ A copper-coloured brew where the light hoppy nose expands to become the dominant flavour. Malt provides major supporting flavour to produce a slightly sweeter finish with a hint of raspberries.

Mild *(OG 1042, ABV 4.2%)* ◆ Light roast malt airs introduce a solid old-style mild where sweetness vies with roast malt for dominance. A rich roast beefiness emerges from the long unwavering finish that complements the deep red hues of this ale.

Polly's Folly *(OG 1043, ABV 4.3%)* ◆ A full-flavoured bitter with malt the dominant flavour in both taste and nose. Hops, noticeable in the bouquet, provide a counter to the maltiness as the long finish develops a bitter-sweet fruitiness.

Hopleaf *(OG 1044.5, ABV 4.5%)* ◆ An amber brew with a smoothness often associated with larger breweries. Sweet hoppy notes with a hint of vanilla provide an easy-drinking feel. A gently fading finish with honey overtones.

India Ale *(OG 1046, ABV 4.6%)* ◆ Hops, malt and bitterness blend to give a full-flavoured but well-balanced beer. The light malty/hop nose belies the robustness of the taste. The bitterness and hops continue to a clean, dry and lingering finish.

Norwegian Blue *(OG 1049, ABV 4.9%)* ◆ Hints of malt and hops give this copper bitter a soft nose. This is at odds with a strong, smooth taste, with equal amounts of malt and hops balancing a bitter-sweet gooseberry body. Short malty, bitter end.

Ale *(OG 1055, ABV 5.5%)* ◆ A tawny, old-fashioned Christmas pudding beer. Rich, plummy aroma emerges from a sweet fruity flavour laced with a malty platform. The finish continues through to a smooth malty flavour abetted by sweet bitterness.

Festival 9X *(OG 1090, ABV 9.0%)*

BULLMASTIFF

Bullmastiff Brewery, 14 Bessemer Close, Leckwith, Cardiff, CF11 8DL
Tel (029) 20665292
Website www.bullmastiffbrewery.com

An award-winning small craft brewery run by the brothers Bob and Paul Jenkins. The name stems from their love of the bullmastiff breed. They have won many awards for the beers, including Champion Beer of Wales 1999 and 2000 and joint gold medal for bitter at the 2000 Great British Beer Festival, but have no ambitions for expansion or owning any pubs, preferring to concentrate on quality control. 30 outlets are supplied direct. Seasonal beers: Summer Moult (ABV 4.3%), Mogadog (ABV 10%, winter).

Gold *(OG 1038, ABV 3.8%)* ◆ Champion Beer of Wales 1999 and 2000. A hoppy aroma invites you taste a fine blend of hops and fruit with malt to balance. A refreshing juicy hop finish completes the beer. Golden beer to match its awards.

Best Bitter *(OG 1042, ABV 4%)* ◆ Good hop aroma with a fruity, hoppy bitterness in the mouth. Lasting hop bitterness in the finish. A tasty best bitter.

Thoroughbred *(OG 1047, ABV 4.5%)* ◆ A tasty, premium bitter with hops strong on the aroma and flavour balanced by fruit and malt with a bitter finish.

Snarlsberg Llager *(OG 1045, ABV 5%)* A break from tradition, a cask-conditioned Welsh 'llager'.

Brindle *(OG 1051, ABV 5%)* ◆ A full-bodied, flavoursome pale beer. Good hop aroma with a mix of malt, hops, fruit and bitterness in the taste. A lasting and satisfying finish.

Son of A Bitch *(OG 1059, ABV 6%)* ◆ An amber beer with a complex mix of hops, fruit and malt balanced by good bitterness. Rich, lasting finish to this warming, tasty and drinkable beer.

BUNTINGFORD*

Buntingford Brewery Co Ltd, Unit 2A, Watermill Industrial Estate, Buntingford, Herts, SG9 9JS
Tel (07956) 246215/(07949) 438353
E-mail enquiries@buntingford-brewery.co.uk
Website www.buntingford-brewery.co.uk
Tours by arrangement

⊗ Set up in August 2001 by Steve Banfield of Banfield Ales and Andrew Potter using the plant purchased for the Woodlands Brewery. A part-time venture, many special ales are produced as well as the regular beers.

Highwayman Best Bitter *(OG 1038, ABV 3.7%)* Pale-brown in colour, gentle smooth maltiness and a good hoppy character.

Templars Gold *(OG 1040, ABV 4%)* A golden beer, lightly hopped and flavoured with cloves.

Hurricane Force *(OG 1045, ABV 4.3%)* Light brown in colour, this is a pleasantly hoppy beer with light malty undertones.

Station Porter *(ABV 4.4%)*

Watermill Stout *(OG 1048, ABV 4.8%)*

BURTON BRIDGE

Burton Bridge Brewery, Bridge Street, Burton upon Trent, Staffs, DE14 1SY
Tel (01283) 510573
Email bbb@burtonbridgebrewery.fsnet.co.uk
Website midlandspubs.co.uk
Shop Bridge Inn 11.30-2.15pm, 5.30-11pm
Tours Wednesday evenings.

☺ A craft brewery established in 1982 by Bruce Wilkinson and Geoff Mumford, two refugees from Allied Breweries who finished up at Ind Coope of Romford. Burton Bridge now has three pubs in the town including an enlarged brewery tap. It supplies 300

outlets direct. Seasonal beers: Old Expensive (ABV 6.5%, winter 🂠), Battle Brew (ABV 5%, July/Aug), Staffordshire Knot Brown Ale (ABV 4.8%, Sept/Oct), Spring Ale (ABV 4.7%, March/Apr). Gold Medal Ales (ABV 4.5%), a range of monthly beers. Bottle-conditioned beers: Burton Porter (ABV 4.5%), Bramble Stout (ABV 5% 🂠), Empire Pale Ale (ABV 7.5%), Tickle Brain (ABV 8%).

Golden Delicious *(OG 1037, ABV 3.8%)* ◆
Gold-coloured, hoppy and fruity. Well balanced with a dry, mouth-watering finish.

XL Bitter *(OG 1039, ABV 4%)* ◆
A golden, malty bitter, with a faint hoppy and fruity aroma. An excellent mix of flavours follows, with fruitiness dominating.

Bridge Bitter *(OG 1041, ABV 4.2%)* ◆
Pale brown coloured with hoppy aroma. Good bitter taste with hops lingering to give a long, bitter finish.

Burton Porter *(OG 1044, ABV 4.5%)* 🂠◆
Dark red, with a faint roast aroma. The taste combines some liquorice flavour with hops and fruit; slightly sweet. A dry, astringent aftertaste.

Top Dog Stout *(OG 1049, ABV 5%)* ◆
A winter-brew with a strong roast malt and fruit mix, developing into a potent malt and roast malt aftertaste.

Stairway to Heaven *(OG 1049, ABV 5%)* ◆
Golden bitter. A perfectly balanced, moreish beer. The malty and bitter start lead to a hoppy body with a moreish astringency.

Burton Festival Ale
(OG 1054, ABV 5.5%) ◆
A full-bodied, tawny-coloured, strong but sweet beer. The aroma is hoppy, malty and slightly fruity. Fruit and hops in the flavour give way to a fruity finish. Tremendous sparkling mouthfeel.

Thomas Sykes *(OG 1095, ABV 10%)* ◆
Very rich, and sweet and sticky. Warm and fruity, heady and hoppy. A true barley wine to be handled with caution.

BURTONWOOD

Thomas Hardy Burtonwood Ltd,
Bold Lane, Burtonwood, Warrington,
Cheshire, WA5 4PJ
Tel (01925) 220022
Tours by arrangement (charge)

⊛ A family-run brewery that merged its brewing operation in 1998 with Thomas Hardy of Dorchester (qv) to form Thomas Hardy Burtonwood Ltd. The brewery is still 40% owned by Burtonwood Brewery plc, which is now a pub-owning group. The other 60% is owned by Thomas Hardy. Occasional beers: Black Parrot (ABV 4%), Forshaws Bitter (ABV 4%), Hoppers (ABV 4.2%).

Bitter *(OG 1036.8, ABV 3.7%)* ◆
A well-balanced, refreshing, malty bitter, with good hoppiness. Fairly dry aftertaste.

Top Hat *(OG 1046, ABV 4.8%)* ◆
Soft, nutty, malty and a little sweet.

BURY STREET*

⚲ Bury Street Brewery,
t/a The Stag Tavern, 44-46 Bury Street,
Stowmarket, Suffolk, IP14 1HF
Tel (01449) 613980

Patrick Murphy built his small brewery in 2001. It has a nine-gallon brew length, and most of the beer is sold through the pub, with some going to CAMRA beer festivals.

Mr Murphy's Mild (Dark)
(OG 1036, ABV 3.6%)
A dark mild with distinct chocolate and slight roast notes. A soft medium/low bitterness.

Bridget's Best Bitter (BBB)
(OG 1037, ABV 3.7%)
Moderately but subtly bitter, slightly malty but dry with delicate late and dry hop.

Blonde Bombshell *(OG 1037, ABV 3.7%)*
Lager-coloured. Dry and bitter with a citrus late hop character. Very refreshing.

Tawny Owl *(OG 1037, ABV 3.7%)*
A darkish bitter with a touch of chocolate and a single hop bitterness. Slightly fruity.

Pat Murphy's Porter *(OG 1043, ABV 4%)*
Distinct roast and chocolate notes balanced by hop bitterness. Complex, fruity undertones.

Tawny Special *(OG 1040, ABV 4.2%)*
Big Brother of Tawny Owl. A totally separate brew with a bit more of the same in all respects, specially the fruity notes.

BUSHY'S

The Mount Murray Brewing Co Ltd,
Mount Murray, Castletown Road,
Braddan, Isle of Man, IM4 1JE
Tel Office (01624) 611101
Tel/Fax Brewery (01624) 611244
Website www.bushys.com
Tours by arrangement

⊛ Set up in 1986 as a brew-pub, Bushy's moved to its present site in 1990 when demand outgrew capacity. It owns four tied houses and the beers, all brewed to the stipulations of the Manx Brewers' Act of 1874, are also supplied to 25 other outlets. Bottle-conditioned beer: Bushys Premium Manx Ale (ABV 4.5%).

Ruby (1874) Mild *(OG 1035, ABV 3.5%)*

Castletown Bitter *(OG 1035, ABV 3.5%)*

Bushy's Export Bitter

(OG 1038, ABV 3.8%) ♦
An aroma full of pale malt and hops introduces you to a beautifully hoppy, bitter beer. Despite the predominant hop character, malt is also evident. Fresh and clean-tasting.

Manannan's Cloak *(OG 1040, ABV 4%)*

Celebration Ale *(OG 1040, ABV 4%)*

Classic *(OG 1042, ABV 4.3%)*

Piston Brew *(OG 1045, ABV 4.5%)*

Old Sea Dog *(OG 1045, ABV 4.5%)*

Old Bushy Tail *(OG 1045, ABV 4.5%)*

Lovely Jubbly *(OG 1052, ABV 5.2%)*

BUTCOMBE

Butcombe Brewery Ltd, Butcombe, Bristol, BS40 7XQ
Tel (01275) 472240
Fax (01275) 474734
E-mail butcombebrewery@talk21.com
Tours by arrangement (trade only)

⊗ One of the most successful of the newer breweries, set up in 1978 by a former Courage Western director, Simon Whitmore. During 1992-93, the brewery virtually doubled in size (for the third time) and, after 18 years of brewing just a single beer, a second ale went into production in 1996 after further plant development. Butcombe has an estate of six houses (although none is tied) and it also supplies 350 other outlets within a 50-mile radius as well as wholesalers and pub companies.

Bitter *(OG 1039, ABV 4%)* ♦
Amber-coloured, malty and notably bitter beer, with subtle citrus fruit qualities. Hoppy, malty, citrus and very slightly sulphur aroma, and a long, dry, bitter finish with light fruit notes. Consistent and refreshing.

Gold *(OG 1047, ABV 4.7%)* ⊡♦
Aroma of pale malt, citrus hops and fruit. Medium bodied, well-balanced, with good pale malt, hops and bitterness. Yellow-gold in colour, it is quite fruity, slightly sweet, with an abiding dryness.

BUTTS

Butts Brewery Ltd, Northfield Farm, Great Shefford, Hungerford, Berkshire, RG17 7BY
Tel (01488) 648133
Fax (0118) 375 9341
Tours by arrangement

⊗ The brewery, established in 1994, is housed in an old Dutch barn on a farm. The 18-barrel brewery supplies some 200 pubs as far afield as Dartford and Taunton, with an emphasis on direct supply to ensure that high quality standards are maintained. Barbus Barbus has won the Champion Beer of the Festival award three years running at the Steventon (Oxfordshire) Beer Festival. Seasonal beer: Golden Brown (ABV 5%, spring and autumn). Bottle-conditioned beers: Golden Brown (ABV 5%), Le Butts (ABV 5%), Blackguard (ABV 4.5%), Barbus Barbus (ABV 4.6%).

Jester *(OG 1035, ABV 3.5%)* ⊡♦
This amber-coloured beer is fruity and slightly buttery, with an excellent hop aroma supported by pale malt. Aroma and bittering hops balance in the mouth, leading to a dry, hoppy finish.

Bitter *(OG 1040, ABV 4%)* ♦
A traditional southern-style bitter, pale brown in colour with a good bitter hop character and some fruity tendencies.

Blackguard *(OG 1045, ABV 4.5%)* ♦
A rich, fruity red-brown porter with hints of crystal and chocolate malt in the mouth. A blackcurrant aroma and taste are well-balanced with bitterness and malt characters, followed by a dry, bitter and roast finish.

Barbus Barbus *(OG 1046, ABV 4.6%)* ⊡♦
The pale malt in this amber beer is tempered with a hint of crystal malt, well balanced by hops and fruit, leading to a long, complex and bitter-sweet finish. Very drinkable.

Le Butts *(ABV 5.0%)*
A French-style bière.

CAINS

Robert Cain Brewery Ltd, Stanhope Street, Liverpool, Merseyside, L8 5XJ
Tel (0151) 709 8734
Fax (0151) 708 8395
E-mail info@cainsbeers.com
Website www.cainsbeers.com
Tours by arrangement Mon-Thu evenings

⊛ Brewery Group Denmark, the owner of Robert Cain, sold the brewery in July 2002 to Gardner-Shaw, a drinks distribution company, which pledged to maintain production in Liverpool. The Robert Cain Brewery was first established on the site in 1850, but was bought by Higsons in the 1920s, then by Boddingtons in 1985. Whitbread took control of the Boddingtons' breweries in 1990 and closed the site. It reopened as Robert Cain Brewery, and became a division of Brewery Group Denmark A/S. Cain's has ten tied houses and 300 outlets are supplied direct. Occasional/seasonal beers: Dragon Heart (ABV 5%, Jan/Feb), Dr Duncans Elixir (ABV 4.5%, March/April), Sundowner (ABV 4.5%, May/June), Triple Hop (ABV 4.5%, July/Aug), Cains Red (ABV 4.5%, Sept/Oct), First Class Ale (ABV 4.3%, Nov/Dec).

Dark Mild *(OG 1033.5, ABV 3.2%)* ⊡♦
A smooth, dry and roasty dark mild, with some chocolate and coffee notes.

Dr Duncans IPA *(OG 1036, ABV 3.5%)*

Traditional Bitter *(OG 1038.5, ABV 4%)* ♦
A darkish, full-bodied and fruity bitter, with a good hoppy nose and a dry aftertaste.

Formidable Ale *(OG 1048, ABV 5%)* ♦
A bitter and hoppy beer with a good dry aftertaste. Sharp, clean and dry.

CAIRNGORM*

Cairngorm Brewery Co. Ltd., Unit 12, Dalfaber Estate, Aviemore, Inverness-shire, PH22 1PY
Tel (01479) 812222
Fax (01479) 811465

E-mail info@cairngormbrewery.com
Website www.cairngormbrewery.com
Shop 9-530, Mon-Fri
Tours by arrangement

Aviemore Brewery started brewing in 1997. Tomintoul Brewery was acquired by Aviemore in 2000. Cairngorm Brewery Co was established in 2001 to market and produce both Aviemore and Tomintoul beers from the plant in Aviemore. Eight regular cask-conditioned beers are produced and 476 outlets are supplied direct. A series of seasonal ales are available throughout the year.

Highland IPA *(OG 1036, ABV 3.6%)*
A light ale with a crisp freshness.

Ruthven Brew *(OG 1039, ABV 3.8%)*
Copper-coloured ale with nice hop and roast balance, and a malty body. Good hoppy aftertaste.

Stag *(OG 1039.5, ABV 4.1%)*
A powerful malty nose with less hop character on the palate than in early brews. This tawny brew has a lingering malty, gently bitter aftertaste.

Nessie's Monster Mash *(OG 1044, ABV 4.4%)*
A mahogany-coloured, full malty brew with a creamy mouthfeel leading to a satisfying, fruity finish.

Black Gold *(OG 1048.5, ABV 4.4%)*

Cairngorm Gold *(OG 1046, ABV 4.5%)*
A golden beer with a good balance between continental hops and fine Scottish malt.

Wee Murdoch *(OG 1046, ABV 4.8%)*
A strong, robust, deep copper-coloured beer.

Wild Cat *(OG 1049.5, ABV 5.9%)*
A fruity aroma leads to a sweetish fruity beer with much malt in evidence. Hops and caramel add complexity to this pale brown ale.

CALEDONIAN

Caledonian Brewing Company Ltd, 42 Slateford Road, Edinburgh, EH11 1PH
Tel (0131) 337 1286
Fax (0131) 313 2370
E-mail info@caledonian-brewery.co.uk
Website www.caledonian-brewery.co.uk
Shop 9-5 Mon-Fri.
Tours by arrangement

Established in 1869, the brewery was bought by Vaux (now closed) in 1919 then saved from closure in 1987 by a management buy-out led by Russell Sharp. Caledonian still brews in three direct-fired open coppers, the last of their type still in use in Britain. Beers are fermented in open squares and are all blessed by the Sabbath. The brewery supplies more than 650 outlets but does not own any pubs or bars of its own. Monthly seasonals are brewed (see web site). Golden Promise Organic Cask Ale is suitable for vegetarians/vegans.

Murrays Summer Ale *(OG 1036, ABV 3.6%)*
A clean-tasting, thirst-quenching, golden session beer, with hop and fruit evident throughout. A bitter beer, balanced by malt in the taste and aftertaste.

Deuchars IPA *(OG 1039, ABV 3.8%)*
At its best, an extremely tasty and refreshing amber-coloured session beer. Hops and fruit are very evident and are balanced by malt throughout. The lingering aftertaste is delightfully bitter and hoppy.

80/- *(OG 1042.5, ABV 4.1%)*
A predominantly malty, copper-coloured beer with hop and fruit. A Scottish heavy that now lacks the complex taste and hoppiness of old.

Golden Promise Organic Ale *(OG 1045, ABV 4.4%)*
The original organic beer, pale in colour, with pronounced hop character. Floral and fruity on the nose.

Lorimer and Clark IPA *(OG 1054, ABV 5.3%)*

CAMBRINUS

Cambrinus Craft Brewery, Home Farm, Knowsley Park, Knowsley, Merseyside, L34 9EL
Tel (0151) 546 2226
E-mail cambrinus@talk21.co

Cambrinus opened in 1997 but closed in 1999 due to lack of income. It re-opened in October 1999 and is now run by John Aspinall. Approximately 32 outlets are supplied direct. Seasonal beers: St George's Ale (ABV 4.5%, Apr), Clogdance (ABV 3.6%, May), Solstice (ABV 3.8%, June), Bandstand (ABV 3.7%, July), Dark Harvest (ABV 4%, Sept), The Reckoning (ABV 5.3%, Oct), Bootstrap (ABV 4.5%, early new year), Lamp Oil (ABV 4.5%, late year), Celebrance (ABV 5.5%, Christmas).

Herald *(OG 1036, ABV 3.7%)*

Yardstick *(OG 1040, ABV 4%)*

Deliverance *(OG 1040, ABV 4.2%)*

Endurance *(OG 1045, ABV 4.5%)*
An India Pale Ale.

CAMERONS

See Castle Eden & Camerons

CANNON ROYALL

Cannon Royall Brewery, the Fruiterer's Arms, Uphampton Lane, Ombersley, Droitwich, Worcs, WR9 0JW
Tel (01905) 621161
Fax (01562) 743262
Tours by arrangement (CAMRA groups only)

The first brew was in 1993 in a converted cider house behind the Fruiterer's Arms pub. It has increased capacity from five barrels to more than 16 a week. The brewery has a tied house, the Fox at Monkwood Green. Cannon Royall supplies a number of outlets in the West Midlands and Worcestershire and plans to bottle. There are occasional seasonal and special beers.

Fruiterer's Mild *(OG 1037, ABV 3.7%)*
A hint of burnt malt in the aroma makes way for the powerful roasted flavours that are prominent throughout this luxuriant black beer. A fruity sweetness balances the flavour.

King's Shilling *(OG 1038, ABV 3.8%)*
The blend of sharp hoppy and mild cereal flavours are well balanced so both can be enjoyed in equal measure.

Arrowhead *(OG 1039, ABV 3.9%)* ◆
Crisp drinking bitter with a powerful aroma of hops leading to a mixture of tastes dominated by a satisfying citrus hoppy bitterness.

Muzzle Loader *(OG 1042, ABV 4.2%)* ◆
A carefully balanced combination of fruity bitterness and light malt.

Heart of Oak *(OG 1054, ABV 5.4%)* ◆
The accent is on malt in this strong ale with a plum fruitiness on the palate.

CAPTAIN COOK

Captain Cook Brewery Ltd,
The White Swan, 1 West End,
Stokesley, N Yorkshire, TS9 5BL
Tel (01642) 710263
Fax (01642) 714245
E-mail Joonanbri@aol.com
Website www.thecaptaincookbrewery.co.uk
Tours by arrangement

Not brewing at present – owner Brian Skipp says it's in 'hibernation'.

CAPTAIN GRUMPY*

Captain Grumpy's Brewery, Ship,
Brandon Creek, Downham Market,
Norfolk, PE38 0PP
Tel (01353) 676228

Brewery started May 2002 at the Ship pub, which is in Cambridgeshire despite postal address. The brewery is supplying the pub and CAMRA beer festival and may move to new premises.

Best Bitter *(ABV 3.9%)*

Busted Flush *(ABV 4.5%)*

Golden Rivet *(ABV 5.1%)*

CARTERS

White Hart Inn, White Hart Lane,
Machen, Caerphilly, CF83 8QQ
Tel (01633) 441005

⊗ Formerly trading as White Hart, Carters is a small plant currently supplying the White Hart plus occasional beer festivals only. Owner Alan Carter is currently looking for new plant and premises to expand production.

Fawn *(ABV 3.8%)*

Rhymney Valley Bitter *(ABV 4%)*

Machen Bitter *(ABV 4.2%)*

T.U. *(ABV 5%)*

Gordon the Gofer *(ABV 5.2%)*

CASTLE EDEN & CAMERONS*

Castle Eden & Camerons Brewing Co Ltd,
Lion Brewery, Hartlepool,
Co Durham, TS24 7QS
Tel (01429) 266666
Fax (01429) 868198
E-mail sales@castleedenbrewery.com
Website www.castleedenbrewery.com

◎ In March 2002, David Soley, owner of Castle Eden Brewery, purchased Camerons from Wolverhampton & Dudley (qv) and formed the Castle Eden & Camerons Brewing Company. Brewing ceased at the Castle Eden site and production moved to the Lion Brewery at Hartlepool, thus securing the future of regional brewing in the North-east. The brewery has the ability to brew specialist ales for cask and bottle due to the installation of a micro plant. 30 pubs are owned, all tied, 20 of which serve cask-conditioned beer. Some 200 other outlets are supplied direct. Seasonal ales: Spring Knights (ABV 4%), Summer Knights (ABV 4%), Autumn Knights (ABV 4.2%), Winter Royal Knights (ABV 5%).

Nimmos 3X *(OG 1036, ABV 3.6%)*
Well hopped and rounded.

Castle Eden Bitter *(OG 1039, ABV 3.9%)*
Chestnut-coloured beer with an interesting contrast between an initial sweet surge of flavour followed by a slightly bitter aftertaste.

Camerons Bitter *(OG 1039, ABV 3.6%)* ◆
A light bitter, but well-balanced, with hops and malt.

Castle Eden Classic *(OG 1040, ABV 4%)*
Pale and smooth with a fine hop character and mellow drinkable fullness.

Camerons Strongarm
(OG 1041, ABV 4%) ◆
A well-rounded, ruby-red ale with a distinctive, tight creamy head; initially fruity, but with a good balance of malt, hops and moderate bitterness

Castle Eden Ale *(OG 1042, ABV 4.2%)* ◆
A light, creamy, malty sweet ale with fruit notes and a mellow dry bitterness in the finish.

Nimmos XXXX *(OG 1044, ABV 4.4%)* ◆
Light golden beer with a well-balanced character derived from the best English malt and Golding hops.

CASTLE ROCK

Castle Rock Brewery, Queensbridge Road,
Nottingham, NG2 1NB
Tel (0115) 985 1615
Fax (0115) 985 1611
E-mail Castlerock@Tynemill.co.uk
Shop being built.
Tours by arrangement

◎ Castle Rock started life in 1996 as the Bramcote Brewery. It moved in 1998 to its current site in conjunction with the Tynemill pub group. In 2001, Tynemill took a 100% interest in the company. Plans are in hand to rebuild the brewery at its current location, increasing capacity from a maximum of 30 barrels a week to a maximum of 120. The adjacent Vat & Fiddle pub will become part of the brewery, with customers able to see into the brewery from one of the bars. The brewery owns 20 pubs, of which 18 are tied houses. All sell cask-conditioned beer. Seasonal beers: Wildlife Beers. One is brewed each month, in support of endangered species.

Gold Bitter (branded for each outlet)
(ABV 3.5%)

Black Gold Dark Mild *(ABV 3.5%)*

Daze Bitter *(ABV 3.8%)*

Hemlock Best Bitter *(ABV 4%)*

Snow White Best Bitter *(ABV 4.2%)*

Elsie Mo Strong Bitter *(ABV 4.7%)*

CATHEDRAL'S*

Cathedral Brewery Co Ltd., Court Lane, Durham, DH1 3JS
Tel (0191) 370 9632
Fax (0191) 370 9633
E-mail enquiries@cathedrals-online.co.uk
Website www.cathedrals-online.co.uk
Shop Yes, at pub opening times
Tours by arrangement

Brew-restaurant opened in 2001, closed 2002 but may re-open.

CAYTHORPE

Caythorpe Brewery, 3 Gonalston Lane, Hoveringham, Nottingham, NG14 7JH
Tel/Fax (0115) 966 4376

⊗ Caythorpe was set up in 1997 by an ex-Home Brewery employee, Geoff Slack, and his wife Pam. The beers are brewed at the Black Horse, Caythorpe, and demand is high from local outlets. Occasional/seasonal beers: Too Grand (ABV 4.8%, winter), Santa's Stiffener (ABV 4.7%, winter), Saucy Susan (ABV 3.8%, summer).

Light Horse Bitter *(OG 1034.7, ABV 3.7%)*
Light in strength but richly coloured. A malty-flavoured session bitter with a dry finish. Dry hopped in cask for aroma.

Dover Beck Bitter *(OG 1037, ABV 4%)*
A light, dry, well-hopped beer, dry hopped in cask. The house beer at the Black Horse.

Old Nottingham Extra Pale Ale *(OG 1038.6, ABV 4.2%)*
The recipe comes from a Home Brewery brewing book of 1914 and offers a taste of old Nottingham. Very light in colour, hoppy and crisp.

Birthday Brew *(OG 1040, ABV 4.5%)*
A golden-coloured bitter with a full malt feel. Late hopping in the copper using Styrian Goldings gives a pleasant aroma.

CHALK HILL

Chalk Hill Brewery, Rosary Road, Norwich, Norfolk, NR1 4DA
Tel/Fax (01603) 477078
Tours by arrangement

⊗ Run by former Reindeer brew-pub owner Bill Thomas and his partners Tiny Little and Dave Blake, Chalk Hill began production with a 15-barrel plant in 1993. It is developing plans for expansion and new brews. Chalk Hill supplies its own two pubs and 20 local free trade outlets. The beers are also available nationwide via beer agencies. Occasional beer: IPA (ABV 5.3%).

Brewery Tap *(OG 1036, ABV 3.6%)*
Hops dominate the bouquet and taste of this pale brown session bitter. A malty bitterness adds weight to the balance but the long finish turns toward a sweeter tone.

CHB *(OG 1042, ABV 4.2%)*
A delicate fruity aroma introduces a beer of many flavours. Malt and hops mingle with a peppery sweetness. These combine to a complex but smooth feel that lasts throughout. Little loss of flavour in the lingering finish.

Dreadnought *(OG 1050, ABV 4.9%)*
A rich toffee sweetness jostles for recognition with a fruity maltiness. The redness of colour is not matched by the light fruity nose. Towards the finish a distinctive bitterness makes an appearance.

Flintknapper's Mild *(OG 1050, ABV 5%)*
Dark brown and heavy, this strong mild has a heavy roasted malt bias. Traces of caramel can be detected in the coffee-like dry roast base. Little sweetness as flavour remains solid to the end.

Old Tackle *(OG 1056, ABV 5.6%)*
A heavy old ale with a port and lemon freshness that softens the heavy malt base. Some caramel and singular dryness comes to the fore as the quick but balanced finish fades.

CHERITON

Cheriton Brewhouse, Cheriton, Alresford, Hampshire, SO24 0QQ
Tel /Fax (01962) 771166
E-mail bestbeer1@aol.com
Tours by arrangement

⊗ The brewery was founded in 1993 by the owners of the adjacent Flower Pots pub, and two working partners, Ray Page and Martin Roberts. With an emphasis on quality rather than quantity the beers soon gained an appreciative audience in local pubs. Full capacity has been achieved. This is a truly local brewery producing good ales for discerning drinkers. 45-50 outlets are supplied direct.

Pots Ale *(OG 1038.5, ABV 3.8%)*
Pale brown, with a hoppy nose. A well-balanced bitter and hoppy taste leads through to the aftertaste.

Village Elder *(OG 1038.5, ABV 3.8%)*

Cheriton Best Bitter *(OG 1043, ABV 4.2%)*
A malty and fruity taste continues into the aftertaste. A dark brown beer with a malty and fruity nose.

Diggers Gold *(OG 1044.5, ABV 4.6%)*
A golden beer with a citric, hoppy aroma; bitter and hoppy in all respects. A dry finish.

Turkey's Delight *(OG 1060, ABV 5.9%)*

CHILTERN

Chiltern Brewery, Nash Lee Road, Terrick, Aylesbury, Bucks, HP17 0TQ
Tel (01296) 613647
Fax (01296) 612419
E-mail info@chilternbrewery.co.uk
Website www.chilternbrewery.co.uk
Shop 9-5 Mon-Sat. Tours by arrangement (individual tour most Saturdays at noon)

⊗ Established by Richard and Lesley Jenkinson in 1980, the first brew, Chiltern Ale, was followed in 1982 by Beechwood Bitter. Three Hundred Old Ale joined the ranks in 1988 to celebrate the eighth anniversary, with Bodgers Barley Wine in 1990 for the 10th, and John Hampden's Ale in 1995 for the 15th anniversary. A brewery shop opened in 1989, followed by a small museum in 1994. Buckinghamshire County Celebration Ale has been replaced with Lord Lieutenant's Ale. Bottle-conditioned beer: Bodgers Barley Wine (ABV 8.5%). The brewery now offers own label bottled beers for customers who choose a name or supply a design.

Chiltern Ale *(OG 1038, ABV 3.7%)* ◆
A refreshing session bitter, amber in colour, with a predominantly malty character. The aroma is of pale malt with a hint of grape, with some sweetness in the mouth and a short finish.

Beechwood Bitter *(OG 1043, ABV 4.3%)* ◆
A pale brown, refreshing beer with a rich butter-toffee aroma, lots of pale malt and fruit in the mouth and a finish that is more sweet and fruity than bitter.

Three Hundred Old Ale
(OG 1049/50, ABV 4.9%) ◆
A strong old ale with some crystal malt and roast character plus hints of liquorice. Deceptively strong.

CHURCH END

Church End Brewery Ltd, Ridge Lane, Nuneaton, Warwickshire, CV10 0RD
Tel (01827) 713080
Fax (01827) 717328
Tours by arrangement

⊗ Church End opened in 1994 as a small brewery in a 350-year-old stable workshop adjacent to the Griffin Inn, Shustoke, with a four-barrel capacity. It moved to new premises in 2001 with 10-barrel equipment and the potential for building a tap room on site. The brewery produces unusual beers (banana, lemon, spices and herbs) made at different times of the year. Church End supplies 50-100 outlets. Occasional beers: Anchor Bitter (ABV 4%), Hooker Ale or Rusty Dudley (ABV 4.5%), Pews Porter (ABV 4.5%), Silent Night (ABV 4.5%, Christmas), Stout Coffin (ABV 4.6%), Shustoke Surpryes (ABV 4.8%), Cracker or Four King Ale (ABV 5%, Christmas), Father Brown (ABV 6%), Rest in Peace (ABV 7%). Bottle-conditioned beer: Ruby Ale (ABV 5%).

Cuthberts *(OG 1038, ABV 3.8%)* ◆
A refreshing, hoppy beer, with hints of malt, fruit and caramel taste. Lingering bitter aftertaste.

Gravediggers *(OG 1038, ABV 3.8%)* ◆
A premium mild. Black and red in colour, with a complex mix of chocolate and roast flavours, it is almost a light porter. Available in spring and summer.

Without-a-Bix *(OG 1042, ABV 4.2%)* ◆
A wheat beer; clear, malty and pale, combining German hops and English wheat. (Note: the name has had to change from Wheat-a-Bix.)

What the Fox's Hat
(OG 1043, ABV 4.2%) ◆
A beer with a malty aroma, and a hoppy and malty taste with some caramel flavour.

Pooh Beer *(OG 1044, ABV 4.3%)* ◆
A bright golden beer brewed with honey. Sweet, yet hoppy; moreish.

Vicar's Ruin *(OG 1044, ABV 4.4%)* ◆
A straw-coloured best bitter with an initially hoppy, bitter flavour, softening to a delicate malt finish.

Old Pal *(OG 1055, ABV 5%)* ◆
A strong, copper-coloured ale, full of rich, malty flavours. Three different types of hops are used; dry finish.

CITY OF CAMBRIDGE

City of Cambridge Brewery Co Ltd, Ely Rd, Chittering, Cambridge, CB5 9PH
Tel (01223) 864864
Website www.cambridge-brewery.co.uk

⊗ City of Cambridge opened in 1997 with a five-barrel brew plant and moved in 2001 to new site out of town with room to expand to a 10-barrel brew length. A bottling plant will be installed to extend the type and range of beers. The company supplies 25 outlets direct. Bottle-conditioned beer: Hobson's Choice (ABV 4.1%). Seasonal beer: Michaelmas (ABV 4.6%, Christmas). The brewery has launched a new beer, Rutherford's IPA (3.8%), which may become a regular brew.

Boathouse Bitter *(OG 1038, ABV 3.8%)* ◆
Copper-brown and full-bodied session bitter, starting with impressive citrus and floral hop; grassy, fruity notes and cooked vegetables are present with finally a fading, gentle bitterness.

Hobson's Choice
(OG 1041, ABV 4.1%) ◻◆
A highly-drinkable, golden brew with a pronounced hop aroma and taste, and a fruity, bitter balance in the mouth, finishing gently dry. Vegetable notes occur when young.

Atom Splitter *(OG 1047, ABV 4.7%)* ◆
Robust copper-coloured strong bitter with hop aroma and taste, and a distinct vegetably sulphur edge.

Darwin's Downfall *(ABV 5%)*
A blended, ruby-golden coloured beer. Hoppy with a fruity character and a refreshing citrus aftertaste.

Parkers Porter *(ABV 5.3%)* ◆
Impressive reddish brew with a defined roast character throughout, and short, fruity, bitter-sweet palate.

Bramling Traditional *(OG 1055, ABV 5.5%)*
Made with Bramling Cross hops; fruity and delicious.

CLARK'S

HB Clark Co (Successors) Ltd, Westgate Brewery, Wakefield, W Yorkshire, WF2 9SW Tel (01924) 373328 Fax (01924) 372306
Tours by arrangement

⊛ Founded in 1905, Clark's ceased brewing during the keg revolution of the 1960s and 1970s. It resumed cask ale production in 1982 and now supplies by direct delivery to 100 outlets, in addition to wholesalers and distributors throughout England and Scotland. Clark's has five tied houses, four of which serve cask-conditioned beer. Seasonal and monthly beers are produced. Beer of the month is available to wholesalers and distributors. Clark's T'owd Dreadnought is brewed specifically for beer festivals.

Traditional *(OG 1038, ABV 3.8%)* ◆
A copper-coloured, well-balanced, smooth beer, with a malty and hoppy aroma, leading to a hoppy, fruity taste and a good, clean, strong malt flavour. Bitterness and dryness linger in the taste and aftertaste.

Classic Blonde *(OG 1039 ABV 3.9%)*
A light blond ale with a citrus and hoppy flavour, a distinctive grapefruit aroma and a dry finish.

Festival Ale *(OG 1042, ABV 4.2%)* ◆
A light, fruity, pleasantly hopped premium bitter with a good fruity, hoppy nose. Moderate bitterness follows, with a dry, fruity finish. Gold in colour.

Burglar Bill *(OG 1044, ABV 4.4%)* ◆
A good hoppy, fruity aroma precedes an enjoyable, strongly hoppy and fruity taste, with moderate bitterness and good malt character. A lingering, dry, hoppy finish follows. Dark brown in colour.

Rams Revenge *(OG 1046, ABV 4.6%)* ◆
A rich, ruby-coloured premium ale, well-balanced with malt and hops, with a deep fruity taste and a dry hoppy aftertaste, with a pleasant hoppy aroma.

Golden Hornet *(OG 1050, ABV 5%)* ◆
A crisp golden premium beer with a full fruity taste, with full hop aroma and dry hop aftertaste.

T'owd Dreadnought *(OG 1090, ABV 9%)* ◆
An exceptionally strong nut-brown super premium ale with a full malt flavour. Not too sweet, with a lingering full hop character.

CLEARWATER

Clearwater Brewery, 2 Devon Units, Hatchmoor Industrial Estate, Great Torrington, Devon, EX38 7HP Tel (01805) 625242
Tours by arrangement

⊗ Clearwater took on the closed St Giles in the Wood brewery in 1999 and has steadily grown since. Around 70 outlets are supplied direct. Bottle-conditioned beers: Cavalier (ABV 4%), 1646 (ABV 4.8%), Oliver's Nectar (ABV 5.2%).

Cavalier *(ABV 4%)* ◆
Mid-brown, full-bodied best bitter with a burnt, rich malt aroma and taste, leading to a bitter, well-rounded finish.

Beggars Tipple *(ABV 4.2%)*

Ramblers Special *(ABV 4.4%)*

1646 *(ABV 4.8%)*

Oliver's Nectar *(ABV 5.2%)*

CLOCKWORK

🛢 RH & JG Graham t/a Graham Enterprises, The Clockwork Beer Co, 1153/55 Cathcart Road, Glasgow, G42 9HB Tel/Fax (0141) 6490184 E-mail rhg@talk21.com
Tours by arrangement

Robin and Gay Graham, a husband-and-wife partnership, purchased a Glasgow pub in 1997, gutted it and rebuilt it to include a micro-brewery in the middle of the bar. Beers, which use primarily American hops: Amber IPA (ABV 3.8%), Red Alt Beer (ABV 4.4%), either Oregon IPA (ABV 5.5%) or Thunder and Lightning (ABV 6%) – the uncut versions of the Amber IPA and Red Alt Beer, Original Lager (ABV 4.8%), Hazy Daze fruit range (ABV 5%): Seriously Ginger is permanent, with others produced as the fruit is available (eg Kiwi, Raspberry and Banana). A German Weisse [wheat] Beer and a Raspberry Weisse Beer (both ABV 5%) are also produced. A Monthly Special (ABV 4.1/4.2%) is always available and uses European/British hops for customers who are not keen on the more flowery American hops. The Specials tend to be quite eclectic, ranging from Original Kelpie [seaweed] Ale, Scottish Oatmeal Stout to Organic Rowan Ale. They are on sale for approximately four weeks at a time. The ales are only available in the pub itself. All the beers are cold conditioned and, with the exception of the strong ales (ie 5.5% ABV plus) are sold from five-barrel conditioning tanks. The Original Lager, the Weisse beer and the Hazy Daze range are served under artificial CO_2 pressure, while the Amber, Red Alt ale and the Special utilise a system in which they are covered with a blanket of the gasses naturally produced by their fermentation: no pressure is involved. The strong ales (ie 5.5% plus) are cask conditioned and dispensed in the traditional Scottish spear extraction method.

COACH HOUSE

Coach House Brewing Company Ltd, Wharf Street, Howley, Warrington, Cheshire, WA1 2DQ E-mail info@coach-house-brewing.co.uk Tel (01925) 232800 Fax (01925) 232700
Tours by arrangement for CAMRA groups

⊛ The brewery was founded in 1991 by four ex-Greenall Whitley employees. In 1995 Coach House increased its brewing capacity to cope with growing demand and it now delivers to some 250 outlets throughout England, Wales and Scotland, either direct or via wholesalers. The brewery also produces specially commissioned beers. Seasonal beers: Ostlers (ABV 4%, summer), Squires Gold (ABV 4.2%, spring), Summer Sizzler (ABV 4.2%, summer), Countdown (ABV 4.7%, Dec), Taverners (ABV5%, autumn), Blunderbus (ABV 5.5% winter).

Coachman's Best Bitter *(OG 1037, ABV 3.7%)* ◆
A well-hopped, malty bitter, moderately fruity with a hint of sweetness and a peppery nose.

Honeypot Bitter *(OG 1037, ABV 3.8%)*

Gunpowder Strong Mild *(OG 1037, ABV 3.8%)* ◆
Dark brown, lightly hopped, malty mild with faint roast undertones. Easy drinking but not as characterful as it once was.

Turnpike *(OG 1037, ABV 3.8%)*

Dick Turpin *(OG 1042, ABV 4.2%)* ◆
Malty, hoppy pale brown beer with some initial sweetish flavours leading to a short, bitter aftertaste. Also sold under other names as a pub house beer.

Flintlock Pale Ale *(OG 1044, ABV 4.4%)*

Innkeeper's Special Reserve *(OG 1044, ABV 4.5%)* ◆
A darkish, full-flavoured bitter. Quite fruity, with a strong, bitter aftertaste.

Postlethwaite *(OG 1045, ABV 4.6%)*

Gingernut Premium *(OG 1049, ABV 5%)*

Posthorn Premium Ale *(OG 1049, ABV 5%)* ◆
Well-hopped and fruity, with bitterness and malt also prominent. Hoppy aroma and fruity aftertaste.

COLES

Coles Family Brewery, White Hart Thatched Inn & Brewery, Llanddarog, Nr Carmarthen, SA32 8NT
Tel (01267) 275395
Tours by arrangement

Coles is based in an ancient inn built in 1371. Centuries ago it brewed its own beer, but only started brewing again in 1999. The site has its own water supply 320 feet below ground, free from pollution. Coles makes a large selection of cask ales due to a system that allows small-batch production. Two pubs are owned.

Cwrw Nadolig *(OG 1030, ABV 3%)*
Christmas Ale.

Summer Harvest *(OG 1038, ABV 3.8%)*

Nettle Ale *(OG 1039, ABV 3.8%)*

Oaten Barley Stout *(OG 1042, ABV 4%)*

Liquorice Stout *(OG 1042, ABV 4%)*

Black Stag *(OG 1042, ABV 4%)*

Amber Ale *(OG 1042, ABV 4%)*

Roasted Barley Stout *(OG 1042, ABV 4%)*

Cwrw Betys (Beetroot Ale) *(OG 1042, ABV 4%)*

Cwrw Llanddarog *(OG 1043, ABV 4.1%)*

Cwrw Blasus *(OG 1044, ABV 4.3%)*

Dewi Sant *(OG 1045, ABV 4.4%)*

CONCERTINA

Concertina Brewery, 9A Dolcliffe Road, Mexborough, S Yorkshire, S64 9AZ
Tel (01709) 580841
Tours by arrangement

A club once famous for its concertina band, where brewing started in the cellar in 1992. The plant is continuously upgraded and produces eight barrels a week and supplies 25 outlets.

Club Bitter *(ABV 3.9%)* ◆
A fruity session bitter with a good bitter flavour.

Old Dark Attic *(OG 1038, ABV 3.9%)*
A dark brown beer with a fairly sweet, fruity taste.

Best Bitter *(OG 1038.5, ABV 3.9%)* ◆
This mid-brown bitter has lots of hops on the nose, a hoppy taste and a dry finish, plus gentle fruitiness throughout.

One-eyed Jack *(OG 1039, ABV 4%)*
Fairly pale in colour, with plenty of hop bitterness. Brewed with the same malt and hops combination as Bengal Tiger, but more of a session beer. Also known as Mexborough Bitter.

Bengal Tiger *(OG 1043, ABV 4.6%)* ◆
Light amber ale with an aromatic hoppy nose followed by a wonderful combination of fruit and bitterness. A very smooth finish.

New Imperial *(ABV 4.6%)*
An amber malty-flavoured beer with an aromatic nose. The flavour is complemented by fruity overtones.

Dictators *(OG 1044, ABV 4.7%)*

Ariel Square Four *(OG 1046, ABV 5.2%)*

CONISTON

Coniston Brewing Co Ltd, Coppermines Road, Coniston, Cumbria, LA21 8HL
Tel (015394) 41133 Fax (015394) 41177
E-mail i.s.bradley@btinternet.com
Website www.conistonbrewery.com
Shop 11-11.
Tours by arrangement.

A 10-barrel brewery set up in 1995 behind the Black Bull inn, it achieved national fame when it won the Champion Beer of Britain competition in 1998 for Bluebird Bitter. It is now brewing 30 barrels a week and supplies 25 local outlets direct. Brakspear brews and bottles Bluebird for Coniston in bottle-conditioned form. Seasonal beer: Blacksmith's Ale (ABV 5%, Dec-Feb).

Bluebird Bitter *(OG 1036, ABV 3.6%)* ◆
A yellow-gold, predominantly hoppy and fruity beer, well-balanced with some sweetness and a rising bitter finish.

Opium *(OG 1040, ABV 4%)* ◆
Copper-coloured with distinctly fruity, hoppy aromas; a well-balanced flavour with malt, hops and fruit, and more bitter and astringent in the aftertaste.

Bluebird XB *(OG 1040.5, ABV 4.2%)* ◆
Well balanced, hoppy and fruity golden bitter. Bitter-sweet in the mouth with dryness building.

Old Man Ale *(OG 1042.5, ABV 4.4%)* ◆
Delicious fruity, winey beer with complex, well-balanced richness.

CORVEDALE

Corvedale Brewery, The Sun Inn, Corfton, Craven Arms, Shropshire, SY7 9DF
Tel (01584) 861239
E-mail thesun@corfton.co.uk
Tours by arrangement

Brewing started in 1999 in a building behind the pub. Landlord Norman Pearce is also the brewer and he uses only British malt and hops, with water from the local borehole. Corvedale swaps its beer with those of other small craft breweries, making them available in many parts of the country. Seasonal beers: Teresa Pride (ABV 4.2%, Jan-Feb), Katie Pride (ABV 4%, May-Jun), Martine Pride (ABV 4.1%, Nov-Dec). All brews are on sale in the pub in bottle-conditioned form and not fined, making them suitable for vegetarians and vegans.

Junior Ale *(OG 1038, ABV 3.8%)*

Norman's Pride *(OG 1043, ABV 4.3%)*
A golden amber beer with a refreshing, slightly hoppy taste and a bitter finish.

Secret Hop *(OG 1045, ABV 4.5%)*
A clear, ruby bitter with a smooth malty taste. Customers are invited to guess the hop!

Dark and Delicious *(OG 1046, ABV 4.6%)*
A dark ruby beer with hops on the aroma and palate, and a sweet aftertaste.

COTLEIGH

Cotleigh Brewery, Ford Road, Wiveliscombe, Somerset, TA4 2RE
Tel (01984) 624086
Fax (01984) 624365
E-mail cotleigh@cloveruk.net
Website www.cotleighbrewery.co.uk

Situated in the historic brewing town of Wiveliscombe, Cotleigh Brewery is one of the oldest and most successful small breweries in the West Country. The brewery, which started trading in 1979, is housed in specially converted premises with a modern plant capable of producing 140 barrels a week. 150 pubs, mostly in Devon and Somerset, are supplied direct from the brewery, and the beers are also widely available across the country via selected wholesalers. The brewery has recently obtained a horse-drawn dray for local deliveries. A number of beers are produced on a monthly guest beer rota: Kiwi Pale Ale (ABV 3.9%), Harvest Ale (ABV 4%), Blue Jay Bitter (ABV 4.2%), Kookaburra Bitter (ABV 4.4%), Peregrine Porter (ABV 4.4%), Old Buzzard (ABV 4.8%, Oct-Mar), Osprey (ABV 5%), Snowy Ale (ABV 5%). Seasonal: Red Nose Reinbeer (ABV 5%, Christmas). Bottle conditioned beer: Old Buzzard (ABV 4.8%).

Tawny Bitter *(OG 1038, ABV 3.8%)* ◆
Well-balanced bitter with malt to the fore, followed by hop fruit and satisfying bitterness at the finish.

Golden Eagle *(OG 1042, ABV 4.2%)* ◆
A gold, well-hopped premium bitter with fruity-hoppy flavour, clean mouthfeel, leading to a dry, hoppy finish.

Barn Owl Bitter *(OG 1045, ABV 4.5%)* ◆
A dark amber beer with a malty aroma backed by hops; smooth, full-bodied taste with hops dominating, followed by malt. The finish is hoppy, balanced with a little malt.

COTTAGE

Cottage Brewing Co Ltd, The Old Cheese Dairy, Hornblotton Road, Lovington, Somerset, BA7 7PS
Tel (01963) 240551 Fax (01963) 240383
Website www.cottagebrewing.com
Tours by arrangement

The brewery was founded in West Lydford in 1993 and upgraded to a 10-barrel plant in 1994. Owned by former airline pilot Chris Norman and his wife Helen, the company got off to a flying start with Norman's Conquest winning the Champion Beer of Britain title at the 1995 Great British Beer Festival. Other awards followed and, on the strength of this success, the brewery moved to larger premises in 1996, doubling the brewing capacity at the same time. In early summer 2001, Cottage installed a 30-barrel plant, which will enable head brewer Daren Godfrey to brew four times a week, instead of six or seven times a week on the previous 20-barrel kit. 1,500 outlets are supplied direct. The malt used is Maris Otter and hops come mainly from Kent. In 1997 Golden Arrow won the silver medal for Best Bitter at the Great British Beer Festival. In 1999 Norman's Conquest won the Gold Medal for strong beers at the Great British Winter Beer Festival. No pubs are owned but the beers are supplied as far away as Liverpool and Yorkshire. The names of beers mostly follow a railway theme. Seasonal beers: Goldrush (ABV 5%), Santa's Steaming Ale (ABV 5.5%, Christmas). Occasional beer: Broadgauge Bitter (ABV 3.9%).

Southern Bitter *(OG 1037, ABV 3.7%)* ◆
Gold-coloured beer with malt and fruity hops on the nose. Malt and hops in the mouth with a long fruity, bitter finish.

Champflower Ale *(OG 1043, ABV 4.2%)* ◆
Amber beer with fruity hop aroma, full hop taste and powerful bitter finish.

Somerset & Dorset Ale *(OG 1044, ABV 4.4%)*
A well-hopped, malty brew, with a deep red colour.

Golden Arrow *(OG 1044, ABV 4.5%)* ◆
Golden beer with powerful floral hoppy aroma, a fruity, full-bodied taste with a dry, bitter finish.

Norman's Conquest *(OG 1066, ABV 7%)* ◆
A dark strong ale, with plenty of fruit in the aroma and taste; rounded vinous, hoppy finish.

COTTAGE SPRING

See Cwmbran

COUNTRY LIFE

Country Life Brewery, Pig on the Hill, Pusehill, Westward Ho!, Devon, EX39 5AH
Tel (01237) 477615, Fax (01237) 425979
E-mail simon@countrylife.freeserve.co.uk
Website www.pigonthehill.co.uk
Shop open during pub hours.
Tours by arrangement

⊗ The original 2.5-barrel plant was bought from the Lundy Island brewery in the Bristol Channel and set up by Simon Lacey at the Pig on the Hill pub. The Lundy plant was replaced with a five-barrel one producing some 15 barrels per week, still visible through viewing screens in the pub. 20 outlets are supplied direct. Bottle-conditioned beers: Wallop, Golden Pig, Country Bumpkin.

Old Appledore *(OG 1038, ABV 3.7%)*

Wallop *(OG 1044, ABV 4.4%)*

Golden Pig *(OG 1046, ABV 4.7%)*

Country Bumpkin *(OG 1058, ABV 6%)*

COX & HOLBROOK

Cox & Holbrook, Manor Farm, Brettenham Road, Buxhall, Suffolk, IP14 3DY
Tel/Fax (01449) 736323
Tours by arrangement

David Cox, an accountant by profession, bought his five-barrel plant in 1997. It's one of the most travelled micro-breweries, having started life as Mackintosh Croft Head Brewery, and became Sutherland's of Edinburgh before journeying south to Suffolk. The emphasis is on dark ales, stouts and porters. The short-term plan is to concentrate on free trade outlets and to expand the range of products in bottle and cask. Bottle-conditioned beers: Albion Pale Ale, East Anglian Pale, Stowmarket Porter, Iron Oak, Remus, and Uncle Stan.

Crown Dark Mild *(OG 1032, ABV 3.2%)*
Malty and full bodied for its strength.

Old Mill Bitter *(OG 1036, ABV 3.8%)*
A good, middle of the road, session bitter.

Albion Pale Ale *(OG 1047, ABV 5%)*

East Anglian Pale Ale *(OG 1050, ABV 5%)* ◆
A very drinkable pale beer with a hoppy taste and fruit to follow.

Stormwatch *(OG 1050, ABV 5%)* ◆
An amber, fruity beer with a bitter aftertaste. Does not taste as strong as it really is: beware.

Stowmarket Porter *(OG 1050, ABV 5%)*
Keeping tradition alive: a soft, well-rounded example of this enigmatic style, which is full of both body and malty, chocolate flavours.

Remus *(OG 1050, ABV 5%)*
A complex, malty amber ale.

Uncle Stan *(OG 1050, ABV 5%)*
A single brown stout, a rare and possibly unique example of a late 19th-century style. It is rich, malty and firm bodied.

Iron Oak *(OG 1050, ABV 5%)*
A luscious, full-flavoured stout in the Victorian style.

COX'S YARD

Cox's Yard Brewery, Stratford-on-Avon, Warwickshire, CV37 6YY
Owners Charles Wells of Bedford closed the brewery attached to the Jester pub but says it may reopen it.

CROPTON

Cropton Brewery, Woolcroft, New Inn, Cropton, Nr Pickering, N Yorkshire, YO18 8HH
Tel (01751) 417330
Fax (01751) 417582
E-mail newinn@cropton.fsbusiness.co.uk
Website www.croptonbrewery.co.uk
Shop 10-4 summer. Tours by arrangement

Brewing returned to Cropton in 1984 when the cellars of the pub were converted to accommodate a five-barrel plant. The plant was extended in 1988, but by 1994 it had outgrown the cellar and a purpose-built brewery was installed in the grounds of Woolcroft Farm behind the pub. Production fluctuates between 35 and 50 barrels a week according to the season. Cropton's seven additive-free beers are supplied to more than 100 independent outlets direct and nationwide through wholesalers. All the beers, with the exception of Balmy Mild and Yorkshire Moors Bitter are available bottle-conditioned and can be purchased from the visitor centre attached to the pub. The bottled beers are suitable for vegetarians and vegans. Special brew: Rudolph's Revenge (ABV 4.6%).

King Billy *(OG 1039, ABV 3.6%)* ◆
A refreshing, straw-coloured bitter, quite hoppy, with a strong, but pleasant, bitter finish that leaves a clean, dry taste on the palate.

Two Pints *(OG 1040, ABV 4%)* ◆
A good, full-bodied bitter. Malt flavours initially dominate, with a touch of caramel, but the balancing hoppiness and residual sweetness come through.

Honey Gold Bitter *(ABV 4.2%)* ◆
A medium-bodied beer, ideal for summer drinking. Honey is apparent in both aroma and taste but does not overwhelm. Clean finish with a hint of hops.

Scoresby Stout *(OG 1044, ABV 4.2%)* ◆
A classic of the style. A jet-black stout whose roast malt and chocolate flavours contrast with a satisfying bitter finish.

Balmy Mild *(ABV 4.4%)* ◆
Dark and full-flavoured with a malty aroma and taste. Milk chocolate and slight coffee notes. Moreish.

Uncle Sam's *(OG 1044, ABV 4.4%)* ◆
A clean-tasting and refreshing premium pale ale. The overriding characteristic is the fruity bouquet yielded by authentic American ingredients.

Yorkshire Moors Bitter *(ABV 4.6%)*

Backwoods Bitter *(OG 1049, ABV 4.7%)* ◆
A malty premium bitter, tawny-coloured and full-bodied. A long and satisfying, sweet finish contains an abundance of fruit flavours.

Monkmans Slaughter
(OG 1060, ABV 6%) ◆
Rich-tasting and warming; fruit and malt in the aroma and taste, with dark chocolate, caramel and autumn fruit notes. Subtle bitterness continues into the aftertaste. Winner of the Strong Beer category in Champion Beer of Britain competition 2000.

CROUCH VALE

Crouch Vale Brewery Limited,
12 Redhills Road,
South Woodham Ferrers, Chelmsford,
Essex, CM3 5UP
Tel (01245) 322744
Fax (01245) 329082
E-mail info@crouch-vale.co.uk
Website www.crouch-vale.co.uk
Tours by arrangement

⊗ Founded over 20 years ago by two CAMRA enthusiasts, Crouch Vale is now well established as a major craft brewer in Essex. They are still brewing in their original premises in the industrial area of South Woodham Ferrers. The company is also a major wholesaler of cask ale from other independent breweries, which they supply to more than 250 direct outlets as well as beer festivals throughout the region. Two tied houses are owned, both serving a range of Crouch Vale beers with additional guest ales. The beer range has been substantially revamped in 2002. Seasonal beers: two beers are available each month, details on website.

Essex Boys Bitter *(OG 1035, ABV 3.5%)*

Blackwater Mild *(OG 1037, ABV 3.7%)* ◆
A fruity mild with a full body, in spite of its name.

Crouch Best *(OG 1040, ABV 4%)* ◆
Clean-tasting, tawny bitter with a fruity aroma, followed by a taste that balances malt and hops, leading to a dry finish.

Brewers Gold *(OG 1040, ABV 4%)* ◆
An impressive, refreshing, grapefruity, hoppy beer.

Anchor Street Porter *(OG 1049, ABV 4.9%)*
A strong and substantial dark ale, flavoured with roast barley and primed with brewing sugar for a fuller flavour.

CROWN

The Crown Country Inn, Munslow,
nr Craven Arms, Shropshire, SY7 9ET
Tel (01584) 841205 Fax (01584) 841255
E-mail crowncountryinn@ntlworld.com
Website www.crowncountryinn.co.uk

The pub was bought in 2001 and brewing ceased. The new owners hope to re-start brewing during the life of this edition of the Guide.

CROWN*

Crown Brewery Sheffield,
The Hillsborough Hotel, Longsett Road,
Sheffield, S6 2UB
Tel/Fax 0114 2322100
E-mail reception@hillsboroughhotel.com
Website www.crownbrewery.com
Tours by arrangement

Brewing started in 2001 using a five-barrel plant. Loxley Gold was the top selling beer at the 2001 Sheffield Beer Festival and Stannington Stout received a bronze award at the First Yorkshire Champion Beer Festival. Head brewer Brian Hendry produced his first Heritage Ale, Mappins 1937 IPA, after researching defunct local breweries. More are planned. Bottle-conditioned beers: Mappins 1937 (ABV 5.2%) and Stannington Stout (ABV 5%). Beers suitable for vegetarians/vegans are planned.

Hillborough Pale Ale (HPA)
(OG 1039, ABV 3.9%)
Very pale, hoppy, session beer with a bitter finish.

Loxley Gold *(OG 1045, ABV 4.5%)*
Single hopped with Goldings. A beautifully balanced beer.

Stannington Stout *(OG 1050, ABV 5%)*
Delicious and well-balanced with chocolate overtones.

CUCKMERE HAVEN

Cuckmere Haven Brewery,
Exceat Bridge, Cuckmere Haven,
East Sussex, BN25 4AB
Tel (01323) 892247
Fax (01323) 892555
E-mail info@goldengalleon.co.uk
Website goldengalleon.co.uk
Tours by arrangement

◎ Alan Edgar set up the brewery in 1994 adjacent to the Golden Galleon inn overlooking Cuckmere Haven. Hops from his own hop garden are now used in production. A bottled beer is planned.

Downland Bitter *(OG 1035, ABV 3.4%)*
Light bitter brewed with Fuggles and Goldings hops. High proportion of old style amber malt for toffee notes in the aftertaste. Dry and hoppy on the palate.

Best Bitter *(OG 1041, ABV 4.1%)* ◈
Medium colour bitter. Dry hopping with full flower Goldings gives strong hop aroma and fruity aftertaste.

Saxon King Stout *(OG 1042, ABV 4.2%)*
Dark and rich. A nice balance between sharp and soft tastes.

Guvnor *(OG 1045, ABV 4.7%)*
Tawny strong ale. Dry hopped with Goldings for aroma.

Golden Peace *(OG 1054, ABV 5.5%)*
A light-coloured strong ale brewed originally in May 1995 as a celebration of the 50th anniversary of VE Day.

Saxon King Stout Extra *(ABV 5.5%)*

Saxon Berserker *(ABV 7%)*

CWMBRAN

Cwmbran Brewery, Gorse Cottage, Graig Road, Upper Cwmbran, Cwmbran, Torfaen, NP44 5AS
Tel (07788) 100043/ (0776) 1186400
Tours by arrangement

⊛ Cwmbran Brewery (formerly Cottage Spring) is a craft brewery on the slopes of Mynydd Maen in Upper Cwmbran in Gwent's Eastern Valley. With an output of up to 24 barrels a week, the brewery is built alongside the brewer's cottage home. A mountain spring supplies the water used for brewing liquor. The brewery has produced a range of six cask beers that are all produced using traditional methods and ingredients. 30-plus outlets are supplied direct. Seasonal/occasional beer: Drayman's Gold (ABV 3.8%, May-Sept). Bottle-conditioned beer: Crow Valley Bitter (ABV 4.2%)

Drayman's Choice *(OG 1038, ABV 3.8%)* ◈
A pale-brown mild with a balance of malt and sweetness giving way to a gentle bitterness in the finish. A faint fruit and hop presence throughout.

Double Hop *(OG 1039, ABV 4%)*

Crow Valley Bitter *(OG 1042, ABV 4.2%)* ◈
A gentle hop and malt aroma is followed by a crisp, clean mix of malt, hop and fruit flavours. Moderate bitterness builds, leaving a lasting finish.

Crow Valley Stout *(OG 1054, ABV 4.2%)*
Also known as Deryn Du

Four Seasons *(OG 1048, ABV 4.8%)*

The Full Malty *(OG 1050, ABV 4.8%)*

For People's Pub Company
People's Cask Ale *(OG 1035, ABV 3.4%)*

DALESIDE

Daleside Brewery Ltd, Unit 1, Camwal Road, Starbeck, Harrogate, N Yorkshire, HG1 4PT
Tel (01423) 880022
Fax (01423) 541717
E-mail dalesidebrewery@hotmail.com
Website www.dalesidebrewery.co.uk
Shop 9-5 Mon-Fri
Tours by arrangement

⊛ After years of gradual expansion, capacity at Daleside was greatly increased in 2000 when plant was bought from Vaux. Around 200 barrels a week are brewed, half of which is cask beer. Daleside has no tied pubs but the beers are available nationwide. 2002 saw the introduction of a range of different and seasonal styles to be brewed throughout the year as part of the 'Ales from t' Dales' campaign, including new stouts and 'real' lagers.

Bitter *(OG 1038, ABV 3.7%)*

Blonde *(OG 1041, ABV 3.9%)*
A refreshing golden beer with a hoppy aroma and crisp palate.

Old Legover *(OG 1043, ABV 4.1%)* ◈
A well-balanced, mid-brown, refreshing beer that leads to an equally well-balanced, fruity and bitter aftertaste.

Old Lubrication *(OG 1043, ABV 4.1%)* ◈
Plenty of malt, fruit and hops with a hint of sweetness leading to a moderate-to-strong bitter aftertaste in this complex dark ale.

Greengrass Old Rogue Ale *(OG 1046, ABV 4.5%)* ◈
A well-balanced, robust, tawny bitter with strong hop and fruit overtones, with a long, dry finish.

Monkey Wrench *(OG 1053, ABV 5.3%)* ◈
A powerful strong ale, mid-brown to ruby in hue. Aromas of fruit, hops, malt and roast malt give way to well-balanced fruit, malt and hoppiness on the tongue, with some sweetness throughout. A very flavoursome beer.

Morocco Ale *(OG 1058, ABV 5.5%)* ◈
A powerful, dark brew with malt and fruit in the taste. A spicy beer in which ginger predominates and can at times overpower. Brewed to an Elizabethan recipe found at Levens Hall in Cumbria and using a 'secret' spice, the beer is becoming increasingly more widely available.

For AVS Wholesalers of Gravesend:
Shrimpers *(OG 1043, ABV 4.1%)*
An amber to dark amber bitter with a malty nose and a hint of fruitiness. Hops and malt carry over to leave a clean, hoppy aftertaste.

DARK STAR

Dark Star Brewing Co Ltd, Moon Hill Farm, Burgess Hill Road, Ansty, Haywards Heath, W Sussex, RH17 5AH
Tel/Fax (01444) 412311
Email sales@darkstarbrewing.co.uk
Website www.darkstarbrewing.co.uk
Shop Planned for the near future
Tours by arrangement

⊗ The brewery was originally set up in 1994 in the cellar of the Evening Star public house in Brighton. It moved in 2001 to new, purpose built premises to cope with increasing demand for the beers. An on-site shop is planned. Seasonal beers: City Porter (ABV 5.5%) and Critical Mass (ABV 6%). Bottle-conditioned beers: Espresso Stout (ABV 4.2%), Critical Mass (ABV 6%).

Hophead *(OG 1036-1040, ABV 3.8%)*
A light, hoppy, refreshing bitter.

Over the Moon *(OG 1036-1040, ABV 3.8%)*

Landlords Wit *(OG 1039-1042, ABV 4.1%)*

Golden Gate *(OG 1041-1045, ABV 4.3%)*

Starbock *(OG 1043-1047, ABV 4.5%)*

Meltdown *(OG 1046-1050, ABV 4.8%)*
Well-balanced and smooth, flavoured with genuine Chinese stem ginger.

Sunburst *(OG 1046-1050, ABV 4.8%)*
Strong, full-flavoured golden ale.

Red Ale *(OG 1048-1052, ABV 5%)*
Malty, full-flavoured, dry-hopped red ale.

Dark Star *(OG 1048-1052, ABV 5%)* ◆
Dark full-bodied ale with a roast malt aroma and a dry, bitter stout-like finish.

DARKTRIBE

DarkTribe Brewery, 25 Doncaster Road, Gunness, Scunthorpe, Lincs, DN15 8TG
Tel (01724) 782324
E-mail dixie@darktribe.co.uk

⊠ The small brewery was built during the summer of 1996 in a workshop at the bottom of the garden by Dave 'Dixie' Dean. The beers generally follow a marine theme, recalling Dixie's days as a marine engineer in the Merchant Navy and his enthusiasm for sailing. DarkTribe merged with Duffield of Harmston, Lincs: at present, the Duffield beers are not being brewed. Currently, the old building is being demolished and a slightly larger one is being built on the same site. Occasional/seasonal beers: Gunness Stout (ABV 4.1%), Futtocks (ABV 4.2%), Dixie's Bollards (ABV 4.5%), Sixteen Bells (ABV 6.5%, Christmas/New Year), Dixie's Midnight Runner (ABV 6.5%), Dark Destroyer (ABV 9.7%).

Dixie's Mild *(OG 1036, ABV 3.6%)*

Honey Mild *(OG 1036, ABV 3.6%)*

Full Ahead *(OG 1037, ABV 3.8%)* ◆
A malty smoothness backed by a slightly fruity hop give a good bitterness to this amber-brown bitter.

Albecore *(ABV 4%)*

Dr Griffin's Mermaid *(OG 1043, ABV 4.5%)*

Galleon *(OG 1044, ABV 4.7%)* ◻◆
A tasty, golden, smooth, full-bodied ale with fruity hops and consistent malt. The thirst-quenching bitterness lingers into a well-balanced finish.

Old Gaffer *(ABV 4.5%)*

Aegir Ale *(OG 1044, ABV 4.7%)*

Twin Screw *(OG 1047, ABV 5.1%)* ◆
A fruity, rose-hip tasting beer, red in colour. Good malt presence with a dry, hoppy bitterness coming through in the finish.

DARWIN

Darwin Brewery Ltd, 63 Back Tatham Street, Sunderland, SR1 2QE
Tel (0191) 514 4746
Fax (0191) 515 2531
E-mail info@darwinbrewery.com
Website www.darwinbrewery.com
Tours by arrangement (including tasting at local venue)

◎ The Darwin Brewery first brewed in 1994 and has expanded into larger scale production with the construction of its Wearside brewery in central Sunderland in 2002 after a move from the Hodges brewhouse in Crook, Co Durham. The current brewery uses the brewplant from Butterknowle brewery and produces a range of high-quality beers with the strong individual character of the North-east region. Darwin Brewery specialises in historical recreations of past beers such as Flag Porter, a beer produced with a yeast rescued from a shipwreck in the English Channel. The brewery also produces trial beers from the Brewlab training and research unit at the University of Sunderland, and experiments in the production of novel and overseas styles for occasional production. The brewery now produces the beers of the High Force Brewery in Teesdale. Bottle conditioned beer: Cauldron Snout.

Darwin's Bitter *(OG 1038, ABV 3.8%)*

Ghost Ale *(OG 1037, ABV 3.8%)*

Sunderland Best
(OG 1041, ABV 3.9%)

Evolution Ale *(OG 1042, ABV 4%)*
A dark amber, full-bodied bitter with a malty flavour and a clean, bitter aftertaste.

Durham Light Ale *(OG 1042, ABV 4%)*

Smugglers Mild *(OG 1044, ABV 4%)*

Richmond Ale *(OG 1048, ABV 4.5%)*

Saints Sinner *(OG 1052, ABV 5%)*
A rich, smooth-tasting, ruby-red ale with a fruity aroma and hop character in the taste.

Killer Bee *(OG 1054, ABV 6%)*

Imperial Stout *(OG 1072, ABV 7%)*

Extinction Ale *(OG 1086, ABV 8.3%)*

For High Force Hotel
Teesdale Bitter *(OG 1040, ABV 3.8%)*

Forest XB *(OG 1044, ABV 4.2%)*

Cauldron Snout
(OG 1056, ABV 5.6%)

DENT

Dent Brewery, Hollins, Cowgill, Dent, Cumbria, LA10 5TQ
Tel (01539) 625326
Fax (01539) 625033
E-mail martin@dentbrew.u-net.com
Tours by arrangement (minimum six people)

◎ A brewery set up in a converted barn in the Yorkshire Dales in 1990, originally to supply just three local pubs. It now has two tied houses and supplies 50 free trade outlets direct. Its own distribution company, Flying Firkin (01282 865923), delivers all over northern England and is making some inroads into the south. All Dent's beers are brewed using the brewery's own spring water.

Bitter *(OG 1036, ABV 3.7%)* ◆
Fruity throughout and lightly hopped. This beer has a pervading earthiness that is evident to a lesser extent in other Dent beers. A short, bitter finish.

Rambrau *(OG 1039, ABV 4.2%)*
A cask-conditioned lager.

Ramsbottom Strong Ale *(OG 1044, ABV 4.5%)* ◆
This complex, mid-brown beer has a warming, dry, bitter finish to follow its unusual combination of roast, bitter, fruity and sweet flavours.

T'Owd Tup *(OG 1058, ABV 6%)* ◆
A rich, fully-flavoured, strong stout with a coffee aroma. The dominant roast character is balanced by a warming sweetness and a raisiny, fruit-cake taste that linger on into the finish.

For Flying Firkin:

Aviator *(OG 1038, ABV 4%)* ◆
This medium-bodied amber ale is characterised by strong citrus and hoppy flavours that develop into a long bitter finish.

Kamikaze *(OG 1048, ABV 5%)* ◆
Hops and fruit dominate this full-bodied, golden, strong bitter, with a dry bitterness growing in the aftertaste. While still enjoyable, this beer has lost the sparkle it once had.

DERWENT

Derwent Brewing Co,
Units 2a/2b Station Road Industrial Estate, Silloth, Cumbria, CA5 4AG
Tel (016973) 31522
Fax (016973) 31523
Tours by arrangement

Set up in 1997 in Cockermouth by Hans Kruger and Frank Smith, both ex-Jennings, together with Mike Askey, as the Bitter End Brewing Co. In 1996 it moved to Silloth as Derwent Brewery. It supplies beers throughout the North of England and organises the Silloth Beer Festival in August. It now brews the beers formerly brewed at Bitter End. Voted Best Beer at the Cumberland Beer Festival 2002. Now with outlets in Cumbria, Lancashire, Yorkshire, Cheshire and Staffordshire.

Carlisle State Bitter *(OG 1037, ABV 3.7%)*

Parsons Pledge *(OG 1040, ABV 4%)*

Winter Gold *(OG 1041, ABV 4.1%)*

Hansi's Oktober Fest *(OG 1042, ABV 4.2%)*

Teachers Pet *(OG 1043, ABV 4.3%)*

W & M Pale Ale *(OG 1044, ABV 4.4%)*

Bill Monk *(OG 1045, ABV 4.5%)* ◆
A mid-brown ale with a faintly flowery and fruity aroma. Fruity in the mouth and then a quickly arriving intense bitterness.

DERWENT ROSE

Derwent Rose Brewery, Grey Horse, 115 Sherburn Terrace, Consett, Co Durham, DH8 6NE
Tel (01207) 502585
E-mail paul@thegreyhorse.co.uk
Website www.thegreyhorse.co.uk

A micro-brewery based in Consett's oldest surviving pub, 154 years old in 2000. It produced its first brew in a former stable block behind the pub in 1997. Seasonal: St Patricks.

3 Giants *(ABV 3.2%)*

Mutton Clog *(ABV 3.8%)*

Steel Town *(ABV 3.8%)*

Target Ale *(ABV 4%)*

Conroy's Stout *(ABV 4.1%)*

Red Dust *(ABV 4.2%)*

Potts' Clock *(ABV 4.2%)*

Swordmaker *(ABV 4.5%)*

Angel Ale *(ABV 5%)*

Coast 2 Coast *(ABV 5%)*

Derwent Deep *(ABV 5%)*

DEVON

Devon Ales Ltd, 7 Main Street, Sauchie, Alloa, FK10 3JR
Tel (01259) 722020
Tours by arrangement

The brewery was set up in outbuildings at the rear of the Mansfield Arms in Sauchie for the pub and The Inn at Muckhart.

Original *(OG 1037, ABV 3.7%)*

Thick Black *(OG 1041, ABV 4.2%)*

Pride *(OG 1046, ABV 4.8%)*

DOGHOUSE*

Doghouse Brewery, Scorrier, Redruth, Cornwall, TR16 5BN
Tel/Fax (01209) 822022
E-mail i.spencerbrown@btinternet.com
Tours by arrangement

The brewery started brewing in 2001 in former Dog Rescue Kennels. It is owned and run by stalwart CAMRA and SIBA members Ian Spencer-Brown and Steve Wilmott. The five-barrel plant has the capacity to produce a wide range of beers, with blends for individual pubs. Seasonal beers: Muddy Paws (ABV 4.9%, Jan-April), Retriever (ABV 5%, autumn), Christmas Tail (ABV 5.5%, Christmas), Winter Tail (ABV 5.5%, winter).

Wet Nose *(ABV 3.8%)*
A gold-coloured, quaffing bitter with plenty of hoppy bite in the aftertaste.

Biter *(ABV 4%)*
Mid-brown, standard strength bitter.

Loyal Corgi *(ABV 4.5%)*
Gold-coloured beer first brewed for the Royal Jubilee but maintained.

Bow Wow *(ABV 5%)*
Dark ruby-coloured premium ale; well rounded maltiness gives way to a more bitter aftertaste.

DOLPHIN

Dolphin Brewery,
48 St Michael's Street,
Shrewsbury, SY1 2EZ
Tel (01743) 350419
E-mail brewers@thedolphinbrewery.co.uk
Website thedolphinbrewery.co.uk

⊗ Started in 2000 by Peter Buy and Nigel Morton, the original two-barrel plant was upgraded to 4.5 barrels in 2001. Three brews are always available plus seasonal and special brews.

Best *(OG 1040, ABV 4%)*

Gold *(OG 1045, ABV 4.2%)*

Amber *(OG 1046, ABV 4.7%)*

Brew *(OG 1050, ABV 5%)*

DONNINGTON

Donnington Brewery, Stow-on-the-Wold,
Cheltenham, Gloucestershire, GL54 1EP
Tel (01451) 830603

Thomas Arkell bought a 13th-century watermill in idyllic countryside in 1827, and he began brewing on the site in 1865. It is owned and run by a direct family descendant, Claude Arkell, and the millwheel is still used to drive small pumps and machinery. Donnington supplies its own 15 tied houses and a number of free trade outlets.

BB *(OG 1035, ABV 3.6%)* ◆
A pleasant amber bitter with a slight hop aroma, a good balance of malt and hops in the mouth and a bitter aftertaste.

SBA *(OG 1045, ABV 4.6%)* ◆
Malt dominates over bitterness in the subtle flavour of this premium bitter, which has a hint of fruit and a dry malty finish.

DONOGHUE

Donoghue Brewing Co,
The Orchard, Butt Gate, Grainthorpe,
Louth, Lincs, LN11 7HU
Tel (01472) 389543

Experimental brews were conducted in 1999 but brewing did not start on a regular basis until 2001. In 2002, the brewery left the Black Horse inn and is now operating from new premises, but it still supplies the pub.

Fiddlers Elbow *(ABV 3.5%)*

The Pipes *(ABV 3.7%)*

Danny Boy *(ABV 4%)*

DOWBRIDGE*

Dowbridge Brewery, 3 Rugby Road,
Catthorpe, Leics, LE17 6DA.
Tel (01788) 869121.

Russell Webb launched his brewery in May 2002 using a 2.5-barrel plant. He plans to upgrade to a five-barrel kit. His beers are available at the Cherry Tree, Catthorpe, the Victoria, Rugby, and Coventry Flying Club.

Mild *(ABV 3.4%)*

Bitter *(ABV 3.8%)*

Rat Eyed *(ABV 4.3%)*

DRIFTWOOD

Driftwood Spars Hotel,
Trevaunance Cove, St Agnes,
Cornwall, TR5 0RT
Tel (01872) 552428/553323
Fax (01872) 553701
E-mail driftwoodspars@hotmail.com
Website www.driftwoodspars.com
Tours by arrangement

Gordon Treleaven started brewing in 2000 in this famous Cornish pub and hotel that dates back to 1660. The brewery is based in the former Flying Dutchman café across the road from the hotel. The one-barrel plant was bought from the Royal Inn, Horsebridge, Devon and has since been added to. Plans are afoot for more equipment. Pale malt comes from Tuckers of Newton Abbot and the hops are Fuggles.

Cuckoo Ale *(OG 1045, ABV 4.5%)*

DUNN PLOWMAN

Dunn Plowman Brewery,
The Brewhouse, Bridge Street, Kington,
Herefordshire, HR5 3DW
Tel (01544) 231993
Fax (01544) 231985
E-mail dunnplowman.brewery@talk21.com
Tours by arrangement

⊗ The brewery was established in 1987 as a brew-pub, moved to Leominster in 1992, and to its present site in 1994. The brewery supplies the Queen's Head, its brewery tap, and 18 other outlets within a 30-mile radius. It is run by husband and wife team Steve and Gaye Dunn. Seasonal beers: Crooked Furrow (ABV 6.5%, Nov-Jan, all year in bottle), Parsons Nose (ABV 5.5%, Nov-Jan). Bottle-conditioned beers: Old Jake Stout (ABV 4.8%), Kyneton Ale (ABV 5%), Golden Haze Wheat Beer (ABV 5%),Crooked Furrow (ABV 6.5%). In June 2002 Dunn Plowman bought SP Sporting Ales of Leominster.

Thomas Bewick Bitter
(OG 1036, ABV 3.7%)

Brewhouse Bitter *(OG 1037, ABV 3.8%)*

Early Riser *(OG 1039, ABV 4%)*

Kingdom Bitter *(OG 1043, ABV 4.5%)*

Under the SP Sporting Ales name:

Winners *(ABV 3.5%)*

Dove's Delight *(ABV 4%)*

Joust Bootiful *(ABV 4.2%)*

Sting *(ABV 4.2%)*

Joust Perfick *(ABV 4.5%)*

Marathon *(ABV 5.1%)*

DURHAM

Durham Brewery Ltd, Unit 5A,
Bowburn North Industrial Estate,
Bowburn, Co Durham, DH6 5PF
Tel (0191) 3771991
Fax (0191) 3770768
E-mail gibbs@durham-brewery.co.uk
Website www.durham-brewery.co.uk
Shop open during business hours.
Tours by arrangement

Established in 1994, Durham now has a portfolio of around 20 beers plus a bottle-conditioned range. Bottles can be purchased via the online shop and an own label/special message service is available. News from the brewery is delivered by e-mail newsletter by free subscription on the website. Bottle-conditioned beers (suitable for vegetarians): Evensong (ABV 5%), Sanctuary (ABV 6%), Benedictus (ABV 8.4%), Imperial Stout (ABV 10%).

Magus *(OG 1038.5, ABV 3.8%)* ◆
Golden, refreshing dry bitter. An excellent session and summer ale, with a medium fruity/dry aftertaste.

White Gold *(OG 1040, ABV 4%)*
Pale and aromatic, mouth-filling and thirst-quenching with citrus aromas and flavours.

White Velvet *(OG 1041.5, ABV 4.2%)* ◆
Smooth, golden bitter with a tangy hop and fruit taste. The aftertaste lingers with a pleasant fruitiness.

Prior's Gold *(OG 1044, ABV 4.5%)*
A very round, full hop aroma and flavour.

Evensong *(OG 1049.5, ABV 5%)*
A deep ruby bitter. Based on an original 1937 recipe with a traditional English character.

Sanctuary *(OG 1057, ABV 6%)*
A ruby coloured traditional old ale. Named after the Sanctuary knocker at Durham Cathedral.

Benedictus *(OG 1072, ABV 8.4%)*
This barley wine is golden in colour with a luscious malty body. A complex blend of hops give an interesting depth and balancing bitterness. The finish lingers with a rich warmth.

Imperial Stout *(OG 1088, ABV 10%)*
Massive body and sense of alcohol. This classic beer is deep black with coffee and liquorice flavours.

EARL SOHAM

Earl Soham Brewery, The Old Forge, The Street, Earl Soham, Suffolk, IP13 7RL
Tel (01728) 684097
E-mail fram.station@btinternet.com & malc@walker173.freeserve.co.uk

⊗ The brewery, initially set up behind the Victoria pub in 1984 to supply just that outlet, moved 200 yards down the road in 2001 to bigger, purpose-built premises in an old converted garage. The building also houses the village sub-post office. The new plant has five times the capacity of the old site. Earl Soham owns a second pub, the Framlingham Station, and enjoys healthy sales to the free trade. Seasonal beer: Jolabrugg (ABV 5%, Christmas).

Gannet Mild *(OG 1034, ABV 3.3%)*
An unusual, full-tasting mild with a bitter finish and roast flavours that compete with underlying maltiness.

Victoria Bitter *(OG 1037, ABV 3.6%)*
A characterful, well-hopped, malty beer with a tangy, hoppy aftertaste.

Low House Bitter *(OG 1040, ABV 3.9%)*
First brewed for the King's Head (Low House) in Laxfield, but now available to other pubs.

Sir Roger's Porter *(OG 1043, ABV 4.2%)*
Full-flavoured dark brown malty beer with bitter overtones, and a fruity aftertaste.

Albert Ale *(OG 1045, ABV 4.4%)*
Hops dominate every aspect of this beer, but especially the finish. A fruity, astringent beer.

EASTWOOD & SANDERS*

Eastwood & Sanders (Fine Ales) Ltd, Units 3-5 Heathfield Industrial Estate, Heathfield Street, Elland, W. Yorkshire, HX5 9AE.
Tel (01422) 377677

The new brewery is the result of a merger between Barge & Barrel and West Yorkshire. Beers are produced on a 10-barrel plant bought from a former Firkin brew-pub, but the West Yorkshire four-barrel plant has been retained for small-batch brews.

First Light *(OG 1035, ABV 3.5%)*

Bargee *(OG 1038, ABV 3.8%)* ◆
Pale bitter with a well-balanced malt, fruit and hoppy character, and slightly sweet citrus taste.

Beyond the Pale *(OG 1040, ABV 4%)*
Pale golden bitter with an intensely citrus flavour that predominates the underlying biscuity malt and fruity character. The finish is long, dry and hoppy

Best Bitter *(OG 1040, ABV 4%)*
A straw-coloured bitter with a strong hoppy aroma and taste. Fruity and malty in character, the dry citrus, bitter flavour lingers to the end.

Fireball *(OG 1042, ABV 4.2%)*

Nettlethrasher *(OG 1044, ABV 4..4%)*
A premium bitter brewed with three different malts, and English and American hops.

Halifax Bomber *(OG 1048, ABV 4.8%)* ◆
Dark amber malty bitter with initial fruitiness through which the hoppy character predominates.

ECCLESHALL

Eccleshall (Slaters Ales) Brewery, Castle Street, Eccleshall, Staffordshire, ST21 6DF
Tel (01785) 850300
Fax (01785) 851452
Tours by arrangement

⊗ The brewery was set up by Ged Slater in outbuildings behind the George Hotel. The first beers were launched in 1995 and became so popular that the brewery was extended twice and bigger premises are now being considered. Ged's son, Andrew, is head brewer and there are three other staff. Two pubs are owned and 250 outlets are supplied directly. Slaters Bitter was Champion West Midlands Beer of the Year 2000, and Slaters Supreme was a bronze winner for Strong Ales GBBF 2001. The company also owns the Monkey at Crewe.

Monkey Magic *(ABV 3.4%)*
Red beer with malt, liquorice and caramel aromas. Tastes sweet and malty with some hops to start. Fruit comes through later as bitterness develops.

Slaters Bitter *(ABV 3.6%)*
Golden bitter with hop and fruit aroma. A malty start with hops giving a good balance and a superb bitter finish.

Slaters Original *(ABV 4%)*
Well-balanced hops and fruit with a hint of caramel. The sweet and bitter mix leads to an astringency difficult to resist.

Slaters Top Totty *(ABV 4%)*
Pale best bitter with hoppy aroma and taste, and a bitter and dry finish.

Slaters Premium *(ABV 4.4%)*
Creamy start to this mid brown beer. Quite bitter, with an astringent finish. Subtle flavours come and go.

Slaters Shining Knight *(ABV 4.5%)*
Copper coloured with a fruity aroma. Very hoppy taste leading to a bitter and dry finish.

Slaters Supreme *(ABV 4.7%)*
A well-hopped, tawny bitter. Fresh and fruity with a hoppy aroma; the hops linger through the developing bitterness to a moreish finish.

EGLESBRECH

Eglesbrech Brewing Co, Eglesbrech at Behind the Wall,
14 Melville Street, Falkirk, FK 1HZ
Tel (01324) 633338

Scott Robertson brews for the Ale House section upstairs in this large pub, using a 4.5-barrel plant. He brews a new seasonal beer every six weeks and plans a Czech-style Pilsner for what he calls (the other side) of the pub, where lager drinkers congregate.

Falkirk 400 *(ABV 3.8%)*

Antonine *(ABV 3.9%)*

Tall Blonde *(ABV 4%)*

EGYPTIAN

The Egyptian Sand & Gravel Brewery Ltd,
The Leggers Inn, Robinson's Boat Yard,
Mill Street East, Savile Town, Dewsbury,
W Yorkshire, WF12 9BD
Tel (01924) 502846
Tours by arrangement

Previously called Sunset Cider & Wine, the brewery is based under the Leggers pub and brews twice a week. Beers are brewed for any beer festival or pub that provide a cask and collect it from the brewery.

Marriots Mild *(OG 1040, ABV 4%)*

Prospect Road *(OG 1040, ABV 4%)*

Golden Eye 700 *(OG 1042, ABV 4.2%)*
Pale golden bitter, lightly hopped, with well-balanced fruity and malty character, and smooth finish.

Pharoes Curse *(OG 1046, ABV 4.6%)*

Dark Old Ale *(OG 1048, ABV 4.8%)*

ELGOOD'S

Elgood & Sons Ltd, North Brink Brewery,
Wisbech, Cambridgeshire, PE13 1LN
Tel (01945) 583160
Fax (01945) 587711
E-mail info@elgoods-brewery.co.uk
Website www.elgoods-brewery.co.uk
Shop 1-5 Wed, Thur, Fri & Sun and Bank Holiday Mondays; closed Sat (May-Sept). Tours by arrangement

⊗ The North Brink Brewery was established in 1795 and was one of the first classic Georgian breweries to be built outside London. In 1878 it came under the control of the Elgood family and is still run today as one of the few remaining independent family breweries, with the fifth generation of the Elgood family now coming through to run the brewery. Belinda Sutton has become managing director, with her father, Nigel Elgood, as chairman. Elgoods stands on the north bank of the river Nene, in the heart of the Fens in Wisbech, Cambridgeshire. Over the years Elgoods have remained loyal to traditional brewing methods. The beers go to 43 Elgood's public houses within a 50 mile radius of the brewery and free-trade outlets throughout East Anglia, while wholesalers distribute nationally. Elgoods has a visitor centre, offering the opportunity to combine a tour of the brewery and the magnificent gardens. Seasonal beers: Old Black Shuck (ABV 4.5%, Nov/Dec.), Barleymead (ABV 4.8%, Sept/Oct), Reinbeer (ABV 5.9%, December), Wenceslas Winter Warmer (ABV 7.5%, December), Golden Newt (ABV 4.6%, March-April), Double Swan (ABV 4.5%, May-June), Mad Dog (ABV 4.4%, July-Aug), Thin Ice (ABV 4.7%, Jan-Feb). Occasional: North Brink Porter (ABV 5%).

Black Dog Mild *(OG 1036, ABV 3.6%)*
Muscular ruby/black, dry mild with a defined liquorice character. Raisin fruit, malt and hops are in balance, and the dry, bitter finish does not fade

Cambridge Bitter *(OG 1038, ABV 3.8%)*
Impressive copper-coloured session bitter with a light fruity aroma, a malty palate and a long bitter, dry aftertaste.

Pageant Ale *(OG 1043, ABV 4.3%)*
A premium beer, with a good aroma of hops and malt, giving a well-balanced bitter-sweet flavour and a satisfying finish

Golden Newt *(OG 1046, ABV 4.6%)*
A well balanced, but dry palate with very prominent bitterness; the unusual malted grain types used give a clean but slightly fruity depth to the finish of this dry, hopped beer

Thin Ice *(OG 1047, ABV 4.7%)*
Fragrant hops and orange fruit aromas introduce this golden bitter. Citrus, resiny

hop fills the mouth, and the finish is delightfully bitter, with hops and fruit persisting

North Brink Porter *(ABV 5%)*
Dark in colour resembling a dry stout, although less creamy and lighter in body with a coffeeish dryness.

Greyhound Strong Bitter
(OG 1052, ABV 5.2%) ◆
Full-bodied, tawny brew, with a mouth-filling blend of malty sweetness and fruit. Starts with berry fruits on the nose and ends surprisingly bitter.

ENVILLE

Enville Ales, Enville Brewery, Cox Green, Enville, Stourbridge, W Midlands, DY7 5LG
Tel (01384) 873728
Fax (01384) 873770
E-mail info@envilleales.com
Website www.envilleales.com

⊛ A brewery based on a picturesque Victorian farm complex. Using the same water source as the original village brewery (closed in 1919), the beers also incorporate more than three tons of honey annually, produced on the farm, using recipes passed down from the proprietor's great-great aunt. Enville's owner, H Constantine-Cort, had originally intended to go into full-time beekeeping with brewing as a sideline, but the position is now reversed. The brewery grows its own barley, too. Seasonal beer: Phoenix IPA (ABV 4.8%, April-Sept).

Chainmaker Mild *(OG 1036-38, ABV 3.6%)*

Bitter *(OG 1036-38, ABV 3.8%)* ◆
A straw-coloured, hoppy and bitter beer that leaves a malty, moreish aftertaste.

Simpkiss Bitter
(OG 1036-38, ABV 3.8%) ◆
A medium-bodied, golden bitter. The refreshing, hoppy taste lingers.

Nailmaker Mild *(OG 1040-42, ABV 4%)*

Enville White *(OG 1040-42, ABV 4.2%)* ◆
A clean, well-balanced, golden, sweet bitter, light in flavour. An appealing beer.

Czechmate Saaz *(OG 1041-43, ABV 4.2%)*

Enville Ale *(OG 1044-45, ABV 4.5%)*
A pale gold, medium-bodied bitter. Light hops and sweet fruit in the taste; a hint of honey in the aroma and aftertaste.

Enville Porter *(OG 1044-1045, ABV 4.5%)*

Ginger Beer *(OG 1044-46, ABV 4.6%)*

Gothic *(OG 1050-52, ABV 5.2%)* ◆
Malt, hops and caramel combine with a strong roast malt taste in this dark, stout-like beer. Well-balanced, with lurking hints of honey. Available Oct-March.

EVERARDS

Everards Brewery Ltd, Castle Acres, Narborough, Leicester, LE9 5BY
Tel (0116) 201 4100
Fax (0116) 281 4199
E-mail: mail@everards.co.uk
Website www.everards.co.uk
Shop Mon-Fri 9-5, Sat 9-2.30.
Tours by arrangement (CAMRA branches)

⊠ An independent, family-owned brewery run by the great-great grandson of the founder. Based at Narborough on the outskirts of Leicester, Everards celebrated its 150th anniversary in 1999. A developing estate of 144 high-quality pubs is based largely in Leicestershire and surrounding counties. Nearly all the pubs serve a full range of cask-conditioned ales and many serve guest ales. Everards ales are all brewed to individual recipes using only the finest English hops and barley. The principal ales are all dry-hopped and conditioned for a week prior to dispatch from the brewery. Tiger Best Bitter is the most widely distributed ale and can be found all over Britain. Daytime weekday tours can be arranged for CAMRA branches. 500 outlets are supplied direct. Seasonal beers: Perfick (ABV 4.5%, spring), Lazy Daze (ABV 4.6%, summer), Equinox (ABV 4.8%, autumn), Triple Gold (ABV 5%, winter), Terra Firma organic beer (ABV 4.5%, spring); suitable for vegetarians and vegans.

Beacon Bitter *(OG 1036, ABV 3.8%)* ◆
The aroma of this copper-coloured session beer presages a malty-hop bitterness that continues into a long bitter-sweet finish.

Tiger Best Bitter
(OG 1041, ABV 4.2%) ◻ ◆
Mid-brown in colour, this somewhat unexciting brew has a malty nose and a well-balanced palate that continues into a long, bitter-sweet finish.

Original *(OG 1051, ABV 5.2%)* ◆
Beautifully full-bodied, the hop-malt aroma of this red-brown strong beer is followed by a malty bitterness that continues into a late finish. Very smooth and well-balanced.

EVESHAM

SM Murphy Associates Ltd, t/a The Evesham Brewery, r/o Green Dragon, 170 Oat Street, Evesham, Worcestershire, WR11 4PJ
Tel/Fax (01386) 443462
E-mail asumgold@aol.com
Tours by arrangement

⊛ A brewery set up in 1992 in the old bottle store at the Green Dragon Inn in Evesham. The owner and licensee, Steve Murphy, currently supplies another four outlets direct. The brewery has become a tourist attraction, drawing thousands of visitors each year. 'Asum' in the beer names is the local pronunciation of Evesham. Seasonal beer: Santa's Nightmare (ABV 6%, Christmas).

Asum Ale *(OG 1038, ABV 3.8%)* ◆
A subtle mix of hops and malt throughout this quaffable session bitter.

Asum Gold *(OG 1052, ABV 5.2%)* ◆
A well-balanced premium ale that has all the range of tastes from malt to a fruity hoppiness that make it a very satisfying drink.

EXE VALLEY

Exe Valley Brewery, Silverton, Nr Exeter, Devon, EX5 4HF
Tel (01392) 860406
Fax (01392) 861001

Email guysheppard@supanet.com
Website www.execamra.freeserve.co.uk /brewery/exe
Brewery tours not available except to pre-arranged groups — charge made

⊠ Established in a redundant barn in 1984 as Barron's Brewery by former publican Richard Barron, it expanded in 1991, when Richard was joined by former brewers' agent Guy Sheppard, and the name was changed to Exe Valley. The beers are brewed traditionally from their own spring water, using Devon malt and English hops. Approximately 50 outlets are supplied direct. Occasional/seasonal beers: Devon Summer (ABV 3.9%, June-Aug), Barron's Dark (4.1%, occasional), Spring Beer (ABV 4.3%, March-May), Autumn Glory (ABV 4.5%, Sept-Nov), Devon Dawn (ABV 4.5%, Dec-New Year), Curate's Choice (ABV 4.8%, occasional), Winter Glow (ABV 6%, Dec-Feb). Bottle-conditioned beer: Devon Glory (ABV 4.7%).

Bitter *(OG 1036, ABV 3.7%)* ◆
Mid-brown bitter, pleasantly fruity with underlying malt through the aroma, taste and finish.

Barron's Hopsit *(OG 1040, ABV 4.1%)* ◆
Straw-coloured beer with strong hop aroma, hop and fruit flavour and a bitter hop finish.

Dob's Best Bitter *(OG 1040, ABV 4.1%)* ◆
Light brown coloured bitter. Malt and fruit predominate the aroma and taste with a dry, bitter, fruity finish.

Devon Glory *(OG 1046, ABV 4.7%)*
Mid-brown, fruity-tasting pint with a sweet, fruity finish.

Mr Sheppard's Crook *(OG 1046, ABV 4.7%)* ◆
Smooth, full-bodied, mid-brown beer with a malty-fruit nose and a sweetish palate leading to a bitter, dry finish.

Exeter Old Bitter *(OG 1046, ABV 4.8%)* ◆
Mid-brown old ale with a rich fruity taste and slightly earthy aroma and bitter finish.

EXMOOR

Exmoor Ales Limited, Golden Hill Brewery, Wiveliscombe, Somerset, TA4 2NY
Tel (01984) 623798
Fax (01984) 624572
Website www.exmoorales.co.uk
Tours by arrangement

⊠ Somerset's largest brewery was founded in 1980 in the old Hancock's plant, which had been closed since 1959. It quickly won national acclaim, as its Exmoor Ale took the Best Bitter award at CAMRA's Great British Beer Festival that year, the first of many prizes. The brewery has enjoyed many years of continuous expansion and steadily increasing demand. Around 250 pubs in the South-west are supplied direct, and others nationwide via wholesalers and pub chains. Seasonal/occasional beers: Hound Dog (ABV 4%, March-May), Wild Cat (ABV 4.4%, Sept-Nov), Beast (ABV 6.6%, Oct-April), Exmas (ABV 5%, Nov-Dec).

Ale *(OG 1039, ABV 3.8%)* ◆
A pale brown bitter with a good balance of malt and hops. Some fruitiness with a hoppy, bitter aftertaste.

Fox *(OG 1043, ABV 4.2%)*
Crafted from a special blend of several malts and hops to produce a mid-brown beer of unusual subtlety and taste. The slight maltiness on the tongue is followed by a burst of hops with a lingering bitter-sweet aftertaste.

Gold *(OG 1045, ABV 4.5%)* ◆
Yellow/golden in colour, with a malty aroma and flavour, and a slight sweetness and hoppiness. Sweet, malty finish.

Hart *(OG 1049, ABV 4.8%)* ◆
Mid-brown beer with a hoppy aroma, rich malty, full-bodied palate, following through to a sharp, hoppy finish.

Stag *(OG 1050, ABV 5.2%)* ◆
A pale brown beer, with a malty taste and aroma, and a bitter finish.

FAINT HOPE*

Faint Hope Brewing Co. Ltd., Horse and Cart, 185 Scawby Road, Scawby Brook, Brigg, Lincs, DN20 9JX
Tel (01652)652150

A new brewery providing beer for the Horse and Cart, but willing to brew for beer festivals and free trade outlets.

Lazy Drayman *(OG 1050, ABV 4%)*

Honest Lawyer *(OG 1052, ABV 4.1%)*

Undertaker *(OG 1062, ABV 5.2%)*

FAR NORTH

Far North Brewery, Melvich Hotel, Melvich, Thurso, KW14 7YJ
Tel (01641) 531206
Fax (01641) 531347
E-mail melvichtl@aol.com
Website www.smoothhound.co.uk/hotels/melvich
Tours for hotel residents

Most northerly brew pub in Britain, it originally brewed just one cask a week for hotel guests working at Dounray nuclear power site. Owner Peter Martin bought the brewing plant from Dark Star in Brighton in 2001 to enable him to have limited distribution in the northern Highlands. He plans to add a bottle-conditioned John o'Groats Ale for summer tourist outlets.

Real Mackay *(OG 1037, ABV 3.8%)*

Split Stone Pale Ale *(OG 1042, ABV 4.2%)*

Fast Reactor *(OG 1047, ABV 4.8%)*

FEATHERSTONE

Featherstone Brewery, Unit 3, King Street Buildings, King Street, Enderby, Leicestershire, LE9 5NT
Tel (0116) 275 0952
Mobile 0966 137762

⊠ Small brewery that specialises in supplying custom-brewed beers to pubs for sale under house names. Personalised beers are brewed to order, minimum volume four barrels.

Howes Howler *(OG 1035, ABV 3.6%)*

Best Bitter *(OG 1041, ABV 4.2%)*

Vulcan Bitter *(OG 1048, ABV 5.1%)*

FEDERATION

Northern Clubs Federation Brewery Ltd, Lancaster Road, Dunston, Tyne and Wear, NE11 9JR
Tel (0191) 460 9023
Fax (0191) 460 1297
Production (0191) 460 8853
E-mail enquiries@federation-brewery.co.uk
Website www.federation-brewery.co.uk
Tours by arrangement to special interest groups

A brewery owned by working-men's clubs that produces only bright beers. The Buchanans range of cask beers is produced under licence by Robinson's of Stockport. Seasonal ale: Tummy Tickler (ABV 5%).

Buchanan's Best Bitter *(OG 1035, ABV 3.5%)*

Buchanan's Original *(OG 1041, ABV 4.2%)*

FELINFOEL

Felinfoel Brewery Co Ltd, Farmers Row, Felinfoel, Llanelli, Carmarthenshire, SA14 8LB
Tel (01554) 773357 Fax (01554) 752452
E-mail enquiries@felinfoel-brewery.com
Website www.felinfoel-brewery.com
Shop 9-5 Mon-Fri; 10-12 Sat

Founded in 1830 by David John, the company is still family-owned and is now the oldest brewery in Wales. The present buildings are Grade II* listed and were built in the 1870s. Felinfoel was the first brewery in Europe to can beer in the 1930s. It supplies cask ale to 50% of its 84 houses, though some use top pressure, and to approximately 350 free trade outlets.

Dragon Bitter Ale *(OG 1034, ABV 3.4%)*

Best Bitter *(OG 1038, ABV 3.8%)*
A balanced beer, low aroma, bitter-sweet initially with an increasing moderate bitterness.

Double Dragon Ale *(OG 1042, ABV 4.2%)*
Malty, fruity aroma, fruity, sweetish flavour with malt and caramel. Gentle hop and bitterness adds to the mostly fruity finish.

FELSTAR*

Felstar Brewery, Felstead Vineyard, Crix Green, Felsted, Essex, CM6 3JT
Tel (01245) 361504, (07973) 315503
Fax (01245) 361504
Shop 10-dusk 7 days/week. Ring to engage if on long journey. Tours by arrangement

The Felstar Brewery opened in 2001 and is based in the Felsted Vineyard, the oldest commercial vineyard in East Anglia. It occupies the old bonded stores of the vineyard and is a five-barrel plant. Seasonal beer: Haunted Hen (ABV 6%, Nov-Feb). Bottle-conditioned beers: Hop-Hop-Hurray (ABV 4%), Hopsin (ABV 4.6%), Felstar Glory (ABV 5%), Haunted Hen (ABV 6%).

Rooster's Knight *(OG 1035, ABV 3.4%)*

Rooster's Ale *(OG 1037, ABV 3.8%)*

Hop-Hop-Hurray *(OG 1040, ABV 4%)*

Hopsin *(OG 1046, ABV 4.6%)*

Golden Egg *(OG 1052, ABV 5.4%)*

Haunted Hen *(OG 1058, ABV 6%)*

FENLAND

Fenland Brewery, Unit 4, Prospect Way, Chatteris, Cambridgeshire, PE16 6TZ
Tel/Fax (01354) 695776 (brewery)
Tours by arrangement

The brewery was set up in 1997 by Dr Rob Thomas and his wife, Liz. Rob was formerly a research chemist and lecturer in Switzerland, where he was born. He was a home brewer for 15 years before embarking on commercial brewing in Chatteris. Fenland became the first brewery in the town for 65 years, converting an industrial unit to a self-designed brewery. Beers are supplied throughout Bedfordshire, Cambridgeshire, Lincolnshire, Norfolk, and Northamptonshire, and have been steadily winning both awards and customer loyalty. 100 outlets are supplied direct. Occasional/seasonal beers: Tell Tale Pale Ale (ABV 3.6, summer), Drayman's Draught (ABV 4%, autumn/winter), Paranoia (ABV 4.2%, autumn), Sparkling Wit (ABV 4.5%, May-Sept), Fractale (ABV 4.5%, spring), Winter Warmer/Rudolph's Rocket Fuel (ABV 5.5%, Nov-Jan. This is the same beer; it's available as Winter Warmer but can be re-badged as Rocket Fuel in December).

Doctor's Orders *(ABV 5%)*
A russet best bitter with a ruby glint and a complex malty fruit aroma, with a blend of First Gold hops and three varieties of Norfolk malts.

FERNANDES

Fernandes Brewery, The Old Malt House, 5 Avison Yard, Kirkgate, Wakefield, W Yorkshire, WF1 1UA
Tel (01924) 291709
Tours by arrangement

The brewery opened in 1997 and is housed in a 19th-century malthouse. It incorporates a home-brew shop and a brewery tap that won Wakefield CAMRA's Pub of the Year in 1999 and in 2000, and has also won Yorkshire Regional Pub of the Year 2001. Seasonal beer: 12 monthly special beers, named after the months, are brewed.

Best Bitter *(OG 1040, ABV 3.8%)*
A light-coloured, spritzy, lightly hopped and refreshing session beer, with a long lasting hoppy finish.

Malt Shovel Mild *(OG 1045, ABV 3.8%)*
A dark, full-bodied, malty mild with an abundance of roast malt and chocolate flavours, leading to a lingering, dry, malty finish.

Ale to the Tsar *(OG 1042, ABV 4.1%)*
A pale, smooth, well-balanced beer with some sweetness leading to a nutty, malty and satisfying aftertaste.

To be Joyfull *(OG 1044, ABV 4.3%)*
An extremely fruity and hoppy, bitter beer with a long lasting fruity aftertaste. Pale in colour.

Jacobs Well Premium *(OG 1045, ABV 4.5%)*
A pale coloured, hoppy beer with a clean hoppy aftertaste, leading to a long hoppy finish with some maltiness.

Wakefield Pride *(OG 1047, ABV 4.5%)*
A light-coloured and full-bodied, clean-tasting malty beer with a good hop character leading to a dry, bitter finish.

Empress of India *(OG 1055, ABV 6%)*
A strong, light-coloured and dangerously drinkable fruity and malty beer with a complex bitter palate. Fruit and malt dominate the aftertaste.

Double Six *(OG 1057, ABV 6%)*
A powerful, dark and rich strong beer with an array of malt, roast malt and chocolate flavours and a strong, lasting malty finish, with some hoppiness.

FILO

First In Last Out Brewery,
14-15 High Street, Old Town, Hastings, E Sussex, TN34 3EY
Tel (01424) 425079
Fax (01424) 420802
E-mail mike@thefilo.co.uk
Website www.thefilo.co.uk
Tours by arrangement

⊠ The Filo Brewery (previously named St Clements Brewery) has been brewing its own beer since 1985 with only a short break in 2000 when the brewery was refurbished. Since that time the pub has also added a covered brewery yard and a special window in the bar to observe the brewing.

Crofters *(OG 1040, ABV 4%)*

Cardinal *(OG 1045, ABV 4.4%)*

Cloudesly *(OG 1048, ABV 4.8%)*

FISHERROW

Fisherrow Brewery Limited,
Units 11 & 12, Duddingston Yards, Duddingston Park South, Edinburgh, EH15 3NX
Tel (0131) 621 5501
Fax (0131) 621 9552
E-mail sales@fisherrow.co.uk
Website www.fisherrow.co.uk
Tours by arrangement

◎ The 13-barrel brewery — the name is pronounced 'Fisher Row' — is based in council-owned industrial units with the plant converted from dairy equipment. The first brew was in late 1999 and growth has been good. Over 200 outlets are supplied direct, including the Home Counties, M4 Corridor, Wales, Northern Ireland, Belgium and the Netherlands. There is always at least one new 'Beer of the Month' with the stronger beers appearing more frequently in the winter. Seasonal/occasional beers:

Three Bears Ale (ABV 4%, for Six Nations Rugby championship), Klondyke Mild (ABV 3.5%, May).

India Pale Ale *(ABV 3.8%)*

Burgh Bitter *(ABV 4.2%)*

Nut Brown Ale *(ABV 4.8%)*

Export Pale Ale *(ABV 5.2%)*

FLAGSHIP

Flagship Brewery Ltd, Unit 2 Building 64, The Historic Dockyard, Chatham, Kent, ME4 4TE
Tel (01634) 832828
Tours by arrangement

⊠ The brewery was established in 1995 by home-brewing enthusiast Andrew Purcell in partnership with his father-in-law. It became a limited company in 2000. It is located in Chatham's Historic Dockyard, a uniquely preserved Georgian dockyard and premier tourist attraction in the South-east. Production has steadily increased, with at least 70 regular outlets served direct and further outlets supplied by wholesalers and other breweries. The brewery now has its own tied house. Occasional/seasonal beers: Victory Mild (ABV 3.5%), Spring Pride (ABV 4.4%), Frigging Yuletide (ABV 5.5%), Old Sea Dog Stout (ABV 5.5%), Nelson's Blood (ABV 6%), Powder Monkey (ABV 4.4%), Moby Dick (ABV 4.4%), Pembroke Old Ale (ABV 4.4%).

Admiral's Bitter *(OG 1038, ABV 3.8%)*

Destroyer *(OG 1039, ABV 4%)*

Trafalgar Bitter *(OG 1040, ABV 4.1%)*

Ensign *(OG 1042, ABV 4.2%)*
A fruity ale, with a good balance of malt and hops.

Spanker *(OG 1042, ABV 4.2%)*
A version of Ensign.

Friggin in the Riggin *(OG 1045, ABV 4.7%)*
A premium bitter with a smooth malt flavour and a bitter-sweet aftertaste.

Crow's Nest *(OG 1048, ABV 4.8%)*
A straw-coloured, sweet and fruity ale with a hoppy aroma.

Shipwrecked *(OG 1048, ABV 5%)*

Futtock *(OG 1050, ABV 5.2%)*
A fruity, ruby-coloured ale, with a roast malt aftertaste.

FORTH

Forth Brewery Co Ltd, Eglinton, Kelliebank, Alloa, FK10 1NU
Tel (01259) 725511
Fax (01259) 725522

◎ A brewing company set up by former partners when Maclay stopped brewing in 1999. Forth's beers are distributed by Belhaven, Caledonian, Beer Seller, Flying Firkin and Maclay. Forth will contract-brew for micro-breweries that need to supplement their production.

Steamboat Ale *(ABV 4%)*

Puffer Ale *(ABV 4.1%)*

FOX*

Fox Brewery, Fox & Founds, 22 Station Road, Heacham, Norfolk, PE31 7EX
Tel (01485 570345)

New brewery that opened in June 2002 and brews for the pub and other outlets.

Heacham Gold *(ABV 3.9%)*

Grace & Favour *(ABV 4.4%)*

FOXFIELD

Foxfield Brewery, Prince of Wales, Foxfield, Broughton in Furness, Cumbria, LA20 6BX
Tel (01229) 716238
E-mail foxfieldbrewery@aol.com
Website www.drink.to/foxfieldbrewery
Tours by arrangement

◎ Foxfield is a three-barrel plant run by Stuart and Lynda Johnson in old stables attached to the Prince of Wales inn. A few other outlets are supplied direct. The Johnson's also own Tigertops in Wakefield (qv). There are many occasional and seasonal beers.

Black Hoad *(OG 1036, ABV 3.5%)*
A dark roast mild with a fruity nose and a sweet finish.

Sands *(OG 1038, ABV 3.6%)*
A pale, light, aromatic quaffing ale.

Brief Encounter *(OG 1042, ABV 4.1%)*
A fruity beer with a long, bitter finish.

Foxfield Flyer *(OG 1048, ABV 4.6%)*
A full-flavoured bitter with loads of middle.

Black Coombe *(OG 1048, ABV 5%)*
A bitter stout.

FRANCAISE*

Brasserie Francaise Ltd, Brasserie les Sans-Culottes, 27-29 Endell Street, Covent Garden, London, WC2H 9BA
Tel (020) 7379 8500
Fax (020) 7836 4540
Email sansculottesuk@aol.com
Tours by arrangement

⊗ A brasserie with a small brewing plant that produces Franco-Belgian style beers The beers are neither filtered nor pasteurised but are pressurised. The beers are only for sale on site. Beers: Blonde (ABV 4%), Rousse (4.6%), Blonde Speciale

FRANKLIN'S

Franklin's Brewery, Bilton Lane, Bilton, Harrogate, N Yorkshire, HG1 4DH
Tel/Fax (01423) 322345
E-mail Tommy2Tom@yahoo.co.uk

A brewery set up in 1980 by Sean Franklin and run by Leeds CAMRA founder-member Tommy Thomas and stepson Tim Osborne. 10-20 outlets are supplied direct. Seasonal beers: Summer Blotto (ABV 4.7%), Winter Blotto (ABV 4.7%).

Bitter *(OG 1038, ABV 3.8%)* ◆
A tremendous hop aroma precedes a flowery hop flavour, combined with malt. Long, hoppy, bitter finish. A fine, unusual amber bitter.

DT's *(OG 1045, ABV 4.5%)*

My Better Half *(OG 1060, ABV 5%)*

FRANKTON BAGBY

The Old Stables Brewery, Green Lane, Church Lawford, Rugby, Warwickshire, CV23 9EF
Tel (02476) 540770
Tours by arrangement

◎ Frankton Bagby was set up in 1999 by three local families. The five-barrel plant is housed in a small, 18th-century stable block that has been carefully renovated by Warwickshire craftsmen. A specialist micro-brewery engineer undertook the design and installation of the equipment for the brewhouse. More than 150 outlets are supplied direct. Seasonal beers: Dark Secret (ABV 4.8%, winter), Top Tipple (ABV 4.2%, summer), Christmas Pud (ABV 7%).

Peeping Tom *(OG 1038, ABV 3.8%)*
Light brown ale packed with a traditional hoppy, bitter flavour.

Old Chestnut *(OG 1040, ABV 4%)*
A chestnut-coloured bitter brewed using a combination of Green Bullet and Fuggles hops that give the beer a distinctive mellow flavour; the late addition of Styrian Goldings adds a fruity nose.

Chicken Tackle *(OG 1041, ABV 4.1%)*
A hoppy but mellow beer with a tantalising hint of ginger.

Squires Brew *(OG 1042, ABV 4.2%)*
A straw-coloured best bitter, smooth on the palate with a good, hoppy aftertaste. A mix of Challenger and Fuggles hops are used in the main brew and Styrian Goldings are added for late hopping.

Top Tipple *(OG 1042, ABV 4.2%)*
Brewed using American Liberty hops, which gives this best bitter a unique flavour and a memorable aftertaste.

Rugby Special *(OG 1045, ABV 4.5%)*
A reddy-brown, full-bodied, well-balanced and pleasantly hoppy best bitter. First brewed in the borough of Rugby to celebrate Rugby Union's World Cup, the beer proved so popular it became a regular brew.

FREEDOM

Freedom Brewing Company Ltd, The Coachworks, 80 Parsons Green Lane, Fulham, London, SW6 4HU

Tel (020) 7731 7372
Fax (020) 7731 1218
E-mail info@freedombrew.com
Website www.freedombrew.com
Tours by arrangement

⊗ The Freedom Brewing Company opened in 1995 in Fulham as the first dedicated lager micro-brewery in Britain. All the beers comply with the 1516 German Beer Purity Law, the Reinheitsgebot, and are now brewed in Germany and at the company's two bars at Covent Garden (41 Earlham St, London WC2; and off Carnaby St (14/16 Ganton St, London W1). The beers are available on draught in the bars, while Freedom Beer and Organic Ale are also available in bottle. More than 300 outlets in London are supplied. The draught beers are unpasteurised but are pressurised. Beers: Freedom Red (ABV 4.2%); Freedom Pale (ABV 4.3%); Freedom Organic (ABV 4.8%); Freedom Wheat (ABV 5%); Freedom Beer (ABV 5%).

FREEMINER

Freeminer Brewery Ltd,
Whimsey Road, Steam Mills, Cinderford,
Gloucestershire, GL14 3JA
Tel (01594) 827989 Fax (01594) 829464
E-mail alesales@freeminer.com
Website www.freeminer.com
Tours by arrangement

⊗ Freeminer Brewery was established in the Forest of Dean in 1992 and has expanded from a five-barrel to a 40-barrel plant. The expansion was due to national sales and increased bottle production, especially new export orders. There are plans to fit a five-barrel plant in the outbuildings of a local public house, to create the Forest of Dean's first brew-pub. Even though it has a rural location, the brewery makes great efforts through a network of national distributors to ensure that its beers can be enjoyed nationwide. Occasional/seasonal beers: Gold Standard (ABV 5%, summer/autumn), Strip and At It (ABV 4%, spring), Iron Brew (ABV 4.2%, spring/summer), Celestial Steam Gale (ABV 5%, summer), Slaughter Porter (ABV 5%, winter), Deep Shaft Stout (ABV 6.2%, autumn/winter), Northern United (ABV 7%, winter). Bottle-conditioned beers: Bitter, Speculation Ale, Deep Shaft Stout, Shakemantle Ginger Ale, Speculation Ale, Trafalgar IPA ⊡, and Slaughter Porter are bottled-conditioned versions of the cask ales. Shakemantle Ginger Ale and Deep Shaft Stout are suitable for vegetarians.

Bitter *(OG 1038, ABV 4%)* ◆
A light, hoppy session bitter with an intense hop aroma and a dry, hoppy finish.

Speculation Ale *(OG 1047, ABV 4.8%)* ◆
An aromatic, chestnut-brown, full-bodied beer with a smooth, well-balanced mix of malt and hops, and a predominantly hoppy aftertaste.

Shakemantle Ginger Ale
(OG 1050, ABV 5%) ⊡◆
A refreshing ginger ale. Unfined, with a high wheat content, it is like a European-style wheat beer. Ginger dominates throughout, mingled with a light hoppiness. Champion Beer of Britain Speciality Beer 1998.

Trafalgar IPA *(OG 1060, ABV 6%)* ◆
Pale, heavily hopped traditional IPA with a pronounced bitterness; hoppy nose, malt and hops on the palate and a dry, hoppy finish.

FROG ISLAND

Frog Island Brewery, The Maltings,
Westbridge, St James' Road,
Northampton, NN5 5HS
Tel (01604) 587772
Fax (01604) 750754
E-mail beer@frogislandbrewery.co.uk
Website www.frogislandbrewery.co.uk
Shop by arrangement
Tours by arrangement

⊗ Started in 1994 by home-brewer Bruce Littler and business partner Graham Cherry in a malt house built by the long-defunct brewery Thomas Manning & Co, Frog Island expanded by doubling brew length to 10 barrels in 1998. It specialises in beers with personalised bottle labels, available by mail order. Up to 40 free trade outlets are directly supplied with the beer occasionally available through other micro-brewers. Seasonal beers: Fuggled Frog (ABV 3.5%, May), Head in the Clouds (ABV 4.5%, August). Bottle-conditioned beers: Fire Bellied Toad (ABV 5%), Croak & Stagger (ABV 5.6%).

Best Bitter *(OG 1040, ABV 3.8%)* ◆
Blackcurrant and gooseberry enhance the full malty aroma with pineapple and papaya joining on the tongue. Bitterness develops in the fairly long Target/Fuggle finish.

Shoemaker *(OG 1043, ABV 4.2%)* ■◆
Cascade aroma hops create a cauldron of tastes and the full mouthfeel complements the strong orangy/malty aromas that precede the citrus and hoppy bitterness lasting into a long, dry finish. Amber.

Natterjack *(OG 1048, ABV 4.8%)* ◆
Deceptively robust, golden and smooth. Fruit and hop aromas fight for dominance before the grainy astringency and floral palate give way to a long, dry aftertaste with a hint of lingering malt.

Fire Bellied Toad *(OG 1050, ABV 5%)* ■◆
Amber-gold brew with an extraordinary long bitter/fruity finish. Huge malt and Phoenix hop flavours have a hint of apples after the pink grapefruit nose belies its punchy overall hit.

Croak & Stagger *(OG 1056, ABV 5.8%)* ◆
The initial honey/fruit aroma is quickly overpowered by roast malt then bitter chocolate and pale malt sweetness on the tongue. Gentle, bitter-sweet finish. A dark winter brew.

FULLER'S

Fuller, Smith and Turner PLC,
Griffin Brewery, Chiswick Lane South,
Chiswick, London, W4 2QB
Tel (020) 8996 2000
Fax (020) 8995 0230
E-mail fullers@fullers.co.uk
Website www.fullers.co.uk
Shop 10-6 Mon-Sat.
Tours by arrangement

produces that essential bite that makes you want more.

Iron Horse *(OG 1049, ABV 4.8%)* ◆
Superb roast old ale/porter style beer with complex roast malty-fruity bitterness consistent through the tasting experience – and what an experience. Available late autumn.

Inspiration Ale *(OG 1050, ABV 5.2%)* ◆
Straw-coloured pale strong ale with a predominantly bitter fruity flavour balanced by a sweet undertone.

Winter Warmer *(OG 1052, ABV 5.2%)* ◆
Good example of a winter ale with a refreshing bitterness that cleans the palate of the sweetness inherent in this style of beer.

GOFF'S

Goff's Brewery Ltd, 9 Isbourne Way, Winchcombe, Cheltenham, Gloucestershire, GL54 5NS
Tel (01242) 603383 Fax (01242) 603959
E-mail goffsbrewery@yahoo.co.uk
Tours by arrangement

⊗ Goff's is a family concern that started brewing in 1994, using plant purchased from Nethergate Brewery. Now brewing to capacity, it supplies beer direct to 200 outlets and through wholesalers. One pub is owned in Cheltenham.

Jouster *(OG 1040, ABV 4%)* ◆
A drinkable, tawny-coloured ale, with a light hoppiness in the aroma. It has a good balance of malt and bitterness in the mouth, underscored by fruitiness, with a clean, hoppy aftertaste.

Tournament *(OG 1038, ABV 4%)*

Fallen Knight *(OG 1044, ABV 4.4%)* ◆
A tawny-coloured premium bitter, dry hopped for a delicate floral aroma. A good balance of malt and fruit in the mouth with a bitter-sweet finish. Autumn ale now brewed all year round.

White Knight *(OG 1046, ABV 4.7%)* ◆
A well-hopped bitter with a light colour and full-bodied taste. Bitterness predominates in the mouth and leads to a dry, hoppy aftertaste. Deceptively drinkable for its strength.

Black Knight *(OG 1053, ABV 5.3%)* ◆
A dark, ruby-red tinted beer with a strong chocolate malt aroma. It has a smooth, dry, malty taste, with a subtle hoppiness, leading to a dry finish. A classic winter porter.

GOLCAR*

Golcar Brewery, Swallow Lane, Golcar, Huddersfield, Yorkshire, HD7 4NB.
Tel (01484) 644241
E-mail jbltd111@aol.com

Golcar started brewing in 2001. It owns one pub and three outlets in total are served.

Dark Mild *(OG 1033, ABV 3.2%)* ◆
Dark mild with a light roasted malt and liquorice taste. Smooth and satisfying.

Bitter *(OG 1038, ABV 3.8%)* ◆
Amber bitter with a hoppy, citrus taste, with fruity overtones and bitter finish.

GOLDFINCH

Goldfinch Brewery, 47 High East Street, Dorchester, DT1 1HU
Tel (01305) 264020

⊗ A brewery established in 1987 at the rear of Tom Brown's public house in Dorchester. Originally a one-barrel plant, it has been increased to four barrels. The brewery supplies Tom Brown's pubs in Dorchester and Salisbury, and 10 free trade outlets direct, plus others via wholesalers. Occasional beer: Mayor J Porter (ABV 4.5%, Nov-Feb). Seasonal: Flashman's (ABV 4.5%, brewed alternately with Midnight Sun in summer).

Tom Brown's Best Bitter *(OG 1039, ABV 4%)* ◆
Clean, refreshing session beer. Moderate fruit and hops in the aroma and taste, balanced well with a little sweetness.

Midnight Sun *(OG 1045, ABV 4.5%)* ◆
A well-balanced golden bitter, light in body with hops, fruit and bitterness in moderation.

Flashman's Clout Strong Ale *(OG 1045, ABV 4.5%)* ◆
A tawny/mid-brown beer with an attractive, honeyed aroma, and a bitter-sweet taste with malt and some hops. Hoppiness continues through to give a bitter edge to the aftertaste.

Midnight Blinder *(OG 1050, ABV 5%)* ◆
A reddish brown, full-bodied strong bitter. Dark malts dominate the bitter-sweet flavour, continuing into the hoppy aftertaste.

GOLDTHORN

Goldthorn Brewery & Co Ltd, Imex Unit 60, Sunbeam Street, Wolverhampton, WV2 4NU
Tel (01902) 756920
Fax (01902) 579108
E-mail paul@goldthornbrewery.co.uk
Website www.goldthornbrewery.co.uk
Tours by arrangement

☺ Goldthorn has a five-barrel plant based in the former Sunbeam car and motorcycle factory. Brewing started in 2001. 30-plus outlets are supplied and there are plans to increase capacity, and brew occasional and bottled beers. Seasonal: Deadly Nightshade (ABV 6%, autumn-winter), Out of Darkness (ABV 4.3%, spring-summer).

Ge It Sum Ommer *(OG 1039, ABV 3.8%)*

Wulfrun Gold *(OG 1043, ABV 4.3%)*

GOODMANHAM*

Goodmanham Brewery, Goodmanham Arms, Main Street, Goodmanham, York, YO43 3JA
Tel (01430) 873849
Email geoff.cawthray@goodmanhampubco.fsnet.co.uk
Tours by arrangement

☺ Geoff Cawthray started brewing in 2002 and is concentrating on producing high-quality beers for the one pub owned, and then developing and marketing into the local free trade: currently six outlets are supplied. It is housed in an out-building behind the Goodmanham Arms.

Cream of the Wold *(OG 1036, ABV 3.4%)*

Wolds Delight *(OG 1038, ABV 3.8%)*

Randy Monk *(OG 1044, ABV 4.2%)*

Goodman Hammer *(OG 1048, ABV 4.5%)*

Monk's Revenge *(OG 1050, ABV 5%)*

GOOSE EYE

Goose Eye Brewery, Ingrow Bridge, South Street, Keighley, W Yorkshire, BD21 5AX
Tel (01535) 605807 Fax (01535) 605735
E-mail goose-eye@totalise.co.uk
Website www.goose-eye-brewery.co.uk
Tours by arrangement

Goose Eye supplies 50-60 regular outlets, mainly in West and North Yorkshire, and Lancashire. Its beers are also available through national wholesalers and pub chains. It produces an ever-expanding and diverse range of occasional beers, sometimes brewed to order, and is diversifying into wholesaling and bottled beers (filtered but not pasteurised). No-Eyed Deer is often re-badged under house names.
Occasional/seasonal beers: Spellbound (ABV 4%, Halloween), Summer Jack's (ABV 4.2%, summer), Wandy Wabbit (ABV 4.2%, Easter), Cockeyed Goose (ABV 6.2%, Christmas), Christmas Goose (ABV 5.2%).

Barm Pot Bitter
(OG 1038, ABV 3.8%)
A golden, citrus-hoppy quaffing ale with a dry, bitter finish

No-Eyed Deer *(OG 1040, ABV 4%)*
A faint fruity and malty aroma. Hoppy fruit flavours, and a long, bitter finish characterise this refreshing, copper-coloured beer.

Bronte Bitter *(OG 1040, ABV 4%)*
A pale brown beer with a faint fruity aroma. Fruit and bitterness dominate the taste with some background malt and hops. The lingering aftertaste is dry and bitter.

Wharfedale *(OG 1045, ABV 4.5%)*
Malt and hops dominate the taste of this copper-coloured premium bitter. Bitterness comes through into the finish.

Golden Goose *(OG 1045, ABV 4.5%)*

Pommies Revenge *(OG 1052, ABV 5.2%)*
A light-coloured, full-bodied and fruity, strong bitter.

Over and Stout *(OG 1052, ABV 5.2%)*

GRAINSTORE

Davis'es Brewing Company Ltd, The Grainstore Brewery, Station Approach, Oakham, Rutland, LE15 6RE
Tel (01572) 770065
Fax (01572) 770068
E-mail grainstorebry@aol.com
Website www.rutnet.co.uk/grainstore
Tours by arrangement

Grainstore, the smallest county's largest brewery, has been brewing since 1995. The brewery's curious name comes from the fact that it was founded by Tony Davis and Mike Davies. After 30 years in the industry, latterly with Ruddles, Tony decided to set up his own business after finding a derelict Victorian railway grainstore building. The brewing is designed traditionally, relying on whole hops and Maris Otter barley malt. 60 outlets are supplied direct. Future plans include relocating and expanding the brewery, and incorporating a bottling line. Seasonal beers: Springtime (ABV 4.5%, March-May), Gold (ABV 4.5%, May-Oct), Harvest IPA (ABV 4.5%, Sept-Oct), Three Kings (ABV 4.5%, Nov-Dec), Winter Nip (ABV 7.3%, Nov-Dec).

Rutland Panther *(OG 1034, ABV 3.4%)*
Formerly Grainstore Dark Mild. Smooth and well-rounded with a balance of hop and malt.

Cooking Bitter *(OG 1036, ABV 3.6%)*
A smooth, copper-coloured beer, full-bodied for its gravity. Malt and hops on the nose; malt and fruit to taste, with a malty aftertaste.

Triple B *(OG 1042, ABV 4.2%)*
Initially, hops dominate over malt in both the aroma and taste, but fruit is there, too. All three linger in varying degrees in the sweetish aftertaste of this tawny brew.

Steamin' Billy Bitter
(OG 1043, ABV 4.3%)
Brewed for the Steaming Billy Brewing Co of Leicester (qv).

Ten Fifty *(OG 1050, ABV 5%)*
This full-bodied, tawny beer is hoppy and fruity right into the aftertaste. A little malt on the nose and in the initial taste, with an underlying sweetness and an increasing bitterness.

GRAND UNION*

Grand Union Brewery, Brewhouse Lock, 10 Abenglen, Betam Road, Hayes, Mddx, UB3 1SS
Tel (020) 8573 9888
Fax (020) 8573 8885
E-mail info@gubc.co.uk
Website www.gubc.co.uk

The Grand Union opened in June 2002 and is owned by John Brigden, who also runs the Old Kent Brewery (qv). The 10-barrel plant was originally installed at Mash & Air in Manchester, and will be used to brew premium lagers as well as cask beers. The cask beers will be sold mainly in West London and surrounding counties.

Union Bitter *(OG 1037, ABV 3.6%)*
Refreshing session ale with light hoppiness.

Union Best *(OG 1038, ABV 4.1%)*
Aromatic, fruity and smooth.

Union Special *(OG 1043.5, ABV 4.5%)*
Full flavoured with a good balance of malt and hops.

GREAT GABLE*

Great Gable Brewing Co Ltd, Wasdale Head Inn, Wasdale, Cumbria, CA20 1EX
Tel (019467) 26333 Fax (019467) 26334
E-mail wasdaleheadinn@msn.com
Website www.wasdale.com

◎ A new pub brewery opened in 2002 as part of the famous Wasdale Head Inn in an idyllic location in Wasdale. It brews 4.5 barrels of Great Gable and three barrels of Wasd'ale a week. There are plans to bottle the beers.

Great Gable *(ABV 3.7%)*

Wasd'ale *(ABV 4.38%)*

GREEN DRAGON

⚲ Green Dragon Free House & Brewery, 29 Broad Street, Bungay, Suffolk, NR35 1EE
Tel/Fax (01986) 892681
Tours by arrangement

⊗ The Green Dragon was purchased from Brent Walker in 1991 and the buildings at the rear converted to a brewery. In 1994 the plant was expanded and moved into a converted barn across the car park. The doubling of capacity allowed the production of a larger range of ales, including seasonal and occasional brews. The beers are available at the pub and in three other outlets. A new cask beer is planned and the bottled range will be expanded. Seasonal: Wynter Warmer (ABV 6.5%). Bottle-conditioned beers: Dragon (ABV 5.5%), Wynter Warmer (ABV 7%).

Dark Mild *(OG 1034, ABV 3.4%)*

Chaucer Ale *(OG 1037, ABV 3.7%)*

Bridge Street Bitter *(OG 1046, ABV 4.5%)*

Dragon Gold *(OG 1055, ABV 5.5%)*

GREEN JACK

See Oulton Ales

GREENE KING

Greene King PLC, Westgate Brewery, Bury St Edmunds, Suffolk, IP33 1QT
Tel (01284) 763222 Fax (01284) 706502
Website www.greeneking.com

⊗ Founded in 1799, Greene King celebrated its 200th birthday in 1999 and transformed itself into a 'super regional' with the acquisition of the Morland and Ruddles brands. It closed the Morland Brewery in Abingdon. Greene King now owns 1,600 pubs in East Anglia, the Thames Valley and South-east England, 99 per cent of them serving cask beer. In June 2002 it bought the bulk of the Morrells pub company outlets in the Thames valley. 3,500 free trade outlets are supplied direct. A brewery museum opened in 2001 and it includes a new oak vat that stores 5X, a 12% beer that is blended with a 5% BPA to form Strong Suffolk Ale (ABV 6%), a bottled beer that is available on draught in the winter. Seasonal beers: Black Baron (ABV 4.3%, Sept-Oct), The Sorcerer (ABV 4.5%, March-April), Ruddles Organic Ale (ABV 5.1%). Bottle-conditioned beer: Hen's Tooth (ABV 6.2%).

XX Mild *(OG 1036, ABV 3%)* ◆
Smooth and sweet, with a bitter aftertaste. The beer is enjoying greater promotion and has increased sales.

IPA *(OG 1036, ABV 3.6%)* ◆
An easy-drinking, amber-coloured session bitter. Bitterness predominates throughout, leading to a somewhat astringent finish. Sweetness and hoppiness can be variable, depending on age.

Ruddles Best *(OG 1037, ABV 3.7%)* ◆
An amber/brown beer, strong on bitterness but with some initial sweetness, fruit and subtle, distinctive Bramling Cross hop. Dryness lingers in the aftertaste.

Morland Original Bitter *(OG 1039, ABV 4%)*

Ruddles County Ale *(OG 1047, ABV 4.3%)* ◆
Richer and slightly darker than Ruddles Best, this premium ale shares similar characteristics. Sweetness and fruit on the palate give way to bitterness and a distinctive hoppy, dry finish. Good body for its strength

Abbot Ale *(OG 1048, ABV 5%)* ◆
A full-bodied, very distinctive beer with a bitter-sweet aftertaste

Old Speckled Hen *(OG 1050, ABV 5.2%)* ◆
This full-flavoured, smooth strong ale has a good sweetness/bitterness balance, and rich fruit, particularly on the nose. The finish is dryish and very pleasant

GREEN TYE

Green Tye Brewery, Green Tye, Much Hadham, Hertfordshire, SG10 6JP
Tel/Fax (01279) 841041
E-mail enquiries@gtbrewery.co.uk
Website www.gtbrewery.co.uk
Tours by arrangement

⊗ Established in 1999 by William Compton and Gary Whelan, Green Tye supplies direct to local outlets, nationally via a wholesaler, and by arrangement with other micros. Occasional beers include a mild, beers for special events and a spiced winter beer. Seasonal beers: Snowdrop (ABV 3.9%, spring), Mad Morris (ABV 4.2%, summer), Autumn Rose (ABV 4.2%, late autumn), Conkerer (ABV 4.7%, early autumn), Coal Porter (ABV 4.5%, winter).

Shot in the Dark *(OG 1036, ABV 3.6%)*
A dark, hoppy bitter, with a pleasant, lingering aftertaste. A stronger flavour than its strength suggests.

Union Jack *(OG 1036, ABV 3.7%)*
A copper-coloured bitter. A hoppy aroma, with strong hops in the mouth and finish. Clean tasting, with a dry finish.

Wheelbarrow *(OG 1044, ABV 4.3%)*
A soft, fruity nose and taste. Gentle malt, with underlying hop bitterness, with a fruity and slightly dry finish.

GRIBBLE INN

Gribble Brewery, Gribble Inn,
Oving, nr Chichester,
W Sussex, PO20 2BP
Tel (01243) 786893
Fax (01243) 788841
E-mail brianelderfield@hotmail.com
Tours by arrangement

The Gribble Brewery has been on the site for 22 years. After a brief interlude, it has been in operation in its current form for 11 years. It is owned by Hall & Woodhouse, but the brewer and manager are given a free hand in the production of their beers, which are distributed throughout the H&W estate, which now includes the former King & Barnes houses. There are plans for a bottle-conditioned beer. Eight outlets are supplied, with a further 25-30 via Blandford. Seasonal beers: Wobbler (ABV 7.8%, winter), Porterhouse (ABV 5.2%, winter & spring), Plucking Pheasant (ABV 5.2%, spring & summer), Wobbler (7.8%, Nov-Feb).

Fursty Ferret *(OG 1041, ABV 4%)*
For selected H & W houses, all year round. This fine golden beer with its light nutty and slightly hoppy flavour is very easy on the palate.

Gribble Ale *(OG 1041, ABV 4.1%)*
The original brewhouse bitter, second only to Fursty Ferret in popularity.

Reg's Tipple *(OG 1048, ABV 5%)*
Reg's Tipple was named after a customer from the early days of the brewery. It has a smooth nutty flavour with a very pleasant afterbite.

Pig's Ear *(OG 1060, ABV 5.8%)*
A full-bodied old ale with a rich ruby-brown colour.

For Hall & Woodhouse.
King & Barnes Mild Ale
(OG 1030, ABV 3.5%)
A truly dark mild with a smoky roast malt character that is present throughout. Short aftertaste. Nothing like the old K&B Mild, but pleasant nonetheless.

King & Barnes Sussex Bitter
(OG 1035, ABV 3.5%)
Reasonably well-balanced mid-brown bitter. Hints of pear fruit in the flavour.

GUERNSEY

Guernsey Brewery Co (1920) Ltd,
South Esplanade, St Peter Port,
Guernsey, Channel Isles, GY1 1BJ
Tel (01481) 720143 Fax (01481) 710658
E-mail frank.morris@bucktrouts.com
Website www.bucktrouts.com

Known first as the London Brewery, it opened in 1856 and became Girling Bros a few years later. The brothers ceased trading in 1889. The foundations of the present company were laid in 1895 when B A P Schreiber and Thomas Skurray leased the property and formed the Guernsey Brewery Company. The company traded through the First World War and expanded its trade up to the Second World War. The German occupation in 1940 caused immense difficulties. It continued production, however, during the Occupation, ultimately brewing with sugar, sugar beet and parsnips. After the war the premises were enlarged, the plant completely modernised and the tied estate increased. In 1978, Guernsey merged with Bucktrouts wine merchants. In 1988, Ann Street brewery group of Jersey acquired Bucktrout. As a result, Guernsey cask ale is available in six selected Jersey Brewery houses. 30 pubs are owned and tied.

Braye Mild *(OG 1037, ABV 3.8%)*
Copper-red in colour, with a complex aroma of malt, hops, fruit and toffee. The rich, mellow flavour combines malt, fruit, hops and butterscotch, while the finish has malt and hops. Full-flavoured, surprisingly dry and hoppy.

Pirates Ale *(OG 1042, ABV 4.2%)*

Sunbeam Bitter *(OG 1042, ABV 4.2%)*
Golden in colour, with a fine malt aroma. Malt and fruit are strong on the palate and the beer is quite dry for its strength. Excellent, dry malt and hop finish.

HADRIAN & BORDER

Hadrian & Border Brewery,
Unit 10, Hawick Crescent Industrial Estate,
Newcastle upon Tyne, NE6 1AS
Tel (0191) 276 5302 Fax (0191) 265 5312
Email border@rampart.freeserve.co.uk
Tours by arrangement

Hadrian & Border is the result of a merger between Border Brewery of Berwick-on-Tweed and Four Rivers of Newcastle. Shona and Andy Burrows of Border joined forces with Trevor Smith of Four Rivers (and formerly of Hadrian) and the new company is based at the ex-Four Rivers 20-barrel site in Newcastle. Trevor Smith has now left the company. The new company's brands are available from Glasgow to Yorkshire, and nationally through wholesalers. They are hard to find on Tyneside, though the Sir John Fitzgerald group stocks them from time to time. Seasonal beer: Yule Fuel (ABV 5%, December).

Vallum Bitter *(OG 1034, ABV 3.6%)*
A well-hopped, amber-coloured bitter with a distinctive dry refreshing taste. The ultimate session bitter.

Gladiator *(OG 1038, ABV 3.8%)*
Medium-bodied bitter with plenty of malt in the aroma and palate, leading to a strong bitter finish.

Farne Island *(OG 1038, ABV 4%)*
An amber/mid-brown bitter with a refreshing hop/malt balance.

Flotsam *(OG 1038, ABV 4%)*
Bronze coloured with a citrus bitterness and a distinctive floral aroma.

Legion Ale *(OG 1041, ABV 4.2%)*
Well-balanced, amber-coloured beer, full bodied with good malt flavours. Well hopped with a long bitter finish.

New Secret Kingdom *(OG 1042, ABV 4.3%)*
Dark, rich and full bodied, slightly roasted with a malty palate ending with a pleasant bitterness. A new brew for this old favourite.

Reiver IPA *(OG 1042, ABV 4.4%)*
Dark golden bitter with a clean citrus palate

and aroma with subtle malt flavours breaking through at the end.

Northumbrian Gold *(OG 1044, ABV 4.5%)*
Dark golden coloured ale with a biscuity malt flavour countered with floral and citrus aromatic hops.

Centurion Bitter *(OG 1045, ABV 4.5%)*
Golden-coloured bitter with a distinct hop palate, some fruit, smooth, clean tasting and refreshing.

Rampart *(OG 1046, ABV 4.8%)*
Golden bitter; complex hopping gives this beer a clean, refreshing taste with plenty of character.

Jetsam *(OG 1046, ABV 4.8%)*
Pale golden bitter, clean and fresh with a flowery, hoppy nose.

HAGGARDS

Haggards Brewery Limited,
c/o 577 King's Road, London, SW6 2EH
Tel (020) 7731 3845
E-mail andrewhaggard@haggardsbrewery.fsnet.co.uk
Tours by arrangement

The brewery was set up in 1998 to supply beer to the Imperial pub on King's Road. It is owned and run by the Haggard brothers, who worked in the City of London but gave up their jobs to run the pub and establish the brewery. The brewery has a five-barrel capacity, and was designed by Rob Jones of Dark Star in Brighton. Haggards supplies other pubs only on request. Only one beer is brewed.

Horny Ale *(OG 1043, ABV 4.2%)*
Tawny beer that is fruity and sweet with little hop character.

HALIFAX

Halifax Steam Brewing Co, The Conclave, Southedge Works, Hipperholme, Halifax, W Yorkshire, HX3 8EF
Tel (07974) 544980
Fax (01484) 715074 (Phone first)
E-mail davidearnshaw@blueyonder.co.uk
Tours by arrangement

David Earnshaw started brewing in 2001 in a converted garage, inspired by CAMRA's series of home-brewing books. He learnt his brewing skills at Barge & Barrel, and now produces one regular beer from a seven-barrel plant. He bought the 6.25-barrel plant from the Fox & Firkin in Lewisham, south London, and has moved to new premises to meet demand. He supplies 12 pubs and Flying Firkin wholesales further afield. The beers are based on old Whitaker's of Halifax brands, and David plans to revive Ramsden's beers as well.

Bantam *(OG 1043, ABV 4.1%)*

Top o' the Morning *(OG 1043, ABV 4.3%)*

Cock o' t' North *(OG 1048, ABV 4.9%)*

HAMBLETON

Nick Stafford Hambleton Ales, Holme-on-Swale, Thirsk, N Yorkshire, YO7 4JE
Tel (01845) 567460
E-mail sales@hambletonales.co.uk
Website www.hambletonales.co.uk
Shop 9-4 Mon-Fri. Tours by arrangement

Hambleton was established in 1991 by Nick Stafford on the banks of the River Swale in the heart of the Vale of York. The bottling line caters for micro and large brewers, handling more than 20 brands. New brewing equipment was installed in 2000, doubling capacity to 100 barrels a week. A mail-order service for all bottle brands is available from the brewery or its website. 100 outlets are supplied direct. Hambleton brews beers under contract for the Village Brewer wholesale company (01325) 374887, and Black Dog of Whitby (qv).

Bitter *(OG 1036.5, ABV 3.6%)*
Rich, hoppy aroma rides through this light and drinkable beer. Taste is bitter with citrus and marmalade aroma and solid body. Ends dry with a spicy mouthfeel.

Goldfield *(OG 1040, ABV 4.2%)*
A light amber bitter with good hop character and increasing dryness. A fine blend of malts gives a smooth overall impression.

Stallion *(OG 1040, ABV 4.2%)*
A premium bitter, moderately hoppy throughout and richly balanced in malt and fruit, developing a sound and robust bitterness, with earthy hop drying the aftertaste.

Stud *(OG 1042, ABV 4.3%)*
A strongly bitter beer, with rich hop and fruit. It ends dry and spicy.

Nightmare *(OG 1050, ABV 5%)*
Fully deserving its acclaim, this impressively flavoured beer satisfies all parts of the palate. Strong roast malts dominate, but hoppiness rears out of this complex blend.

For Village Brewer:
White Boar *(OG 1037.5, ABV 3.7%)*
A light, flowery and fruity ale; crisp, clean and refreshing, with a dry-hopped, powerful but not aggressive, bitter finish.

Bull *(OG 1039, ABV 4%)*
A fairly thin, but well-hopped bitter, with a distinct dryness in the aftertaste.

Old Ruby *(OG 1048, ABV 4.8%)*
A full-bodied, smooth, rich-tasting dark ale. A complex balance of malt, fruit character and creamy caramel sweetness offsets the bitterness. A classic old ale.

HAMPSHIRE

Hampshire Brewery Ltd, 6-8 Romsey Industrial Estate, Greatbridge Road, Romsey, Hampshire, SO51 OHR
Tel (01794) 830529
Fax (01794) 830528
E-mail online@hampshirebrewery.com
Website www.hampshirebrewery.com
Shop 9-5 Mon-Fri.
Tours by arrangement. CAMRA groups/customers only

Set up in 1992, the brewery outgrew its capacity in Andover and moved in 1997 to a larger site in Romsey. Pride of Romsey was launched to celebrate the move and has already won several awards in both cask and bottle-conditioned form. In 1999 the brewery started to brew Strong's Best Bitter, to the old Romsey Brewery's original recipe, by arrangement with Whitbread, who bought and closed Strong's. Seasonal ales: Grim Reaper (ABV 4.4%, Jan), Not Tonight Josephine (ABV 5%, Feb), Temptation (ABV 4.2%, Oct), Desperate Dan (ABV 5%, April), Manneken (ABV 4.6%, May), Uncle Sam (ABV 5%, June), Porky & Best (ABV 4.5%, July), Wild Thing (ABV 4.2%, Nov), Bohemian Rhapsody (ABV 5%, Sept), Californian Red (ABV 5%, Oct), Penny Black Porter (ABV 4.5%, Nov), Good King 'Censlas (ABV 5%, Dec).

King Alfred's *(OG 1038, ABV 3.8%)* ◆
A mid-brown beer, featuring a malty and hoppy aroma. A malty taste leads to a hoppy, malty and bitter finish.

Strong's Best Bitter
(OG 1038, ABV 3.8%)
A deep copper-coloured bitter with rich malt complexity brewed with classic English aroma hops.

Ironside *(OG 1042, ABV 4.2%)* ◆
A beer with little aroma, but some malt. The taste has solid fruit with lasting hops and malt. The aftertaste is more bitter and malty. Pale brown in colour.

Gold Reserve *(OG 1046, ABV 4.8%)*
Golden ale with an inviting citrus fragrance of late added Golding hops. The fine hop and light malt aromas carry through to the palate to give an ale that is full but refreshing and with a clean bitter finish.

Pride of Romsey *(OG 1050, ABV 5%)*
Abundant aroma of the fruit of the hop, citrus and fragrant with orange, grapefruit and lemon hints. Powerful hop aroma through to the aftertaste with distinctive bitterness complemented by good strength of malt character.

HANBY

Hanby Ales Ltd, New Brewery,
Aston Park, Soulton Road, Wem,
Shropshire, SY4 5SD
Tel/Fax (01939) 232432
E-mail hanby@dial.pipex.com
Tours by arrangement

⊗ Hanby was set up in 1990 by three partners. The 12-barrel plant was upgraded to 20 barrels in 2000 to cope with demand. Hanby supplies some 200-300 pubs direct and others via wholesalers. Bottle-conditioned beers: Hanby Premium (ABV 4.6%), Rainbow Chaser and Cherry Bomb.

Black Magic Mild *(OG 1033, ABV 3.3%)* ◆
A dark, reddish-brown mild, which is dry and bitter with a roast malt taste.

Drawwell Bitter *(OG 1039, ABV 3.9%)* ◆
A hoppy beer with excellent bitterness, both in taste and aftertaste. Beautiful amber colour.

All Seasons Bitter *(OG 1042, ABV 4.2%)*

Rainbow Chaser *(OG 1043, ABV 4.3%)*
A pale beer brewed with Pioneer hops.

Wem Special *(OG 1044, ABV 4.4%)*
A pale, smooth, hoppy bitter.

Cascade *(OG 1045, ABV 4.5%)*

Golden Honey *(OG 1045, ABV 4.5%)*
A beer made with the addition of Australian honey.

Premium Bitter *(OG 1046, ABV 4.6%)* ◆
Formerly Treacleminer, a pale brown beer that is sweeter and fruitier than most of the beers above. Slight malt and hop taste.

Old Wemian Ale *(OG 1049, ABV 4.9%)*
Golden-brown colour with an aroma of malt and hops and a soft, malty palate.

Taverners Ale *(OG 1053, ABV 5.3%)*

Cherry Bomb *(OG 1060, ABV 6%)*
Beer made with the addition of cherries.

Nutcracker *(OG 1060, ABV 6%)*

Joy Bringer *(OG 1060, ABV 6%)*
Beer made with the addition of ginger.

HANSON'S

See Banks's.

HAPPY HOOKER

Happy Hooker Brewery Ltd,
30 St Edmunds Road, Sleaford,
Lincs, NG34 7LS
Tel (01529) 307499
E-mail brent@happyhookersbeers.com
Website www.happyhookerbeers.com
Shop via internet
Tours by arrangement

⊗ A small brewery launched in 2001 by Brent Day, a CAMRA member from the early 1970s who home-brewed with enthusiasm when stationed abroad with the RAF. His other passion is Rugby Union, hence the name of the company. He bought a 2.5-barrel plant with the aid of his RAF pension and is currently based in the back garden of his home, but plans to move either to an industrial unit or a pub. Increased demand has been met by increasing the number of conditioning vessels. The brewery serves the free trade throughout the country. Brent planned to move to new premises and expand production in summer 2002. Small-scale bottling will follow. Seasonal beers: Stay On Your Feet (ABV 5.8%, Oct-March), Santas Scored (ABV 5.2%, Nov-Dec).

Up And Under *(OG 1042, ABV 3.9%)*
A hoppy session beer.

Loosehead *(OG 1044, ABV 4.2%)*
A tawny-coloured, malty brew.

Tighthead *(OG 1049, ABV 4.8%)*
A darker, stronger, full-flavoured ale.

THOMAS HARDY

Thomas Hardy Brewery,
Weymouth Avenue, Dorchester,
Dorset, DT1 1QT
Tel (01305) 250255 Fax (01305) 258381
Website www.thomashardybrewery.co.uk

⊗ In March 1997, ex-Courage manager Peter Ward bought Dorchester Brewery from Eldridge Pope. The next year he acquired the majority share of Burtonwood Brewery. Peter Ward declines to reveal what is being brewed at Dorchester, on the grounds that he has confidentiality agreements with all his customers. The brewery is thought to be brewing secret trial brews for various customers. As a contract brewer, the customer retains ownership of the brands. In a shock move, Eldridge Pope, the former owners of the brewery and now a pub retailer, discontinued the contract in September 2001 to brew Royal Oak, Hardy Country Bitter and Popes Traditional, ending at a stroke the long Eldridge Pope brewing tradition in Dorset. The brewery occupies about 80% of the freehold site, which Eldridge Pope plans to sell. THB holds two 24-year leases from 1997, and any developer will need to buy out the leases. Although one major customer, Refresh UK, has bought the Wychwood Brewery (qv), it says it does not plan to move its Usher's brands from Thomas Hardy, as Wychwood is brewing to capacity. Seasonal beers (for Morrells): Old Don (ABV 4.6%, Jan-Feb), Blustering Bursar (ABV 4.3%, March-April), Trinity (ABV 4.1%, May-June), Scorcher (ABV 3.8%, July-Aug), Pickled Proctor (ABV 4%, Sept-Oct), Advent (ABV 4.4%, Nov-Dec). Seasonal beers (for Refresh UK): Spring Fever (March-May), Summer Madness (June-Aug), Autumn Frenzy (Sept-Nov), Winter Storm (Dec-Feb), all ABV 4%.

For Morrells of Oxford:
Oxford Blue *(OG 1036, ABV 3.7%)*

Varsity *(OG 1042, ABV 4.3%)*

Graduate *(OG 1048, ABV 4.8%)*

For Refresh UK:
Usher's Best Bitter *(OG 1039, ABV 3.8%)*

Founders Ale *(OG 1046, ABV 4.5%)*

The Bishops Tipple (ex-Gibbs Mew)
(OG 1054, ABV 5.2%)

HARDYS & HANSONS

Hardys & Hansons PLC,
Kimberley Brewery, Kimberley,
Nottingham, NG16 2NS
Tel (0115) 938 3611
Fax (0115) 945 9055
Tours by arrangement

Established in 1832 and 1847 respectively, Hardys & Hansons were two competitive breweries until a merger in 1931 produced the present company. The brewery is still run by descendants of the original families. The majority of its 246 tied houses take its award-winning real ales, mostly drawn by metered dispense into oversized glasses, although Kimberley Classic, and increasingly the Bitter, are served by handpumps. Around 100 other outlets are also supplied direct. A range of seasonal ales, with a rotation or new beer every month under the Cellarman's Cask banner, has extended Hardys & Hansons' geographical availability and reputation. Occasional/seasonal beers: Frolicking Farmer (ABV 4.2%), Peddler's Pride (ABV 4.3%), Guzzling Goose (ABV 4.4%), Rocking Rudolph (ABV 5%), Guinea Gold (ABV 4.5%), Original Gravity (ABV 4.1%), Old Kim (ABV 4.5%), Ye Olde Trip Ale (ABV 4.7%).

Kimberley Best Mild
(OG 1035, ABV 3.1%)
A deep ruby mild dominated by chocolate malt. The fruitiness and caramel sweetness are well balanced in the taste, with a faintly hoppy finish.

Kimberley Best Bitter
(OG 1039, ABV 3.9%)
A beer with a flowery, hoppy and fruity nose, although malt is never far away. Fruity hop is evident in the taste and there is a consistent bitterness.

Kimberley Classic *(OG 1047, ABV 4.8%)*
A light brown beer with an amber hue. Bitter throughout, it has a fruity hop nose, with malt behind the hops in the taste and aftertaste. It is not always easy to find (occasionally alternating with seasonals).

HART

Hart Brewery, Cartford Hotel,
Cartford Lane, Little Eccleston,
Lancs, PR3 0YP
Tel (01995) 671686 Fax (01772) 797069
Tours by arrangement on Thursdays

The brewery was founded in 1994 in a small private garage in Preston. It moved to its present site at the rear of the Cartford Hotel in 1995. With a 10-barrel plant, Hart now supplies direct to more than 100 outlets nationwide. The company plans to buy a pub in the future. Seasonal beers: Knights Wheat Beer (ABV 4%, spring, summer, autumn, winter), Amethyst Seasonal (ABV 4.2%, twice a year), No Balls (ABV 4.5%, winter).

Dishy Debbie *(OG 1040, ABV 4%)*

Imposter *(OG 1040, ABV 4%)*

Squirrels Hoard *(OG 1040, ABV 4%)*
Brewed for the Cartford Hotel and CAMRA festivals.

Nemesis *(OG 1045, ABV 4.5%)*
A light amber-coloured beer with a refreshing flavour.

HARVEYS

Harvey & Son (Lewes) Ltd, The Bridge Wharf Brewery, 6 Cliffe High Street, Lewes, E Sussex, BN7 2AH
Tel (01273) 480209 Fax (01273) 486074
E-mail maj@harveys.org.uk
Website www.harveys.org.uk
Shop 9.30-4.45 Mon-Sat
Tours by arrangement (two-year waiting list)

⊠ Established in 1790, this independent family brewery operates from the Bridge Wharf Brewery on the banks of the River Ouse in Lewes. The brewery was rebuilt in 1881. A major development in 1985 doubled the brewhouse capacity and subsequent additional fermenting capacity has seen production rise to more than 34,000 barrels a year. Harveys supplies real ale to all its 44 pubs and 400 free trade outlets in Sussex and Kent. Seasonal beers: Knots of May Light Mild (ABV 3%, May), Sussex XXXX Old Ale (ABV 4.3%, Oct-May), Kiss (ABV 4.8%, February), Southdown Harvest Ale (ABV 5%, September), 1859 Porter (ABV 4.8%, March), Tom Paine (ABV 5.5%, July), Copperwheat (ABV 4.8%, June), Bonfire Boy (ABV 5.8%, November), Christmas Ale (ABV 8.1%, December). Bottle-conditioned beer: Imperial Extra Double Stout (ABV 9%); annual vintages in limited supply.

Sussex XX Mild Ale
(OG 1030, ABV 3%)
A dark copper-brown colour. Roast malt dominates the aroma and palate leading to a sweet, caramel finish.

Sussex Pale Ale *(OG 1033, ABV 3.5%)*
An agreeable, light bitter with malt and hops dominating the aroma, while a hoppy bitterness develops throughout the taste, to dominate the finish.

Sussex Best Bitter
(OG 1040, ABV 4%)
Full-bodied brown bitter. A hoppy aroma leads to a good malt and hop balance and a dry aftertaste.

Sussex XXXX Old Ale
(OG 1043, ABV 4.3%)
A rich, dark beer with a good malty nose, with undertones of roast malt, hops and fruit. The flavour is a complex blend of roast malt, grain, fruit and hops with some caramel. Malty caramel finish with roast malt.

Armada Ale *(OG 1045, ABV 4.5%)*
Hoppy amber best bitter. Well-balanced fruit and hops dominate throughout with a fruity palate.

HARVIESTOUN

Harviestoun Brewery Ltd, Devon Road, Dollar, Clackmannanshire, FK14 7LX
Tel (01259) 742141
Fax (01259) 743141
E-mail harviestoun@talk21.com

⊛ Hand-built in a 200-year-old stone byre by two home-brew enthusiasts in 1985, this small brewery operates from a former dairy at the foot of the Ochil Hills, near Stirling. A new custom-built brewing plant was installed in 1991, and Harviestoun now serves 70 outlets in central Scotland as well as wholesalers' customers throughout Britain. There is planning permission approval to build a new brewery in Hillfoots Village Industrial Estate, Alva. It should be re-located and operational by the end of 2002. Harviestoun bottles a range of beers (not bottle conditioned). Occasional beers: Spring Fever (ABV 3.8%, March), Fresher's Bitter (ABV 3.9%, October), Cutlass Sharp (ABV 4%, August), Lochinvar (ABV 4%, April), American Red (ABV 4.1%, September), Belgian White (ABV 4.3%, July), Mayfest Wheat Beer (ABV 4.4%, May), Old Engine Oil (ABV 4.4%, November), Black Lager (ABV 4.5%, February), Good King Legless (ABV 4.5%, December), Burn's Ale (ABV 4.6%, January), Auld Lang Syne (ABV 4.7%, December), Natural Blonde (ABV 4%), Gremlin (ABV 4.3%), Hitchhiker Bitter (ABV 4%), Sandpiper (ABV 3.9%, June), Storm Force (ABV 4.2%, February), Liberation (ABV 4.5%, January).

Brooker's Bitter & Twisted
(OG 1038, ABV 3.8%)
Refreshingly hoppy beer with fruit throughout. A bitter-sweet taste with a long, dry, bitter finish. A golden session beer, 1999 Champion Beer of Scotland.

Turnpike *(ABV 4.1%)*

Ptarmigan *(OG 1045, ABV 4.5%)*
A well-balanced, bitter-sweet beer in which hops and malt dominate. The blend of malt, hops and fruit produces a clean, hoppy aftertaste.

Schiehallion *(OG 1048, ABV 4.8%)*
A Scottish cask lager, brewed using a lager yeast and Hersbrucker hops. A hoppy aroma, with fruit and malt, leads to a malty, bitter taste with floral hoppiness and a bitter finish.

HAWKSHEAD*

Hawkshead Brewery Co,
Town End Farm, Colthouse,
Hawkshead, Cumbria, LA22 0JU
Tel 015394 36111

⊛ Brewery opened summer 2002 in an industrial barn, using plant from the former Border Brewery. It's run by BBC radio presenter Alex Brodie.

Hawkshead Bitter *(ABV 3.7%)*

Hawkshead Best Bitter *(ABV 4.2%)*

HEATHER

Heather Ale Ltd/Craigmill Brewery Ltd, Strathaven, Lanarkshire, ML10 6PB
Tel (01357) 529529
Fax (01357) 522256
E-mail fraoch@heatherale.co.uk
Website heatherale.co.uk
Tours by arrangement

Heather and Craigmill are based in a18th-century watermill on the banks of the River Avon, restored for use as a brewery in 1998. Plans for a Scottish Heather Ale Centre may be developed once the brewing side of the business is optimised. All cask beers are made in Strathaven, while the bottled products are brewed and bottled at Forth Brewery (qv). Heather Ale is made with flowering heather, while Pictish is a stronger version for the dark winter months. The Craigmill side of the business has been developed to produce conventional cask beers. 100 outlets are supplied direct. Seasonal beers: Grozet Gooseberry Wheat Ale (ABV 4.5%, Aug-Sept), Pictish Heather Ale (ABV 5.4%, Dec-Jan), Ebulum Elderberry Black Ale (ABV 5.8%, Oct-Nov), Kelpie ABV 4.4% , May-July), Alba (ABV 6%, March-April), AT Bob Ale (ABV 4.2%. Aug-Sept).

Swallow IPA *(OG 1041, ABV 4%)*
A light fresh golden ale with a soft malt character and crisp hop finish.

Fraoch Heather Ale
(OG 1043, ABV 4.1%)
Light amber ale with fresh heather spice aroma, firm malt flavour, and dry wine finish.

HEBRIDEAN*

Hebridean Brewing Company, Bells Road, Stornoway, Isle of Lewis, HS1 2RA
Tel (01851) 700123
Fax (01851) 700234
Website www.hebridean-brewery.co.uk

The company was set up in 2001 by Andy Ribbens, whose family came from Lewis. The plant is steam powered with a 14-barrel brew length. Plans for bottling are underway.

Clansman Ale *(OG1037, ABV 3.9%)*

Islander Strong Premium Ale *(OG 1047, ABV 4.8%)*

HEPWORTH

Hepworth & Co, The Beer Station, Railway Goods Yard, Nightingale Road, Horsham, W. Sussex, RH12 2NW
Tel (01403) 269696
E-mail fineale@ouvip.com
Tours by arrangement

Andy Hepworth, former head brewer at King & Barnes, together with K&B's key personnel set up independently in February 2001. The Beer Station's own range of bottled beers includes Pullman (ABV 4.2%) and Iron Horse (ABV 4.8%). A bottle-conditioned range is expected shortly. Andy also brews for Salopian, the Brilliant Beer Company and Weltons. The brewery is certificated by the Soil Association to produce organic beers.

For Salopian
Firefly *(ABV 5%)*

For the Brilliant Beer Company
Brilliant Gold *(ABV 5.4%)*

For Weltons:
Pride & Joy *(ABV 2.8%)*

Kid & Bard *(ABV 3.5%)*
Mid-brown bitter with predominantly malty aroma that also has toffee, hops and fruit present. The flavour reflects the aroma, with a bitterness growing towards the finish.

Old Cocky *(ABV 4.3%)*

Horsham Old *(ABV 4.5%)*
Very dark old ale with roast malt aroma that is reflected in the taste. Hints of caramel also present. Full bodied with bitter-sweet aftertaste.

HESKET NEWMARKET

Hesket Newmarket Brewery Ltd, Old Crown Barn, Hesket Newmarket, Cumbria, CA7 8JG
Tel/Fax (016974) 78066
E-mail breweryhesket@talk21.com
Website www.bdksol.demon.co.uk/hesket
Tours Booking essential (016974) 78288

A brewery run as a co-operative by the villagers. Hesket Newmarket was set up in 1988 in a converted barn behind the Old Crown pub by Jim and Liz Fearnley. In 1999 they said they planned to retire. The villagers, anxious to save the brewery as a community resource, raised the funds to buy the site. The beers are named after local fells, with the notable exception of Doris's 90th Birthday Ale (Doris died in 1995, aged 96). Around 20 pubs take the beers regularly and many more on an occasional basis.

Great Cockup Porter *(OG 1035, ABV 3%)*
A refreshing, dark and chocolatey porter with a dry finish.

Blencathra Bitter *(OG 1035, ABV 3.2%)*
A malty, tawny ale, mild and mellow for a bitter, with a dominant caramel flavour.

Skiddaw Special Bitter
(OG 1035, ABV 3.6%)
An amber session beer, malty throughout, thin with a dryish finish.

Doris's 90th Birthday Ale
(OG 1045, ABV 4.3%)
Golden brown with a caramel and barley sugar aroma. Full tasting and satisfying, drying in the aftertaste to a more balanced finish.

Catbells Pale Ale *(OG 1050, ABV 5%)*
A powerful golden ale with a well-balanced malty bitterness, ending with a bitter and decidedly dry aftertaste.

Old Carrock Strong Ale
(OG 1060, ABV 5.9%)
A dark red, powerful ale.

Ayala's Angel *(OG 1069, ABV 6.9%)*
A black, dark, strong beer, with a complex, nutty character.

HEXHAMSHIRE

Hexhamshire Brewery, Leafields, Ordley, Hexham, Northumberland, NE46 1SX
Tel (01434) 606577

Brewing started in 1993 as a partnership and the present brewer, one of the original partners, took over in 1997. He plans to introduce bottle-conditioned beers.

Devil's Elbow *(OG 1036, ABV 3.6%)*
Amber brew full of hops and fruit, leading to a bitter finish.

Shire Bitter *(OG 1037, ABV 3.8%)*
Good balance of hops with fruity overtones, this amber beer makes an easy-drinking session bitter.

Devil's Water *(OG 1041, ABV 4.1%)*
Copper-coloured best bitter, well-balanced with a slightly fruity, hoppy finish.

Whapweasel *(OG 1048, ABV 4.8%)*
An interesting smooth, hoppy beer with a fruity flavour. Amber in colour, the bitter finish brings out the fruit and hops.

Old Humbug *(OG 1055, ABV 5.5%)*

HIGH FORCE

See Darwin

HIGHGATE

Highgate Brewery Ltd,
Sandymount Road, Walsall,
W Midlands, WS1 3AP
A subsidiary of Aston Manor of Birmingham
Tel (01922) 644453
Fax (01922) 644471
Tours by arrangement

Built in 1898, Highgate was an independent brewery until 1938 when it was taken over by Mitchells & Butlers and subsequently became the smallest brewery in the Bass group. It was brought back into the independent sector in 1995 as the result of a management buy-out, and was subsequently bought by Aston Manor in 2000. Some of the original equipment in the traditional Victorian brewery is still in use, but a new racking line and laboratory have been added along with a visitor facility. Highgate has now acquired 12 tied houses towards a target of 50, including the City Tavern, a restored Victorian ale house off Broad Street in Birmingham. All but one of the tied houses take real ale, which is also supplied direct to around 200 outlets. The company also has a major contract to supply Six Continents (former Bass) pubs. Seasonal beer: Highgate Old Ale (ABV 5.3%), Bain's 535 (ABV 5.3%), Beezone (ABV 4%). Highgate Old, Fox's Nob, Balti Beer, Davenports Top Brew de Luxe & Piddle in the Hole are all suitable for vegetarians.

Dark Mild *(OG 1036, ABV 3.4%)*
A dark brown Black Country mild with a good balance of malt and hops, and traces of roast flavour following a malty aroma.

Special Bitter *(OG 1037, ABV 3.8%)*

Saddlers Best Bitter
(OG 1043, ABV 4.3%)
A fruity, pale yellow bitter with a strong hop flavour and a light, refreshing bitter aftertaste.

Old Ale *(OG 1055, ABV 5.3%)*
A dark brown/ruby-coloured old ale, full-flavoured, fruity and malty, with a complex aftertaste with hints of malt, roast, hops and fruit.

For Coors:
M&B Mild *(OG 1034, ABV 3.2%)*

HIGHWOOD

Highwood Brewery Ltd, Melton Highwood, Barnetby, Lincs, DN38 6AA
Tel (01652) 680020
Fax (01652) 680010
E-mail tomwood@tom-wood.com
Website www.tom-wood.com
Tours by arrangement, occasionally

Highwood started brewing in a converted Victorian granary on the family farm in 1995. The brew-length was increased from 10 barrels to 30 in 2001, using plant from Ash Vine brewery. More than 100 outlets are supplied direct. Seasonal beers: Mill Race (ABV 4.2%, Jan-Feb), Fathers Pride (ABV 4.5%, March), Wagoners Ale (ABV 4.8%, April), Barndance (4.2%, June-July), Summer Days (ABV 4.4%, July-Aug), Lincolnshire Longwool (4.4%, Sept-Oct), Jolly Ploughman (ABV 5%, Oct-Nov), Christmas Cheers (ABV 5%, December).

Tom Wood's Dark Mild
(OG 1034, ABV 3.5%)

Tom Wood's Best Bitter
(OG 1034, ABV 3.5%)
A good citric passion fruit hop on the nose and taste, which dominates the background malt. A lingering hoppy and bitter finish makes this amber bitter very drinkable.

Tom Wood's Shepherd's Delight
(OG 1040, ABV 4%)
Malt is the dominant taste in this amber brew, although the fruity hop bitterness complements it all the way.

Tom Wood's Harvest Bitter
(OG 1042, ABV 4.3%)
A well-balanced amber beer where the hops and bitterness just about outdo the malt.

Tom Wood's Old Timber
(OG 1043, ABV 4.5%)
Hoppy on the nose, but featuring well-balanced malt and hops otherwise. A slight, lingering roast/coffee flavour develops, but this is generally a bitter, darkish brown beer.

Tom Wood's Bomber County
(OG 1046, ABV 4.8%)
An earthy malt aroma but with a complex underlying mix of coffee, hops, caramel and apple fruit. The beer starts bitter and intensifies but all its mahogany characteristics stay on until the end.

HILDEN

Hilden Brewing Company, Hilden House, Hilden, Lisburn, Co Antrim, BT27 4TY
Tel (028 92) 663863 Fax (028 92) 603511
E-mail hilden.brewery@uk.gateway.net
Shop 10-5 Mon-Sat.
Tours by arrangement

Hilden Brewery Company was established by Ann and Seamus Scullion in 1981. Then it was the first of a wave of small breweries in Ireland, north and south. The others all switched to keg beer and finally went out of business. Hilden is now the oldest independent brewery in Ireland and is looking forward, in conjunction with the latest wave of small breweries on the island, to meet a growing demand for choice in a market dominated by a beer monopoly. Bottle-conditioned beer: Original (ABV 4.6%).

Hilden Ale *(OG 1038, ABV 4%)* ◆
An amber-coloured beer with an aroma of malt, hops and fruit. The balanced taste is slightly slanted towards hops, and hops are also prominent in the full, malty finish. Bitter and refreshing.

Molly Malone's Porter *(OG 1048, ABV 4.6%)*
Dark ruby-red porter with complex flavours of hop bitterness and chocolate malt.

Scullion's Irish *(OG 1048, ABV 4.6%)*
Initially smooth on the palate, it finishes with a clean, hoppy aftertaste.

HOBDEN'S*

Hobden's Wessex Brewery (t/a CF Hobden), Farm Cottage, Norton Ferris, Warminster, BA12 7NT
Tel/Fax (01985) 844532
Email wessexbrewery@tinyworld.co.uk

A new brewery that went into production in 2002.

Blackmore Ale *(OG 1037, ABV 3.5%)*

Norton's Ferret *(OG 1037, ABV 3.5%)*

Best Bitter *(OG 1041, ABV 4%)*

Golden Delirious *(OG 1046, ABV 4.5%)*

Paze Zeals Ale (PZ) *(OG 1044, ABV 4.5%)*

Lost Dog in the Dark *(OG 1047, ABV 4.5%)*

Old Deverill *(OG 1060, ABV 6%)*

HOBSONS

Hobsons Brewery & Co Ltd, Newhouse Farm, Tenbury Road, Cleobury Mortimer, nr Kidderminster, Worcestershire, DY14 8RD
Tel (01299) 270837
Fax (01299) 270260
E-mail beer@hobsons-brewery.co.uk
Shop 8-5 weekdays. Tours by arrangement

⊗ Established in 1993, Hobsons moved to its current premises in 1996. Production has grown to 75 barrels a week. An extension was built in 2001 that allowed production to grow by 50% and to include a bottling plant. More than 100 outlets are supplied direct.

Best Bitter *(OG 1038.5, ABV 3.8%)* ◆
A pale brown to amber, medium-bodied beer with strong hop character throughout. It is consequently bitter, but with malt discernible in the taste.

Town Crier *(OG 1045, ABV 4.5%)*
An elegant straw-coloured bitter. The hint of sweetness is complemented by subtle hop flavours, leading to a dry finish.

Old Henry *(OG 1051, ABV 5.2%)*
Authentic winter ale. Complex malty flavours give a richness that is balanced by the clean, hoppy finish.

For Three Tuns, Bishop's Castle:
Three Tuns XXX *(OG 1041, ABV 4.3%)*

HOGS BACK

Hogs Back Brewery, Manor Farm, The Street, Tongham, Surrey, GU10 1DE

Tel (01252) 783000
Fax (01252) 782328
E-mail info@hogsback.co.uk
Website www.hogsback.co.uk
Shop 10-6 Mon-Tue; 10-8.30 Wed-Fri; 9-6 Sat; 10-4.30 Sun. Tours by arrangement 6.30 Wed-Fri; 11am and 2.30 Sat; 2.30 Sun

⊗ The purpose-built brewery was set up in a restored, 18th-century farm building in 1992 and the popularity of its ales — particularly the award-winning TEA — resulted in a major plant change to double capacity. From small beginnings, with just a single beer, Hogs Back now brews nearly 20 beers on a regular or occasional basis. The brewery has commissioned a new bottling hall to expand its bottle beer range to cope with exporting to the US. There are plans to install a single, larger copper to replace the existing two smaller vessels, and to upgrade the older fermenting vessels to 40-barrel size. Planning permission to build a brewery tap on site is planned. E-commerce and mail order continue to grow. Seasonal beers: Dark Mild (ABV 3.4%), APB or A Pinta Bitter (ABV 3.5%), Spring Call (ABV 4%), Summer Capers (ABV 4%), Easter Teaser (ABV 4.2%), Friday 13th (ABV 4.2%), Blackwater Porter (ABV 4.4% ■), BSA or Burma Star Ale (ABV 4.5%), Autumn Seer (ABV 4.8%, autumn), Tattoo (ABV 4.8%), Arena (ABV 4.8%), YES or Your Every Success (ABV 5%), Fuggles Nouveau (ABV 5%), Goldings Nouveau (ABV 5%), Utopia (ABV 5.4%), OTT or Old Tongham Tasty (ABV 6%), Brewster's Bundle (ABV 7.6%), Santa's Wobble (ABV 7.5%, Christmas), A over T or Aromas over Tongham (ABV 9%), Wheat Your Whistle (ABV 4.8%, summer), Spring Call (ABV 4%, spring). Bottle-conditioned beers: TEA (ABV 4.2%), BSA (ABV 4.5%), Vintage Ale (ABV 6%), Brewster's Bundle (ABV 7.4%), Wobble in a Bottle (ABV 7.5%), A over T (ABV 9%), OTT (ABV 6%), Hop Garden Gold (ABV 4.6%).

Hair of the Hog *(OG 1038, ABV 3.5%)* ◆
An honest, refreshing pale brown session beer with a good bitter hop character balanced with pale malt and fruit. A dry, bitter finish.

Legend *(OG 1038, ABV 4%)* ◆
Complex and drinkable, this golden-coloured beer contains both wheat and lager malts, and has a dry, malty and bitter taste that lingers. Available September.

TEA or Traditional English Ale
(OG 1044, ABV 4.2%)
The brewery's flagship beer is pale brown, with a hoppy and slightly fruity aroma, supported by malt, which is more noticeable in the taste. A long dry aftertaste.

Advent Ale *(OG 1046, ABV 4.4%)*
Dark red-brown in colour, this easy-to-drink winter ale tastes of dark malts and roast barley, with liquorice hints in the finish. Available Christmas.

Hop Garden Gold
(OG 1048, ABV 4.6%)
Pale golden beer with fruity, malty aroma. Delicate flowery-citrus hop flavours are balanced by malt and fruit. Hoppy bitterness grows in aftertaste.

Rip Snorter *(OG 1052, ABV 5%)*
Strongish malty and fruity tawny-brown bitter with a slight hop flavour.

HOLDEN'S

Holden's Brewery Ltd Co,
Hopden Brewery, George Street,
Woodsetton, Dudley,
W Midlands, DY1 4LN
Tel (01902) 880051
Fax (01902) 665473
E-mail holdens.brewery@virgin.net
Website www.holdensbrewery.co.uk
Shop Mon-Thu 11-3, 5-9. Fri-Sat 11-9. Sun 12-3, 5-9
Tours by arrangement

A family brewery going back four generations, Holden's began life as a brew-pub when Edwin and Lucy Holden took over the Park Inn (now the brewery tap) in the 1920s; the inn has been refurbished to its former Victorian heritage. Holden's also renovated a Grade II listed building in Codsall and have restored it to a traditional drinkers pub that will also interest railway fanatics. Codsall Station is one of the newest additions to the Holden's estate, which with 22 pubs, is continually growing. Some 45 other outlets are also supplied with Holden's cask ales. Seasonal: Old Ale (ABV 7.2%, Christmas).

Black Country Mild
(OG 1037, ABV 3.7%)
A good, red/brown mild; a refreshing, light blend of roast malt, hops and fruit, dominated by malt throughout.

Black Country Bitter
(OG 1039, ABV 3.9%)
A medium-bodied, golden ale; a light, well-balanced bitter with a subtle, dry, hoppy finish.

XB *(OG 1042, ABV 4.1%)*
Named after founder Lucy Blanche Holden, this is a sweeter, slightly fuller version of the Bitter. Sold in a number of outlets under different names.

Golden Glow *(OG 1045, ABV 4.4%)*
A pale golden beer, with a subtle hop aroma plus gentle sweetness and a light hoppiness.

Special Bitter *(OG 1052, ABV 5.1%)*
A sweet, malty, full-bodied amber ale with hops to balance in the taste and in the good, bitter-sweet finish.

HOLLAND

Holland Brewery, 5 Brown Flatts,
Brewery Street, Kimberley, Notts, NG16 2JU
Tel (0115) 938 2685
E-mail hollandbrew@btopenworld.com

Len Holland, a keen home-brewer for 30 years, went commercial in 2000, cheek-by-jowl with mighty Hardys & Hansons. He has a nine-gallon plant in his back yard. Seasonal beers: Holly Hop Gold (ABV 4.7%, Xmas), Dutch Courage (ABV 5%, winter), Glamour Puss (ABV 4.2%, spring).

Golden Blond *(OG 1040, ABV 4%)*

Lip Smacker *(OG 1040, ABV 4%)*

Cloghopper *(OG 1042, ABV 4.2%)*

Double Dutch *(OG 1045, ABV 4.5%)*

HOLT

Joseph Holt Group plc,
Derby Brewery, Empire Street,
Cheetham, Manchester, M3 1JD
Tel (0161) 834 3285
Fax (0161) 834 6458
Tours 10-11.15am Sat, £10 per person donation to Holt Radium Institute at the Christie Hospital. Groups of 12-15 only.

A family brewery established in 1849 by Joseph Holt, it celebrated 150 years in brewing in 1999. In recent years new equipment for the brewing process has been installed to cope with demand for the ever-expanding estate of pubs. Bitter is often delivered in 54-gallon hogsheads and the brewery hopes that one day there will be a demand for Mild in hogsheads, too. 127 pubs are owned, all serving cask-conditioned beer. Holts became a limited company in 1951 and was quoted on the Stock Exchange, but in 2000 the company applied to re-purchase all the shares and to become de-listed. This will make the company even more secure from takeovers, being family-run and truly independent once more. A new 30-barrel plant is being installed to produce small one-off brews to different recipes on an ad hoc basis.

Mild *(OG 1032, ABV 3.2%)*
A dark brown beer with a fruity, malty nose and taste. Strong in bitterness for a mild, with a dry, hoppy finish.

Bitter *(OG 1040, ABV 4%)*
A tawny beer with a good hop aroma. Although balanced by malt and fruit, the uncompromising bitterness can be a shock to the unwary.

HOME COUNTY

Home County Brewers,
The Old Brewery, Wickwar Trading Estate,
Station Road, Wickwar,
Gloucestershire, GL12 8NB

Tel/Fax (01454) 294045
No shop Polypins to order
Tours by arrangement

⊗ The brewery opened in 1997. Production was stopped in its tracks when the Wickwar railway tunnel suffered a flood that breached the nearby brewery in 2000. There was a complication with insurers and the brewery did not re-open until 2001. Home County now brews five barrels a week and anticipates expansion, once the trade lost has been made up. 24 outlets are supplied direct.

Golden Brown *(OG 1035, ABV 3.5%)* ◆
Gentle and clean-tasting ale. Golden brown in colour, this is a light malty ale with a very subtle aroma. Moderately bitter and slightly dry. Malty and dry finish.

Wichen *(OG 1042, ABV 4.2%)* ◆
Pale brown, this has a malty and fruity aroma with a little hop. Medium bodied, with a good, malty taste throughout, some hops and complex fruit, and a slightly dry, bitter finish.

Pit Orchard Pale *(OG 1045, ABV 4.5%)*

Old Tradition *(OG 1048, ABV 4.8%)* ◆
Malty throughout, but with balancing fruit and hops. Mid to full-bodied, brown in colour, and bitter-sweet. Predominantly malty aroma.

County Pride *(OG 1050, ABV 5%)* ◆
Pale and crystal malts and fruit aroma. Mid-brown and bitter-sweet tasting, with a slightly dry, malty aftertaste. Medium-bodied for its strength.

HOOK NORTON

Hook Norton Brewery Co Ltd,
Brewery Lane, Hook Norton, Banbury,
Oxon, OX15 5NY
Tel (01608) 737210
Visitor Centre (01608) 730784
Fax (01608) 730294
E-mail info@hooknorton-brewery.co.uk
Website www.hook-norton-brewery.co.uk
Shop in visitor centre (01608) 730384, with a small museum 10-4.30 Mon-Fri
Tours by arrangement

⊗ The Hook Norton Brewery can trace its origins back to 1849 when John Harris set up in business as a maltster. He soon started brewing and in 1872 built a small, three-storey brewery. In 1896 major building work started with new stables and offices, followed by the six-storey tower brewery still in use today. Much of the original brewing equipment is still in use, including a 25hp steam engine that provides nearly all the motive power. Hook Norton owns 42 pubs and supplies approximately 300 free trade accounts. All Hook Norton draught beers are cask conditioned and dry hopped. All the beers use water drawn from wells beneath the brewery, Maris Otter malt and English Challenger, Fuggles and Goldings hops. Seasonal beers: First Light (ABV 4.3%, May-June), Steam Ale (ABV 4.4%, Sept-Oct), Copper Ale (ABV 4.8%, March-April), Double Stout (ABV 4.8%, Jan-Feb), Haymaker (ABV 5%, July-Aug), Twelve Days (ABV 5.5%, Nov-Dec).

Best Mild *(OG 1032, ABV 3%)* ◆
A dark, red/brown mild with a malty aroma and a malty, sweetish taste, tinged with a faint hoppy balance. Malty in the aftertaste.

Best Bitter *(OG 1035, ABV 3.4%)* ◆
A fruity and hoppy aroma introduces this complex, well-crafted amber bitter. Moderate maltiness underpins the hops, leading to a long, bitter-sweet finish.

Generation *(OG 1041, ABV 4%)* ◆
A pale brown best bitter, predominantly hoppy but balanced with moderate malt and banana fruit. The fruit and malt decline to a relatively short, hoppy finish.

Old Hooky *(OG 1048, ABV 4.6%)* ◆
A well-balanced and full-bodied pale copper beer that is fruity with pale and crystal malt and hops on the aroma and taste. The hoppy character gives way to a sweet and fruity finish.

Double Stout *(OG 1050, ABV 4.8%)* ◆
This dry, dark red-brown stout has masses of roast malt flavour but not too much depth of character. The finish is dry and powdery.

HOP BACK

Hop Back Brewery plc,
Unit 22 Downton Business Centre,
Downton, Salisbury, Wilts, SP5 3HU
Tel (01725) 510986
Fax (01725) 513116
E-mail sales@hopback.co.uk
Website www.hopback.co.uk
Tours by arrangement

⊗ Started by John Gilbert in 1987 at the Wyndham Arms in Salisbury, the brewery has expanded steadily ever since. It went public via a Business Expansion Scheme support plan in 1993, and has enjoyed rapid continued growth. Summer Lightning has won many awards. The brewery has seven tied houses and also sells direct to 200 other outlets. Seasonal beers are produced on a monthly basis. Bottle-conditioned beers: Thunderstorm (ABV 5%), Summer Lightning (ABV 5%), Taiphoon (ABV 4.2%), Crop Circle (ABV 4.2%).

GFB/Gilbert's First Brew *(OG 1035, ABV 3.5%)* ◆
A golden beer, with the sort of light, clean quality that makes it an ideal session ale. A hoppy aroma and taste lead to a good, dry finish. Refreshing.

Best Bitter *(OG 1040, ABV 4%)*

Crop Circle *(OG 1041, ABV 4.2%)*

Entire Stout *(OG 1043, ABV 4.5%)* ◆
A rich, dark stout with a strong roasted malt flavour and a long, sweet and malty aftertaste. A beer suitable for vegans. Also produced with ginger.

Thunderstorm *(OG 1048, ABV 5%)* ◆
A softly bitter, easy-drinking wheat beer.

Summer Lightning *(OG 1049, ABV 5%)* ◆
A pleasurable pale bitter with a good, fresh, hoppy aroma and a malty, hoppy flavour. Finely balanced, it has an intense bitterness leading to a long, dry finish. Though strong, it tastes like a session ale.

HOPDAEMON

Hopdaemon Brewery Co,
18a-18b Canterbury Hill,
Tyler Hill, Canterbury,
Kent CT2 9LS
Tel (01227) 784962
E-mail hopdaemon@supanet.com

Tonie Prins, former brewer at Swale Brewery, opened a 12-barrel plant in 2001 and within six months was supplying more than 30 pubs in the area, as well as exclusive bottled-conditioned, own-label beers for the British Museum and Southwark Cathedral, named Beer and Pilgrim's Pleasure respectively, and for the Science Museum, Deep Blue, all 5% ABV. Seasonal beer: Leviathan (ABV 6%), winter. Bottle-conditioned beers: Skrimshander, Leviathan.

Golden Braid *(ABV 3.7%)*

Skrimshander IPA *(ABV 4.5%)*

Dominator *(ABV 5.1%)*

HOSKINS & OLDFIELD

Ceased brewing 2002. The beers will be contract brewed, range unknown. For further information contact Steve and Phil Hoskins on (0116) 262 3330.

HOUSTON

Houston Brewing Company,
South Street, Houston,
Renfrewshire, PA6 7EN
Tel (01505) 614528
Fax (01505) 614133
E-mail ale@houston-brewing.co.uk
Website www.houston-brewing.co.uk
Shop open all day, every day. Tours by arrangement

Brewing since 1997 from one of Renfrewshire CAMRA's favourite pub/restaurants, the Fox and Hounds, Houston has expanded rapidly and the beers are now available throughout Britain. Silver Medal winner, Champion Beer of Scotland 2000 and 2001, and Bronze Medal winner, Best Bitter category, Champion Beer of Britain 2000, for Peter's Well, which is now available in bottle but not bottle-conditioned. Seasonal beers: Champion (ABV 4%, summer), Formakin (ABV 4.3%, spring), Jock Frost (ABV 4.5%, winter), Texas (ABV 4.5%, autumn).

Killellan *(OG 1037, ABV 3.7%)*
Light session ale, with a floral hop and fruity taste. The finish of this amber beer is dry and quenching.

Barochan
(OG 1041, ABV 4.1%)
A red, malty beer, in which fruit is balanced by roast and hop overtones; dry, bitter-sweet finish.

Peter's Well
(OG 1042, ABV 4.2%)
Well-balanced fruity taste with sweet hop, leading to an increasingly bitter-sweet finish.

Teuchter
(OG 1048, ABV 4.8%)
Strong, dark, porter style ale full of body and character.

SARAH HUGHES

Sarah Hughes Brewery,
Beacon Hotel, 129 Bilston Street,
Sedgley, W Midlands, DY3 1JE
Tel (01902) 883380
Tours by prior arrangement

Opened originally in the 1860s behind the Beacon Hotel, Sarah Hughes bought the brewery in 1921 and started to brew the beer now called Dark Ruby. After lying idle for 30 years, the brewery was re-opened in 1987 by John Hughes, who continued the tradition and recipe of his grandmother. One pub is owned and more than 100 outlets are supplied direct. The beers are now exported to the United States. Seasonal beer: Snow Flake (ABV 8%). Bottle-conditioned beer: Dark Ruby (ABV 6%).

Pale Amber *(OG 1038, ABV 4%)*
A well-balanced beer, initially slightly sweet but with hops close behind.

Sedgley Surprise *(OG 1048, ABV 5%)*
A bitter-sweet, medium-bodied, hoppy ale with some malt.

Dark Ruby *(OG 1058, ABV 6%)*
A dark ruby strong ale with a good balance of fruit and hops, leading to a pleasant, lingering hops and malt finish.

HUMPTY DUMPTY

Humpty Dumpty Brewery, Church Road,
Reedham, Norfolk, NR13 3TZ
Tel (01493) 701818.
Fax (01493) 700727
E-mail mick@humptydumptybrewery.com
Shop 9-6 daily
Tours by arrangement

Humpty Dumpty Brewery was opened in 1998 by Mick Cottrell and it moved to its present site in 2001. Brewing capacity expanded from five to 11 barrels and the brewery is currently producing 25 to 35 barrels a week. The brewery shop sells a wide range of bottle-conditioned beers (their own and other breweries), and home-brew kits, plus a full off-licence. There are plans to develop other buildings on site for retail, and Mick is actively looking for a free house to buy. He sells to the Railway Tavern in Reedham and some 150 pubs nationwide. There is a full range of bottle-conditioned ales.

Nord Atlantic *(ABV 3.7%)*
Tawny coloured with light fruity airs, giving little hint of the heavily-hopped bitterness that leaves little room for other flavours. A lingering finish with little appreciable diminishing of bitterness.

Little Sharpie *(ABV 3.8%)*
A delicate hoppy aroma is a forerunner to a sweet hoppy, lagerish flavour. A clean golden yellow bitter with a finish in which bitterness grows.

Ferryman *(ABV 3.8%)*

Four Spot Chaser *(ABV 3.9%)*

Swallow Tail *(ABV 4%)*

Lemon and Ginger *(ABV 4%)*

Tender Behind *(ABV 4%)*

Swingbridge Ale *(ABV 4%)*

Humpty Dumpty *(ABV 4.1%)* ◆
A complex mix of delicate flavours. A malty fruitiness gives balance to the dry, hoppy bitterness. A light fruity nose and an amber colour generate a feeling of smooth bitterness with hoppy overtones.

'Ops on Train *(ABV 4.1%)*

Reed Cutter *(ABV 4.2%)*

Claud Hamilton *(ABV 4.3%)* ◆
With its dark brown colouration, this old-style oyster stout is a stirring mix of roast fruity sweetness. The bitter-sweet finish draws out a hint of caramelised toffee.

Brief Encounter *(ABV 4.3%)*

Iron Duke *(ABV 4.6%)*

Butt Jumper *(ABV 4.8%)* ◆
Toffee and malt dominate the aroma of this tawny-hued ale. Full-flavoured, with malt vying with a fruity bitterness for dominance. Long, lingering finish does not fade as a nutty bitterness becomes prevalent.

Spark Arrester *(ABV 4.8%)*

Railway Sleeper *(ABV 5%)* ◆
Hops with a citrus hint introduce this mid-brown strong bitter. This blend continues through the first taste, and although a bitter-sweet influence grows, later the strong hop character dominates a short ending.

Peto's Porter *(ABV 6%)*

Broadland Gold *(ABV 6%)* ◆
Easy-drinking and smooth, this old ale introduces itself with a well-rounded, fruity aroma. This is followed by a deep hoppy introduction with a bitter vine, fruity edge. A well-defined finish with lots of malt.

HYDES

Hydes' Brewery Ltd,
46 Moss Lane West,
Manchester, M15 5PH
Tel (0161) 226 1317
Fax (0161) 227 9593
E-mail pauljefferies@hydesbrewery.com
Website www.hydesbrewery.com
Tours by arrangement

◎ In the past five years, management changes have revitalised the brewery's fortunes, with major investments in the brewery and its tied estate. Over this period cask beer output has more than doubled due to the introduction of Hydes bi-monthly craft ales programme, contract brewing Whitbread Trophy for Interbrew, and a major expansion in the number of free trade accounts. There has also been substantial investment in Hydes' tied estate, with the acquisition of new pubs and the refurbishment of existing pubs. A third of a million pounds was spent on the brewery to increase capacity to keep up with demand. This investment will allow the barrelage to increase from 40,000 barrels to 60,000 barrels a year. Currently Hydes has 68 tied houses (32 tenanted, 36 managed) and is actively seeking to acquire more pubs. Hydes supplies cask ale to all but two of its outlets and it has more than 100 free trade accounts. Hydes is one of the few breweries to still brew three milds. The craft ale programme will feature beers brewed from a single hop variety and will be marketed under the 'Pick of the Hop' banner with the name indicative of the variety of hop used. Seasonal beers: Bramling Cross (ABV 4.8%, Jan-Feb), Styrian Spring (ABV 4.2%, March-April), Red Admiral (ABV 4.4%, May-June), Summer Challenger (ABV 4%, July-Aug), Autumn Goldings (ABV 4.5%, Sept-Oct), Winter Fuggle (ABV 5%, Nov-Dec).

Light Mild *(OG 1033.5, ABV 3.5%)* ◆
A lightly-hopped, amber-coloured session beer with a fresh, fruity taste and a brief but dry finish.

Traditional Mild *(OG 1033.5, ABV 3.5%)* ◆
A mid-brown beer with malt and citrus fruit in the aroma and taste. Short dry aftertaste.

Dark Mild *(OG 1033.5, ABV 3.5%)* ◆
Dark brown/red in colour with a fruit and roast malt nose. Complex taste, including berry fruits, malt and a hint of chocolate. Satisfying aftertaste.

Traditional Bitter
(OG 1036.5, ABV 3.8%) ◆
Amber beer with a fruity nose, citrus fruit and hops in the taste, and a good bitterness through into the finish.

Trophy Bitter *(OG 1036, ABV 3.8%)*
Now brewed for Interbrew, this is a beer with a mellow balance of hop, malt and grain flavours with a malty and light, floral hop aroma. Dry hop finish.

Jekyll's Gold Premium Ale
(OG 1042, ABV 4.3%) ◆
Pale gold in colour, with a fruity, hoppy nose. A well-balanced beer with hops, fruit and malt all in evidence, and a dry, hoppy finish.

ICENI

Iceni Brewery, 3 Foulden Road,
Ickburgh, Mundford,
Thetford, Norfolk, IP26 5BJ
Tel (01842) 878922
Fax (01842) 879216
E-mail icenibrewe@aol.com
Shop 830-230, Mon-Sat
Tours by arrangement

⊠ Brendan Moore started the Iceni Brewery in 1995 after having a dream about owning a brewery. Seven years on, it now has its own hop garden and barley plot aimed at amusing the many visitors that now flock to the brewery shop to buy the 28 different ales, stout and lagers bottled on-site. Beer as a gift is an increasingly important trend at Iceni. 35 outlets are supplied direct. Special beers are brewed for festivals. All cask ales are bottle-conditioned. Deirdre of the Sorrows (ABV 4.4%) is suitable for vegetarians/vegans.

Thetford Forest Mild
(OG 1036, ABV 3.6%)

Fine Soft Day *(OG 1038, ABV 4%)* ◆
Full-bodied and hoppy amber ale with a lingering aftertaste of hops and malt.

Celtic Queen *(OG 1038, ABV 4%)*
A light summer ale, packed with flavour.

Fen Tiger *(OG 1040, ABV 4.2%)*

It's a Grand Day *(OG 1040, ABV 4.5%)*

Gold *(OG 1045, ABV 5%)*
A strong ale, sun gold in colour. Crisp taste; smooth and deceptive for its strength.

LAD Lager *(OG 1046, ABV 5%)*

Raspberry Wheat *(OG 1046, ABV 5%)*

Men of Norfolk *(OG 1062, ABV 6.2%)*

INVERALMOND

Inveralmond Brewery Ltd,
1 Inveralmond Way, Perth, PH1 3UQ
Tel/Fax (01738) 449448
E-mail info@inveralmond-brewery.co.uk
Website www.inveralmond-brewery.co.uk
Shop 9-5

Established in April 1997, the Inveralmond Brewery is the first brewery in Perth for more than 30 years. The brewery has gone from strength to strength since opening with a string of awards, culminating in winning Champion Beer of Scotland in November 2001 with Ossian's Ale. Around 150 outlets are supplied direct, with wholesalers supplying beers nationwide. Ossian's Ale and Lia Fail are now also available in bottle (not bottle conditioned). Seasonal ales: Inkie Pinkie (ABV 3.7%), Amber Bead (ABV 4.1%), Pint Stowp (ABV 4.2%), Pundie (ABV 5%).

Independence *(OG 1040, ABV 3.8%)*
Well-balanced Scottish ale with fruit and malt tones. Hop provides an increasing bitterness in the finish.

Ossian's Ale *(OG 1042, ABV 4.1%)*
Well-balanced, moreish best bitter with a dry finish. This full-bodied amber ale is dominated by fruit and hop with a bitter-sweet character. Champion Beer of Scotland 2001.

Thrappledouser *(OG 1043, ABV 4.3%)*
A refreshing amber beer with reddish hues. The crisp, hoppy aroma is finely balanced with the tangy but quenching taste.

Lia Fail *(OG 1048, ABV 4.7%)*
The name is the Gaelic title for the Stone of Destiny. A dark, robust, full-bodied beer with a deep malty taste. Smooth texture and balanced finish.

ISLE OF SKYE

Isle of Skye Brewing Company
(Leann an Eilein), The Pier, Uig,
Isle of Skye, IV51 9XY
Tel (01470) 542477
Fax (01470) 542488
E-mail info@skyebrewery.co.uk
Website www.skyebrewery.co.uk
Shop 10-6 Mon-Sat; 12-5 Sun Apr-Oct
Tours by arrangement

Established in 1995, Isle of Skye's trade continues to expand steadily, both directly and via wholesalers, to cover most of mainland Britain. The island now has 11 hotels serving cask ale from the brewery and many others stock the bottled range. The company serves 60 outlets direct.

Young Pretender *(OG 1039, ABV 4%)*
Golden amber ale with hop and fruit on the nose. The bitter taste is dominated by fruit and hop, the latter lingering into the dry, bitter finish.

Red Cuillin *(OG 1041, ABV 4.2%)*
A burst of fruit with malt and hop notes introduce this tawny reddish beer. These characteristics continue into the wonderful bitter-sweet taste. A very dry and bitter finish.

Hebridean Gold
(OG 1041.5, ABV 4.3%)
A superb golden-coloured beer that is brewed using oats. Hops and fruit dominate the bitter taste and increasingly dry, citrus finish.

Black Cuillin *(OG 1044, ABV 4.5%)*
A dark, reddish-brown old ale with a predominately malty taste persisting into a slightly astringent finish. Summer fruits and roast can also be detected in this rather complex beer.

Blaven *(OG 1047, ABV 5%)*
An amber-coloured, sweetish beer with a rich mango fruit aroma. There is plenty of fruit and malt in the taste with some bitterness in the long, dry finish.

ITCHEN VALLEY

Itchen Valley Brewery Ltd,
Unit 4, Shelf House, New Farm Road,
Alresford, Hampshire, SO24 9QE
Tel (01962) 735111
Fax (01962) 735678
Website www.itchenvalley.com
Shop 9-5 Mon-Fri.
Tours by arrangement

The brewery, founded in 1997, enjoyed immediate success by winning the bronze medal award for its Godfathers beer at the 1998 Great British Beer Festival, Olympia. This set a precedent for winning awards that continues today. Over the past few years, the brewery has expanded and its enlarged range of beers is now sold in more than 150 pubs across Hampshire, Surrey, Sussex and Berkshire. The brewery also offers bottle-conditioned ales, not only in supermarkets and independent off-licences but also direct to the public online and at farmers' markets and agricultural shows. There is an extensive seasonal programme featuring at least 15 different cask ales each year, including Hambledon Bitter (ABV 4%), brewed with elderflower and honey extract.

Godfathers *(OG 1039, ABV 3.8%)*
Brewed from a secret recipe using a unique combination of four hops. A crisp

distinctive quaffing ale with a bitter-sweet edge. Full in flavour, golden in colour with a unique hoppiness.

Fagin's *(OG 1042, ABV 4.1%)*
Brewed from a traditional recipe using a combination of three hops. A light brown, well-balanced beer with fine malts, dry citrus flavours and well hopped.

Wykehams Glory *(OG 1043, ABV 4.3%)*
Nut brown in appearance, malty flavour, with a hoppy nose.

Pure Gold *(OG 1048, ABV 4.8%)*
A light golden, refreshing beer, with a unique, deliciously hoppy nose.

JENNINGS

Jennings Bros PLC, Castle Brewery, Cockermouth, Cumbria, CA13 9NE
Tel (01900) 823214 Fax (01900) 827462
E-mail tour@jenningsbrewery.co.uk
Website www.jenningsbrewery.co.uk
Shop 9-5 Mon-Fri, 10-4 Sat, 10-5 Sun (July & Aug)
Tours by arrangement

Founded in 1828, Jennings moved to its present idyllic site by the River Derwent and at the foot of Cockermouth Castle in 1874, where it still uses its own well water. Although there is no longer any family involvement, many of the company's shares are owned by local people. Around 200 free trade outlets are supplied direct with many more via a network of wholesalers throughout the country. A £1 million investment programme, launched in 1999 to upgrade the brewery and increase output, was completed in the summer of 2002. Real ale is available in most of Jenning's 165 tied houses, which has expanded outside Cumbria into the North-east and Lancashire. The company is committed to an integrated pub and brewery business, and has converted managed houses back to tenancies. Seasonal beers: John Jennings No 1 (ABV 4.3%, spring), Crag Rat (ABV 4.3%, summer), Cross Buttock (ABV 4.5%, autumn), La'al Cockle Warmer (ABV 6.5%, winter).

Dark Mild *(OG 1031, ABV 3.1%)*
A well-balanced dark brown mild with a malty aroma, strong roast taste, not over-sweet, with some hops and a slightly bitter finish.

Bitter *(OG 1035, ABV 3.5%)*
A mid-brown bitter with pronounced malt and roast flavours and aftertaste. Some hoppiness and a rising bitter, dry finish. Good mouth-feel.

Cumberland Ale *(OG 1040, ABV 4%)*
A creamy amber-gold malty ale with hop resin and fruity notes; rising bitterness balances well.

Cocker Hoop *(OG 1047, ABV 4.6%)*
A rich, creamy, copper-coloured beer with raisiny maltiness balanced with a resiny hoppiness, with a developing bitterness towards the end.

Sneck Lifter *(OG 1055, ABV 5.1%)*
A strong, dark brown ale with a complex balance of fruit, malt and full roast flavours right through to the finish.

JERSEY

Ann Street Brewery Co Ltd, t/a Jersey Brewery, 57 Ann Street, St Helier, Jersey, JE1 1BZ
Tel (01534) 731561 Fax (01534) 767033
Tours by arrangement

Jersey, better known as Ann Street, phased out cask ale after a brief flirtation in the 1980s and '90s. It has 50 tied houses, of which 12 take real ale, including beers from its sister company, Guernsey Brewery. Jersey Brewery also has an interest in the Tipsy Toad brew-pub (qv).

JOHN O'GAUNT

John O'Gaunt Brewing Co Ltd, 1 Chapel Close, Melton Mowbray, Leicestershire, LE14 3HW
Tel/Fax (01664) 820103
E-mail jogbrewery@aol.com
Tours Not yet, but soon

The brewery was set up by Celia Frew (nee Atton) in 1997 next to the Stag and Hounds at Borough on the Hill, and moved in 1998 to share the equipment of the Parish Brewery. Celia took over the Old Brewery Inn in 1998, first as manager then as licensee until 2000. She then bought her own pub, the Fox Inn at Thorpe Satchville, which is now leased out. One pub sells the John O'Gaunt Ales. She has now bought her own brewing plant, which will be set up and available for visits during the lifetime of this edition of the Guide.

Robin a Tiptoe *(OG 1043, ABV 3.9%)*

Cropped Oak *(OG 1047, ABV 4.4%)*

Coat O' Red *(OG 1052, ABV 5%)*

JOLLYBOAT

Jollyboat Brewery (Bideford) Ltd, The Coach House, Buttgarden Street, Bideford, Devon, EX39 2AU
Tel (01237) 424343
Tours by arrangement

The brewery, named after sailors' leave boats, was established in 1995 by Hugh Parry and his son Simon. The brewery went into receivership in 2000 but brewing didn't stop, and the new company is now in the sole hands of Hugh. It is now expanding, with new beers added. It currently supplies some 204 outlets. Seasonal beer: Contraband (ABV 5.8%, Nov-March). Bottle-conditioned beers: Privateer (ABV 4.8%). Contraband (ABV 5.8%) and Plunder (ABV 4.8%) will be added.

Buccaneers *(OG 1036, ABV 3.7%)*
A pale brown summer bitter with a pleasant presence of hops and bitterness from the nose through to the aftertaste.

Freebooter *(OG 1040, ABV 4%)*

Mainbrace *(OG 1041, ABV 4.2%)* ◆
Pale brown brew with a rich fruity aroma and a bitter taste and aftertaste.

Privateer *(OG 1046/48, ABV 4.8%)*

Plunder *(OG 1046/48, ABV 4.8%)* ◆
A good balance of malt, hops and fruit are present on the aroma and palate of this red/brown beer with a bitter finish. Winner of Best in Class at the 2001 Maltings Festival, Newton Abbot.

Contraband *(OG 1054/56, ABV 5.8%)*

JUWARDS

See Blackdown

KELBURN*

Kelburn Brewing Company Ltd, 10 Muriel Lane, Barrhead, Glasgow, G78 1QB
Tours by arrangement

Kelburn started brewing in February 2002. It is run by father and son, Derek and Ross Moore. Two further beers were planned for late 2002. The brewery is situated a few minutes from Barrhead Station.

Goldihops *(ABV 3.8%)*

Red Smiddy *(ABV 4.1%)*

KELHAM ISLAND

Kelham Island Brewery Ltd, 23 Alma Street, Sheffield, South Yorkshire, S3 8SA
Tel (0114) 249 4804
Fax (0114) 249 4803
E-mail sales@kelhambrewery.co.uk
Website www.kelhambrewery.co.uk
Tours by arrangement

Kelham Island Brewery was purpose built in 1990 on land adjoining the Fat Cat pub in Alma Street. The area is known as Kelham Island as the land is on an island formed by a mill race, leaving then running back into the River Don. The brewing equipment was purchased from the Oxford Brewery and Bakehouse, and allowed for full mash brewing of approximately 20 barrels a week. Kelham Island was the first new independent brewery in Sheffield in the last century. Due to its success in its early years the brewery has now moved into new, purpose built premises at Kelham Island, with five times the capacity of the original premises. 150 outlets are supplied direct. Seasonal beers: Wheat Beer (ABV 5%, summer), Bete Noire (ABV 5.5%, winter), Grand Pale (ABV 6.6%, winter).

Devonshire Cat Bitter
(OG 1038, ABV 3.8%)

Best Bitter *(OG 1038.8, ABV 3.8%)* ◆
A clean, characterful, crisp, pale brown beer. The nose and palate are dominated by refreshing hoppiness and fruitiness, which, with a good bitter dryness, lasts in the aftertaste.

Easy Rider *(OG 1043, ABV 4.3%)* ◆
A pale, straw-coloured beer with a sweetish flavour and delicate hints of citrus fruits. A beer with hints of flavour rather than full-bodied.

Fat Cat Bitter *(OG 1044, ABV 4.4%)*

Pride of Sheffield
(OG 1045, ABV 4.5%)
A full-flavoured, amber-coloured, premium strength bitter.

Pale Rider *(OG 1052, ABV 5.2%)* ◆
A full-bodied, straw pale ale, with a good fruity aroma and a strong fruit and hop taste. Its well-balanced sweetness and bitterness continue in the finish.

Bete Noire *(OG 1055, ABV 5.5%)*

KELTEK

Keltek Brewery, Unit 3A, Restormel Industrial Estate, Liddicoat Road, Lostwithiel, Cornwall, PL22 0HG
Tel/Fax (01208) 871199
Tours by arrangement

Keltek Brewery moved to Lostwithiel in 1999 and started brewing again in March of that year. Monthly specials and house beers for pubs are brewed. 50 outlets in Cornwall and North Devon are supplied direct. Seasonal/occasional beers: Olde Smugglers Ale (ABV 4.2%, September), Olde Pirates Ale (ABV 4.8%, March). Bottle-conditioned beers: King (ABV 5.1%), Revenge (ABV 7%).

4K Mild *(OG 1038, ABV 3.8%)*
Dark and fruity.

Golden Lance *(OG 1038, ABV 3.8%)*
Light golden, refreshing brew.

Magik *(OG 1042, ABV 4.2%)*
Good balance of malt and hops. Tawny red in colour.

King *(OG 1051, ABV 5.1%)*
A light brown beer with a bitter taste, then a sweetness through the middle.

Revenge *(OG 1066, ABV 7%)*
Dark ruby in colour; sweetish with a bitter edge.

KEMPTOWN

Kemptown Brewery Co Ltd, 33 Upper St James's Street, Brighton, E Sussex, BN2 1JN
Tel (01273) 699595
Fax (01273) 696483
E-mail kemptownbrewery@btinternet.com
Website www.kemptownbrewery.com
Tours by arrangement

A brewery established in 1989 and built in the tower tradition behind the Hand in Hand, which is possibly the smallest pub in England with its own brewery. It takes its name and logo from the former Charrington's Kemptown Brewery 500 yards away, which closed in 1964. Six free trade outlets are supplied.

Black Moggy Mild *(ABV 3.6%)*

Brighton Bitter *(ABV 3.6%)* ◆
A refreshing, dry beer, with malt and hops in the flavour and a dry, hoppy finish.

Ye Old Trout Ale *(OG 1045, ABV 4.5%)*

Kemptown *(ABV 4%)*

SID/Staggering in the Dark *(ABV 5.2%)* ◆
A dark, almost black beer with a vinous nose and a complex flavour, with roast and bitterness giving way to a dry finish.

Old Grumpy *(ABV 6.2%)*

KING

W J King & Co (Brewers), 3-5 Jubilee Estate, Foundry Lane, Horsham, W Sussex, RH13 5UE
Tel (01403) 272102
Fax (01403) 754455
E-mail sales@kingfamilybrewers.co.uk
Website www.kingfamilybrewers.co.uk
Tours by prior arrangement

⊗ Brewing started in mid-2001 using former Firkin brand pub equipment. King, run by former King & Barnes managing director Bill King, has developed two main beers similar in style to the old K&B Sussex Bitter and Festive but deliberately different in flavour. After six months, he was brewing to capacity of 20 barrels a week. A new fermenter has increased capacity by 25 per cent. Bill should have a tied house by 2003 and he will introduce a bottle-conditioned version of Red River Ale by putting in a small bottling line. His long-term plan is to build an estate of five or six pubs by 2006. Seasonal beer: Merry Ale (ABV 6.5%, Nov-Dec).

Horsham Best Bitter *(OG 1038, ABV 3.8%)*

Red River Ale *(OG 1048, ABV 4.8%)* ◆
Tawny red with a fruity malt aroma balanced by faint hops. Malty sweet and fruity taste with a little hoppy bitterness. Dry, bitter aftertaste.

KINGS HEAD

Kings Head Brewing Co, Kings Head, 132 High Street, Bildeston, Ipswich, Suffolk, IP7 7ED
Tel/Fax (01449) 741434
E-mail enquiries@bildestonkingshead.co.uk
Website www.bildestonkingshead.co.uk

⊗ Kings Head has been brewing since 1996, originally as Brettvale Brewing Co. A five-barrel plant is based in an old stable block behind the pub. Brewing takes places two or three times a week and six other outlets are supplied direct. Seasonal beers: Crowdie (ABV 5%, winter). Bottle-conditioned beers: Blondie, Apache, Crowdie and Dark Vader (same strengths as cask versions).

Not Strong Beer (NSB)
(OG 1030, ABV 2.5%)

Best Bitter *(OG 1040, ABV 3.8%)*

Blondie *(OG 1041, ABV 4%)*

Apache *(OG 1046, ABV 4.5%)*

Billy *(OG 1050, ABV 4.8%)*

Dark Vader *(OG 1055, ABV 5.4%)*
Champion beer Ipswich Beer Festival 1999. Best in class Ipswich Beer Festival 2000.

LANGTON

🍺 The Langton Brewery, Bell Inn, Main Street, East Langton, Market Harborough, Leicestershire, LE16 7TW
Tel (01858) 545278
Fax (01858) 545748
Website www.thebellinn.co.uk
Tours by arrangement

⊛ Langton is run by two partners, Alistair Chapman and Derek Hewitt, publican and customer respectively of the Bell Inn. Derek is a retired banker who brought his business experience to underscore Alistair's knowledge of the pub trade. They installed a 2.5-barrel brewing plant in outbuildings of the 17th century Bell. They now brew 90 gallons a time of Caudle Bitter (named after the range of local hills) and Bowler, which celebrates the Bell Inn's long association with Langton Cricket Club, whose ground is opposite the inn. Boxer Heavyweight is named after Jack Gardner, British Heavyweight champion, who was resident in the village. The brewery owns one pub and supplies eight outlets.The beers are available for take-away in nine-gallon casks or 10-litre polypins. Seasonal beers are produced and various occasional beers are available throughout the year.

Caudle Bitter *(OG 1039, ABV 3.9%)*
A session bitter, close to a pale ale in style.

Bowler Strong Ale
(OG 1048, ABV 4.8%)
A strong traditional ale with a deep red colour and a hoppy nose.

Boxer Heavyweight
(OG 1055, ABV 5.2%)
A dark, well-hopped winter warmer.

LARKINS

Larkins Brewery Ltd, Larkins Farm, Chiddingstone, Edenbridge, Kent, TN8 7BB
Tel (01892) 870328
Fax (01892) 871141
Tours by arrangement Nov-Feb

⊗ Larkins Brewery was founded in 1986 by the Dockerty family, farmers and hop growers, who bought the Royal Tunbridge Wells Brewery. The company moved to Larkins Farm in 1987. Since then production of three regular brews and a Porter in the winter months have steadily increased. Brews are made using only Kentish hops, yeast and malt; no sugars or brewing adjuncts are added to the beers. Larkins owns one pub, the Rock at Chiddingstone Heath, and supplies around 70 free houses within a radius of 20 miles.

Traditional Ale *(OG 1035, ABV 3.4%)*
Tawny in colour, a full-tasting hoppy ale with plenty of character for its strength.

Chiddingstone *(OG 1040, ABV 4%)*
Named after the village where the brewery is based, Chiddingstone is a mid-strength, hoppy/fruity ale with a long, bitter-sweet aftertaste.

Best *(OG 1045, ABV 4.4%)*
Full-bodied, slightly fruity and unusually bitter for its gravity.

Porter *(OG 1052, ABV 5.2%)*
Each taste and smell of this potent black winter beer (Nov-April) reveals another facet of its character. An explosion of roasted malt, bitter and fruity flavours leaves a bitter-sweet aftertaste.

LEADMILL

Leadmill Brewery, Park Hall, Park Hall Road, Denby, Ripley, Derbyshire, DE5 0PS
Tel (01332) 883577
or (07971) 189915 (m)
Tours started in 2002

The brewery has moved from Selston, Notts to Denby, Derbyshire, and is housed in an old mill building, dating back to the 1800s. Future plans include using local well water, buying a pub, and seeking to expand further.

Wild Weasel *(OG 1038, ABV 3.9%)*

Arc-Light *(OG 1041, ABV 4.2%)*

Rolling Thunder *(OG 1044, ABV 4.5%)*

Saigon *(OG 1044, ABV 4.5%)*

Linebacker *(OG 1045, ABV 4.6%)*

Festival Stout *(OG 1046, ABV 4.5%)*

Red River *(OG 1047, ABV 4.8%)*

Agent Orange *(OG 1047, ABV 4.9%)*

Sidewinder *(OG 1047, ABV 5%)*

Niagara *(OG 1048, ABV 5%)*

Firebird *(OG 1048, ABV 5%)*

Rampage *(OG 1049, ABV 5.1%)*

Apocalypse Now *(OG 1050, ABV 5.2%)*

Park Hall Porter *(OG 1058, ABV 6%)*

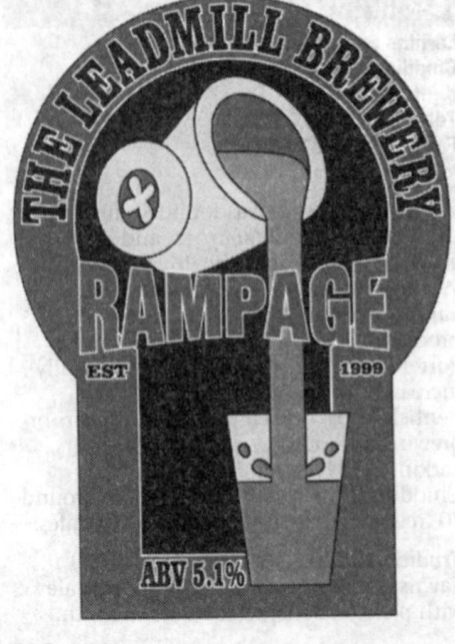

LEATHERBRITCHES

Leatherbritches Brewery, Bentley Brook, Fenny Bentley, Ashbourne, Derbyshire, DE6 1LF
Tel (01335) 350278
Fax (01335) 350422
E-mail all@bentleybrookinn.co.uk
Website www.bentleybrookinn.co.uk

Leatherbritches Brewery is part of the Bentley Brook Inn, just north of Ashbourne. Inn and brewery are owned by David and Jeanne Allingham, with their son Edward as general manager, and David Corby as head brewer. Both cask-conditioned and bottle-conditioned beers are brewed. Hairy Helmet was Beer of the Festival at Derby 2001 event. Production averages 10 barrels a week and supplies approximately 40 selected real ale specialist pubs in the Midlands and North West. Bottle-conditioned beer: Bespoke (ABV 5%), Ale Conners Porter (ABV 5.4%).

Goldings *(OG 1036, ABV 3.6%)*
A light hoppy session beer with a fruity finish.

Ashbourne Ale *(OG 1040, ABV 4%)*
Bitter with fruity hints from fresh Goldings hops with a crisp lasting taste.

Belter *(OG 1040, ABV 4.4%)*
Maris Otter malt produces a pale but interesting beer.

Hairy Helmet *(OG 1047, ABV 4.7%)*

Bespoke *(OG 1050, ABV 5%)*
Mid-brown in colour, with a well-balanced sweet finish. Full bodied.

LEES

J W Lees & Co (Brewers) Ltd, Greengate Brewery, Middleton Junction, Manchester, M24 2AX
Tel (0161) 643 2487
Fax (0161) 655 3731
Website www.jwlees.co.uk
Tours by arrangement

Family-owned brewery founded in 1828 by John Lees, operated by the sixth generation of the family. Still brewing in the 1876 brewhouse designed and built by John Willie Lees, the grandson of the founder. All 170 pubs (most in north Manchester) serve cask beer. The range of Lees Bitter and GB Mild is supplemented by six seasonal ales every year. Seasonal beers: Archer Stout (March-April), Fudger Ale (May-June), Scorcher (July-Aug), Sloeberry Ale (Sept-Oct), MM (Nov-Dec).

GB Mild *(OG 1032, ABV 3.5%)*
Malty and fruity in aroma. The same flavours are found in the taste, but do not dominate in a beer with a rounded and smooth character. Dry, malty aftertaste.

Bitter *(OG 1037, ABV 4%)*
An amber beer with a malty and citrus fruit aroma. Distinctive, malty, dry and slightly metallic taste. Clean, dry Lees finish.

Moonraker *(OG 1073, ABV 7.5%)*
A reddish-brown beer with a strong, malty, fruity aroma. The flavour is rich and sweet, with roast malt, and the finish is fruity yet dry. Available only in a handful of outlets.

LEITH HILL

Leith Hill Brewery,
The Plough Inn & Leith Hill Brewery,
Coldharbour Lane, Coldharbour,
nr Dorking, Surrey, RH5 6HD
Tel (01306) 711793 Fax (01306) 710055
E-mail theploughinn@btinternet.com
Website www.ploughinn.com
Tours by arrangement

Leith Hill started in the summer of 1996 to supply the Plough Inn. Formerly using home-made equipment, a new 2.5-barrel ex-micro brewery plant was installed in 2001 in another part of the pub to halve brewing times and improve consistency.

Crooked Furrow *(OG 1040, ABV 4%)*
Sharp, tangy bitter with strong malt and citrus hop flavours. Long, hoppy bitter aftertaste.

Tallywhacker *(OG 1056, ABV 5.6%)*
Medium to full-bodied, dark brown old ale. Fruity, malty aroma leads to a fruity sweet taste, balanced by roast. Sweet malty finish with some astringency.

LEYDEN

Leyden Brewery, (Lord Raglan),
Nangreaves, Bury, Lancs, BL9 6SP
Tel (0161) 764 6680
Tours by arrangement
E-mail leydenbrewery@tinyworld.co.uk
Website leydenbrewery.com
Tours by arrangement

A brewery built by Brian Farnworth that started production in 1999. Additional fermenting vessels have been installed, allowing a maximum production of 12 barrels a week. One pub is owned. There are plans to bottle Raglan Sleeve.

Nanny Flyer *(OG 1040, ABV 3.8%)*
A drinkable session bitter with an initial dryness, a hint of citrus, followed by a strong, malty finish.

Black Pudding *(OG 1040, ABV 3.9%)*
A dark brown, creamy mild with a malty flavour, followed by a faint, balanced finish.

Light Brigade *(OG 1043, ABV 4.2%)*
Copper in colour with a citrus aroma. The flavour is a balance of malt, hops and fruit, with a bitter finish.

Raglan Sleeve *(OG 1047, ABV 4.6%)*
Dark red/brown beer with a hoppy aroma and a dry, roasty, hoppy taste and finish.

Heavy Brigade *(OG 1048, ABV 4.7%)*
A traditional strong bitter beer, pale colour, with malt and a touch of bitterness coming through in the finish.

Crowning Glory *(OG 1069, ABV 6.8%)*
A surprisingly smooth-tasting beer for its strength, ideal for cold winter nights.

LIDSTONES

Lidstones Brewery,
Coltsfoot Green, Wickhambrook,
Newmarket, Suffolk, CB8 8UW
Tel (01440) 820232: brewery;
Fax/pub (01223) 319414
E-mail Lidstones.brewery@btopenworld.com
Tours by arrangement

Lidstones was founded by Peter Fairhall in 1998. His sister, Jane, joined the business in 1999 to run sales and administration. In 2000 they took over the Kingston Arms in Cambridge, which was awarded Pub of the Year status in 2001 by Cambridge & District CAMRA. Plans to install a brewery at the pub are now in progress, as is a bottling plant at the existing site. Seasonal beers: Various flavoured (ginger, orange, berry & spiced) wheat beers (ABV 4.2%), Old Ale (ABV 6%, winter).

Rowley Mild *(ABV 3.2%)*
Chocolate and toffee aromas lead into what, for its strength, is an impressively rich and flavoursome ale. The finish is pleasantly bitter-sweet.

Session Bitter *(ABV 3.7%)*
Intensely aromatic, straw-coloured ale offering a superb balance of malt and hops on the tongue; an ideal session beer by any standards.

Liberty Golden Ale *(ABV 4.1%)*
Golden in colour, hoppy in taste, brewed with Liberty hops.

Lucky Punter *(ABV 4.3%)*
Golden ale with a hint of banana on the nose. The taste is clean, crisp and moreishly hoppy, with grapefruit flavours also present.

Suffolk Draught *(ABV 4.3%)*
A straw-coloured bitter with great depth of character with a strong fruit and hop aroma.

Colquhoun's Dark Mischief Stout *(ABV 4.4%)*
Less full-bodied than many stouts, this has a dry, burnt roast and coffee flavour, and a long, bitter follow-through.

Bookies Revenge *(ABV 4.6%)*
A hoppy bitter.

Rawalpindi IPA *(ABV 5%)*
Citrus flavours dominate both aroma and taste in this pale, smooth, refreshing beer; the aftertaste is quite dry.

LINFIT

Linfit Brewery, Sair Inn,
139 Lane Top, Linthwaite,
Huddersfield, W Yorkshire, HD7 5SG
Tel (01484) 842370
Tours by arrangement

A 19th-century brew-pub that started brewing again in 1982, producing an impressive range of ales for sale at the pub and in the free trade as far away as Manchester (27 regular outlets). New plant installed in 1994 has almost doubled capacity. Occasional/seasonal beers: Smoke House Ale (ABV 5.3%), Springbok Bier (ABV 5.7%), Xmas Ale (ABV 8.6%), Ginger Beer (ABV 4.2%), Janet Street Porter (ABV 4.5%). Dark Mild and English Guineas Stout are suitable for vegetarians and vegans as isinglass finings are not used in their production.

Dark Mild *(OG 1032, ABV 3%)*
Roast grain dominates this straightforward dark mild, which has some hops in the aroma and a slightly dry flavour. Malty finish.

Bitter *(OG 1035, ABV 3.7%)* ◆
A refreshing session beer. A dry-hopped aroma leads to a clean-tasting, hoppy bitterness, then a long, bitter finish with a hint of malt.

Cascade *(OG 1038, ABV 4%)*

Gold Medal *(OG 1040, ABV 4.2%)*

Special *(OG 1041, ABV 4.3%)* ◆
Dry-hopping provides the aroma for this rich and mellow bitter, which has a very soft profile and character: it fills the mouth with texture rather than taste. Clean, rounded finish.

Autumn Gold *(OG 1045, ABV 4.7%)* ◆
Straw-coloured best bitter with hop and fruit aromas, then the bitter-sweetness of autumn fruit in the taste and the finish.

English Guineas Stout *(OG 1050, ABV 5.3%)* ◆
A fruity, roast aroma preludes a smooth, roasted barley, chocolatey flavour that is bitter but not too dry. Excellent appearance; good, bitter finish.

Old Eli *(OG 1050, ABV 5.3%)*
A well-balanced premium bitter with a dry-hopped aroma and a fruity, bitter finish.

Leadboiler *(OG 1060, ABV 6.6%)* ◆
Powerful malt, hop and fruit in good balance on the tongue, with a well-rounded bitter sweet finish.

Enoch's Hammer *(OG 1075, ABV 8%)* ◆
A straw-coloured beer with malt, hop and fruit aromas. Mouth-filling, smooth malt, hop and fruit flavours with a long, hoppy bitter finish. Dangerously drinkable.

LIVERPOOL

Liverpool Brewing Company Ltd. Subsidiary of Bispham Green Brewery Co Ltd, 21-23 Berry Street, Liverpool, L1 9DF
Tel (0151) 709 5055
Fax (0151) 707 9926
Shop Mon-Sat 12-2, Sun 12-1030. Ask bar staff.
Tours by arrangement

The Liverpool Brewing Company is based in the Brewery public house on Berry Street, 300 yards from Europe's largest Chinese arch. The brewhouse was installed at the front of the premises with views from the street, the bar and the entrance hall (via a porthole) in 1990, when the pub was called the Black Horse and Rainbow. In 1996 it was bought by the Bispham Green Brewing Company and continued to brew ales for sale on the premises. The new, tawny-coloured, fruity ale called Scouse Mouse (after the book by Liverpudlian George Melly) was formulated. A bottle-conditioned ale called Super Scouse Mouse is planned, and a cask-conditioned lager is undergoing trial brews. Seasonal beers are available and bottle-conditioned beers are planned. Six pubs are owned with three serving cask-conditioned beer. Six outlets are supplied direct. Seasonal: Berry Street Mild (ABV 3.4%, May), Red (ABV 3.8%, various times).

Blondie *(OG 1040, ABV 4.1%)*
Creamy, light, best bitter.

First Gold *(OG 1041, ABV 4.2%)*
A light, single hop brew.

Scouse Mouse *(OG 1040, ABV 4.2%)*
A tawny, fruity best bitter.

Devil in Disguise *(OG 1047, ABV 4.8%)*
An amber ale with a spicy/peppery aftertaste.

Celebration *(OG 1048, ABV 4.8%)*
Premium bitter.

LORD RAGLAN

Lord Raglan, High Street, Cefn-Coed, Merthyr Tydfil, Mid-Glamorgan, CF48 2PN
Tel (01685) 721445

Brewing started in 2000. The plant, based in the pub, can produce just one barrel at a time. There are plans to move to bigger premises and to supply other outlets.

Ale *(ABV 4.1%)*

LOWES ARMS*

Lowes Arms Brewery, The Lowes Arms, 301 Hyde Road, Denton, Manchester, M31 3FF
Tel (0161) 336 3064
Fax (0161) 285 9015
Email brewer@thelab.biz
Web www.thelab.biz
Shop during pub opening hours
Tours by arrangement

The brewery, known as 'the Lab', was set up by Peter Wood, landlord of the Lowes, who had brewed as a student, and Anthony Firmin, a keen home-brewer. The brewery is located in the cellars of the pub; the first brew of St Anns Ale was produced in August 2001. It now produces a range of five beers named after local landmarks and sites of interest. The brewery is a 2.5 barrel system, but two new fermenting vessels have been added to enable Lab to brew four times a week, so producing 10 barrels. A campaign to wholesale the beer is planned.

Jet Amber *(OG 1040, ABV 3.5%)*
Brewed for the Stockport and Manchester Mild challenge.

Frog Bog *(OG 1040, ABV 3.9%)*
A light, easy-drinking bitter with an orange aroma and a light hoppy taste.

Wild Wood *(OG 1040-1046, ABV 4.1%)*
A spicy session bitter with a malty and fruity aroma, and spicy hop tastes leading to a tingling sensation on the tongue.

Broomstairs *(OG 1040-1046, ABV 4.3%)*
A dark best bitter with distinct roast flavours and a hoppy aftertaste.

Haughton Weave *(OG 1040-1046, ABV 4.5%)*
Distinct tangerine aromas in this light-coloured beer are followed by lots of bitterness and hoppy tastes in the mouth.

McGUINNESS

Thomas McGuinness Brewing Co, Cask & Feather, 1 Oldham Road, Rochdale, Lancs, OL16 1UA
Tel (01706) 711476

Fax (01706) 669654
E-mail tonycask@hotmail.com
Website www.mcguinnessbrewery.com
Tours by arrangement

⊗ McGuinness opened in 1991 and now averages 15-20 barrels a week. It supplies real ale to its own pub and several other outlets direct. Various seasonal beers at ABV 3.8-4.2%.

Feather Plucker Mild *(ABV 3.4%)* ◆
A dark brown beer, with roast malt dominant in the aroma and taste, with hints of chocolate. Satisfying bitter and roast finish.

Best Bitter *(ABV 3.8%)* ◆
Gold in colour with a hoppy aroma: a clean, refreshing beer with hop and fruit tastes and a hint of sweetness. Bitter aftertaste.

Utter Nutter *(ABV 3.8%)*

Special Reserve Bitter or SRB *(ABV 4%)* ◆
A tawny beer, sweet and malty, with underlying fruit and bitterness, and a bitter-sweet aftertaste.

Junction Bitter *(ABV 4.2%)* ◆
Mid-brown in colour, with a malty aroma. Maltiness is predominant throughout, with some hops and fruit in the taste and bitterness coming through in the finish.

Tommy Todd's Porter *(ABV 5%)* ◆
A winter warmer, with a fruit and roast aroma, leading to a balance of malt and roast malt flavours, with some fruit. Not too sweet for its gravity.

McMULLEN

McMullen & Sons Ltd,
The Hertford Brewery, 26 Old Cross,
Hertford, SG14 1RD
Tel (01992) 584911
Fax (01992) 500729
Tours by arrangement

⊗ The future of Hertfordshire's oldest independent brewery, founded in 1827 by Peter McMullen, is in doubt as a result of splits in the ruling family. The company is controlled by a series of trusts, and in 2002 a majority of shareholders decided to cash in their shares. The sale is being resisted by David and Fergus McMullen, who want to keep the company going as an integrated brewery and pub business. Ironically, while other members of the family were keen to quit the business, McMullen was reporting record sales for its cask beers. While the original brewery building of 1890 still stands, brewing is now undertaken in a new brewhouse built in 1984. Brewing 'liquor' (water) is still drawn from three deep artesian wells. Cask ale is served in all McMullen's 140 pubs in Hertfordshire, Essex and London (although all managed houses use cask breathers on all beers), and also supplies direct to 60 free trade outlets. Seasonal beers are brewed for a limited period under the banner of McMullen Special Reserve. Gladstone, formerly a regular brew, is now part of the Special Reserve portfolio.

Original AK *(OG 1036, ABV 3.7%)* ◆
A pleasant mix of malt and hops leads to a distinctive, dry aftertaste that isn't always as pronounced as it used to be.

Country Best Bitter *(OG 1042, ABV 4.3%)* ◆
A full-bodied beer with a well-balanced mix of malt, hops and fruit throughout.

MALLARD

Mallard Brewery, 15 Hartington Avenue,
Carlton, Nottingham, NG4 3NR
Tel/Fax (0115) 952 1289
E-mail Philip.mallard@ntlworld.com
Website www.mallard-brewery.co.uk
Tours by arrangement (small groups)

⊗ Phil Mallard built and installed a two-barrel plant in a shed at his home and started brewing in 1995. The brewery is a mere nine square metres and contains a hot liquor tank, mash tun, copper, and three fermenters. The brewery was launched at the Nottingham Beer Festival in 1995. Since then production has risen from one barrel a week to between six or eight barrels, which is the plant's maximum. Phil has no plans at present to expand and now supplies around 25 outlets, of which seven are on a regular weekly basis. He has also launched a small-scale bottling enterprise and plans to produce bottled beers as limited editions supplied direct from the brewery by mail order. Seasonal beer: DA (ABV 5.8%, winter), Quismas Quacker (ABV 6%, Christmas). Bottle-conditioned beers: Owd Duck (ABV 4.8%), Friar Duck (ABV 5%), DA (ABV 5.8%), Quismas Quacker (ABV 6%), Duckling (ABV 4.2%), Drake (ABV 4.5%), Duckdown Stout (ABV 4.6%), Spittin' Feathers (ABV 4.4%), Waddlers Mild (ABV 3.7%), Duck & Dive (ABV 3.7%), Feather Light (ABV 4.1%)

Waddlers Mild *(OG 1039, ABV 3.7%)*
A dark ruby mild with a fruity chocolate flavour in the mouth and a fruity finish.

Duck & Dive *(OG 1037, ABV 3.7%)*
A light single-hopped beer made from the hedgerow hop, First Gold. A bitter beer with a hoppy nose, good bitterness on the palate and a dry finish.

Best Bitter *(OG 1038, ABV 4%)* ◆
Golden brown, fruity and hoppy to the nose, with malt more apparent in the taste than anywhere else. The fruity hop carries through to a bitter, dry finish.

Feather Light *(OG 1039, ABV 4.1%)*
A very pale lager-style bitter, floral bouquet and sweetish on the palate, a nice light hoppy session beer.

Duckling *(OG 1039, ABV 4.2%)*
A crisp refreshing bitter with a hint of honey and citrus flavour. Dry hopped.

Spittin' Feathers *(OG 1043, ABV 4.4%)*
A mellow, ruby bitter with a complex malt flavour of chocolate, toffee and coffee, complemented with a full and fruity/hoppy aftertaste.

Drake *(OG 1044, ABV 4.5%)*
A full-bodied premium bitter, with malt and hops on the palate, and a fruity finish.

Duck Down Stout *(OG 1045, ABV 4.6%)*
Black and fruity.

Owd Duck *(OG 1046, ABV 4.8%)*
A dark ruby bitter with a smooth mellow smoky flavour and fruity finish.

Friar Duck *(OG 1048, ABV 5%)*
A pale full malt beer, hoppy with a hint of blackcurrant flavour.

MALTON

Malton Brewery Company Ltd, 12 Wheelgate, Malton, N Yorkshire, YO17 7HP
Tel (01653) 697580 Fax (01653) 691812
E-mail suddaby@crownhotel.plus.com
Website www.suddabys@crown.co.uk
Tours by arrangement

⊗ The Malton Brewery Company was founded in the stable block at the rear of the Crown Hotel, Wheelgate, Malton in 1984. The managing director is Neil Suddaby, who is also licensee of the hotel with Alan Brayshaw as brewer. Seasonal beers: Auld Bob (ABV 6%), Pickwick's Porter (ABV 4.2%), Crown Inn Glory (ABV 4.3%), Ryedale Champion (ABV 4.5%), Stonetrough Bitter (ABV 5.2%), Young Bob (ABV 5.2%). Bottle-conditioned beers: Golden Chance (ABV 4.2%), Auld Bob (ABV 6%).

Double Chance *(OG 1038, ABV 3.8%)* ◆
A clean-tasting, amber bitter in which hops predominate. Little malt character, but hop and fruit flavours lead to a smooth, bitter finish.

Golden Chance *(OG 1039, ABV 4.2%)*
Golden-coloured bitter with a complex hoppy finish. Two distinct varieties of hops combine with English malts to make this mid-strength bitter distinctive and quaffable.

Ryedale Light *(OG 1044, ABV 4.5%)*

Young Bob *(OG 1050, ABV 5.2%)*
Full-bodied, russet-coloured, deceptively strong bitter. Well hopped with a malty bouquet but with a dry, fruity aftertaste.

MALVERN HILLS

Malvern Hills Brewery Ltd, 15 West Malvern Road, Great Malvern, Worcestershire, WR14 4ND
Tel (01684) 560165
Fax (01684) 577336
E-mail MHB.ales@tesco.net
Website www.malvernhillsbrewery.co.uk

⊗ The brewery was set up in 1997, using a converted dynamite store on the north-eastern slopes of the Malvern Hills. Three beers are brewed all year round. There are long-term plans to move into bottling. Existing ventures include a Zero Duty brew kit for the home market.

Red Earl *(OG 1037, ABV 3.7%)* ◆
A very light beer that does not overpower the senses. A hint of apple fruit, it is ideal for slaking the thirst.

Worcestershire Whym *(OG 1042, ABV 4.2%)*

Black Pear *(OG 1044, ABV 4.4%)* ◆
A complex array of flavours including an acidic fruitiness as well as a cereal maltiness make this an absorbing drink.

MANSFIELD

See Banks's

MARBLE

Marble Brewery, 73 Rochdale Road, Manchester, M4 4HY
Tel/Fax (0161) 610 1073
E-mail vance@marblebeers.co.uk
Website www.marblebeers.co.uk
Tours by arrangement

The brewery was established in 1997 at the rear of the Marble Arch pub. It now produces beers made with organic ingredients and GM-free yeast, accredited by Soil Association and Vegetarian Society. There are plans to bottle the stronger beers. A cask-conditioned lager (Stonham) was produced in 2001 and it may be repeated. All the beers are organic and suitable for vegetarians and vegans. Seasonal: Chocolate Heavy (ABV 5.5%, winter).

Chorlton-cum-Hazy *(OG 1038, ABV 3.8%)* ◆
Also sold as N/4. This golden-amber beer has a shy nose with some hops and fruit, a fresh hoppy palate, and a short, dry aftertaste.

Cloudy Marble *(OG 1040, ABV 4%)* ◆
Amber in colour, with a hoppy/fruity nose. Hops, fruit and bitterness in the mouth, with quite a strong bitter finish.

Manchester Bitter *(OG 1042, ABV 4.2%)*

Ginger Marble *(OG 1045, ABV 4.5%)*

Uncut Amber *(OG 1047, ABV 4.7%)* ◆
Red/brown beer with malt, coffee and fruit in the aroma. It has dark chocolate, malt and fruit on the palate, with a dry, roast finish.

Old Lag *(OG 1050, ABV 5%)* ◆
Copper-coloured beer with a fruity and hoppy aroma. The flavour is a balance of malt, fruit and hops with a good bitter aftertaste.

Chocolate Heavy *(OG 1055, ABV 5.5%)* ◆
Black in colour; chocolate, roast malt and fruit nose. A smooth chocolatey, roasty bitter taste with hops and fruit also in evidence. Dry, roast, hoppy finish.

MARCHES

Marches Ales, Unit 6, Western Close, Southern Avenue Industrial Estate, Leominster, Herefordshire, HR6 0QD
Tel (01568) 610063

⊗ Plans to expand the brewery in 2001 had to be put on hold as a result of foot-and-mouth disease in the locality, which meant that engineers could not get on to the site. By the summer of 2002, the owners were ready to brew again but were waiting for an entry road to be completed. They said brewing would start again by the end of 2002.

MARSTON MOOR

Marston Moor Brewery, Crown House, Kirk Hammerton, York, YO26 8DD
Tel/Fax (01423) 330341
E-mail marston.moor.brewery@ic24.net

⊛ A small brewery established in 1983, it also offers a consultancy service to other brewers. Some 40 micro-breweries have been established at home and overseas. Due to increasing commitments with brew plant activity, the range of beers is presently brewed at Rudgate. About 100 outlets are served.

Cromwell Bitter
(OG 1036-38, ABV 3.6%) ◆
A golden beer with hops and fruit in strong evidence on the nose. Bitterness as well as fruit and hops dominate the taste and long aftertaste.

Prince Rupert Mild
(OG 1039-40, ABV 4%)

Mongrel *(OG 1039-40, ABV 4%)*

Brewers Pride
(OG 1040-42, ABV 4.2%) ◆
A light but somewhat thin, fruity beer, with a hoppy, bitter aftertaste.

Merriemaker
(OG 1044-46, ABV 4.5%)

Brewers Droop
(OG 1048-50, ABV 5%)
A pale, robust ale with hops and fruit notes in prominence. A long, bitter aftertaste.

Trooper *(OG 1048-50, ABV 5%)*

MARSTON'S

Marston, Thompson & Evershed PLC, The Brewery, Shobnall Road, Burton upon Trent, Staffs, DE14 2BW.
A subsidiary of Wolverhampton & Dudley Breweries.
Tel (01283) 531131
Fax (01283) 510378
Website www.fullpint.com
Shop 10-3 Mon-Fri; 9.30-12 Sat
Tours by arrangement, ring (01283) 507391 or (01902) 711811 x 7391

⊛ Marston's was bought by Wolverhampton & Dudley Breweries in 1999, and in 2001 W&D pledged to keep the brewery in full production. Marston's is the only brewery still using the Burton Union system of fermentation for Pedigree Bitter. Marston's reinforced its commitment to this method in 1992 with a £1 million investment in a new union room. Real ale is available throughout the Marston's estate, which stretches from Hampshire to Yorkshire. Marston's also enjoys a large free trade, thanks to many regional and national brewers. Marstons brews casual cask ales and bottles for the off trade. Three to four seasonal beers are brewed under the general title of Gooses Revenge. Owd Rodger is now only available in bottled form.

Bitter *(OG 1038, ABV 4%)* ◆
An amber/tawny session beer that can often be sulphury in aroma and taste. At its best, a splendid, subtle balance of malt, hops and fruit follows a faintly hoppy aroma and develops into a balanced, dry aftertaste.

Pedigree *(OG 1043, ABV 4.5%)* ◆
Sulphurous aroma gives way to hops. Tastes hoppy and fruity, and leaves a bitter aftertaste. The classic Burton pale ale rarely found in peak form.

MASH

⌂ Mash Ltd, 19/21 Great Portland Street, London, W1N 5DB
Tel (0207) 637 5555
Fax (0207) 637 7333

Brew-restaurant. The in-house brewery produces international beer styles on a rotation basis, including a Blackcurrant Porter, Scotch, IPA, Peach, Extra Stout and Pils. The beers are stored in cellar tanks using a CO2 system. Regular beer: Mash Wheat (ABV 5.2%).

MAULDONS

Mauldons Brewery Ltd, 7 Addison Road, Chilton Industrial Estate, Sudbury, Suffolk, CO10 2YW
Tel/Fax (01787) 311055
E-mail sims@mauldons.co.uk
Website www.mauldons.co.uk
Tours by arrangement

⊗ The company was bought by Steve and Alison Sims in 2000 from founder Peter Mauldon. Steve is a former sales manager with Adnams. Using traditional methods and quality materials, Mauldons supplies ales throughout East Anglia. There are plans to purchase a brew-pub. Seasonal beers: May Bee (ABV 3.7%, May), Bah Humbug (ABV 4.9%, Christmas), Midsummer Gold (ABV 4%), Mid Autumn Gold (ABV 4.2%), Midwinter Gold (ABV 4.5%), Cuckoo (ABV 4.3%), Ploughmans (ABV 4.3%), Eatanswill Old (ABV 4%). There are also a large number of occasional and one-off brews. Bottle-conditioned beer: Black Adder.

Mauldons Bitter *(OG 1036, ABV 3.6%)*

Moletrap Bitter *(OG 1037.8, ABV 3.8%)* ◆
A well-balanced session beer with a crisp, hoppy bitterness balancing sweet malt.

Dickens *(OG 1039.8, ABV 4%)*
A light-coloured bitter with a fine distinctive hop nose, and a refreshingly dry, fruity finish.

Peggottys Porter *(OG 1041, ABV 4.1%)*

Pickwick *(OG 1042, ABV 4.2%)*
A best bitter with a rich rounded malt flavour with ripe aromas of hops and fruit. A bitter-sweet finish.

Suffolk Pride *(OG 1048, ABV 4.8%)* ◆
A full-bodied strong bitter. The malt and fruit in the aroma are reflected in the taste, and there is some hop character in the finish. Deep tawny/red in colour.

Black Adder *(OG 1053.8, ABV 5.3%)* ◆
A dark stout. Roast malt is strong in the aroma and taste, but malt, hop and bitterness provide an excellent balance and a lingering finish.

White Adder *(OG 1053.8, ABV 5.3%)* ◆
A pale brown, almost golden, strong ale. A warming, fruity flavour dominates and lingers into a dry, hoppy finish.

Suffolk Comfort *(OG 1065.8, ABV 6.6%)*
A clean, hoppy nose leads to a predominantly malty flavour in this full-bodied beer. Dry, hoppy aftertaste.

MAYFLOWER*

Mayflower Brewery, Unit X, Worthington Lakes Business Park, Chorley Road, Standish, Nr Wigan, WN1 2UX
Tel (01257) 400605
Email cat@longen.freeserve.co.uk
Website www.mayflowerbrewery.co.uk
Tours by arrangement

New brewery launched in autumn 2001 on the Mayflower conservation site at Standish. It is a 2.5 barrel plant. There are plans to have beer bottled in production in 2003.

Black Diamond *(OG 1035, ABV 3.4%)*

Best Bitter *(OG 1037, ABV 3.8%)*

Wigan Bier *(OG 1041, ABV 4.2%)*

Hic-Bibi *(OG 1049, ABV 5%)*

MAYPOLE

Maypole Brewery, North Laithes Farm, Wellow Road, Eakring, Newark, Notts, NG22 0AN
Tel (01623) 871690
Tours by arrangement

The brewery was set up in 1995 in an 18th-century converted farm building. It changed hands in December 2001. The new owner, Kenny Munro, also owns the Square & Compass, Normanton-on-Trent where Lions Pride is permanently on sale. The brewery supplies the Angel Inn, Kneesall, with its house beer, Angels Delight (ABV 4.6%) and several Maypole beers are sold under the Bees Knees badge at the Beehive, Maplebeck. The brewery currently supplies around 30 outlets on an occasional basis, and also brews one-off beers for festivals and other events. Seasonal/occasional beers: May Day (ABV 4.5%), Flanagans Stout (ABV 4.4%), Old Homewrecker (ABV 4.7%), Donner and Blitzed (ABV 5.1%, Christmas).

Mayfair *(OG 1037, ABV 3.8%)*
A golden-coloured beer with a bitter hop taste balanced by sweet maltiness, with a long bitter finish.

Lion's Pride *(OG 1038, ABV 3.9%)*
A tawny brown beer with a malty aroma and taste. Fruity hop bitterness comes through in the finish.

Celebration Bitter *(OG 1040, ABV 4%)* ◆
A ruddy-brown bitter in which malt dominates. Some fruity hop in the nose and taste, with an initial sweetness that dries into a bitter finish where the fruit and hops meet the malt.

Loxley Ale *(OG 1041, ABV 4.2%)*
A light golden ale made with local honey. Refreshing, but not too sweet, it has a subtle bitterness.

Wellow Gold *(OG 1044, ABV 4.6%)*
A blonde, Belgian-style beer where citrus flavours predominate in the nose and taste. A deceptively drinkable beer for its strength.

Sells under the Mae West label in some existing outlets.

Poleaxed *(OG 1046, ABV 4.8%)*
A tawny, smooth beer. Damsons come out in the nose and taste, which give way to a slightly burnt aftertaste. A full-bodied, warming beer.

MEANTIME

Meantime Brewing Co, 2 Penhall Road, Greenwich, London, SE7 8RX
Tel (020) 8293 1111
Fax (020) 8293 4004
E-mail sales@mean-time.co.uk
Website www.mean-time.co.uk
Tours by arrangement

A specialist brewery run by Alastair Hook, formerly of Freedom and Mash. He brews bespoke classic beer styles for customers with their own labels and concentrates on cold-fermented lagers and warm-fermented Bavarian-style wheat beers, plus recreations of Kolsch and Vienna Red styles. He also produces bottle-conditioned beers for own-label sales. Bottle-conditioned beer: Meantime White (ABV 5%).

MIGHTY OAK

Mighty Oak Brewing Company Ltd, Units 14A & 14B, West Station Industrial Estate, Spital Road, Maldon, Essex, CM9 6TW
Tel (01621) 843713Fax (01621) 840914
E-mail moakbrew@aol.com
Tours for evening group visits only

Founded in 1996 by former Ind Coope, Romford brewer John Boyce, Mighty Oak has increased capacity three times in five years. In 2001, the brewery moved to its own premises in Maldon, doubling brewing capacity to 60 barrels a week and it continues to prosper. It is brewery policy not to sell via wholesalers, but beers are swapped with other independent brewers. Burntwood Bitter was Champion Beer of East Anglia in 1999, Champion Beer of Britain finalist 1999 and 2000. The brewery has some 200 customers in Essex, Suffolk, Herts, Kent, Wiltshire, Somerset and Gloucestershire. Seasonal beers: Brass Monkey (ABV 4.1%, Nov-Feb), Saffron Gold (ABV 4.3%, March-Aug), Mellow Yellow (ABV 4.2%, Sept-Oct).

IPA *(OG 1035, ABV 3.5%)*
Pleasant golden-amber beer with a warm, malty body and increasingly bitter aftertaste.

Oscar Wilde *(OG 1037, ABV 3.7%)*
Dark mild with a dry aftertaste and roasty character with suggestions of fresh coffee. Rather sulphurous at times. (In Cockney rhyming slang, Oscar Wilde equals Mild.)

Burntwood Bitter
(OG 1040, ABV 4%)
Powerful tawny bitter, with an attractive grainy roastiness underpinning a hoppy taste.

Simply The Best
(OG 1043, ABV 4.4%)
A tawny, full-bodied best bitter with a light balance of malt and hops, and a bitter-sweet finish.

English Oak *(OG 1047, ABV 4.8%)*
A glowing amber ale with full malt flavours balanced by a strong hop finish from First Gold and Bramling Cross hops.

Spice *(OG 1070, ABV 7%)*
Beer brewed with fruits and spices, most obviously cinnamon and orange zest, which dominate over malt and hops.

MILK STREET

The Milk Street Brewery,
The Griffin, 25 Milk Street,
Frome, Somerset, BA11 3DB
Tel (01373) 467766
E-mail
thegriffin@milkstreetbrewery.fsnet.co.uk
Tours by arrangement

The brewery was commissioned in 1999 and has a capacity of 20 barrels a week. Four beers are currently brewed with seasonal beers produced every two months. The brewery currently runs three outlets and is hoping to expand shortly. The brewery was designed by Rik Lyall, using his experience gained as head brewer for Bunce's, Hop Back and Cotleigh breweries. 25 outlets are supplied direct. Seasonal: Funky Monkey (ABV 4%), Mermaid (ABV 4.1%), Aldhelms (ABV 4.3%).

Gulp *(OG 1036, ABV 3.5%)*
An amber beer that is initially fresh and lively on the palate. The bitterness is provided by Northdown hops. The aroma is of toasted grapefruit peel and freshly picked Hawthorne leaves. These are provided by the late addition of Mount Hood hops. Very full-bodied despite its gravity.

Nature Ale *(ABV 3.8%)*

B4 *(OG 1040, ABV 4%)*
Golden in colour, there is an initial softness in the palate due to the use of malted wheat in the malt grist. Smooth and well-rounded, the bitterness comes from Liberty hops. The aroma is that of freshly-rubbed hops with pine notes. These are provided by the use of East Kent Goldings.

Nick's *(OG 1045, ABV 4.4%)*
A clean-drinking bitter, refreshing with an excellent balance of bitterness and malt flavours. The use of East Kent Goldings as both the main and aroma hops creates an excellent length of flavour.

Zig-Zag Stout *(OG 1046, ABV 4.5%)*
A soft start on the palate soon gives way to roasted malts. The subtle flavours in the background are those of bitter chocolate with an edge of citrus fruit. The beer is suitable for vegetarians and vegans.

Beer *(OG 1049, ABV 5%)*
Golden in colour, the mouthfeel has a shortbread finish. The bitterness is provided by Mount Hood hops. The aroma is that of pineapple and lemon with an almost floral hint.

MILTON

Milton Brewery, Cambridge Ltd,
Unit 111, Norman Industrial Estate,
Cambridge Road, Milton,
Cambs, CB4 6AT
Tel (01223) 226198
Fax (01223) 226199
E-mail enquiries@miltonbrewery.co.uk
Website www.miltonbrewery.co.uk
Tours by arrangement

Founded in 1999, the Milton Brewery grew rapidly and now supplies more than 100 pubs in Cambridge and beyond. It has a 15-barrel brew length; further expansion is envisaged, including the purchase of pubs. Seasonal beers: Pyramid (ABV 4.4%, May-July), Artemis (ABV 3.7%, July-Aug), Babylon (ABV 4.4%, Aug-Sept), Zeus (ABV 4.2%, Sept-Oct), Pharos (ABV 4.7%, Oct-Nov), Colossus (ABV 5.6%, Nov-Jan), Mammon (ABV 7%, December).

Minotaur *(OG 1035, ABV 3.3%)*
Rich and very full-bodied for its strength, a malty chocolateyness predominates, but vanilla and liquorice flavours also surface.

Jupiter *(OG 1037, ABV 3.5%)*
Golden session beer whose delicately hoppy flavour leads to a satisfying bitter finish.

Neptune *(OG 1039, ABV 3.8%)*
Delicious hop aromas introduce this well-balanced, nutty and refreshing copper-coloured ale. Good hoppy finish.

Pegasus *(OG 1043, ABV 4.1%)*
Hops dominate the first impression of this majestic ale, but the long, fruity/toffee finish shows that this is anything but a one-dimensional brew.

Electra *(OG 1046, ABV 4.5%)*
Golden colour, hoppy aroma, with a biscuity malt flavour, balanced by a strong and lasting bitterness.

Cyclops *(OG 1055, ABV 5.3%)*
Deep copper-coloured ale, with a rich hoppy aroma and full body; fruit and malt notes develop in the finish. Uses three different malts and four different hops.

MOLES

Moles Brewery (Cascade Drinks Ltd),
5 Merlin Way, Bowerhill,
Melksham,
Wilts, SN12 6TJ
Tel (01225) 704734/708842
Fax (01225) 790770
E-mail cascade@cableinet.co.uk
Website molesbrewery.com
Shop 9-5.
Tours by arrangement

⊗ Moles Brewery was established in 1982 and produces beers for local pubs and also nationwide via other brewers and wholesalers. Over the last 20 years the range of beers has been expanded to meet consumer demand. Molennium (ABV 4.5%) was introduced at the appropriate time while Molecatcher (ABV 5%) was launched at the 2001 Bristol CAMRA Beer Festival. 14 pubs are now owned, 13 serving cask beer. 150 outlets are supplied direct. Seasonal beers: Barleymole (ABV 4.2%, summer), Molegrip (ABV 4.3%, autumn), Holy Moley (ABV 4.7%, spring), Moel Moel (ABV 6%, winter).

Tap Bitter *(OG 1035, ABV 3.5%)*
A top-quality session bitter with a smooth, malty flavour and clean bitter finish.

Best Bitter *(OG 1040, ABV 4%)*
A well-balanced amber-coloured bitter, clean, dry and malty with some bitterness and delicate floral hop flavour.

Landlords Choice *(OG 1045, ABV 4.5%)*
A dark, strong, smooth porter beer, with a rich fruity palate and malty finish.

Moles Molennium *(OG 1045, ABV 4.5%)*
Fruit, caramel and malty overtones in the aroma of this deep amber-coloured ale, balanced by a pleasant bitterness.

Molecatcher *(OG 1050, ABV 5%)*
This copper-coloured ale has a delightfully spicy hop aroma and taste with a long bitter finish.

MOONSTONE

Gem Taverns Ltd t/a Moonstone Brewery, Ministry of Ale, 9 Trafalgar Street, Burnley, Lancs, BB11 1TQ
Tel (01282) 830909
Tours by arrangement

The brewery was built in a pub that had been closed for three years, and the first brew appeared in 2001. New beers planned include Sunstone Anniversary Ale (ABV 3.8%), and Mild (ABV 3.4%).

Tiger's Eye *(OG 1037, ABV 3.8%)*

Moonstone Dark *(OG 1042, ABV 4.8%)*

Red Jasper *(OG 1056, ABV 6%)*

MOOR

Moor Beer Company, Whitley Farm, Ashcott, Bridgwater, Somerset, TA7 9QW
Tel/Fax (01458) 210050
E-mail arthur@moorbeer.co.uk
Website www.moorbeer.co.uk
Tours by arrangement

⊗ Farmer Arthur Frampton and his wife Annette set up Moor Beer in 1996 and since then have become a thriving business, producing beers for local pubs in their corner of Somerset and beyond. Their 10-barrel plant is situated in an old workshop on their former dairy farm, and bottle-conditioned beers are sold through local farmers' markets. Monthly specials with a railway tour theme are produced and 40/50 outlets are supplied direct. Seasonal beer: Avalon (ABV 4%, spring/autumn). Bottle-conditioned beer: Old Freddy Walker (ABV 7.3%), Withy Cutter and Merlins.

Withy Cutter *(OG 1037, ABV 3.8%)*
A lightly malty, pale brown beer with a moderate bitter finish.

Merlin's Magic *(OG 1044, ABV 4.3%)*
Dark amber-coloured, complex, full-bodied beer, with fruity notes.

Peat Porter *(OG 1045, ABV 4.5%)*
Dark brown/black beer with an initially fruity taste leading to roast malt taste with a little bitterness. A slightly sweet malty finish.

Summerland Gold *(OG 1052, ABV 5%)*
Straw-coloured beer with spicy hop aroma, malt with hints of vanilla on the palate, long fruit and hop finish.

Old Freddy Walker
(OG 1074, ABV 7.3%)
Rich, dark, strong ale with a fruity complex taste, leaving a fruitcake finish.

MOORHOUSES

Moorhouses Brewery (Burnley) Ltd, 4 Moorhouse Street, Burnley, Lancs, BB11 5EN
Tel (01282) 422864/416004
Fax (01282) 838493
E-mail moorhouses@moorhouses.fsbusiness.co.uk
Website www.moorhouses.co.uk
Tours by arrangement

Brewers of famous hop bitters from 1865, Moorhouses switched to cask beer production in 1978. A succession of owners failed to develop the company until it was taken over in 1985 by Bill Parkinson, since when it has grown substantially. A modern brewhouse was installed in 1988 and more fermenting vessels were added in 1991 to keep up with demand. The company owns six pubs, all serving cask-conditioned beer, and supplies real ale to 200-250 free trade outlets. Two new 30-barrel fermenters and a 7.5 ton dray were added in 2000 to keep up with demand. Seasonal: Owd Ale (ABV 6%, Nov-Feb).

Black Cat *(OG 1036, ABV 3.4%)*
An excellent dark, fruity ale. Smooth and well-balanced with fruity, chocolate and coffee flavours to complement the bitter roast character that lingers on in the aftertaste. Champion Beer of Britain 2000.

Premier Bitter *(OG 1036, ABV 3.7%)*
A clean and satisfying bitter aftertaste rounds off this consistent, well-balanced hoppy, amber session bitter.

Pride of Pendle *(OG 1040, ABV 4.1%)*
A fine balance of malt and hops give this beer a long, dry and extremely satisfying finish.

Pendle Witches Brew
(OG 1050, ABV 5.1%)
A faint malty nose leads into a rich, sweetish nutty flavour with a subtle hoppy bitterness. This develops into a delightful lasting bitter finish.

MORDUE

Mordue Brewery, Unit 21A, West Chirton North Industrial Estate, Shiremoor, Tyne & Wear, NE29 8SF
Tel/Fax (0191) 2961879

E-mail morduebreweries@hotmail.com
Website www.morduebrewery.com
Shop Mon-Fri 9-5.
Tours by arrangement (Min 15, Max 50)

The Mordue Brewery was the brainchild of home-brewers Garry Fawson and his younger brother Matthew, who lived in a house that in the 18th century was the Mordue Brewery. The brothers leased a unit on an industrial estate, bought a five-barrel plant, and brewed their first beer, Workie Ticket, which was launched at the 1995 Newcastle Beer Festival. It won the Beer of the Festival award, and then went on to win the Champion Beer of Britain accolade at the Great British Beer Festival in 1997. By 1998, demand had outstripped capacity and the brewery moved to new premises with a 20-barrel plant. Bateman's distributes the beers in the south of England, while Caledonian looks after the north. There is a modest but thriving export business in the United States. Seasonal beers: Winter Tyne (ABV 3.9%), Spring Tyne (ABV 4.2%), Summer Tyne (ABV 3.6%), Autumn Tyne (ABV 4%), Wallsend Brown Ale (ABV 4.6%), Black Midden Stout (ABV 4.4%), Xmas Sermon (ABV 5.2%), A'l Wheat Pet (ABV 4.1%, summer).

Five Bridge Bitter *(OG 1038, ABV 3.8%)*
Crisp, golden beer with a good hint of hops. The bitterness carries on in the aftertaste. A good session bitter.

Geordie Pride *(OG 1042, ABV 4.2%)*
Medium-bodied amber brew, well-balanced and hoppy, with a long, bitter finish.

Workie Ticket *(OG 1045, ABV 4.5%)*
Complex, tasty beer with plenty of malt and hops. Long, satisfying, bitter finish.

Radgie Gadgie *(OG 1048, ABV 4.8%)*
Strong, easy-drinking bitter. Plenty of fruit and hops. The flavours extend into a long, lingering finish.

MOULIN

RTR Catering Ltd,
Moulin Hotel & Brewery, Kirkmichael Road,
Pitlochry, Perthshire, PH16 5EW
Tel (01796) 472196
Fax (01796) 474098
E-mail hotel@moulin.u-net.com
Website www.moulin.u-net.com
Shop 12-3 daily. Tours by arrangement

The Moulin Brewery was the first brewery in Perthshire for more than 50 years, and was opened in 1995 during celebrations for the hotel's 300th anniversary. Moulin supplies the Moulin Inn across the road and three other outlets. Bottle-conditioned beer: Ale of Atholl (ABV 4.5%).

Light *(OG 1035, ABV 3.7%)*
Thirst-quenching, straw-coloured session beer, with a light, hoppy, fruity balance ending with a gentle, hoppy sweetness.

Braveheart *(OG 1039, ABV 4%)*
An amber bitter, with a delicate balance of malt and fruit and a Scottish-style sweetness.

Ale of Atholl *(OG 1043, ABV 4.5%)*
A reddish, quaffable, malty ale, with a solid body and a mellow finish.

Old Remedial *(OG 1050.5, ABV 5.2%)*
A distinctive and satisfying dark brown old ale, with roast malt to the fore and tannin in a robust taste.

NAGS HEAD

Nags Head Inn, Abercych, Boncath,
Pembrokeshire SA37 0HJ
Tel (01239) 841200

Pub-brewery producing just one brew for its own consumption. Two outlets are supplied direct.

Old Emrys *(OG 1038-40, ABV 3.8-4%)*

NATHAN'S*

Nathan's Fine Ales, Dovecote Brewery,
The Old Alehouse, Top Street,
Elston, Notts, NE23
Tel (01636) 525197/(07711) 825197
E-mail nathanshome@hotmail.com

The one-barrel plant, based in an old dovecote at the back of the Old Alehouse in Elston, was originally designed and built by the owner as a hobby brewery. It started commercial brewing in 2001. To date, two regular and three seasonal beers have been produced. There are plans to expand capacity and relocate. The brewery supplies 20 outlets direct. Seasonal beers: Dozy Hedgehog Autumn Ale (ABV 4.2%), Arctic Fox Winter Ale (ABV 5.4%), Over the Top Remembrance Ale (ABV 5.4%).

Standard Best Bitter *(ABV 3.6%)*

English Stout *(ABV 4.7%)*

NETHERGATE

Nethergate Brewery Ltd,
11-13 High Street, Clare,
Suffolk, CO10 8NY
Tel (01787) 277244 Fax (01787) 277123
E-mail orders@nethergate.co.uk
Tours by arrangement (trade and CAMRA groups)

Nethergate Brewery was established in 1986 and since then has been in the forefront of innovative brewing, while maintaining strictly traditional methods. Old Growler, introduced in 1989, heralded the new wave of porters, while Umbel Ale reintroduced coriander as an English brewing ingredient for the first time in 150 years. Both these brews became Champion Beers of Great Britain in their respective categories. Nethergate supplies approximately 350 outlets on a direct basis, mainly in East Anglia, with seven regular ales, to which has been added a successful monthly beer programme produced by head brewer Tom Knox. Seasonal brews: Vixen (ABV 4.3%, January), Red Rooster (ABV 4.5%, February), Wild Rox (ABV 4.3%, March), Hares Breadth (ABV 4.4%, April), Wild Goose (ABV 4.5%, May), Painted Lady (ABV 4.2%, June), Sheeps Eye (ABV 4.1%, July), Golden Gate (ABV 4.5%, August),

Greedy Pike (ABV 4.2%, September), Scutchers (ABV 4.3%, October), Monks Habit (ABV 4.2%, November), Winter Draught (ABV 4.8%, December).

Priory Mild *(OG 1036, ABV 3.5%)* ◆
Distinctive, full-flavoured, very dark mild. Pronounced lingering roast and dry hop aftertaste.

IPA *(OG 1036, ABV 3.5%)* ◆
This amber-coloured session bitter is clean, crisp and very drinkable. Plenty of malt and hoppy bitterness together with some fruit are pleasing to the palate. Bitterness lingers in a long dry aftertaste.

Umbel Ale *(OG 1039, ABV 3.8%)* ◆
Wort is percolated through coriander seeds to give a wonderful, warming, spicy fruit tang to both the taste and aroma. The hops are strong enough to make themselves known and a strong, bitter malt finish hits late.

Suffolk County Best Bitter ◆
(OG 1041, ABV 4%)
Formerly Nethergate Bitter, Suffolk County retains the classic Nethergate taste but not so intensely bitter as previously. Still a fine balanced beer with plenty of hops and malt.

Augustinian Ale *(OG 1046, ABV 4.5%)* ◆
A pale, refreshing, complex best bitter. Fruity aroma leads to a bitter-sweet flavour and aftertaste with predominance of citrus tones.

Old Growler *(OG 1050, ABV 5%)* ◆
A complex and satisfying porter, smooth and distinctive. Sweetness, roast malt and fruit feature in the palate, with bitter chocolate lingering. The finish is powerfully hoppy.

Umbel Magna *(OG 1050, ABV 5%)*
The addition of coriander to the Old Growler wort completes the original 1750s recipe for this distinctive dark beer. The powerful spiciness only adds to this porter's appeal.

NEWBY WYKE

Newby Wyke Brewery, Willoughby Arms Cottages, Station Road, Little Bytham, Lincolnshire, NG33 4RA
Tel/Fax (01780) 411119
Tours by arrangement

The brewery, named after a Hull trawler skippered by brewer Rob March's grandfather, was set up in a converted garage at his home in Grantham. Brewing started in 1998 with a 2.5-barrel plant. Rob moved into purpose-built premises with a 10-barrel brewery and capacity for 30 barrels a week at the Willoughby Arms, in 2001. 40 outlets are supplied direct. Stamford Gold (ABV 4.4%) is brewed regularly for the Green Man, Stamford; Lord Willoughby, named after another Hull trawler (ABV 4.8%), and Lord Ancaster (ABV 4.5%) are regular beers for the Willoughby Arms. Seasonal/occasional beers: Summer Session (ABV 3.8%, April-Sept), Red Squall (ABV 4.4%, Oct-March), White Sea (ABV 5.2%, April-Sept), Kingston Amber (ABV 5.2%, June-Aug), Distant Grounds IPA (ABV 5.2%, Nov-March), Black Squall Bitter (ABV 4.6%, Oct-March), The Deep (ABV 5.4%, winter), Homeward Bound (ABV 6%, winter)

Sidewinder *(OG 1038, ABV 3.8%)*

Decade *(OG 1039, ABV 4%)*

Lord Ancaster *(OG 1039, ABV 4%)*

Brutus *(OG 1039, ABV 4%)*

Bardia *(OG 1039, ABV 4%)*

Slingshot *(OG 1041, ABV 4.2%)*

Slipway *(OG 1041, ABV 4.2%)*

Bear Island *(OG 1044, ABV 4.6%)*

White Squall *(OG 1045, ABV 4.8%)*

For Willoughby Arms, Little Bytham
Stamford Gold *(OG 1042, ABV 4.4%)*

Greenman Stamford *(OG 1042, ABV 4.4%)*

NEWTONMORE & KINGUSSIE*

Newtonmore & Kingussie Brewery Ltd, 29 High Street, Kingussie, Inverness-shire, PH21 1HX
Tel (01540) 661236 Fax (01540) 661061

New brewery based in the Royal Hotel and producing Piper's Brew, Third Son, and Just For You.

NORTH COTSWOLD

North Cotswold Brewery, Ditchford Farm, Moreton-in-Marsh, Glos, GL55 9RD
Tel (01608) 663947
E-mail northcotswold@breathe.com

Brothers David and Roger Tilbrook started brewing in 1999 on a 2.5-barrel plant, bought from the closed Viking Brewery. A new 10-barrel plant was installed in 2000. The brewery is in Warwickshire, despite the Gloucestershire postal address, on the estate of Lord Willoughby De Broke. Two mainstream beers are produced with other seasonals planned and 20 outlets are supplied direct.

Christmas Special *(OG 1041, ABV 4.4%)*

NORTH YORKSHIRE

North Yorkshire Brewing Co, Pinchinthorpe Hall, Pinchinthorpe, Guisborough, TS14 8HG
Tel/Fax (01287) 630200
Email nyb@pinchinthorpe.freeserve.co.uk
Website www.pinchinthorpehall.co.uk
Tours by arrangement

The brewery was founded in 1989 and moved in 1998 to Pinchinthorpe Hall, a moated, listed medieval monument near Guisborough that has its own spring water. The site also includes a hotel, restaurant and bistro. More than 100 free trade outlets are currently supplied. In 2002 the brewery converted to organic ingredients for all brews. A special monthly beer is produced monthly together with three beers in the Cosmic range.

Prior's Ale *(OG 1036, ABV 3.6%)* ◆
Light, refreshing and surprisingly full-flavoured for a pale, low gravity beer, with a complex, bitter-sweet mixture of malt, hops and fruit carrying through into the aftertaste.

Best Bitter *(OG 1036, ABV 3.6%)*

Clean tasting, well hopped, pale-coloured traditional bitter.

Archbishop Lee's Ruby Ale *(OG 1040, ABV 4%)*
A full-bodied beer with a malty aroma and a balanced malt and hops taste, with vanilla notes.

Boro Best *(OG 1040, ABV 4%)*
Northern-style, full-bodied beer.

Fools Gold *(OG 1046, ABV 4.6%)*
Hoppy, pale-coloured premium beer.

Golden Ale *(OG 1046, ABV 4.6%)* ◆
A well-hopped, lightly-malted, golden premium bitter, using Styrian and Goldings hops.

Flying Herbert *(OG 1047, ABV 4.7%)*
Full-flavoured premium bitter, smooth and well balanced.

Lord Lee *(OG 1047, ABV 4.7%)* ◆
A refreshing, red/brown beer with a hoppy aroma. The flavour is a pleasant balance of roast malt and sweetness that predominates over hops. The malty, bitter finish develops slowly.

NOTTINGHAM*

The Nottingham Brewing Co Ltd,
The Plough, 17 St Peter's St, Radford,
Nottingham, NG7 3EN
Tel (0115) 9422649 or (0781) 5073447
Fax (0115) 9422649
Tours by arrangement

⊠ Formerly Bramcote Brewery, which went into partnership with Tynemill and became Castle Rock. The owners of Bramcote, Niven Balfour and Philip Darby, sold control to Tynemill, bought the name of Nottingham Brewery and built a purpose-built brewery behind their pub, the Plough Inn at Radford. The 10 barrel plant brews a range of beers based on recipes from the former Nottingham Brewery, which was closed by Whitbread in the 1950s. It supplies six outlets.

Rock Ale Mild Beer *(OG 1038, ABV 3.8%)*

Rock Ale Bitter Beer *(OG 1038, ABV 3.8%)*

Legend *(OG 1040, ABV 4%)*

Extra Pale Ale *(OG 1042, ABV 4.2%)*

Dreadnought *(OG 1046, ABV 4.5%)*

Bullion *(OG 1048, ABV 4.7%)*

Sooty Stout *(OG 1050, ABV 4.8%)*

NURSERY*

Nursery Brewing Co Ltd,
Unit 15, Brookleaze Trading Estate,
Stockwood Vale, Keynsham,
Bristol, BS31 2AL
Tel (0117) 986 1212
Fax (0117) 986 2211
E-mail mail@nurserybrewing.co.uk
Website www.nurserybrewing.co.uk
Shop Open with tours only
Tours by arrangement

⊠ Nursery Brewery was established in 2001 by Malcolm Shipp, who runs Shipping Beer Ltd next door. Steve Cheesewright joined from Sutton Brewery in Plymouth, is head brewer, and brews on a 10-barrel plant three times a week. The Old Bank free house in Keynsham is the brewery tap and serves all the beers plus guests. Bottled beers are exported to Scandinavia and the USA. Seasonal beers: Little Mild Muffet (ABV 3.8%, April- May), Little Jack Horner (ABV 4.8%, Aug-Sept), Queen of Hearts (ABV 4.4%, June-July), Grand Old Duke (ABV 4.6%, Jan-March), Oat King Cole (ABV 6%, winter). Speciality beers: Sugar & Spice (ABV 4.3%, spiced Christmas ale).

Georgie Porgie *(OG 1038, ABV 3.7%)* ◆
Amber session bitter with assertive, dry bitterness, which continues to the finish. Some crystal malt and fruit flavour is dominated by the bitterness.

Three Blind Mice *(OG 1041, ABV 4.2%)* ◆
Amber, full-bodied bitter with more malt and hop flavours than Georgie Porgie, but sharing the same dominant dry bitterness in taste and finish.

Hey Diddle Diddle *(OG 1048, ABV 4.7%)* ◆
Refreshing light amber, bitter-sweet beer with balanced hop and malt flavours. Apple fruit and blackcurrant contribute to some sweetness in the aftertaste. Easy drinking for its strength.

Old Mother Hubbard *(OG 1050, ABV 5.2%)* ◆
Well-crafted dark brown old ale. Complex and well balanced, with roast malt and fruit. Coffee, liquorice, blackcherry, blackcurrant and clove flavours balance the satisfyingly dry bitterness.

O'HANLON'S

O'Hanlon's Brewing Company Ltd,
Great Barton Farm, Whimple,
Devon, EX5 2NY.
Tel (01404) 822412
Fax (01404) 833700
E-mail lizohanlon@aol.com
Website www.ohanlons.co.uk
Tours by arrangement

⊠ The brewery was established in 1996 to supply John O'Hanlon's pub in Clerkenwell, London, but expanded to serve around 80 other outlets direct, with others taking the beers via wholesalers. In the summer of 2000, O'Hanlon's sold its pub and moved the brewery to the West Country. It still supplies O'Hanlon's pub in London as well as other free trade accounts. Seasonal beers: Maltsters Weiss (ABV 4%, spring/summer), Rye Beer (ABV 4.3%, autumn), Christmas Ale (ABV 4.3%, December). Bottle-conditioned: Original Port Stout (ABV

4.8%), Organic Rye Beer (ABV 5%), Wheat Beer (ABV 4%). Organic Rye Beer (ABV 5%) is suitable for vegetarians/vegans.

Fire Fly *(OG 1035, ABV 3.7%)* ◆
Malty and fruity light bitter. Hints of orange in the taste.

Wheat Beer *(ABV 4%)* ◆
1999 SIBA Champion Wheat Beer of Britain has a fine citrus taste.

Blakeley's Best *(OG 1040, ABV 4.2%)* ◆
Premium ale with complex flavours. Hoppy nose and finish are balanced by a fruity malt taste.

Dry Stout *(OG 1041, ABV 4.2%)* ◆
A dark malty, well-balanced stout with a dry, bitter finish and plenty of roast and fruit flavours up front.

Myrica Ale *(OG 1039, ABV 4.2%)* ◆
The use of honey and bog myrtle for flavour produce a sweet, malty yellow beer with no noticeable bitterness.

Port Stout *(OG 1041, ABV 4.4%)* ◆
A black beer with a roast malt aroma that remains in the taste but gives way to hoppy bitterness in the aftertaste.

Yellowhammer *(ABV 4.5%)*
The flavour-packed golden ale.

Red Ale *(OG 1044, ABV 4.5%)* ◆
A typical Irish red ale. Well-balanced but fruity with a good, dry, hoppy finish.

Organic Rye Beer *(ABV 5%)*
Crisp, with a unique nutty flavour that goes wonderfully with bar food.

OAKHAM

Oakham Ales, 80 Westgate, Peterborough, Cambs, PE1 2AA
Tel (01733) 358300
Fax (01733) 310022
Email oakhamales@aol.com
Tours by arrangement

oakham ales

⊗ Peterborough's first brewery for 80 years was opened in 1998 on its present site in one of Europe's largest brew-pubs, with a 35-barrel plant, after being in a 10-barrel plant in Oakham for five years. The present site is still under threat of demolition due to the proposed re-development of the surrounding area. It holds the title of Supreme Champion Beer of Britain 2001 with JHB and Champion Beer in the speciality class at GBBF with White Dwarf. Oakham has won more than 20 beer awards during 2001 at CAMRA beer festivals, plus industry awards. Seasonal beers: Old Tosspot (ABV 5.2%, Dec-Feb), Black Hole Porter (ABV 5.5%, Jan-Feb), Harlequin (ABV 4.9%, March), Mompessons Gold (ABV 5%, April-May), Helterskelter (ABV 5%, June-Aug), Peterborough Beer Festival Special (strength varies, Aug-Sept), Five Leaves Left (ABV 4.5%, Oct-Nov), Cold Turkey (ABV 6.3%, December).

Jeffrey Hudson Bitter or JHB
(OG 1038, ABV 3.8%) ◆
Impressive straw-coloured quaffing bitter with bold floral, grassy hop, grapefruit and kiwi fruit and a little sweetness followed by a long, dry aftertaste.

White Dwarf Wheat Beer
(OG 1043, ABV 4.3%)
Full-bodied yellow-golden beer with a well-defined citrus hop, rounded off with a gentle underlying malty sweetness in the mouth but ending bone-dry with hops holding up well.

Bishops Farewell *(OG 1046, ABV 4.6%)* ◆
A well-rounded, full-bodied strong bitter, yellow in colour with a strong hoppy aroma joined by floral fruity flavours in the mouth with a grainy background and a dry, fruity finish.

OAKHILL

Oakhill Brewery, The Old Maltings, High Street, Oakhill, Radstock, Somerset, BA3 5BX
Tel (01749) 840340
Fax (01749) 840531
E-mail sales@oakhillbrewery.co.uk
Website www.oakhillbrewery.co.uk
Shop Informal, when brewery is open
Tours by arrangement Tue evening, £5.00 per person, max 25 people

⊗ Founded in 1767, Oakhill was a major brewery until 1924, when it closed following a catastrophic fire. The brewery was restarted in 1984 by a local businessman, the business being run for several years by a single brewer-cum-manager. The operation expanded in the early 1990s, taking on more full-time staff and acquiring a number of local pubs. In 1997 it moved from the old brewing site to the refurbished former Oakhill Maltings, expanding its potential capacity to 300 barrels a week. Brewing may move out of the village, as the maltings could be sold for housing development, subject to planning permission. Oakhill supplies some 200 free trade outlets direct. It has signed a deal with the InnSpired pub group (qv) that will offer Oakhill beers to Usher's pubs in the South-west. Seasonal beers: Charioteer (ABV 4.2%, March-Sept), Merry Maltings (ABV 4.8%, December).

XXX Mature *(OG 1038, ABV 3.7%)*
A slightly darker beer that replaced Bitter.

Best Bitter *(OG 1040, ABV 4%)* ◆
A clean-tasting, tangy bitter, with a good hop content and citrus fruit and malt balance. Dry finish; light hop aroma. Very quenching.

Black Magic Stout
(OG 1045, ABV 4.5%) ◆
A black/brown bitter stout with roast malt and a touch of fruit on the nose. Smooth roast malt and bitterness in the taste, with mellow coffee and chocolate.

Mendip Gold *(OG 1045, ABV 4.5%)*

Yeoman 1767 Strong Ale
(OG 1050, ABV 5%) ◆
A strong, pale brown, full-bodied bitter, with a floral hop palate and notable fruitiness. Dry, bitter, lasting finish.

Mendip Twister *(OG 1065, ABV 6.3%)*

OAKLEAF

Oakleaf Brewing Co Ltd, Unit 7, Clarence Wharf Industrial Estate, Mumby Road, Gosport, Hants, PO12 1AJ
Tel (023) 9251 3222
Fax (023) 9251 0148
E-mail info@oakleafbrewing.co.uk
Website www.oakleafbrewing.co.uk
Tours by arrangement

⊗ Brewer Ed Anderson and his father-in-law, Dave Pickersgill, are partners in Oakleaf. Ed was the brewer at the Fuzz & Firkin, Southsea, before moving to brew for Winchester Ale Houses. They have contracts to sell to InnSpired Inns, plus a wholesale deal with Shipping Beer. Seasonal beers: Maypole Mild (ABV 3.8%, Feb-Sept), Stokers Stout (ABV 5%, Oct-Jan), IPA (ABV 5.5%), Blakes Heaven (ABV 7%, December).

Oakleaf Bitter *(ABV 3.8%)*

Nuptu'ale *(ABV 4.2%)*

Squirrel's Delight *(ABV 4.4%)*

Hole Hearted *(ABV 4.7%)*

Blake's Gosport Bitter *(ABV 5.2%)*

OAKWELL

Oakwell Brewery, Pontefract Road, Barnsley, S Yorkshire
Tel (01226) 296161
Fax (01226) 771457

☺ Brewing started in 1997, with plans for expansion. Oakwell supplies some 30 outlets direct. Barnsley Bitter should not be confused with the beer brewed by Barnsley Brewery (qv).

Barnsley Bitter *(OG 1036, ABV 3.8%)*

Old Tom *(OG 1036, ABV 3.8%)*

Old Tom Stout *(ABV 4%)*

ODCOMBE

Odcombe Ales, The Masons Arms, 41 Lower Odcombe, Nr Yeovil, Somerset, BA22 8TX
Tel (01935) 862591

⊗ A one-barrel plant installed in 2000 to produce beer for the pub. Originally it was anticipated that a brew a fortnight would be sufficient but the plant is now producing three beers with occasional specials when time allows. Brewing takes place three times a fortnight where possible. The beers are occasionally found at local festivals.

Lower Odcombe Ale
(OG 1040-1042, ABV 4%)
Pale, dry bitter with a biscuity flavour.

Dunne Lane *(OG 1041-1043, ABV 4.2%)*

Higher Odcombe Ale
(OG 1044-1046, ABV 4.5%)
A sweeter, stronger version of Lower Odcombe Ale.

OKELLS

Okell & Son Ltd, Kewaigue, Douglas, Isle of Man, IM2 1QG
Tel (01624) 661120
Fax (01624) 624253
E-mail mac@okells.co.uk
Website www.okells.co.uk
Tours by arrangement

☺ Founded in 1874 by Dr Okell and formerly trading as Isle of Man Breweries, this is the main brewery on the island, having taken over and closed the rival Castletown Brewery in 1986. The brewery moved in 1994 to a new, purpose-built plant at Kewaigue. All the beers are produced under the Manx Brewers' Act 1874 (permitted ingredients: water, malt, sugar and hops only). All of the company's 55 pubs sell real ale and more than 70 free trade outlets are also supplied direct. Occasional beers: Castletown Bitter (ABV 4%), Manx Cat (ABV 4%), Wheel Ale (ABV 4.2%), Spring Ram (ABV 4.2%), Poleaxed (ABV 4.2%), Autumn Dawn (ABV 4.2%), Chequered Flag (ABV 4.2%), Summer Storm (ABV 4.2%), Hoptunaa (ABV 4.2%), Olde Skipper (ABV 4.5%), St Nick (ABV 4.5%), Falcon Strong Ale (ABV 5%).

Mild *(OG 1034, ABV 3.4%)* ◆
A genuine, well-brewed mild ale, with a fine aroma of hops and crystal malt. Reddish-brown in colour, this beer has a full malt flavour with surprising bitter hop notes and a hint of blackcurrants and oranges. Full, malty finish.

Bitter *(OG 1035, ABV 3.7%)* ◆
A golden beer, malty and superbly hoppy in aroma, with a hint of honey. Rich and malty on the tongue, it has a wonderful, dry, malt and hop finish. A complex but rewarding beer.

Heart-Throb *(OG 1042, ABV 4.5%)*

OLD CANNON

Old Cannon Brewery Ltd, 86 Cannon Street, Bury St Edmunds, Suffolk, IP33 1JR
Tel (01284) 768769
Fax (01284) 701137
E-mail rej@btinternet.com
Website www.oldcannon.co.uk
Tours by arrangement

⊗ St Edmunds Head pub opened in 1845 with its own brewery. Brewing ceased in 1917, and Greene King closed the pub in 1995. It re-opened in 1999 complete with unique state-of-the-art brewery housed in the bar area. There are plans for bottling, further off-sales, more seasonal beers and the acquisition of a further pub. Seasonal beers: Black Pig (ABV 4.5%, winter), Old Chestnut (ABV 4.4%, autumn), Spring Ale (ABV 4.5%, spring), Summer Ale (ABV 4.2%, summer).

Best Bitter *(OG 1040, ABV 3.8%)* ◆
An excellent session bitter brewed using Styrian Goldings, giving a crisp grapefruit aroma and taste. Very refreshing, full of flavour and extremely moreish.

Powder Monkey *(OG 1047, ABV 4.7%)*

Gunner's Daughter
(OG 1052, ABV 5.5%) ◆
A well-balanced strong ale with a complexity of hop, fruit, sweetness and bitterness in the flavour, and a lingering pleasant hoppy, bitter aftertaste.

OLD CHIMNEYS

Old Chimneys Brewery, The Street, Market Weston, Diss, Norfolk, IP22 2NZ (office). Brewery: Hopton End Farm, Market Weston, Diss, Norfolk, IP22 2NX
Tel Office (01359) 221411 Brewery (01359) 221013
Shop by arrangement
Tours by arrangement

⊗ A craft brewery opened in 1995 by former Vaux/Greene King/Broughton brewer Alan Thomson. In 2001 the brewery moved to larger premises in a converted farm building in the same village. Despite the postal address, the brewery is in Suffolk. The beers produced are mostly named after endangered local species. Four strong bottle-conditioned beers are also brewed. Old Chimneys currently supplies 50 outlets direct. Seasonal beers: Polecat Porter (ABV 4.2%, winter), Black Rat Stout (ABV 4.4%, winter), Golden Pheasant (ABV 4.7%, summer), Natterjack Premium Ale (ABV 5%, winter), Winter Cloving (ABV 7.2%, winter), Corn Cleavers Ale (ABV 4.3%, spring/summer). Bottle-conditioned beers: Greenshank Organic (ABV 7%), Brimstone Lager (ABV 6.5%), Redshank Strong Ale (ABV 8.7%), Good King Henry Imperial Stout (ABV 9.6%).

Military Mild *(OG 1035, ABV 3.3%)* ⬥
A rich, dark mild with good body for its gravity. Sweetish toffee and light roast bitterness dominate, leading to a moreish dry aftertaste.

Galingale *(OG 1041, ABV 3.9%)* ⬥
This amber gold bitter has excellent body allied to a clean and refreshing character. Hops, malt and fruit combine to give a well-balanced, bitter-sweet flavour with hop in the early aftertaste, followed by a pleasing dry finish.

Great Raft Bitter *(OG 1043, ABV 4.2%)*
Complex and satisfying for its gravity, this pale copper bitter is bursting with fruit throughout. Malt and hops add to the sweetish fruity flavour, which is nicely rounded off with hoppy bitterness in the aftertaste.

OLD COTTAGE

Old Cottage Beer Co, Unit 3, Eccleshaw Industrial Estate, Hawkins Lane, Burton-on-Trent, Staffs, DE14 1PT
Tel (01283) 511615 or (07780) 90000
E-mail oldcottage@euphony.net
Tours by arrangement

⊗ Kevin Slater bought his brewing equipment from the former Old Cottage Brewery in Kendal and installed it in the Heritage Brewery in Burton. When the site was taken over, he was evicted and set up in a modern industrial unit. The brewery will be moving across the yard to a bigger unit with two floors in the near future.

Oak Ale *(OG 1040, ABV 3.9%)*

Columbus *(OG 1041, ABV 4%)* ⬥
Amber ale, crisp from hops and citrus fruit.

Stout *(OG 1048, ABV 4.7%)* ⬥
Black but not heavy! Full roast aroma with hints of liquorice and chocolate malt; the roast flavours linger to a bitter finish.

Halcyon Daze *(OG 1050, ABV 5.1%)* ⬥
Dark and full bodied, with hops, fruit and malt.

OLD KENT

Old Kent Brewery Co, 11-13 Western Road, Borough Green, Sevenoaks, Kent, TN15 8AL
Tel (01732) 882111
Fax (01732) 882333
Email info@okbc.co.uk
Website www.okbc.co.uk
Opening times Mon-Fri 9-430, Sat 10-2pm

The Old Kent Brewery brewed its first pint in 2000 and has since then developed a growing band of followers in the west Kent area. Started by two cricketers, John Brigden and Mike Canniford, it has named its brews after cricketing terms. It now delivers to more than 30 outlets in the immediate area, with demand coming in from further afield in Kent. The five-barrel equipment was virtually new when purchased, having been bought from a Firkin pub. The mainstay of the brewery is Opener, which accounts for nearly 50 per ent of sales. Seasonal beers: Full Pitch (ABV 5%, winter), Golden Duck (ABV 5.1%, summer) and Golden Duck Lite (ABV 3.5%, summer). The brewery now does a considerable trade in bottle-conditioned beers.

Fine Edge *(OG 1037.5, ABV 3.8%)*
A refreshing golden session ale with light hoppiness.

Opener *(OG 1039, ABV 4.2%)*
Aromatic, fruity and very smooth.

Top Score *(OG 1044, ABV 4.6%)*
Full flavour with a good balance of malt and hops.

Full Pitch *(OG 1048, ABV 5%)*
A classic winter warmer with a hint of chocolate.

Long Hop *(OG 1048, ABV 5%)*
Full bodied and satisfying.

Golden Duck *(OG 1049, ABV 5.1%)*
IPA-style, straw coloured, crisp, smooth and deceptive.

OLD LAXEY

Old Laxey Brewing Co, The Shore Hotel, Old Laxey, Isle of Man, IM4 7DA
Tel (01624) 861509
E-mail shore@advsys.co.uk
Website www.welcome.to/shorehotel
Tours by arrangement

The brewery was designed and constructed in 1997 by Peter Austin, the renowned 'father' of micro-brewing and founder of Ringwood Brewery. The five-barrel plant can be seen through the brewery bar . Various outlets on the island and in Britain are supplied.

Bosun Bitter *(OG 1038, ABV 3.8%)*
Crisp and fresh with a hoppy aftertaste.

OLD LUXTERS

Old Luxters Brewery, Old Luxters Farm, Hambleden, Henley-on-Thames, Oxon, RG9 6JW
Tel (01491) 638330 Fax (01491) 638645
E-mail david@luxters.co.uk
Website www.luxters.co.uk
Shop 7 days a week.
Tours by arrangement 9-6 weekday, 11-6 weekends

⊗ A traditional, full-mash, independent farm brewery established 1990 in a 17th-century barn alongside a winery. Cask ales are supplied through the shop and private clients and some free trade customers. Old Luxters specialises in exclusive bottle-conditioned beers for specialist customers, such as Fortnum & Mason, and Royal Farm Shop. Bottle-conditioned beers: Barn Ale (ABV 5.4%), Dark Roast Ale (ABV 5%), Luxters Gold (ABV 5%), Damson Ale (ABV 7%), Old Windsor Gold, brewed for the Royal Household Farm Shop, Windsor (ABV 5%), Old Windsor Dark Ale (ABV 5%), 21-21 (ABV 4.5%), Fortnum & Mason Ale (ABV 5%). The brewery is in Buckinghamshire, despite the postal address.

Barn Ale Bitter *(OG 1038, ABV 4%)*
A fruity, aromatic, fairly hoppy, bitter beer.

Barn Ale Special *(OG 1042.5, ABV 4.5%)* ◆
The original Barn Ale: predominantly malty, fruity and hoppy in taste and nose, and tawny/amber in colour. Fairly strong in flavour: the initial, sharp, malty and fruity taste leaves a dry, bitter-sweet, fruity aftertaste. It can be slightly sulphurous.

Dark Roast Ale *(OG 1048, ABV 5%)*

Gold *(OG 1048, ABV 5%)*

OLD MILL

Old Mill Brewery Ltd, Mill Street, Snaith, Goole, Yorkshire, DN14 9HU
Tel (01405) 861813
Fax (01405) 862789
Website www.oldmillbrewery.co.uk
Tours by arrangement

⊛ A small craft brewery opened in 1983 in a 200-year-old former malt kiln and corn mill. A new brewhouse was installed in 1991 to increase the brew-length to 60 barrels. The brewery is building its tied estate (now 17 houses). The innovation of selling beer in plastic, non-returnable handicasks has meant that the beer can now be found nationwide. Around 200 free trade outlets are supplied direct from the brewery. A bottling plant installed in 1997 sees occasional use. Seasonal beers: Nellie Dene (ABV 3.5%, August), Black Jack (ABV 5%, winter).

Traditional Mild *(OG 1035, ABV 3.45%)* ◆
A satisfying roast malt flavour dominates this easy-drinking, quality dark mild.

Nellie Dene *(OG 1035, ABV 3.5%)* ◆
A well-hopped, straw-coloured beer with hops throughout, slightly fruity in the middle, and a refreshing bitter finish. Lots of flavour for its strength.

Traditional Bitter *(OG 1038, ABV 3.9%)* ◆
A malty nose is carried through to its initial flavour. Bitterness runs throughout.

Old Curiosity *(OG 1044, ABV 4.5%)* ◆
Slightly sweet amber brew, malty to start with. Malt flavours all the way through.

Bullion *(OG 1045, ABV 4.7%)* ◆
The malty and hoppy aroma is followed by a neat mix of hop and fruit tastes within an enveloping maltiness. Dark brown/amber in colour.

Blackjack *(OG 1050, ABV 5%)*

OLDE SWAN

Olde Swan Brewery, 89 Halesowen Road, Netherton, Dudley, West Midlands, DY2 9PY
Tel (01384) 253075
Tours by arrangement

⊛ The welcome return of a once-famous and much-loved brew-pub, best known in the old days as 'Ma Pardoe's', after the matriarch who ruled it for years. The pub has been licensed since 1835 and the present brewery and pub were built in 1863. Brewing continued until 1988, and restarted in 2001. The plant brews primarily for the on-site pub with some beer available to the trade. Seasonal beer: Black Widow (ABV 6.7%, winter).

Original *(OG 1034, ABV 3.5%)*

Dark Swan *(OG 1039, ABV 3.9%)*
A rich dark mild full of flavour.

Entire *(OG 1043, ABV 4.4%)*
A premium bitter beer.

Bumblehole *(OG 1052, ABV 5.2%)*

OLD WHEELTON

Marsden Inns Ltd, Old Wheelton Brewery, Dressers Arms, Briers Brow, Wheelton, Chorley, Lancs, PR6 8HD
Tel (01254) 830041
Fax (01254) 832899
E-mail dressers.arms@virgin.net
Tours by arrangement

⊛ Steve Turner started brewing at the Dresser's Arms in 2001. A purpose-built, two-barrel plant is situated in the brewery, built next to the pub with a glass-panelled viewing area behind the bar. Old Wheelton is part of the Marsden Inns Group which owns six pubs in the North-west. The beers are currently only supplied to the Dresser's Arms and local beer festivals. Seasonal beer: Winterbrew (ABV 4.5%).

Big Frank's Bitter *(OG 1041, ABV 4.1%)*

Just a Flyer *(OG 1042, ABV 4.2%)*

Milk of Amnesia *(OG 1044, ABV 4.4%)*

OLD WHITE BEAR

Old White Bear and Brewery, 6 Keighley Road, Cross Hills, Keighley, W Yorkshire, BD20 7RN
Tel (01535) 632115
Fax (01535) 634875
Tours by arrangement

⊛ The brewery was founded in 1993 by former Goose Eye Brewer Bryan Eastell, and was taken over by the Naylor family with Keith Allatt as brewer. The brewery is unusual as it is operated in property owned by Laurel, now part of Enterprise Inns, whose tie limits the beers on sale. Six other outlets are supplied.

Old Bear Bitter *(OG 1038, ABV 3.9%)* ◆
A refreshing and easy-to-drink bitter. The balance of malt and hops gives way to a short, dry, bitter aftertaste.

OLDERSHAW

**Oldershaw Brewery,
12 Harrowby Hall Estate,
Grantham, Lincs, NG31 9HB
Tel (01476) 572135
Fax (01476) 572193
E-mail goldbrew@lineone.net
Website www.oldershawbrewery.co.uk**
Tours by arrangement

⊗ Experienced home-brewer Gary Oldershaw and his wife Diane set up the brewery at their home in 1997. Grantham's first brewery for 30 years, Oldershaw now supplies 60 local free houses. It concentrates on supplying outlets direct and is enjoying steady growth. A third fermenting vessel was added in 1999 to increase capacity to 20 barrels a week. The Oldershaws plan to introduce some small-scale bottling, to include Old Boy, Yuletide, Royal Blonde and Grantham Stout. Seasonal beers: Sunnydaze (ABV 4%, summer wheat beer, May-Aug), Topers Tipple (ABV 4.5%, Nov-Feb), Yuletide (ABV 5.2%, Nov-Dec).

Harrowby Bitter *(OG 1036, ABV 3.6%)* ◆
Bitter and hoppy session beer, light brown in colour. Faint fruit and malt support the slow-dying hop character.

High Dyke *(OG 1039, ABV 3.9%)*
Golden and moderately bitter. A predominantly hoppy session beer.

Newton's Drop *(OG 1041, ABV 4.1%)* ◆
Balanced malt and hops but with a strong bitter, lingering taste in this mid-brown beer.

Ermine Ale *(OG 1042, ABV 4.2%)*
Golden brown with a fruity hop the dominant feature on nose and taste giving a bitterness that lasts; malt plays a supporting role.

Caskade *(OG 1042, ABV 4.2%)*
Pale, golden beer brewed with American Cascade hops to give a distinctive floral, hoppy flavour and aroma, and a clean lasting finish.

Grantham Stout *(OG 1043, ABV 4.3%)*
Dark brown and smooth with rich roast malt flavour, supported by some fruit and bitterness. A long, moderately dry finish.

Ahtanum Gold *(OG 1043, ABV 4.3%)*
A gold-coloured, fruity, hoppy beer balanced with some maltiness. Moderately bitter.

Regal Blonde
(OG 1043, ABV 4.4%) ◆
Straw-coloured lager-style beer with a good malt/hop balance throughout; strong bitterness on the taste lingers.

Old Boy *(OG 1047, ABV 4.8%)* ◆
A full-bodied amber ale, fruity and bitter with a hop/fruit aroma. The malt that backs the taste dies in the long finish.

ORCHARD

**Deltacloud Ltd, Orchard Brewery Bar,
15 Market Hill, Barnsley,
Yorkshire, S70 2PX
Tel/Fax (01226) 288906
Email orchard@barboy.net
Website www.orchardbrewery.co.uk**
Tours by arrangement

⊚ The Orchard Brewery Bar opened in 1999 after being converted from a shop. The micro-brewery is situated behind the bar and produces between 10 and 15 barrels a week. The brewery also supplies other pubs within the company and also to the free trade. Eight pubs are owned, three serving cask-conditioned beer.

Orchard Bitter *(OG 1037, ABV 3.9%)*

Pitt Top *(OG 1037, ABV 3.9%)*

Jubilee *(OG 1040, ABV 4.2%)*

Tyke *(OG 1044, ABV 4.6%)*

Orchard Gold *(OG 1050, ABV 5.2%)*

ORGANIC

**Organic Brewhouse,
Unit 1, Higher Bochym Workshops,
Cury Cross Lanes, Helston,
Cornwall, TR12 7AZ
Tel (01326) 241555
E-mail a.hamer@btclick.com**
Tours by arrangement

⊗ The brewery was set up by Andy Hamer in 2000 on the Lizard Peninsular. It is dedicated to brewing exclusively organic beers, using its own source of natural mineral water. Set up as a mini 'tower' system (the brewing process flowing logically from floor to floor), production has increased to three regular beers and Wolf Rock, a winter stout. About 20 local outlets are supplied regularly, and the beers occasionally head north with wholesalers. Lizard Point won its class at Cornwall Beer Festival in St Ives in 2000. Seasonal: Wolf Rock (ABV 5%, winter). All the beers are also available bottle-conditioned and are suitable for vegetarians.

Lizard Point *(OG 1038, ABV 4%)*

Serpentine Dark Ale
(OG 1042, ABV 4.5%)

Black Rock *(OG 1044, ABV 4.7%)*

ORKNEY

Orkney Brewery Ltd, Quoyloo, Sandwick, Orkney, KW16 3LT
Tel (01856) 841802
Fax (01856) 841754
E-mail beer@orkneybrewery.co.uk
Website www.orkneybrewery.co.uk
Tours occasionally by arrangement for CAMRA groups

⊛ Set up in 1988 in an old school building by former licensee Roger White, the brewery was completely modernised in 1995 with new buildings replacing a single cramped room. The brewery is run along strict ecological lines with its own water supply and unique effluent control system. There are plans for a new fermenting room/visitor centre if funds will allow. The beers are available nationwide via wholesalers. Occasional beer: White Christmas (ABV 5%, December).

Raven Ale *(OG 1038, ABV 3.8%)*
Both citrus and hedgerow fruits are evident in this golden brown, quaffable bitter. Hops balance the sweetish taste and carry through to the satisfying dry, bitter finish.

Northern Light *(OG 1040, ABV 4%)*
A lager-coloured beer, hoppy and refreshing. Fruity hop notes can develop a true lager nose. A late copper hop is intense without being cloying.

Dragonhead Stout *(OG 1040, ABV 4%)*
A strong, dark malt aroma flows into the taste in this superb Scottish stout. The roast malt continues to dominate the aftertaste, and blends with chocolate to develop a strong, dry finish. Hard to find.

Red MacGregor *(OG 1040, ABV 4%)*
Smooth-tasting, full-bodied, tawny-red ale. A powerful smack of fruit and hop is a feature of this complex beer.

Dark Island *(OG 1045, ABV 4.6%)*
Dark, beautifully balanced and full of roast, malt and fruit, and a hint of caramel. A sweetish taste leads to a long-lasting, roasted, slightly bitter finish. Full-bodied and deceptively drinkable. If beer was whisky, this would be it. Champion beer of Scotland 2000.

Skullsplitter *(OG 1080, ABV 8.5%)*
An intense velvet malt nose with hints of apple, nutmeg and spice. Hops to the fore balanced by satiny smooth malt with fruity spicy edges leading to a long dry finish with a hint of nut. Champion winter beer of Britain 2001.

OSSETT

Ossett Brewing Company Ltd, t/a Ossett Brewery, Low Mill Road, Ossett, W Yorkshire, WF5 8ND
Tel (01924) 261333
Fax (01924) 261356
E-mail brewery@ossett.co.uk
Website Ossett-brewery.co.uk
Tours by arrangement

⊛ Brewing started in 1998 at the rear of the Brewers Pride public house. The purpose-built brewery is wholly owned by Robert Lawson, an ex-Tetley brewer. When sales rose to 20 barrels a week, new fermenters were installed in mid-2000, increasing capacity to 35 barrels a week. Further expansion is due in the coming year and bottled beers will be introduced. Direct delivery is made to more than 100 outlets and others through selected wholesalers. Silver King won a national SIBA award at the 2001 annual competition in Lincoln. Seasonal Beers: Silver Fox (ABV 4.1%, spring), Silver Link (ABV 4.6%, summer), Ace of Spades Porter (ABV 4.5%, winter), Ruby Mild (ABV 4.2%, autumn), Oregon Pale (ABV 4.7%, Sept-Oct), Hercules (ABV 6.5%, Jan-March), Winter Warmer (ABV 6%, Dec-March).

Pale Gold *(OG 1038, ABV 3.8%)*
A light, refreshing pale ale with a floral/spicy aroma derived from American hops.

Silver Shadow *(OG 1038, ABV 3.9%)*
A pale session beer of considerable character despite its low gravity. The first Ossett brew to use eco-friendly English hedgerow hops.

Silver King *(OG 1041, ABV 4.3%)*
A lager-style beer with a crisp, dry flavour and citrus fruity aroma.

Dazzler *(OG 1044, ABV 4.5%)*
A delicately-flavoured pale ale. The smooth, slightly spicy aroma is derived from use of classic English Goldings hops.

Fine Fettle *(OG 1048, ABV 4.8%)*
A strong yet refreshing pale ale with a crisp clean flavour and citrus fruity aroma.

Excelsior *(OG 1051, ABV 5.2%)*
A mellow yet full flavour that develops into fruity dryness on the palate. A fresh, hoppy aroma with citrus, toffee and floral characteristics.

OTTER

Otter Brewery Ltd, Mathayes, Luppitt, Honiton, Devon, EX14 4SA
Tel (01404) 891285
Fax (01404) 891124
E-mail info@otterbrewery.com
Website www.otterbrewery.com
Tours via trade only

⊗ The Otter Brewery was established in 1990 by David and Mary Ann McCaig. The brewery is beautifully located in the Blackdown Hills, between Taunton and Honiton, and makes the most of the local spring water that feeds the River Otter. David had previously brewed with Whitbread for 17 years and Mary Ann's family have been brewers for a number of generations. Today, still maintaining its family roots, the brewery employs local friends and family and delivers Otter Beers to more than 200 outlets within a 40-mile radius across the West Country. 200 outlets are supplied direct. Seasonal beer: Otter Claus (ABV 5%, Christmas).

Bitter *(OG 1036, ABV 3.6%)*
Well-balanced amber session bitter with a fruity nose and bitter taste and aftertaste.

Bright *(OG 1039, ABV 4.3%)*
Fruit and hop aroma in a straw-coloured bitter with a strong bitter finish.

Ale *(OG 1043, ABV 4.5%)*
Full-bodied best bitter. Malty aroma and

taste predominate with a fruity taste and finish.

Head *(OG 1054, ABV 5.8%)*
Fruity aroma and taste with a pleasant bitter finish. Dark brown and full-bodied.

OULTON

Oulton Ales Ltd,
Harbour Road Industrial Estate,
Oulton Broad, Lowestoft,
Suffolk, NR32 3LZ
Tel (01502) 587905
Tours by arrangement

⊗ Formerly Green Jack, the company was formed in 1993 by Rosemary Moore and Timothy Dunford on the former Forbes site. Tim left in 2002 and has been granted the original name, hence the change to Oulton Ales. The company hopes to increase to 1,200 barrels to meet pub demand and also for bottling. Two fermenting tanks and a mash tun have been purchased to allow for expansion. 20-25 outlets are supplied direct, as well as its own three pubs. Wholesalers also take the beers.

Oulton Bitter *(OG 1037, ABV 3.5%)*

Mild *(OG 1037, ABV 3.7%)*

Albatross *(OG 1043, ABV 4.2%)*

Wet and Windy *(OG 1043, ABV 4.3%)*

Excelsior *(OG 1047, ABV 4.6%)*

Gone Fishing *(OG 1051, ABV 5%)*

OUTLAW

See Rooster's.

PACIFIC ORIENTAL

Pacific Oriental, 1 Bishopsgate,
London, EC2N 3AB
Tel (020) 7621 9988

Pacific Oriental is a state-of-the-art boutique brewery based in the heart of the City of London. Brewing started in 1998 and the permanent brews are a Pilsner lager and a bitter with at least one other beer always on offer. These include a wheat beer, a golden ale and a red beer. The copper brewhouse is on full display at the front of the restaurant. The beers are filtered and served by mixed gas dispense. Beers: Bishops (ABV 4.5%), Pils (ABV 5%).

PACKHORSE

Packhorse Brewing Co Ltd,
5 Somers Road, Southsea,
Portsmouth,
Hampshire, PO5 4PR
Tel (02392) 750450

Packhorse Brewery was resurrected in Portsmouth from the former Ashford Brewery. It produces infusion mash, 100 per cent malt ales as opposed to the decoction lagers of the Ashford days. Seasonal beer: Rudolph's Revenge (ABV 7.9%).

Southern Star ASA *(ABV 3.5%)*

Best Bitter *(ABV 3.8%)*

Old Pompey *(ABV 4.8%)*

PALMER

JC & RH Palmer Ltd, Old Brewery,
Bridport, Dorset, DT6 4JA
Tel (01308) 422396
Fax (01308) 421149
E-mail enquiries@palmersbrewery.com
Website www.palmersbrewery.com
Shop Mon-Thu, Apr-Oct, 9-8, Nov-Mar, 9-6, Fri-Sat 9-8
Tours by arrangement (01308) 427500

⊗ Palmers is Britain's only thatched brewery, founded in 1794, and situated by the sea in an idyllic location in west Dorset. The company is run by brothers John and Cleeves Palmer, great-grandsons of Robert Henry and John Cleeves Palmer, who bought the company in 1896. Its tenanted estate of 56 pubs all offer real ale. A further 150 free trade outlets are supplied direct, and Palmer's beers reach a wider audience throughout the south via wholesalers. Dorset Gold was added to the portfolio in 1999, followed by Copper Ale in 2001. Seasonal beer: Dorset Gold (ABV 3.7%). Occasional beer: Tally Ho! (ABV 5.5%). Bottle-conditioned beers: IPA (ABV 4.2%), Palmers 200 (ABV 5%) and Tally Ho! (ABV 5.5%).

Bridport Bitter *(OG 1030, ABV 3.2%)* ⬘
A light beer with a hoppy aroma, a bitter hoppy taste with some malt, and a bitter aftertaste.

Copper Ale *(OG 1037, ABV 3.7%)*
A fruity, hoppy session ale.

IPA *(OG 1040, ABV 4.2%)* ⬘
A deep copper beer that is hoppy and bitter throughout. Fruit and malt undertones give some balance in the aroma and taste, and there is a lingering bitter aftertaste.

200 *(OG 1052, ABV 5%)* ⬘
Full-bodied, caramel sweetness and fruity aroma are balanced with a dry finish, not excessively bitter; a deep-copper ale, originally brewed to mark the brewery's 200th anniversary.

PARADISE

Unit 2, The Old Creamery, Wrenbury,
Nantwich, Cheshire, CW5 8EX
Tel/Fax (01270) 780916
Tours by arrangement

Paradise was founded by partners John Wood and Nick Platt, who traded as Paradise Plastics and turned to brewing when there was a recession in the plastics industry. The brewery is based in a former creamery. Seasonal beer: Rum Old Ale (ABV 6.3%).

Marbury Mild *(ABV 3.6%)*

Aston Light *(ABV 3.8%)*

Station Master *(ABV 4.3%)*

Dabbers Gold *(ABV 5%)*

Up the Junction *(ABV 5.5%)*

PARISH

Parish Brewery, Courtyard of the Old Brewery Inn, Somerby, Leicestershire, LE14 2PZ
Tel (01664) 454801
Fax (01664) 454777
Tours by arrangement

Parish started life at Burrough on the Hill in 1982 and moved to its present location after expanding to a 20-barrel plant in 1992. The Parish Brewery was one of the first brew-pubs to start up in the Midlands and is famous for brewing the strongest beer in the world, with an ABV of 23%, as listed in the Guinness Book of World Records. It currently supplies 12 local outlets.

Mild *(OG 1038, ABV 3.7%)*

Parish Special Bitter or PSB *(OG 1040, ABV 3.9%)*

Farm Gold *(OG 1039, ABV 3.9%)*

Somerby Premium *(OG 1040, ABV 4%)*

Poachers Ale *(OG 1060, ABV 6%)*

Baz's Bonce Blower *(OG 1100, ABV 10-11%)*

PHOENIX

Oak Brewing Co Ltd t/a Phoenix Brewery, Phoenix Brewery, Green Lane, Heywood, Greater Manchester, OL10 2EP
Tel (01706) 627009
E-mail phoenixbrewery@btclick.co.uk
Tours by arrangement

A company established as Oak Brewery in 1982 at Ellesmere Port, it moved in 1991 to Heywood and changed its name in 1996 to Phoenix (after the original name of the brewery it occupies). It now supplies more than 450 free trade outlets mostly in the North-west and West Yorkshire. Seasonal beers: Black Shadow (ABV 4%, May), Whirlwind (ABV 4.1%, October), Jovian (ABV 4.2%, February), Snowbound (ABV 4.3%, Nov-Feb), Spinning Jenny (ABV 4.3%, October), March Hare (ABV 4.4%, March), May Fly (ABV 4.4%, May), Christmas Kiss (ABV 4.5%, Nov-Dec), Midsummer Madness (ABV 4.5%, June-Aug), Tennis Elbow (ABV 4.5%, July), Sticky Wicket (ABV 4.7%, June-Sept), Struggling Monkey (ABV 4.7%, June), White Tornado (ABV 4.3%, Sept-Oct), Flashflood (ABV 4.1%, Sept-Xmas), Last Leaf (ABV 4.5%, Oct-Nov), Porter (ABV 5%, Nov-Jan), Humbug (ABV 7%, Oct-Jan; matured for six months), Golden Glow (ABV 6.5%, Xmas).

Bantam *(ABV 3.5%)*
Light brown beer with a fruity aroma. Balance of malt, citrus fruit and hop in taste. Hoppy, bitter finish.

Monkey Town Mild *(ABV 3.9%)*

Best Bitter *(ABV 3.9%)*

Arizona *(ABV 4.1%)*

Pale Moonlight *(ABV 4.2%)*

Hopwood Bitter *(ABV 4.3%)*
Amber beer with a hoppy, fruity nose and palate. Dry, hoppy finish.

White Monk *(ABV 4.5%)*

Old Oak *(ABV 4.5%)*
A well-balanced, brown beer with a multitude of mellow fruit flavours. Malt and hops balance the strong fruitiness in the aroma and taste, and the finish is malty, fruity and dry.

Thirsty Moon *(ABV 4.6%)*
Fruity, malty aroma to this amber beer. Malt, fruit and bitter taste and a dry, hoppy finish.

Double Dagger *(ABV 5%)*
A pale brown, malty brew, more pleasantly dry and light than its gravity would suggest. Moderately fruity throughout; a hoppy bitterness in the mouth balances the strong graininess.

Wobbly Bob *(ABV 6%)*
A red/brown beer with a malty, fruity aroma. Strongly malty and fruity in flavour and quite hoppy, with the sweetness yielding to a dryness in the aftertaste.

PICKS

Picks Brewery, Red Lion Hotel, Willows Lane, Green Haworth, Accrington, Lancashire, BB5 3SJ
Tel (01254) 233194
Tours by arrangement

The brewery was originally based in 1998 in the cellar of the Red Lion pub in Green Haworth using home-made equipment, but in 2000 it moved into a nearby industrial unit, converting five-barrel beer tanks to make hot liquor tank, mash tun, copper, one fermenter and two conditioning tanks. Owner Steven Pickles has started supplying the free trade, with just some local outlets. Six regular beers are produced and he plans to produce a real lager for the summer.

Moorgate Mild *(OG 1035, ABV 3.5%)*
A smooth, grainy, chocolate and coffee cream mild. Red-brown in colour, it is not oversweet, with a long, gently hopped aftertaste.

Pale Ale *(OG 1036, ABV 3.7%)*
Soft lemon and honey notes at the beginning, with a lingering bitter-dry end. A straw-coloured refreshing pint.

Bedlam Bitter *(OG 1038, ABV 3.9%)*
Complex sour and barley sugar flavours. Astringent throughout, pepper-dry at the end. A red-gold bitter.

Lions Main *(OG 1041, ABV 4.2%)*

Porter *(OG 1042, ABV 4.5%)*
Impenetrably dark beer, it has an immediate strong black coffee flavour, leading to a dry finish. A pronounced, teeth-coating maltiness throughout.

Lions Pride *(OG 1049, ABV 5.4%)*
A pale premium bitter, strong but sweet and deceptively easy-drinking. Golden in colour, it builds to a malty finish.

PICTISH

Pictish Brewing Company,
Unit 9, Canalside Industrial Estate,
Woodbine Street East, Rochdale,
Lancs, OL16 5LB
Tel/Fax (01706) 522227
Tours by arrangement

⊛ The brewery established in 2000 by Richard Sutton, formerly senior brewer for the north with the Firkin Brewery until Punch Taverns took over the former Allied Domecq estate and closed the Firkin chain in 1999. The brewery supplies free trade outlets in the North-west direct. Seasonal beers: Summer Solstice (ABV 4.7%, May-Aug), Porter (4.4%, Nov-March). There are regular monthly specials.

Brewers Gold *(OG 1038, ABV 3.8%)* ◆
Yellow in colour, with a hoppy, fruity nose. Strong hop/fruit flavour with a dry, bitterness coming through in the aftertaste.

Celtic Warrior *(OG 1042, ABV 4.2%)*

For Crown Inn, Bacup:
Bare Arts *(OG 1035, ABV 3.5%)*

IBA *(OG 1050, ABV 5%)*

PILGRIM

Pilgrim Ales, The Old Brewery,
West Street, Reigate, Surrey, RH2 9BL
Tel (01737) 222651
Fax (01737) 225785
E-mail david@pilgrim.co.uk
Website www.pilgrim.co.uk

⊗ Set up by Dave Roberts in 1982, and based in Reigate since 1985, Pilgrim has gradually increased its capacity and its beers have won both local and national awards, although sales are mostly concentrated in the Surrey area (around 60 outlets). Pilgrim owns one tied house, the Rising Sun, Epsom. Seasonal beers: Autumnal (ABV 4.5%, Sept-Oct), Excalibur (ABV 4.5%, March-May), Pudding (ABV 7.3%, Nov-Jan). Bottle-conditioned beers: Springbock (ABV 5.2%, brewed by Hepworth of Horsham), Pudding (ABV 6.8%). The draught version of Springbock, originally cask-conditioned, is now a pressurised keg beer.

Surrey Bitter *(OG 1037, ABV 3.7%)* ◆
A clean, fruity, well-balanced session bitter with nice citrus hop notes. The hoppy bitterness becomes more pronounced in the finish.

Porter *(OG 1040, ABV 4%)* ◆
Black beer with a good balance of dark malts with hints of berry fruit. Roast character present throughout to give a bitter-sweet finish.

Progress *(OG 1040, ABV 4%)* ◆
Tawny in colour, with a malty flavour and aroma, although hops are more evident in the taste. Some spicy notes.

Crusader *(OG 1049, ABV 4.9%)*

Talisman *(OG 1049, ABV 5%)* ◆
A strong ale with a tawny red colour, a fruity roast malt flavour, and a faint hoppiness. Caramel is also evident.

PITFIELD

Pitfield Brewery, The Beer Shop,
14 Pitfield Street,
London, N1 6EY
Tel (020) 7739 3701
Website www.pitfieldbeershop.co.uk
Shop 11-7 Mon-Fri; 10-4 Sat.
Tours by arrangement

⊗ The Beer Shop was founded in 1980 to supply real ale and international bottled beers. A five-barrel brewery was installed to produce Pitfield Bitter. Dark Star was introduced in 1985 and in 1987 won the title of Best New Beer and was runner-up in the Champion Beer of Britain competition. The following year, it won the overall Champion Beer of Britain title; the beer has now been renamed Black Eagle. In the summer of 1996 the Beer Shop moved into larger premises, with the brewery in one building and the shop next door. In 2000, in response to the success of Eco Warrior, Pitfield converted all its beers to organic ingredients. Six outlets are supplied direct.

Original *(OG 1037, ABV 3.7%)* ◆
Bitterness balanced with sweetness producing a pleasant, hoppy/fruity bitter. Dry finish.

Shoreditch Stout *(OG 1040, ABV 4%)*

East Kent Goldings
(OG 1042, ABV 4.2%) ◆
Impressive, dryish and fruity yellow beer with a pleasant level of bitterness and a lingering citrus flavour. Some floral notes on the aroma.

Eco Warrior *(OG 1045, ABV 4.5%)* ◆
Yellow/gold ale with a smooth, rounded mouthfeel, balanced malt and hops and a bitter, dry aftertaste.

Hoxton Best Bitter
(OG 1048, ABV 4.8%) ◆
Previously named Hoxton Heavy, a smooth, deceptively easy-drinking beer for the strength. Malt and fruit are well-balanced and pear notes persist in the dry aftertaste.

Black Eagle *(OG 1050, ABV 5%)* ◆
A light-drinking strong old ale, black with red hues, a lasting roast malt flavour and a malty, dryish aftertaste.

Shoreditch 1850 Porter
(OG 1050, ABV 5%)

PLASSEY

Plassey Brewery, The Plassey,
Eyton, Wrexham, LL13 0SP
Tel (01978) 780922
Fax (01978) 781195
Website www.plasseybrewery.co.uk
Shop 1.30-5 Wed-Sun winter; 1.30-5 Tue-Sun summer
Tours by arrangement

Brewery founded in 1985 on the 250-acre Plassey Estate, which also incorporates a touring caravan park, craft centres, a golf course, three licensed outlets for Plassey's ales, and a brewery shop. 30 free trade outlets also take the beers. Seasonal beer: Ruddy Rudolph (ABV 4.5%, Christmas). Bottle-conditioned beer: Royal Welch Fusilier (ABV 4.5%).

Bitter *(OG 1041, ABV 4%)* ◆
Full-bodied and distinctive best bitter. Good balance of hops and fruit flavours with a lasting dry bitter aftertaste.

Royal Welch Fusilier
(OG 1046, ABV 4.5%) ▯

Welsh Stout *(OG 1046, ABV 4.6%)* ◆
A dry, roasty stout, sweetish; a long, dry finish.

Cwrw Tudno *(OG 1048, ABV 5%)* ▯◆
A mellow sweetish premium beer with classic Plassey flavours of fruit and hops.

Dragon's Breath *(OG 1060, ABV 6%)*
A fruity, strong bitter, smooth and quite sweet, though not cloying, with an intense, fruity aroma. A dangerously drinkable winter warmer.

PLOUGH INN

Bodicote Brewery, Plough Inn, Bodicote, 9 High Street, Bodicote, Oxford, OX15 4BZ
Tel (01295) 262327
E-mail bodicotebrewery@tinyworld.co.uk
Website www.banbury-cross.co.uk/bodicotebrewery
Tours by arrangement

⊗ Brewery founded in 1982 at the Plough, which has been in the same hands since 1957. Two other outlets are also supplied with its full-mash beers. Two popular, week-long beer festivals are held each year in February and August. Seasonal beers: Three Goslings (ABV 3.9%, May-Oct), Old English Porter (ABV 4.4%, Oct-May).

Bodicote Bitter *(OG 1035, ABV 3.3%)*

No. 9 *(OG 1044, ABV 4.3%)*

Triple X *(OG 1060, ABV 6.3%)*

POACHERS*

Poachers Brewery,
Unit 4, Swinderby Industrial Park, Swinderby, Lincs
Tel 01522 510237
Website www.poachersbeer.co.uk

The brewery was established in 2001 by Ian Baker and George Batterbee on what was formerly an RAF station at Swinderby in Lincolnshire. Initially, a 2.5-barrel plant was used but has now been replaced by a five-barrel one. Regular outlets are supplied direct throughout Lincolnshire and Norfolk with plans to gradually expand the area of operation. Bottling was scheduled to start in 2002. The brewery also owns an off-licence on Lincoln High Street, which stocks bottled beers from micros as well as a selection of Belgian beers.

Trembling Rabbit *(OG 1034, ABV 3.4%)*
Rich dark mild with a smooth malty flavour and a slightly bitter finish.

Shy Talk *(OG 1037, ABV 3.7%)*
Clean-tasting session beer, pale gold in colour; slightly bitter finish, dry hopped.

Pride *(OG 1040, ABV 4%)*
Amber bitter brewed using Cascade hops producing a wonderful flavour and aroma that lingers.

Trail *(OG 1042, ABV 4.2%)* ◆
A flowery hop-nosed, mid-brown beer with a well-balanced but bitter taste that stays with the malt, becoming more apparent in the drying finish.

Den *(OG 1042, ABV 4.2%)* ◆
Pale amber with a musty fruit hop aroma that gives way to a citrus hoppiness in the taste, with a moderate bitterness that brings it to a nice malty aftertaste.

Dick *(OG 1045, ABV 4.5%)*
Ruby red bitter, smooth fruity flavour balanced by the bitterness of Goldings hops.

Black Crow *(OG 1045, ABV 4.5%)*
Dry stout with burnt toffee and caramel flavour.

Pytiak (Per-Tash) *(OG 1049, ABV 5%)*
Cask-conditioned lager brewed in the Czech style using Saaz hops and caramalt.

De Wilderer *(OG 1050, ABV 5.1%)*
Brewed using the famous smoked rauch malts from Bamberg. A smoked beer with depth and character, dark ruby in colour with an intense lingering aftertaste.

POINTS WEST

Points West Brewery,
Plymouth College of Further Education, Kings Road, Devonport, Plymouth, Devon, PL1 5QG
Tel (01752) 305700
Fax (01752) 305888
E-mail broome@scfe.ac.uk
Website www.pcfe.ac.uk
Tours any time

⊗ A five-barrel plant set up for catering students. It is not totally commercial, but will sell to pubs and beer festivals if they approach the college. Most beer is sold through bottling either for individuals or organizations such as the National Trust. It is hoped to expand this side of the production. Bottle-conditioned beers: Players Ale (ABV 4.8%), sold only at Plymouth Argyll Football Club; Buckland Abbey Ale (ABV 4.2%) and Drakes Drum

'A (ABV 4.8%) for National Trust. easonal beer: Christmas Rooster ABV 7.5%, Oct-Jan.)

ilgrim PA *(OG 1041, ABV 4.2%)*

rakes Drum IPA *(OG 1046, ABV 4.8%)*

eonardo Wheat Beer *OG 1054, ABV 5.5%)*

POOLE

Poole Brewery, The Brewhouse, 68 High Street, Poole, Dorset, BH15 IDA
Tel (01202) 682345
Tours by arrangement, limited to CAMRA members

Brewery established in 1980 by David Rawlins, who opened the Brewhouse pub in 1983, relocating the brewery to buildings at its rear. The brewery now has a capacity to brew about 1,000 barrels a year, and serves more than 15 outlets direct with a widespread free trade through wholesalers. Seasonal/occasional beers: Pie-eyed Pudding (ABV 4.5%).

Dolphin Best Bitter *(OG 1038, ABV 3.8%)*
The brewery's original session bitter: amber-coloured and well balanced.

Bedrock Bitter *(ABV 4.2%)*

Bosun Bitter *(OG 1045, ABV 4.6%)*
The brewery's top-selling beer. A rich, amber-coloured beer with a smooth, crisp, powerful malty flavour and a pronounced hoppy aftertaste.

For Hogshead (on demand)
Hedgehog *(ABV 5.2%)*

PORT MAHON*

Port Mahon Brewery, Cask and Cutler, 1 Henry Street, Sheffield, South Yorkshire,S3 7EQ
Tel (0114) 2492295

⊗ Brewing commenced in 2001 in a purpose-built brewery situated behind the Cask and Cutler, initially using a one-barrel plant. Several experimental brews have been produced so far while a four-barrel plant is being commissioned. It is planned to brew a permanent house bitter and a range of other beer styles that will alternate with the other guest ales in the pub. The beer range is yet to be established.

PORTCHESTER

Portchester Brewery, 6 Audret Close, Portchester, Fareham, Hants, PO16 9ER
Tel/Fax (01329) 512918
E-mail gill.stone@portchesterbrewery.co.uk
Website www.portchesterbrewery.co.uk
Tours by arrangement

⊗ A tiny brewery, able to produce just nine gallons a time, set up in the garage of Gill Stone's home. After years of home-brewing, Gill was encouraged by her husband Graham (both are keen CAMRA members) to 'go commercial' in 2000, as they were fed up with over-priced beer in pubs. Dr Graham Stone used his knowledge from his biology and physics doctorate to help Gill make the perfect pint. She is now supplying a few pubs and clubs in the locality, and has upgraded to a 2.5-barrel plant. The beers are named in honour of Portchester Castle. Seasonal: XP (ABV 6.2%, Christmas).

Bastion *(ABV 3.8%)*

Slingshot *(ABV 4.2%)*

Catapult *(ABV 4.8%)*

Battering Ram *(ABV 5%)*

PORTER

Porter Brewing Co Ltd, Rossendale Brewery, The Griffin Inn, 84-86 Hud Rake, Haslingden, Lancs, BB4 5AF
Tel/Fax (01706) 214021
Tours by arrangement

⊗ The Griffin Inn opened in 1994 and now has five tied houses. All four pubs sell a minimum of five house ales. All the pubs serve cask ale and a few other local outlets also take the beer. Occasional/seasonal beers: Timmy's Ginger Beer (ABV 4.2%, March and August), Stout (ABV 5.5%, Sept-Oct), Sleighed (ABV 6.5%, Dec-Jan), Celebration Ale (ABV 7.1%, July-Aug). All beers leave the brewery as vegan products.

Dark Mild *(OG 1033, ABV 3.3%)*
A true dark mild, with a slight maltiness and a good hint of roast in the finish.

Floral Dance *(OG 1035, ABV 3.6%)*
Pale and fruity.

Bitter *(OG 1037, ABV 3.8%)* ◆
Unusually dark for a standard bitter, this beer has a dry and assertively bitter character that develops in the finish.

Railway Sleeper *(OG 1040, ABV 4.2%)*
Intensely bitter and hoppy.

Rossendale Ale *(OG 1041, ABV 4.2%)* ◆
A malty aroma leads to a complex, malt-dominated flavour supported by a dry, increasingly bitter finish.

Porter *(OG 1050, ABV 5%)*
A rich beer with a slightly sweet, malty start, counter-balanced with sharp bitterness and a noticeable roast barley dominance.

Sunshine *(OG 1050, ABV 5.3%)*
An intensely hoppy and bitter golden ale, full-bodied with some malt, a robust mouthfeel and a lingering bitterness.

POTTON

Potton Brewery Company, 10 Shannon Place, Potton, Sandy, Beds, SG19 2PZ
Tel (01767) 261042
Website www.potton-brewery.co.uk
Tours by arrangement

⊗ Run by Clive Towner and Robert Hearson, both ex-managers of Greene King at Biggleswade, they resurrected the Potton Brewery Company name after it disappeared as a result of a takeover in 1922. 100 outlets are supplied direct. Bottle-conditioned beers: Butlers Ale (ABV 4.3%), and Shambles. Potton also makes a draught cider, Sam's Potton Mix (ABV 6%). Seasonal beer: No-Ale (ABV 4.8%, Christmas).

Shannon IPA *(OG 1035, ABV 3.6%)*

Phoenix *(OG 1040, ABV 3.8%)*

Shambles *(OG 1042, ABV 4.3%)*

Village Bike *(OG 1042, ABV 4.3%)*

Potton Gold *(OG 1047, ABV 4.8%)*

Pride of Potton *(OG 1057, ABV 6%)* ◆
Impressive, robust amber ale with a malty aroma, malt and ripe fruit in the mouth, and a fading sweetness.

PRINCETOWN

Princetown Breweries Ltd, The Brewery, Tavistock Road, Princetown, Devon, PL20 6QF
Tel (01822) 890789
Fax (01822) 890798
Tours by arrangement

⊗ A brewery established in 1994 by a former Gibbs Mew and Hop Back brewer, capacity has been increased to 45 barrels a week. It supplies two hotels owned by a sister company, the pub next door and 16 other local outlets. Bottle-conditioned beer: Jail Ale.

Dartmoor IPA *(OG 1039.5, ABV 4%)* ◆
Flowery hop aroma and taste with a bitter aftertaste to this full-bodied, amber-coloured beer.

Jail Ale *(OG 1047.5, ABV 4.8%)* ◆
Hops and fruit predominate in the flavour of this mid-brown beer, which has a slightly sweet aftertaste.

QUAY

Lapin Noir Ltd t/a The Quay Brewery, Hope Square, Weymouth, Dorset, DT4 8TR
Tel/Fax (01305) 777515
E-mail mail@quaybrewery.com
Website quaybrewery.com
Shop at Brewers Quay 10-5.30 daily
Tours by arrangement via Timewalk at Brewers Quay

⊗ Founded in 1996 by Giles Smeath, he brews on a site that was formerly the Devenish & Groves brewery. The rest of the site is open to visitors as a Timewalk attraction showing the history of Weymouth; much of the old brewing plant is still on view. Giles plans to add two new 10-barrel fermenters. Seasonal beers: Silent Knight (ABV 5.9%, winter), Summer Knight (ABV 3.8%). Bottle-conditioned beers: Quay Steam Beer (ABV 4.5%), Organic Gold (ABV 4.7%), Old Rott (ABV 5%), Silent Knight. Organic Gold is suitable for vegetarians and vegans.

Weymouth Harbour Master *(OG 1036, ABV 3.6%)* ◆
Well-balanced, nut-brown session beer, sweetish, but not cloying, thanks to the dry finish. May be badged by pubs as a house beer.

Weymouth Best Bitter *(OG 1038, ABV 3.9%)*

Weymouth JD 1742 *(OG 1040, ABV 4.2%)* ◆
Clean-tasting, easy-drinking bitter. Well-balanced with lingering bitterness after moderate sweetness.

Quay Steam Beer *(OG 1043, ABV 4.5%)*

Weymouth Organic Gold *(OG 1045, ABV 4.7%)*

Old Rott *(OG 1048, ABV 5%)* ◆
Warming finish despite a rather light caramel and malt taste. Hint of sulphur and yeastiness throughout.

QUEEN'S HEAD & FAT GOD'S

🍺 The Queens Head and Fat God's Brewery, Iron Cross, Evesham, Worcs, WR11 8SH
Tel (01386) 871012 Fax (01386) 871362
E-mail andy@fatgodsbrewery.co.uk
Website www.fatgodsbrewery.co.uk
Tours by arrangement

⊗ The brewery, run by Andy and Kym Miller, opened in 1997 and was expanded in 2001. Most of the brewery's production is consumed at the Queens Head. Brewery tours tend to be light-hearted. Seasonal beer: Kym Miller Lager (ABV 5%)

Fat God's Bitter *(OG 1036, ABV 3.6%)* ◆
Balanced between maltiness and hoppiness, this mainly hoppy beer leaves a clean, dry aftertaste.

Morris Dancer *(OG 1039, ABV 3.9%)*

Fat Gods Mild *(OG 1040, ABV 4%)*

Porter of the Vale *(OG 1041, ABV 4.1%)*

Thunder and Lightning *(OG 1042, ABV 4.3%)* ◆
Malt is the main taste in this premium bitter. Hops are there in the mouth, but the final impression is one of malt.

Gods Wallop *(OG 1049, ABV 5%)*

RAILWAY TAVERN

🍺 Famous Railway Tavern Brewing Co, 58 Station Road, Brightlingsea, Essex, CO7 0DT
Tel (01206) 302581
Tours by arrangement

The brewery started life as a kitchen-sink affair, with Crab & Winkle Mild the staple brew. Crouch Vale Brewery obtained two fermenters from Vaux for the Railway Tavern and today two barrels are brewed every fortnight. It is hoped to increase this amount.

Crab & Winkle Mild *(OG 1040, ABV 3.7%)*

Sprat & Oyster Bitter *(OG 1040, ABV 3.7%)*

Bladderwrack Stout *(OG 1050, ABV 4.7%)*

RAINBOW

Rainbow Inn & Brewery, 73 Birmingham Road, Allesley Village, Coventry, W Midlands, CV5 9GT
Tel (024) 76402888
Fax (024) 76407415
Tours by arrangement

Pub brewery that started brewing in 1994 with a two-barrel plant, upgraded to four-barrels in 1996.

Piddlebrook *(OG 1037, ABV 3.8%)*

RAMSGATE*

Ramsgate Brewery, 98 Harbour Parade, Ramsgate, Kent, CT11 8LP
Tel (07967) 660060
Email info@ramsgatebrewery.co.uk
Website ramsgatebrewery.co.uk
Tours by arrangement

⊠ Ramsgate Brewery is part of the Ramsgate Royal Harbour Brewhouse and Bakers, a café bar built by Andy Barrett and Eddie Gadd in an old restaurant building, unused for 30 years. It has a five-barrel capacity and was opened in March 2002. Along with its own beer and bakery products, the site serves Belgian beers on draught an ever-increasing number in bottle.

Gadds No. 7 *(OG 1038, ABV 3.8%)*

Gadds No. 3 *(OG 1049, ABV 5%)*

RANDALLS

RW Randall Ltd, Vauxlaurens Brewery, St Julian's Avenue, St Peter Port, Guernsey, GY1 3JG
Tel (01481) 720134
Fax (01481) 713233
Shop 9-5
Tours by arrangement

⊠ Randalls Brewery was purchased by R H Randall from Joseph Gullick in 1868. With third, fourth and fifth generation Randalls currently working for the company, it is the Channel Islands only family independent brewery. Randalls produces four cask-conditioned beers that are on sale throughout Guernsey and also in some free trade outlets on the south coast of England. Randalls owns 17 pubs, all of which are tied but only seven serve cask beer. Do not confuse with Randalls Vautier of Jersey, which no longer brews.

R.W. RANDALL
BREWER & MALTSTER
BREWED SINCE 1868
VB
PATOIS

Mild *(OG 1034, ABV 3.4%)*

Pale Ale *(OG 1038, ABV 3.8%)*

Patois *(OG 1047, ABV 4.8%)* ◆
Amber in colour, with a hoppy aroma. Bitter and hoppy both in the palate and finish.

Stout *(OG 1058, ABV 5.5%)*

RAT & RATCHET

Rat & Ratchet, 40 Chapel Hill, Huddersfield, W Yorkshire, HD1 3EB
Tel (01484) 516734
Fax (01484) 300196
E-mail mail@ratandratchet.co.uk
Website www.ratandratchet.co.uk

⊛ A brew-pub with an extensive range of beers, it has been brewing since 1994 to supply the pub and beer festivals. The 3.5-barrel brew plant is the ex-Firkin equipment from the Firecracker & Firkin in Crawley. The beers are generally named with a rodent theme and are rarely repeated.

Trap Tickler *(ABV 3.9%)* ◆
Straw-coloured pale bitter with an intense citrus flavour. Fruit and malt are evident throughout, leading to a dry, zesty and bitter finish.

Church Mouse *(ABV 4.2%)*
Winner of Woking Beer Festival 2001 Bitter class.

RCH

RCH Brewery, West Hewish, Weston-super-Mare, Somerset, BS24 6RR
Tel (01934) 834447
Fax (01934) 834167
E-mail rchbrew@aol.com
Website www.rchbrewery.com
Shop. Yes

⊛ The brewery was originally installed by previous owners in the early 1980s behind the Royal Clarence Hotel at Burnham-on-Sea. But since 1993 brewing has taken place on a commercial basis in a former cider mill at West Hewish. A new 30-barrel plant was installed in 2000. RCH now supplies 75 outlets direct and the award-winning beers are available nationwide through its own wholesaling company, which also distributes beers from other small independent breweries. Bottle-conditioned beers: Pitchfork (ABV 4.3%), Old Slug Porter (ABV 4.5%), Firebox (ABV 6%), Ale Mary (ABV 6%).

Hewish IPA *(ABV 3.6%)* ◆
Light, hoppy bitter with some malt and fruit, though slightly less fruit in the finish. Floral, citrus hop aroma, pale brown/amber colour.

PG Steam *(ABV 3.9%)* ◆
Amber-coloured, medium-bodied with a floral hop aroma with some fruit. Hoppy and bitter, with some malt, fruit and subtle sweetness. Finish is similar.

Pitchfork *(ABV 4.3%)*
Floral citrus hop with pale malt. Yellow/gold in colour, hops predominate in a full-bodied taste, which is slightly sweet. Long finish — a class act.

Old Slug Porter *(ABV 4.5%)*
Chocolate, coffee, roast malt and hops with lots of body and dark fruits. A complex, rich stout, dark brown in colour.

East Street Cream *(ABV 5%)*
Superb premium ale, pale brown in colour, it is malty with chocolate hints, hoppy, fruity and bitter-sweet. All flavours vie for dominance in what is a notable and well-crafted ale.

Double Header *(ABV 5.3%)*
Light brown, full-bodied strong bitter. Beautifully balanced flavours of malt, hops and tropical fruits, followed by a long, bitter-sweet finish. Very refreshing and easy drinking for its strength

Firebox *(ABV 6%)*
Aroma and taste of citric hops and pale crystal malt. A strong complex, full-bodied, mid-brown beer with a well-balanced flavour of malt and hops.

READING LION

Reading Lion Brewery, the Hop Leaf, 163-165 Southampton Street, Reading, Berks, RG1 2QZ
Tel (0118) 931 4700

A pub-brewery opened by Hop Back in 1995 at the Hop Leaf pub. Brewing stopped in 2002 but the equipment is still on site.

REBELLION

Rebellion Beer Company, Marlow Brewery, Bencombe Farm, Marlow Bottom, Bucks, SL7 3LT
Tel (01628) 476594
Fax (01628) 476617
E-mail info@rebellionbeer.co.uk
Website www.rebellionbeer.co.uk
Shop 9-530 Mon-Fri; 9-4 Sat
Tours by arrangement

⊠ Opened in 1993, Rebellion fills the gap left in Marlow by Whitbread, which shut down Wethereds in 1988. Rebellion moved to a new site in Marlow and increased brewing capacity from 50 to 200 barrels a week, when it bought a pilot brewery from Courage at Reading. The new brewery will now allow Rebellion to grow and produce a much wider range of beer styles. 160 outlets are supplied direct. Seasonal beers: Overdraft (ABV 4.3%, spring), Zebedee (ABV 4.7%, spring), Blonde (ABV 4.3%, summer), Red (ABV 4.7%, autumn), Roasted Nuts (ABV 4.6%, winter), Old Codger (ABV 5%, winter).

IPA *(OG 1038, ABV 3.7%)*
Copper-coloured bitter, sweet and malty, with resinous and red apple flavours. Caramel and fruit decline to leave a dry, bitter and malty finish.

Smuggler *(OG 1041, ABV 4.1%)*
A red-brown beer, well-bodied and bitter with an uncompromisingly dry, bitter finish.

Mutiny *(OG 1045, ABV 4.5%)*
Tawny in colour, this full-bodied best bitter is predominantly fruity and moderately bitter with crystal malt continuing to a dry finish.

RECTORY

Rectory Ales Ltd, Streat Hill Farm Outbuilding, Streat Hill, Streat, Hassocks, E Sussex, BN6 8RP
Tel/Fax (01273) 890570
E-mail sales@rectory-ales.co.uk
Tours by arrangement

⊠ Rectory was founded in 1995 by the Rector of Plumpton, the Rev Godfrey Broster, to generate funds for the maintenance of his three parish churches. 107 parishioners are shareholders. The brewing capacity is now 20 barrels a week. Some seasonal beers are produced. All outlets are supplied direct. Seasonal beer: Christmas Cheer (ABV 3.8%, December). Bottle-conditioned beer: Rector's Revenge (ABV 5.4%).

The Rector's Ale *(OG 1038, ABV 3.8%)*

Rector's Revenge *(OG 1054, ABV 5.4%)*
Copper-brown strong bitter with a complex aroma, becoming more hoppy in the mouth with a dry, bitter finish.

REDRUTH

Redruth Brewery (1742) Ltd, The Brewery, Redruth, Cornwall, TR15 1RB
Tel (01209) 212244
Fax (01209) 210383
Shop noon-6 Mon-Fri; 10-4 Sat

⊠ Since May 1995, Redruth Brewery (formerly Devenish) has been owned by the Hong Kong-based Dransfield Group. Cask-conditioned beer was re-established in 1998 after a break of nearly 10 years, but production was suspended in February 2002 as a result of poor sales and loss of a wholesaling contract. There were plans to re-start cask beer production in the summer of 2002, but the company's long-term commitment to cask beer is in doubt. It is still a large brewery with the capacity to increase barrelage significantly when required. Most of the activity centres on bottling and canning. There is no tied estate, with cask ale sold through the free trade in the South-west. More than 200 outlets are supplied in the South-west.

Cornish Rebellion *(OG 1049, ABV 4.8%)*

Steam Brewed Bitter *(OG 1050, ABV 5%)*

RED SHOOT

Red Shoot Brewery, Toms Lane, Linwood, Ringwood, Hampshire, SP6 3RB
Tel (01425) 475792
Website www.redshootinn.co.uk

The brewery, owned by Wadworth, was commissioned in 1998 with Forest Gold as the first brew. Tom's Tipple was introduced in 1998 as a winter brew and is now a permanent brand. Red Shoot would like to expand but the size of plant (2.5 barrels) makes this difficult, though some occasional beers are produced.

Forest Gold *(ABV 3.8%)*

Tom's Tipple *(ABV 4.8%)*

REEPHAM

Reepham Brewery, Unit 1, Collers Way, Reepham, Norwich, Norfolk, NR10 4SW
Tel (01603) 871091
Tours by arrangement

Norfolk's oldest working brewery is a family business established in 1983 by a chemical engineer and architect (father and son), who brought back the name and brewing to the small market town west of Norwich. The original Reepham Brewery was closed by Steward and Patteson. Some 20 outlets are supplied direct. Bottle-conditioned beers: Organic Honey Ale (brewed for Fat Cat pub, Norwich), Granary Bitter (ABV 3.5%), Rapier Pale Ale (ABV 4.2%).

Granary Bitter *(OG 1038, ABV 3.5%)*
A gold-coloured beer with a light hoppy aroma followed by a malty sweetish flavour with some smoke notes. A well-balanced beer with a long, moderately hoppy aftertaste.

Rapier Pale Ale
(OG 1042, ABV 4.2%)
A faint toffee nose introduces a honeyed hop beginning. The smooth, clean mouthfeel is matched by a clear golden colour. A vanilla sweetness matches the inherent hoppiness that fades slowly.

Brewhouse *(OG 1052, ABV 5%)*

Velvet Sweet Stout
(OG 1045, ABV 4.5%)
Roast malt dominates the nose and taste of this rich red, smooth-drinking stout. A dry elderberry fruitiness blends in with the malty bitterness. A long finish becomes somewhat fruitier but retains smoothness.

St Agnes *(OG 1046, ABV 4.6%)*
A donation to a local church is made for every pint sold of this golden-hued, hoppy bitter. Bitterness combined with citrus notes provide a counter-balance to the inherent hoppiness. Complex, drawn-out, dry finish.

RIDLEYS

T D Ridley & Sons Ltd, Hartford End Brewery, Chelmsford, Essex, CM3 1JZ
Tel (01371) 820316
Fax (01371) 821216
E-mail pdownes@ridleys.co.uk
Website www.ridleys.co.uk
Shop open via reception, office hours.
Tours by arrangement

Ridleys was established by Thomas Dixon Ridley in 1842 and is still family run. It owns 70 pubs and also supplies some 350 other outlets. A new managing director, Brian Field (ex-Greene King) and head brewer Philip Downes have radically overhauled the portfolio, cutting out a proliferating number of occasional beers. A new regular bitter, Prospect, was introduced in spring 2002. In July 2002, Ridleys merged with Tolly Cobbold (qv). Tolly will stop brewing and Original will be brewed by Ridleys. Seasonal beers: Witchfinder Porter (ABV 4.3%, winter), Spectacular (ABV 4.6%, spring and summer).

IPA *(OG 1034, ABV 3.5%)*
Well-balanced session beer with a delicate orange character yielding to a hoppy aftertaste.

Tolly Original Best Bitter
(OG 1038.5, ABV 3.5%)

Prospect *(OG 1042, ABV 4.1%)*
A new pale and fruity bitter.

Rumpus *(OG 1049, ABV 4.5%)*
Fruity beer with toffee tones and a slight liquorice edge, building to a bitter aftertaste. Brewed with oats.

Old Bob *(OG 1055, ABV 5.1%)*
A good balance of malt and fruit, followed by a slightly bitter finish.

RING O' BELLS

Ring O' Bells Brewery, Pennygillam Way, Pennygillam Industrial Estate, Launceston, Cornwall, PL15 7ED
Tel (01566) 777787
Fax (01566) 777788
Tours by arrangement

The Ring O'Bells started trading in the 13th century as a cider farm-cum-alehouse for the stonemasons of St Torney Church, North Hill. It closed in 1918 and after 79 years of neglect new owners set about restoring the old ale house, and rebuilding the cider press and vat. Intensive research with the help of two micro-biologists re-cultured the old yeast strain that was trapped within the walls of the old vat, and is now used to ferment today's ales, some 600 years later. The success of the beers when launched in 1999 led to the brewery moving to new premises in Launceston, in 2001.There are plans to bottle the beers. Seasonal beers: Surf Boar (ABV 4%, summer), Santa Boars (ABV 5.5%, Christmas).

Porkers Pride *(OG 1036, ABV 3.8%)*
A light, refreshing session ale that is well-balanced with a clean, hoppy finish.

Bodmin Boar *(OG 1041.5, ABV 4.3%)*
Full-flavoured, darkish premium ale, with a fine aroma and malty finish.

Dreckly *(OG 1046, ABV 4.8%)*
A warm, ruby coloured strong premium ale fortified with gorse and heather, rich in malt with a spicy aroma and good malty after taste.

Tipsy Trotters *(OG 1048.2, ABV 5.1%)*
Amber-coloured, full-bodied, malty beer, slightly fruity.

Sozzled Swine *(OG 1051.8, ABV 5.5%)*

RINGWOOD

Ringwood Brewery Ltd,
138 Christchurch Road,
Ringwood,
Hampshire, BH24 3AP
Tel (01425) 471177
Fax (01425) 480273
E-mail info@ringwoodbrewery.co.uk
Website www.ringwoodbrewery.co.uk
Shop 9.30-5 Mon-Fri; 9.30-12 Sat
Tours by arrangement; individual visits every Wednesday May-Sep, but must book in advance

⊗ Ringwood was set up in 1978 by legendary micro-brewery builder Peter Austin. The brewery moved in 1986 to attractive 18th-century buildings, formerly part of the old Tunks Brewery. A new brewhouse was commissioned at the end of 1994, and a new fermenting room completed in 1995. The strong growth enjoyed in 2000 continued throughout 2001, with a brief downturn during the foot and mouth crisis. Additional fermenters were due to be installed. Five pubs are owned, all serving cask-conditioned beer. Ringwood's impressive success, under managing director David Welsh, has moved the brewery out of the ranks of micro-brewers and it's now a small regional. Seasonal beers: Boondoggle (ABV 3.9%, May-Sept), XXXX Porter (ABV 4.7%, Oct-March). Bottle-conditioned beers: Fortyniner (ABV 4.9%), XXXX Porter (ABV 4.7%).

Best Bitter
(OG 1038, ABV 3.8%) ◆
A well-balanced, golden brown beer. A malty and hoppy aroma leads to a malty taste with some sweetness. Malty and bitter finish, with some fruit present.

Fortyniner *(OG 1049, ABV 4.8%)* ◆
Pale brown in colour. A malty and fruity aroma leads to a well-balanced taste of malt and hops. Fruity finish.

Old Thumper
(OG 1056, ABV 5.6%) ◆
A mid-brown beer. A fruity aroma preludes a sweet, malty taste with some fruit. Surprisingly bitter aftertaste, with malt and fruit.

RIVERHEAD

Riverhead Brewery Ltd,
2 Peel Street, Marsden,
Huddersfield, W Yorkshire, HD7 6BR
Tel (01484) 841270
Tours by arrangement

The Riverhead Brewery Tap is a brew-pub that opened in 1995 after its conversion from an old grocery store. The seven beers are named after local reservoirs with the height of the reservoir relating to the strength of the beer. Occasional specials such as Jazz Bitter (ABV 4%, for Marsden Jazz Festival), and Ruffled Feathers Bitter (ABV 4.2%, for Marsden Cuckoo Day) are brewed. The brewery also supplies six local outlets on an occasional basis.

Sparth Mild *(OG 1038, ABV 3.6%)* ◆
A light-bodied, dry mild, with a dark ruby colour. Fruity aroma with roasted flavour and a dry finish.

Butterley Bitter *(OG 1038, ABV 3.8%)* ◆
A dry, amber-coloured, hoppy session beer.

Deer Hill Porter *(OG 1040, ABV 4%)*
A dark brown bitter with the characteristics of stout, but not as strong.

Cupwith Light Bitter *(OG 1042, ABV 4.2%)*
A very pale bitter with a distinctive bitter aftertaste.

Black Moss Stout *(OG 1043, ABV 4.3%)* ◆
Roast malt and fruit aromas from a lightly-hopped dry stout with a chocolatey finish.

March Haigh Special Bitter
(OG 1046, ABV 4.6%)
A smooth, rounded flavour appealing to the taste buds as a result of the interesting selection of hops used.

Redbrook Premium Bitter
(OG 1055, ABV 5.5%) ◆
A rich and malty strong beer, with malt and fruit, and a sweet, fruity aftertaste.

ROBINSON'S

Frederic Robinson Ltd,
Unicorn Brewery, Lower Hillgate,
Stockport, Cheshire, SK1 1JJ
Tel (0161) 612 4061
Fax (0161) 476 6011
E-mail brewery@frederic-robinson.co.uk
Website www.frederic-robinson.com
Shop Visitors shop only
Tours by arrangement

⊗ A major family brewery founded in 1838 in the Unicorn Inn and still run by the descendants of Frederic Robinson. The company moved to the present site in 1865. Robinson's bought Hartleys of Ulverston in 1982 and closed the brewery in 1991. The company supplies real ale to all its 414 tied houses in the North-west and North Wales, and to some 100 free trade outlets. Seasonal: Samuel Oldknow (ABV 3.5%, Jan-Feb), Stockport Arches (ABV 4%, March-April), Young Tom (ABV 4%, May-June), Whistling Will (ABV 4%, July-Aug), Coopers Bell (ABV 4%, Sept-Oct), Robin Bitter (ABV 4.5%, Nov-Dec).

Hatters Mild *(OG 1032, ABV 3.3%)* ◆
A light mild with a fruit and malt aroma, it has a refreshing, dry, malty flavour and

aftertaste. A darkened version is available in a handful of outlets and badged Dark Mild.

Old Stockport Bitter *(OG 1034, ABV 3.5%)* ◆
A beer with a refreshing taste of malt, hops and citrus fruit, a fruity aroma, and a short, dry finish.

Hartleys XB *(OG 1040, ABV 4%)* ◆
An overly sweet and malty bitter with a bitter citrus peel fruitiness and a hint of liquorice in the finish.

Hartleys Cumbria Way *(OG 1040, ABV 4.1%)*
A new pale, refreshing bitter marketed under the Hartley's name and first brewed for the Ulverston Ale Trail in 2001.

Best Bitter *(OG 1040, ABV 4.2%)* ◆
Amber beer with an aroma of citrus fruit, spices and earthy hop. Hoppy, bitter and quite fruity to taste with a short bitter finish.

Frederics *(OG 1049, ABV 5%)* ◆
A gold-coloured beer with an aroma of orange and a hint of spice. Citrus fruit and hops on the taste with a dry hoppy finish.

Old Tom *(OG 1079, ABV 8.5%)* ◆
A full-bodied, dark beer, it has malt, fruit and chocolate in the aroma. A delightfully complex range of flavours including dark chocolate, full maltiness, treacle toffee and fruits lead to a long, bitter-sweet aftertaste.

ROCKINGHAM

Rockingham Ales,
c/o 25 Wansford Road, Elton,
Cambs, PE8 6RZ
Tel (01832) 280722
E-mail brian@rockinghamales.co.uk
Website www.rockinghamales.co.uk

⊗ A part-time micro-brewery established in 1997, which operates from a converted farm building near Blatherwyke, Northamptonshire (business address as above). The two-barrel plant produces a prolific range of beers and supplies half a dozen local outlets. The regular beers are brewed on a rota basis, with special beers brewed to order. Seasonal beers: Fineshade (ABV 3.8%, autumn), Sanity Clause (ABV 4.3%, December), Old Herbaceous (ABV 4.5%, winter).

Forest Gold *(OG 1040, ABV 3.9%)*
A hoppy blonde ale with citrus flavours. Well-balanced and clean finishing.

Hop Devil *(OG 1040, ABV 3.9%)*
Six hop varieties give this light amber ale a bitter start and spicy finish.

A1 Amber Ale *(OG 1041, ABV 4%)*
A hoppy session beer with fruit and blackcurrant undertones.

Saxon Cross *(OG 1041, ABV 4.1%)*
A golden-red ale with nut and coffee aromas. Citrus hop flavours predominate.

Fruits of the Forest *(OG 1043, ABV 4.2%)*
A multi-layered beer in which summer fruits and several spices compete with a big hop presence.

Dark Forest *(OG 1050, ABV 5%)*
A dark and complex beer, similar to a Belgian Dubbel, with numerous malty/smokey flavours that give way to a fruity bitter finish.

ROOSTER'S

Rooster's and Outlaw Brewing Co Ltd,
Grimbald Park, Wetherby Road,
Knaresborough, N Yorkshire, HG5 8LJ
Tel/Fax (01423) 865959
E-mail seanf@roosters.co.uk
Website www.roosters.co.uk
Tours by arrangement

⊛ Rooster's Brewery was opened in 1993 by Sean and Alison Franklin. Outlaw Brewery Co started in 1996 after the original Pioneer label was released. In 2001 the brewery was relocated to larger premises at Knaresborough. Production is close to 80 barrels a week. Under the Rooster's label, Sean and Alison make seven regular beers while Outlaw produces experimental beers. They change materials or process or both to make a new beer every two months. Sean Franklin is a devotee of hops and uses many varieties, including North American, in his brews. 820 outlets are supplied direct

Special *(OG 1038, ABV 3.9%)* ◆
A yellow-coloured beer with an intense fruity/floral aroma, which is carried through the taste, where it is joined by a well-balanced bitter character.

Scorcher *(OG 1042, ABV 4.3%)* ◆
Golden aromatic and fruity, with balancing bitterness. The fruitiness is carried through into the aftertaste, where the bitterness tends to increase. A well-balanced beer.

Yankee *(OG 1042, ABV 4.3%)* ◆
A straw-coloured beer with a delicate, fruity aroma leading to a well-balanced taste of malt and hops with a slight evidence of sweetness, followed by a refreshing, fruity/bitter finish.

Hooligan *(OG 1042, ABV 4.3%)*
A pale, aromatic premium bitter with aromas of tangerine. Moderately bitter.

Cream *(OG 1045, ABV 4.7%)* ◆
A pale-coloured beer with a complex, floral bouquet leading to a well-balanced refreshing taste. Fruit lasts throughout and into the aftertaste.

ROTHER VALLEY

Rother Valley Brewing Co, Gate Court Farm, Station Road, Northiam, E Sussex, TN31 6QT Tel (01797) 252922 Fax (01797) 253550

Tours by arrangement

Rother Valley was established in Northiam in 1993 on a hop farm overlooking the river that marks the boundary between Kent and Sussex. It brews only with hops grown on the farm. In 2000, Colin Smith took over brewing from Martin Christoff. Special beers are brewed to order and 50 outlets are supplied direct. Occasional/seasonal beers: Wheat Beer (ABV 3.8%, summer), Blues (ABV 5%, winter), Holly Daze (ABV varies, Christmas), Hopper's (ABV 4.4%, September).

Level Best *(OG 1040, ABV 4%)* Full-bodied tawny session bitter with a malt and fruit aroma, malty taste and a dry, hoppy finish.

Spirit Level *(OG 1045, ABV 4.6%)* Tawny best bitter. Initial hoppy fruitiness leads to a well-balanced sweet mixture of flavours with a dry aftertaste.

RUDDLES

See Greene King.

RUDGATE

Rudgate Brewery Ltd, 2 Centre Park, Marston Business Park, Rudgate, Tockwith, York, YO26 7QF Tel/Fax (01423) 358382 E-mail sales@rudgate-beers.co.uk Website www.rudgate-beers.co.uk

Tours by arrangement

Rudgate was founded in 1992 and is located in an old armoury building on the edge of a disused World War Two airfield. It supplies 150 outlets with beers fermented in open square vessels and also brews for Marston Moor (qv). A range of seasonal beers has been launched. Awards: Beauty of Hops, English Ale Gold Medal 2000 and 1998, Silver 1999. Seasonal beer: Rudolf's Ruin (ABV 5.4%, Christmas).

Viking *(OG 1038, ABV 3.8%)* An initially warming and malty, full-bodied beer, with hops and fruit lingering into the aftertaste.

Battleaxe *(OG 1042, ABV 4.2%)* A well-hopped bitter with slightly sweet initial taste and light bitterness. Complex fruit character gives a memorable aftertaste.

Ruby Mild *(OG 1044, ABV 4.4%)* Nutty rich ruby ale, stronger than usual for a mild.

RYBURN

Ryburn Brewery, c/o Ram's Head, Wakefield Road, Sowerby Bridge, Halifax, W Yorkshire, HX6 2AZ Tel (01422) 835413/63355876 E-mail ryburnbrewery@talk21.com Web www.ryburnbrewery.co.uk

The brewery was established during 1989 at Mill House, Sowerby Bridge, but has since been relocated beneath the company's single public house, the Tied House. The brewery is once again actively involved in free trade sales, both locally and nationally via wholesalers and the SIBA cooperative scheme. Occasional beers include Stone Troff (ABV 4.6%) and Porter (ABV 4.8%).

Best Mild *(OG 1033, ABV 3.3%)*

Best Bitter *(OG 1038, ABV 3.6%)*

Light *(OG 1042, ABV 4.4%)*

Humpty *(OG 1044, ABV 4.4%)*

Rydale Bitter *(OG 1044, ABV 4.2%)*

Luddite *(OG 1048, ABV 5%)*

Stabbers *(OG 1052, ABV 5.2%)*

Coiners *(OG 1060, ABV 6%)*

SADDLEWORTH

Saddleworth Brewery, The Old Brewhouse, Church Lane, Uppermill, Oldham, OL3 6LW Tel (01457) 872415, (07813) 176121(m)

The brewery is in an old brewhouse that until five years ago had not brewed for more than 130 years. The copper is still fired by direct flame to give a fuller flavour to the beer. In 1999, a new fermentation room, barrelling room and cold room were added. The brewhouse has an additional copper and mash tun. Seasonal/occasional beers: Christmas Carol (ABV 7.4%).

Saddleworth More *(OG 1038, ABV 3.8%)*

Harvest Moon *(OG 1052, ABV 4.1%)* A light golden beer, slightly sweet with bitter aftertaste.

Hop Smacker *(OG 1041, ABV 4.1%)* A golden, refreshing bitter, brewed with five different varieties of hops.

Pete's Dragon *(OG 1044, ABV 4.1%)* A light amber beer with a pleasant hint of caramel.

Robyns Bitter *(OG 1046, ABV 4.8%)* A dark ruby bitter with a rich malty flavour.

Shaftbender *(OG 1054, ABV 5.4%)* A black porter/stout bitter.

ST AUSTELL

St Austell Brewery Co Ltd, 63 Trevarthian Road, St Austell, Cornwall, PL25 4BY Tel (01726) 74444 Fax (01726) 68965 E-mail info@staustellbrewery.co.uk Website www.staustellbrewery.co.uk

Shop 9-5 Mon-Fri

Visitor centre and tours (01726) 66022

St Austell Brewery celebrated 150 years of brewing in 2001. Founded by Walter Hicks in 1851, the company is still family-owned and run, with Walter Hicks' great-great-grandson, James Staughton, at the helm as managing director since 2000. He leads a young team, with head brewer Roger Ryman, and there is a powerful commitment to cask beer. The beer range has been overhauled, with new branding and pump clips in pubs. Cask beer is available in all 150 licensed houses, as well as an increasing presence in the free trade throughout Devon, Cornwall and Somerset. An attractive visitor centre offers guided tours and souvenirs from the brewery. The brewery hosts its own Celtic Beer Festival late in the year. Bottle-conditioned beers: Clouded Yellow (ABV 5%), Hicks Strong Ale (ABV 5%).

IPA *(OG 1034, ABV 3.4%)*
Copper/bronze in colour, the nose blossoms with fresh hops. The palate is clean and full-bodied with a hint of toffee caramel. The finish is short and crisp.

XXXX Mild *(OG 1037, ABV 3.6%)* ☐◆
Little aroma, but a strong, malty character. A caramel-sweetish flavour is followed by a good, lingering aftertaste that is sweet but with a fruity dryness.

Tinners Ale *(OG 1038, ABV 3.7%)* ◆
A deservedly popular, golden beer with an appetising malt aroma and a good balance of malt and hops in the flavour. Lasting finish.

Dartmoor Best Bitter *(OG 1039, ABV 3.9%)*
A delicately hopped golden bitter. Originally brewed at the now-closed Ferguson Brewery in Plymouth, DBB was brewed by St Austell for Carlsberg-Tetley, but it is now owned by St Austell and is spearheading the Cornish company's increased presence in Devon.

Tribute *(OG 1043, ABV 4.2%)*
Pale amber in colour, full-bodied malt flavours are balanced by a fresh citrus nose.

Hicks Special Draught/HSD *(OG 1051, ABV 5%)* ◆
An aromatic, fruity, hoppy bitter that is initially sweet and has an aftertaste of pronounced bitterness, but whose flavour is fully rounded. A good premium beer.

ST GEORGE'S

St George's Brewing Co Ltd, Bush Lane, Callow End, Worcester, WR2 4TF
Tel/Fax (01905) 831316
(07974) 563598 (m)
Tours by arrangement

⊠ St George's, situated halfway between Worcester and Malvern in an old bakehouse, started trading in 1998 and in 2000 was taken over by Brian McCluskie and David Butcher, who both took early retirement after long careers in the brewing industry. They have a strong commitment to traditional brewing and have revised the beer range, which they plan to expand. Several of the beer names pay homage to Sir Edward Elgar, who lived in the area and drew inspiration from the Malvern Hills. Seasonal beer: Paragon Steam (ABV 4%, summer).

Bitter *(OG 1038, ABV 3.7%)*
Light in colour with a pronounced, refreshing hoppy character.

Gold 2000 *(OG 1040, ABV 3.9%)*
A mellow beer using aromatic Goldings hops and a blend of specialist coloured malts.

Enigma *(OG 1042, ABV 4.2%)* ◆
An aromatic bitter beer that lives up to its name, as it is not as it first appears.

Premium Bitter *(OG 1046, ABV 4.3%)* ◆
A fruity but unassertive bitter that allows the flavours of all its constituents to come through and be enjoyed.

St George's Special *(OG 1044, ABV 4.4%)*
A dark, bitter and malty traditional English ale. Locally-grown Fuggles and Goldings hops predominate.

Nimrod *(OG 1045, ABV 4.5%)*
A strong and characterful English pale ale in the Burton style.

Fire 2000 *(OG 1050, ABV 4.9%)*
A pungent, ruby-coloured strong ale using traditional English Fuggles and Brewers Gold hops. A satisfying malt character due to the blend of malts and roasted barley.

ST PETER'S

St Peter's Brewery Co Ltd, St Peter South Elmham, Bungay, Suffolk, NR35 1NQ
Tel (01986) 782322 Fax (01986) 782505
E-mail beers@stpetersbrewery.co.uk
Website www.stpetersbrewery.co.uk
Shop available 9-5
Tours by arrangement

⊠ St Peter's Brewery commenced brewing in 1996 using water from a deep-water bore hole on the site. A wide range of cask-conditioned beers are produced and the beer is also bottled on site. The medieval St Peter's Hall provides a dramatic back-drop to the brewery and is open as a bar and restaurant every Friday, Saturday and Sunday. Pubs in the Home Counties are supplied direct and elsewhere via distributors. Seasonal beers: Winter Ale (ABV 6.5%), Cinnamon & Apple Spiced Ale (ABV 6.5%), Summer Ale (ABV 6.5%).

Best Bitter *(OG 1038, ABV 3.7%)*
A traditional best bitter brewed with pale and crystal malts and Goldings aroma hops. The result is a full-bodied ale with distinctive fruity caramel notes.

Mild *(OG 1038, ABV 3.7%)*
A beer mild in hops but not in flavour. Sweetness is balanced by bitter chocolate malt.

Organic Best Bitter *(OG 1041, ABV 4.1)*
Soil Association accredited, organically-grown Chariot malted barley is used to make the mash for this beer, which is hopped with organic Hallertauer hops.

Extra *(OG 1044, ABV 4.3%)*
A premium beer with hop character is to the fore.

Organic Ale *(OG 1046, ABV 4.5%)*
Soil Association standard, light malted barley from Scotland, with organic Target hops create a refreshingly flavoured ale with a delicate character.

Golden Ale *(OG 1047, ABV 4.7%)*
English Halcyon malts are used together with pale malts, with Goldings hops providing the bitterness and aroma. The result is a highly distinctive light, golden ale.

Wheat Beer *(OG 1048, ABV 4.7%)*
A high proportion of premium wheat is used with modest amounts of Challenger and Goldings hop varieties to produce a light, smooth, clear and refreshing beer with a distinctive palate and a clean, crisp aftertaste.

Elderberry Fruit Beer *(OG 1048, ABV 4.7%)*
This refreshing beer has a wheat beer base complemented by the addition of elderberry. This rare example of an English fruit beer has a delightfully floral fruit nose and refreshing dry finish.

Grapefruit Beer *(OG 1045, ABV 4.7%)*
Wheat Beer as the base for this refreshing beer. The zesty/pithy grapefruit is in complete harmony with the hops and malt. Excellent as an aperitif.

Lemon and Ginger Spiced Ale *(OG 1048, ABV 4.7%)*
A traditional English ale with a light citrus aroma and a delicate ginger aftertaste.

Suffolk Gold *(OG 1050, ABV 4.9%)*
Suffolk-grown First Gold hops provide the inspiration for this premium beer, which is brewed with Suffolk malt to produce a full-bodied ale with a lasting hop aroma.

King Cnut Ale *(OG 1051, ABV 5%)*
This fine ale is based on a recipe from the first Millennium and features roast barley, juniper berries, orange and lemon peel, spices and stinging nettles from a local hedgerow.

Old Style Porter *(OG 1051, ABV 5.1%)*
This beer is a blend of a mature old ale with a younger light beer, just as a true Porter should be. The marriage produces an extremely characterful brew that is dark in colour and complex in taste.

Honey Porter *(OG 1051, ABV 5.1%)*
A traditional English porter finished with honey for a truly unique aroma and taste.

Strong Ale *(OG 1052, ABV 5.1%)*
A fine example of a traditional English strong ale. Challenger and Goldings hops act in perfect harmony with Suffolk malt.

Cream Stout *(OG 1065, ABV 6.5%)*
Challenger and Fuggles hops plus a blend of four local barley malts create an aromatic, strong, dark chocolate cream stout with a satisfying bitter-sweet aftertaste.

SALAMANDER

Salamander Brewing Co,
22 Harry Street, Dudley Hill, Bradford, W Yorkshire, BD4 9PH
Tel (01274) 652323
Fax (01274) 680101
Tours by arrangement

◎ Chris Bee and Daniel Gent launched their brewery in 2001 in a former pie factory. Chris brewed at the Orange Brewery and the Yorkshire Grey brew-pubs in London, and Daniel honed his skills at Freedom, also in London. Their 10-barrel plant is made up of some vessels bought from Mitchells of Lancaster along with ex-dairy equipment. They have quickly established their business with 150 outlets in the North and Midlands. In 2001, more tanks were purchased and capacity doubled to meet growing demand. Most of the beer names have salamander connections.

Axolotl *(ABV 3.8%)*
A pale refreshing session ale with a pleasing Fuggles late hop character.

Mudpuppy *(ABV 4.2%)* ◆
A hoppy fruitiness dominates this beer. A fruity nose gives way to a pleasant nutty character. Then a dry, bitter, hoppy, slightly astringent finish.

Golden Salamander *(ABV 4.5%)*
A golden premium ale, with a refreshing fruity/citrus character.

Hellbender *(ABV 4.8%)*
A light amber strong bitter. A beer with a fruity nose and a clean hop bitterness.

Hammer and Tong *(ABV 5%)*
A pale assertive strong ale.

Titus Tipple *(ABV 5.3%)*
Brewed in honour of philanthropist Sir Titus Salt. This chestnut ale has a spicy/aromatic hop character and a dry finish.

SALOPIAN

Salopian Brewing Co Ltd, 67 Mytton Oak Road, Shrewsbury, Shropshire, SY3 8UQ
Tel (01743) 248414
Shop 9-5 weekdays.
Tours by arrangement

◎ The brewery was opened in 1995 in an old dairy on the outskirts of Shrewsbury. Partners Wilf Nelson and brewer Martin Barry have developed cask sales locally and nationally through wholesalers. They have purchased two new fermenters, and capacity has been increased in size to 50 barrels. Bottle-conditioned beers are brewed at Brakspear, except for Minsterley and Gingersnap at Salopian. The brewery is actively seeking a brewery tap. Fifty-five outlets are supplied direct.

Shropshire Gold *(OG 1037, ABV 3.8%)*

Proud Salopian *(OG 1044, ABV 4.5%)*

Heaven Sent *(OG 1044, ABV 4.5%)*

Goodalls Gold *(OG 1047, ABV 4.7%)*

Puzzle *(OG 1047, ABV 4.8%)*

Golden Thread *(OG 1048, ABV 5%)*

Ironbridge Stout *(OG 1050, ABV 5%)*

SARAH'S HOP HOUSE

Sarah's Hop House Brewery,
131 High Street, Golborne, Warrington, Cheshire, WA3 3TG
Tel (01942) 728202
E-mail jim@tripp.fsnet.co.uk
Tours by arrangement

⊛ Sarah Porter worked in the pub trade for 20 years, bought her own free house eight years ago, and decided to go the next mile and brew her own beer. She learnt the brewing skills by working with John Feeney at Bank Top. Her five-barrel plant is situated in outbuildings behind the Railway Inn. She started brewing in 2000 with Hop House Bitter only and now has 50 outlets (but steadily increasing and spreading) in the locality, plus pubs nationwide supplied by wholesalers. The brewery now has four fermenting vessels.

Hop House Bitter *(OG 1039, ABV 3.9%)* 🗍
An amber beer with a fruity nose. A nice balance of orange fruit and hops with malt and bitterness in the mouth and a satisfyingly bitter, fruity finish.

Black Mamba Mild *(OG 1040, ABV 4%)*
A roast malt and chocolate aroma complements the dark red/brown colour. Hints of treacle toffee join the roast malt and chocolate in the taste, before a dry roast finish.

Hop To It *(OG 1042, ABV 4.2%)* ⬙
Amber beer with a light citrus aroma. Bitter, malty palate with a bitter and very dry aftertaste.

Gordon's Amber Ale *(OG 1042, ABV 4.2%)*

Chocolate Stout *(OG 1047, ABV 4.7%)*
Dark red/brown beer with roast malt and chocolate on the aroma and flavour. Creamy, smooth palate and a fairly dry, roast aftertaste.

Wheels of Fire *(OG 1047, ABV 4.7%)*

Two Harleys *(OG 1047, ABV 4.7%)*

SAWBRIDGEWORTH

**Sawbridgeworth Brewery,
81 London Road, Sawbridgeworth,
Herts, CM21 9JJ
Tel (01279) 722313
Fax (01279) 726060**
Tours by arrangement

⊗ A brew-pub run by former professional footballer Tommy Barnett (Crystal Palace, Orient and St Albans City) with equipment bought from Whitbread. Tommy started brewing in 2000 and he supplies beer festivals as well as the Gate. Lynne Pearce is named in honour of his favourite beer writer, who once wrote that she hoped a brewer would name a beer after her.

Brown Bomber *(ABV 3.7%)*

Selhurst Park Flyer *(ABV 3.7%)*

Teflon *(ABV 3.7%)*

Is It Yourself *(ABV 4.2%)*

Brooklands Express *(ABV 4.6%)*

Lynne Pearce *(ABV 5%)*

Piledriver *(ABV 5.3%)*

SCANLON'S

**Scanlon's Fine Ales, Rainbow Industrial Estate, Trout Road, Yiewsley, Middlesex, UB7 7XT
Tel (01895) 256270**

Scanlon's sells eight beers on a regular basis produced for the company by the following breweries:

**Vale Brewery, Haddenham, Bucks:
Frays Mild** *(OG 1036, ABV 3.6%)*

Colne Valley Bitter *(OG 1042, ABV 4.1%)*

Ealing Porter *(OG 1045, ABV 4.4%)*

Lord Ashford's Special Reserve *(OG 1052, ABV 5%)*
A stout produced Dec-Jan.

**O'Hanlon's Brewery:
Middlesex Gold** *(OG 1039, ABV 3.8%)*

Elthorne White *(OG 1043, ABV 4.2%)*
A wheat beer produced March-Oct.

Brunel Premier Ale *(OG 1050, ABV 4.8%)*

**Rebellion, Marlow, Bucks:
Spike** *(OG 1046, ABV 4.5%)*

Elthorne White, Middlesex Gold, Ealing Porter and Colne Valley Bitter are also available in bottle-conditioned form.

SCARECROW*

**⚲ Scarecrow Brewery,
c/o Dairyman's Daughter,
Arreton Barn, Newport Road,
Arreton, Isle of Wight
Phone (01983) 856161**

3.5-barrel brewery, opened in June 2002, and owned by Ventnor Brewery (qv) and using Ventnor's phone number. It's based in a craft village and supplies four pubs.

Scarecrow Best *(ABV 4.2%)*

SCATTOR ROCK

**Scattor Rock Brewery Ltd,
Unit 5 Gidley's Meadow, Christow,
Exeter, Devon, EX6 7QB
Tel (01647) 252120
E-mail keithscattorrock@aol.com
Website www.scattorrockbrewery.com**
Tours by arrangement

⊗ The brewery was set up in 1998 and is situated within the boundaries of the Dartmoor National Park, and named after a well-known local landmark. 60 plus outlets are supplied direct on a permanent or regular basis. Occasional beers: Quarryman Stout (ABV 4.9%), Scattor Brain (ABV 4.8%), Gidleys Bitter (ABV 4.4%), Completely and Utterly Brain Dead (ABV 9%). There is a seasonal beer available every month and branded as the 'Tor collection'.

Scatty Bitter *(OG 1040, ABV 3.8%)*

Teign Valley Tipple *(OG 1042, ABV 4%)*
A well-balanced tawny coloured beer with a hoppy aroma.

Skylark *(OG 1043, ABV 4.2%)*
A refreshing, light brown session ale.

Devonian *(OG 1045, ABV 4.5%)*
A strong, fruity, light-coloured ale.

Golden Valley *(OG 1046, ABV 4.6%)*
A golden refreshing ale.

Valley Stomper *(OG 1051, ABV 5%)*
Light brown and deceptively drinkable.

SELBY

Selby (Middlebrough) Brewery Ltd,
131 Millgate, Selby,
N Yorkshire, YO8 3LL
Tel (01757) 702826
Shop 10-12 and 6-10 Mon-Sat

☺ Old family brewery that resumed brewing in 1972 after a gap of 18 years but which is now mostly involved in wholesaling. Its beers, which are brewed on an occasional basis, are available, while stocks last (only in bulk) at the shop and not at the company's single pub. They are also sold as guest beers in the local free trade.

No. 1 *(OG 1040, ABV 4%)*

No. 3 *(OG 1040, ABV 4%)*

Old Tom *(OG 1065, ABV 6.5%)*

SHARDLOW

Shardlow Brewing Company Ltd,
The Old Brewery Stables,
British Waterways Yard,
Cavendish Bridge,
Leicestershire, LE72 2HL
Tel (01332) 799188 Fax (01530) 416368
Tours by arrangement

⊗ Brewing in the Old Brewery Stables since 1996, Shardlow works in part of the Eatons Brewery (established 1815) and was subsequently Offilers. The premier bitter takes its name from John Trussel Eaton, the vicar for 40 years of Shardlow, and a member of the Eaton Brewing dynasty. Shardlow supplies beer throughout the Midlands and plans to expand its pub estate.

Chancellors Revenge *(ABV 3.6%)*
A light-coloured, refreshing, full-flavoured and well-hopped session bitter.

Cavendish Dark *(ABV 3.7%)*

Best Bitter *(ABV 3.9%)*
A well-balanced, amber-coloured, quaffable bitter.

Goldenhop *(ABV 4.1%)*
A golden bitter, dry hopped with Goldings for added flavour and aroma.

Narrowboat *(ABV 4.3%)*
A pale amber bitter, with a short, crisp hoppy aftertaste.

Cavendish Gold *(ABV 4.5%)*
A premium pale bitter.

Reverend Eaton's *(ABV 4.5%)*
A smooth, medium-strong bitter, full of malt and hop flavours with a sweet aftertaste.

Whistle Stop *(OG 1050, ABV 5%)*
Maris Otter pale malt and two hops produce this smooth and surprisingly strong pale beer.

SHARP'S

Sharp's Brewery,
Pityme Industrial Estate, Rock,
Wadebridge, Cornwall, PL27 6NU
Tel (01208) 862121
Fax (01208) 863727
Tours by arrangement

⊗ Founded in 1994 in one industrial unit, the brewery has enjoyed rapid expansion and now occupies nearly half the estate. It supplies the free trade in Devon and Cornwall, and the beers are also widely available via wholesalers. Eden Ale won the Supreme Champion award at the 2000 Falmouth Beer Festival. The brewery is currently upgrading its equipment to cope with continued demand for the beers. Eden Ale is now being bottled with other beers from the range to follow.

Cornish Coaster
(OG 1037, ABV 3.6%) ◆
A smooth, easy-drinking beer, golden in colour, with a fresh hop aroma and dry malt and hops in the mouth. The finish starts malty but becomes dry and hoppy.

Doom Bar Bitter *(OG 1040, ABV 4%)* ◆
A rich, golden brown beer with a hint of barley. Dry malt and hops in the mouth. The malty finish becomes dry and hoppy. Fresh hop aroma.

Eden Ale *(OG 1043, ABV 4.4%)*
Brewed in celebration of Cornwall's Eden Project, it boasts a full and rounded flavour with a distinctively crisp and refreshing, dry hop finish.

Sharp's Own *(OG 1043, ABV 4.4%)* ◆
A deep golden brown beer with a delicate hops and malt aroma, and dry malt and hops in the mouth. Like the other beers, its finish starts malty but turns dry and hoppy.

Will's Resolve *(OG 1046, ABV 4.6%)*
A rich golden brown beer with fresh hop aroma and with dry malt and hops in the mouth.

Special *(OG 1052, ABV 5.2%)* ◆
Deep golden brown with a fresh hop aroma. Dry malt and hops in the mouth; the finish is malty but becomes dry and hoppy.

SHAWS*

Shaws Brewery, The Old Stables,
Dukinfield, Cheshire, SK16 5LX
Tel (0161) 330 5471

New brewery producing one beer at present: Best Bitter.

SHEPHERD NEAME

Shepherd Neame Ltd, 17 Court Street, Faversham, Kent, ME13 7AX
Tel (01795) 532206
Fax (01795) 538907
E-mail company@shepherd-neame.co.uk
Website www.company@shepherd-neame.co.uk
Shop 9-5 Mon-Fri. Tours by arrangement

⊗ Kent's major independent brewery is believed to be the oldest continuous brewer in the country since 1698, but records show brewing began on the site as far back as the 12th century. The same water source is still used today, steam engines are still usable, and the mash is produced in two teak tuns that date from 1910. A visitors' reception hall is housed in a restored medieval hall (tours by arrangement). In 2000, Shepherd Neame invested £2.2 million in a new brewhouse that boosted production to 200,000 barrels a year. The company has 370 tied houses in the South-east, nearly all selling cask ale, but tenants are encouraged to keep beers under blanket pressure if the cask is likely to be on sale for more than three days. 500 other outlets are also supplied direct. Seasonal beers: Early Bird (ABV 4.3%, spring), Late Red (ABV 4.5%, autumn), Goldings (ABV 4.7%, summer), Herald (ABV 4.5%, winter).

Master Brew Bitter *(OG 1032.6, ABV 3.7%)* ◆
A distinctive bitter, mid-brown in colour, with a hoppy aroma. Well-balanced, with a nicely aggressive bitter taste from its hops, it leaves a hoppy/bitter finish, tinged with sweetness.

Best Bitter *(OG 1036.2, ABV 4.1%)* ◆
Mid-brown, with less marked characteristics than the bitter. However, the nose is very well-balanced and the taste enjoys a malty, bitter smokiness. Malty, well-rounded finish. It also appears under the name Canterbury Jack.

Spitfire *(OG 1039, ABV 4.5%)*
A commemorative Battle of Britain brew for the RAF Benevolent Fund's appeal, now a permanent feature.

Bishops Finger *(OG 1045.7, ABV 5%)*
A cask-conditioned version of a famous bottled beer, introduced in cask in 1989.

SHOES

Shoes Brewery, Three Horseshoes Inn, Norton Canon, Hereford, HR4 7BH
Tel/Fax (01544) 318375

Landlord Frank Goodwin had long been a home brewer, but decided in 1994 to brew on a commercial basis for his pub. The beers are brewed from malt extract, stored in casks and dispensed under a blanket of mixed gas. Beers: Norton Ale (ABV 3.6%), Canon Bitter (ABV 4.1%). Limited edition only: Farriers Beer (ABV 13.9%, unfiltered, bottle-conditioned).

SHUGBOROUGH

See Titanic.

SIX BELLS

The Six Bells Brewery, Church Street, Bishop's Castle, Shropshire, SY9 5AA
Tel (01588) 638930
Fax (01588) 630132
Website bishops-castle.co.uk/SixBells / brewery
Tours by arrangement

⊗ Neville Richards – 'Big Nev' – started brewing in 1997 with a five-barrel brew length and two fermenters. Alterations in 1999 included two more fermenters, a new grain store and mashing equipment, and some automation. He currently supplies 15 regular accounts plus the brewery tap, with regular contract brews for the Kangaroo Inn and Ystwyth Ales. Seasonal beers: Cloud Nine (ABV 4.2%, spring-Oct), Old Recumbent (ABV 5.2%, Oct-spring).

Big Nev's *(OG 1037, ABV 3.8%)*
A pale, fairly hoppy bitter.

Roo Brew *(OG 1038, ABV 3.8%)*
Brewed exclusively for the Kangaroo Inn Aston on Glen, to the publican's recipe. Copper-coloured, hoppy and heavily late hopped with Goldings.

Marathon Ale *(OG 1040, ABV 4%)*
Dark and malty.

Full Moon *(OG 1044, ABV 4.5%)*
Brewed for Ystwyth Ales of Capel Bangor. A new distributor, run by Chris Giles who worked for Flannery's of Aberystwyth before it closed.

Spring Forward *(OG 1044, ABV 4.6%)*
Originally a spring beer but now permanent: dry, hoppy and amber in colour.

Brew 101 *(OG 1048, ABV 4.8%)*

Festival Pale *(OG 1051, ABV 5.2%)*

SKINNER'S

Skinner's Brewery, Riverside View, Newham, Truro, Cornwall, TR1 2SU
Tel (01872) 271885
Fax (01872) 271886
E-mail info@skinnersbrewery.com
Website www.skinnersbrewery.com
Tours by arrangement

⊗ A brewery founded in 1997 by Steve and Sarah Skinner, formerly of the Tipsy Toad

Brewery in Jersey. The beer names are based on Cornish folklore characters. The brewery has won many awards in its short life, including Supreme Champion at the SIBA Maltings Festival, Newton Abbot, in 1998, with Cornish Knocker. This was followed in 1999 with a repeat performance with Betty Stogs. Also in 1999 Who Put the Lights Out? won a gold medal in the National Beauty of Hops competition. Ice Blonde won Beer of the Festival at the Cotswold Festival in 2000. Skinner's owns one pub, the Skinner's Ale House in Newquay. Occasional beer: Jingle Knockers (ABV 5.5%, Christmas), Mild Oatmeal Stout (ABV 4%, April/May). Bottle-conditioned beers: Who Put the Lights Out? (ABV 5%), Cornish Knocker Ale (ABV 4.5%), Jingle Knockers (ABV 5.5%).

Coast Liner *(ABV 3.4%)*
A crisp, light brown, hoppy session bitter.

Spriggan Ale *(OG 1038, ABV 3.8%)*
A light golden, hoppy bitter. Well-balanced with a smooth bitter finish.

Betty Stogs Bitter *(ABV 4%)*
A pale amber, mid-strength bitter with hoppy overtones.

Cornish Knocker Ale
(OG 1044.5, ABV 4.5%)
A strong, clean-tasting golden ale. Distinctive flowery aroma with a lasting finish.

Figgy's Brew *(ABV 4.5%)*
A classic dark premium-strength bitter. Full-flavoured with a smooth finish.

Who Put the Lights Out? *(ABV 5%)*
Strong single hop amber ale first brewed to mark the solar eclipse in 1999.

Cornish Blonde Wheat Beer
(OG 1050, ABV 5%)

Ice Blonde *(OG 1050, ABV 5%)*
Wheat beer served at 4 degrees C.

SMILES

Smiles Brewing Co Ltd, Colston Street, Bristol, BS1 5BD
Tel (0117) 929 9308
Fax (0117) 925 8235
E-mail mort@smiles.co.uk
Website www.smiles.co.uk
Shop Normal opening hours
Tours by arrangement

⊗ Smiles Brewing Co, founded in 1978, is a traditional tower brewery located in the heart of the city. The mainstream brands are complemented by monthly specials. Quentin Williams is now the chief executive of a leaner and meaner machine that is targeted to achieve increased sales. The company sold 16 pubs to Young's; Smiles owns only its Brewery Tap. The brewery supplies more than 250 other outlets. The brewery has an e-store on the website where fresh beer and memorabilia can be purchased. Seasonal beers: April Fuel (ABV 4.8%, April), Mayfly (ABV 4.5%, May), Holly Hops (ABV 5%, December).

Original *(OG 1038, ABV 3.8%)*
Aroma of pale/crystal malt, fruit and floral hop, with similar, bigger taste. Good dry bitterness, with a finish less sweet and more dry. Amber-coloured, it is light, hoppy, dry and refreshing.

Best *(OG 1041, ABV 4.1%)*
Nicely balanced, mid-bodied and bitter-sweet ale, with malt, hops and fruit lasting throughout. Pale brown in colour.

Bristol IPA *(OG 1044.4, ABV 4.5%)*
Crisp, hoppy, dry bitter. Pale and crystal malts combine with peppery Styrian hops to create a pleasing tart acidity, balanced by malt. Long dry finish.

Heritage *(OG 1052, ABV 5.2%)*
Aroma of malt, chocolate and hops, this is a medium to full-bodied, fruity ale, with a lasting, bitter-sweet finish. Red-brown in colour.

SAMUEL SMITH

Samuel Smith Old Brewery (Tadcaster), High Street, Tadcaster, N Yorkshire, LS24 9SB
Tel (01937) 832225
Fax (01937) 834673
Tours by arrangement

Samuel Smith's brews is Yorkshire's oldest brewery, which dates from 1758. Although related to the nearby much larger John Smith's (now owned by Scottish Courage), who originally owned the old brewery, Samuel Smith's is a radically different company, still family-owned, fiercely independent and with a great belief in tradition. Cask-conditioned Old Brewery Bitter is brewed with well water without the use of adjuncts or any brewing aids and fermented in traditional Yorkshire Squares. All real ale is supplied in wooden casks made and repaired by the brewery's own cooper. Cask ale is sold in the majority of the 200 odd tied houses, although there is now only one cask brand, and the company has gone over to nitro-keg in a number of outlets, including London.While not bottle conditioned, Sam Smith's range of bottled beers, including Taddy Porter, Imperial Stout, and Organic Best Ale, are of outstanding quality.

Old Brewery Bitter (OBB)
(OG 1040, ABV 4%)
Malt dominates the aroma, with an initial burst of malt, hops and fruit in the taste, which is sustained in the aftertaste.

SNOWDONIA

Snowdonia Brewery, Snowdonia Parc Hotel, Waunfawr, Caernarfon, Gwynedd, LLS5
Tel/Fax (01286) 650409
Tours by arrangement

Snowdonia started brewing in spring 1998 in a two-barrel brew length brewhouse. The pub is the station master's house for the Welsh Highland Railway. Waunfawr station opened in summer 2000 and is now the railway terminus. The owners bought the Prince of Wales in Caernarfon, which is a second outlet for the brewery's beers. The brewery is now a member of SIBA.

Welsh Highland Bitter
(OG 1050, ABV 5%)

SPINNING DOG

Spinning Dog Brewery,
88 St Owen's Street,
Hereford, HR1 2QD
Tel (01432) 342125/274998
Fax (01432) 342125
E-mail jfkenyon@aol.com
Tours by arrangement

The brewery was built in a room of the Victory in 2000 by Jim Kenyon, following the purchase of the pub. Initially the brewery served only the pub, but is now supplying some 250 other outlets. As a result of the closure of Flannery's of Aberystwyth, Jim has taken on some of its beers. Two pubs are owned. The brewery, with a four-barrel brew length, can be seen from a window in the pub. Seasonal ale: Santa Paws (ABV 5.2%), Springer (ABV 4.4%), Mutleys Pale Ale (ABV 4.2%).

SPINNING DOG BREWERY
CHASE YOUR TAIL
HEREFORD
OG. 1036°

Mutleys Bark Mild *(OG 1035, ABV 3.5%)*
A dark, malty mild with a hint of bitterness and a touch of roast.

Chase Your Tail *(OG 1036, ABV 3.6%)*
A good session beer with an abundance of hops and bitterness. Dry, with citrus aftertaste.

Mutleys Mongrel *(OG 1039, ABV 3.9%)*
Brewed with a blend of three different hops to create a very hoppy ale.

Mutleys Dark *(OG 1040, ABV 4%)*

Top Dog *(OG 1042, ABV 4.2%)*
A hoppy beer with both malt and fruit flavours, a hoppy aroma with a slight bitter, hoppy aftertaste.

Mutleys Oatmeal Stout
(OG 1044, ABV 4.4%)

Harvest Moon *(OG 1045, ABV 4.5%)*

Celtic Gold *(OG 1045, ABV 4.5%)*

Rheidol Reserve *(OG 1048, ABV 4.8%)*

Mutleys Revenge
(OG 1048, ABV 4.8%)
A strong, smooth, premium hoppy beer, amber in colour. Full-bodied with a dry, citrus-like aftertaste.

SP SPORTING ALES

Sold to Dunn Plowman (qv) in June 2002

SPRINGHEAD

Springhead Fine Ales Ltd,
Old Great North Road, Sutton-on-Trent,
Newark, Notts, NG23 6QS
Tel (01636) 821000
Fax (01636) 821150
E-mail springhead@compuserve.com
Website www.springhead.co.uk
Tours by arrangement

The brewery opened in 1990 and moved to larger premises in 1994, where brewer Shirley Reynolds has increased the range. Brewery tours are available in the Tap Room and 'Meet the Brewster' nights feature regularly at the Bramley Apple in Southell. Most of the beer names are associated with the English Civil War. One pub is owned and supplies are made to some 300 other outlets. Bottle-conditioned beers: Roundheads Gold (ABV 4.2%), The Leveller (ABV 4.8%), Roaring Meg (ABV 5.5%), Cromwell's Hat (ABV 6%), Gardener's Tap (ABV 5%), all suitable for vegetarians and vegans.

Hersbrucker Wheatbeer *(ABV 3.6%)*

Surrender *(OG 1035, ABV 3.6%)*
A burnished, copper-coloured bitter with a stunning combination of malt and hops. Long dry finish. Wonderfully refreshing.

Bitter *(OG 1040, ABV 4%)*
A clean-tasting, easy-drinking hoppy beer.

Puritans Porter *(OG 1040, ABV 4%)*
A porter, dark but not heavy. Smooth with a lingering finish of roasted barley.

Roundhead's Gold
(OG 1042, ABV 4.2%)
Golden light, made with wild flower honey. Refreshing but not too sweet with the glorious aroma of Saaz hops.

Rupert's Ruin *(ABV 4.2%)*
A coppery, complex beer with a fruity aroma and a long, malty aftertaste.

Goodrich Castle
(OG 1044, ABV 4.4%)
Brewed following a 17th-century recipe using rosemary. Pale ale, light on the palate with a bitter finish and a delicate flavour.

Sweet Lips *(ABV 4.6%)*
A light, smooth and refreshing beer with some grapefruit notes from American Cascade hops.

The Leveller *(OG 1046, ABV 4.8%)*
Dark, smoky, intense flavour with a toffee finish. Brewed in the style of Belgian Trappist ales.

Gardener's Tap *(ABV 5%)*
A rich, smooth, aromatic beer, specially brewed for Chatsworth House.

Roaring Meg
(OG 1052, ABV 5.5%)
Smooth and sweet with a dry finish and citrus honey aroma.

Cromwell's Hat *(ABV 6%)*

Tumbledown Dick *(ABV 8%)*
A dark winter warmer with oak flavourings and a hint of vanilla.

STANWAY

Stanway Brewery, Stanway, Cheltenham, Glos, GL54 5PQ
Tel (01386) 584320
Website www.stanwaybrewery.co.uk

⊠ Small brewery founded in 1993 with a five-barrel plant, which confines its sales to the Cotswolds area (around 25 outlets). Seasonal beers: Lords-a-Leaping (ABV 4.5%, Christmas), Cotteswold Gold (ABV 3.9%, summer).

Stanney Bitter *(OG 1042, ABV 4.5%)* ◆
A light, refreshing, amber-coloured beer, dominated by hops in the aroma, with a bitter taste and a hoppy, bitter finish.

STEAMIN' BILLY

Steamin' Billy Brewing Co Ltd, 5 The Oval, Oadby, Leics, LE2 5JB
Tel (0116) 271 2616
E-mail enquiries@steaminbilly.co.uk
Website www.steamin-billy.co.uk

The Steamin' Billy Brewing Co, despite the name, doesn't brew any beer. It was set up to supply three pubs it owned in 1996. It now has just one outlet, but is planning to expand. The beers are brewed at Grainstore of Oakham. Seasonal beers: Lazy Summer (ABV 4.4%, summer), Robert Catesby (ABV 4.5%, autumn), Merry Christmas (ABV 4.4%, December), Knock Out (ABV 7.1%, winter).

Scrum Down Mild *(OG 1039, ABV 3.9%)*
A refreshing, dark, well-balanced mild whose chocolatey fruity flavours complement its roasted bitter finish, with a hint of Golding hops coming through.

Country Bitter *(OG 1040, ABV 4%)*
A full-bodied, copper-coloured beer.

Billy the Porter *(OG 1042, ABV 4.2%)*
Smooth and dry with a bitter-sweet, roasted malt aftertaste.

Steamin' Billy Bitter *(OG 1043, ABV 4.3%)*
The floral flavour and aroma are derived from dry hopping with Golding hops. A well-rounded beer with a satisfying aftertaste.

Lazy Summer *(OG 1044, ABV 4.4%)*
Both Goldings and Saaz hops are used in this refreshing golden brew with a subtle floral aroma, belying its strength.

Robert Catesby *(OG 1045, ABV 4.5%)*
Originally brewed as the house beer for the Catesby in Norfolk, it is now brewed as a seasonal around the time of Fifth of November, commemorating the gunpowder plot. Mainly Goldings hops are used.

Skydiver *(OG 1050, ABV 5%)*
A strong, rich, mahogany-coloured beer with malty sweetness and pronounced hop bitterness.

STONEHENGE

Stonehenge Ales Ltd, The Old Mill, Mill Road, Netheravon, Salisbury, Wilts, SP4 9QB
Tel (01980) 670631
Fax (01980) 671187
E-mail Stonehenge_ales@bigfoot.com
Website www.stonehengeales.co.uk
Tours by arrangement

⊠ A tower brewery, originally named Bunce's Brewery after late founder Tony Bunce, is housed in a listed building on the River Avon. It was established in 1984, and sold to Danish master brewer Stig Anker Andersen in 1993. Its cask-conditioned beers are delivered to around 60 free trade outlets within a radius of 50 miles, and a number of wholesalers are also supplied. Seasonal beers: Sign of Spring (ABV 4.6%, spring), Second to None (ABV 4.6%, summer), Old Smokey (ABV 5%, autumn), Rudolph (ABV 5%, Christmas).

Benchmark *(OG 1035, ABV 3.5%)* ◆
A pleasant, bitter ale of remarkable character which maintains one's interest for a long time. The taste is malty, the aroma subtle and the very long finish is quite dry on the palate.

Pigswill *(OG 1040, ABV 4%)*
A full-bodied beer, rich in hop aroma, with warm amber colour.

Body Line *(OG 1042, ABV 4.3%)*

Heel Stone *(OG 1042, ABV 4.3%)*
A crisp, clean, refreshing bitter, deep amber in colour, well balanced with a fruity blackcurrant nose.

Danish Dynamite *(OG 1050, ABV 5%)*
A light golden, dry strong ale, slightly fruity with a well-balanced hop flavour and bitterness.

Old Smokey *(OG 1050, ABV 5%)* ◆
A delightful, warming, dark bitter ale, with a roasted malt taste and a hint of liquorice surrounding a developing bitter flavour.

STORM

Storm Brewing Co, 2 Waterside, Macclesfield, Cheshire, SK11 7HJ
Tel (01625) 432978/615856
Tours by arrangement

Storm started brewing in 1998 under the guidance of Brian Rides of Wickwar Brewery. Two partners, Hugh Thompson and Dave Stebbings, brew five barrels a week on a part-time basis. Storm currently supplies approximately 30 outlets in the Macclesfield area.

Beaufort's Ale *(OG 1036, ABV 3.8%)*
Golden brown, full-flavoured session beer with a lingering hoppy taste.

Bitter Experience *(ABV 4%)*

Desert Storm *(ABV 4%)*

Ale Force *(OG 1038, ABV 4.2%)* ◆
Amber, smooth-tasting, complex beer that balances malt, hop and fruit on the taste, leading to a roasty, slightly sweet aftertaste.

Windgather *(OG 1043, ABV 4.5%)*
Pale brown, refreshing, clean-tasting best bitter, complex and highly flavoured.

Storm Damage *(ABV 4.7%)*
A light-coloured, well-hopped beer with a distinct fruitiness from start to finish.

SULWATH

Sulwath Brewers Ltd, The Brewery, 209 King Street, Castle Douglas, Dumfries & Galloway, DG7 1DT
Office: Strathmore, 14 Babbington Gardens, Hardthorn, Dumfries, DG2 9JB
Tel/Fax (01556) 504525
E-mail allen@scottdavid98.freeserve.co.uk
Website www.sulwathbrewers.co.uk
Shop Mon-Sat 10-4. Tours Mon-Sat.

A small, privately-owned company that started brewing in 1995. It sells cask ales direct to the licensed trade and currently has 53 outlets and three wholesalers for draught, with a further 25 supermarkets and licensed shops for bottled Criffel, Knockendoch and Galloway Gold (lager); all brewery conditioned. Seasonal/occasional beers: The Black Galloway (ABV 4.4%), John Paul Jones (ABV 4%), Hawkhill Best (ABV 3.8%). All the beers are suitable for vegetarians.

Cuil Hill *(OG 1039, ABV 3.6%)*
Distinctively fruity session ale with malt and hop undertones. The taste is bitter-sweet with a long-lasting dry finish.

The Black Galloway *(OG 1046, ABV 4.4%)*
Named after the native castle of Galloway, this dark porter derives its colour from the abundance of deeply roasted malts used.

Criffel *(OG 1043, ABV 4.6%)*
Full-bodied beer with a distinctive bitterness. Fruit is to the fore of the taste, with hop becoming increasingly dominant in the taste and finish.

Knockendoch *(OG 1047, ABV 5%)*
Dark, copper-coloured, reflecting a roast malt content, with bitterness from Challenger hops.

Galloway Gold (cask-conditioned lager) *(OG 1048, ABV 5%)*
A lager with full, refreshing taste. Best lager and wheat malts with Continental hops are used. There is a hint of citrus on the palate.

SUMMERSKILLS

Summerskills Brewery, 15 Pomphlett Farm Industrial Estate, Broxton Drive, Billacombe, Plymouth, Devon, PL9 7BG
Tel/Fax (01752) 481283
E-mail Summerskills@cs.com

Originally established in a vineyard in 1983 at Bigbury-on-Sea, Summerskills moved to its present site two years later. National distribution via carefully vetted wholesalers ensures nationwide coverage for the company's prize-winning beers. Occasional/seasonal beers: Menacing Dennis (ABV 4.5%), Turkey's Delight (ABV 5.1%, Christmas).

Cellar Vee *(OG 1037, ABV 3.7%)*

Tamar *(OG 1037, ABV 3.7%)*
A tawny-coloured bitter with a fruity aroma, and a hop taste and finish.

Best Bitter *(OG 1042, ABV 4.3%)*
A mid-brown beer, with plenty of malt and hops through the aroma, taste and finish. A good session beer.

Whistle Belly Vengeance *(OG 1046, ABV 4.7%)*
A red/brown beer with a beautiful malt and fruit taste and a pleasant, malty aftertaste.

Indiana's Bones *(OG 1055, ABV 5.6%)*
A mid-brown beer with a good balance of fruit and malt in the aroma and taste, and a sweet, malty finish.

SUSSEX

The Sussex Brewery, Pett Road, Pett, E Sussex, TN35 4HB
Tel (01424) 813927 Fax (01424) 813928
Tours by arrangement

Formerly Pett Brew Company, then Old Forge and for the past 12 months Sussex Brewery run by Robbie Chapman. The brewery is sited in buildings in the grounds of the Two Sawyers public house in Pett. The equipment has a capacity to brew five barrels and normally brews on Mondays, Wednesdays and Fridays.

Forge Bitter *(ABV 3.2%)*

Brothers Best *(ABV 3.9%)*
A hoppy, amber-coloured, session beer.

Pett Progress *(ABV 4.6%)*
Hoppy aroma, full body and a slightly bitter aftertaste.

SUTTON

Sutton Brewing Co, 31 Commercial Road, Coxside, Plymouth, Devon, PL4 0LE
Tel/Fax (01752) 205010
E-mail qnahoon@aol.com
Tours by arrangement

The brewery was built alongside the Thistle Park Brewhouse, near Plymouth's Sutton Harbour, in 1993. It went into production the following year to supply the pub and one other outlet. It now sells to more than 50 outlets in and around Plymouth, and is now expanding out of the South-west through wholesalers. A bigger plant and additional fermenters were installed in 1998 to cope with demand. Occasional/seasonal beers: Pandemonium (ABV 4.8%, autumn), Wild Blonde (ABV 4.4%, summer), Sleigh'd (ABV 5.5%, Christmas).

Plymouth/Dartmoor Pride *(OG 1039, ABV 3.8%)*

XSB *(OG 1042, ABV 4.2%)*
Amber nectar with a fruity nose and a bitter finish.

Sutton Comfort *(OG 1045, ABV 4.5%)*
Hoppy-tasting, mid-brown beer with a bitter hop finish underscored by malt and fruit.

Knickadroppa Glory *(OG 1050, ABV 5%)*

SWALE

Swale Brewery, Little Telpits Farm, Grafty Green, Maidstone ME17 2AY
Tel (01622) 851996
E-mail swalebrewery@aol.com

Swale Brewery was opened by John Davidson in 1995 in Milton Regis, expanded and moved to new premises in Sittingbourne in 1997. He moved again in 2001. Cask ales are brewed on a regular basis and are changed four times a year.

Four bottle-conditioned beers are brewed all year. The brewery has a capacity of 80 barrels a week. 200 outlets are supplied direct. Seasonal beers: Mild (ABV 3.8%), Whitstable Oyster Stout (ABV 4.5%), Pickled Porter (ABV 5%), Mad Tom Courtney (ABV 5%), Cocklewarmer (ABV 5%, winter). Bottle-conditioned beers: Whitstable Oyster Stout, Indian Summer Ale, Kentish Gold (ABV 5%), Old Dick (ABV 5.2%).

Kentish Admiral *(OG 1038.5, ABV 3.5%)*
Russet-coloured, fresh clean flavour from Kentish Admiral hops, giving a light, bitter aroma and finish.

Kentish *(OG 1040, ABV 3.8%)*
A clean-tasting, light brown-coloured ale, dry hopped with East Kent Goldings.

Indian Summer Ale *(OG 1043, ABV 4.2%)*
Pale ale rich in citrus grapefruit aroma and flavour. Crisp bitter finish.

Bizarre *(OG 1048.5, ABV 4.8%)*

SWAN

Gimbal Trading Ltd,
Swan on the Green, West Peckham,
Kent, ME18 5JW
Tel (01622) 812271 Fax (0870) 0560556
E-mail goodbeer@swan-on-the-green.co.uk
Website www.swan-on-the-green.co.uk
Tours by arrangement

⊗ A pub brewery that opened in 2000 on a site that dates back to 1526, when an inn was first recorded. Over the centuries it has been variously known as the Millers Arms (when it included a bakery), the Myllers Arms on the Greene, and Honest Tom after landlord Thomas Oliver. It became the Swan in 1852. The current owner, Gordon Milligan, looked at micro-breweries in the US and Britain, and picked up brewing skills with Rob Jones at Dark Star in Brighton, honing the skills on courses with Brewlab at Sunderland University. Gordon built his two-barrel plant himself and supplies just the pub with beer. There are plans for an organic beer and a 2.6% ABV beer aimed at drivers. The pub stages a 'green beer' festival in September, offering six different beers made with hops harvested straight from the hop fields.

Whooper Pale *(OG 1036, ABV 3.5%)*

Old Fashioned Mild *(OG 1036, ABV 3.5%)*

Ginger Swan *(OG 1036, ABV 3.6%)*

Organic Swan *(ABV 4%)*

Trumpeter Best *(OG 1040, ABV 4%)*

Stout *(OG 1048, ABV 4.8%)*

Parliament Ale *(OG 1050, ABV 4.8%)*

Swan Porter *(OG 1051, ABV 5.1%)*

SWANSEA

Swansea Brewing Company,
Joiners Arms, 50 Bishopston Road,
Bishopston, Swansea, SA3 3EJ.
Office: 74 Hawthorne Avenue, Uplands,
Swansea, SA2 0LY
Tel (01792) 232658 brewery,
(01792) 290197 office
E-mail rorygowland@fsbdial.co.uk
Tours by arrangement

Opened in 1996, it was the first commercial brewery in the Swansea area for almost 30 years and is Swansea's only brew-pub. It doubled its capacity within the first year and now produces four regular beers and occasional experimental ones. The founder, Rory Gowland, learned his trade working in the chemistry department of Swansea University. Four regular outlets are supplied direct plus free trade outlets in the South Wales area. Seasonal: St Teilo's Tipple (ABV 5.5%), Barland Strong (ABV 6%), Pwll Du XXXX (ABV 4.9%).

Deep Slade Dark *(OG 1034, ABV 4%)*

Bishopswood Bitter
(OG 1038, ABV 4.3%)
Pale brown, delicate aroma of malt and hops. A balanced mix of flavours and bitterness lead to a long, dryish finish.

Three Cliffs Gold *(OG 1042, ABV 4.7%)*
Hops and fruit aroma leads to a tasty mix of hops, fruit and malt. Moderate bitterness quickly builds, leaving a hoppy, bitter finish.

Original Wood *(OG 1046, ABV 5.2%)*

SWEET WILLIAM

Sweet William Brewery, William IV,
816 High Road, Leyton, London, E10
Tel (020) 8556 2460
Tours by arrangement

A new brew-pub that came on stream in 2000. The beers are currently available only in the pub and a few selected outlets.

East London Mild *(OG 1039, ABV 3.6%)*

Just William *(OG 1039, ABV 3.8%)*

E10 Red Ale *(ABV 4.1%)*

William the Conqueror
(OG 1045, ABV 4.4%)

TALLY HO!

Tally Ho! Country Inn & Brewery,
14 Market Street, Hatherleigh,
Devon, EX20 3JN
Tel (01837) 810306
Fax (01837) 811079
E-mail tally.ho@virgin.net
Tours by arrangement

Not currently brewing.

TAYLOR

Timothy Taylor & Co Ltd,
Knowle Spring Brewery,
Belina Street, Keighley,
W Yorkshire, BD21 1AW
Tel (01535) 603139 Fax (01535) 691167
Website www.timothy-taylor.co.uk

One of the classic brewers of pale ale, Timothy Taylor is an independent family-owned company established in 1858. It moved to the site of the Knowle Spring in 1863. Its prize-winning ales, which use Pennine spring water, are served in all 22 of the brewery's pubs as well as 400 other outlets. A new boiler and cask washer were installed in 1999 and the fermentation capacity was increased in 2000. While organic beers are not yet produced, none of the ales contains animal products. Seasonal beer: Ram Tam (ABV 4.3%, winter).

Golden Best *(OG 1033, ABV 3.5%)*
A clean-tasting and refreshing amber-coloured mild with fruit on the nose, a light hoppy taste, a bitter finish and background malt throughout. A good session beer.

Dark Mild *(OG 1034, ABV 3.5%)*
The hops of the underlying Golden Best combines with malt and a caramel sweetness and lead to a dry, bitter-sweet finish.

Porter *(OG 1041, ABV 3.8%)*
Sweetness and caramel can dominate this beer if it is served too young. However, when mature, the sweetness is balanced by fruity flavours and bitterness in the finish.

Best Bitter *(OG 1038, ABV 4%)*
Hops and a citrus fruitiness combine well with some biscuity malt in this drinkable bitter. Bitterness increases down the glass and lingers in the aftertaste.

Landlord *(OG 1042, ABV 4.3%)*
An increasingly dry, bitter finish complements the spicy, citrus hop character and complex fruitiness of this full-flavoured and well-balanced beer.

TEIGNWORTHY

Teignworthy Brewery, The Maltings,
Teign Road, Newton Abbot,
Devon, TQ12 4AA
Tel (01626) 332066
Fax (01626) 330153
E-mail john@teignworthy.freeserve.co.uk
Shop 10-5 weekdays at Tuckers Maltings

John and Rachel Lawton founded the brewery in 1994 and they now produce on average 30-35 barrels a week. Teignworthy is based in the historic Tuckers Maltings, and has first call on traditional, floor-malted grain. There are tours of the brewery and the maltings every 45 minutes between Easter and the end of October. Teignworthy is the only brewery producing a 12% ale in bottle-conditioned form exclusively for Tuckers Maltings. One brew of approximately 2000 bottles is done yearly; this is then sold to Tuckers. Bottles can be purchased from Tuckers shop or via mail order. Bottle-conditioned beers: Reel Ale, Springtide, Old Moggie, Beachcomber, Maltsters (ABV 5%), Strong Ale Christmas Cracker (ABV 6%).

Reel Ale *(OG 1039.5, ABV 4%)*
Clean, sharp-tasting bitter with lasting hoppiness; predominantly malty aroma.

Springtide *(OG 1043.5, ABV 4.3%)*
An excellent, full and well-rounded, mid-brown beer with a dry, bitter taste and aftertaste.

Old Moggie *(OG 1044.5, ABV 4.4%)*

Beachcomber *(OG 1045.5, ABV 4.5%)*
A pale brown beer with a light, refreshing fruit and hop nose, grapefruit taste and a dry, hoppy finish.

TEME VALLEY

Teme Valley Brewery, The Talbot Hotel,
Knightwick, Worcs, WR6 5PH
Tel (01886) 821235
Fax (01886) 821060
E-mail temevalley@aol.com
Website www.temevalley.co.uk
Tours by arrangement

The Teme Valley Brewery opened in 1997 behind the Talbot, with both brewery and inn owned by the farming and hop-growing Clift family. The brewery was the only privately-owned British brewery that grew and used its own hops, but in September 2000, after the hop harvest, Lulsley Court Estate was sold. The Clifts had grown hops at Lulsley Court since the late 19th century, had been heavily involved in the history of hop growing in the area, and were among the first to change to mechanical hop picking in 1947. The new owner at Lulsley Court continues to supply all the brewery's hops. With a 360-gallon weekly capacity, the brewery is on the smaller scale of micro plants, supplying the Talbot and 10 other pubs. Chris Gooch, the brewer, uses a full barley mash and ferments in traditional, open-topped fermenting vessels. Seasonal beers: The Hops Nouvelle is a range of single-hop varietal beers, using fresh, unkilned hops, Challenger, Earlybird Goldings, Fuggles, Mathon Goldings and Northdown: Spring Wot (ABV 4.7%, Jan-March), Fool's Gold (ABV 4.5%, April-May), The Dark Stranger (ABV 4.4%, June-Aug), Wassail (ABV 5.5%, Dec-Jan), Talbot Porter (ABV 4.4%, Nov & Jan), 3 Pears (ABV 3.9%, July-Aug). Bottle-conditioned beers: This; That.

T'Other *(OG 1035, ABV 3.5%)*
A powerfully pungent nose is not lived up to in the flavour with the fruity hops coming through in a very refreshing drink.

This *(OG 1037, ABV 3.7%)* ◆
Quaffing bitter with plenty of hops in the aroma, joined by a dry maltiness when drunk, ending with a light dry aftertaste.

That *(OG 1041, ABV 4.1%)* ◆
A refreshing premium bitter that doesn't overpower the senses but delivers a fruity aroma and taste with malty undertones on the tongue.

JOHN THOMPSON*

John Thompson Brewery, John Thompson Inn, Ingleby, Derbyshire, DE73 1HW
Tel (01332) 863426/(01332) 862469 (pub)
Tours by arrangement

The departure of both Lichfield and Lloyds breweries has turned the site into a brew-pub, producing two beers for the inn.

JTS Bitter *(ABV 4.1%)*

JTS Summer Ale *(ABV 4.5%)*

THREE B'S

Three B's Brewery, Unit 5, Laneside Works, Stockclough Lane, Feniscowles, Blackburn, Lancs, BB2 5JR
Tel (01254) 207686
Tours by arrangement

Robert Bell designed and began building his two-barrel brewery in 1997 and in 1998 he obtained premises in Hamilton Street, Blackburn, to set up the brewery and complete the project. It is now a 10-barrel brewery. The first beers went on sale in 1999. 20 outlets are supplied direct.

Stoker's Slake *(ABV 3.6%)*
A traditional dark mild with roast malt aromas and creamy chocolate notes.

Bobbin's Bitter *(ABV 3.8%)*
Warm aromas of malt, Goldings hops and nuts; a full, fruity flavour with a light dry finish.

Tackler's Tipple *(ABV 4.3%)*
A best bitter with full hop flavour, biscuit tones on the tongue and a deep, dry finish. A darker coloured ale with a fascinating blend of hops and dark malt.

Pinch Noggin' *(ABV 4.6%)*
A luscious balance of malt, hops and fruit, with a lively, colourful spicy aroma of citrus fruit. A quenching golden beer.

Knocker Up *(ABV 4.8%)*
A porter with an exotic ebony texture and a deep, rich palate of roast barley and chocolate malt.

Shuttle Ale *(ABV 5.2%)*
A strong pale ale, light in colour with a balanced malt and hop flavour, and superb Goldings aroma, long dry finish and delicate fruit notes.

THREE TUNS

Three Tuns Brewing Co Ltd, Three Tuns Inn, Salop Street, Bishop's Castle, Shropshire, SY9 5BW
Tel (01588) 638797 Fax (01588) 638081
E-mail info@thethreetunsinn.co.uk

Brewing suspended. The management is seeking planning permission to turn the site into holiday accommodation.

THWAITES

Daniel Thwaites Brewery PLC, PO Box 50, Star Brewery, Blackburn, Lancs, BB1 5BU
Tel (01254) 686868
Fax (01254) 681439
E-mail info@thwaites.co.uk
Website www.thwaites.co.uk
Tours by arrangement

For 200 years Daniel Thwaites has successfully combined traditional brewing recipes and techniques with modern technology to produce an excellent range of quality beers. Passionate about cask ales, Thwaites is committed to traditional brewing with a range of standard and seasonal ales. The pub estate has 65 managed houses and 390 tenanted, with 850 free trade accounts. Seasonal beers, available in both cask and bottle: Daniel's Hammer (ABV 5%, May-June), Good Elf (ABV 4.9%, Nov-Dec), Swashbuckler (ABV 4.5%, dates to be announced).

Mild *(OG 1033, ABV 3.3%)* ◆
A rich, dark mild presenting a smooth, malty flavour and a pleasant, slightly bitter finish.

Bitter *(OG 1036, ABV 3.6%)* ◆
A clean-tasting, refreshing session bitter, combining bitterness and biscuity flavours, and with a lingering bitter finish.

Thoroughbred *(OG 1040, ABV 4%)*
A robust golden colour with a good hop aroma, with dry hops added to the cask.

Lancaster Bomber *(OG 1044, ABV 4.4%)*
Beer bought from Mitchells of Lancaster.

TIGERTOPS

Tigertops Brewery, 22 Oakes Street, Flanshaw Lane, Wakefield, W Yorkshire, WF2 9LN
Tel (01229) 716238 or (01924) 897728
Tours by arrangement in August only

Tigertops was established in 1995 by Stuart Johnson, a former chairman of the Wakefield branch of CAMRA, and his wife, Lynda. The Johnsons also own the Foxfield Brewery in Cumbria. Barry 'Axeman' Smith, the brewer, produces Continental

beer styles, using imported malts and yeasts. The brewery supplies mainly beer festivals and three or four other outlets. Seasonal beer: Marzen (ABV 5%, March).

Dark Mild Wheat *(OG 1036, ABV 3.6%)*
An unusual mild made primarily with wheat malt.

Axeman's Light *(OG 1035, ABV 3.6%)*
A hoppy pale ale.

Axeman's Block *(OG 1036, ABV 3.6%)*
A malty beer with a good hop finish.

Blanche de Newland
(OG 1044, ABV 4.6%)
A Belgian-style wheat beer.

Bock *(OG 1058, ABV 6.4%)*
A fruity, full-bodied complex beer.

TINDALL

Tindall Ale Brewery, Toad Lane, Seething, Norfolk, NR35 2EQ
Tel/Fax (01508) 483844
Shop ring for appointment
Tours by arrangement

⊗ Tindall Ales was established in 1998 and was situated on the edge of the medieval Tindall Wood. It moved to new premises, a converted stable block, in 2001. It is a family-run business with the main objective of producing a good quality, locally-produced ale for local outlets. All the beers are made from best local malt and the finest Kentish hops. Seasonal beers: Lovers' Ale (ABV 4%), Christmas Cheer (ABV 4%), Summer Loving (ABV 3.6%), Fuggled Up (ABV 3.7%), Resurrection (ABV 3.8%), Mundham Mild (ABV 4%), Autumn Brew (ABV 4%), Suffolk 'n' See (ABV 4.6%), Norfolk 'n' Good (ABV 4.6%). All the beers are available in bottle-conditioned form.

Mild *(ABV 3.7%)*
A good dark mild.

Best Bitter *(ABV 3.7%)* ◆
Complex nose with a mixture of malt, honey and sulphur. Malt continues throughout as hops and vanilla combine to produce a light, clean signature. A steady finish develops a slightly smoky overtone.

Resurrection *(ABV 3.8%)* ◆
A golden-coloured, crisp-tasting bitter. The Cascade hops give a popcorn aroma and a clean peachy feel to the dominant hop beginning. A long fruit finish with marmalade and malt add to the persistent hoppiness.

Alltime *(ABV 4%)* ◆
A malt-based best bitter. This amber-coloured bitter has a malty nose as a lead into a malty freshness that complements the sweet, fruity overtones. A long ending develops a filling hop and caramel feel.

Ditchingham Dam *(ABV 4.2%)* ◆
Initial malt flavour with a treacle toffee edge adds to the rich malty aroma. Some hints of dried vine fruits develop before the quick finish gives a dryish roast farewell befitting a mid-brown coloured beer.

Ale Extra *(ABV 4.5%)* ◆
A sweet, fruity ale with a distinct malt beginning. This fades as bitterness comes through to give a quick, dry finish. Amber in colour, with low malt notes in a gentle hoppy aroma.

Norwich Dragon *(ABV 4.6%)*
A lighter ale brewed with American Cascade hops for a fruitier finish.

TIPSY TOAD

Tipsy Toad Brewery,
St Peter's Village,
Jersey, CI, JE3 7AA
Tel (01534) 485556
Fax (01534) 485559
Tours by arrangement

⊗ A brew-pub launched in 1992 and taken over by Jersey Brewery in 1997. Jersey Brewery distributes the beers through its tied estate. Seasonal/rotating beers: Festive Toad (ABV 8%), Horny Toad (ABV 5%), Dixie's Wheat Beer (ABV 4%), Naomh Padraig's Porter (ABV 4.4%).

Tipsy Toad Ale *(OG 1038, ABV 3.8%)*

Jimmy's Bitter *(OG 1042, ABV 4.2%)*

TIRRIL

Tirril Brewery Ltd,
Brougham Hall, Brougham,
Cumbria, CA10 2DE
Tel (01768) 863219
Fax (01768) 863243
E-mail brewery@queensheadinn.co.uk
Website www.queensheadinn.co.uk
Tours by arrangement

◎ Tirril started brewing 100 years after J Siddle's Brewery was closed in Tirril in 1899. It brewed to full capacity of 2.5 barrels a week at the Queens Head in Tirril, until in June 2002 it moved to a 10-barrel plant in nearby Brougham Hall, an ancient castle with a 19th-century brewhouse.

John Bewsher's Best Bitter
(OG 1037.5, ABV 3.8%)
Lightly-hopped, pale brown coloured bitter. A popular session beer.

Charles Gough's Old Faithful
(OG 1039, ABV 4%)
A pale colour, hoppy, aromatic bitter.

Thomas Slee's Academy Ale
(OG 1040.5, ABV 4.2%)
A dark, full-bodied traditional style, rich malty bitter.

TITANIC

Titanic Brewery, Harvey Works,
Lingard Street, Burslem,
Stoke-on-Trent, Staffs, ST6 1ED
Tel (01782) 823447
Fax (01782) 812349
E-mail titanic@titanicbrewery.co.uk
Website www.titanicbrewery.co.uk

◎ Founded in 1985, the brewery is named in honour of Captain Smith who hailed from the Potteries, and had the misfortune to captain the Titanic. In 1996 Titanic Brewery resurrected the log-fired Victorian micro-brewery at Shugborough, home of Lord Lichfield, and brews for demonstration purposes there, producing one-off brews for festivals and special occasions. Titanic's increasing presence in the free trade led to

another move to larger premises in 2002 and a visitor centre is planned. The company now supplies more than 250 free trade outlets as well as its own tied house, the Bulls Head in Burslem. For Shugborough Brewery: Coachman's Tipple (ABV 4.7%, Jan-Feb), Butler's Revenge (ABV 4.9%, March-April), Milady's Fancy (ABV 4.6%, May-June), Farmer's Half (ABV 4.8%, July-Aug), Gardener's Retreat (ABV 4.7%, Sept-Oct), Lordship's Own (ABV 5%, Nov-Dec). Shugborough brews are also available in bottle-conditioned form in the same periods. Titanic seasonal beers: A monthly seasonal beer is brewed, all named with Titanic connections.

Mild *(OG 1035, ABV 3.5%)*
A mild of classic style, full of roast malt flavours and balanced by delicate hops. True to type, it has rounded sweetness and a smooth, dry finish.

Best Bitter *(OG 1036, ABV 3.5%)* ◆
A malty and hoppy beer throughout. Hoppy and bitter finish; excellent for a light bitter.

Lifeboat Ale *(OG 1040, ABV 4%)* ◆
A fruity and malty, dark red/brown beer, with a fruity finish.

Iceberg *(OG 1042, ABV 4.1%)*
A combination of Maris Otter pale malt and fine wheat malt, give this refreshing beer real zest. The hops are Yakima Galena and Cascade from the U.S.

Premium Bitter
(OG 1042, ABV 4.1%) ◆
An impressive, well-balanced pale brown bitter with hops and fruit in the aroma, which develop into a full flavour and a dry, hoppy finish.

Stout *(OG 1046, ABV 4.5%)* ◆
Full roast with great liquorice taste. Hopped to give dryness and astringency, but roast is well balanced and lingers.

White Star *(OG 1050, ABV 4.8%)* ◆
An amber ale with a fruity taste and long bitter-sweet, fruity aftertaste.

Captain Smith's *(OG 1054, ABV 5.2%)* ◆
A full-bodied, dark red/brown beer, hoppy and bitter with malt and roast malt flavours, and a long, bitter-sweet finish.

Wreckage *(ABV 7.2%)* ◆
This sweet malty winter ale has a port-like aroma and walnut aftertaste.

TOLLY COBBOLD

Tollemache & Cobbold Brewery Ltd, Cliff Road, Ipswich, Suffolk, IP3 0AZ
Tel (01473) 231723

Tolly Cobbold, founded in 1723, merged with Ridleys of Chelmsford in July 2002. Brewing will cease at Ipswich and the brewery museum will close.

TOWER

Tower Brewery, The Old Water Tower, Walsitch Maltings, Glensyl Way, Burton-on-Trent, Staffs, DE14 1PZ
Tel/Fax (01283) 530695
Tours by arrangement

⊗ The brewery was built and situated in the old water tower of Thomas Salt's brewery, once the second-biggest brewery in Burton and in the vanguard of the pale ale revolution of the 19th century. The height of the building provides gravity feed for malt grist, cold liquor and hot liquor. Owner John Mills started trading in 2001 after nine months restoring the derelict building. It had been empty for seven and a half years before purchase. John has 50 regular outlets for his beers. Seasonal beers: Sundowner (ABV 4%, May-Aug), Spring Equinox (ABV 4.6%, March-May), Autumn Equinox (ABV 4.6%, Sept-Nov).

Bitter *(OG 1041, ABV 4.2%)* ◆
Gold coloured with a malty aroma, with hops and caramel. A full hop and fruit taste with the fruit lingering; almost grassy fresh. A bitter and astringent finish that lingers.

Malty Towers *(OG 1044, ABV 4.4%)* ◆
Yellow with a malty aroma as named, with a hint of tobacco. Strong hops give a long, dry, bitter finish with pleasant astringency.

Pale Ale *(OG 1047, ABV 4.8%)*

Winter Spirit *(OG 1050, ABV 5%)*

Walsitch Wobbler *(OG 1052, ABV 5.2%)* ◆
Blackberry and liquorice flavours abound in this strong red beer. A dry finish with some background roast.

Tower of Strength *(OG 1075, ABV 7.6%)*

TOWNES

⌂ Townes Brewery, Speedwell Inn, Lowgates, Staveley, Chesterfield, Derbyshire, S43 3TT
Tel (01246) 472252
Tours by arrangement

⊗ Townes Brewery started in 1994 in an old bakery on the outskirts of Chesterfield using a five-barrel plant; it was the first brewery in the town for more than 40 years. After a period of steady progress, the Speedwell Inn at Staveley was bought and the plant was moved to the rear of the pub. Brewing at Staveley started in 1997 and, after a period of renovation, the pub opened a year later. It was the first brew-pub in north Derbyshire in the 20th century. It sells the full range of Townes Beers. There are plans to bottle the beers and to buy another tied house in the area. More than 20 outlets are supplied direct. Reciprocal deals with other micros are being extended. Seasonal beers: GMT (ABV 4.2%, winter), Speedwell Bitter (ABV 3.9%, winter), IPA (ABV 4.5%, summer), Sunshine (ABV 3.6%, summer). A monthly Special is available, always over ABV 4.5%, but in varying styles.

Speedwell Bitter *(OG 1038, ABV 3.8%)*

Golden Bud *(OG 1038, ABV 3.8%)*

Best Lockoford Bitter *(OG 1040, ABV 4%)*

IPA *(OG 1045, ABV 4.5%)*

Pynot Porter *(OG 1045, ABV 4.5%)*

Muffin Ale *(OG 1045, ABV 4.5%)*

TOWN HOUSE*

Town House, 2 Town House Studios, Town House Farm, Alsager Road, Audley, Staffs, ST7 8JQ
Tel (07976) 209437

Small brewery based in units on a farm and supplying eight free houses.

Audley Bitter *(ABV 3.8%)*

Parker's Pride *(ABV 4.6%)*

Standard *(ABV 4.1%)*

TRAQUAIR

Traquair House Brewery Ltd, Innerleithen, Peeblesshire, EH44 6PP
Tel (01896) 830323
Fax (01896) 830639
E-mail enquiries@traquair.co.uk
Website www.traquair.co.uk
Shop and Brewery Museum 12.30-5.30 daily April-Oct, 10.30-5.30 daily June-Aug.
Tours by arrangement April-Sept

The 18th-century brewhouse is based in one of the wings of the 1,000-years-old Traquair House, Scotland's oldest inhabited house, visited by Mary Queen of Scots and Prince Charles Edward Stuart. The brewhouse was rediscovered by the 20th Laird, the late Peter Maxwell Stuart, in 1965. He began brewing again using all the original equipment, which remained intact, despite having lain idle for more than 100 years. The brewery has been run by Peter's daughter, Catherine Maxwell Stuart, since his death in 1990. The Maxwell Stuarts are members of the Stuart clan, and the main Bear Gates will remain shut until a Stuart returns to the throne. All the beers are oak-fermented and 60 per cent of production is exported (mostly bottled Traquair House Ale and Jacobite Ale). Some five outlets take the cask beer. Seasonal beers: Stuart Ale (ABV 4.5%, summer), Bear Ale (ABV 5%, winter).

House Ale *(ABV 7.2%)*

Jacobite Ale *(ABV 8%)*

TRAVELLERS INN

Travellers Inn Brewing Company, Tremerchion Road, Pen-y-Cefn, Caerwys, Flintshire, CH7 5BL
Tel (01352) 720251

Roy Morgan's Original Ale *(ABV 3.8%)*

TRING

Tring Brewery Co Ltd, 81-82 Akeman Street, Tring, Herts, HP23 6AF
Tel (01442) 890721
Fax (01442) 890740
E-mail info@tringbrewery.com
Website www.tringbrewery.com
Tours by arrangement

Tring Brewery was founded in 1992 and, after a break of more than 50 years, restored brewing to the West Hertfordshire town. The company was started by Richard Shardlow, who had brewed with Devenish, Greene King and Ruddles, who was joined by Andrew Jackson from Whitbread. A new range of beers has been developed for the 32-barrel plant, backed by contemporary marketing. Tring has leased the Two Brewers in Luton, which is run as a free house but always stocks two or three of the brewery's beers. The company plans to add five to 10 pubs in the next few years. The brewery supplies 60-100 outlets. As well as seasonal beers, there is a vast range of one-off specials. Seasonal beers: Cuckoo's Coming (ABV 4.5%, spring), Mother Haggy's Finest Summer Ale (ABV 3.7%), Reap the Rye (ABV 4.7%, autumn), Santa's Little Helper (ABV 4.8%).

Side Pocket for a Toad *(OG 1035, ABV 3.6%)*
Unmistakable citrus notes from American Cascade hops balanced with a floral aroma and crisp dry finish in a straw-coloured ale.

Jack O'Legs *(OG 1041, ABV 4.2%)*
A combination of four types of malt and two types of aroma hops provide a copper-coloured premium ale with full fruit and a distinctive hoppy bitterness.

Colley's Dog *(OG 1051, ABV 5.2%)*
Dark but not over-rich, strong yet drinkable, this premium ale has a long dry finish with overtones of malt and walnuts.

TRIPLE FFF

Triple fff Brewing Company, Unit 3, Old Magpie Works, Four Marks, Alton, Hampshire, GU34 2DN
Tel/Fax (01420) 561422
Website www.triplefff.co.uk

Established in 1997, and now under the sole proprietorship of Graham Trott, Triple fff has made steady progress. It has expanded from five to 18 barrel brew-lengths. Winner of 14 awards, the brewery supplies around 200 outlets, and also uses wholesalers to distribute outside its own delivery area. Seasonal beers: Apache Rose Peacock (ABV 4.2%), Goldfffinger (ABV 5.4%), Witches Promise (ABV 6%).

Alton's Pride *(ABV 3.8%)*
Excellent, clean-tasting, hoppy bitter with a pleasant fruitiness to balance. Nice hop aroma and long hoppy, bitter finish.

Pressed Rat & Warthog *(ABV 3.8%)*
A dry, roasty red-black mild with good body and hints of blackcurrant and caramel. Moderately bitter, with a short but well-balanced aftertaste.

After Glow *(ABV 4%)*
A superbly hoppy, award-winning bitter. Straw-coloured, with honey and citrus fruit on the nose, the beer is well-balanced, with a good body and an aromatic hoppy and fruity finish.

Moondance *(ABV 4.2%)*
An amber-coloured best bitter, wonderfully hopped, with a huge hop aroma, balanced by bittering hops and malt. Bitterness increases in the finish as the fruit declines.

Stairway to Heaven *(ABV 4.6%)*
An aroma of pale and crystal malts introduces this pale brown beer with a flavour of summer fruits. Well-balanced, with a dry and fruity finish.

Dazed and Confused *(OG 1048, ABV 4.6%)*
An aroma of pale and crystal malts introduces this pale brown beer with a flavour of summer fruits. Well balanced, with a dry and fruity finish.

Comfortably Numb *(ABV 5%)*

Little Red Rooster *(ABV 5%)*

TRUEMAN'S

Sam Trueman's Brewery, Henley House, School Lane, Medmenham, Marlow, Bucks, SL7 2HJ
Tel (01491) 576100
Fax (01491) 571764
E-mail bar@crownandanchor.co.uk
Website www.crownandanchor.co.uk

⊗ Sam Trueman's beer was available through wholesalers throughout the country but, as a result of wholesalers not paying bills, the owners bought the Crown & Anchor in Marlow, where Best (cask) and Lager (unfiltered but pressurised) were always available, but the pub has now been sold. Bottle-conditioned beers: Percy's Downfall (ABV 8.2%), No Name (ABV 6%) and Lager (ABV 4.2%). Seasonal beer: Percy's Downfall (ABV 8.2%).

Best *(OG 1036, ABV 3.5%)*

Tipple *(OG 1041, ABV 4.2%)*

Bees Knees *(OG 1043, ABV 4.3%)*

Gold *(OG 1050, ABV 5%)*

TURKEY

Turkey Inn, Goose Eye, Oakworth, Keighley, West Yorkshire, BO22 0PD
Tel (01535) 681339
Tours by arrangement

A purpose-built brewhouse with walls four feet thick, built into the hillside at the back of the pub, it took three years to build. All the beers are named after caves. Brewery trips are free, with a small donation to Upper Wharfdale Fell Rescue. Beer Festivals every May Bank Holiday, finishes first Monday in May. Black Shiver is suitable for vegetarians/vegans.

Turkey Bitter *(OG 1038)*

White Sear *(OG 1046)*

Lost John's *(OG 1048)*

Black Shiver *(OG 1040)*

ULEY

Uley Brewery Ltd, The Old Brewery, Uley, Dursley, Glos, GL11 5TB
Tel (01453) 860120
Web www.uleybrewery.com

⊗ Brewing at Uley began in 1833 at Price's Brewery. After a long gap, the premises were restored and Uley Brewery opened in 1985. It has its own spring water, which is used to mash with Tuckers Maris Otter malt and boiled with Hereford hops. No sugar or additives are used. Uley serves 40-50 free trade outlets in the Cotswolds area and, says owner Chas Wright, contrary to 'decline in cask ales, we have never been busier!' Seasonal beer: Pigor Mortis (ABV 6%, Dec-Jan).

Hogshead PA *(OG 1036, ABV 3.5%)*
A pale-coloured, hoppy session bitter with a good hop aroma and a full flavour for its strength, ending in a bitter-sweet aftertaste.

Uley Bitter *(OG 1040, ABV 4%)*
A copper-coloured beer with hops and fruit in the aroma and a malty, fruity taste, underscored by a hoppy bitterness. The finish is dry, with a balance of hops and malt.

Old Ric *(OG 1045, ABV 4.5%)*
A full-flavoured, hoppy bitter with some fruitiness and a smooth, balanced finish. Distinctively copper-coloured.

Old Spot Prize Ale *(OG 1050, ABV 5%)*
A distinctive full-bodied, red/brown ale with a fruity aroma, a malty, fruity taste, with a hoppy bitterness, and a strong, balanced aftertaste.

Pig's Ear Strong Beer
(OG 1050, ABV 5%) ◆
A pale-coloured beer, deceptively strong. Notably bitter in flavour, with a hoppy, fruity aroma and a bitter finish.

UPPER AGBRIGG*

Upper Agbrigg Brewery, 17 The Village, Holme, Holmfirth, Huddersfield, HD9 2QG
Tel (01484) 685143
E-mail andy@balmfontla.freeserve.co.uk

☺ The brewery is named after Wapentake of Agbrigg, dating back to the 1200s. Brewing started with a one-barrel plant run by an ex-process chemist. The intention is to move to new premises and a five-barrel plant. The brewery aims to develop and produce Continental-style cask ales, using Belgian and German malts and hops. Six outlets are supplied directly.

Spring/Summer Ale *(ABV 3.8%)*

Agbrigg Alt *(ABV 4-4.2%)*
Old German ale.

Black Beauty Porter *(ABV 4.1-4.2%)*

ESB *(ABV 4.3%)*

Kellerbier *(ABV 5-5.2%)*
Bavarian-style beer

VALE

Vale Brewery Company, Thame Road, Haddenham, Bucks, HP17 8BY
Tel (01844) 290008 Fax (01844) 292505
E-mail valebrewery@ntlworld.com
Website www.valebrewery.co.uk
Tours by arrangement

⊗ After many years working for large regional breweries and allied industries, brothers Mark and Phil Stevens opened a small, purpose-built brewery in Haddenham. This revived brewing in a village where the last brewery closed at the end of World War Two. The plant was expanded in 1996 and now has a capacity of 40 barrels. All the beer is traditionally brewed without adjuncts, chemicals, or preservatives. A bottling line has been added, now producing a range of 10 different ales plus own label beers in short runs and the cask beers are also available in bottle-conditioned form. Around 200 local outlets take the beers. Seasonal beers: Hadda's Spring Gold (ABV 4.6%), Hadda's Summer Glory (ABV 4%), Hadda's Autumn Ale (ABV 4.5%), Hadda's Winter Solstice (ABV 4.1%). Bottle-conditioned beers: As for regular ales, except Notley Ale. All are suitable for vegetarians and vegans.

Black Swan Dark Mild
(OG 1033, ABV 3.3%)

Notley Ale *(OG 1033, ABV 3.3%)* ◆
A refreshing copper-coloured session bitter with some malt in the aroma and taste, and an uncompromisingly dry finish.

Best Bitter *(OG 1036, ABV 3.7%)*

Wychert Ale *(OG 1038, ABV 3.9%)*
A full-flavoured beer with nutty overtones.

Black Beauty Porter
(OG 1043, ABV 4.3%)

Edgar's Golden Ale
(OG 1043, ABV 4.3%) ◆
A golden, hoppy best bitter with some sweetness and a dry, bitter-sweet finish. An unpretentious and well-crafted beer.

Grumpling Old Ale *(OG 1046, ABV 4.6%)*

Haddas Headbanger *(OG 1050, ABV 5%)*

VALHALLA

Valhalla Brewery, Shetland Refreshments Ltd, Baltasound, Unst, Shetland, ZE2 9DX
Tel/Fax (01957) 711658
Website www.valhallabrewery.co.uk
Tours by arrangement

Valhalla Brewery opened in 1997 on the island of Unst in the Shetland Isles, making it the most northerly brewery in Great Britain. It is run by husband and wife team Sonny and Sylvia Priest plus some part-timers. The latest acquisition was a bottling plant in 1999, which has greatly increased sales.

White Wife *(ABV 3.8%)* ◆
Predominantly malty aroma with hop and fruit, which remain on the palate. The aftertaste is increasingly bitter.

Simmer Dim *(ABV 4%)* ◆
A light golden bitter, named after the long Shetland twilight. The sulphur features do not mask the fruits and hops of this well-balanced beer.

Auld Rock *(ABV 4.5%)* ◆
A full-bodied, dark Scottish-style best bitter, it has a rich malty nose but does not lack bitterness in the long dry finish.

Sjolmet Stout *(ABV 5%)* ◆
Full of malt and roast barley, especially in the taste. Smooth, creamy, fruity finish, not as dry as some stouts.

VENTNOR

Ventnor Brewery Ltd, 119 High Street, Ventnor, Isle of Wight, PO38 1LY
Tel (01983) 856161
Website www.ventnorbrewery.co.uk
Shop 9-5. Tours by arrangement

⊗ Ventnor Brewery has been brewing since the early 1840s. Using traditional recipes of malt, hops and the unique ingredient of St Boniface natural spring water, Ventnor Brewery continues the tradition of brewing high quality, hand-crafted cask and bottled ales for the island and beyond. More than 60 outlets are supplied direct. All the beers are available in bottle, all but SunFire are available bottle-conditioned. Bottles are available nationally. A celebration ale called Admirals Ale was brewed to commemorate the America's Cup. Due to its success, it has been continued as is now the biggest-selling bottled beer. It won Celebration Label of the Year. Seasonal ales are also available.

Golden *(OG 1039, ABV 4%)* ◆
Well-balanced, easy-drinking bitter with an interesting slight honey/yeasty aftertaste.

SunFire *(OG 1043, ABV 4.3%)* ◆
A generously and distinctively bittered amber beer that could be toned down if pulled through a sparkler.

Oyster Stout *(OG 1045, ABV 4.5%)* ◆
A thin stout/dark mild with real oysters in the brew.

Old Ruby *(OG 1048, ABV 4.7%)*
A deep ruby-coloured bitter, with a good body and well balanced hop.

Wight Spirit *(OG 1050, ABV 5%)* ◆
Interesting pale, hoppy, strong bitter with a surprising reversal of flavours from taste to aftertaste.

Sandrock Smoked Ale *(OG 1055, ABV 5.6%)*
Brewed using a selected peated malt from Scotland. This dark ruby-coloured winter ale brings the aromas of a blazing fire direct to you in a pint.

VERULAM

Verulam Brewery, 134 London Road, St Albans, Herts, AL1 1PQ
Tel (01727) 766702
Tours by arrangement

⊠ A brewery housed behind the Farmers Boy pub run by Viv and Tina Davies. There are monthly specials.

Best Bitter *(OG 1035, ABV 3.5%)*

Special *(OG 1037, ABV 3.8%)* ◆
Well-balanced session beer with a dryish aftertaste.

IPA *(OG 1039, ABV 4%)* ◆
Impressive straw-coloured, very hoppy beer.

Farmers Joy *(OG 1043, ABV 4.5%)* ◆
A malty beer with overtones of sweetness.

WADWORTH

Wadworth & Co Ltd, Northgate Brewery, Devizes, Wilts, SN10 1JW
Tel (01380) 723361
Fax (01380) 724342
E-mail sales@wadworth.co.uk
Website www.wadworth.co.uk
Shop 9-7.30 Mon-Fri. 9-530 Sat.
Tours Trade April-Oct. Public June-Sept & Devizes Arts Festival. Stables open weekday afternoons.

⊠ A market town brewery set up in 1885 by Henry Wadworth, and one of the few remaining breweries to sell beer locally in oak casks; the brewery still employs a cooper. Though solidly traditional, with its own dray horses, it continues to invest in the future and to expand, producing up to 2,000 barrels a week to supply a wide-ranging free trade in the South of England, as well as its own 250 pubs. All but two of the tied houses serve real ale and 6X remains one of the south's most famous beers, with national distribution through Interbrew. Up to 350 outlets are supplied. Wadworth also owns a brew-pub, the Red Shoot (qv). Seasonal beers: Old Father Timer (OG 1055, ABV 5.8%, Dec-Jan), Malt 'n' Hops (OG 1043, ABV 4.5%, Sept-Oct), Summersault (ABV 4%, May-Sept). Bottle-conditioned beer: Strongest Ale (ABV 11.3%).

Henry's Original IPA *(OG 1035, ABV 3.6%)* ◆
A golden brown-coloured beer with a gentle, malty and slightly hoppy aroma, a good balance of flavours, with maltiness gradually dominating, and then a long-lasting aftertaste to match, eventually becoming biscuity. A good session beer.

6X *(OG 1041, ABV 4.3%)* ◆
Copper-coloured ale with a malty and fruity nose and some balancing hop character. The flavour is similar, with some bitterness and a lingering malty, but bitter finish. Full-bodied and distinctive.

JCB *(OG 1045, ABV 4.7%)*
A deep amber, robust but perfectly balanced, traditional English ale with a rich, malty body, complex hop character and a hint of tropical fruit in the aroma and taste. A gentle 'boiled sweet'/barley sugar sweetness blends wonderfully with smooth nutty malt and rounded hop bitterness before a dry, biscuity, bitter finish.

WAPPING*

Wapping Beers, The Baltic Fleet, 33A Wapping, Liverpool, L1 8DQ
Tel (0151) 709 3116
Tours by arrangement

⊛ Wapping Beers is a scaled-down plant from Passageway, expertly installed in the cellar to maximise heat retention both in the copper and hot liquor tank. As a result, the energy saving is significant and consistency of brew very good. The fermentation vessels are cooled on the outside and lagged, and there is an area in the brewery for warm conditioning as well as cool conditioning for which old smugglers' tunnels are used. Production started in January 2002.

Wapping Bitter *(OG 1036, ABV 3.6%)*
A light chestnut colour with a lingering aftertaste.

Cornhill Summer Ale *(OG 1042, ABV 4.2%)*
Straw coloured with a good bite.

Baltic Extra *(OG 1045, ABV 4.5%)*
Chestnut in colour with a big whack of bitterness.

WARCOP

Warcop Country Ales, 9 Nellive Park, St Brides Wentlooge, S Wales, NP10 8SE
Tel/Fax (01633) 680058
E-mail williampicton@compuserve.com

Small brewery based in a converted milking parlour, with 30 outlets delivered direct and others supplied by two wholesalers. Seasonal beer brewed normally at Christmas: Red Hot Furnace (ABV 9%), Furnace Fire (ABV 7.2%), Oil Fire (ABV 6-6.7%).

Pit Shaft *(ABV 3.4%)*
Dark mild.

Pitside *(ABV 3.7%)*
The delicate taste of malt beer.

Arc *(ABV 3.8%)*
Light session beer with a dry, hoppy taste.

Pit Prop *(ABV 3.8%)* ◆
Fruit and roast aroma, dark brown in colour. A mixture of roast, malt, caramel and fruit in taste and aftertaste. The bitterness builds, adding to the character.

Hackers *(ABV 4%)*
Pale yellow lightly-hopped bitter.

Black and Amber *(ABV 4%)*
A traditional pale ruby bitter, lightly hopped and full of flavour.

Casnewydd *(ABV 4%)*
Light, easy-drinking beer.

Hilston Premier *(ABV 4%)*
Rustic coloured, medium dry autumnal beer.

Drillers *(ABV 4%)*
A lightly hopped yellow ale.

Steelers *(ABV 4.2%)*
Light red malty-tasting brew.

Rollers *(ABV 4.3%)*
A light ruby-coloured, well-hopped bitter.

Raiders *(ABV 4.3%)*
A lightly hopped strong yellow ale.

Zen *(ABV 4.4%)*
A light yellow ale with a dry finish.

Riggers *(ABV 4.5%)*
A strongly hopped golden beer with body.

Furnace *(ABV 4.5%)*
Ruby-coloured, malty beer with a dry finish.

Printers *(ABV 4.6%)*
Pale yellow strong ale.

Dockers *(ABV 5%)*
Golden, fruity, full-bodied beer.

Deep Pit *(ABV 5%)*
Ruby full-bodied beer with distinctive taste.

Painters *(ABV 5%)*
Pale yellow, full-bodied strong ale.

WARWICKSHIRE

Warwickshire Beer Co Ltd, The Brewery, Queen Street, Cubbington, Leamington Spa, Warwickshire, CV32 7NA
Tel (01926) 450747
Fax (01926) 450763
Website www.warwickshirebeerco.co.uk
Shop 8-12 Sat (weekdays ring first)
Tours by arrangement

A six-barrel plant opened in a former village bakery by Phil Page in 1999, it was commissioned by Warwick District Council to produce a commemorative bottled beer to celebrate the redevelopment of Warwick market place. Capacity was increased in 2000 to 26 barrels. In 2001 it acquired its first pub, the Market Tavern in Atherstone. 80 outlets are supplied direct. Seasonal beer: Xmas Bare (ABV 4.9%). Bottle-conditioned beer: King Maker (ABV 5.5%)

Best Bitter *(OG 1039, ABV 3.9%)*
A golden brown session bitter flavoured with First Gold hops.

Lady Godiva *(OG 1042, ABV 4.2%)*
Blond, gentle, and full-bodied.

St Patricks *(OG 1044, ABV 4.4%)*
A rich porter brewed in the Irish tradition.

Falstaff *(OG 1044, ABV 4.4%)*
A mahogany-coloured bitter flavoured with Cascade and First Gold hops.

Castle *(OG 1046, ABV 4.6%)*
A premium full-bodied and malty bitter.

Golden Bear *(OG 1049, ABV 4.9%)*
Golden in colour with well-balanced bitterness and spicy/fruity notes.

King Maker *(OG 1055, ABV 5.5%)*
Its subtlety belies its strength with flavour dominated by Challenger hops.

TOMOS WATKIN

Hurns Brewing Co Ltd, Phoenix Brewery, Unit 3, Century Park, Valley Way, Swansea Enterprise Park, Swansea, SA6 8RP
Tel (01792) 797300 Fax (01792) 775779
E-mail enquiries@tomoswatkin.com
Website www.tomoswatkin.com
Tours by arrangement

⊛ Convulsive changes at Tomos Watkin in 2002 saw the brewery bought by the Hurns wholesaling group, the abrupt and angry departure of the former owners, and the purchase of some of the company's nine pubs by a company called Celtic Inns. For a time there was talk of legal action by the former directors, but the action was abandoned. At present, Tomos Watkin is a stand-alone brewery without pubs, but it is supplying some beer to the Celtic outlets. The brewery was established by Simon Buckley (ex Buckley's and Usher's) at Llandeilo in 1995, adopting the name of a Llandovery company that ceased production in 1928. In 2000, the brewery moved to Swansea to a bigger custom-built brewhouse. Buckley is no longer connected with the brewery. Seasonal beers: Warrior (ABV 4.2%, spring), Canons Choice (ABV 4.5%, winter), Dewi Sant (ABV 4.3%, March-April), Cwrw Haf (ABV 4.2%, summer), Owain Glyndwr (ABV 4.2%, autumn), Cwrw Santa (ABV 4.6%, Dec-Jan).

Whoosh *(OG 1037.5, ABV 3.7%)* ◆
Amber-coloured, gentle malt and hop aroma. A similar flavour with fruit and moderate bitterness leads to a fading finish.

Brewery Bitter (BB)
(OG 1040.5, ABV 4%) ◆
Pale brown, a faint malt, hop and fruit aroma. A rounded mix of these flavours is joined by a balancing bitterness in the finish.

Merlin Stout *(OG 1043, ABV 4.2%)*
A roast and malt aroma, dark brown in colour. A pleasing mix of roast and malt flavours with some caramel and hop. A good roast and malt finish, with moderate bitterness. A long finish adds to a rounded stout.

Old Style Bitter (OSB)
(OG 1045, ABV 4.5%)
Malt, hop and fruit aroma, full bodied, balanced mix of hop and fruit flavours. Increasing bitterness leads to a lasting finish. Satisfying.

WAWNE

Wawne Brewery, Hodgson's Public House, Flemingate, Beverley, E Yorkshire, HU17 0NU
Tel (01482) 880484Fax (01482) 880980
Website www.wawne-brewery.com
Shop Merchandise for sale in pub
Tours by appointment

The brewery moved to Hodgson's from the Tickton Arms in 2001. A new copper and fermenter were added. There are plans to get back into wholesaling and direct selling to all parts of the country.

Monks Mild *(OG 1032, ABV 3.2%)*
This dark brown mild has a fairly fruity aroma. It is well balanced with a rich roasted caramel flavour and hints of fruit. Tasty throughout.

Infringement Bitter
(OG 1038, ABV 3.8%)
Fresh and fruity, this golden/copper-coloured beer mixes both bitterness and sweetness well. The hop flavours come through to give a dry, crisp finish.

Hodgsons Best *(OG 1039, ABV 3.9%)*
This amber-coloured session beer has a distinctly hoppy aroma and taste throughout. The aftertaste is dry and bitter

Waghen *(OG 1041, ABV 4.1%)*
An easily drinkable premium beer, amber in colour with a crisp mix of floral hops and fruitiness. Full flavoured with a hint of caramel.

Melsa *(OG 1043, ABV 4.3%)*
This delightful, complex beer is copper coloured. An aroma of pear drops is followed by a lovely balanced taste of fruit/hops and malt, which brings out sweetness in the tasse. A bitter finish.

WEATHEROAK

Weatheroak Brewery, Coach & Horses Inn, Weatheroak Hill, Alvechurch, Birmingham, B48 7EA
Tel (0121) 445 4411 (eves)
E-mail dave@weatheroakales.co.uk
Website www.weatheroakales.co.uk
Shop Real ale Off-Licence, Alvechurch. Tue-Fri 5.30-830. Fri-Sat 5-9. Tours by arrangement

The brewery was set up in 1997, in an outhouse of the Coach & Horses, by Dave and Pat Smith by arrangement with pub owners Phil and Sheila Meads. The first brew was produced in 1998. A real ale off-licence has been opened in nearby Alvechurch. Weatheroak supplies 40 outlets direct.

Light Oak *(ABV 3.6%)*
A well-hopped beer with an abundance of bitter flavours. A very quaffable, low-gravity beer

Ale *(ABV 4.1%)*
Floral hops dominate throughout in this tangy session bitter. This very aromatic drink is finished with a distinct dryness.

Redwood *(ABV 4.7%)*
This medium-bodied ale has an emphatic maltiness in the nose and on the tongue, with an undercurrent of hops and fruit, leaving a slight bitterness in the mouth

Triple Tee *(ABV 5.1%)*
The strong hoppiness of this refreshing premium bitter starts in its aroma and is joined by a fruity taste ending with a light dryish aftertaste.

WEETWOOD

Weetwood Ales Ltd, Weetwood Grange, Weetwood, Tarporley, Cheshire, CW6 0NQ
Tel (01829) 752805
or Tel/Fax (01829) 752377
E-mail sales@weetwoodales.co.uk
Website www.weetwoodales.co.uk

The brewery was set up at an equestrian centre in 1993. In 1998, the five-barrel plant was replaced by a 10-barrel kit. Around 100 regular customers are now supplied.

Best Bitter *(OG 1038.5, ABV 3.8%)*
A clean, dry and malty bitter with little aroma. Bitterness dominates the finish.

Eastgate Ale *(OG 1043.5, ABV 4.2%)*
Well-balanced, pale, refreshing beer with malty, fruity taste and short, dry finish.

Old Dog Bitter *(OG 1045, ABV 4.5%)*
A fuller-bodied version of the bitter: fruitier, with a hint of sweetness.

Ambush Ale *(OG 1047.5, ABV 4.8%)*
Smooth, dark, amber-coloured beer with the fruity flavour balanced by the addition of Styrian Goldings hops.

Oasthouse Gold *(OG 1050, ABV 5%)*
Sweet, golden beer with some light malt and hop flavours. Typical Weetwood sharp aftertaste. It is deceptively drinkable for a beer of this strength.

WELLS

Charles Wells Ltd, Eagle Brewery, Havelock Street, Bedford, MK40 4LU
Tel (01234) 272766
Fax (01234) 279000
E-mail info@charleswells.co.uk
Website www.charleswells.co.uk
Tours by arrangement

The largest independent, family-owned brewery in the country established in 1876 and still run by descendants of the founder. The brewery has been on this site since 1976 and 290 of its 300 pubs serve cask ale, though about 50 per cent use cask breathers. Wells also supplies around 600 other outlets direct. A bottling line was added in 1996. Its export market of 23 countries earned it a Queen's Award for Export in 1997. In 2000 Charles Wells bought the John Bull Pub Company in

Europe from Allied Domecq, giving it a dedicated estate of 28 franchised outlets from central to eastern Europe. The company runs 40 other retail outlets in Europe, mainly in Italy and Spain. In 2001 it launched cask-conditioned Bombardier in vented cans for supermarket sales. Seasonal beers: Summer Solstice (ABV 4.1, May), Lock Stock and Barrel (ABV 4.3%, Sept), Naked Gold (ABV 4.5%, Dec).

Eagle IPA *(OG 1035, ABV 3.6%)* ◆
A refreshing, amber session bitter with pronounced citrus hop aroma and palate, faint malt in the mouth, and a lasting dry, bitter finish.

Bombardier Premium Bitter
(OG 1042, ABV 4.3%) ◆
Gentle citrus hop is balanced by traces of malt in the mouth, and this pale brown best bitter ends with a lasting dryness. Sulphur often dominates the aroma, particularly with younger casks.

Banana Bread Beer
(OG 1045, ABV 4.5%)

WELTONS

See Hepworth.

WENTWORTH

Wentworth Brewery Ltd,
The Powerhouse, Gun Park,
Wentworth, Rotherham,
S Yorkshire, S62 7TF
Tel (01226) 747070
Fax (01226) 747050
Website www.wentworthbrewery.co.uk
Tours by arrangement

⊛ Wentworth was built during the summer of 1999, using equipment from two defunct Sheffield breweries, Stones and Wards. Brewing started in 1999 and the first brew, WPA, won Best Beer of the Festival at CAMRA's Sheffield festival. Wentworth has installed three 15-barrel fermenters, boosting production to 70 barrels. One pub is owned and the owners plan to create a small tied estate. Approximately 140 outlets are supplied direct. Bottle-conditioned beers: WPA (ABV 4%), Oatmeal Stout (ABV 4.8%), Rampant Gryphon (ABV 6.2%).

Needles Eye *(ABV 3.6%)*
A session bitter with a rather bitter taste that dominates the aftertaste.

WPA *(ABV 4%)* ◆
An extremely well-hopped IPA-style beer that leads to some astringency. A very bitter beer.

Best Bitter *(ABV 4.3%)* ◆
A hoppy, bitter beer with hints of citrus fruits. A bitter taste dominates the aftertaste.

Spalt *(ABV 4.5%)*
Straw-coloured, aromatic, dry and drinkable. Spalt is the German variety of hop used.

Black Zac *(ABV 4.6%)*
A mellow, dark ruby-red ale with chocolate and pale malts leading to a bitter taste, with a coffee finish.

Oatmeal Stout *(ABV 4.8%)* ◆
Black, smooth, with roast and chocolate malt and coffee overtones.

Gryphon *(ABV 5.1%)* ◆
A golden, clean-tasting, full-bodied bitter with a bitter-sweet taste and aftertaste.

Rampant Gryphon *(ABV 6.2%)* ◆
A strong, well-balanced golden ale with hints of fruit and sweetness but which retains a hoppy character.

WEST BERKSHIRE

West Berkshire Brewery Co Ltd,
The Old Bakery, Yattendon,
Thatcham, Berks, RG18 0UE
Tel (01635) 202968
Fax (01635) 202638
E-mail davemaggs@wbbrew.co.uk
Website www.wbbrew.co.uk
Shop Mainly a Craft Shop
Tours strictly by arrangement only

⊗ A brewery established in 1995 by Dave and Helen Maggs in the grounds of the Pot Kiln, Frilsham, although the businesses are separate. They added a 25-barrel plant in 1999 at a converted bakery in nearby Yattendon, together with a small bottling plant and a craft shop where the brewery's T-shirts, mugs and jugs are sold. Over 90 pubs, mostly in the upper Thames valley, stock their beers. With a conscious policy of reducing 'food miles', a local farmer has been commissioned to grow Maris Otter for malting and Berkshire-grown hops are included in many of their beers. In 2000 a programme of additional monthly beers was started, using a different new dwarf hop variety each month. Brick Kiln Bitter (ABV 4%) is only available at the Pot Kiln. Old Tyler (ABV 4%) is an extra-hopped version of Good Old Boy. Seasonal Ales: Koenig's Half English (ABV 5%, summer), Spiced Porter (ABV 4.5%, winter). Bottle-conditioned beer: Full Circle (ABV 4.5%).

Mr Chubb's Lunchtime Bitter
(OG 1039, ABV 3.78%)
A traditional beer with all English hops and a good bitterness balanced by Maris Otter malts from Wiltshire and Suffolk. This beer is named in memory of the brewer's father who was the lock-keeper at Whitchurch-on-Thames and sometimes nick-named Mr. Chubb.

Maggs Magnificent Mild
(OG 1039, ABV 3.8%) ◆
An easy-to-drink southern mild with a good balance of malt and hops for the style. This dark red-brown beer has a short, dry finish.

Good Old Boy *(OG 1043, ABV 4%)* ◆
A well-balanced, fruity and hoppy beer with some sweetness in the finish.

Dr Hexter's Wedding Ale
(OG 1044, ABV 4.1%)

There are hints of grapefruit in this pale-coloured beer, with strong hop aromas and a long, bitter finish.

Full Circle *(OG 1047, ABV 4.5%)*

Dr Hexter's Healer
(OG 1051, ABV 5%) ◆
A full-bodied, vinous and sweet, end-of-the-evening beer that tastes stronger than it is. Tawny in colour, fruity and warming, with masses of malt and roast character.

Gold Star *(OG 1053, ABV 5.2%)* ◆
A pale brown beer, fruity and deceptively strong, with well-balanced fruit, malt and hops.

THE WEST BERKSHIRE BREWERY CO. LTD.
EST. 1995

WEST YORKSHIRE

West Yorkshire Brewery, Victoria Buildings, Burnley Road, Luddendenfoot, Halifax, Yorkshire, HX2 6AA
Tel (01422) 885930
Tours by arrangement

The brewery has merged to form Eastwood & Sanders (qv) but brewing continues on this site for the time being. Eight barrels a week are produced. Originally brewed as a house beer, First Light is a permanent beer at the Cricketers, Keighley, but is now also a permanent addition to the range.

First Light *(OG 1037, ABV 3.5%)* ◆
Pale golden mild with a good balance of maltiness and bitterness.

Baht'At *(OG 1038, ABV 3.8%)* ◆
Amber-coloured bitter with a hoppy and well-balanced malt and fruity character, and dry finish.

Beyond The Pale
(OG 1040, ABV 4%) ◆
Pale golden bitter with an intensely citrus flavour that predominates the underlying biscuity malt and fruity character. The finish is long, dry and hoppy.

Night Porter *(ABV 4.3%)* ◆
Very dark porter with a bitter chocolatey flavour and hints of liquorice. The finish is slightly dry and sweet with a bitter end.

Jet Stout *(ABV 4.4%)* ◆
A dark stout with a bitter, roasted malt and not too strong coffee flavour, with a dry finish.

1872 Porter *(ABV 6.5%)* ◆
Dark with a good roasted aroma, slightly sweetish, with a smooth coffee and liquorice flavour, and dry roasted coffee finish.

Imperial Stout *(ABV 11.8%)* ◆
This intensely dark, powerful stout is surprisingly well attenuated, not cloying, but eminently drinkable. It has a vinous sweet and fruity liquorice taste and aroma, with a dry finish.

WHIM

Whim Ales, Whim Farm, Hartington, Nr Buxton, Derbyshire, SK17 0AX
Tel (01298) 84991
Fax (01298) 84702

⊠ A brewery opened in 1993 in outbuildings at Whim Farm by Giles Litchfield who bought Broughton Brewery (qv) in 1995. Whim's beers are available in 50-70 outlets and the brewery's tied house, the Wilkes Head in Leek, Staffs. Some one-off brews are produced. Occasional/seasonal beers: Snow White (ABV 4.5%, a wheat beer), Special Ale (ABV 4.7%), Old Izaak (ABV 5%, winter), Black Christmas (ABV 6.5%, winter).

Arbor Light *(OG 1035, ABV 3.6%)*
Light-coloured bitter, sharp and clean with lots of hop character and a delicate light aroma.

Magic Mushroom Mild
(OG 1037, ABV 3.8%)
Ruby-black in colour, well-balanced with a complex mix of flavours and a sweet finish.

Hartington Bitter *(OG 1038, ABV 4%)*
A light, golden-coloured, well-hopped session beer. A dry finish with a spicy, floral aroma.

Hartington IPA *(OG 1045, ABV 4.5%)*
Pale and light-coloured, smooth on the palate allowing malt to predominate. Slightly sweet finish combined with distinctive light hop bitterness. Well rounded.

WHITE

White Brewing Company, The 1066 Country Brewery, Pebsham Farm Industrial Estate, Pebsham Lane, Bexhill, E Sussex, TN40 2RZ
Tel (01424) 731066
Tours by arrangement

⊠ Brewery founded in May 1995 by husband-and-wife team David and Lesley White to serve local free trade outlets and some wholesalers, brewing five to 10 barrels a week. Seasonal beer: MM (ABV 4.9%, summer.) It appears under various labels, all with 'millennium' in the name.

1066 Country Bitter *(OG 1040, ABV 4%)*
Amber-gold in colour, a light, sweetish beer with good malt and hop balance, and a bitter, refreshing finish.

White Dark *(ABV 4%)*

WHITEWATER

Whitewater Brewing Co, 40 Tullyframe Road, Kilkeel, Co Down, N Ireland, BT34 4RZ
Tel/Fax 028417 69449
Website www.whitewaterbrewing.co.uk
Tours by arrangement

◎ Set up in 1996 and nestling in the idyllic setting of the heart of the Mourne Mountains, Whitewater is now the largest micro-brewery in Northern Ireland. It produces 11 different cask-conditioned ales. The plant was designed and built by Kerry and Bernard Sloan, and, with an expansion in 2000, it now boasts a 15-barrel brew length. With its stainless-steel construction, the plant has fermenting capacity of 2,000 gallons a week. The brewery is currently supplying 25 outlets in Northern Ireland.

Mill Ale *(ABV 3.7%)*

Solstice Pale *(ABV 4%)*

Cascade *(ABV 4%)*

Nutbrown Ale *(ABV 4%)*

Mayflower *(ABV 4.1%)*

Glen Ale *(ABV 4.2%)*

Dappled Mare *(ABV 4.3%)*

Northern Brewer *(ABV 4.4%)*

Belfast Ale *(ABV 4.5%)*

Bee's Endeavour *(ABV 4.8%)*

Knight Porter *(ABV 5%)*

WICKED HATHERN

Wicked Hathern Brewery Ltd,
46 Derby Road, Hathern,
Loughborough, Leics, LE12 5LD
Tel (01509) 842585
E-mail Beer@Hathern.com
Website www.wicked-hathern.co.uk
Tours by arrangement, small charge

Opened in the first month of the new millennium, the 2.5-barrel brewery is owned and operated by four men, John and Marc Bagley, John Worsfold and Sean O'Neill, in their spare time. They supply beers on a guest basis to many local pubs, and also brew commissioned beers for special occasions. In 2002 they began to bottle beers to supply their local shop. Seasonal beers: Doble's Dog (ABV 3.5%, autumn/winter), Hawthorn Gold (ABV 3.5%, spring/summer), Gladstone Tidings (ABV 5.1%, Christmas).

WHB (Wicked Hathern Bitter) *(OG 1038, ABV 3.8%)*
A light-tasting session bitter with a dry palate and good hop aroma.

Cockfighter *(OG 1043, ABV 4.2%)*

Soar Head *(OG 1048, ABV 4.8%)*
A dark ruby bitter with a complex rich fruit taste and a mellow aroma.

WICKWAR

Wickwar Brewing Co, Arnolds Cooperage,
Station Road, Wickwar, Glos, GL12 8NB
Tel/Fax (01454) 294168/299868
E-mail info@wickwarbrewing.co.uk
Website www.wickwarbrewing.co.uk
Shop 9.30-4.30 Mon-Fri, 10-12 Sat.
Tours by arrangement

⊗ The brewery was launched in 1990 by two Courage tenants, Brian Rides and Ray Penny, with the aim of providing guest ales for their three tenancies. The business proved so successful that they dropped the

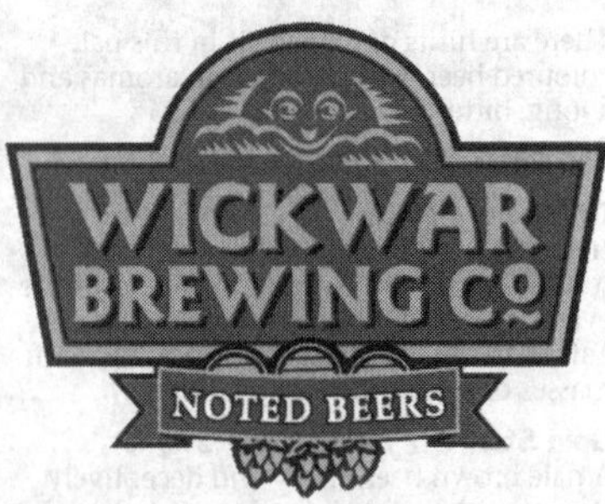

pubs to concentrate on supplying their other regular outlets (now totalling around 200). The brewery operates from the cooper's shop of the old Arnold, Perret & Co brewery and is currently brewing to capacity. Brian Rides has retired, but Ray Penny continues to run the company with an ambitious and adventurous team, led by head brewer Steve Mcdonald. They plan to move to the Arnold Perrett & Co brewery across the road, so that production can increase to 25 barrels per brew. Two pubs have been bought, the Princess of Wales, Bedminster, and the White Lion in Bristol. They plan to create a small tied estate. Seasonal beers: Mr Perret's Traditional Stout (ABV 5.9%), Spring Ale (ABV 3.8%, March-May), Sunny Daze (ABV 4.2%, June-Aug), Christmas Cracker (ABV 4.3%). Bottle-conditioned beers: Old Arnold (ABV 4.8%), Station Porter (ABV 6.1%), Brand Oak Bitter (BOB) (ABV 4%), Mr Perretts Traditional Stout (ABV 5.9%).

Coopers WPA *(OG 1034.5, ABV 3.5%)*
Golden-coloured, this well-balanced beer is light, refreshing, with hops, citrus fruit, apple/pear flavour and notable pale malt character. Bitter, dry finish. A crisp and quenching ale.

Brand Oak Bitter (BOB)
(OG 1038.5, ABV 4%)
Amber-coloured, this has a distinctive blend of hop, malt and apple/pear citrus fruits. The slightly sweet taste turns into a fine, dry bitterness, with a similar malty-lasting finish.

Cotswold Way *(OG 1041, ABV 4.2%)*
Amber-coloured, it has a pleasant aroma of pale malt, hop and fruit. Good dry bitterness in the taste with some sweetness. Similar though less sweet in the finish, with good hop content.

Old Arnold *(OG 1045.5, ABV 4.6%)*
Named after the founder of the original brewery (around 1800), this is a ruby-red ale, sweetish with malt and bitter overtones and Challenger hops providing rich fruitiness. It is brewed to a similar recipe used by Arnold in his Strong Old Beer.

Olde Merryford Ale
(OG 1047, ABV 4.8%)
Full-flavoured and well-balanced ale, with malt, hops and cherry fruit throughout. Amber/pale brown, it is slightly sweet, with a long-lasting, malty, dry, fruity and increasingly bitter finish.

Mr Perretts Traditional Stout
(OG 1059-61, ABV 5.9%)
Aroma and taste of smoky chocolate malts

and peppery hops. Dark fruits of black cherry and blackcurrant give hints of sweetness to the dry, quite bitter, slightly spicy, well-balanced taste.

Station Porter *(OG 1059.5, ABV 6.1%)* ◆
Available Oct-Feb, this is a rich, smooth, dark ruby-brown ale. Starts with roast malt; coffee, chocolate and dark fruit then develops a complex, spicy, bitter-sweet taste and a long roast finish.

WILLY'S

Willy's Brewery Ltd, 17 High Cliff Road, Cleethorpes, Lincs, DN35 8RQ
Tel (01472) 602145
Fax (01472) 603578
Tours by arrangement

The brewery opened in 1989 to provide beer for two outlets in Grimsby and Cleethorpes. It has a five-barrel plant with maximum capacity of 15 barrels a week. The brewery can be viewed at any time from pub or street.

Original Bitter *(OG 1038, ABV 3.8%)* ◆
A light brown 'sea air' beer with a fruity, tangy hop on the nose and taste, giving a strong bitterness tempered by the underlying malt.

Burcom Bitter *(OG 1044, ABV 4.2%)* ◆
A dark ruby colour, sometimes known as Mariner's Gold, although the beer is dark ruby in colour. It is a smooth and creamy brew with a sweet chocolate-bar maltiness, giving way to an increasingly bitter finish.

Last Resort *(OG 1044, ABV 4.3%)*

Weiss Buoy *(OG 1045, ABV 4.5%)*
A cloudy wheat beer.

Coxswains Special *(OG 1050, ABV 4.9%)*

Old Groyne *(OG 1060, ABV 6.2%)* ◆
An initial sweet banana fruitiness blends with malt to give a vanilla quality to the taste and slightly bitter aftertaste. A copper-coloured beer reminiscent of a Belgian ale.

WINTER'S*

Winter's Brewery, 8 Keelan Close, Norwich, NR6 6QZ
Tel/Fax (01603) 787820
Email sales@wintersbrewery.com
Website www.wintersbrewery.com

Dave Winter, who has had previous award-winning success as brewer for both Woodforde's and Chalk Hill breweries, decided to set up his own brewery in 2001. He purchased the brewing plant from the now defunct Scott's Brewery in Lowestoft. He produces five ales at present, and sells direct to the local free trade.

Mild *(OG 1036.5, ABV 3.6%)*
Mild in strength but strong in flavour; roast tones come through.

Bitter *(OG 1039.5, ABV 3.8%)*
East Anglian malted barley, East Kent Goldings and Fuggles hops makes for a delicious session drink.

Golden *(ABV 4.1%)*

Revenge *(OG 1047, ABV 4.7%)*
Golden coloured and well-hopped for a distinct bitterness with a sweetish finish that makes this a warmer beer.

Storm Force *(OG 1053, ABV 5.3%)*
Light amber, malty, sweetish brew with a delicate hop aroma and a moderate bitter finish.

Tempest *(OG 1062, ABV 6.2%)*

WOLF

Wolf Brewery Ltd, 10 Maurice Gaymer Road, Attleborough, Norfolk, NR17 2QZ
Tel (01953) 457775
Fax (01953) 457776
E-mail info@wolf-ales.co.uk
Website www.wolf-brewery.ltd.uk
Tours by arrangement

The brewery was founded by the former owner of the Reindeer Brewery in 1996, using a 20-barrel plant housed on the site of the old Gaymer's cider orchard. 200 outlets are supplied direct. All the beers are also sold in bottle-conditioned form.

Golden Jackal *(OG 1039, ABV 3.7%)* ◆
Distinctive honey aroma introduces this amber brew. A bitter-sweet fruitiness is the mainstay of the refreshingly complex mix of flavours. A growing honeyed hoppiness can be detected in the short, crisp ending.

Wolf In Sheeps Clothing *(OG 1039, ABV 3.7%)* ◆
A malty aroma with fruity undertones introduces this reddish-hued mild. Malt, with a bitter Bisto-like background that remains throughout, is the dominant flavour of this clean-tasting beer.

Bitter *(OG 1041, ABV 3.9%)* ◆
A blend of bitterness and hop dryness gives this clean-tasting bitter its character. Some fruit can be detected in the background. A bitter finish with some hop nuances.

Coyote Bitter *(OG 1044, ABV 4.3%)* ◆
A pale brown bitter with light, fruit-enhanced hoppy vapours. A complex but well-balanced mix of hops and malt with more than a hint of citrus leads on to a crisp, well-hopped finale.

Newshound 2001 *(ABV 4.5%)* ◆
Copper coloured with a light hop and malt nose. Malt takes the edge off the bitter backbone of this solid tasting beer. Vanilla and citrus hints can be detected as the long finish grows into a dry hoppiness.

Woild Moild *(OG 1048, ABV 4.8%)*
A big roast coffee bean aroma leads into a distinctively roasted barley base. A good balance of malt with a liquorice bitterness aids this dark-red mild towards a smoky, dark and long-lasting rich finish.

Granny Wouldn't Like It *(OG 1049, ABV 4.8%)*
Dark red, rich and filling, the swirling mix of flavours produces a complex but satisfying experience. Both the nose and taste have a fruity blend of malt and bitter-sweet hoppiness with smoky overtones.

Lupus Lupus *(ABV 5%)*
A soft blackurrant nose introduces this red-coloured brew. Hops vie with bitterness in the initial taste. Fruity malt notes soon fade to leave a long bitter finish with just a hint of blackcurrant fruitiness.

Timber Wolf *(OG 1060, ABV 5.8%)*
A rich and warming winter ale. A solid currant bun aroma combines with a rich fruit and nut beginning to give this red-hued beer a sweet, spicy feel. A long, drawn-out bitter-sweet finale completes the experience.

WOLVERHAMPTON & DUDLEY

See Banks's and Marston's.

WOOD

Wood Brewery Ltd, Wistanstow, Craven Arms, Shropshire, SY7 8DG
Tel (01588) 672523
Fax (01588) 673939
E-mail mail@woodbrewery.co.uk
Website www.woodbrewery.co.uk
Shop. Goods available at brewery, working hours & by mail
Tours by arrangement

⊗ The brewery opened in 1980 in buildings next to the Plough Inn, still the brewery's only tied house. Steady growth over the years included the acquisition of the Sam Powell Brewery and its beers in 1991. Building work started in 2002 to enlarge fermentation, storage and office space. Production averages 60 barrels a week. 200 outlets are supplied direct.
Seasonal/occasional beers: Summer That! (ABV 3.9%, summer), Woodcutter (ABV 4.2%, autumn), Saturnalia (ABV 4.2%, Jan-Feb), Get Knotted (ABV 4.7%, February), Hopping Mad (ABV 4.7%, March), Anniversary Ale (ABV 5%, April), Christmas Cracker (ABV 6%, Nov-Dec), plus a series under the Shropshire Heroes label. Bottle-conditioned beer: Armada (ABV 4%).

Wallop *(OG 1035, ABV 3.4%)*

Sam Powell Original Bitter *(OG 1038, ABV 3.7%)*

Parish Bitter *(OG 1040, ABV 4%)*
A blend of malt and hops with a bitter aftertaste. Pale brown in colour.

Special Bitter *(OG 1042, ABV 4.2%)*
A tawny brown bitter with malt, hops and some fruitiness.

Shropshire Lad *(OG 1045, ABV 4.5%)*

Sam Powell Old Sam *(OG 1047, ABV 4.6%)*

Wonderful *(OG 1048, ABV 4.8%)*
A mid-brown, fruity beer, with a roast and malt taste.

WOODFORDE'S

Woodforde's Norfolk Ales
(t/a Woodforde's Ltd),
Broadland Brewery, Woodbastwick, Norwich, Norfolk, NR13 6SW
Tel (01603) 720353
Fax (01603) 721806
E-mail info@woodfordes.co.uk
Website www.woodfordes.co.uk
Shop 10.30-4.30 Mon-Fri; open most weekends & Bank Holidays, telephone 01603 722218 to confirm.
Tours by arrangement

⊗ Founded in 1981 in Drayton near Norwich, Woodforde's moved to Erpingham, near Aylsham in 1982, and then moved again to a converted farm complex, with greatly increased production capacity, in the picturesque Broadland village of Woodbastwick in 1989. A major expansion of Broadland Brewery took place in 2001/2002 to more than double production capacity and included a new brewery shop and visitor centre. It brews an extensive range of beers and runs three tied houses with some 300 other outlets supplied on a regular basis.
Seasonal/occasional beers: Wherry Best Bitter (ABV 3.8%), Great Eastern (ABV 4.3%), Nelson's Revenge (ABV 4.5%), Norfolk Nog (ABV 4.6%), Norfolk Nip (ABV 8.5%). Bottle-conditioned beers: Wherry, Nelson's Revenge, Norfolk Nog, Headcracker, Norfolk Nip. There are plans to introduce a new 5% beer to celebrate the 21st Anniversary of Woodforde's in 2002.

Mardler's *(OG 1035, ABV 3.5%)*
A gentle dark red mild with a soft fruity, chocolate aroma. First impressions reinforce this as a roasted malt smoothness takes hold. As flavour develops, a dry fruitiness emerges into the long, sustained finish.

Kett's Rebellion *(OG 1034.4, ABV 3.5%)*
Brewed to celebrate the 450th anniversary of Kett's land workers' rebellion, this moderately bitter session beer retains a hoppiness to the finish. Sweet caramel notes fade in the finish.

Fur & Feather *(ABV 36%)*
House beer for the brewery tap. Copper coloured with a soft fruity aroma that leads to a well-balanced sweet, malty flavour with bitter echoes. The quick finish sustains the maltiness but loses bitterness.

Wherry Best Bitter *(OG 1037.4, ABV 3.8%)*
Consistent, award-winning bitter with a soft citrus nose and matching flavour. Grapefruit and coriander can be found in the first taste. Hops also come to the fore as a residual bitterness is maintained to the end.

Great Eastern *(OG 1039.8, ABV 4.3%)*
A bitter hoppy character dominates the initial taste and the quick defined finish. Vanilla airs can be detected in the nose and a faint banana fruitiness, fitting for a rich yellow beer, intrudes in the beginning.

Nelson's Revenge *(OG 1042.7, ABV 4.5%)*

Heavy fruity notes in the nose continue well into the first taste. Aided by a sweet malty, bitter background, this pale brown bitter settles to a glowing richness, with a solid, filling feel. Quick bitter end

Norfolk Nog *(OG 1046.8, ABV 4.6%)*
Dark red with a fruity roast malt aroma. A heavy bitter-sweet introduction underpins the dry roast backbone. Some chocolate and vanilla notes can be found as the long finish becomes noticeably sweeter

270 *(ABV 5%)*
A deceptively clean-tasting, mid-brown bitter with a gentle hoppy nose. A solid bitterness knits together the complex mix of malt, fruit and hops that competes for attention. The finish turns to a dry lingering bitterness.

Headcracker *(OG 1065.7, ABV 7%)*
A starburst of malty fruitiness follows on from a rich, rolling, malty bouquet. A date-like sweetness adds to the complexity of this rich and filling barley wine. The delicate colour deceives the drinker

WOODLANDS

Woodlands Brewery,
c/o Buntingford Brewery Co Ltd,
27 Woodlands, Bishops Stortford,
Herts, CM23 5BS
Tel (07949) 438353
E-mail woodlandsbrewery@yahoo.co.uk
Website
www.geocities.com/woodlandsbrewery.uk

Woodlands beers are brewed by Andrew Potter on a part-time basis. The 2.5 barrel plant produces beer on demand, alongside Buntingford Brewery (qv) range.

Dark Wood *(OG 1035, ABV 3.5%)*

Bitter *(OG 1039, ABV 3.9%)*

Red Squirrel *(OG 1042, ABV 4.2%)*

WORFIELD

Worfield Brewing Co Ltd,
Unit 1A The Bullring, Station Lane,
Bridgnorth, Shropshire, WV16 4AR
Tel (01746) 769606

Set up in 1994 at the Davenport Arms, known as the Dog, in Worfield, it relocated in 1998 with plant from the Red Cross Brewery and moved again to Bridgnorth. The brewery sells to some 50 free trade outlets, mainly in Shropshire and the West Midlands. Seasonal beers: Hermitage Old Ale (ABV 8.8%), Christmas Classic (ABV 5%), Winter Classic (ABV 5%), Reynolds Redneck (ABV 5.5%).

Hopstone Bitter *(OG 1040, ABV 4%)*

Nailers OBJ *(OG 1041, ABV 4.2%)*

Shropshire Pride *(OG 1046, ABV 4.5%)*

Burcote Premium Pale *(OG 1050, ABV 4.9%)*

WYCHWOOD

Wychwood Brewery Co Ltd,
Eagle Maltings, The Crofts,
Witney, Oxon, OX28 4DP
Tel (01993) 890800
Fax (01993) 772553
E-mail imray@wychwood.co.uk
Website www.wychwood.co.uk
Shop 9-5 Mon-Fri. On-line shopping on website
Tours only for CAMRA branch visits

Wychwood was bought in June 2002 by Refresh UK, a drinks retailing company that also markets Usher's brands brewed by Thomas Hardy (qv). Refresh says it is committed to maintaining brewing at Wychwood, which started life as Glenny Brewery in 1983, in the old maltings of the extinct Clinch Brewery. It moved to a modern site in the late 1980s and then back again to the Clinch's site in 1994. The brewery has a brew length of 150 barrels using a variety of old and new plant. About 60 per cent of the capacity is bottled. 30 pubs are now owned most called Hobgoblinn, a mixture of freeholds and leased pubs. 12 seasonal beers are brewed.

Shires *(OG 1034, ABV 3.7%)*
A copper-coloured session beer with a fruity and malty aroma and admirable hop character. Good body for its strength. Fruit declines to a dry finish.

Fiddler's Elbow *(OG 1039, ABV 4.1%)*
A spicy amber beer, complex, with a spicy hop aroma and a suggestion of cinnamon. Easy to drink, with a crisp and refreshing finish.

NEW BREWERIES

The following new breweries have been notified to the Guide and should come on stream in 2002/2003:

Anchor Brewery, King's Lynn, Norfolk
Bedrock, Toppesfield, Essex
Belfast Brewery, Belfast
Borough Arms, Crewe
Bragdy Ty Crwr Glan yr Afon, Holywell, Flintshire
Briarsway, Edinburgh
Brimstage Brewing Co, Thornton Heath, Merseyside
Carpenters Arms, Slapton, Bucks
Cross Hands, near Ammanford, Dyfed
Crown & Anchor, Newport, E. Yorks
Edale Brewery, Edale, Derbyshire
Gretna Green, Cumbria
Jarrow Brewery, Jarrow, Tyne & Wear
Joule's, Stone, Staffs
Kingston Arms, Kingston Street, Cambridge
Maldon, Essex
Matfen, Newcastle upon Tyne
Nantwich, Cheshire
Pheasant Inn, Broseley, Telford, Shropshire
Queen's Head, Earsham, Norfolk
Red Lion, Ossett, W. Yorkshire
Slaughterhouse Brewery, Warwick
Stanton, Northumberland
Star Inn, Crowlas, Penzance, Cornwall
Tickenham, Somerset

Hobgoblin *(OG 1043, ABV 4.5%)* ◆
Powerful, full-bodied, copper-red, well-balanced brew. Strong in roasted malt, with a moderate, hoppy bitterness and a slight fruity character.

WYE VALLEY

Wye Valley Brewery Ltd, Stoke Lacy, Herefordshire, HR7 4HG
Tel/Fax 01885 490505
E-mail wvb@freeuk.com
Website www.wyevalleybrewery.com

⊗ The Wye Valley Brewery was launched in 1985 at the Nags Head in Canon Pyon, Herefordshire. It moved to the rear of the Barrels pub in 1986 and then in 2002 it moved again to the site of the former Symonds cider works at Stoke Lacy in the north of the county. The brewery has been completely re-equipped and has the capacity to brew 400 barrels a week. The beers are distributed locally on a weekly basis, and monthly to many parts of the country by its own transport. Seasonal beers: Golden Ale (ABV 4.2%, March-Oct), Winter Tipple (ABV 4.4%, Nov-Feb), Christmas Ale (ABV 6%, Nov-Dec). Bottle-conditioned beers: DG Golden Ale (ABV 4.2%), DG Wholesome Stout (ABV 4.6%), DG Christmas Ale (ABV 6%), Winter Tipple (ABV 5.3%).

Bitter *(OG 1038, ABV 3.7%)* ◆
A beer whose aroma gives little hint of the bitter hoppiness that follows right through to the aftertaste.

Hereford Pale Ale
(OG 1040, ABV 4%) ◆
A pale, hoppy, malty brew with a hint of sweetness before a dry finish.

Dorothy Goodbody's Golden Ale
(OG 0142, ABV 4.2%)

Butty Bach *(OG 1046, ABV 4.5%)*
Three times winner at the Cardiff Beer Festival

Dorothy Goodbody's Wholesome Stout
(OG 1046, ABV 4.6%) ◆
A smooth and satisfying stout with a bitter edge to its roast flavours. The finish combines roast grain and malt. Supreme champion, Winter Beer Festival 2002.

R.I.P.

The following breweries have closed, gone out of business, suspended operations, or merged with another company since the 2002 Guide was published:

Ales of Kent
Aviemore
Bragdy Ty Bach
Cape Hill (Bass, Mitchells & Butlers)
Castle Eden
Cox's Yard
Crewkerne
Dark Horse
Frome Valley
Grimsdale
Henry's Butcher's Yard
Heritage
Hoskins & Oldfield
Hull
Lakeland
Lichfield
Lloyds
Millers Thumb
Marches
Northumberland
Orchard (Lincs)
Passageway
Payn
Pembroke
Reading Lion
Shraley Brook
Spinnaker
SP Sporting Ales
Strawberry Bank
Swaled Ale
Tally Ho!
Three Tuns
Tolly Cobbold
Trimdon
Woodbury
Woodhampton

WYLAM

Wylam Brewery Ltd, South Houghton, Heddon on the Wall, Northumberland, NE15 0EZ
Tel (01661) 853377
E-mail admin@wylambrew.co.uk
Website www.wylambrew.co.uk
Tours by arrangement

⊗ Wylam was set up by John Boyle and Robin Leighton in a converted farm dairy in 2000, with a brew length of 4.5 barrels. They plan to commission a bottling machine soon. The brewery delivers to more than 100 local outlets.

Bitter *(OG 1039, ABV 3.8%)*
A refreshing lighter version of the 4.4 Rocket using similar ingredients but producing a beer with its own distinctive character.

Gold Tankard *(OG 1041, ABV 4%)* ◆
Fresh, clean flavour, full of hops, this golden ale has a hint of citrus in the finish.

Turbinia *(OG 1041, ABV 4%)*
Rich ruby-coloured beer full of hops, with a long, bitter finish.

Rocket *(OG 1044, ABV 4.4%)* ◆
A gold-coloured beer packed with flavour. Hops and malt come out in the flavour and lead to a smooth, bitter finish.

80/- *(OG 1045, ABV 4.5%)*
A traditional brown beer in the style favoured in Scotland and the North-east by the 'old school' of beer connoisseurs. Smooth with complex malts and subtle hops.

Landlord's Choice *(OG 1046, ABV 4.6%)* ◆
A complex ale full of interesting flavours and aromas. Plenty of malt in the aroma, then a burst of hops and bitter finish.

Bohemia Pilsner
(OG 1046, ABV 4.6%) ◆
Deep gold in colour with a heady bouquet of malt and hops, and a deep finish of fruit.

The Haugh *(OG 1046, ABV 4.6%)* ◆
A smooth velvet porter packed with flavour. Roast malt and a slight fruitiness provide a satisfying pint with a smooth finish.

WYRE PIDDLE

Wyre Piddle Brewery, Highgrove Farm, Peopleton, Nr Pershaw, Worcs, WR10 2LF
Tel/Fax (01905) 841853

⊗ A brewery established in a converted stable by a former publican and master builder in 1992. Some 200 pubs in the Midlands take the beer. The brewery relocated and upgraded its equipment in 1997 and has now moved again to Highgrove Farm. It also brews for Green Dragon, Malvern: Dragon's Downfall (ABV 3.9%), Dragon's Revenge (ABV 4%). For Severn Valley Railway: Royal Piddle (ABV 4.2%). Seasonal beers: Piddle in the Sun (ABV 5.2%, summer), Yule Piddle (ABV 4.5%, Christmas). Bottle-conditioned beer: Piddle in the Hole (ABV 4.6%).

Piddle in the Hole *(OG 1039, ABV 3.9%)* ◆
Copper-coloured and quite dry, with lots of hops and fruitiness throughout.

Piddle in the Wind *(ABV 4.5%)* ◆
This drink has a superb mix of flavours. A nice hoppy nose through to a lasting aftertaste makes it a good, all-round beer.

Piddle in the Dark *(ABV 4.5%)*
A rich ruby red bitter with a smooth flavour.

Piddle in the Snow *(ABV 5.2%)* ◆
A dry, strong taste all the way through draws your attention to the balance between malt and hops in the brew. A glorious way to end an evening's drinking.

YATES

Yates Brewery, Ghyll Farm, Westnewton, Wigton, Cumbria, CA5 3NX
Tel/fax (016973) 21081
E-mail graeme@yatesbrewery.freeserve.co.uk
Website yatesbrewery.com
Tours by arrangement

⊚ Established in 1986 in a range of outbuildings at Ghyll Farm, Westnewton, the brewery was bought in 1998 by Graeme and Caroline Baxter, who had previously owned High Force Brewery in Teesdale. More beers have been added to the range and direct distribution now includes Tyneside and Wearside, in addition to the traditional stronghold of the Lake District. 65 outlets are supplied direct. Seasonal beers: Spring Fever (ABV 4.7%), Summer Fever (ABV 3.9%), Autumn Fever (ABV 4%), Winter Fever (ABV 4%), Best Cellar (ABV 5.8%, winter).

Bitter *(OG 1035, ABV 3.7%)* ◆
Distinctive golden bitter, powerful hop and fruit aroma. Strong hop flavour with lingering bitterness.

No 3 *(OG 1040, ABV 4.2%)* ◆
A pale brown beer with a prominent butterscotch aroma. It has a strong roast and caramel taste with some maltiness. Full-bodied with a pleasant bitter taste.

XB *(OG 1043, ABV 4.5%)*

Premium *(OG 1048, ABV 5.2%)* ◆
A golden beer with hops and lingering fruity sweetness. Rising bitterness with some malt and good mouthfeel.

YATES

Yates Brewery, The Inn at St Lawrence, Undercliff Drive, St Lawrence, Ventnor, Isle of Wight, PO38 1XG
Tel (01983) 854689(b) 730398(h)
E-mail info@yates-brewery.fsnet.co.uk
Website www.yates-brewery.co.uk
Tours by arrangement

Dave Yates previously worked for the original Burts Brewery in Ventnor, which went into receivership in 1992. He started brewing for Hartridge at the Island Brewery. Hartridge sold its pubs and brewery to Usher's of Trowbridge and Dave was made redundant four months later. He has now installed his own five-barrel brewery at The Inn at St Lawrence. Brewing started in 2000 and he now has regular outlets on the Isle of Wight. Seasonal beer: Xmas Pud (ABV 5%).

Undercliff Experience *(OG 1042, ABV 4.1%)*

Holy Joe *(OG 1050, ABV 4.9%)*

Wight Winter Ale *(OG 1052, ABV 5%)*

YORK

York Brewery Company Ltd, 12 Toft Green, Micklegate, York, YO1 6JT
Tel (01904) 621162
Fax (01904) 621216
E-mail andrew@yorkbrew.co.uk
Website www.yorkbrew.co.uk
Shop Mon-Sat 11.30-7 daily.
Tours Mon-Sat 12.30, 2.00, 3.30, 5.00 daily

⊚ York started production in 1996, the first brewery in the city for 40 years. A visitor centre, gift shop and bar were added in 1999. It is designed as a show brewery, with a gallery above the 20-barrel brew plant giving visitors a view of the fermenting and conditioning rooms. In 2000, York bought its first pub, the Last Drop inn, in Colliergate in the city; a second pub opened in 2001, the Three-legged Mare, and York is negotiating for a third pub in Micklegate in the city. More than 400 pubs take the beers. Occasional/seasonal beers: York IPA (ABV 5%, summer), Stocking Filler (ABV 4.8%, December).

Stonewall *(OG 1037, ABV 3.7%)* ◆
A light amber bitter with little maltiness but strong hop and fruit aromas and flavours. Clean-tasting, its hoppiness leads to a dry, bitter finish.

York Bitter *(OG 1039, ABV 4%)* ◆
A fine, easy-drinking session beer with a fresh floral aroma, well-balanced malt and hops in the mouth, and a hint of marmalade in the aftertaste.

Yorkshire Terrier
(OG 1041, ABV 4.2%) ◆
Refreshing and distinctive, well-balanced fruit and hops in the aroma and taste, with a background of malt. Hoppy bitterness remains assertive in the aftertaste of this amber-gold brew.

Centurion's Ghost Ale
(OG 1045, ABV 5.4%) ◆
Dark ruby in colour, full-tasting with mellow roast malt character balanced by bitterness that lingers into the aftertaste. Hops and fruit in the mouth.

YOUNG'S

Young & Co's Brewery PLC, The Ram Brewery, High Street, Wandsworth, London, SW18 4JD
Tel (020) 8875 7000
Fax (020) 8875 7100
Website www.youngs.co.uk
Shop 10-6, Mon-Sat. Daily tours of the brewery and stables (020) 8875 7005

⊗ Beer has been brewed continuously alongside the River Wandle since 1581, making it the oldest site in Britain for beer production. The present brewery was founded in 1675 and bought by Charles Young & Anthony Bainbridge in 1831; the business was continued by the Young family and, although it is a public company, it remains very much a family affair. The company brews award-winning beers in the traditional manner and also produces up to four seasonal beers. 500-600 free-trade outlets are supplied throughout Britain, concentrated in London and the South-east. Young's growing tied estate stands at more than 205 pubs. The brewery has outlawed pouring back spilt or unsold beer in its tied houses, and recommends the use of cask breathers only if its smallest casks cannot be consumed within three days. Bottle-conditioned beer: Special London Ale (ABV 6.4%).

Bitter
(OG 1036, ABV 3.7%) ◆
A light-drinking bitter with a hoppy, malty nose and a dryish palate and finish, with hops predominating.

Triple A *(OG 1040, ABV 4%)* ◆
Creamy-textured dark amber beer with malty notes and a low aroma due to being served cold. Becomes cloying as it warms.

Special *(OG 1046, ABV 4.6%)* ◆
Smooth, fruity beer with a good malty/hoppy balance, and a fruity, bitter aftertaste with hoppy notes.

Waggle Dance *(OG 1049, ABV 5%)*
Beer brewed with honey. The brand was bought from the Vaux/Swallow Group in the summer of 1999 and is available cask-conditioned and in bottle.

Winter Warmer *(OG 1055, ABV 5%)* ◆
Impressive ruby/black, smooth beer with a roast malt aroma, a sweet fruity flavour and finish, and caramel notes throughout.

ZERO DEGREES

Zero Degrees, (Forthglen Investments Ltd), 29-31 Montpelier Vale, Blackheath, London, SE3 0TJ
Tel (020) 8852 5619
Fax (020) 8852 4463
E-mail
maria@zerodegrees-microbrewery.co.uk
Website
www.zerodegrees-microbrewery.co.uk
Shop 12-12 daily
Tours by arrangement

⊗ Brewing started in 2000. The brewery incorporates a state-of-the-art, computer-controlled German plant, producing unfiltered and unfined ales and lagers, served from tanks using air pressure (not CO_2). The brewery won three out of four awards at SIBA's first London Brewers Competition, with Champion Beer of London for Pale Ale. A new brew-restaurant is planned for Bristol. All beers are suitable for vegetarians/vegans.

WIT (Belgian-style wheat beer)
(OG 1042, ABV 4.2%)

Hefe-Weizen (German wheat beer)
(OG 1042, ABV 4.2%)

American Wheat *(OG 1042, ABV 4.2%)*

Brown Ale *(OG 1044, ABV 4.4%)*
A deep brown-red coloured ale with full malt flavours of caramel and chocolate, mildly hopped with East Kent Golding hops. Smooth and malty.

Pale Ale *(OG 1046, ABV 4.6%)*
A copper-coloured pale ale with a good malt character using American hop varieties Cascade and Centennial. Well-hopped and dry.

Global giants

Eight out of ten pints of beer brewed in Britain today come from the groups listed below...

ANHEUSER-BUSCH UK

Anheuser-Busch UK, a wholly-owned subsidiary of Anheuser-Busch of St Louis, Missouri, has complained that it has not been listed previously in this section. We apologise for this egregious error.

Anheuser-Busch UK, Thames Link House, 1 Church Road, Richmond, Surrey, TW9 2QW. Tel (020) 8332 2302

The company brews Budweiser at the Stag Brewery, Lower Richmond Road, Mortlake, London SW14 7ET, the former Watneys plant. Budweiser is brewed from rice (listed first on the label), malt and hops, with chips of wood used to clarify the beer. Mortlake can be roughly rendered in modern English as 'dead water', which some may consider is the ideal location for a brewery producing Budweiser. A-B's Budweiser should not be confused with the classic Czech beer Budweiser Budvar. Visitors to the area are recommended to visit the Hare & Hounds, 216 Upper Richmond Road, a Young's pub, where they will find some decent beer. Hope this helps, guys.

CARLSBERG-TETLEY

Carlsberg-Tetley Brewing Ltd, PO Box 142, The Brewery, Leeds, W Yorkshire, LS1 1QG
Tel (0113) 259 4594
Fax (0113) 259 4000
E-mail comms.website@carlsbergtetley.co.uk
Websites www.carlsbergtetley.co.uk/ www.smoothlydoesit.co.uk

⊚ A wholly-owned subsidiary of Carlsberg Breweries A/S of Copenhagen, Denmark. Carlsberg is an international giant best known for its pale lagers, though in Denmark it brews a large range of beers, including brown lagers and a porter-stout, all made by cold fermentation. In Britain its lagers are brewed at a dedicated plant in Northampton, while Carlsberg-Tetley in Leeds produces ales and some Carlsberg products. Some 250,000 barrels are produced annually. The website above, www.smoothlydoesit.co.uk, suggests where C-T's interests lie as far as ale brewing is concerned.

Tetley's Dark Mild *(OG 1031, ABV 3.2%)* ◆
A reddish, mid-brown beer with a light malt and caramel aroma. A well-balanced taste of malt and caramel follows, with good bitterness and a satisfying finish.

Tetley's Mild *(OG 1034, ABV 3.3%)* ◆
A mid-brown beer with a light malt and caramel aroma. A well-balanced taste of malt and caramel follows, with good bitterness and a satisfying finish.

Ansells Mild *(OG 1035, ABV 3.4%)*

Ansells Best Bitter *(OG 1035, ABV 3.7%)*

Tetley's Cask Bitter
(OG 1035, ABV 3.7%) ◆
A variable, amber-coloured light, dry bitter with a slight malt and hop aroma, leading to a moderate bitterness with a hint of fruit, ending with a dry and bitter finish.

Tetley's Imperial *(ABV 4.3%)*

Draught Burton Ale (DBA)
(OG 1047, ABV 4.8%) ◆
A beer with hops, fruit and malt present throughout, and a lingering complex aftertaste, but lacking some hoppiness compared to its Burton original.

Carlsberg-Tetley also brews Greenalls Bitter (ABV 3.8%) for former Greenalls pubs supplied by Scottish & Newcastle Retail and other wholesalers. Benskins Bitter and Friary Meux Bitter have been discontinued.

COORS

Coors Brewers Ltd, PO Box 217, High Street, Burton-on-Trent, Staffs, DE14 1BG.
Tel (01283) 511000
Fax (01283) 513873
Website www.coorsbrewers.com

Coors of Colorado is a giant brewer in the United States but has a much lower profile outside the US than Anheuser-Busch (Budweiser) or Miller, the latter now owned by South African Breweries. In 2002 Coors established itself in Europe by buying part of the former Bass brewing empire, when Interbrew was instructed by the British government to divest itself of some of its interests in Bass. Coors now owns several cask ale brands. It brews 110,000 barrels of cask beer a year and also provides a further 50,000 barrels of cask beer from other breweries. A new premium cask beer under the Worthington label was planned for autumn 2002. Coors plans to close the Mitchells & Butlers brewery in Birmingham at the end of 2002.

M&B Mild *(OG 1034/7, ABV 3.4%)*
Brewed under licence by Highgate Brewery, Walsall

Stones Bitter *(OG 1037, ABV 3.7%)*

Hancock's HB *(OG 1038, ABV 3.6%)*
A pale brown, slightly malty beer whose initial sweetness is balanced by bitterness but lack a noticeable finish. A consistent if inoffensive 'Welsh' beer.

Worthington's Bitter *(OG 1038, ABV 3.6%)*
A pale brown bitter of thin and unremarkable character.

M&B Brew XI *(OG 1039.5, ABV 3.8%)*
A sweet, malty beer with a hoppy, bitter aftertaste, brewed under licence by Brains of Cardiff.

Worthington's 1744
A new premium bitter due to launched in autumn 2002; Coors replacement for Draught Bass.

MUSEUM BREWING CO

Bass Museum, Horninglow Street, Burton-on-Trent, Staffs, DE14 1YQ
Tel (0845) 6000598
Fax (01283) 513509
E-mail brewery@museum.brewers.bass.com
Website www.bass-museum.com
Shop (in Bass Museum) 9.30-4.30
Tours by arrangement

The Museum Brewing Co, based in the Bass Museum (the name is due to change), is part of Coors but has a large degree of independence. It began brewing in 1994 and has a licence to recreate some of the older Bass beers that have been discontinued. The brewery dates from 1920 with some equipment going back to 1840. It has a maximum capacity of 60 barrels a week. Production is divided 50:50 between cask and bottled beers. As well as historic beers, the brewery produces seasonal brands and creates ales for CAMRA festivals.

Victoria Ale *(ABV 3.5%)*
Aroma of malt and fruit leads to a well-balanced beer with a bitter-sweet, almost dry aftertaste.

No. 6 Mild *(ABV 3.9%)*

Offilers Bitter *(ABV 4%)*
An amber beer with a hint of malt leading to a fruity start developing into hoppiness. The hops linger without astringency.

Joules Bitter *(ABV 4.1%)*
Malty with a bitter finish.

Massey's Bitter *(ABV 4.1%)*
Easy-drinking golden bitter with a hoppy bite.

Centennial *(ABV 4.3%)*
A light golden bitter, refreshing and aromatic. It is named after the American hop variety used for bittering.

Five Hides *(ABV 4%)*
Little aroma but a flowery taste initially leading to a sharp hoppiness that lingers.

Masterpiece *(ABV 5.4%)*

Worthington's White Shield *(ABV 5.6%)*
Brewed virtually unchanged since 1829. A bottle-conditioned IPA with a clean fruit aroma and a fruity/nutty taste.

Wulfric *(ABV 5.5%)*
Bottle-conditioned beer brewed with ginger.

P2 Imperial Stout *(ABV 8%)*
A black, sweetish, complex stout. Available in bottle and draught.

Bass No 1 Barley Wine *(ABV 10.5%)*
A dark ruby winter beer brewed in summer and fermented in casks for 12 months. Available in bottle and on draught.

GUINNESS

Guinness Brewing GB, Park Royal Brewery, London, NWI0 7RR
Tel (020) 8965 7700
Fax (020) 8963 5120

An Anglo-Irish giant with world-wide brewing operations and distribution. In London it brews draught keg and pasteurised bottled stouts only.

INTERBREW

Interbrew UK Ltd, Porter Tun House, 500 Capability Green, Luton, Beds, LU1 3LS
A wholly-owned subsidiary of Interbrew of Leuven/Louvain, Belgium.
Tel (01582) 391166
Fax (01582) 397397
E-mail name.surname@interbrew.co.uk
Website www.interbrew.com

Interbrew of Belgium is a major player in the European market with such lager brands as Stella Artois and Jupiler, and internationally with Labatt and Molson of Canada. It has some interest in ale brewing with the cask- and bottle-conditioned wheat beer, Hoegaarden, and the Abbey beer Leffe. It has a ruthless track record of closing plants and disposing of brands. In the summer of 2000 it bought both Bass's and Whitbread's brewing operations, giving it a 32 per cent market share. The British government told Interbrew to dispose of parts of the Bass brewing group, which were bought by Coors (qv).

Draught Bass *(OG 1043.3, ABV 4.4%)*
Amber-coloured, with some sweet fruit aroma. A touch of caramel and malt with the hoppy bitterness developing later. 150,000 barrels of Draught Bass are brewed a year, making it Britain's biggest-selling premium cask ale. It is currently brewed under licence by Coors in Burton for Interbrew. Coors has a three-year contract for the beer, after which the beer may be moved to a different site, ending its historic connection with Burton, the home of pale ale brewing.

BODDINGTONS

Boddingtons Brewery, PO Box 23, Strangeways, Manchester, M60 3WB
Tel (0161) 828 2000
Fax (0161) 828 2213
Website www.boddingtons.com
Tours by arrangement

Founded in 1778, acquired by the Boddington family in 1835, sold to Whitbread in 1989, the brewery became part of Interbrew in May 2000. Following the closure of the Cheltenham Brewery, Flowers brands have been transferred to Manchester. The brewery now produces more nitro-keg and packaged Boddingtons than the once-revered cask version.

Boddingtons Bitter
(OG 1035, ABV 3.8%) ◆
A golden straw-coloured beer in which the grainy malt, hop and bitter character can be spoiled by a cloying sweetness.

Flowers IPA *(OG 1035, ABV 3.6%)*
A copper-coloured, refreshing fruity and hoppy beer.

Flowers Original Bitter
(OG 1043, ABV 4.3%)
A copper-coloured, malty beer with a fruity, hoppy taste.

FELLOWS, MORTON & CLAYTON

Fellows, Morton & Clayton Brewhouse Company,
54 Canal Street,
Nottingham, NG1 7EH
Tel (0115) 950 6795
Fax (0115) 953 9838
E-mail fellowsgalley@aol.co.uk
Website www.galleyrestaurant.co.uk

A pub that began brewing in 1980 and still uses malt extract.

Fellows *(OG 1039, ABV 3.8%)*

Post Haste *(OG 1048, ABV 4.5%)*

FROG & PARROT

Frog & Parrot Brewhouse, Division Street, Sheffield, S Yorkshire, S1 4GF
Tel (0114) 272 1280

Brew-pub launched in 1982. The beers are brewed from malt extract and stored in casks and are occasionally available in a few other pubs. Brewing is suspended during long students' vacations. Occasional/one-off brews. Beer: Roger & Out (ABV 12.5%).

LASS O'GOWRIE

Lass O'Gowrie Brewhouse,
36 Charles Street, Manchester, M1 7DB
Tel (0161) 273 6932
Tours by arrangement

Victorian pub that was revamped and reopened as a malt extract brew-pub in 1983. The brewery in the cellar is visible from the bar and the beer is now stored in casks. Occasional/one-off brews. Beers: Lass Ale (ABV 4.1%), Mukka (ABV 4.4%).

SCOTTISH COURAGE

Fountain House, 160 Dundee Street, Edinburgh, EH11 1DQ
Tel (0131) 656 5000
Fax (0131) 656 5217

Scottish Courage is Britain's biggest brewing group with close to 30 per cent of the market. It joined the ranks of the global brewers in 2000 when it negotiated to buy Brasseries Kronenbourg and Alken Maes from the French group Danone; Kronenbourg is the biggest French beer brand and is exported internationally. Alken Maes is a major Belgian group that produces lagers and the Grimbergen abbey beers range. ScotCo also sells the Italian beer Peroni in the off-trade in Britain, and owns Hartwall of Finland, which gives it access to Russia and the Baltic. Scottish & Newcastle was formed in 1960, a merger between Scottish Brewers (Younger and McEwan) and Newcastle Breweries. In 1995 it bought Courage from its Australian owners, Foster's. Since the merger that formed Scottish Courage, the group has rationalised by closing its breweries in Nottingham, Halifax and the historic Courage [George's] Brewery in Bristol, a

dedicated cask ale plant. The remaining beers were transferred to John Smith's in Tadcaster. In June 2001, ScotCo sold 432 managed pubs to Enterprise Inns and 214 pubs to Robert Breare's Noble House for £360 million. In July 2002 the group organised a sale and lease-back scheme for its remaining 1,500 pubs to raise £1.5bn for brewery investments.

FOUNTAIN

Fountain Brewery, 159 Fountainbridge, Edinburgh, EH3 9YY
Tel (0131) 229 9377
Fax (0131) 228 9522

The once-legendary home of McEwan's and Younger's cask ales has now axed all its real ales save for one.

McEwan's 80/- *(OG 1042, ABV 4.2%)*
Thin-bodied with a cloying metallic, caramel flavour. Once a classic, now bland and sweet with maltiness and fruit. Occasionally labelled Younger's IPA.

JOHN SMITH'S

Scottish Courage Brewing Ltd, John Smith's Brewery, Tadcaster, N Yorkshire, LS24 9SA
Tel (01937) 832091
Fax (01937) 833766
Tours by arrangement.

☺ The brewery was built in 1879 by a relative of Samuel Smith (qv). John Smith's became part of the Courage group in 1970. Major expansion has taken place since the formation of Scottish Courage, with 11 new fermenting vessels installed. However, traditional Yorkshire square fermenters have been replaced by conical vessels.

Webster's Green Label Best *(OG 1031.8, ABV 3.2%)*

Webster's Bitter *(OG 1034.8, ABV 3.5%)*

John Smith's Bitter *(OG 1035.8, ABV 3.8%)*
A copper-coloured beer, well-balanced but with no dominating features. It has a short hoppy finish.

Courage Best Bitter *(OG 1038.3, ABV 4%)*
Pale brown beer with hops throughout and a bitter aftertaste.

John Smith's Magnet *(OG 1039.8, ABV 4%)*
An almost ruby-coloured beer with a complex aroma of hops, malt and citrus fruit. Malt dominates the taste and aftertaste.

Directors Bitter *(OG 1045.5, ABV 4.8%)*
Fruity, medium-bodied, pale brown beer with hoppy and yeasty notes throughout.

THEAKSTON

T&R Theakston Ltd, Wellgarth, Masham, Ripon, N Yorkshire, HG4 4YD
Tel (01765) 680000
Fax (01765) 689414
Website www.theakstons.co.uk
Shop April-Oct, open every day; Nov-Dec limited opening.
Brewery tours (01765) 684333

☺ Founded in 1827 and based on the present site since 1875, Theakston became part of S&N in 1987. More than £1 million has been invested in the brewery and in developing a museum of brewing, but most of Theakston's production now takes place in Newcastle (see below). Best Bitter and Cool Cask are brewed exclusively at Tyne; all packaged Old Peculier is also brewed at Tyne. The same pump clips are used for both Masham and Newcastle beers so the consumer is not told where the beers are sourced. The brewery still employs a cooper. Masham has started a seasonal ale programme in which each of these beers is available for a month: Youngers No 3, Masham Ale (ABV 6.6%), Hogshead (ABV 4.1%) and Lightfoot (ABV 5.4%).

Mild Ale *(OG 1035, ABV 3.6%)*
A rich and smooth mild ale with a creamy body and a rounded liquorice taste. Dark ruby/amber in colour, with a mix of malt and fruit on the nose, and a dry, hoppy aftertaste.

Black Bull Bitter *(OG 1037, ABV 3.9%)*
A distinctively hoppy aroma leads to a bitter, hoppy taste with some fruitiness and a short bitter finish. Rather thin.

XB *(OG 1044, ABV 4.6%)*
A sweet-tasting bitter with background fruit and spicy hop. Some caramel character gives this ale a malty dominance.

Old Peculier *(OG 1057, ABV 5.7%)*
A full-bodied, dark brown, strong ale. Slightly malty but with hints of roast coffee and liquorice. A smooth caramel overlay and a complex fruitiness lead to a bitter chocolate finish.

TYNE

Tyne Brewery, Gallowgate, Newcastle upon Tyne, Tyne & Wear, NE99 1RA
Tel (0191) 232 5091
Fax (0191) 261 2301

☺ Home of Newcastle Breweries formed in 1890 from the amalgamation of five local companies. Cask ale production started in the 1970s.

Theakston Mild Ale *(OG 1035, ABV 3.6%)*

Theakston Best Bitter *(OG 1036, 3.6%)*
A dry and metallic bitter with light hop character when fresh. Older samples lose character and end watery and pale.

Theakston Cool Cask *(OG 1042, ABV 4.2%)*
A beer served through special cooling equipment at 10 degrees C. Launched in the north of England in 2001, due to be nationally available by the summer of 2002.

Theakston XB *(OG 1044, ABV 4.6%)*

Theakston Old Peculier *(OG 1057, ABV 5.7%)*

McGOWANS

McGowans Brewhouse, Unit 1, Fountain Park Dundee Street, Edinburgh, E11 1AJ
Tel (0131) 228 8198
Fax (0191) 228 8201

S&N brew pub that opened in 1999.

Pub Groups

Pubs groups or 'Pubcos' [pub companies] now dominate beer retailing in Britain.The national brewers have largely disengaged from running pubs, preferring to sell beer to the pub groups. As a result of the deep discounts demanded by the pubcos, most sell beers mainly from the nationals, thus restricting drinkers' choice, and forming a barrier to regional and micro-breweries. The three biggest pub companies are Enterprise, Punch and Pubmaster, owning more than 11,000 pubs.

AVEBURY

Avebury Taverns Ltd, Sterling House, 20 Station Road, Gerrards Cross, Bucks, SL9 8EL
Tel (01753) 482600

Avebury operates 800 tenanted and leased pubs throughout England and Wales. All pubs trade as independent free houses with tenants able to choose 'market-leading brands' supplied by national, regional and local brewers. Its main suppliers are Coors, Carlsberg-Tetley, Interbrew, and Scottish Courage. Cask beers include Marston's Pedigree.

BARRACUDA

Barracuda Group Ltd, Henley Road, Medmenham, Marlow, Bucks, SL7 2ER
Tel (0845) 345 2528
Fax (0845) 345 2527

Barracuda was formed in 2000. It runs 131 managed outlets. The main pub brands in Barracuda are the 20-strong Smith & Jones chain and Varsity student bars. It takes its main cask beers from Adnams, Coors, Interbrew, Greene King, and Scottish Courage.

BARTER

Barter Inns, 132 Gypsy Hill, London, SE19 1PW
Tel (020) 8670 7001.
Email barterinns@aol.com

Barter has 27 managed pubs in the South-east. It takes ales from Interbrew and Scottish Courage, but its best-selling beer is Fuller's London Pride.

BURTONWOOD

Burtonwood Brewery plc, Bold Lane, Burtonwood, Warrington, WA5 4PJ
Tel (01925) 225131

Brewing at the Burtonwood, Cheshire site is operated by Thomas Hardy Burtonwood, a joint venture formed in 1998 between Burtonwood Brewery and Thomas Hardy Brewery of Dorchester. Burtonwood operates 480 pubs, the majority of which are traditional tenancies. Burtonwood's cask ales and a monthly changing cask beer from an independent brewer are made available to all Burtonwood tenancies. Fewer than half the Burtonwood estate stocks cask ale.

CALEDONIAN HERITABLE

4 Hope Street, Edinburgh, EH2 4DB.
Tel (0131) 220 5511.
Fax (0131) 225 6546

A group with 16 tenanted pubs, 42 managed and 66 leased, all in Scotland. Beers come mainly from Scottish Courage, but the best-selling ale is Caledonian Deuchars IPA.

CATMERE

Catmere Group, Station Road, Scunthorpe, Lincs, DN15 6PY
Tel (01724) 861703
Fax (01724) 861708

Catmere owns eight pubs in Leicestershire and Lincolnshire. Five serve cask beer from both national and regional brewers.

CCT

CCT Group, 76 Mitcham Road, Tooting, London, SW17 9NG.
Tel (020) 8767 8967.
Fax (020) 8767 3675

A South-east based company with 38 managed pubs. Beer is supplied by Scottish Courage and Greene King.

TOM COBLEIGH

Tom Cobleigh, Spencer House, Cliftonville Road, Northampton, NN1 5BU
Tel (01604) 745000

Established in 1992 with just two pubs, the estate has grown to 116 across England. The company was taken over by the Rank Group in 1996 but was bought back by its management. Licensees choose beers from a head office range of national and regional ales, with Scottish Courage as the main supplier. A list of rotating guest beers is also offered.

TOM COBLEIGH

COMMER INNS

Commer Group Ltd, Commer House, Station Road, Tadcaster, N Yorkshire,LS24 9JF
Tel (01937) 833311
Fax (01937) 834236
E-mail commer@commer.co.uk
Website www.commer.co.uk

Commer has scaled down its pub operation from 75 to just five outlets but plans to buy a further 20.

CONQUEST INNS

14 Theobald Steet, Borehamwood, Herts, WD6 4SE
Tel (020) 8207 5656.
Fax (020) 8207 1211
Email info@conquest-inns.co.uk
Website www.conquest-inns.co.uk
Tel (01992) 717718
Fax (01992) 717788

A company with 66 pubs in London, the South-east and East Anglia. Beers are supplied by Interbrew, Scottish Courage and Greene King.

JT DAVIES

JT Davies & Sons Ltd, 7 Aberdeen Road, Croydon, Surrey, CR0 1EQ
Tel (020) 8681 3222
Fax (020) 8760 0390

Wine merchants now controlling 51 tenancies and leased houses in the South-east. Its main suppliers are Interbrew and Scottish Courage, with some beers from Fuller's and Harveys. In June 2002, the company bought a 28% share of Henley brewer W H Brakspear.

DAVY'S

Davy's, 59-63 Bermondsey Street, London, SE1 3XF
Tel (020) 7407 9670
Fax (020) 7407 5844

Wine merchants and shippers since 1870, Davy's has been opening wine bars/restaurants in the London area since 1965, taking previously unlicensed properties and creating a Dickensian, sawdust, nooks-and-crannies type of establishment. Its Davy's Old Wallop (ABV 4.8%) is a re-badged brew of undeclared origin (though Courage Directors fits the bill). This is usually served in pewter tankards or copper jugs. The company currently runs around 50 outlets, including a few pubs.

ELDRIDGE POPE

Eldridge Pope & Co plc, Weymouth Avenue, Dorchester, ST1 1QT

Founded as the Green Dragon Brewery in 1837, Eldridge Pope divorced itself from brewing in 1996 when it split into two wings, the brewing side becoming known as Thomas Hardy Brewery (see Independents). The company now runs 188 pubs, 124 managed, the rest tenanted. It has axed Eldridge Pope beers from Thomas Hardy and has supply agreements with Coors, Interbrew and Scottish Courage. See also Burtonwood.

ENTERPRISE INNS

Enterprise Inns plc, Cranmore Avenue, Shirley, Solihull, W Midlands, B90 4LE
Tel (0121) 733 7700
Fax (0121) 733 6447

Formed in 1991 with an initial acquisition of 372 pubs from Bass, the company has grown rapidly and is now Britain's biggest pub group. In 2002 it bought the former Whitbread tenanted estate from Laurel Inns, and has a 20% stake in New Company, which has acquired the Unique and Voyager pub estates from Nomura. Enterprise has an option to buy both estates. Enterprise previously purchased pubs from John Labatt Retail, Discovery Inns, Gibbs Mew, Mayfair Taverns, Century Inns (Tap & Spile), and Swallow Inns. Enterprise added to this number by buying 439 former Whitbread pubs, and then in June 2001 bought 432 managed houses from Scottish & Newcastle, taking its estate to 3,400. Chief Executive Ted Tuppen says he plans to build an estate of 6,500. A range of cask beers from all the major brewers, as well as many of the regionals, is available through the Enterprise central distribution network.

FITZGERALD

Sir John Fitzgerald Ltd, Cafe Royal Buildings, 8 Nelson Street, Newcastle upon Tyne, NE1 5AW
Tel (0191) 232 0664
Fax (0194) 261 4509

Long-established, family-owned property and pubs company. Its pubs convey a free house image, most offering a good choice of cask beers, including guest ales from smaller craft breweries. The 31 pubs are mainly in the North-east but there are also outlets in Edinburgh, Harrogate and London.

GRAY

Gray & Sons (Chelmsford) Ltd, Rignals Lane, Galleywood, Chelmsford, Essex,CM2 8RE
Tel (01245) 475181
Fax (01245) 475182

Former Chelmsford brewery that ceased production in 1974 and which now supplies its 49 tied houses in Essex with a choice of cask beers from Adnams, Greene King and Mighty Oak. The tenants are also free to choose from a monthly guest list that features at least 10 different ales.

HEAVITREE

Heavitree Brewery plc, Trood Lane, Matford, Exeter, EX2 8YP
Tel (01392) 217733 Fax (01392) 229939

A West Country brewery, established in 1790, which gave up production in 1970 to concentrate on running pubs. The current estate, which is mainly confined to Devon, stands at 112: 12 managed, and the rest tenanted or leased. The pubs are tied to beers from Interbrew.

HERITAGE

Heritage Pub Co, Donnington House, Riverside Road, Pride Park, Derby, DE24 8HY
Tel (01332) 384808. Fax (01332) 384818
Email heritage@heritagepubs.com

Heritage runs 65 tenanted pubs in the East Midlands. Its main suppliers are Coors, Hardy's & Hanson's and W & D. Its best-selling cask beer is Marston's Pedigree.

HOBGOBLINNS

Hobgoblinns, Eagle Maltings, The Crofts, Corn Street, Witney, Oxon, OX8 7AZ
Tel (01993) 702574.
Fax (01993) 772553
Email intray@hobgoblinss.co.uk
Website www.hobgoblinns.co.uk

Formerly the pub-owning subsidiary of Wychwood Brewery. But Wychwood was bought by Refresh UK in June 2002 and the pub group now stands alone. It has 31 managed houses aimed primarily at young people. The main beer supplier is Wychwood.

HONEYCOMBE

Honeycombe Leisure, Muldoons, 50 Water Lane, Ashton, Preston, Lancs, PR2 2NL
Tel (01772) 723764

This 25 year-old company bought the Devonshire Pub Co in 2000 and now has 89 managed houses. Beers are supplied by the nationals plus Burton Bridge, Eccleshall, Moorhouses, Phoenix and Timothy Taylor, and most micro-brewers in the North-west. It is one of the biggest sellers of Black Sheep, Moorhouses and Timothy Taylor in the north of England. Honeycombe also has its own micro-brewery based in Salford.

INN BUSINESS

See Punch

INN PARTNERSHIP

See Pubmaster

INNSPIRED

InnSpired Pubs & Taverns, Wiltshire Drive, Trowbridge, Wilts, BA14 0TT
Tel (01225) 763171
Website www.innspired.co.uk

InnSpired represents the remains of Ushers of Trowbridge, a famous West Country brewery founded in 1824. Ushers became part of Grand Metropolitan in 1960. The brewery passed into Courage's control, but a management buy-out restored its independence in 1991. In 1999 Ushers merged with the Alehouse Company of Southampton. With the involvement of the Alchemy group, it was always likely that the new owners would opt to concentrate on real estate and retailing. Brewing ceased early in 2000. InnSpired has an estate of more than 1,000 pubs. It bought 50 outlets in the North of England and plans to grow the estate to 2,000. Usher's cask beers are brewed for InnSpired by Thomas Hardy of Dorchester; other brands, such as Manns Brown Ale and the Lowenbrau range of lagers, are brewed by Burtonwood. A separate company, Refresh UK, retails the Usher's brands, and bought the Wychwood Brewery in June 2002. Under new tenancy agreements, InnSpired's landlords can offer a wide range of beers that often includes ales from specialist and local breweries.

INNTREPRENEUR

Once a mighty pub company created by Courage and Grand Metropolitan, it was bought by Nomura, which sold its entire pub estate in 2002. See Enterprise.

LAUREL

Laurel was created in 2001 by Morgan Grenfell/Deutsche Bank, who bought the Whitbread pub estate. Laurel sold the tenanted pubs to Enterprise Inns a year later but kept the managed houses, including the Hogshead chain. See Enterprise.

MACLAY

Maclay Group plc, Thistle Brewery, Alloa, FK10 1ED
Tel (01259) 723387
Fax (01259) 216511

Maclay, founded in 1830, stopped brewing in September 1999. It owns 35 pubs and its full range of cask ales is brewed under licence by Belhaven (qv).

McMANUS

McManus Taverns, Kingsthorpe Road, Northampton, NN2 6HT
Tel (01604) 713601

Company with 19 pubs in the East Midlands, Essex and Kent. Half serve cask beer mainly from ScotCo and Wadworth.

MERCURY

Mercury Management (UK) Ltd, Mercury House, Amber Business Village, Amington, Tamworth, Staffs, B77 4RP
Tel (01827) 62345
Fax (01827) 64166
E-mail headoffice@mercurymanagement.co.uk
Website www.mercurymanagement.co.uk

Mercury Management is the result of a 1999 buy-out of Mercury Taverns. It has slimmed down its estate from 45 pubs to 16.

MILL HOUSE

Mill House Inns, Century House, Westcott Venture Park, Westcott, Bucks, HP18 0XB
Tel (01296) 652600
Fax (01296) 652626

Mill House has 54 managed pubs nationwide, ranging from town bars to country pubs and family pub-diners. Its main supply agreement is with Interbrew.

MORRELLS

Morrells of Oxford Ltd,
Ferry Hinskey Road,
Oxford, OX2 0ES
Tel (01865) 727722
Fax (01865) 794262

In June 2002 Greene King paid £60 million for 107 Morrells' pubs. Michael Cannon keeps control of the remaining 25 outlets. The pubs are all that remain of the once much-loved Oxford brewery that closed in 1998 following a boardroom split and the eviction of two members of the Morrell family. Morrells beers are brewed by Thomas Hardy of Dorchester, but will be replaced by Greene King brands in 107 pubs. Get ready for 'Morrells Oxford Bitter' brewed in Bury St Edmunds.

NOBLE HOUSE

Noble House Pub Company,
4 Thamesside Centre, Kew Bridge,
Brentford, Mddx TW8 0HF
Tel (020) 8847 9100

A subsidiary of Noble House Leisure, which owns hotels and restaurants. The group is run by Robert Breare, who masterminded the exit from brewing by Ushers of Trowbridge to become the pub company InnSpired (qv). Mr Breare was interested in making a bid for Wolverhampton & Dudley in 2000, but withdrew to allow Pubmaster to make its own unsuccessful bid. Noble House owns 240 managed pubs.

OLD ENGLISH

Old English was bought by Greene King for £59 million in 2001.

OLD MONK

Old Monk Company, Walter House,
418/422 The Strand,
London, WC2R 0PT
Tel (020) 7836 6002.
Fax (020) 7836 6003
Website www.theoldmonk.co.uk

Old Monk runs 31 traditional pubs and eight Springbok theme bars. It takes some cask beers from Nethergate.

PUB ESTATE

Pub Estate Company Ltd,
3-5 Ashfield Road, Chorley,
Lancs, PR7 1LH
Tel (01257) 238800
Fax (01257) 233918

A company established with the purchase of 230 pubs from Scottish & Newcastle, it currently has 335 pubs (28 managed, the rest tenanted or leased) based in the north of England and Scotland. The pubs offer beers from Coors, Interbrew, Carlsberg-Tetley and Scottish Courage but some licensees have guest beer rights. The company's aim is to convert all pubs to three-year leases that would offer no guest beer entitlement and would mean all pubs being served by a favoured supplier, probably Scottish Courage.

PUBMASTER

Pubmaster Ltd, Greenbank,
Hartlepool, TS24 7QS
Tel (01429) 266699
Fax (01429) 278457
Website www.pubmaster.co.uk

Pubmaster was formed in 1991 to take over the pub estate of Brent Walker, the property group that also owned Cameron's and Tolly Cobbold breweries in the 1980s. Following a management buy-out in 1996, Pubmaster continued to grow, with acquisitions from Mercury Taverns, Devonshire Pub Company and Swallow. Swallow, the remant of the Vaux brewing group, sold 662 pubs to Pubmaster. In 2000, the initial investors in the group sold their stake to West LB (a German financial company), First Principal Finance Group/Nomura of Japan, Rotch Property Group, and St Modwen Properties. Nomura sold all its pub interests in 2002, with the exception of Wizards Inns (qv). Pubmaster acquired 1,200 Inn Partnership outlets from Nomura as a result, followed by 38 pubs from Pub.com in Scotland. In the summer of 2002, it bought the 45-strong pub estate of White Rose of Leeds. It is currently operating more than 3,200 pubs and stocks beers from Coors, Interbrew, Carlsberg-Tetley, and some independents.

PUNCH GROUP

Punch was formed in 1998 by a team led by Hugh Osmond, founder of Pizza Express, with the purchase of the Bass leased pub estate. In 1999, Punch, with the backing of Bass, bought Allied Domecq's pub estate. It sold 550 former managed houses to Bass and now owns some 5,000 pubs itself. Punch claims its lessees are free to take guest beers, but brewers who supply the group are closely monitored and have to offer substantial discounts to be accepted. In 2001, Punch launched a specialist cask ale initiative to supply some of its pubs with a wider portfolio of beers but the problem of discounts restricts the number of participating brewers. The main cask ales sold by Punch are Tetley and Worthington, with guest ales from a number of regionals.

SPIRIT GROUP

107 Station Road, Burton-on-Trent,
Staffs, DE14 1BZ
Tel (01283) 545320
Website www.spiritgroup.co.uk

The new name (previously Punch Retail) for the managed side of the business, based in the former offices of Allied Domecq. It operates 1,046 pubs.

PUNCH PUB COMPANY

Lincoln House, Wellington Crescent,
Fradley Park, Lichfield, Staffs, WS13 8RZ
Tel (01543) 443500 Fax (01543) 443502
Website www.punchpubs.co.uk

Punch Pub Co, which includes the Inn Business estate, is the tenanted and leased division of the Punch Pub Company. It owns some 4,000 pubs.

PYRAMID

Pyramid Pub Co Ltd, Suite H3, Steam Mill Business Centre, Steam Mill Street, Chester, CH3 5AN
Tel (01244) 321171. Fax (01244) 317665
Email amandab@pyramidpub.co.uk

Manages 475 pubs, formerly known as Paramount and bought from Royal Bank of Scotland. The pub estate is widely spread, mainly in towns and cities. Beers are supplied by Burtonwood, Interbrew, Scottish Courage and Wolverhampton & Dudley. Banks's is the leading cask ale.

RANDALL VAUTIER

Randall Vautier Ltd, PO Box 43, Clare Street, St Helier, Jersey, JE4 8NZ
Tel (01534) 887788
Fax (01534) 888350

A brewery that ceased production in 1992. It now runs 30 pubs on Jersey selling beers from Interbrew, Scottish Courage, and Marston's. Not to be confused with Randalls of Guernsey (see Independents).

REGENT INNS

Regent Inns PLC, 77 Muswell Hill, London, N10 3PJ
Tel (020) 8375 3000
Fax (020) 8375 3001
Website www.regentinns.co.uk

Founded in 1980, Regent owns 123 managed pubs in London and the Home Counties, and is growing by 20 pubs a year. Expansion into the Midlands and the north is taking place. Most of the pubs are unbranded, are allowed to retain their own identities, and are not tied to any supplier. Most pubs feature a wide range of national, local and seasonal cask ales chosen by managers. The company has contracts with Coors, Interbrew and Scottish Courage plus half a dozen regional breweries, but licensees can also take beer from the Beer Seller wholesaler. Branded pubs include Walkabout Inns and Jongleurs.

RYAN

Ryan Elizabeth Holdings plc, Ryan Precinct, 33 Fore Street, Ipswich, IP4 1JL
Tel (01473) 217458
Fax (01473) 258237

The company's 63 pubs in East Anglia, many bought from national brewers, are mostly leased to individual operators on 35-year contracts, although eight are managed. The pubs are generally free of the tie but some have a tie to Interbrew. A subsidiary company, Elizabeth Hotels, operates independent bars/pubs in its hotels with a local community focus, offering four to five real ales and live entertainment. The main beer supplier is Interbrew but Adnams, Greene King and Nethergate also supply beers.

SCORPIO INNS

Scorpio Inns Ltd, Commerce House, Abbey Road, Torquay, TQ2 5PJ
Tel (01803) 296111
Fax (01803) 296202

Formed in 1991, it now runs 111 pubs (nearly all tenanted). These stock beers from Interbrew and are located in South Wales, the Bristol and Hereford areas, and along the M4 corridor to Swindon.

SFI

SFI Group plc, SFI House, 165 Church Street East, Woking, Surrey, GU21 1HJ
Tel (01483) 227900 Fax (01483) 227903

Established in 1986, the SFI Group, formerly Surrey Free Inns, runs around 180 pubs and café bars in England, Scotland and Wales. The number is set to increase, with further acquisitions planned. Beers come from national brewers and a range of smaller regional brewers. Cask ale is a feature of the Litten Trees outlets. Not all the pubs are branded: around 20, such as the Ostrich Inn, at Colnbrook, near Heathrow, have kept their own identity. SFI bought the Slug & Lettuce group in 2000.

SIX CONTINENTS

Six Continents, Cape Hill, PO Box 27, Birmingham, B16 0PQ
Tel (0121) 558 1481
Fax (0121) 558 2515

Following the sale of its brewing interests to Interbrew, Bass had to change the name of its pubs division. In 2001 it became Six Continents, to reflect its role as a leisure and retail company; it is one of the world's leading hoteliers through ownership of Holiday Inns. Six Continents runs more than 2,000 pubs, bars and restaurants and employs around 40,000 people. Its brands include Vintage Inns (traditional pubs), Ember Inns (local pubs), and Goose (traditional pubs offering good food and drink). All these outlets offer cask ales: Ember Inns always have one cask ale available and could have as many as four if the volume is sustainable. Ember Inns also hold Cask Ale Celebrations: the 2001 event featured more than 30 cask ales. Vintage Inns will always stock Draught Bass and one other cask beer, if the volume is sustainable. Goose pubs have the highest sales of cask ale. The company acquired 550 pubs from Allied Domecq in late 1999, the majority of which stock Tetley Bitter and Draught Bass. This acquisition has given the group some historic gems such as the Philharmonic in Liverpool, the Bear in Oxford, and several in London, including the Black Friar. Six

Continents offers a selection of cask beers: as well as Draught Bass, Worthington Bitter, Stones, Hancocks, M&B Mild and Brew XI, a number of guest ales are also available, including Adnams, Highgate Bitter, Fuller's London Pride and Greene King Old Speckled Hen. In 2002 there were persistent rumours that Six Continents might merge with the pub division of Scottish & Newcastle, which would make such a merged group the biggest pub retailer in the country.

TYNEMILL

Tynemill Ltd,
2nd Floor, Victoria Hotel,
Dovecote Lane, Beeston,
Nottingham, NG9 1JG
Tel (0115) 925 3333
Fax (0115) 922 6741

Founded by former CAMRA chairman Chris Holmes, Tynemill has been established in the East Midlands for more than 20 years, and now owns 17 pubs. It has a 'pubs for everyone' philosophy, avoiding trends and gimmicks, and concentrating on quality cask ales and food in good surroundings, including public bars where space permits. It sold more than 1,500 different cask ales during 2000, thought to be more than anyone else in the industry. Managers have complete autonomy on guest beers they sell. During 2000, Tynemill entered into two joint ventures: the Mildly Mad Pub Co with York Brewery, to develop an estate in the York region, and with Breakthroughpoint in Nottingham. Tynemill is now the sole owner of the Castle Rock Brewery in Nottingham (qv). Regional and micro-brewers make up the bulk of Tynemill's products.

UNIQUE

See Enterprise

WETHERSPOON

JD Wetherspoon plc, PO Box 616,
Watford, WD1 1YN
Tel (01923) 477777 Fax (01923) 219810
Website www.jdwetherspoon.co.uk

Wetherspoon is a vigorous and independent pub retailer that currently owns more than 580 managed pubs, with rapid plans for expansion. No music is played in any of the pubs, all offer no-smoking areas, and food is served all day. Two standard beers from Scottish Courage are available to managers: Theakston Best Bitter and Courage Directors. Each pub also stocks regional ales from the likes of Cains, Fuller's, Greene King, Shepherd Neame and Wolverhampton & Dudley, plus at least two guest beers. There are usually two beer festivals a year, one in the spring, the other in the autumn, at which up to 30 micro-brewery beers are stocked over a four-day period. Wetherspoon joined the Cask Marque scheme in 2000 and now enjoys CM accreditation in more than 435 pubs.

WHARFEDALE

Wharfedale Taverns Ltd,
Highcliffe Court, Greenfold Lane,Wetherby,
W Yorkshire, LS22 6RG
Tel (01937) 580805
Fax (01937) 580806
E-mail wharfedale_taverns@compuserve.com

A company set up in 1993 by former Tetley employees to lease 90 pubs from that company, it currently owns 60 pubs, mainly in the north. The main beers come from Carlsberg-Tetley; guest beers are from C-T's Tapster's Choice.

WHITE ROSE

See Pubmaster

WILLIAMS

James Williams (Narberth),
7 Spring Gardens, Narberth,
Pembrokeshire, SA67 7BP
Tel (01834) 862200
Fax (01834) 862202

A privately-owned concern that operates 55 pubs in West and mid-Wales. Tenants are mainly supplied by Coors, Interbrew, Brains, and Carlsberg-Tetley. A house ale, James Williams IPA, brewed by Brains, is also available. Regional brands are also supplied, including beers from Adnams, Banks, Bateman, Everards, Jennings and Shepherd Neame. The company has a regular, extensive guest cask beer policy.

WIZARD INNS

City Gate, 17 Victoria Street,
St Albans, Herts, AL1 3JJ
Tel (01727) 792200
Fax (01727) 792210

Former CAMRA national chairman Chris Hutt, also the ex-boss of Midsummer Inns and Unicorn Inns, purchased 30-40 former Phoenix Inns pubs to set up this new company. Nomura, the Japanese bank that owned Unique Pub company, has a £9.5 million stake. Wizard Inns operates traditional, unbranded pubs. All the pubs, now numbering 46, are managed and serve a selection of real ales.

YATES'S

Yates's Wine Lodges Ltd,
Peter Yates House, Manchester Road,
Bolton, BL3 2PY
Tel (01204) 373737
Fax (01204) 388383

Company founded in Oldham in 1884 by wine merchant Peter Yates, it now runs 150 managed pubs in locations from Scotland to London. Beers are mainly from Coors, Interbrew and Scottish Courage, with some regional ales also featured. Boddingtons Bitter is sold at one price nationwide but many branches do not serve real ale.

The Beers Index

Over 2,000 beers are listed. They refer to beers in bold type in the Breweries section

A

B

C

D

E

F

H

M

N

O

P

R

S

T

U

V

W

X

Y

Z

Readers' recommendations

Suggestions for pubs to be included or excluded

All pubs are surveyed by local branches of the Campaign for Real Ale. If you would like to comment on a pub already featured, or any you think should be featured, please fill in the form below (or copy it), and send it to the address indicated. Your views will be passed on to the branch concerned. Please mark your envelope with the county where the pub is, which will help us to sort the suggestion efficiently.

Pub name:

Address:

Reason for recommendation/criticism:

Pub name:

Address:

Reason for recommendation/criticism:

Pub name:

Address:

Reason for recommendation/criticism:

Your name and address:

Please send to: [Name of county] Section, Good Beer Guide,
230 Hatfield Road, St Albans, Hertfordshire AL1 4LW

Readers' recommendations

Suggestions for pubs to be included or excluded

All pubs are surveyed by local branches of the Campaign for Real Ale. If you would like to comment on a pub already featured, or any you think should be featured, please fill in the form below (or copy it), and send it to the address indicated. Your views will be passed on to the branch concerned. Please mark your envelope with the county where the pub is, which will help us to sort the suggestion efficiently.

Pub name: ....

Address: ....

Reason for recommendation/criticism: ....

....

....

....

....

Pub name: ....

Address: ....

Reason for recommendation/criticism: ....

....

....

....

....

Pub name: ....

Address: ....

Reason for recommendation/criticism: ....

....

....

....

....

Your name and address: ....

....

....

....

....

Please send to: [Name of county] Section, Good Beer Guide,
230 Hatfield Road, St Albans, Hertfordshire AL1 4LW

Readers' notes

CAMRA Books and Gifts

CAMRA Books (non-members' prices)	Price	Quantity	Total
Good Beer Guide 2003	£12.99		
Good Beer Guide 2002	£3.00		
Good Beer Guide 2001	£3.00		
Good Beer Guide 2000	£3.00		
Good Beer Guide 1999	£3.00		
50 Pub Crawls	£9.99		
Heritage Pubs (Hardback)	£15.99		
Pubs for Families (3rd edition)	£7.99		
London Pub Guide (3rd edition)	£9.99		
Guide to Northern France	£7.99		
Guide to Home Brewing (3rd edition)	£7.99		
Brew British Real Ales at Home	£7.99		
Brew Classic European Beers at Home	£7.99		
Homebrew Classics – India Pale Ale	£8.99		
Guide to Cellarmanship	£4.99		
CAMRA Guide to Good Pub Food (5th edition)	£8.99		
Good Bottled Beer Guide (Hardback – 3rd edition)	£8.99		
Real Ale Almanac (6th edition)	£8.99		
Pub Superchefs	£7.99		
Good Cider Guide (4th edition)	£9.99		
Dictionary of Beer	£9.99		
CAMRA Beer and Pubs Quiz Book	£1.00		
Kegbuster Remembers by Bill Tidy	£1.00		
Cidermaking on a Small Scale	£5.95		
Ciders Story Rough and Smooth	£9.99		
Country Ales and Breweries (Hardback)	£15.99		
Historic Inns of England (Hardback)	£14.99		
Historic Inns of Dublin (Hardback)	£14.99		
Britain's 500 Best Pubs	£9.99		
London by Pub	£10.00		
Born and Brewed in Yorkshire	£9.99		
A History of Brewing Industry in Scotland	£7.50		
	TOTAL		

- Prices include postage and packing to the UK
- Add £2.00 per book in European Union (£4 for the 2001 Good Beer Guide)
- Add £4.00 per book elsewhere (£7 for the 2001 Good Beer Guide)

Credit Card Orders can be placed by calling **01727 867201**
or via our website **www.camra.org.uk**

- **Please allow up to 21 days for delivery, up to 35 days for delivery overseas**

Please send your order for books, CAMRA products and clothing to:
CAMRA, 230 Hatfield Road,
St Albans,
Hertfordshire AL1 4LW

(cheques made payable to CAMRA must accompany all orders). To place a credit card order, phone (01727) 867201 and ask for the Products Secretary.

NAME ....

ADDRESS ....

....

....

....

....

Postcode ....

CAMRA Products	**Price**	**Quantity**	**Total**
Spinning Key Fob	£2.95		
CAMRA Lapel Badge	£2.50		
Cider Lapel Badge	£2.50		
Beer Style Lapel Badge – Mild	£2.50		
Beer Style Lapel Badge – Bitter	£2.50		
Beer Style Lapel Badge – Stout	£2.50		
Beer Style Lapel Badge – Old Ale	£2.50		
GBBF 10 Year @ Olympia Badge Set (Limited Edition)	£27.50		
CAMRA Bar Towel *Black* (10 for £12.50)	£2.00		
CAMRA Tea Towel (How a Brewery Works)	£3.00		
Hop Lady Beach Towel	£9.95		
CAMRA Hanging Neck Pen	£1.50		
CAMRA Ballpoint Pen	£0.50		
Embroidered Material Badge *Red and Black*	£2.00		
CAMRA Handpump Bookmark	£1.00		
Bottle Opener/Fridge Magnet (2 in 1)	£2.00		
Fridge Magnet – Hop Lady	£1.50		
Fridge Magnet _ Pulling Power	£1.50		
CAMRA Wallet (Embroidered Logo) *Red*	£3.75		
PVC Glass Cooler *Red*	£3.00		
PVC Good Beer Guide Cover *Burgundy*	£2.95		
Flashing Rubber Ball	£3.00		
CAMRA Squezzy Stress Bottle	£2.95		
CAMRA Notelets with Holder	£4.95		
CAMRA Darts Flights (pack of 3)	£1.00		
Beanie Bear	£3.00		
'Full Pint' Wristwatch	£14.95		
Desk Clock	£9.75		
Wall Clock	£19.50		
CAMRA Mouse Mat	£3.00		
CAMRA Coaster (6 for £8.50)	£1.75		
CAMRA Model Van *Red*	£9.50		
Ask if it's Cask Model Van *White*	£9.50		
Metal Waiters Tray	£14.95		
Golf Umbrella	£16.75		
Record Bag *Black with Grey and Red*	£14.95		

CAMRA Clothing			
CAMRA Tie (Help Save Real Ale) *Navy Blue*	£8.50		
Mild Logo Silk Tie *Navy Blue* SALE	£9.95		
CAMRA T-Shirt Embroidered Logo *Red/Back/Green* (M to XXL)	£950		
Save Your Local T-Shirt *Sky Blue* (S to XXL)	£850		
Pub is for Life (not just Christmas) *White* (S to XXL)	£850		
Cider & Perry T-Shirt *White* (S to XXL)	£8.50		
Life's Simple T-Shirt *Sky Black* (S to XXL)	£8.50		
Endangered Species T-Shirt *White* (S to XXL)	£8.50		
Genuine Taste T-Shirt *White* (S to XXL)	£7.50		
Goddess Ninkasi T-Shirt *White* (M to XXL)	£12.50		
Beer Warriors Rugby Shirt *Blue* (L to XXL)	£29.95		
CAMRA Sweatshirt *Navy Blue* (M to XXL)	£12.50		
CAMRA Polo Shirt *Crimson* (S to XXL)	£16.50		
Life Member Polo Shirt *Crimson* (M to XXL)	£16.50		
Lads Polo Shirt (Light and Dark Supporters) *Green* (S to XXL)	£17.50		
EBCU Polo Shirt *Blue* (M to XXL)	£14.50		
Denim Shirt *Pale Blue* (M to XL)	£12.50		
CAMRA Summer Jacket *Navy Blue* (XL only)	£27.50		
CAMRA Fleece *Red or Green* (M to XXL)	£24.95		
Apron (Champion Beers of Britain) *White*	£9.50		
Baseball Caps *Black*	£8.95		
CAMRA Socks 'Mine's a Full Pint' *Grey*	£4.50		
Children's 'Half Pint Kids' T-Shirt *Red* (3 – 13 years old; Please state age required)	£5.00		
	TOTAL		

- Prices include postage and packing to the UK
- Please add £1.50 per item In European Union
- Please add £2.50 per item elsewhere

- **Please allow up to 21 days for delivery**
- **Please allow up to 35 days for delivery overseas**

An offer for CAMRA members
GOOD BEER GUIDE Annual Subscription

Being a CAMRA member brings many benefits, not least the big discount on the Good Beer Guide. Now you can take advantage of an even bigger discount on the Guide by taking out an annual subscription.

Simply fill in the form below and the Direct Debit form opposite (photocopies will do if you don't want to spoil your book), and send them to CAMRA at the usual St Albans address.

You will then receive the *Good Beer Guide* automatically every year. It will be posted to you before the official publication date and before any other postal sales are processed.

You won't have to bother with filling in cheques every year and you will receive the book at a lower price than other CAMRA members (the 2002 edition, for instance, was sold to annual subscribers at only £7.50).

So sign up now and be sure of receiving your copy early every year.

Note: This offer is open only to CAMRA members and is only available through using a Direct Debit instruction to a UK bank (use the form opposite, or copy it if you do not want to spoil your book). This offer applies to the 2004 *Guide* onwards.

Name ....

CAMRA Membership No. ....

Address and Post code ....

....

....

....

....

I wish to purchase the *Good Beer Guide* annually by Direct Debit and I have completed the Direct Debit instructions to my bank which are enclosed.

Signature   Date

....

....

Instruction to your bank or building society to pay by Direct Debit

Please fill in and send to the Campaign for Real Ale Limited, 230 Hatfield Road, St Albans, Herts AL1 4LW

Name and full postal address of your bank or building society

To the manager **Bank or building society**

Address

Postcode

Name(s) of Account Holder(s)

Bank or building society account number

☐☐☐☐☐☐☐☐

Branch sort code

☐☐☐☐☐☐

Reference number

☐☐☐☐☐☐☐☐☐☐☐☐☐☐☐☐☐☐

Banks and building societies may not accept Direct Debit instructions for some types of account

Originator's identification number

9 2 6 1 2 9

For CAMRA official use only

This is not part of the instruction to your bank or building society

Membership number

Name

Postcode

Instruction to your bank or building society

Please pay CAMRA Direct Debits from the account detailed on this instruction subject to the safeguards assured by the Direct Debit Guarantee. I understand this instruction may remain with CAMRA and, if so, will be passed electronically to my bank/building society.

Signature(s)

Date

Postcode

Direct Debit

This Guarantee should be detached and retained by the payer.

The Direct Debit Guarantee

- This Guarantee is offered by all banks and building societies that take part in the Direct Debit Scheme. The efficiency and security of the scheme is monitored and protected by your own bank or building society.
- If the amounts to be paid or the payment dates change, CAMRA will notify you within ten working days in advance of your account being debited or as otherwise agreed.
- If an error is made by CAMRA or your bank or building society, you are guaranteed a full and immediate refund from our branch of the amount paid.You can cancel a Direct Debit at any time by writing to your bank or building society. Please also send a copy of your letter to CAMRA

Join CAMRA

Free for three months!

- **Has a pub near you been closed or ruined?**
- **Has your local brewery been taken over or its beers lost their flavour?**
- **Are you concerned about the price of a pint?**

If you can answer 'yes' to any or all of these questions you are sure to benefit from becoming a member of CAMRA.

The Campaign for Real Ale is a voluntary organisation consisting of over 64,000 drinkers, run by an unpaid, elected National Executive and backed by a small core of professional executives. It speaks for drinkers everywhere in fighting to save pubs and breweries from closure, and in attempting to improve quality and to ensure pub standards are raised.

- As a member you can have your say about issues which effect you. You can stand for election to office, attend the annual conference to speak and vote, and help organise local campaigns.
- You can help select pubs for the Good Beer Guide, help out at beer festivals and enjoy some excellent social activities.
- You can receive big discounts on the Good Beer Guide and other CAMRA books and products, free or reduced price admission to CAMRA beer festivals, plus the What's Brewing newspaper, delivered to your door each month. All new members receive the Members' Handbook as soon as they are registered.

All this is available at the bargain price of just £16 per year (£19 per year for two people living at the same address).

- What's more if you join by Direct Debit you will receive three month's membership free, so you can see for yourself how worthwhile being a member can be.
- Fill in the application form below (or a photocopy of it) and the Direct Debit form on the previous page. If after three months of membership you decide not to continue just write to CAMRA, cancel your membership and you will owe nothing.

Note: If you do not wish to take up the trial offer, but wish to join CAMRA anyway, fill in the application form and return it to us with a cheque for your first years subscription. To pay by credit card, contact the Membership Secretary on (01727) 867201 (or Join online on our National Web-site at www.camra.org.uk)

- Full annual membership £16
- Joint annual membership (two people at the same address) £19
- Life membership £192 (single)/£288 (joint)
- Under-26 membership £9 single/£12 joint.

Concessionary rates available on request.

Please delete as appropriate:

- ☐ I/We wish to take advantage of the trial membership, and have completed the instructions overleaf.
- ☐ I/We wish to become members of CAMRA
- ☐ I/We agree to abide by the memorandum and articles of association of the company.
- ☐ I/We enclose a cheque/PO for £ (payable to CAMRA)

NAME(S) ....

Address and Post Code ....

....

....

Date of birth .... E-mail address ....

Signature(s) ....

☐ Tick here if you would like to receive occasional e-mails from CAMRA.
(At no point will your details be released to a third party) Opt-in

Signature(s) ....

To: **CAMRA, 230 Hatfield Road, St Albans, Hertfordshire AL1 4LW**